McGRAW-HILL CHEMICAL ENGINEERING SERIES

Texts and Reference Works Outlined by the Following Committee

THE SERIES

CONTRIBUTORS

M. R. FENSKE, D.Sc., Professor of Chemical Engineering and Director of Petroleum Refining Laboratory, Pennsylvania State College. *Hydrogenation.*

P. H. GROGGINS, B.S., Senior Chemist, U. S. Department of Agriculture. *Nitration, Amination by Reduction, Halogenation, Sulfonation, Amination by Ammonolysis, Friedel and Crafts Reaction.*

S. J. LLOYD, Ph.D., Dean, School of Chemistry, University of Alabama. *Hydrolysis.*

L. F. MAREK, M.S., Chemical Engineer, Arthur D. Little, Inc. *Oxidation.*

H. P. NEWTON, M.A., Research Chemist, U. S. Department of Agriculture. *Halogenation, Compilation of Indices.*

A. J. NORTON, B.S., Consulting Chemist. *Polymerization.*

G. D. PALMER, JR., Ph.D., Associate Professor of Chemistry, University of Alabama. *Hydrolysis.*

E. EMMET REID, Ph.D., LL.D. *Esterification.*

R. N. SHREVE, A.B., Professor of Chemical Engineering, Purdue University. *Alkylation.*

W. A. SIMPSON, B.S., Chemical Engineer, Charles Pfizer and Company, Inc. *Sulfonation.*

A. J. STIRTON, Ph.D., Research Chemist, U. S. Department of Agriculture. *Amination by Ammonolysis.*

H. E. WOODWARD, Ph.D., Research Chemist, E. I du Pont de Nemours & Co. *Diazotization.*

CHEMICAL ENGINEERING SERIES

UNIT PROCESSES

IN

ORGANIC SYNTHESIS

P. H. GROGGINS, EDITOR-IN-CHIEF

Senior Chemist, Bureau of Chemistry and Soils, U. S. Department of Agriculture; Author of "Aniline and Its Derivatives"

SECOND EDITION
FIFTH IMPRESSION

McGRAW-HILL BOOK COMPANY, INC.

NEW YORK AND LONDON

1938

THE MAPLE PRESS COMPANY, YORK, PA.

PREFACE TO THE SECOND EDITION

In the preface to the first edition, the editor distinguished between the now generally accepted terms *unit operations* and *unit processes* and showed how they were intimately related in the solution of chemical engineering problems involving organic synthesis. The widespread acceptance of the book since it made its appearance about three and a half years ago and the adoption of unit processes and unit operations as complementary phases of chemical engineering have been a source of genuine gratification to the authors.

The object of this volume continues to be the presentation of an outline of the industrial technic generally employed in attacking problems involving organic synthesis. In the first edition it was recognized that specialized experience was necessary to amass, digest, and interpret the voluminous literature relating to each unit process. This experience was also an important asset in keeping the present volume within practical limits without the sacrifice of important new material.

The synthetic organic chemical industry in the United States has made remarkable progress during the past decade, the production having more than trebled since 1929. The indications are that this upward trend will continue. The importance of a text of this character has consequently been greatly increased. It is hoped that the organized fundamental information which the authors bring to this volume will in some measure assist in the training of personnel for this expanding industry.

In this second and enlarged edition, the general plan of the book remains unchanged, but every chapter has been revised and brought into line with current developments as revealed by the technical and patent literature. Some chapters retain their former outline, while others have undergone marked transformation. The chapter on Diazotization has been augmented to include Coupling; those on Alkylation and Polymerization have been substantially enlarged. Mention should also be made of (1) the increased emphasis on the synthesis of aliphatic compounds; (2) the incorporation of a substantial number of new flow

vii

sheets; and (3) the introduction of sections explaining the theoretical basis of halogenation and hydrogenation reactions by means of thermodynamics.

The editor is deeply obligated to many individuals for their constructive criticism of certain aspects of the first edition, and he takes this opportunity to acknowledge gratefully the helpful suggestions of Professor H. B. Hass and his colleagues of Purdue University and those of Professor Henry Gilman of Iowa State College and Dr. H. W. Elley of the du Pont Company.

P. H. GROGGINS.

WASHINGTON, D. C.
July, 1938.

PREFACE TO THE FIRST EDITION

During the past half century, the activities of workers in the field of organic synthesis have swelled to unwieldy proportions our store of information regarding new products. As a result thereof, most organic chemists have been constrained to focus their interest to some restricted field. Beyond his immediate professional problems, the chemist is generally not so much interested in the countless new carbon compounds that are synthesized as he is in the reaction mechanism and technic employed. To derive the fullest benefit from the accumulated knowledge and current contributions, it is obviously advantageous to record the development of organic synthesis in terms of the comparatively few underlying unit processes.

In this book, an attempt is made to present in a systematic manner the principles and practice of the more important and well-defined reactions in organic synthesis. In commercial operations, it is found necessary to bring to the application of such reactions the pertinent information derived from inorganic and physical chemistry as well as the contributions of the chemical engineer. Hence, attention is directed not only to the chemistry and products of reaction but equally to the contributing factors and agencies which lead to efficient operation. The term *unit processes* is used here to represent the embodiment of all the factors in the technical application of an individual reaction in organic synthesis.

The desirability of employing such a concise and descriptive term can be appreciated readily from the following illustration: In the process of synthesizing dimethylaniline from benzene, three distinct unit processes are involved, *viz.* (1) nitration; (2) amination by reduction; and (3) alkylation. Similarly, in each of the two current methods of synthesizing phenol from benzene, two unit processes are required; thus: (1) sulfonation followed by hydrolysis or (2) halogenation followed by hydrolysis.

Perhaps a few words of explanation are warranted here to distinguish between the term *unit process* as we have used it and the term *unit operation*, which now has a definite significance to the chemical engineer. Unit processes deal principally with chemical reactions, whereas unit operations relate largely to physical phenomena. The former are based on changes in chemical constitution or molecular structure, while the latter involve changes of state or position. Unit processes bring about distinctive chemical transformations in the materials treated, these changes being conditioned largely by the intrinsic properties of the

ix

reactants. On the other hand, the factors affecting physical movements or changes, *i.e.*, the underlying principles of unit operations, may in many instances be discussed apart from the chemical nature of the materials handled.

Unit processes and unit operations have, however, important inter-relations for no reaction or series of reactions can be carried out commercially without the application of one or more unit operations. Thus, in nitration, some of the unit operations that are involved are conveying and feeding materials; mixing; heat transfer; separation of materials; filtration; and distillation. In this volume, however, the authors have assumed that the reader is familiar with the principles of the chemical engineering unit operations, which are competently discussed in other texts of this series. A knowledge of these is essential to the technical application of chemical engineering to unit processes in organic synthesis.

Examination of the literature relating to any unit process in organic synthesis reveals that there may be many means to the same end. In this work, an effort is made to codify the underlying principles and factors, for the satisfactory interpretation of any unit process depends on discovering the common among the apparently diverse reactions. The formulation of a practical philosophy of each reaction should consequently include (1) an examination of the reactants; (2) an inquiry into the mechanism of the reaction; (3) a knowledge of the chemical and physical factors involved; (4) observations regarding the design and construction of equipment; and, finally, (5) a study of typical technical applications. Once the principles are mastered, it matters little in what branch of chemical technology these processes are carried out.

This volume is therefore intended for advanced students in chemistry and chemical engineering. An attempt has been made to coordinate the study of fundamental principles of organic synthesis with the requirements of the industrial plant. The text may be viewed as a semi-works course to facilitate the transition from the class room to the works laboratory.

To amass, digest, and interpret the literature of each unit process was recognized as a task calling for specialized experience. To assure the practicability and reliability of the text, it has been considered essential to make the work a collaborative effort. In addition, individual chapters have been sent to industries and universities for critical examination, and the able and valuable assistance given by members of such organizations and institutions is hereby gratefully acknowledged.

P. H. GROGGINS.

WASHINGTON, D. C.,
November, 1934.

CONTENTS

PAGE

PREFACE TO THE SECOND EDITION. vii

PREFACE TO THE FIRST EDITION. ix

CHAPTER I

NITRATION. 1

Survey of Nitro Compounds, 2; Nitric Acid in the Nitration Process, 11;
Mechanism of the Nitration Reaction, 12; Examination of Nitrating Agents,
14; Mixed Acid for Nitrations, 21; Factors Affecting Nitration, 24; Equipment for Nitrations, 26; Technical Nitrations, 33; Thermal Data Relating to
the Preparation and Use of Nitro Compounds, 53; Recovery of Spent Acid
from Nitrations, 55.

CHAPTER II

AMINATION BY REDUCTION 63

Outline of Processes for the Preparation of Amines, 63; The Reduction of
Nitro Compounds, 64; Reduction with Iron in Acid or Neutral Solutions, 68;
Tin and Hydrochloric Acid Reduction, 77; Reduction with Zinc in Weakly
Alkaline Solutions, 82; Reduction of Nitro Compounds with Alkali or Metal
Sulfides, 83; Ferrous Sulfate in Alkaline Solution as a Reducing Agent, 86;
Reduction of Nitro Compounds with Hydrogenated Quinoline Bases, 87;
Sodium Hyposulfite (Hydrosulfite) in Alkaline Solutions as a Reducing
Agent, 87; Reduction by Hydrogen with the Aid of a Catalyst, 88; Design
and Construction of Equipment, 92; Technical Preparation of Amines, 96.

CHAPTER III

DIAZOTIZATION AND COUPLING 115

Introduction, 115; Uses and Reactions of Diazo Compounds, 115; Properties
and Reactions of Diazonium Salts, 119; Properties and Reactions of
Diazonium Sulfonates, 123; Properties and Reactions of Diazonium Carboxylates, 125; Properties and Reactions of Diazo Oxides, 125; Factors
Affecting Diazotization, 126; Design and Construction of Equipment, 130;
Technical Diazotizations, 131; Analysis of Diazo Compounds, 140; Coupling,
140; Mechanism of the Coupling Reaction, 144; Factors Affecting Coupling,
145; Technical Couplings, 148.

CHAPTER IV

HALOGENATION 153

Introduction, 153; The Theoretical Basis of Halogenation Reactions, 159;
Survey of Halogenations, 165; Chlorination in the Presence of a Catalyst,
206; Photo-catalytic Chlorinations, 209; Design and Construction of Equipment for Halogenation, 211; Technical Halogenations, 213.

                                                                            PAGE
                              CHAPTER V
SULFONATION. 233
   Introduction, 233; Sulfonating Agents and Their Principal Applications,
   234; Separation of Sulfonic Acids, 263; Physical and Chemical Factors in
   Sulfonation, 265; Formation of Addition Compounds in Sulfonation, 274;
   Technical Methods of Sulfonation, 277; Design and Construction of Appa-
   ratus, 281; Technical Preparation of Sulfonic Acids, 283; Concentration of
   Spent Sulfuric Acid, 297.

                              CHAPTER VI
AMINATION BY AMMONOLYSIS 299
   General Discussion, 299; Reactions and Properties of Aqueous Ammonia,
   303; Survey of Amination Reactions, 309; Physical and Chemical Factors
   Affecting Ammonolysis, 327; Metal Catalysts in Ammonolysis of Halogeno
   Compounds, 334; Corrosion and the pH of the Autoclave Charge, 336;
   Equilibrium Considerations in Ammonolysis, 337; Speculation Regarding
   Mechanism of the Reaction, 339; Design and Construction of Equipment,
   340; Technical Manufacture of Amino Compounds, 342; Control of the
   Ammonia Recovery System, 359.

                              CHAPTER VII
OXIDATION. 362
   Types of Oxidative Reactions, 362; Oxidizing Agents, 365; Liquid-phase
   Oxidation with Oxidizing Compounds, 376; Liquid-phase Oxidation with
   Oxygen, 382; Vapor-phase Oxidation of Aliphatic Compounds, 390; Vapor-
   phase Oxidation of Aromatic Hydrocarbons, 405; Apparatus for Oxidations,
   413.

                              CHAPTER VIII
HYDROGENATION 419
   Introduction, 419; Production of Hydrogen, 422; Type Hydrogenations,
   429; Physical Factors Other than Catalysts Affecting Hydrogenation, 444;
   General Principles Concerning Hydrogenation Catalysts, 455; Apparatus
   and Materials of Construction, 461; Industrial Processes, 464.

                              CHAPTER IX
ALKYLATION 485
   Introduction, 485; Alkylating Agents, 487; Types of Alkylation, 490;
   Factors Controlling Alkylation, 500; Equipment for Alkylations, 503;
   Effect of Alkylation, 506; Technical Alkylations, 509.

                              CHAPTER X
ESTERIFICATION 533
   Esterification Reactions, 533; Speeding Up Esterification, 544; Completing
   Esterification, 548; Vapor-phase Esterification, 556; Alcoholysis, 558;
   Acidolysis, 561; Esterification of Amides, 562; Use of Acid Anhydride, 562;
   Use of Acid Chlorides, 563; Esters from Metal Salt and Alkyl Halide, 565;
   Esters from Anhydrides of Dibasic Acids, 566; Preparation of Xanthate, 567;
   Esterification by Ketene, 567; Addition of an Acid to an Unsaturated
   Hydrocarbon, 568; Esters from Acetylene, 568; Esters from Nitriles, 569;

Esterification with Ethylene Oxide, 570; Esters from Aldehydes, 570; Esters from Alcohols, 570; Esters from Carbon Monoxide, 571; Design and Operation of Esterification Plant, 572; Technical Esterifications, 578.

CHAPTER XI

HYDROLYSIS 590

Definition and Scope, 590; Hydrolyzing Agents, 591; Materials Susceptible to Hydrolysis, 596; Theory and Mechanism of Hydrolysis, 602; Construction and Control of Equipment for Hydrolysis, 607; Technical Operations Involving Hydrolysis, 608.

CHAPTER XII

THE FRIEDEL AND CRAFTS REACTION 634

Introduction, 634; Classification of Syntheses, 637; Chemical and Physical Factors, 657; Chemical Engineering Problems, 668; Mechanism of the Friedel and Crafts Reaction, 675; Technical Syntheses, 677.

CHAPTER XIII

POLYMERIZATION 692

Introduction, 692; Classification of Synthetic Resins and Plastics, 696; Chemical Constitution and Polymerization, 699; Factors Influencing Polymerization, 703; Thermosetting Resins, 707; Thermoplastic Resins, 717; Polymer Resins, 722; Methods of Manufacture, 730; Applications, 737.

INDEX. 741

UNIT PROCESSES IN ORGANIC SYNTHESIS

CHAPTER I

NITRATION

BY P. H. GROGGINS

Nitration may be considered as the process by which the union of the nitro (—NO$_2$) group to a carbon atom is effected. Generally, it is the hydrogen atom which is replaced; thus:

$$R \cdot H + HO \cdot NO_2 \rightarrow R \cdot NO_2 + H \cdot OH$$

Although a number of methods for the preparation of nitro compounds are available, the nitro group is usually introduced by the action of nitric acid admixed with some other acid which preferentially combines with the water in the reaction system. The comparative ease with which nitration occurs in the presence of such dehydrating agents has led to the belief that nitration is probably due to the activity of either nitric acid anhydride or mixed acid anhydrides. These compounds possess pronounced additive properties and contain a labile —NO$_2$ group, e.g., O$_2$N·O·NO$_2$, H$_3$C·CO·O·NO$_2$. Generally, however, the representation of the reaction involves the union of the hydrogen which is replaced with the hydroxyl of nitric acid to form water.

The agents generally employed for the preparation of nitro compounds are the following:

1. Nitric acid, concentrated.
2. Mixed acids, i.e., nitric acid admixed with a dehydrating acid such as oleum, sulfuric acid, acetic anhydride, acetic acid, phosphorus pentoxide.
3. Alkali nitrates in the presence of sulfuric acid.
4. Organic nitrates, such as acetyl and benzoyl nitrates.
5. Metal nitrates with acetic acid.
6. Nitrosulfonic acid.
7. Nitrogen tetroxide.

It is apparent from the preceding tabulation of nitrating agents that the nitro group can be introduced by various procedures. The choice of agent and the technic employed will be governed by such factors as

1

the chemical constitution and physical properties of the organic compound as well as by the economics of competitive methods. Such variations in any unit process are instructive and to be expected.

A parallelism exists in other unit processes. In the preparation of amino compounds, a wide variety of aminating agents are available. Thus, NH_3 $aq.$, NH_3 (in organic solvents), NH_2OH, $(NH_2)_2 \cdot CO$, $R \cdot SO_2 \cdot NH_2$, etc., may be effectively employed. The satisfactory interpretation of any unit process obviously depends on discovering the common among the apparently heterogeneous reactions.

In a few cases, not a hydrogen atom but another group, such as the sulfonic acid ($-SO_3H$) or acetyl ($-COCH_3$) group, is replaced. Examples of interest are the nitration of phenoldisulfonic acid, which is thereby converted into picric acid; and the nitration of 3, 4-dimethoxyacetophenone in glacial acetic acid to 4, 5-dinitroveratrole.

Phenol   Phenoldisulfonic Acid   Picric Acid

3, 4-Dimethoxyacetophenone   4, 5-Dinitroveratrole

It is possible to replace more than one hydrogen atom by nitro groups, and in this way dinitro and trinitro compounds may be formed. The preparation of mononitro compounds is comparatively easy. It is more difficult, however, to bring about the introduction of the second and third nitro groups. In the last case, it is necessary to use an excess of mixed acid containing a high nitric acid concentration and to nitrate at higher temperatures.

I. SURVEY OF NITRO COMPOUNDS

The Nitroparaffins.—Hitherto, the nitroparaffins have been unimportant industrially. This situation has, however, been altered because of a number of technical and economic developments; $viz.$,

1. Chemical engineering progress, which has made available at a low cost an abundance of lower paraffins in a high state of purity;

2. The advent of cheap nitrogen peroxide and nitric acid from the oxidation of synthetic ammonia; and

3. The development of vapor-phase nitration processes.

The nitration of paraffins has an added interest because the familiar method of direct nitration with mixed acids which is generally used in the treatment of aromatic compounds here finds only a limited application. Whereas low temperatures—0 to 50°C.—and high HNO_3 concentrations are advantageously employed for the nitration of aromatic compounds, the most favorable conditions for nitrating the higher paraffins in the liquid phase are provided by using higher temperatures—130 to 140°— and relatively dilute acids.

Nitric acid can both nitrate and oxidize organic compounds. These activities are functions of the nitric acid concentration and the temperature, and each appears to be accelerated by the presence of oxides of nitrogen. From this generalization, it may be concluded that the limiting factor in accelerating nitrations is the susceptibility of the organic compound to undergo oxidation. By and large, in the nitration of aromatic compounds, the concentration of the nitrating agents is more influential than the temperature, whereas in the treatment of paraffins the effect of temperature is greater.

Some oxidative action accompanied by the liberation of oxides of nitrogen, however, appears to be a necessary prerequisite to the nitration of alkanes. Theoretical considerations, which are discussed later, lead to the belief that NO_2 and N_2O_4 are indeed the real nitration agents. This presumably accounts for the higher yields of nitroparaffin when the reaction is carried out in a sealed vessel. It is also in harmony with the successful non-catalytic vapor-phase nitrations of paraffins[1] with nitric acid or nitrogen dioxide.

In the nitration of paraffins with nitric acid, in both the liquid and vapor phase, the hydrocarbons having tertiary carbon atoms form nitro derivatives most readily. This is to be expected from the relative ease of nitration of aromatic compounds wherein all carbon atoms are necessarily tertiary. The secondary carbon atoms take on nitro groups with greater difficulty, and the primary compounds require the most drastic treatment.

The nitroparaffins can be made by the reaction of alkyl halides with certain metal nitrites, and alkali metal nitrites.

$$C_2H_5 \cdot 1 + AgO \cdot NO \rightarrow Ag1 + C_2H_5 \cdot O \cdot N \cdot O \qquad \text{Ethyl Nitrite} \qquad IA$$

$$C_2H_5 \cdot 1 + Ag.N{\overset{O}{\underset{O}{\diagdown}}} \rightarrow Ag1 + C_2H_5 \cdot N{\overset{O}{\underset{O}{\diagdown}}} \qquad \text{Nitroethane[2]} \qquad IB$$

$$CH_3Cl + NaNO_2 \rightarrow CH_3NO_2 + NaCl[3] \qquad II$$

---

[1] McCleary and Degering, *Ind. Eng. Chem.*, **30**, 64 (1938); Hass and Hodge, U. S. 1,969,667 (1934); 2,071,122 (1937); Hass and Patterson, *Ind. Eng. Chem.*, **30**, 67 (1938).

[2] The parachors for nitromethane, etc., show only one double bond, but dipole moment measurements indicate that the two oxygen atoms are in all probability equivalent because of a condition of resonance.

$$R:N::\overset{..}{O} \qquad ; \qquad R:N:\overset{..}{O}:$$
$$:\overset{..}{O}: \qquad\qquad :\overset{..}{O}:$$

[3] U. S. 2,105,581 (1938).

The two isomers, ethyl nitrite and nitroethane, are always formed together in reactions IA and IB. This is a characteristic phenomenon of such double decompositions and is ascribed to the fact that nitrous acid, as well as its noble metal salts, exists in isomeric forms. The alkali nitrites are strong electrolytes, whereas the colored noble metal nitrites do not dissociate. This difference arises because the former are probably derived from the true acid form and the latter from the neutral form of nitrous acid. The nitrous esters, having lower boiling points, may be separated from the nitro compounds by distillation.

The boiling points of nitromethane, methyl nitrite, and methyl nitrate are as follows:

$$CH_3-\overset{\overset{\displaystyle O}{\|}}{N} \rightarrow O \qquad 101°C.$$
$$CH_3-O-N{=}O \qquad -12°C.$$
$$CH_3-O-\underset{\underset{\displaystyle O}{\|}}{N} \rightarrow O \qquad 66°C.$$

The nitration of the lower saturated paraffins is probably best accomplished in the vapor phase by treatment with nitric acid or nitrogen dioxide. This is due to the fact that the alkanes of less than five carbon atoms are gases at the temperatures usually employed in liquid-phase nitrations and, furthermore, they are not appreciably soluble in aqueous nitric acid. Ethane, for example, is bubbled through boiling nitric acid at a rate which will provide one mole of the acid for two moles of hydrocarbon.[1] The mixture, at atmospheric or superatmospheric pressure, is led through a reaction tube at 420°C. The effluent gases from the reactor, which contain practically no unreacted nitrogen peroxide, are cooled to 0°C. to condense the nitroethane and spent nitric acid. These form layers, and the supernatant nitroethane is separated by decantation. The product, which is contaminated by some nitromethane, is thoroughly washed and is then purified by rectification. In addition to nitric oxide, the gases leaving the condenser contain some carbon monoxide, carbon dioxide, and water. The presence of these constituents is evidence of oxidative action which may involve the direct oxidation of the paraffins or the further oxidation of aldehydes and olefins which are formed during the nitration process.

The nitroparaffins are colorless when pure and almost insoluble in water and have a characteristic mild chloroformlike odor. The physical properties of the simplest members are given in Table I on page 5.

The reaction of nitroparaffins with alkali and the displacement of an α-hydrogen atom by a metal are the reactions of the enol form. When

---

[1] Hass, Hodge, and Vanderbilt, *Ind. Eng. Chem.*, **28**, 339 (1936).

TABLE I.—PHYSICAL PROPERTIES OF NITROPARAFFINS

Compound	Boiling point, °C.	Density	Refractive index
Nitromethane	101	1.1382 (20/20)	1.39348 (20/D)
Nitroethane	115	1.0461 (25/25)	1.39007 (24.3)
1-Nitropropane	131	1.0023 (25)	1.40027 (24.3)
2-Nitropropane	118	1.024 (0)	
1-Nitrobutane	151		
2-Nitrobutane	139	0.9877	
2-Methyl-1-nitropropane	140.5	0.9625 (25/25)	1.4050 (25)
2-Methyl-2-nitropropane	126.4 (m. p., 25.6)	0 9501 (28/4)	

nitroethane is treated with potassium hydroxide, the corresponding potassium derivative of the acinitro (nitronic acid) form, which is soluble in water is obtained:

$$CH_3\overset{\overset{\displaystyle H}{|}}{\underset{\underset{\displaystyle H}{|}}{C}}-N\underset{O}{\overset{O}{\diagup}} + KOH \rightarrow CH_3CH=N\underset{OK}{\overset{O}{\diagup}} + H_2O$$

The nitroparaffins are quite reactive and can be employed as the raw materials for numerous syntheses, some of which have potential industrial importance. They can all be reduced to primary amines. The primary isomers can be hydrolyzed with boiling concentrated hydrochloric acid to form fatty acids and hydroxylamine hydrochloride:

$$RCH_2NO_2 + HCl + H_2O \rightarrow RCOOH + NH_2OH \cdot HCl$$

It is apparent that this procedure affords a simple and inexpensive method for the production of propionic and butyric acids which are useful as the raw materials for other syntheses. Controlled reduction of the sodium salt of the acinitro form $-C=NO(ONa)$ with $SnCl_2$ in concentrated hydrochloric acid yields oximes. When steam is introduced into the acid solution, hydrolysis takes place and aldehydes or ketones are obtained depending respectively on whether primary or secondary nitroparaffins are employed:

$$CH_3CH=N\underset{ONa}{\overset{O}{\diagup}} \rightarrow CH_3CH=NOH \rightarrow CH_3C\underset{H}{\overset{O}{\diagup}} + NH_2OH$$

$$\underset{CH_3}{\overset{CH_3}{\diagdown}}C=N\underset{ONa}{\overset{O}{\diagup}} \rightarrow \underset{CH_3}{\overset{CH_3}{\diagdown}}C=NOH \rightarrow CH_3COCH_3 + NH_2OH$$

The primary and secondary nitro compounds are characterized by further reactions due to α-hydrogen atoms and give the aldol condensation with aldehydes resulting in the formation of nitroalcohols or nitroölefins, depending on conditions.

$$2RCHO + R'CH_2NO_2 \xrightarrow{KHCO_3} R'-C \begin{cases} CHOH \\ NO_2 \\ CHOH \end{cases} \quad \begin{matrix} R \\ | \end{matrix} \quad \begin{matrix} | \\ R \end{matrix}$$

$$RCHO + R'CH_2NO_2 \xrightarrow[160°C.]{ZnCl_2} RCH{=}C \begin{cases} R' \\ NO_2 \end{cases} + H_2O$$

As many molecules of the aldehyde unite with one molecule of nitro-paraffins as there are α-hydrogen atoms, thus:

$$3HCHO + CH_3NO_2 \rightarrow O_2NC \begin{cases} CH_2OH \\ CH_2OH \\ CH_2OH \end{cases} \xrightarrow[]{HONO_2} O_2NC \begin{cases} CH_2O{\cdot}NO_2 \\ CH_2O{\cdot}NO_2 \\ CH_2O{\cdot}NO_2 \end{cases}$$

Tris (hydroxymethyl) nitromethane

The nitroalcohols on further esterification with nitrating acids yield nitrates having the structure and properties similar to the well-known glyceryl trinitrate.

Nitric Acid Esters of Aliphatic Compounds.—The nitration of aliphatic polyhydroxy alcohols and of carbohydrates results in the formation of nitric acid esters. These compounds, although popularly referred to as nitro compounds, are true nitrates:

$$K{-}O{-}NO_2; \qquad C_3H_5(O{-}NO_2)_3; \qquad C_{24}H_{30}O_{10}(O{-}NO_2)_{10}$$

Potassium Nitrate   Glyceryl Trinitrate   Cellulose Decanitrate

The nitrates of glycerol, glycol, cellulose, starch, and sugar are probably the most important members of this group of esters and are discussed in greater detail under Esterification. Although these compounds are used as military explosives, their principal uses are in normal and highly important industrial undertakings. The employment of cellulose esters in the manufacture of synthetic ivory, lacquers, cellophane, artificial leathers, etc., is well known. The mining of coal, copper, and other minerals; the blasting of rocks and stumps; the excavating and irrigating operations are only a few of the normal activities which require several hundred millions of pounds of explosives annually.

The nitrating agent generally employed in the preparation of these esters is a mixed acid comprising nitric and sulfuric acids in varying proportions. In the nitration of glycerol, both the total acidity and nitric acid concentration of the mixed acid are greater than those employed for the nitration of carbohydrates. Typical analyses would show the following composition:

Compound nitrated	Composition of nitrating acid, %			
	H_2SO_4	HNO_3	HNO_2	H_2O
Glycerol................................	55	44.8	0.2	0
Cellulose................................	74	18.0	0.6	7.4

Mixed acids containing free SO_3, *i.e.*, having an acidity of over 100 per cent, have been used for the manufacture of glyceryl trinitrate but the practice is not so general.

Aromatic Nitro Compounds.—Practically all the nitrating agents previously enumerated (page 1) are used in the preparation of nitro-aromatic compounds. Economic considerations are generally the determinants in the choice of the agent. Often, however, certain inherent chemical or physical properties, or the presence of substituents, necessitate the use of specific nitrating agents. The choice of the nitrating agent may furthermore determine the position of the entering nitro group. The important subject of orientation therefore merits a brief consideration at this time.

Orientation of Nitro Groups in Aromatic Compounds.—*In the benzene series*, three different dinitrobenzenes can be obtained—the ortho, meta, and para compounds. The position taken by the entering nitro group depends on the group already present. As a rule, it enters in a position *meta* to a nitro, sulfonic acid, carboxyl, or carbonyl group; and *ortho* and *para* to a chloro, bromo, alkyl, amino, or hydroxyl group. The proportions in which the isomerides are formed depend to a slight extent on

TABLE II.—THE NITRATION OF VARIOUS MONOSUBSTITUTED BENZENES[1]

Group already present	Percentage of		
	Ortho	Meta	Para
F..	12.4	Trace	87.6
Cl..	30.1	Trace	69.9
Br..	37.6	Trace	62.4
I..	41.1	Trace	58.7
CH_3..	58.8	4.4	36.8
CH_2Cl..	40.9	4.2	54.9
$CHCl_2$..	23.3	38.8	42.9
CCl_3..	6.8	64.5	28.7
$COOC_2H_5$..	28.3	68.4	3.3
COOH..	18.5	80.2	1.3
NO_2..	6.4	93.2	0.25

[1] HOLLEMAN, *Chem. Rev.*, **1**, 187 (1925).

the nitrating temperature. A lower temperature of nitration is conducive to the exclusive formation of the meta derivatives in the first group, and a preponderance of para compound in the second. In case two or more groups are already present, it is difficult to predict which compound will be formed owing to the conflicting influences of these groups, and often a mixture of different compounds will result upon nitration. In most cases, however, it is possible to regulate the conditions to be optimal for a certain compound and thus minimize the formation of undesirable by-products. Upon purification, it is generally possible to obtain a product suitable for technical operations.

The influence of substituents in the benzene ring upon the orientation of the entering —NO_2 group is shown in Table II.

Naphthalene Series.—In the naphthalene series, it is possible to have two different mononitro derivatives, *viz.*, the alpha and beta compounds, but the beta compound is formed only to a slight extent by direct nitration. Upon nitration, the first nitro group enters almost exclusively into the alpha position; a second nitro group enters into position 5 or 8.

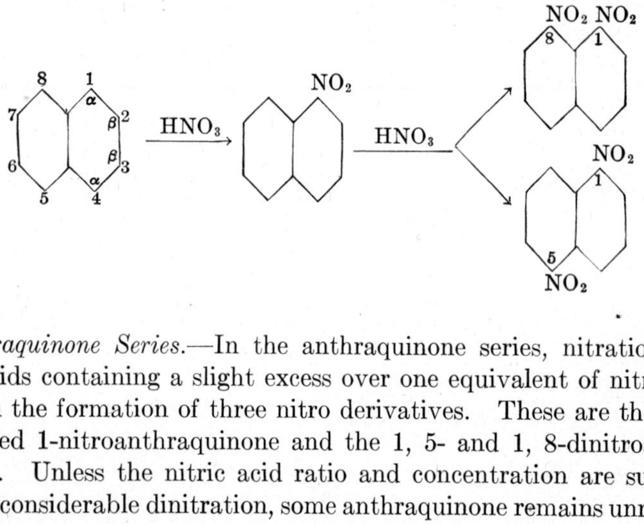

Anthraquinone Series.—In the anthraquinone series, nitration with mixed acids containing a slight excess over one equivalent of nitric acid results in the formation of three nitro derivatives. These are the alpha substituted 1-nitroanthraquinone and the 1, 5- and 1, 8-dinitroanthraquinones. Unless the nitric acid ratio and concentration are sufficient to insure considerable dinitration, some anthraquinone remains unreacted.

Nitration of Amines and Phenols. Acylation.—Since amino compounds are very susceptible to oxidation, it is generally necessary to protect the —NH_2 group during nitration. This is accomplished by converting the amine to its acyl derivative. Acylation may be carried out by heating the amine under a vented reflux with acids or acid chlorides.

$$R \cdot NH_2 + R \cdot COOH \rightarrow R \cdot NH \cdot CO \cdot R + H_2O \qquad (I)$$
$$R \cdot NH_2 + R \cdot CO \cdot Cl \rightarrow R \cdot NH \cdot CO \cdot R + HCl \qquad (II)$$

Acetic acid and, to a lesser extent, oxalic and formic acids are employed for acylations according to Eq. (I); acetyl chloride, benzoyl chloride, and *p*-toluenesulfonyl chloride are suitable for reactions according to Eq. (II).

TABLE III.—NITRATION OF ANILINE AND ANILIDES[1]

A. Nitration with 80 Per cent HNO_3 in Glacial Acetic Acid

Amine	Per cent			Ratio ortho:para
	Para	Ortho	Meta	
Free amine....................	64	38	..	1:1.8
Acetyl........................	70	30	..	1:2.3
Benzoyl.......................	72	28	..	1:2.6
Formyl........................	74	26	..	1:2.8
Chloroacetyl..................	75	25	..	1:3.0
Amino oxalyl..................	79	21	..	1:3.8
Toluenesulfonyl...............	84	16	..	1:5.3

B. Nitration with 94 Per Cent HNO_3 in Concentrated H_2SO_4

Amine	Per cent			Ratio ortho:para
	Para	Ortho	Meta	
Free amine....................	50	1	49	
Acetyl........................	92	8	..	1:11.5
Benzoyl.......................	93	7	..	1:13.3
Formyl........................	94	6	..	1:15.6
Chloroacetyl..................	96	4	..	1:24.0
Amino oxalyl..................	98	2	..	1:49.0
Toluenesulfonyl...............	98	2	..	1:49.0

C. Nitration in HNO_3

Amine	Per cent			Ratio ortho:para
	Para	Ortho	Meta	
Aniline nitrate...............	56	4	40	
Acetyl........................	58	42	..	1:1.4
Benzoyl.......................	60	40	..	1:1.5
Formyl........................	65	35	..	1:1.9
Chloroacetyl..................	73	27	..	1:2.7
Oxalyl........................	85	15	..	1:5.7
Toluenesulfonyl...............	88	12	..	1:7.3

Temperature, 20°C.; time, 24 hr.

[1] According to K. LAUER, *J. prakt. Chem.*, **137**, 175 (1933).

The choice of acylating agent and nitrating agent is often a matter of importance, since the orientation of the entering —NO_2 group is, as can be seen from Table III, affected by the agents employed. When acetanilide is nitrated with a mixed acid in the presence of an excess of sulfuric acid (see pages 44, 45) at 3 to 5°C., the product is principally *p*-nitroacetanilide, only a small quantity—2 to 5 per cent of the ortho isomer—being formed. When the nitration of acetanilide is carried out with a mixed acid comprising glacial acetic acid and fuming nitric acid at 0 to 5° in the presence of a small quantity of urea, the ratio of ortho to para isomerides is 3 : 1. When nitration is accomplished by acetyl nitrate in acetic anhydride, the ortho compound is obtained almost exclusively.[1]

The nitration of *p*-toluenesulfonyl derivatives of amines is effected with (1) nitric acid alone; (2) a mixture comprising nitric and acetic acids; or (3) boiling glacial acetic acid containing sodium nitrite. Nitration with mixed acids, *i.e.*, HNO_3—H_2SO_4 mixtures may result in nitration in the toluene nucleus also. Thus, Reverdin[2] found that the *p*-toluenesulfonyl derivative of *p*-anisidine gave 3-nitro-*p*-anisidine on nitration with nitric acid (sp. gr., 1.4) in acetic acid at 10 to 22°C., whereas a nitro group was also introduced into the toluene nucleus when nitration was effected with mixed acid at subzero temperatures.

It is interesting to note that in exceptional cases, where it is possible to nitrate amino compounds without resorting to previous acylation, the product differs from that obtained by the nitration of the acyl derivative. When *p*-toluidine is dissolved in a large quantity of sulfuric acid and nitrated with mixed acid (HNO_3—H_2SO_4 mixture) at low temperatures, 2-nitro-*p*-toluidine is obtained. The nitration of the acetyl derivative yields 3-nitro-*p*-toluidine.

Phenols, like amines, are particularly susceptible to oxidation, and in some nitrations it is therefore advisable to acylate first, *i.e.*, to form an ester. The nitrated derivative, on hydrolysis, yields the nitrophenol. When the ester is nitrated with mixed acid, the procedure frequently yields two nitro compounds of technical value, since a nitro group also enters the esterifying component.

When *p*-toluenesulfonyl chloride is added to a hot solution of sodium phenolate, phenyl *p*-toluenesulfonate is formed. On cooling, this compound separates out as a nearly colorless solid.[3] Nitration with a mixed acid containing 2.2 moles of nitric acid to each mole of phenyl ester in an excess of sulfuric acid results in a nitro group entering the toluene nucleus as well as in the phenol nucleus. The alkaline hydrolysis of the inter-

[1] PICTET, *Ber.*, **40**, 1165 (1907).

[2] REVERDIN, *Bull. soc. chim. ind.*, **35**, 1168 (1924).

[3] Ger. 91,314 (1895).

mediate compound—*p*-nitrophenyl *o*-nitro-*p*-toluenesulfonate—results in the formation of *p*-nitrophenolate and *o*-nitrotoluene-*p*-sulfonate.

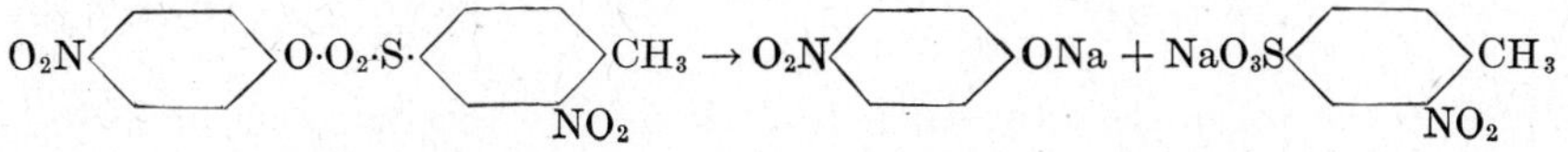

$$O_2N\langle\ \rangle O\cdot O_2\cdot S\cdot\langle\ \rangle \overset{CH_3}{\underset{NO_2}{}} \rightarrow O_2N\langle\ \rangle ONa + NaO_3S\langle\ \rangle \overset{CH_3}{\underset{NO_2}{}}$$

II. NITRIC ACID IN THE NITRATION PROCESS

Assuming that nitric acid reacts according to the following equation:

$$R\cdot H + HO\cdot NO_2 \rightarrow R\cdot NO_2 + H_2O$$

it can be seen that the aqueous solution containing the active nitrating agent becomes more and more dilute as nitration progresses. For example, when 2 moles of 90 per cent aqueous HNO_3 are used to effect the nitration, the HNO_3 concentration of the residual acid, after 1 mole of the mononitro compound is formed, will be

$$\frac{63}{140 - 63 + 18} = 66.3\% \; HNO_3$$

If 3 moles of 70 per cent aqueous HNO_3 are employed, the HNO_3 concentration after mononitration will be

$$\frac{126}{270 - 63 + 18} = 56\% \; HNO_3$$

With diminishing HNO_3 concentration, two important problems are introduced: (1) The nitrating capacity of the acid is greatly reduced; and (2) its activity as an oxidizing agent is relatively increased. Obviously, also, the factor of cost is involved in the employment of such large excesses of nitric acid.

The dual activity of nitric acid may be explained as follows:[1] Spectroscopic investigations show that alkali salts and esters of nitric acid show quite a different absorption spectra in the ultra-violet and must therefore be differently constituted. The concentrated acid shows a spectrum that is identical with that of esters, while that of the dilute acid is the same as that of the alkali salts.[2] Acids of medium concentration can give both spectra together. Now the salts certainly dissociate in solution and the esters are undissociated, but the mere process of dissociation into ions of a similar structure, according to Hantzsch, causes no change in the spectrum. A formula must therefore be assumed for the salts (and for dilute nitric acid) which permits dissociation (I), and

[1] EPHRAIM, "Inorganic Chemistry," p. 583, 1926 ed.
[2] Radiation with respect to Raman effect also indicates the molecular form $NO_2\cdot OH$ exists in concentrated nitric acid. BRUNETTI and OLLANO, *Atti accad. Lincei*, **13**, 52 (1931).

for the esters and the concentrated acid a formula which excludes dissociation (II).

$$\{N(O_3)\}H \qquad\qquad (I) \qquad\qquad \left\{N^{(O)_2}_{OH}\right\} \qquad\qquad (II)$$

Both forms are present together in nitric acid of medium concentration. Nitric acid is thus a true acid in dilute solution and a neutral complex when concentrated. In the former, the hydrogen atom stands in the same relation to all, or at least two, of the oxygen atoms. In the second formulation, it is more closely attached to one oxygen atom. The vapor of the acid gives the same spectrum as the liquid concentrated acid, showing that the dissociating form is not present.

In studying the equilibrium of aqueous nitric acid solutions, Hantzsch[1] found that liquid nitric acid is dimolecularly associated. The relationship between the pseudo-acid (neutral form) $HO \cdot NO_2$ and the true acid $H \cdot NO_3$ for acids of varying concentrations was found by him to be as follows:

HNO_3, %	Normality	Moles H_2O per mole HNO_3	Pseudo-acid, %[1]	Undissociated true acid, %	Ionized true acid NO_3^- H^+, %
77.3	18	1.0	70	25	5
48.3	10	3.75	50	32	18
31.6	6	7.5	2	60	38

[1] Hantzsch further indicated that strong nitric acid is a mixture of pseudo-acid $(NO_2)(OH)$, nitronium nitrate $((HO)_3N)(NO_3)_2$, and hydroxonium nitrate $(NO_3)(H \cdot OH_2)$, or $(NO_3)'(OH_3)^+$.

Since the character and behavior of aqueous nitric acid undergo change as a result of dilution and since success in practically all nitrations depends on the absence of the acid or dissociating form, it is apparent that provision against dilution should be made in nitration operations. This problem is solved by adding compatible acids or their anhydrides which preferentially combine with the water in the system.

The mixture of nitric and concentrated sulfuric acids is the one most commonly used. This mixture is generally referred to as *mixed acid* and is so designated in this text. Mixtures of nitric acid and acetic acid or acetic anhydride[2] are also extensively employed, and such combinations are specifically designated.

III. MECHANISM OF THE NITRATION REACTION

Aromatic Compounds.—According to Michael[3] the first phase of nitration is an 'aldolization. Acceptance of this viewpoint not only

[1] HANTZSCH, *Ber.*, **58**, 954 (1925).

[2] May react with explosive violence.

[3] MICHAEL, *Ber.*, **29**, 1795 (1896); MICHAEL and CARLSON, *J. Am. Chem. Soc.*, **57**, 1269 (1935).

accounts for the nitration of aromatic compounds, but also elucidates the mechanism through which the nitro group actually becomes attached to the carbon. Accordingly, in the nitration of aromatic compounds, a reactive nuclear hydrogen unites with a Δ-oxygen, *i.e.*, $=O$, of the acid, and the residual aromatic group with the nitrogen, the elements of water then separating from the addition product. The nitration of benzene with nitric acid and nitrosulfuric acid may be set forth as follows:

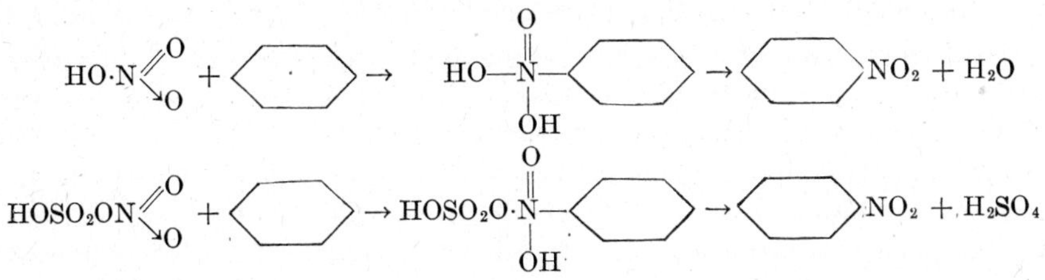

The course of nitration through aldolization is coordinated with one of the largest classes of organic reactions. These are nucleus syntheses, *i.e.*, condensations, and are based on the fundamental organic principle that substitution reactions involving a delta group always proceed through addition at the delta atoms followed by elimination; *i.e.*, they are pseudo substitutions.[1] In the nitration process the dominating forces in nitric acid and its anhydrides are the chemical potential and chemical affinity of a Δ-oxygen for a reactive nuclear H and that of N for aryl as indicated graphically above.

Olefins.—Nitrogen tri- and tetroxides, which may be considered as simple and mixed anhydrides of nitrous and nitric acids, show a highly developed additive capacity to ethylene derivatives forming nitro and nitroso derivatives instantaneously. Correspondingly, nitrosulfuric acid should form nitrosulfuric ester addition products with ethylene;[2] the

$$CH_2:CH_2 + HOSO_2 \cdot NO_2 \rightarrow CH_2OSO_2OH \cdot CH_2NO_2$$

sulfuric ester group being subsequently displaced by the stronger nitric ester radical forming the nitro nitric ester and pyrosulfuric acid as follows:

$$CH_2OSO_2OHCH_2NO_2 + HOSO_2ONO_2 \rightarrow CH_2(ONO_2)CH_2NO_2 + H_2S_2O_7$$

Michael and Carlson[3] have shown quite conclusively that the formation of the nitric acid ester of ethylene nitrohydrine with a mixture of fuming sulfuric and nitric acids does not proceed as Wieland[4] had postulated, *viz.*, by addition of HO and NO_2 to ethylene and subsequent action

[1] MICHAEL, *Ber.*, **29**, 1795 (1896); MICHAEL and CARLSON, *J. Am. Chem. Soc.*, **57**, 2169 (1935).

[2] MICHAEL and CARLSON, *J. Am. Chem. Soc.*, **57**, 1269 (1935).

[3] *Ibid.*

[4] WIELAND and coworkers, *Ber.*, **53**, 201 (1920); **54**, 1770 (1921).

of nitric acid. The acid mixture must contain the mixed anhydride, nitrosulfuric acid, which reacts as indicated above.[1]

When concentrated nitric acid is employed in the nitration of alkylenes, the nitroalkane nitric esters obtained are *not* direct products of nitration but are due to the union of ethylene with nitric oxides formed in the deoxidation of nitric acid. Oxidation is always apparent in such indirect nitrations.

Paraffins.—The nitration of paraffins with nitric acid in the liquid phase is known to be accompanied by oxidative reactions leading to the formation of higher oxides of nitrogen. The mechanism of nitration is, however, quite obscure. In the vapor phase, the reaction appears to involve a free radical mechanism.[2] Evidence in support of this theory has been adduced.[2] It has shown that every nitroparaffin has been obtained which is theoretically derivable by adding a nitro group to the free radicals obtainable from a given hydrocarbon, *e.g.*, butane and pentane, by loss of hydrogen or by fission of a carbon-to-carbon linkage (see pages 50–53). As is to be expected, the nitration of paraffins appears to be governed by the same factors as the oxidation of paraffins, in either the liquid or vapor phase (see Chap. VII). Reactions at ordinary pressures and high temperatures result in a more extensive formation of compounds of lower carbon content. Increased pressure leads to the highest yield of nitro or oxidation derivative corresponding to the paraffin employed.

IV. EXAMINATION OF NITRATING AGENTS

It is of interest, in the light of the previous discussion, to examine the more important of the nitrating agents which are tabulated on page 15.

It is apparent from an examination of the formulations for the nitrating agents that the following generalizations can be made. The nitrating agents are complexes which

1. Contain the —NO₂ group as part of a labile complex.

2. Are similar in structure to nitric acid esters, or acid anhydrides and generally the —NO₂ group is held by a shared oxygen atom.

3. Possess pronounced auxiliary valence or free energy for addition, presumably through an oxonium linkage.

4. On stabilization after nitration, an acid is split off.

5. Under certain circumstances, *e.g.*, nitration of amines, the acid split off may participate in a second reaction. *o*-Nitroacetanilide is thus made directly from aniline by reacting with acetyl nitrate or diacetyl-*o*-

---

[1] MARKOWNIKOW, *Ber.*, **32**, 1444 (1899).

[2] McCLEARY with DEGERING; *Ind. Eng. Chem.*, **30**, 64 (1938); HASS and PATTERSON; *Ind. Eng. Chem.*, **30**, 67 (1938).

nitric acid. The fission in the nitrating complex occurs in the —O|·NO$_2$ group.

EXAMINATION OF NITRATING AGENTS

Nitrating agents	Remarks	Structural formulation	Acid liberated
Nitric acid[1]	Pseudo-acid	$(HO·NO_2)_2$	$(H·OH_2)^+, (NO_3)^-$
Nitric acid anhydride[2]	N_2O_5	$O_2N·O·NO_2$	HNO_3
Nitrosulfuric acid	Mixed acid anhydride	$HO\diagdown_{\diagup}{O\ NO_2}$ (S with O, O)	H_2SO_4
Acetyl nitrate	Mixed acid anhydride	$CH_3CO·O·NO_2$	CH_3COOH
Benzoyl nitrate	Mixed acid anhydride	$C_6H_5CO·O·NO_2$	C_6H_5COOH
Diacetyl-o-nitric acid[1]	From nitrates and glacial acetic acid	$(CH_3·COOH)_2HO·NO_2$	CH_3COOH
Nitrogen tetroxide	Mixed acid anhydride, probably yielding indicated addition complex	$\begin{smallmatrix}R\diagdown\\H\diagup\end{smallmatrix}O\diagup^{NO_2}_{\diagdown NO_2}$	HNO_2

---

[1] Hantzsch has shown that concentrated nitric acid is dimolecular and exists principally in the pseudo-acid form. The reaction with the formation of hydroxonium nitrate represents the viewpoint of Hetherington and Masson. The reaction of metal nitrates and acetic acid results in an addition compound of this pseudo-acid.

[2] When alkali nitrates and sulfuric acid are used, the HNO_3 liberated in the presence of the dehydrating agents H_2SO_4—$NaHSO_4$ presumably reacts as N_2O_5. The qualitative study of mixtures of H_2SO_4, HNO_3 and H_2O by the Raman effect has shown that, in mixtures which contain little water, nitric acid is totally or partially dehydrated into its anhydride, N_2O_5.

Mixed Acids for Nitrations.—It has been shown that nitric acid alone is generally a poor nitrating agent, since its constitution undergoes change during the nitration process because water is introduced. To overcome this difficulty, it would be necessary to employ a very large excess of nitric acid. Under such circumstances, polynitro derivatives may be formed by the substitution of nitro groups for two or more hydrogen atoms. In the presence of dehydrating acids, most mononitrations can be carried out with approximately the theoretical amount of nitric acid, because nitration is presumably carried out with the mixed anhydride $HOSO_2·O·NO_2$

$$HONO_2 + H_2SO_4 \rightarrow HOSO_2O·NO_2 + H_2O$$
$$\text{Nitrosulfuric acid}$$
$$HOSO_2·ONO_2 + R·H \rightarrow R·NO_2 + H_2SO_4$$

As nitration progresses, sulfuric acid is split off and forms hydrates, and its capacity for further dehydration diminishes.

Notwithstanding the widespread belief that nitrosulfuric acid is the active nitrating agent, there is evidence that N_2O_5 is also formed as a result of the dehydrating action of concentrated sulfuric acid.   From a study of mixed acids of 100 per cent total acidity by the Raman effect, Chedin[1] obtained the following data:

HNO_3	10	20	40	60	80
H_2SO_4	90	80	60	40	20
N_2O_5	10	12.5	11.5	10	7.8
$HONO_2$	0	7.5	28.5	50	72.2

When water is present in the mixed acid, the per cent of nitric acid anhydride is markedly diminished.   Thus a mixed acid comprising 80, 10 and 10 per cent H_2SO_4, HNO_3 and H_2O, respectively, contains only 3.4 per cent N_2O_5.   Inasmuch as the water content of the nitrating acid increases during the progress of the reaction and because the nitric acid content of the mixed acid is practically exhausted in effecting mono-nitrations, it is necessary to assume that nitric acid is present also in another active form throughout the nitration process.   By combining with sulfuric acid it forms a compound with greater chemical energy. The similar preparation and successful employment of other analogous mixed anhydrides, *e.g.*, benzoyl nitrate and acetyl nitrate, constitute further evidence that nitrosulfuric acid ($HOSO_2O \cdot NO_2$) is the reactive component in mixed acid.

It is important to observe that the employment of mixed acids rather than an excess of nitric acid results in certain technical advantages. Since nitric acid is much more expensive than sulfuric acid, a considerable saving is effected.   The sulfuric acid, moreover, is recovered from the spent acid with only a slight loss.   In addition to serving as an economical dehydrating agent, the presence of sulfuric acid (as will be shown later) makes it easier to keep the reaction under control, and the milder conditions that are thus provided are instrumental in inhibiting the formation of oxidation products.   The greatest advantage, however, relates to the industrial use of mixed acid, for, unlike nitric acid, it corrodes the storage equipment and nitrating apparatus only to a very slight extent.   The low hydrogen ion concentration of mixed, or spent, nitrating acids having a total acidity in excess of 78 per cent explains why they do not appreciably attack steel at ordinary nitrating temperatures.   This fact is of great engineering importance, as it makes possible the use of iron apparatus in nitration operations.

Nitrations with Alkali Nitrates and Sulfuric Acid.—The nitric acid in mixed acids may be prepared *in situ* by using alkali nitrates and sulfuric acid.   When this method is employed, it is necessary to use somewhat more sulfuric acid, since the reaction

$$NaNO_3 + NaHSO_4 \rightarrow HNO_3 + Na_2SO_4$$

[1] CHEDIN, *Compt. rend.*, **202**, 1067 (1936).

takes place best at temperatures so high that the equilibrium

$$2HNO_3 \rightleftarrows N_2O_5 + H_2O$$

is effected. The increased velocity of decomposition of N_2O_5 results in the formation of NO_2 and O, and in the reestablishment of the preceding equilibrium more water is introduced. Therefore, any method that diminishes the temperature at which HNO_3 is liberated is favorable. For this reason, the cheaper $NaNO_3$ which decomposes at a lower temperature than does KNO_3 is used. The nitric acid liberated in this way is practically free of water.

It is interesting to recall that in the infancy of the dye industry, Perkin employed this method of nitration because no other satisfactory method was then available for obtaining nitrating acids of high total acidity.

A number of patents have been taken out utilizing this procedure, particularly for the preparation of nitrochlorobenzenes. This method of nitration is unquestionably of great value in plants not possessing facilities for the denitration and concentration of spent acids. Generally speaking, however, the substitution of nitrates introduces mechanical difficulties as well as problems in obtaining a pure product and consequently has been adopted to only a limited extent.

Nitrations with Organic Nitrates.—Pictet[1] found that acetic anhydride and nitric acid anhydride N_2O_5 combined to form acetyl nitrate:

$$\begin{matrix} CH_3 \cdot CO \\ \diagdown \\ CH_3 \cdot CO \diagup \end{matrix} O + O \begin{matrix} \diagup NO_2 \\ \diagdown NO_2 \end{matrix} \rightarrow 2CH_3 \cdot CO \cdot O \cdot NO_2.$$

An analogous nitrate was prepared by Francis[2] through a double decomposition involving benzoyl chloride and silver nitrate:

$$C_6H_5 \cdot CO \cdot Cl + AgO \cdot NO_2 \rightarrow AgCl + C_6H_5 \cdot CO \cdot O \cdot NO_2$$

Both acetyl and benzoyl nitrates are energetic nitrating agents for aromatic compounds dissolved in carbon tetrachloride or acetic anhydride. These nitrates react readily with alcohols yielding nitric acid esters. Acetyl nitrate as well as diacetyl nitrate can nitrate and acetylate amines. When 1 mole of acetyl nitrate reacts with 2 moles of aniline dissolved in carbon tetrachloride at $-15°C.$, equimolecular proportions of acetanilide and aniline nitrate are obtained. On further nitration with a larger ratio of acetyl nitrate, o-nitroacetanilide is obtained.

In carbon tetrachloride, both acetyl nitrate and benzoyl nitrate convert acetanilide principally to o-nitroacetanilide[3] ($o = 84.9$ per cent; $m = 2.2$ per cent; $p = 14.9$ per cent).

[1] PICTET, *Ber.*, **40**, 1163 (1907).
[2] FRANCIS, *Ber.*, **39**, 3798 (1906).
[3] HOLLEMAN, *Ber.* **44**, 717 (1911).

Nitrations with Metal Nitrates.—Numerous metal nitrates, particularly those that have a low decomposition temperature, can, in acetic anhydride, or glacial acetic acid solution, serve as nitrating agents.[1] Cupric, ferric, and aluminum nitrates are satisfactory substitutes for nitric acid in this process. The procedure is characterized by the dual activity of the acetyl nitrate mixture. When amines are reacted upon, both acetylation and nitration occur. Thus, o-nitroacetanilide is obtained by treating aniline in acetic anhydride with cupric nitrate at 30°C.

When phenol in acetic anhydride is reacted upon by ferric nitrate dissolved in acetic anhydride, picric acid is obtained directly. Benzene, chlorobenzene, etc., can similarly be converted to mononitro compounds.

The nitration method employing nitrates and acetic anhydride or glacial acetic acid appears to proceed through the intermediate formation of diacetyl-o-nitric acid. Pictet first prepared this compound from glacial acetic acid and nitric acid and ascribed to it the formula (I). Spectroscopic studies by Hantzsch indicated the complex involving

$$\begin{array}{c} CH_3 \cdot COO \\ \\ CH_3 \cdot COO \end{array} \!\! N \!\! < \!\! \begin{array}{c} OH \\ OH \\ OH \end{array} \qquad \text{(I)}$$

$$[(CH_3 \cdot COOH)_2 HO \cdot NO_2] \qquad \text{(II)}$$

pseudo-nitric acid (II). Bacharach[2] has established the existence of diacetyl-o-nitric acid in the nitration mixture, $Cu(NO_3)_2 \cdot 3H_2O$—$(CH_3 \cdot CO)_2O$, and has employed it for the preparation of o-nitroacetanilide from aniline.

Nitrations in the Presence of Nitrosulfonic Acid.—Although nitrosulfonic acid is introduced or formed in certain nitration operations, its rôle in the reaction is still obscure. Generally, its activity is interpreted as being that of an energetic dehydrating agent.

The constitution of nitrosulfonic acid itself is still uncertain, but it appears capable of existing in isomeric forms.[3] The formulations below indicate that three isomers are possible.

$$O_2S \!\! < \!\! \begin{array}{c} NO_2 \\ OH \end{array} \qquad \text{(I)}$$

$$O_2S \!\! < \!\! \begin{array}{c} O \cdot NO \\ OH \end{array} \qquad \text{(II)}$$

$$O \cdot S \!\! < \!\! \begin{array}{c} O \cdot NO_2 \\ OH \end{array} \qquad \text{(III)}$$

In (I), nitrogen is attached to sulfur as a comparatively stable complex. The structure of (II) corresponds to the colorless crystals of nitrosyl-

---

[1] MENKE, *Rec. trav. chim.*, **44**, 141, 270 (1925).

[2] BACHARACH, *Ber.*, **64**, 2136 (1931).

[3] BEHRINGER and BORSUM, *Ber.*, **49**, 1402 (1916).

sulfuric acid. In concentrated sulfuric acid, some of this acid is converted to the nitro form, as indicated by the appearance of the yellow color, but it cannot nitrate benzene. The —O·NO form, since it is the anhydride of nitrous and sulfuric acid, presumably is responsible for the nitrosations of aniline and naphthalene obtained by Gerard and Pabst.[1] The existence of isomer (III) is hypothetical. It is doubtful whether nitrosulfonic acid could nitrate directly unless it was available in this form.

Varma[2] produced a whole series of nitro compounds employing nitrosulfonic acid in fuming nitric acid. He concluded that nitrosulfonic acid functions because of its dehydrating action, in which respect it is more efficacious than sulfuric acid. The nitrating agent was prepared by passing a stream of sulfur dioxide into cold fuming nitric acid (sp. gr., 1.502) until the yield of nitrosulfonic acid was about 50 per cent. Crystals of the acid have *no* effect on benzene, whereas a mixture of benzene, sulfuric acid, and nitrosulfonic acid blackens on warming but yields no nitrobenzene. However, when a 46 per cent solution of nitrosulfonic acid in fuming nitric acid is used, a good yield of nitrobenzene is obtained. The constitution of the real nitrating acid is, however, obscure because of the probable oxidizing action of fuming nitric acid.

Nitration with Nitrogen Tetroxide.[3]—Whereas nitric acid anhydride is one of the most vigorous of nitrating agents, nitrogen tetroxide alone exhibits very little reactivity with benzene, chlorobenzene, or toluene. By allowing such reactions to proceed for weeks, only small quantities of oxidation and reduction products are formed. This behavior is to be attributed to the weak capacity of N_2O_4 to add to benzenoid compounds not containing the —OH group. Although nitrogen tetroxide adds immediately to olefins, the reaction is very complex, since mixtures of easily decomposed substances are obtained. Such heterogeneous activity is believed to be due to the existence of isomers of N_2O_4 in equilibrium, dependent on the concentration and temperature.[4]

With increasing substitution in the benzene ring, the capacity of the aromatic compound to react with N_2O_4 alone increases. Naphthalene is readily nitrated by means of nitrogen tetroxide. The initially formed N_2O_4 addition compound decomposes soon after its formation into nitrous acid and nitronaphthalene. Aniline and phenol react with N_2O_4 with similar ease, catalysts being unnecessary in the treatment of these compounds. If $AlCl_3$ be added, N_2O_4 exerts a violent oxidizing effect. It is interesting to note that naphthalene reacts smoothly with N_2O_4

[1] Gerard and Pabst, *Ber.*, **12**, 365 (1879).

[2] Varma, *J. Am. Chem. Soc.*, **47**, 143 (1925).

[3] At low temperatures, nitrogen peroxide has a molecular weight corresponding to N_2O_4; on vaporization it is practically completely dissociated to the dioxide.

[4] Schaarschmidt, *Z. angew. Chem.*, **37**, 933 (1924).

in carbon tetrachloride solution but is indifferent in ether solution. This difference is due to the formation of an addition compound of N_2O_4 with ether, which no longer is capable of addition to naphthalene.

In the presence of anhydrous aluminum chloride (or, preferably, stannic chloride), benzene, chlorobenzene, and toluene form stable addition compounds with N_2O_4,[1] *e.g.*, $2AlCl_3 \cdot 3(C_6H_5 \cdot Cl : N_2O_4)$. On hydrolysis, these hygroscopic metal complexes are decomposed and yield a nitro compound and nitrous acid. When nitric oxide or nitrous oxide is treated similarly with chlorobenzene, no reaction takes place. If, however, N_2O_3 is employed, the result is different. In the latter instance, the NO_2 portion of the nitrogen trioxide reacts, with the liberation of the corresponding quantity of NO.

Silica gel, like $AlCl_3$, apparently has the power to activate a hydrogen atom in the benzene ring, and at 310°C. it can be used as a specific catalyst for the vapor-phase nitration of benzene with nitrogen dioxide (NO_2). McKee and Wilhelm[2] found that the percentage nitration was a function of the ratio $NO_2 : C_6H_6$. When the mole fraction of NO_2 in the binary reaction mixture is 0.88, the conversion of benzene to nitrobenzene is approximately 83 per cent. Accompanying the nitration reaction there is a reduction of approximately 1.5 moles of nitrogen dioxide to nitric oxide per mole of nitrobenzene produced. In operations involving the recycling of exit gases, the nitric oxide would of course have to be reoxidized.

$$2NO + O_2 \rightleftharpoons 2NO_2 \rightleftharpoons N_2O_4$$
$$\text{Colorless} \qquad \text{Brown} \quad \text{Colorless}$$

When phenols are dissolved in a benzene solution of nitrogen tetroxide, they are readily nitrated. In this way *o*- and *p*-nitrophenols are obtained from phenol. Similarly, *o*-cresol yields 3- and 5-nitro-*o*-cresols, and cellulose yields cellulose nitrates.[3]

Nitrogen tetroxide in the presence of strong sulfuric acid[4] is a good nitrating agent, and yields of approximately 90 per cent of the theoretical have been obtained with it in the nitration of benzene, toluene, and naphthalene. Pinck states that "in such a system, about 50 per cent of the nitrogen tetroxide[4] is utilized in the nitration of the organic substance, and approximately 50 per cent is combined with the sulfuric acid in the form of nitrosylsulfuric acid." The complete reaction for a single-step nitration for benzene, for example, can be represented by the following equation:

$$C_6H_6 + N_2O_4 + H_2SO_4 \rightarrow C_6H_5NO_2 + O_2S\begin{smallmatrix} OH \\ NO_2 \end{smallmatrix} + H_2O$$

[1] Schaarschmidt; *Z. angew. Chem.*, **39**, 1459 (1926); *Ber.*, **58**B, 499 (1925).
[2] McKee and Wilhelm, *Ind. Eng. Chem.*, **28**, 662 (1936).
[3] U. S. 1,917,400 (1933).
[4] Pinck, *J. Am. Chem. Soc.*, **49**, 2536 (1927).

The intermediate steps of the nitration process are as yet obscure. The addition complex of nitrogen tetroxide with sulfuric acid (A), which would contain the —O—NO$_2$ group, may well be the active agent. The formation of similar oxonium compounds presumably accounts for the successful nitration of phenols and carbohydrates with N$_2$O$_4$.

(A)

$$\underset{O}{\overset{HO}{\diagdown}}\ \underset{O}{\overset{O\,H}{\diagup}}\ S \cdots \underset{NO_2}{\overset{NO_2}{\diagup}}$$

$$\nearrow HNOSO_4 + HNO_3 \qquad (B)$$
$$\searrow HOSO_2O\cdot NO_2 + HNO_2 \qquad (C)$$

There is also the possibility that the moderately active nitric acid may be liberated along with nitrosylsulfuric acid (B).[1,2] Most probably the addition complex liberates the mixed anhydride nitrosulfuric acid (HOSO$_2$O·NO$_2$) and HNO$_2$. Nitrosulfuric acid is definitely known to be an active nitrating agent and, furthermore, the liberation of nitrous acid is in accordance with the findings of Schaarschmidt using AlCl$_3$. The HNO$_2$ will here combine with the excess of H$_2$SO$_4$ to produce the end product found by Taylor[2] and by Pinck,[1] *viz.*, HNOSO$_4$.

Table IV presents data relating to the preparation of nitrobenzene.

TABLE IV.—NITRATION OF BENZENE[1]
Molecular Ratio of N$_2$O$_4$ to C$_6$H$_6$ = 1.05

Expt. No.	Molar ratio H$_2$SO$_4$:C$_6$H$_6$	Conc. of H$_2$SO$_4$	Temp., °C.	Yield of nitrobenzene (steam distilled), %
1	1.25	95	40 to 50	81.3
2	1.50	95	50 to 60	89.5
3	1.75	95	55 to 60	94.4
4	1.25	85	40	70.2
5	1.50	85	40 to 50	80.7
6	1.50	90	40 to 50	86.3

[1] According to Pinck.

V. MIXED ACID FOR NITRATIONS

Discussion.—The nitrating acid best suited for the preparation of each nitro compound should be the subject of thoughtful consideration. It is apparent, for example, that mononitrations may be carried out with more dilute acids and under milder conditions of temperature than are required for polynitro compounds.   Moreover, the nitration of the former may be made with only a slight excess (1 to 2 per cent) of nitric acid in the mixed acid, whereas in the preparation of the higher nitrated compounds the nitric acid content of the spent acid ranges from 3 to 10 per cent.

[1] PINCK. *J. Am. Chem. Soc.*, **49**, 2536 (1927).
[2] Taylor and Richardson, U. S. 1,640,737 (1927).

In considering the composition of mixed acids, it is necessary to arrive at an understanding regarding the relationship of the three constituents HNO_3, H_2SO_4, and H_2O.   For example, if the total acidity or water content of a mixed acid is kept constant and H_2SO_4 is replaced by HNO_3, it would appear possible under such circumstances to maintain a definite excess of HNO_3 to organic compound and to nitrate progressively increasing quantities of material.   Accompanying the replacement of H_2SO_4 by HNO_3 under such conditions, there will be a proportionate increase in the water of reaction, and a corresponding decrease in the ratio of H_2SO_4 to H_2O at the close of nitration.   Since excessive dilution of the nitric acid at the end of a run is conducive to incomplete nitration and loss of volatile organic compounds, such a practice is productive of low yields of nitro compound.   If, on the other hand, HNO_3 is similarly replaced by H_2SO_4, still maintaining the same total acidity and nitric acid ratio to the organic compound, it is obvious that the productive capacity of the nitrator will be diminished, and a larger amount of spent acid will be produced.

It appears advisable, therefore, to formulate the composition of the mixed acid so that a definite optimum relationship exists at the close of nitration between the sulfuric acid and water.   This relationship is usually termed the *dehydrating value of sulfuric acid* (*D.V.S.*).[1]   It is expressed numerically by the quotient obtained by dividing the actual sulfuric acid content of the mixed acid by the total water present when nitration is completed.   The latter figure includes, in addition to the water of reaction, the water that is introduced with the mixed acid and organic compound.

If, for example, a mixed acid of the following composition is used for the nitration of benzene, the dehydrating value of sulfuric acid may be calculated as follows:

$$\text{Composition of mixed acid} \begin{cases} H_2SO_4 = 60\,\% \\ HNO_3 = 32\,\% \\ H_2O \;\;= \;\,8\,\% \end{cases}$$

Mol. wts.	$\begin{cases} \text{Benzene} \\ \;\;78 \end{cases}$	$+$	nitric acid 63	$\rightarrow$	water 18	$+$	nitrobenzene 123

When molecular proportions of acid and hydrocarbon are used, the water formed per 100 lb. of mixed acid (32 per cent HNO_3) will be

$$\frac{63}{18} : \frac{32}{X} \qquad X = 9.14 = \text{water of nitration}$$

To this must be added the water that already exists in the mixed acid.

$$D.V.S. = \frac{\text{actual } H_2SO_4 = 60}{9.14 + 8} = 3.50$$

[1] In some chemical plants, this relationship is called *spent-acid concentrations.*

The calculations in terms of hydrocarbon are

$$\frac{78}{63} = 1.238 = \text{factor hydrocarbon to HNO}_3$$

$1.238 \times 32 = 39.62 = $ pounds of hydrocarbon to be used per 100 lb. of mixed acid containing 32 per cent HNO_3.

$$\frac{78}{18} : \frac{100}{X} \qquad X = 23.08 = \text{water of nitration per 100 lb. hydrocarbon}$$

$$23.08 \times \frac{39.62}{100} = 9.14 \text{ lb. water of nitration per 100 lb. of mixed acid}$$

In actual practice, the relationship between hydrocarbon and nitric acid is worked out in advance, and allowance is made for the presence of an excess over theory of HNO_3 during nitration. The calculations may be made with reference to either hydrocarbon or nitric acid, thus: when 95 per cent of the theoretical hydrocarbon is used, the hydrocarbon factor is

$$\frac{C_6H_6}{HNO_3} = \frac{78}{63} = 1.24 \div 1.05\,\% = 1.18 = \text{hydrocarbon factor}$$

$1.18 \times \%HNO_3$ in M/A* (32) $= 37.76 = $ lb. of hydrocarbon per 100 lb. M/A

Water of nitration per 100 lb. hydrocarbon $\frac{78}{18} : \frac{100}{X} = 23.08$

$$\frac{37.76 \times 23.08}{100} = 8.71 = \text{water of nitration per 100 lb. mixed acid}$$

The same results are obtained by making the calculations with reference to a nitric acid ratio; thus, if instead of a 95 per cent hydrocarbon ratio, a 105 per cent nitric ratio is used:

Ratio HNO_3 to hydrocarbon $\frac{63}{78} = 0.808 \times 105\,\% = 0.848$

$\dfrac{\text{Per cent HNO}_3 \text{ in mixed acid} = 32}{\text{HNO}_3 \text{ ratio to hydrocarbon} = 0.848} = 37.74$ lb. of hydrocarbon per 100 lb. mixed

acid of 32 % HNO_3 content

$\text{D.V.S.} = \dfrac{\text{actual H}_2\text{SO}_4 \text{ in } M/A = 60}{\text{H}_2\text{O of nitration, 8.71} + \text{water in } M/A, 8} = 3.59$

The control of the D.V.S. is a matter of great practical importance in maintaining high efficiencies in nitrating operations. In the nitration of benzene, for example, when acids of the following compositions were used, (I) would often show the presence of unnitrated benzene and generally gave lower yields in spite of the fact that the total acidities are the same.

(I) D.V.S. 2.96		(II) D.V.S. 3.51
%		%
54.0	H_2SO_4	60.0
38.0	HNO_3	32.0
8.0	H_2O	8.0

* M/A = mixed acid.

Use of Cycle Acid in Nitration.—The term *cycle acid* is used to describe that portion of the spent acid from nitrations that is used over again in ensuing operations. The use of cycle acid, which is essentially diluted sulfuric acid, in starting a nitration is merely another phase of the well-founded practice of using mixed, instead of straight nitric acid. From experience, it has been found that the use of an acid having approximately the same composition as that naturally formed in the reaction would accentuate the smoothness of react on and furthermore introduce a factor of safety by causing the organic compound to come in contact first with dilute sulfuric acid and then gradually with the stronger nitrating acid which was delivered to the nitrator. The approximate composition of spent acid from the mononitration of benzene is as follows:

H_2SO_4... 80 to 85 %
HNO_3... 3 to 0 %
H_2O... 17 to 15 %

The principle underlying the use of cycle acid is based on the fact that, compared to cycle acid, the concentrated sulfuric and nitric acids employed for nitration possess a high integral heat of dilution[1] and com-

TABLE V.—HEAT CAPACITY OF SULFURIC ACID (15°C.)

Sp. gr.	H_2SO_4, %	Specific heat	Sp. gr.	H_2SO_4, %	Specific heat
1.841	98.5	0.33	1.71	77.5	0.41
1.839	95.0	0.34	1.61	69.0	0.45
1.820	90.0	0.36	1.53	62.5	0.49
1.77	83.4	0.38	1.45	55.0	0.55

paratively low heat capacity. This accounts for the difficulty in controlling nitrating operations at the start and the fact that the reaction runs smoothly as soon as some of the nitric acid is replaced by the water of nitration. The problem of temperature control is thus simplified by the use of cycle acid which quickly absorbs the heat developed and transfers it to the cooling system that is provided.

The method of nitrating with cycle acid is consequently characterized by the introduction into the nitrator of a considerable weight of material, inert as far as conditions of nitration are concerned. This would be a serious handicap if provisions were not made systematically to remove this diluent from the vessel. The withdrawal of cycle acid is termed *bleeding* the nitrator, and this acid resulting from the bleeding process is, of course, subsequently returned to the nitrator.

VI. FACTORS AFFECTING NITRATION

Influence of Nitration Temperature.—In contradistinction to sulfonation, the nitrating temperature has comparatively no directive influence

[1] RHODES and NELSON, *Ind. Eng. Chem.*, **30**, 648 (1938).

on the position taken by the entering —NO₂ group, but it is of importance in controlling the purity of the reaction product. With ascending temperatures, the degree of nitration is increased so that a proportional amount of a higher nitrated product is formed. The deleterious influence which such impurities may exercise in subsequent operations is apparent. Nitric acid is furthermore a good oxidizing agent, its activity becoming more pronounced at higher temperatures. Part of the raw material may thus be converted into valueless products which not only lower the

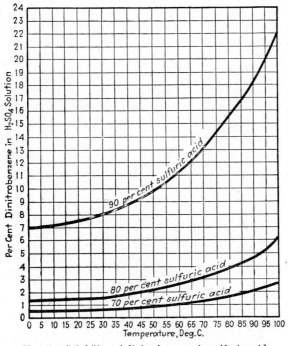

Fig. 1.—Solubility of dinitrobenzene in sulfuric acid.

direct yields but also make purification of the nitro compound imperative. The presence of sulfuric acid, along with red oxide of nitrogen (NO₂), tends to the formation of nitrosylsulfuric acid, a compound possessing strong oxidizing properties, which may also cause oxidation when the dehydrating strength of the mixed acid is low. It is therefore of the greatest importance, especially when nitrating a compound that is easily oxidized, to keep the temperature sufficiently low to prevent this action. Oxidation is accompanied by the development of nitrogen oxides, which may cause further complications in case the material being nitrated will react with nitrous acid. Included in this category are amino compounds which may first be converted to diazo compounds and subsequently to hydroxy compounds; also, the alkylated amino compounds and hydroxy compounds which are able to form nitroso compounds by the action of nitrous acid. For this reason, it is advisable to protect amino and hydroxyl groups by converting them into their acetyl compounds by means of glacial acetic acid. Formic acid and benzaldehyde may also be used for this purpose but for economic reasons they have not been widely adopted. By hydrolyzing the nitrated acyl compound, the desired nitro derivative is obtained.

The nitration process is distinctly exothermic, partly on account of the heat of nitration of the nitro compounds (see page 53) and partly from the heat of hydration of the sulfuric acid that is present. It is necessary, therefore, to provide the nitrator with cooling surfaces to maintain the desired operating temperature. Such heat-exchange surfaces may also be used to heat the charge at the close of the run, should this be necessary to complete the reaction. Since polynitro derivatives are unstable at high temperatures, it is important to keep the operating temperature under control. Picric acid and trinitrotoluene obtained by the nitration of phenol and toluene, respectively, are widely used as military explosives, and the necessity for maintaining a safe operating technic in their preparation is thoroughly appreciated.

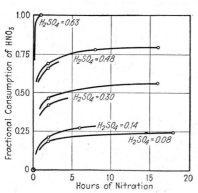

Fig. 2.—Speed of consumption of nitric acid in certain nitrating acids with the molar fractions of H_2SO_4 shown.

Solubility.—The solubility of the nitro compounds in sulfuric acid is another factor of primary importance. The increase in solubility with rise of temperature and decrease with dilution of the acid are shown in Fig. 1 for dinitrobenzene. Since nitro compounds are more soluble in the more concentrated sulfuric acid, a mixed acid of high H_2SO_4 concentration increases the speed of arrival at the eventual degree of nitration. The effect which the sulfuric acid content has on the speed of dinitration of nitrobenzene is shown by the curves of Fig. 2. Here the fractional consumption of nitric acid plotted against the reaction time is shown.[1]

VII. EQUIPMENT FOR NITRATIONS

Nitrating Apparatus.—Most nitrations are carried out in closed iron vessels which are provided with an agitating mechanism and means for controlling the reaction temperature. Nitrators are usually constructed

[1] HETHERINGTON and MASSON, *J. Chem. Soc.*, **1933**, 109.

of acid-resisting cast iron, but often steel and acid-resistant alloys are used, particularly in the manufacture of polynitro compounds. These vessels may be obtained in sizes ranging from 1 gal. capacity for laboratory use to 1,600 gal. or more capacity for economical industrial operations. Most of the tools provided by equipment manufacturers possess some valuable characteristics which make each one particularly useful for a definite set of conditions. Three types of apparatus are discussed in these pages in order to provide a basis for studying the two essential attributes of a safe and efficient nitrator, heat exchange, and agitation.

The importance of temperature control arises from the fact that the nitration process is highly exothermic. Furthermore, the additional heat introduced because of the heat of hydration of the sulfuric acid that is present penalizes the reaction by increasing the time cycle. In this connection, it must be noted that when temperature regulation is dependent solely on external jackets, a disproportional increase in nitrator capacity as compared with jacket surface occurs when the size of the machine is enlarged. Thus, if the volume is increased from 400 to 800 gal., the heat-exchange area increases as the square and the volume as the cube of the expanded unit. To overcome this fault, internal cooling coils and tubes are introduced, and these have proved satisfactory when installed on the basis of sound calculations which include the several thermal factors entering into this unit process.[1]

The necessity for providing an efficient agitation inside the nitrator is of great importance. Reference has already been made to the increased reaction velocity resulting from a more efficient agitation. Of equal importance is the fact that, in a properly designed apparatus, local overheating at the point where the acid and organic compound first make contact is avoided and a safer operation is insured. Furthermore, the smoothness of the reaction depends on the dispersion of the reacting material as it comes in contact with the charge in the nitrator so that a fairly uniform temperature is maintained throughout the vessel.

Nitrators are usually equipped with one of three general types of agitating mechanism. These may be designated as (1) single or double impeller; (2) propeller or turbine, with or without sleeve; and (3) outside tunnel circulation. Reproductions of such vessels along with pertinent operating data are given on following pages.

The *single-impeller* agitator consists of one vertical shaft containing horizontal arms. The shaft may be placed off center in order to create rapid circulation past, or local turbulence at, the point of contact between the nitrating acid and the organic compound.

[1] Reference to works on *unit operations* in chemical engineering is valuable for such studies (see WALKER, LEWIS, and MCADAMS, "Principles of Chemical Engineering"; also BADGER and MCCABE, "Elements of Chemical Engineering").

The *double-impeller* agitator consists of two vertical shafts rotating in opposite directions.   To each shaft is attached a series of horizontal arms.   The lower blades have an upward thrust while the upper ones repel the liquid downward.   The contents of such nitrators are practically homogeneous.   The volume increases as the nitration progresses, and in such vessels it is not advantageous to use cycle acid, for it cannot be drawn off.

The term *sleeve-and-propeller* agitation is usually applied when the nitrator is equipped with a vertical sleeve through which the charge is

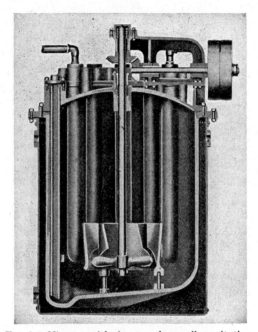

Fig. 3.—Nitrator with sleeve-and-propeller agitation.

circulated by the action of a marine propeller or turbine.   The sleeve is usually made of a solid bank of acid-resisting cooling coils through which cold water or brine is made to circulate at a calculated rate.   In order to obtain the maximum efficiency with this type of nitrator, it is essential to maintain a rapid circulation of liquid upward or downward in the sleeves and past the coils.   Obtaining the desired velocity of the liquid is a matter of regulating the speed of the propeller used.

The size of the propeller is determined by the diameter of the machine, and when a ratio of 1:3 is maintained, the r.p.m. of the propeller may be kept fairly low, *i.e.*, 150 to 250 r.p.m., and still obtain the desired velocity. The sleeve, which is slightly larger in diameter than the propeller used, can be made of cast iron (Fig. 3) or preferably may consist of lead or iron cooling coils (Fig. 5) placed in the center of the nitrator and supported by legs at the desired height to allow sufficient space for the liquid to be returned to the sleeve after it has been forced out of the top and down past the coils. The height of the sleeve must be such that it comes within 2 or 3 in. of the top layer of cooling coils, which usually occupy about one-half the depth of the nitrator.

Two stationary propellers of opposite pitch are often placed inside the sleeve, a few inches above the revolving propeller, in order to cut down the swirl, thus increasing the pumping capacity of the propeller. As the propeller revolves, the liquid is forced up through it and strikes an annular baffle plate, elevated above the top of the sleeve, thus diverting the flow of the liquid first in a lateral and then in a vertical direction downward past the cooling coils. The distance of the baffle above the top of the sleeve must be such as to cause no appreciable resistance to the liquid, or excessive nitration will take place inside the sleeve.

When nitrating aromatic hydrocarbons, the nitrating acid is generally fed into the spent or cycle acid by means of an annular acid distributor placed a few inches directly under the revolving propeller. By delivering the mixed acid into the cycle acid, the nitration is made with a fortified spent acid, and this practice is conducive to a better control of temperature. In the nitration of polyhydric alcohols, the organic compound may be distributed over the charge and then drawn or beaten into the acid, which may be either a concentrated mixed acid or a fortified cycle acid.

When nitrating benzene or toluene in the sleeve-and-propeller type of nitrator, two distinct layers of liquid are maintained throughout most of the nitration—a lower one of spent acid and an upper one consisting of hydrocarbon and nitrohydrocarbon. As the propeller forces the cycle acid, which has been fortified by the addition of mixed nitrating acid, through the sleeve, it attacks a portion of the hydrocarbon layer without breaking the surface. As nitration nears completion, the specific gravity of the cycle acid decreases and the nitrated hydrocarbon increases to approximately the same density, after which the two liquids are uniformly mixed by the agitation but separate very rapidly when agitation is discontinued.

A syphon or overflow system is used to maintain constant level in the nitrator. The withdrawal of the cycle acid is generally made from the bottom of the nitrator, as near the center as is possible. The amount of hydrocarbon carried off through the bleeding system is governed by the following factors: (1) speed of agitation; (2) distance of propeller from the bottom of the nitrator; and (3) the shape of the bottom of the nitrator.

The most satisfactory results may be obtained by running the propeller at a speed that insures turning the charge over from two to three times per minute and placing the propeller at such a distance from the bottom of the nitrator that very little agitation occurs at the bottom level of the cycle acid. A cone-shaped nitrator bottom, or one having a deep well at the base, is undoubtedly the most practical, for in this way a dead pocket of cycle acid would be formed, thus eliminating the probability of a large amount of hydrocarbon being carried off with the cycle acid.

Outside Tunnel Circulation.—Agitation which is brought about by circulating the cooled nitrator charge through outside tunnels is a char-

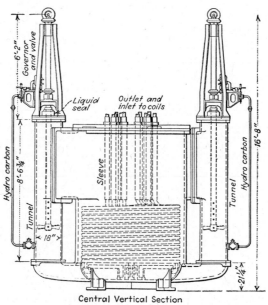

Central Vertical Section

Fig. 4.—Hough nitrator, cast iron, with external tunnels.

acteristic of the *Hough nitrator*. This nitrator, is built with two tunnels, one on either side of the body of the nitrator. There are two impellers revolving at from 200 to 400 r.p.m., according to the size of the machine. In this type, the contents of the nitrator are completely circulated once each minute, the rate of circulation of the liquid through the tunnels in a large-size machine being about 2,500 gal. per minute.

Well down the tunnels, and under the impellers, is the injector for the hydrocarbon to be nitrated and for the nitration acid. The latter is forced in a small stream into the benzene-cycle acid mixture so that approximately 1 lb. of incoming nitrating acid comes in contact with 1,000 lb. of material in the nitrator. This is a desirable condition to obtain in nitration and prevents any local rise of temperature.

By referring to the drawing of this machine (Fig. 4), it will be seen that the circulation of the liquid is from the lower part of the tunnel over the port and into the body of the machine. Obviously, in order to function properly, the ports must be covered at the start with a liquid heavier then the hydrocarbon or substituted hydrocarbon to be introduced. The cycle acid system of nitration brings this condition about in an ideal manner.

For the first run of the nitrator, a charge of sulfuric and nitric acid corresponding to the normal spent acid obtained from the nitration must be prepared. This acid is placed in the nitrator so as to cover and just overflow the ports of the machine. The agitator (impeller) is now started up, and the whole of the benzene charge is run into the machine through the injector pipes at the side of the tunnels. It is quite immaterial how fast it is run in, as the agitation is efficient, and the amount of nitric acid in the cycle acid so small that practically no elevation of temperature occurs. As soon as all the benzene is in, the nitrating mixed acid is forced in through the injector pipes, keeping the temperature within the desired limit. It is quite possible to conduct a run in this way at a temperature of 60°C., without the least danger of the temperature's rising beyond control.

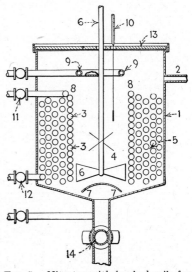

FIG. 5.—Nitrator with banked coils for continuous or batch nitrations.

After all the nitrating acid has been added, the temperature may be held at 90°C. for two hours to complete the reaction.

The withdrawal of the original cycle acid is started at the moment the nitrating acids are being added. Just as much cycle acid is drawn from the nitrator as nitration acid is added, the volume in the nitrator being maintained practically constant. The withdrawal of the cycle acid is done from a cock placed at the lowest point of the nitrator, where there is least agitation. A very small amount of nitrobenzene, of course, is carried along with the cycle acid. The acid collected from the *bleeding* process is subsequently returned to the nitrator, fresh benzene is added, and then nitrated in the manner previously described.

Continuous Nitrations.—The apparatus shown in Fig. 5[1] may be employed for both batch and continuous operations. The nitrator comprises two compartments, an inner mixing chamber 4 surrounded by a

[1] U. S. 1,893,447 (1933).

solid bank of cooling coils 3 and an outer cooling zone 5 containing an elaborate system of cooling coils.

In the nitration of polyhydric alcohols, the vessel is charged with sufficient cycle acid just to overflow through pipe 2, and the concentrated nitrating acid is admitted at the lower portion of the vessel under the distributer baffle 7. The stirrer causes the fortified acid mixture to travel upward through the outer cooling chamber, and as it flows over the coils at 8 it receives the polyhydric alcohol, *e.g.*, glycerol, or glycol, which is delivered through the distributor pipe 9.

The heat of reaction is taken up by the precooled acid, and therefore no appreciable rise in temperature occurs in the reaction zone. The passage of the charge downward through the inner mixing chamber is sufficiently rapid, and the reaction mixture is quickly forced into the dense network of cooling coils in the cooling chamber. Because the mixing zone is free of pockets or obstacles, there is a thorough incorporation of the newly formed nitro compound, and local temperature differences do not arise.

When polyhydric alcohols are to be nitrated in a continuous manner, a quantity of the reaction mixture corresponding to the quantity of reactants introduced is run off through the overflow pipe 2, this outlet maintaining a practically constant level of liquid during nitration. Since the reaction temperature is practically constant and uniform throughout the process, there is a possibility that the yields of organic nitrate may not be so high as that obtained in batch operations wherein the temperature is slightly raised at the close of the operation to insure complete nitration. The nitrator is emptied through connection 14 at the base when operations are suspended.

This system may be employed for nitrations in general, since the circulation of the charge can readily be directed up or down in the mixing chamber and the nitrating acid and organic compound may be admitted through any suitable connections.

For the nitration of hydrocarbons, it is desirable to equip the propeller with emulsifying vanes and to ensure the admission of air into the free space in the nitration. The air which is drawn into the mixing chamber serves to disperse the drops of hydrocarbon; *e.g.*, toluene delivered by distributer 9, and thus facilitates nitration.[1]

McCormack has found that the process of adding the material to be nitrated to the mixed acid is likely to be successful when the desired compound is the highest nitro derivative readily formed.[2] When this is the case, the process has some operating advantages and can be conducted with a somewhat lower cost for nitrating acid.

[1] Brit. 455,570 (1935).
[2] McCormack, *Ind. Eng. Chem.*, **29**, 1335 (1937).

VIII. TECHNICAL NITRATIONS

General Remarks Regarding the Technical Preparation of Inter-mediates.—The following paragraphs present methods for the production of some of the more important nitro compounds. In these syntheses, as in the other technical operations described in this volume, the heavy chemicals used are the usual high-grade technical quality. The cyclic hydrocarbons or their derivatives are generally purchased in quantity by contract according to well-defined specifications regarding their physical properties and chemical behavior. It is common practice to analyze samples of each shipment received, and these analyses form the basis for subsequent yield calculations. It is customary in chemical plants to take stock of all materials monthly and to calculate the yields obtained, the latter being usually expressed as pounds of finished product per 100 lb. of raw material used.

PREPARATION OF NITROBENZENE

In the following paragraphs, a study will be made of some of the more important details of nitrobenzene manufacture in order that the observations may be of value in the preparation of the other nitro compounds that will later be described. The description which follows assumes the use of cycle acid, although this practice is neither general nor essential, particularly when the problem of heat transfer has been satisfactorily solved.

Nitration.—The operation commences by delivering to the nitrator sufficient cycle acid, *i.e.*, spent acid from a previous charge in which some nitrobenzene and nitric acid are still present. The amount of such acid required depends on the type of nitrator used. In the sleeve-and-propeller type, it must cover the propeller; and in the Hough nitrator, it must cover and overflow through the ports of the machine. Cold water is then circulated through the heat-exchange medium; and when the temperature is 50°C. or lower, the charge of benzene is pumped from the scale tank into the nitrator.

The mixed acid for nitration can be fed on top of the hydrocarbon or under the surface. When top feed is used, there is always a slight loss of benzene vapors due to the reaction with surface hydrocarbon accompanied by the local evolution of heat. When undersurface feed is used in conjunction with paddle-type agitators, the acid runs into a lead funnel placed on the agitator just above the top paddle. A lead pipe leads from the funnel to one of the lower paddles, where it makes a loop upward. The loop in the lead pipe is always full and prevents spluttering, as the mixed acid now comes in contact with the cycle acid at the lower part of the nitrator instead of making direct contact with benzene. A similar feeding arrangement is made for the sleeve-and-propeller type of machine by terminating the lead pipe just under the propeller. In the Hough nitrator, this is all taken care of in the design of the machine, as the mixed acid is forced in a small stream into the benzene-cycle-acid mixture.

The temperature of nitration for benzene may vary within fairly wide limits. When no cycle acid is used, it is inadvisable to exceed 50°C.; but when fortified spent acid is employed, the nitration temperature may be kept between 50 and 55°C. The efficiency of agitation and heat exchange are also important considerations, which affect not only the control of temperature but also the rate of feed.

To arrive at the proper amount of mixed acid to be used per charge, it is necessary to multiply the weight of benzene by the acid factor which is used in making the calculations for the D.V.S. (see page 23), provision being made for the presence of a slight excess of nitric acid.

Separation and Neutralization.—The separation and neutralization of the nitrobenzene are accomplished in large conical-bottomed lead tanks, each capable of holding one or more charges. The nitrator charges are permitted to settle here for approximately 12 hr., when the spent acid is drawn off from the bottom of the lead tanks and delivered to the spent acid tanks for additional settling or for treatment with benzene next to be nitrated, in order to extract the residual nitrobenzene. The nitrobenzene is then delivered to the neutralizing house.

The neutralizing tub may be either a large, lead, conical-shaped tub containing an air spider, which is used for agitating the charge of nitrobenzene during the washing process, or a standard cast-iron kettle similar to the nitrator with sleeve-and-propeller agitation. The neutralizing vessel is prepared with a "heel" of warm water, which is delivered from an adjacent vat, and the nitrobenzene is blown into it. The charge is thoroughly agitated and warmed with live steam for 30 min. and then allowed to settle for a similar period. The supernatant acid water is then run off through side outlets into a labyrinth where practically all the enmeshed nitrobenzene will settle out.

The charge is now given a neutralizing wash at 40 to 50°C. with a warm sodium carbonate solution. When the nitrobenzene is intended for aniline production, this may be followed by a wash with aniline water from the reducer house if any has to be worked up. Otherwise, a final washing with a small quantity of warm water is made. The nitrobenzene is then delivered to its storage tanks where it is again settled to remove final traces of water. The crude product can now be distilled for commerce or used directly for the preparation of aniline. In some plants where the nitrobenzene is used almost exclusively in the aniline plant, the neutralizing and subsequent washes are omitted. The nitrobenzene delivered to the reducer houses is consequently acid. No harmful effects

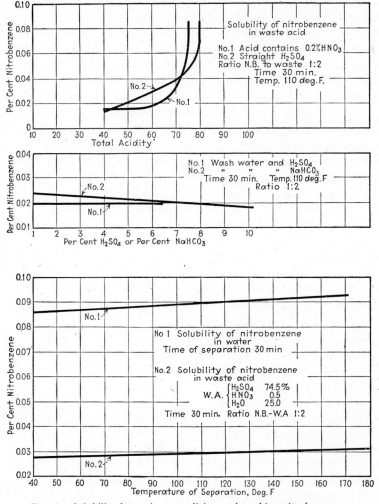

Fig. 6.—Solubility losses in neutralizing and washing nitrobenzene.

on the equipment are noticeable, provided the acidity is kept below 0.5 per cent.

Operating Losses of Nitrobenzene. *Loss in Waste Acid.*—When the nitrobenzene in the spent acid is not extracted by countercurrent washing with benzene next to be nitrated, it is recovered by permitting the acid to settle in large lead-lined vats from 8 to 24 hr., the duration depending on production demands.   The percentage of nitrobenzene being removed in waste acid depends upon the temperature and efficiency of separation. The amount of nitrobenzene carried along with the spent acid is approximately 0.5 per cent of the yield.   These losses are in excess of the true solubility losses (Fig. 6), being caused by incomplete separation of the nitrobenzene from the spent acid.

Loss in Wash Waters.—The losses incidental to the neutralization of the nitrobenzene are directly proportional to the number of washes given and the amount of water used.   In neutralizing, three washes may be given, the second of which contains sodium carbonate.   The washes are made at a temperature of about 45°C. and are agitated with air and steam and then permitted to settle.   The wash waters are drawn off at different levels and are delivered to a series of wood catch boxes, the overflow from the last one going to waste.   The quantity of nitrobenzene actually lost at this source is always slightly higher than what might be expected from the curves in Fig. 6 showing the solubility of nitrobenzene in wash waters.

NITRATION OF BENZENE: OPERATING DATA[1]
HOUGH NITRATOR

Initial charge of weak acid to represent cycle acid...................... 9,000 lb.
Composition of above:

H_2SO_4.. 83 %
HNO_3... 2.3 %
H_2O... 14.7 %

Nitric content includes low oxides of nitrogen.
Charge of benzene... 10,000 lb.
Charge of mixed acid.. 23,300 lb.
Nitric acid ratio.. 1.04
Composition of mixed acid (99 % acidity):

H_2SO_4.. 62.8 %⎫
HNO_3... 36.1 % ⎬ 5.7 D.V.S.
H_2O... 1.1 %⎭

Nitric content includes low oxides of nitrogen amounting to about 0.2 %.
Yield of nitrobenzene[2] about 15,698 lb. = 156.9 lb. nitrobenzene per 100 lb. benzene.
Length of time required to introduce benzene into inert (cycle) acid, about ½ hr.
Time required to inject nitrating acid, 1 hr.
Time required to cook at 90°C., 2 hr. 5 min.
Total time for run, 3 hr. 35 min.

NITRATION WITH SLEEVE-AND-PROPELLER AGITATION

Charge of benzene.................................... 6,000 lb.
Time of nitration...................................... 2.5 hr.
Temperature of nitration............................. 50 to 60°C.
Time of digestion or cooking at 50 to 60°C.............. 2 hr.
Yield per 100 lb. benzene............................. 154–155 lb.
HNO_3 in waste acid.................................. 0.3 %

The above results are obtained in a closed system of nitration, using cycle acid and top feed.   No HNO_3 remains in spent acid when benzene is used in excess.

[1] From GROGGINS, "Aniline and Its Derivatives," D. Van Nostrand Company.
[2] The above yields are based on 100 per cent C_6H_6 as used.   No allowance is made for losses in handling.   The nitrobenzene dissolved in the waste acid is recovered by washing, with the benzene next to be nitrated either in the nitrator or in a separate vessel.

Cost Factors in Production of Nitrobenzene

Nitration of benzene to nitrobenzene:

Molecular weight benzene (C_6H_6)..................................... 78

Molecular weight nitrobenzene ($C_6H_5NO_2$).......................... 123

Theoretical yield per 100 lb. C_6H_6.................................... 157.6

Standard yield for determining costs (98 % of theory)................. 154.5

Materials to produce 100 lb. nitrobenzene:

65.15 lb. benzene, at $0.028[1]....................................... $1.82

71.00 lb. H_2SO_4, at $0.0075... 0.54

55.00 lb. HNO_3, at $0.05... 2.75

1.00 lb. Na_2CO_3, at $0.012... 0.01

Total material cost.. $5.12

Credits:

69.0 lb. H_2SO_4 in waste acid, at .0.005............................ $0.345

0.9 lb. HNO_3 in waste acid, at $0.03............................... 0.027

$0.372

Therefore, net material cost per 100 lb. nitrobenzene................... $4.748

Operating costs:

Operating labor and direct supervision⎫

Repairs labor

Repairs material } $0.15

Supplies ⎭

Power costs:

Electricity⎫

Steam

Air } 0.20

Water

Brine ⎭

Overhead:

Administration⎫

Depreciation

Insurance } 0.52

Fixed charges ⎭

Net cost per 100 lb. of nitrobenzene................................. $5.62

ANALYSIS OF NITROBENZENE COST DATA

Percentage Cost Analysis:[2]

% of total cost

Operating cost..................................... $\dfrac{0.15}{5.62}$ = 2.67

Power cost... $\dfrac{0.20}{5.62}$ = 3.56

Overhead... $\dfrac{0.52}{5.62}$ = 9.25

Raw materials...................................... $\dfrac{4.75}{5.62}$ = 84.52

[1] Benzene at 20 cts. per gallon; add ⅛ ct. per pound to final cost for every cent increase above 20 cts. per gallon as cost of benzene.   The above figures do not include packaging, storing, or sales costs.

[2] Numerator = cost of each phase of production; denominator = total net cost.

When the nitration operations are conducted according to the methods noted on page 36, the yields range from 153 to 156.9 lb. of nitrobenzene obtained per 100 lb. of benzene used. The latter figure closely approaches the theoretical 157.6; and since each percentage increase in yield is equivalent to about a third of the operating cost (see cost sheet, page 37), it is a matter of great moment to maintain high operating efficiencies.

PREPARATION OF m-DINITROBENZENE

$$\text{C}_6\text{H}_6 + 2\text{HO·NO}_2 \rightarrow \text{C}_6\text{H}_4(\text{NO}_2)_2 + 2\text{H}_2\text{O}$$

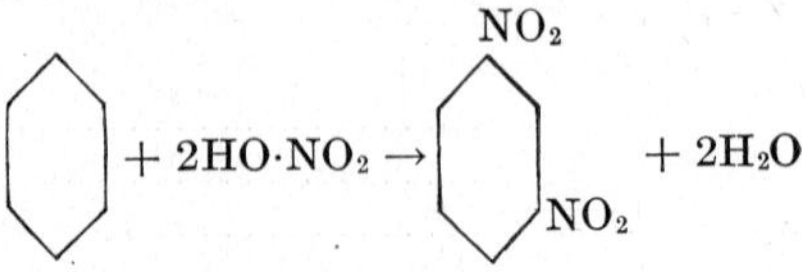

The preparation of m-dinitrobenzene from benzene is usually accomplished in two stages of nitration. Both may, however, be made to take place in the same vessel.

The first stage is carried out under the conditions previously described for nitrobenzene. At the conclusion of the first nitration, the spent acid is run off from the base of the machine and is replaced by a stronger nitrating acid for the second stage of nitration. The composition of the nitrating acids for the two stages of nitration is as follows:

MIXED ACID COMPOSITIONS

(I) For Mononitration %		(II) For Dinitration %
60.0	H_2SO_4	75
32.0	HNO_3	20
8.0	H_2O	5
3.52	D.V.S.	7.36
1.01	HNO_3 ratio	1.1

It is readily seen from the above acid compositions that the second nitration requires a more concentrated acid. Moreover, the reaction must be controlled at a higher temperature, i.e., 100 to 110°C. Although the heat of nitration for the second nitro group is not so great as for the introduction of the first, the operation is nevertheless much slower on account of the lower specific heat and greater integral heat of dilution[1] of the more concentrated acids that are used. Since the rate of feed and time of reaction are determined by the efficiency of agitation and heat exchange, these are therefore matters of special importance in this nitration.

Stirring is continued after the acid is all in and until the nitration is finished, this being indicated by the solidification, upon cooling, of the oily portion of a sample withdrawn from the machine. By stopping the agitation and maintaining the temperature at approximately 100°C., the contents of the nitrator are made to separate in two layers—an upper, lighter, aromatic nitro compound; and a lower, spent acid. After drawing off the spent acid, the dinitrobenzene is run into a vat containing boiling water, which is thoroughly agitated, preferably by live steam admitted

[1] RHODES and NELSON, *Ind. Eng. Chem.*, **30**, 648 (1938).

through a circular spider. The washing is repeated with the addition of
alkali, as in the preparation of nitrobenzene, to insure an acid-free product.
A final treatment with boiling water completes the preparation of the
crude product. The dinitrobenzene obtained in this way melts at
78 to 80°C. and contains about 8 per cent of ortho and para isomers.

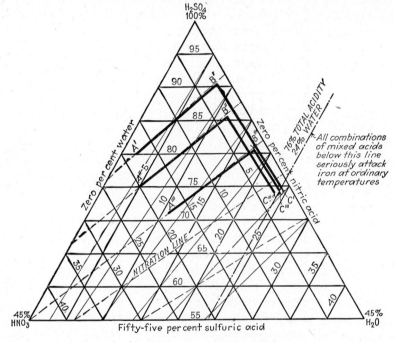

Fig. 7.—Mixed acid system for nitrations.

Figure 7 is a three-coordinate chart having sulfuric and nitric acids and water percentages as variables. A percentage of any one of the constituents is represented by a line. A dot-and-dash line represents 24 per cent water, which is the limit of dilution permissible for nitration in iron vessels. Above this, practically no hydrogen ions are present at the nitrating temperatures, and a mixed or spent acid with less than 24 per cent water does not appreciably attack steel. The percentages of any two constituents fix the third and locate a joint, A'' for instance being 5 per cent water, 75 per cent sulfuric, and 20 per cent nitric acid. The dotted fine lines are the loci of molecular substitution of nitric acid by water and represent the sulfuric-water concentration throughout the mixed acid medium.

The spent acid from the dinitration (approximately 85 per cent H_2SO_4)
contains from 8 to 10 per cent nitro compound in solution (see solubility
curves, Fig. 1), and this must therefore be diluted to precipitate the
dissolved dinitrobenzene.

Hough[1] has suggested the preparation of *m*-dinitrobenzene directly
from benzene. By using a mixed acid A' (Fig. 7), the highest yield

Mixed acid A'
H_2SO_4	80.0
HNO_3	18.0
H_2O	2.0
D.V.S.	11.96
HNO_3 ratio	1.1

[1] Hough, *Chem. & Met. Eng.*, **23**, 668 (1920).

of the meta compound is obtained, the product having a melting point of 83°C.   Mixed acid A″ gives a product setting at 79°C.; and A‴, 75°C. The temperature must be held at 30°C. while the benzene is being added to the cycle acid and then permitted to rise gradually to 100°C. during the time for completion of the reaction.   The spent acid from A′ will be B′, which is located below the perfect nitration line due to the reduction of a small part of the nitric acid and the formation of nitrosylsulfuric acid. The only method known for recovering B′ spent acid is to dilute to C′, practically all of the nitrosylsulfuric acid being decomposed and 7 of the 8 per cent dinitrobenzene dissolved in the acid being liberated by the operation.   After denitration, the last traces of organic matter are removed by concentrating the sulfuric acid to a strength of 96 per cent.

The purification of m-dinitrobenzene may be effected by making a paste with the least possible quantity of warm benzene or toluene and then filtering the cooled mass.   Another method of purification[1] is based on the greater instability of the ortho and para isomers in dilute caustic.   When crude m-dinitrobenzene containing 6 to 10 per cent impurities in the form of isomers is treated with a 5 to 10 per cent caustic solution at a temperature above the melting point of the product (90 to 100°C.), the ortho and para isomers which are converted to the corresponding nitrophenols are removed as soluble alkali salts with the alkaline solution.   The o-nitrophenol present in the largest amount in the alkaline wash waters may be recovered by acidifying and distilling with steam.   This method of purification has been used extensively in the separation of isomeric compounds, e.g., the removal of o- from p-nitro-aniline.   When basic substances are being purified, acids are used as solvents.   Under such circumstances, the meta compounds, which are usually the strongest bases, dissociate most and remain in solution, while the ortho and para compounds are separated by precipitation.

Purification may also be effected by suspending 100 parts of the crude product in 200 parts of water at 85 to 90°C., and then rapidly cooling to 45°C. to obtain a fine crystalline dispersion of dinitrobenzenes.   To this suspension, 15 parts sodium sulfite and 20 parts sodium bisulfite are added and the charge is stirred for about 2 hr. at a temperature of 60°C. Upon cooling to 30°C. and then filtering and washing, m-dinitrobenzene (m.p., 90.6°C.) is obtained in a yield of 84 per cent.[2]

PREPARATION OF o- AND p-CHLORONITROBENZENE

The preparation of chloronitrobenzene is of particular interest because of its commercial preparation by nitrating with an alkali nitrate and sulfuric acid.

[1] U. S. 1,665,005 (1928).   [2] U. S. 2,040,123 (1936).

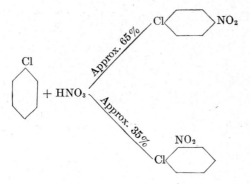

In carrying out the process,[1] a mixture of 1,000 lb. sulfuric acid, 81 per cent strength, and 200 lb. chlorobenzene is heated to 100°C. in a jacketed nitrator equipped with an effective stirrer. To the hot agitated emulsion, which is controlled by the use of steam or water in the jacket, at 110 to 130°C., are added 1,175 lb. of dried, pulverized, commercial sodium nitrate and about 1,600 lb. of 93 per cent sulfuric acid. Concurrently 1,240 parts of chlorobenzene are added at such a rate that proportional parts of the reactants are admitted in about the same period of time. Under such conditions, nascent HNO₃ is progressively generated; and with optimal conditions, not more than small amounts of unreacted sodium nitrate are present in the charge. The heat of nitration raises the temperature above 110°C., and at first the use of cooling water is necessary to limit the temperature to a maximum of 130°C. The addition of the reacting materials requires about 5 hr., after which the temperature is maintained by the existing heat-exchange facilities at 110 to 130°C. for 1 hr.

The contents of the nitrator are permitted to settle, and the waste acid and dissolved sulfate are drawn off from the bottom. The mixture of isomeric chloronitrobenzenes is then delivered to a vat in which the oil is washed with hot water and hot dilute alkali.

Some of the calculations pertaining to the above nitration are as follows:

$$\frac{\text{(Chlorobenzene) } 112.5}{\text{(HNO}_3) \quad 63} : \frac{1440}{X} \quad X = 806 = \text{lb. HNO}_3 \text{ required for}$$
$$1{,}440 \text{ lb. charge chlorobenzene.}$$

1,175 lb. NaNO₃ × 96 % purity × .741 (HNO₃ factor) = 836 lb. HNO₃ available.

The ratio HNO₃ to chlorobenzene $\dfrac{836}{806}$ = 1.037

[1] Livingston, U. S. 1,586,253 (1926).

The D.V.S. of the nitrating acid may be calculated from the acid components used.

$$
\begin{array}{lrl}
1,000 \text{ lb. } H_2SO_4 \text{ at } 81\% = & 810 \\
1,600 \text{ lb. } H_2SO_4 \text{ at } 93\% = & 1,448
\end{array} \Big\} \; 65.4\% \; H_2SO_4
$$

Estimated 850 lb. HNO_3 = 836 24.3% HNO_3

H_2O by difference 356 10.3% H_2O

3,450 lb. 3,450 100.0%

Water of nitration per 100 lb. $M/A = 6.47$

$$\text{D.V.S.} = \frac{65.4}{6.47 + 10.32} = 3.9$$

The above acid mixture is as has been previously observed satisfactory for carrying out mononitrations.

By the substitution of nitrate and H_2SO_4 for mixed acid, it appears that a great economy has been effected, because it would have required about 1,200 lb. of sulfuric acid to produce the necessary amount of nitric acid from sodium nitrate for the above operation. Furthermore, the yields in nitric acid operations are usually about 98 per cent of theory, whereas no appreciable losses are sustained in this procedure. On the other hand, the nitration waste from this operation is a mixture of dilute sulfuric acid and impure sodium acid sulfate as compared with a completely recoverable sulfuric acid from mixed acid nitrations. A further disadvantage arises from the fact that nitration with nitrates requires a slightly greater excess of HNO_3, which is not susceptible to economical recovery.

When the nitration of chlorobenzene is made with mixed acid, Hough[1] recommends an acid of the following composition:

$$
\begin{aligned}
H_2SO_4 &= 71.0\% \\
HNO_3 &= 18.0\% \\
H_2O &= 11.0\% \\
\text{D.V.S.} &= 4.41 \\
HNO_3 \text{ ratio} &= 1.01
\end{aligned}
$$

The D.V.S. in this acid is close to that used in making the nitration of benzene; and when only a slight excess over the required amount of nitric is used, the yield of nitroaromatic compound is practically theoretical.

The separation of the nitrochlorobenzenes is a tedious and difficult matter. The solidifying points of mixtures of *o*- and *p*-nitrochlorobenzenes are given in Table VI.

From this table, it is seen that the eutectic point is 14.65°C., corresponding to a composition of 33.1 per cent of para and 66.9 per cent of ortho compound. The crude compound in Holleman's experiments had a solidifying point of 59°C., which corresponds to a mixture of 70 per cent para and 30 per cent ortho compound.

[1] Hough, *Chem. & Met. Eng.*, **23**, 668 (1920).

TABLE VI.—SOLIDIFYING POINTS, MIXTURES, *o*- AND *p*-NITROCHLOROBENZENES[1]

Percentage of para	Solidifying point, °C.	Percentage of para	Solidifying point, °C.
0	32.09	35.43	18.43
1.05	31.06	37.53	21.90
4.60	29.92	39.96	26.10
6.54	29.00	41.67	28.50
8.88	27.89	45.86	33.98
12.61	26.10	48.94	37.65
16.26	24.19	60.18	50.10
19.22	22.65	64.66	54.32
22.91	20.75	68.54	57.83
26.89	18.30	70.02	59.22
30.26	16.29	71.93	60.80
32.39	15.35	75.48	63.97
32.71	14.94	81.93	69.10
32.90	14.85	86.70	72.77
33.07	14.77	90.30	75.40
33.10	14.65	95.57	79.13
34.09	16.73	100.00	82.15
34.94	17.47		

[1] According to HOLLEMAN, *Proc. Acad. Sci. Amsterdam*, **11**, 248 (1908).

The separation of the isomers may be accomplished by alternate crystallizations and distillations, taking advantage of the slight differences in their physical constants. From the melting and boiling points of the two compounds which are given below, along with the information derived from the melting points of the mixtures, it can be predicted that considerable of the para content will be thrown out upon cooling. Half of the para compound is recovered in this way by first cooling the nitration

	Melting point, °C.	Boiling point, °C.	
		760 mm.	8 mm.
Ortho......................	32.5	245.7	119
Para......................	83.5	242.0	113

product to 16°C., *i.e.*, a little above the eutectic point. The filtrate is then distilled *in vacuo*. The product first coming over is essentially the para, and that coming over last is essentially the ortho compound. By cooling these fractions, the isomers may be separated.

The separation of the isomers may also be effected by dinitrating the oily eutectic fractions at 60 to 100°C., whereby the ortho isomer reacts preferentially and is to a large extent converted to 2, 4-dinitrochlorobenzene. Upon distillation, a low boiling fraction consisting of 60 per cent *p*- and 40 per cent *o*-nitrochlorobenzene is obtained.[1]

According to Molinari,[2] excellent results are obtained by making the distillation in a very high vacuum, using a tall column filled with rings and maintaining a vapor velocity of 0.5 m. per second (see Separation of Nitrotoluenes, page 47, form ore complete description of the apparatus). According to this procedure, practically pure compounds are obtained, except in separating part of the para fraction when a liquid mixture containing 35 per cent of *p*-nitrochlorobenzene remains. This mixture is incorporated with fresh material to be rectified.

PREPARATION OF *p*-NITROACETANILIDE

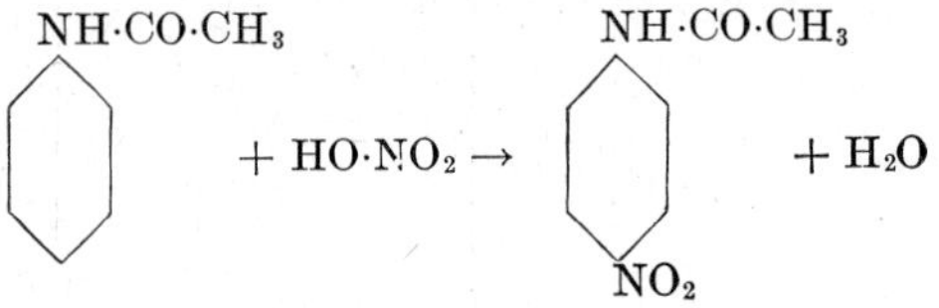

$$NH \cdot CO \cdot CH_3 \qquad\qquad NH \cdot CO \cdot CH_3$$

$$\text{(ring)} \quad + HO \cdot NO_2 \rightarrow \quad \text{(ring)} \quad + H_2O$$

$$NO_2$$

In the nitration of acetanilide, it is important, in order to prevent hydrolysis, to conduct the nitration at 3 to 5°C. It is necessary, therefore, to equip the nitrator with brine coils for controlling the reaction temperature. To insure further a maximum yield of product, use is made of cycle acid, which in this instance is water-white 66°Bé. sulfuric acid.

Into 4,000 lb. of sulfuric acid that is free of nitrous acid is delivered very slowly 1,000 lb. of dry acetanilide (m.p., 113°C.). During the 3 to 4 hr. that are consumed in this operation, the temperature is maintained at 25°C. The charge is cooled to 2°C., and 1,450 lb. of mixed acid of the following composition is then slowly run into the nitrator, the rate of feed being regulated by the capacity of the brine coils to control the temperature at 3 to 5°C.

	HNO₃	33 %
Composition of	H₂SO₄	47 %
nitrating acid	H₂O	20 %
	HNO₃ ratio	1.015

Agitation is continued for 1 hr. longer, the entire operation consuming from 10 to 12 hr. When the temperature rises above 5°C. during nitration, there is a distinct tendency toward the formation of the ortho isomeride. To test for complete nitration, a sample is drawn from the nitrator and poured on ice, and the *p*-nitroacetanilide washed with cold water. The precipitate is hydrolyzed in a test tube with boiling dilute caustic, and the resulting *p*-nitroaniline should yield a clear yellow solu-

---

[1] U. S. 1,981,311 (1934).

[2] MOLINARI, *Atti congr. naz. chim. ind.*, **1924,** 402.

tion with hydrochloric acid. If the acetanilide has not been completely nitrated, the odor of aniline may be detected.

The batch is run from the nitrator on to a suction filter containing 600 gal. of water and sufficient ice (or a brine coil) to keep the temperature below 15°C. The filter is a large wooden tub 8 ft. in diameter having a false bottom of filtros tile. It is provided with a stirrer which is set in motion just prior to receiving the charge from the nitrator. The temperature should be kept close to 5°C.; otherwise, the weak mineral acid present will hydrolyze some of the *p*-nitroacetanilide and the mixture will turn yellow owing to the formation of *p*-nitroaniline sulphate. Part of the amino compound will consequently be lost during the ensuing filtering and washing operations, and a low yield will be the result. The *p*-nitroacetanilide, which is brown as it runs from the nitrator, is changed to a milky-white mass as it comes into contact with the cold water.

When the *p*-nitroacetanilide is to be sold, it is twice washed on the filter with cold water until practically free of acid and then with a minimum of 3 per cent caustic soda or sodium carbonate solution. The neutralized cake is finally washed to remove the excess of alkali and then removed and dried. For the production of *p*-nitroaniline, the filter cake is merely washed and delivered to the hydrolyzing kettle.

Any *o*-nitroaniline can be separated on the filter by making the batch slightly alkaline with 20 to 30 lb. of 3.5 per cent sodium hydroxide and heating the charge containing a minimum amount of water up to 80°C. The alkaline liquor containing the soluble salt of the enolized ortho isomeride can then be filtered off. The ortho compound may similarly be removed by continued washing with hot water at 80°C. Separation of the ortho isomeride may also be effected by diluting the nitrator charge with cold water so as to obtain a sulfuric acid concentration of 65 per cent. The suspension is then warmed to 70°C., whereby hydrolysis of the acetyl group is effected. Upon cooling to 0°C., the *p*-nitroaniline sulfate separates out and is recovered by filtration.[1]

The yield of *p*-nitroacetanilide is 88 to 90 per cent of theory, or 160 to 162 lb. per 100 lb. acetanilide taken.

PREPARATION OF MONONITROTOLUENES

[1] Flett, U. S. 2,012,307 (1935).

The nitration of toluene is carried out in a manner similar to that used in the preparation of nitrobenzene and the chloronitrobenzenes. The presence of the methyl group may, however, give rise to the formation of oxidation impurities if the temperature is excessive. Thus, whereas a temperature in excess of 100°C. may be used for the nitration of chlorobenzene, that during the mononitration of toluene is controlled between 30 to 60°C. The ease of oxidation increases as methyl groups are added to the ring. It is necessary, therefore, to moderate progressively the nitrating conditions in the series toluene, xylene, and cumene.

Toluene is first run into the nitrator containing cycle acid, and the mixture is cooled to approximately 30°C. Mixed acid is added slowly to the well-stirred charge, controlling the temperature at 50°C. The agitation is continued under these conditions for 2 hr. after the acid is all delivered.

The nitrating acid need not be quite so concentrated as that used in the preparation of nitrobenzene, for in this case the reaction takes place more readily. The composition of typical mixed acids, according to Holleman[1] (I) and Gibson[2] (II), are as follows:

I		II
57.6%	H_2SO_4	58.7%
30.0%	HNO_3	23.8%
12.4%	H_2O	17.5%
2.84%	D.V.S.	2.42%
1.09	HNO_3 ratio	1.01

The yield of mixed nitrotoluenes is about 96 per cent of theory. The relative proportion of each isomer is approximately 60 per cent ortho, 4 per cent meta, and 36 per cent para. These proportions are practically

TABLE VII.—NITRATION OF TOLUENE

Toluene, grams	Wt. of nitrating acid, gm.			Temp., °C.	Crystallization point, °C.	Calculated composition		
	H_2SO_4	HNO_3	H_2O			Ortho	Meta	Para
75	....	282	18	40	30.8	60.7	4.3	35
75	....	282	18	0	31.7	60.3	2.5	37.2
35	58.7	23.8	17.5	50	30.3	62.5	4.3	33.5
35	58.7	23.8	17.5	40	29.8	63.6	4.2	32.2
35	58.7	23.8	17.5	20	30.35	61.9	4.5	33.6
35	58.7	23.8	17.5	0	30.6	61.1	4.5	34.4
35	112	23.8	38.2	40	30.25	62.7	3.9	33.4
36	112	23.8	38.2	0	31.3	60.5	3.3	36.2

[1] HOLLEMAN, *Proc. Acad. Sci. Amsterdam*, **11**, 248 (1908).
[2] GIBSON, DUCKHAM, and FAIRBARN, *J. Chem. Soc.*, **121**, 270 (1922).

constant and do not appear to be affected sufficiently by variations in the process (see Table VII, according to Gibson *et al.*) to make the suppression of *m*-nitrotoluene feasible.

The separation of the mixed nitrotoluenes may be carried out in a manner similar to that used for the isomeric chloronitrobenzenes. When the nitration product is distilled *in vacuo*, the first fraction is essentially the ortho compound. When cooled to 10°C., this liquid fraction deposits any accompanying para compound. After the distillation has gone halfway, the contents of the still are cooled and crystallized, and the para compound may thus be separated by centrifuging. The middle fraction is added to new material and redistilled.

Isomeride	Melting point, °C.	Boiling point, °C.
Ortho, α^1......	−10.56	222.3
Ortho, β........	− 4.14	222.3
Meta..........	16.10	230.3
Para..........	51.60	238.0

See Bell and Spry[1] for discussion of two forms of *o*-nitrotoluene.
[1] BELL and SPRY, *Ind. Eng. Chem.*, **13,** 59 (1921).

According to Molinari,[1] ordinary methods for the separation of *o*- and *p*-nitrotoluene give either impure products or are uneconomical because of repeated distillations and low yields. By distilling *in vacuo*, decomposition is avoided, the power consumption is less, and the boiling-point curve of the mixture has neither a maximum nor a minimum, making possible a separation of the two compounds in a state of great purity. A simple plate rectifying column or a Kubiershky column is, however, inefficient, and resort must be had to a system which brings about a minimum velocity of vapors, such as a column filled with Raschig or similar chemical-ware rings. Distilling under 20 mm. pressure, with a velocity of the vapors of 0.5 m. per second, excellent results may be obtained. It is also necessary to maintain a constant dephlegmator temperature in order to obtain both efficient rectification and uniformly pure products. This is accomplished by using a self-regulating dephlegmator, a device which functions in such a way that with an increase in the temperature of the distillation vapors a corresponding and automatic increase in the circulation of the cooling liquid is obtained. This is accomplished by cooling the dephlegmator by suitable oil or solution which when cold enters the dephlegmator by a tube and is heated by the vapors. Convection then causes a circulation of the solution or oil, and the more heat it extracts from the vapor the more rapid this circulation

[1] MOLINARI, *Atti congr. naz. chim. ind.*, **1924,** 402.

and the faster the removal of heat. The circulating liquid is, in turn, cooled artificially outside the dephlegmator. The system can be used for either a continuous or a discontinuous dephlegmation. Applied to the separation of o- and p-nitrotoluenes prepared according to the preceding outline, a 45 per cent yield based on the total charge of commercial ortho compound is obtained. The para isomeride is then recovered by cooling the residue with brine or by continuing the rectification and separating the intermediate fraction from which more para compound may be recovered on cooling.

The Preparation of Nitrophenols

The preparation of o- and p-nitrophenol is usually accomplished by treating the corresponding chloronitrobenzene derivatives with dilute alkali. This procedure, which is productive of practically theoretical yields of the desired product, is described under Hydrolysis.

When phenol is nitrated under conditions optimal for the substitution of one nitro group, the reaction product consists of a mixture of o- and p-nitrophenols. The nitration process is similar to that used for the preparation of chloronitrobenzene. Ninety-four pounds of phenol are liquefied by the addition of 20 lb. of water, and the phenolic solution is gradually added to cycle acid which is fortified with 150 lb. of sodium nitrate and 250 lb. of 95 per cent sulfuric acid. The use of approximately 1.8 moles nitric acid has been found necessary to reduce the amount of unreacted phenol to a minimum. The temperature of nitration is kept at 20 to 25°C. while the contents of the nitrator are thoroughly agitated, the stirring continuing for 2 hr. after the ingredients are added.

The resinous mixture of nitro compounds is then separated from the spent acid and boiled with 60 gal. of water to which is added sufficient chalk to insure complete neutrality to litmus. The washing is again repeated, discarding all the wash waters.

The separation of the isomers may easily be accomplished by distilling with steam, whereby the ortho compound is recovered with the condensed distillate. Any unreacted phenol is also carried over and remains in solution, whereas the o-nitrophenol separates out on standing overnight. It may be purified by redistilling, whereby bright canary-yellow crystals (m.p., 45°C.; b.p., 214°C.) are obtained.

The para compound which remains behind is boiled up with dilute hydrochloric acid and filtered. The *p*-nitrophenol crystallizes out from the hot solution in long, practically white needles (m.p., 114°C.).

PREPARATION OF α-NITRONAPHTHALENE

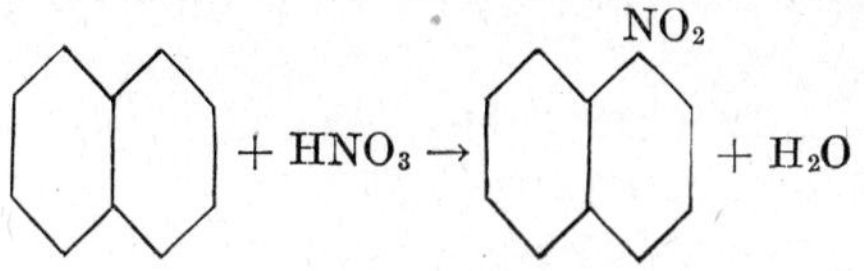

$$\text{+ HNO}_3 \rightarrow \text{+ H}_2\text{O}$$

When naphthalene is nitrated under optimal conditions, the product consists principally of α-nitronaphthalene. The reaction takes place vigorously; and unless precautions are taken, polynitro compounds are formed. If impure naphthalene is used, the nitration product will be unsatisfactory; and inasmuch as it is difficult to isolate α-nitronaphthalene in a pure state, it is advisable to prevent further complications and to use a pure raw material.

When the nitration is made without the use of cycle acid, a mixed acid of the following composition may be used:

	%		%
H_2SO_4	59.55	HNO_3 ratio	1.01
HNO_3	15.85	D.V.S	2.04
H_2O	24.60		

According to Fierz,[1] this will yield a product consisting of 95 per cent α-nitronaphthalene together with some unchanged naphthalene and very little dinitro derivative.

By using cycle acid[2] to dissolve the naphthalene to be nitrated and then proceeding with the nitration in the usual way, the operating steps are as follows: The naphthalene—1,280 lb.—is suspended in 4,500 lb. of dilute sulfuric acid or spent acid containing about 65 per cent H_2SO_4. The whole is thoroughly stirred, and 2,350 lb. of mixed acid of the following composition is slowly added:

	%
H_2SO_4	56.60
HNO_3	28.30
H_2O	15.10
HNO_3 ratio	1.03

During the addition of the acid the temperature is kept at 25 to 30°C.; but after the whole of the acid has been run in, the temperature is raised slowly to 65 to 70°C. and maintained at that point for 1 hr. The agita-

---

[1] FIERZ-DAVID, "Dye Chemistry," p. 79, D. Van Nostrand Company, Inc., (1921).
[2] Brit. 133,918 (1919).

tion is then stopped, and the nitronaphthalene which floats on the surface as a porous cake is separated from the spent acid in a separator.

The crude product is delivered to the neutralizing kettle, where it is made free of acid by repeated washings with boiling water and alkali. Any free naphthalene that may be present is removed by steam during the washing process.

The purification of the crude product is accomplished by recrystallizing it from 10 per cent of its weight of ligroin or solvent naphtha. The success of the purification depends upon certain details of manipulation,[1] which include (1) use of a minimum of solvent and (2) constant agitation while recrystallization takes place in order to assure the formation of small crystals. The nitronaphthalene is dissolved in 10 per cent of its weight of solvent naphtha and heated above the melting point of the crude, i.e., above 50°C., until a homogeneous mixture is formed. The resulting solution is cooled to 25°C. with constant agitation, and the thick slurry that is formed is centrifuged. The α-nitronaphthalene obtained in this manner has a solidifying point above 54.4°C. This is not yet pure, as the c.p. material comes as glistening yellow crystals which melt at 61°C. To obtain the pure product, it is necessary to resort to further purification by recrystallization.

THE PREPARATION OF NITROPARAFFINS[2,3]

The liquid-phase nitration of paraffinic hydrocarbons is confronted with certain inherent difficulties. Nitric acid and the alkanes are mutually insoluble, whereas the nitrated product is considerably more soluble in the nitric acid layer and is there subjected to further nitration and oxidation. These particular difficulties may be obviated by operating in the vapor phase. The reactants may then be mixed in any desired proportions, and, inasmuch as reaction is almost instantaneous, practically no polynitro derivatives are formed. Operations according to this method are particularly suitable for the lower paraffins and such nitrations may be carried out in the apparatus shown diagrammatically in Fig. 8.

The alkane, at atmospheric or superatmospheric pressure and in the vapor phase, is delivered to a mixing tube where it is intimately mixed with an atomized stream of nitric acid delivered under pressure. To increase the yield of nitroparaffins and to decrease explosion hazards, it is important to regulate the proportions of the reactants so as to have at least 2 moles of alkane per mole of nitric acid. The mixture of hydro-

---

[1] U. S. 1,581,258 (1926).

[2] HASS, HODGE, and VANDERBILT, *Ind. Eng. Chem.*, **28**, 339 (1936); U. S. 1,967,667 (1934); 2,071,122 (1937).

[3] McCLEARY with DEGERING, *Ind. Eng. Chem.*, **30**, 64 (1938).

carbon and acid vapors passes through a stainless steel reaction tube, immersed in a suitable salt bath maintained at 410 to 430°C. Above 250°C., nitric acid is completely decomposed yielding nitrogen peroxide as the principal product, and this is the active nitrating agent. The concurrent formation of nitric oxide and oxygen exert an unfavorable oxidizing action which markedly penalizes the yields.

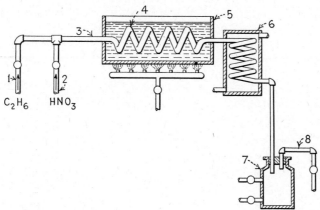

FIG. 8.—Reaction system: vapor-phase nitration of paraffins.
1. Metered inlet for alkanes.
2. Inlet for nitric acid vapors.
3. Mixing tube.
4. Reaction coil.
5. Furnace containing molten salt.
6. Cooling coil.
7. Liquid-gas separator.
8. Vent for uncondensed gases.

The mixed gases from the reaction tube pass through a cooler maintained at a temperature which will insure condensation of the nitroparaffin at atmospheric pressure. The condensed liquid and accompanying gases pass to a liquid-gas separator in which the liquid nitro compounds and spent acid are collected. The liquid product separates into two layers and the supernatant mixture of nitroparaffins is drawn off and subsequently purified by washing thoroughly with water and then rectifying in a Podbielniak column. The gases leaving the separator consist of excess alkane, nitric oxide, carbon dioxide, carbon monoxide, water, and some vapor of nitroparaffins. The alkane is recovered and recycled. The lower oxides of nitrogen are reoxidized and reemployed.

The results of nitrations carried out substantially as noted above gave the results which are set forth in Table VIII.

In general, it is found that the use of superatmospheric pressures in the reactor leads to an increase in the yield of nitroparaffins and a large increase in the reaction rate. The yield also increases with increasing hydrocarbon concentration in the reacting gases up to a ratio of 14:1

TABLE VIII.—NITRATION OF PARAFFINS: RESULTS OF ANALYSES, %

Hydro-carbon	Ace-tone	Nitro-me-thane	Nitro-eth-ane	1-Nitro-pro-pane	2-Nitro-pro-pane	1-Nitro-bu-tane	2-Nitro-bu-tane	1-Nitro-isobu-tane	2-Nitro-isobu-tane	Yield per pass
Methane	..	.....	.....	..	..	..	..	..	..	0
Ethane	..	10–20	80–90	..	..	..	..	..	..	9
Propane	..	9	(26?)	32	33	..	..	..	..	21
Butane	..	6	12	5	..	27	50	..	..	28
Isobutane	5	3	.....	..	20	..	..	65	7	25

According to Hass, Hodge, and Vanderbilt.

The introduction of oxygen-containing gases favors oxidation with no increase in nitration. This is probably due to the fact that the equilibrium

$$2NO_2 \rightleftarrows 2NO + O_2$$

is displaced completely to the right, above 154°C.; and, as is well known, the lower oxides of nitrogen are the more vigorous oxidizing agents. These considerations suggest further research at lower temperatures and under superatmospheric pressures, as well as the use of addition agents which inhibit oxidation.

Effect of Temperatures.—When operating at higher temperatures, the ratio of primary nitro compound to secondary nitro compound becomes larger. This change in ratio is probably due primarily to a change of the relative reaction rates of the primary and secondary hydrogen atoms with the change in temperature. The results obtained in the nitration of butane are presented in Table IX.[1]

TABLE IX.—EFFECT OF TEMPERATURE: NITRATION OF BUTANE

Run No.	Temp., °C.	Nitro-methane, %	Nitro-ethane, %	1-Nitro-propane, %	2-Nitro-butane, %	1-Nitro-butane, %
1	395	2.1	12.7	4.9	49.0	30.5
2	393	6.0	19.0	7.0	41.0	27.0
3	393	5.0	11.0	5.0	46.0	32.0
4	445	5.9	18.2	6.5	37.0	31.8
5	450	9.0	25.0	7.0	28.0	31.0

Material Cost of Production of Nitroparaffins.—Yields of 40 per cent per pass have been obtained in the nitration of the butanes. Since not more than 5 per cent of the nitric acid is reduced to free nitrogen, this means a net, over-all yield of $(40 \times 100)/(40 + 5)$ or 89 per cent, based upon nitric acid, assuming that the nitric oxide can all be reconvered

[1] McCleary with Degering, Ind. Eng. Chem. **30**, 64 (1938).

to nitric acid. The hydrocarbon which is not nitrated is converted to carbon monoxide, carbon dioxide, and water. This reaction requires something like 7 moles of nitric acid for each mole of butane. Based on the absence of HNO_3 and NO_2 in the exit vapors, about 60 per cent of the nitric acid is used as oxidizing agent, consequently, one-seventh of 60 per cent or 0.08 mole of hydrocarbon is oxidized by the nitric acid for each mole of nitric acid reacting. The percentage of hydrocarbon nitrated is therefore approximately $(0.40 \times 100)/(0.40 + 0.08)$ or 83 per cent.

Nitric acid can be produced by the oxidation of ammonia at a cost of approximately 1.75 cents per pound on an anhydrous basis. Butane is available at about 0.6 ct. per pound. The raw material cost of a pound of crude, nitrated butane, using the above figures, is approximately 1.8 cts. per pound.

When *n*-pentane is similarly nitrated at 400°C., the approximate composition of the products obtained is as follows:[1]

Nitromethane, b.p., 101.7°C. = 1.1 %	1-Nitropentane, b.p., 172°C. = 20.6 %
Nitroethane, b.p., 114.0°C. = 7.19%	2-Nitropentane, b.p., 152°C. = 20.8 %
1-Nitropropane, b.p., 131.0°C. = 13.85 %	3-Nitropentane, b.p., 152°C. = 23.0 %
1-Nitrobutane, b.p., 151.0°C. = 12.5 %	

The presence of all these nitroderivatives is reasonable evidence for a free radical mechanism during the vapor-phase nitration process.[1]

IX. THERMAL DATA RELATING TO THE PREPARATION AND USE OF NITRO COMPOUNDS

From the previous paragraphs, it has become apparent that the nitration process is accompanied by the development of a considerable amount of heat. A discussion of nitration processes would therefore be incomplete without taking into consideration some of the thermal factors involved in this reaction.

Garner and Abernethy[2] found (Figs. 9, 10) that certain regularities exist between the heats of formation and nitration of the benzene, toluene, and phenol series. The heats of nitration decrease with the increase in the number of nitro groups, but the heats of formation tend to a maximum for the second or third member of the series and then diminish. An exception is seen in the benzene series, but it is probable that the maximum is shifted to the fourth member of the series and that the same relationship would hold if the more highly nitrated benzenes could be obtained.

[1] HASS and PATTERSON, *Ind. Eng. Chem.*, **30**, 67 (1938).

[2] GARNER and ABERNETHY, *Proc. Roy. Soc.* (*London*), **99A**, 213 (1921), from which the following paragraphs were abstracted. The reader is referred to this excellent article for a more complete discussion of the subject. The more recent work of Rinkenbach of the Picatinny Arsenal [*J. Am. Chem. Soc.*, **52**, 115 (1930)] is also an important study in this field.

In the benzene, toluene, and phenol series, it is clear (Tables X, XI, XII) that the nearer the nitro groups are to one another in the benzene ring the greater is the strain in the molecule and the lower the heat of

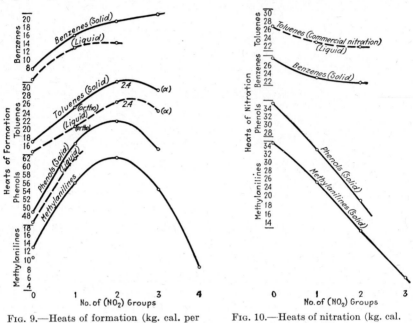

FIG. 9.—Heats of formation (kg. cal. per mole).

FIG. 10.—Heats of nitration (kg. cal. per mole).

TABLE X.—HEATS OF COMBUSTION, FORMATION, NITRATION, AND CRYSTALLIZATION
Benzene Series

Substance	Mol. wt.	Heat of combustion, kg. cal. per mole		Heat of formation, kg. cal. per mole		Heat of nitration, kg. cal. per mole	Heat of crystallization, kg. cal. per mole
		Const. vol.	Const. press.	C. amorph.	C. diamond		
Benzene....................	78	780.4	781.3	+ 5.6	− 10.6	+27.0	2.35
Nitrobenzene..............	123	739.9	739.7	+13.1	− 3.1	+25.6	2.78
o-Dinitrobenzene...........	168	703.8	702.6	+16.0	− 0.2		
m-Dinitrobenzene...........	168	700.6	699.4	+19.2	+ 3.0	+21.4	4.87
p-Dinitrobenzene...........	168	693.7	692.5	+26.1	+ 9.9		
1,3,5-Trinitrobenzene.......	213	665.6	663.4	+21.1	+ 4.9		
1,2,4-Trinitrobenzene.......	213	675.9	673.7	+10.8	− 5.4		

formation. Thus *o*-dinitrobenzene and the ortho mononitro compounds of the toluene and phenol series have the smallest heats of formation. The differences between the ortho and para derivatives are, however, greatest for the benzene and least for the phenol series. In the case of

TABLE XI.—HEATS OF COMBUSTION, FORMATION, NITRATION, AND CRYSTALLIZATION
Phenol Series

Substance	Mol. wt.	Heat of combustion, kg. cal. per mole		Heat of formation, kg. cal. per mole		Heat of nitration, kg. cal. per mole	Heat of crystallization, kg. cal. per mole
		Const. vol.	Const. press.	C. amorph.	C. diamond		
Phenol..............	94	736.9	737.5	+49.4	+33.2	+35.0	2.34
o-Nitrophenol.......	139	689.9	689.4	+63.4 } 64.9	+47.3 } 48.7	+24.5	4.30
p-Nitrophenol.......	139	687.0	686.5	+66.3	+50.1		
2, 4-Dinitrophenol...	184	650.2	648.7	+69.9	+53.7	+12.9	
Picric acid..........	229	623.7	621.2	+63.3	+47.1		

di- and trinitro derivatives also, the proximity of the groups has the same effect.

Some regularities have been observed in the heats of formation of members of the toluene series. Thus, there appears to be a definite *increase* in the internal energy (lower value for heat of formation) associated with groups in the ortho position, and especially when nitro groups are ortho to one another. Thus, of the isomeric trinitrotoluenes, β-(2, 3, 4) trinitrotoluene (Table XII) has the lowest heat of formation. *i.e.*, contains the greatest internal energy per gram; and α-(2, 4, 6) trinitrotoluene the highest heat of formation, *i.e.*, contains the least internal energy per gram. If on detonation these two substances gave the same products of decomposition, β-trinitrotoluene would have an advantage over α-trinitrotoluene of 54 cal. per gram. For the same reason, the unsymmetrical trinitrobenzene should be a more powerful explosive than the symmetrical body. In general, the greater the number of adjacent groups in a molecule of high explosive the greater will be the heat of detonation, but there are often practical limitations to this choice on account of the greater reactivity and lower stability of the less symmetrical nitro compounds.

X. RECOVERY OF SPENT ACID FROM NITRATIONS[1]

The economical recovery and utilization of the large amounts of spent acids necessarily produced as a by-product in the manufacture of nitrohydrocarbons or other organic compounds are problems of great importance. In the early days of the synthetic organic chemical industry, practically all the spent acid was wasted. In the course of time, however, the disposition of nitration spent acid became an acute problem, for the continued pollution of streams constituted a serious menace. Thus,

[1] Acknowledgment is made of the following sources of information: MARX, *Chem. Age*, **29**, 253 (1921); WEBB, *J. Soc. Chem. Ind.*, **40**, 265 (1921); ZEISBERG, *Chem. & Met. Eng.*, **30**, 781 (1924).

TABLE XII.—SUMMARY OF HEATS OF COMBUSTION, FORMATION, AND NITRATION PER MOLECULE, AND FIGURES OF INSENSITIVENESS

Substance	Mol. wt.	Heat of combustion (kg. cal. per mole)		Heat of formation (kg. cal. per mole)		Heat of nitration, kg. cal. per mole. One NO$_2$ group inserted in the following positions relative to existing NO$_2$ groups			Heat of crystallization (kg. cal. per mole)	Gas evolution at 120°C. c.c. per 40 hr.	Figure of insensitiveness (picric acid = 100)
		Const. vol.	Const. press.	C. amorph.	C. diamond	Ortho position	Meta position	Para position			
Toluene	92	935.9	937.1	+15.1	− 3.8	+25.3	+29.4	+33.7	2.4		
Mononitrotoluene:											
Ortho (liquid)	137	897.0	897.2	+20.9	+ 2.0	2:3+22.9	2:4+29.7; 2:6+28.2	2:5+27.3			
Meta (liquid)		892.9	893.1	+25.0	+ 6.1	2:3+18.8; 3:4+18.5	3:5+25.4	2:5+23.2	4.3		
Para		888.6	888.8	+29.3	+10.4	3:4+14.2	2:4+21.3				
Dinitrotoluene:											
2:3	182	860.5	859.6	+24.3	+ 5.4	2:3:4+12.1	2:3:5+21.2	2:3:6+19.7; 2:3:5+21.2	4.80		
2:4		853.7	852.8	+31.1	+12.2	3:4:6 12.6; 2:3:4 5.3	2:4:6 17.5	3:4:6 12.6			
2:5		856.1	855.2	+28.7	+ 9.8	2:3:5 16.8; 3:4:6 15.0	2:3:5 16.8; 3:4:6 15.0; 2:3:6 15.3				
2:6		855.2	854.3	+29.6	+10.7	2:3:6 14.4	2:4:6 19.0	2:3:6 14.4			
3:4		860.8	859.9	+24.0	+ 5.1	2:3:4 12.4; 3:4:5 17.2	3:4:6 19.7	3:4:6 19.7			
3:5		853.9	853.0	+30.9	+12.0	2:3:5 14.6; 3:4:5 10.3		2:3:5 14.6			
Trinitrotoluene:											
α (2:4:6)	227	822.5	820.7	+29.1	+10.2				4.88	0.03	114
β (2:3:4)		834.7	832.9	+16.9	− 2.0					0.73	92
γ (3:4:6)		827.4	825.6	+24.2	+ 5.3					1.40	102
δ (3:4:5)		829.9	828.1	+21.7	+ 2.8					1.60	95
ε (2:3:5)		825.6	823.8	+26.0	+ 7.1					0.40	101
ζ (2:3:6)		827.1	825.3	+24.5	+ 5.6						

as in the case of waste SO_2 fumes from the smelters, a new industry was born of legal necessity. Later economical reasons brought further pressure to bear, so that at present a number of satisfactory means are available for effecting both the recovery and concentration of spent acids from nitrations. Without such means, the producer of nitro compounds operates under a distinct economic handicap.

In normal times, there are but two principal sources of spent nitrating acids—those from the nitration of aromatic compounds, such as benzene, chlorobenzene, toluene, or phenol; and those resulting from the esterification of glycerol and the carbohydrates cellulose, starch, and sugar. While the spent acids from the former consist of sulfuric acid with but minimal amounts of nitric acid and relatively large amounts of water, those from the latter source contain many times more nitric acid and therefore are first denitrated before being delivered to the sulfuric acid concentrating plant.

Denitration of Spent Acid.—The initial step in the recovery of spent acids consists in the removal of the residual nitric and nitrous acids from the bulk of diluted sulfuric acid. The nitrous acid in spent acid is, however, not present as HNO_2 but as nitrosylsulfuric acid $HO \cdot SO_2 \cdot ONO$, since spent acid does not give many of the ordinary tests for nitrous acid unless diluted with water. The operating details relating to the recovery of the nitrogen compounds in spent acid must therefore be preceded by a study of their reactions.

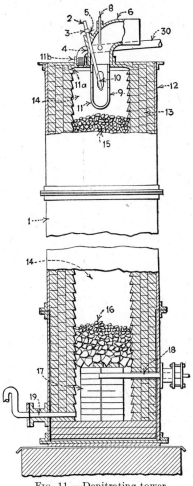

Fig. 11.—Denitrating tower.

1. Steel.
2. Spent acid delivery.
8. Thermometer.
9. Distributor for spent acid.
10. Openings for HNO_3 vapors.
12. Steel shell.
13. Inner brick lining.
15–16. Chemical ware packing.
17. Tiles, arranged in checkered layers.
18. Steam inlet.
19. Outlet for denitrated sulfuric acid.

Nitrosylsulfuric acid ($HO \cdot SO_2 \cdot ONO$) is quite stable in the presence of concentrated sulfuric acid. In concentrations below 70 per cent H_2SO_4, the velocity of decomposition is much greater, increasing with the temperature and dilution of the sulfuric acid; *e.g.*, in 72.8 per cent H_2SO_4, considerable decomposition occurs at 100°C.; at 68.5 per cent, the whole of nitrosylsulfuric acid is decomposed at the boiling point of the solution; while with acids of concentration below 64.26 per cent H_2SO_4, crystals of nitrosylsulfuric acid do not dissolve in the cold without decomposition.

In order to effect complete separation of nitrous and nitric acid from mixtures with sulfuric acid, it is necessary first to dilute the mixture until

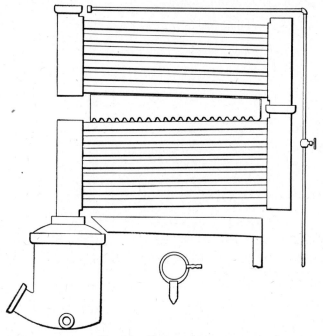

Fig. 12.—Hart condenser.

Complete assembly; showing arrangement of bleacher, manifolds, cooling tubes, water supply, and water trough.

the concentration of the sulfuric acid is about 70 per cent and then to heat the same to a sufficiently high temperature to drive off the volatile constituents. The resulting vapors of nitric acid are condensed while the nitrous gases, consisting essentially of NO and NO_2, are absorbed in dilute nitric acid of 35 to 55 per cent strength, the final oxidation of the absorbed gases being effected by admixture and agitation with atmospheric oxygen.

These operations are best carried out in denitration towers constructed of acid-resistant material. The spent acid is delivered to a distributor on top of the tower (Fig. 11) and is allowed to trickle down through the packing while being subjected to an ascending current of saturated or superheated steam, the steam serving both to dilute the mixture and to drive off the nitric acid.

The reactions which take place may be summarized as follows: Spent acid entering the top of the tower is heated by escaping oxides of nitrogen, and any nitric acid present is decomposed by nitrosylsulfuric acid with the formation of NO_2 according to the following reversible reaction:

$$HNO_3 + HO \cdot SO_2 \cdot ONO \rightleftarrows H_2SO_4 + 2NO_2 \quad (1)$$

Farther down, the remaining nitrosylsulfuric acid is decomposed by steam.

$$2OH \cdot SO_2 \cdot ONO + H_2O \rightarrow \\ 2H_2SO_4 + NO + NO_2 \quad (2a)$$

$$OH \cdot SO_2 \cdot ONO + H_2O \rightarrow H_2SO_4 + HNO_2 \quad (2b)$$

The nitrous acid thus formed is decomposed at the elevated temperatures that prevail, probably according to the following equations:

$$2HNO_2 \rightarrow NO + NO_2 + H_2O \quad (3)$$
$$3HNO_2 \rightleftarrows 2NO + HNO_3 + H_2O \quad (4)$$

the nitric acid distilling off. The denitrated sulfuric acid, containing about 67 to 70 per cent of H_2SO_4, which flows off from the bottom of the tower, will retain not over 0.15 per cent of nitric acid and is suitable for concentration and reuse. The nitric acid in the gases leaving the tower is first led through a set of condensers (Fig. 12) where any nitric acid is liquefied and recovered, the non-condensable gases, consisting of

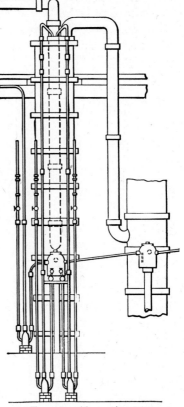

Fig. 13.—Absorption tower. Complete assembly showing arrangement of overflow pots, air lifts for nitric acid, and gas lines.

NO and NO_2, passing on to an absorption system (Fig. 13) where they encounter a downward current of nitric acid, experience having shown that 55 per cent nitric acid possesses the maximum absorptive capacity. The air which is introduced through the pulsometers, *i.e.* air lifts, serves to oxidize the absorbed NO to NO_2, thus enriching the nitric acid.

The strength of the recovered nitric acid from spent acids is greatly increased by returning the comparatively weak absorption-tower acid to the denitrating column.[1] In this way, the concentration of the nitric acid is increased from the usual 55 to 60 per cent strength to 90 per cent

[1] U. S. 1,590,043 (1926).

or more. The usual denitration and absorption system is employed
(Fig. 14). This comprises a denitrating tower similar to that shown in
detail in Fig. 11, a "bleaching" tower filled with disks or cylinders, a
stoneware condenser, and a series of absorption towers. The dilute
acid that accumulates in the absorption system is pumped back to the
top of the denitrating tower, where it is mixed with the spent acid as it
enters the tower. The spent acid contains sufficient H_2SO_4 to combine

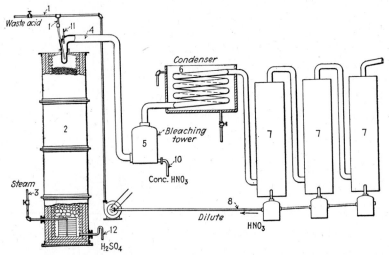

FIG. 14.—System for the production of concentrated nitric acid.

1. Spent acid delivery.
2. Denitrating tower.
3. Steam inlet.
4. Outlet for nitric acid vapors.
5. Bleaching tower.
6. Chemical ware condenser.

7. Absorption towers (see Fig. 13).
8. Dilute nitric acid—returned to denitrating tower.
10. Outlet for concentrated nitric acid.
11. Thermometer.
12. Outlet for diluted sulfuric acid.

with the H_2O of the absorption-tower acid to form nonvolatile hydrates
of sulfuric acid under the conditions existing in the denitrating tower,
thus permitting the HNO_3 content of this acid to be vaporized in comparatively anhydrous condition from the top of the denitrating tower.

This scheme works satisfactorily only for spent acids that are comparatively free of dissolved hydrocarbons and in which the free HNO_3
content is two or more times that of the nitrosylsulfuric acid. The
unsuitability of acids like trinitrotoluene spent acid is due to the excessive
reduction of nitric acid which occurs at the top of the denitrating tower.

Concentration of Nitric Acid.—The concentrating of dilute nitric acid
obtained from denitration systems or ammonia-oxidation operations can
be accomplished in a vertical tower in which the ternary mixture, nitric
acid, sulfuric acid, and water, passes downward countercurrent to a hot
gaseous medium composed largely of steam.[1]

[1] Pauling, U. S. 1,031,864 (1912); Zeisberg, U. S. 1,292,948 (1919).

It is clear, however, that the direct contact of steam with the dehydrating sulfuric acid necessitates using larger quantities of this acid than would be required if the necessary heat were supplied through a heat

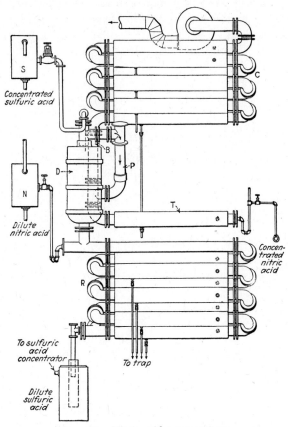

FIG. 15.—Nitric acid concentrator.

Sulfuric acid flows from the tank *S* downward through the dehydrating tower *D* and thence into a mixing tube. The dilute nitric acid to be concentrated flows from the tank *N* into the mixing tube where it is mixed with the sulfuric acid. The acid mixture flows downward through a vertically superimposed bank of retort tubes *R* heated by individual steam jackets, the temperature being automatically controlled by the temperature of the nitric acid vapors leaving the dehydrating tower *D* [U. S. 1,921,255 (1933)]. These tubes contain a body of acid retained by dams located at the discharge end.

Nitric acid vapor is evolved from the acid mixture in each of the retort tubes, and this vapor, along with some water vapor incidentally evolved therewith, flows upward through the retort tubes *R*, the mixer tube, and the dehydrating tower *D*. During its passage through the tower *D* the water vapor is removed by the descending sulfuric acid. The dehydrated nitric acid vapor passes from the top of the tower downward through the interconnecting pipe *P* and then upward through the bleacher pipe *B* and into a bank of water-jacketed condenser tubes *C* in which the nitric acid vapor is condensed to a liquid. The liquid flows back down through bleacher pipe *B* in which it is bleached by the rising nitric acid vapor, and thence to a water-jacketed collecting tube *T* from which the concentrated nitric acid is led to any suitable storage.

exchanger. A large number of such improved concentrating systems have been devised.[1] These are of either the tower or the tubular type, and their performance indicates that the quantity of sulfuric acid required

[1] U. S. 1,772,122 (1930); 1,920,307; 1,921,255; 1,922,278; 1,922,289; 1,924,312 (1933).

to concentrate a ton of 36°Bé. nitric acid (53 per cent) can thereby be reduced from 2.5 to 1.5 tons.   The tubular equipment shown in Fig. 15[1] is an example of a modern economical nitric acid concentrating system. Any vapors leaving the nitric acid condenser may be removed under reduced pressure and delivered to the concentrated sulfuric acid to be used for dehydration.[2]

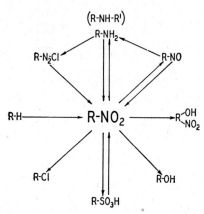

[1] U. S. 1,916,837 (1933).
[2] U. S. 1,920,307 (1933).

CHAPTER II

AMINATION BY REDUCTION

By P. H. Groggins

I. OUTLINE OF PROCESSES FOR THE PREPARATION OF AMINES

A compound containing the —NH₂ group united to a radical of acid character is called an amide, or an amido compound. An amine, or amino compound, is one containing the —NH₂ group united to a radical other than an acid radical. Acetanilide ($CH_3 \cdot CO \cdot NHC_6H_5$), formamide ($H \cdot CO \cdot NH_2$), and benzamide ($C_6H_5 \cdot CO \cdot NH_2$) are amido compounds, as they may be regarded as being derived from ammonia by the substitution of an acidic residue in place of hydrogen; *e.g.*,

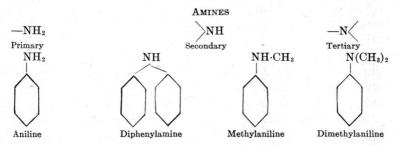

$$N \Big\langle \begin{matrix} H \\ H \\ H \end{matrix} \qquad\qquad N \Big\langle \begin{matrix} H \\ H \\ CO-CH_3 \end{matrix}$$

Ammonia   Acetamide

Aniline and 2-aminoanthraquinone are examples of amino compounds. The process of preparing these compounds may be termed *amidation* and *amination*, respectively.

Amines are divided into three classes—primary, secondary, and tertiary—the distinguishing characteristic being the number of hydrogen atoms in the parent substance *ammonia* that have been replaced by organic radicals. The classification may be illustrated graphically as follows:

AMINES

—NH₂	>NH	—N<
Primary	Secondary	Tertiary

NH₂   NH   NH·CH₃   N(CH₃)₂

Aniline   Diphenylamine   Methylaniline   Dimethylaniline

With respect to amination by reduction, the most important of these compounds are the aromatic primary amines, since they are almost invariably the starting materials for the preparation of amines of other classes.

63

A number of methods may be utilized for the preparation of amines, and oftentimes only a change in economic factors or the presence of patent barriers is responsible for the selection of a manufacturing technic for the production of a particular compound. Thus, aniline may be prepared commercially by the ammonolysis of chlorobenzene, the acid or alkaline reduction of nitrobenzene, or the catalytic hydrogenation of nitrobenzene in the vapor phase.

The methods generally used for the preparation of primary amines are the following:

1. The reduction of nitro compounds, also of the intermediate products of reduction, as the nitroso, azo, and hydrazo compounds.

2. Ammonolysis. The treatment of compounds containing labile nitro groups, sulfonic acid groups, hydroxy groups and oxygen atoms, or halogen atoms with ammonia.

3. The reduction of nitriles.

4. Intramolecular rearrangement of such compounds as secondary or tertiary amines, hydrazobenzenes, and hydroxylamine derivatives.

5. From amides, by hydrolysis or the action of alkaline hypochlorite.

6. The direct introduction of the amino group by means of agents other than ammonia.

    a. Treatment with hydroxylamine in sulfuric acid solutions.

    b. Fusion of polynitroaromatic compounds containing halogen atoms with urea, or other dibasic amides.

    c. Treatment with *p*-toluenesulfonamide.

To insure a proper balance in this work, only the two most important methods of amination are considered. The present discussion relates to amination by reduction; and later, in Chap. VI, the process of amination by ammonolysis is given consideration.

Aromatic and Aliphatic Compounds.—In this chapter emphasis is placed on the reduction of aromatic rather than aliphatic nitro compounds. Such accentuation is considered desirable because (1) The arylnitro compounds are readily available and are used extensively for the technical preparation of arylamines; (2) the processes are generally susceptible to close control and give high yields; (3) the fundamental principles have been more exhaustively studied; and (4) the principles based on aromatic chemistry can to a considerable extent be applied in the treatment of aliphatic compounds. In Chap. VI, however, the preparation of alkylamines is given adequate and merited consideration.

II. THE REDUCTION OF NITRO COMPOUNDS

Introduction.—The reduction of nitro compounds involves the progressive replacement of oxygen in the —NO_2 group by hydrogen. There are two groups of reduction products, *viz.*, the primary, which have one benzene ring; and the secondary, which contain two benzene rings. The intermediate compounds obtained from the reduction of nitrobenzene are shown in the accompanying chart on page 66.

Under suitable conditions, gaseous hydrogen in the presence of a metal catalyst, such as nickel, tin, or copper, may be used as the reducing agent. This method finds widespread and important application in the industrial synthesis of both aliphatic and aromatic amines. Here it is generally found most effective and economical to utilize the hydrogen liberated on metal surfaces by acid, alkaline, or neutral solution. Such *active* hydrogen possesses a larger amount of free energy than hydrogen gas.[1]

Since *active* hydrogen can be produced by diverse reactions, it follows that reductions may be accomplished by many methods. It is important to bear in mind that the metals iron, tin, and zinc, which are customarily employed in reduction processes, each have characteristic properties when used in acid or alkaline solutions. Conditions must therefore be

---

[1] The term *active* hydrogen is used by Prins, Haber, and others, as we have used it above, to mean hydrogen activated by contact with a metal. There seems to be no question that contact with different metals confers on free hydrogen the ability to produce different chemical changes in the same substance. Thus, hydrochloric acid and some nitric acid with zinc give ammonia; with magnesium, no ammonia; with tin, ammonia and hydroxylamine. Here the hydrogen is the same, but the metallic contact agent is different, and the free energy of the acid with each metal is different. If, now, hydrogen gas is led through the cold nitric acid solution, little or no action occurs. To explain the apparently greater activity of the hydrogen in the first three experiments, we note the fact that the hydrogen is liberated on the surface of the metals.

Alexander Smith ("Inorganic Chemistry") has deplored the use of the term nascent as confusing and states that the activity of the hydrogen liberated by the hydrolysis of salts in the presence of metals or by the action of acids on metals is "due to the larger amount of free energy contained in zinc plus acid plus reducible substance as compared with the free energy contained in free hydrogen plus reducible substance." In a similar manner, it can be shown that the oxygen liberated in the decomposition of hypochlorous acid is a more active oxidizing agent than is free oxygen gas. "The energy liberated in the decomposition of hypochlorous acid has to be added to that which free oxygen could give if performing the same oxidation, in order that the total fall in energy, which measures the tendency of the reaction to take place, may be estimated. Hence, substances that are not affected by free oxygen may be changed instantly by hypochlorous acid. This explains, for example, the oxidation by hypochlorous acid of many organic compounds, including those that are colored, when atmospheric air is without action. Thus, the heat liberated in the oxidation of indigo to isatin by oxygen gas, if it could be carried out, would be 1,800 cal. The much greater heat liberated when hypochlorous acid is used is obtained by adding the thermochemical equations."

$$2HClO = 2HCl + 2O + 18,600 \text{ cal.}$$
$$C_{16}H_{10}N_2O_2 + 2O = 2C_8H_5NO_2 + 1,800 \text{ cal.}$$
$$C_{16}H_{10}N_2O_2 + 2HClO = 2C_8H_5NO_2 + 2HCl + 20,400 \text{ cal.}$$

chosen with respect to the compound to be treated and the degree of reduction desired.

By controlling the reducing activity of the system, *i.e.*, by regulating the energy potential at which hydrogen is liberated, it is possible to obtain intermediate products of reduction from nitro compounds. In the following chart (Fig. 1) are shown the reduction products of nitro-

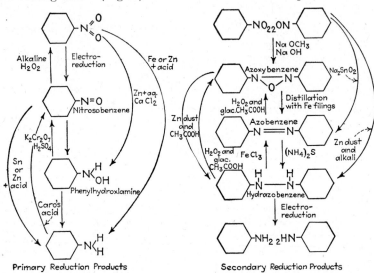

Fig. 1.—Reduction of nitrobenzene: intermediate products.

benzene, and below is given the value of potentials of reducing agents with reference to the normal hydrogen electrode using platinum poles.

$SnCl_2$ in KOH	0.861 volt	Hydrogen in HCl	0.311 volt
Na_2S	0.651 volt	I_2 in KOH	0.070 volt
Hydroxylamine in KOH	0.616 volt	$SnCl_2$ in HCl	0.064 volt

Nitrosobenzene can be obtained by electro-reduction of nitrobenzene.

Phenylhydroxylamine is obtained by treating an alcoholic solution of nitrobenzene with zinc dust and a small quantity of calcium chloride.

Azoxybenzene is produced by boiling nitrobenzene with an alcoholic solution of potassium hydroxide. A whole series of azoxy compounds has been prepared by reducing nitrotoluene, *p*-nitrochlorobenzene, etc., in alcoholic solution with ammonium chloride and magnesium.[1]

When nitrobenzene is reduced with a solution containing Na_2SnO_2 made from stannous chloride in an excess of sodium hydroxide, a partial reduction to the azo stage is obtained. In hydrochloric acid solution, stannous chloride converts the nitro compound to the amino derivative. Azobenzene can also be obtained by distilling azoxybenzene in the presence of finely divided iron.

[1] Ger. 446,867 (1924).

Hydrazobenzene is formed when nitrobenzene is reduced by zinc dust in alkaline solution. The presence of alkali is necessary, as in neutral solution phenylhydroxylamine is formed, and in acid solution aniline is the reduction product.

Outline of Methods.—The most useful methods for carrying out the reduction of nitro compounds are the following:

1. Iron, tin, and zinc—in the presence of water and (*a*) certain mineral or organic acids, (*b*) sulfur dioxide, (*c*) salts, particularly those derived from the neutralization of strong acids.

2. Alkali or metal sulfides in solution or suspension as dilute sodium, calcium, ammonium, manganese, or iron sulfides.

3. Ferrous sulfate in alkaline solution.

4. Hydrogenated bases of the quinoline series.

5. Sodium hydrosulfite in alkaline solution.

6. Zinc and iron in the presence of solutions of the strong alkalis.

7. Gaseous hydrogen or carbon monoxide in the presence of a catalyst (*a*) in alkaline solution, (*b*) in vapor phase.

By a proper selection of the reducing agents and careful regulation of the process, the reduction may be stopped at intermediate stages, and valuable products other than amino compounds may thus be obtained. The metal-acid reductions are the most vigorous, and only amino compounds are obtained as end products. When nitrobenzene is treated with zinc and a mineral acid solution, the end product is aniline; when an alkaline solution is employed, the end product is hydrazobenzene. When zinc dust and water are employed, the reaction product is phenylhydroxylamine. The following structural formulas represent the three modifications of this reduction process:

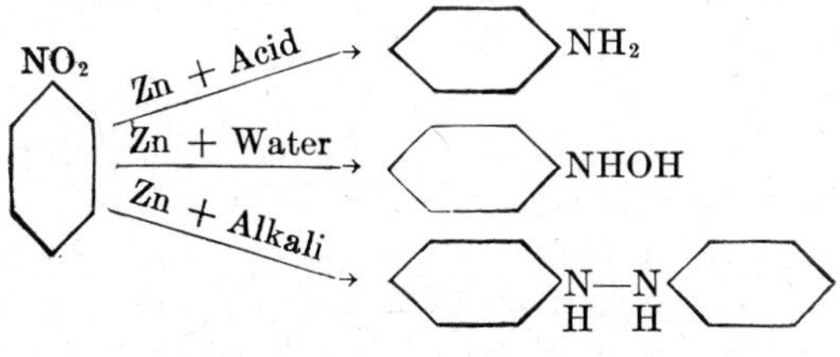

When the compound to be treated contains more than one nitro group, the products of reduction depend on the agents used; thus, *m*-phenylenediamine is obtained by the iron-acid reduction of *m*-dinitrobenzene, while the alkaline sulfide reduction yields *m*-nitroaniline.

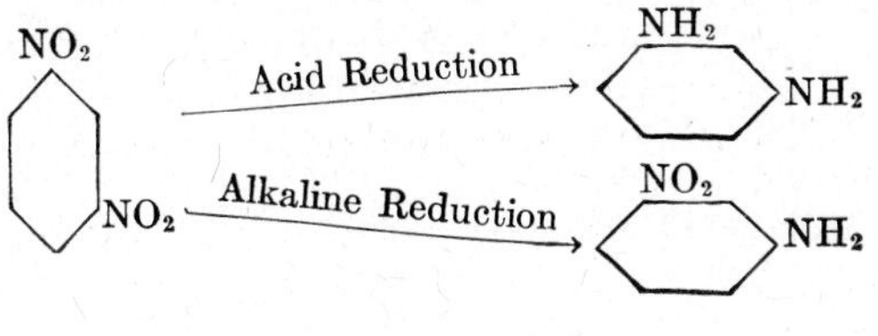

Under certain conditions, the mineral acid is replaced by an organic acid—acetic acid. This is essential in order to avoid decomposition in the treatment of complex compounds, *e.g.*, nitroaminobenzoylbenzoic acids, and also in the reduction of nitroanilides, for here

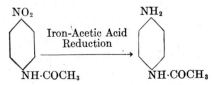

the presence of hydrochloric acid would tend to hydrolyze the anilide to a nitroamino compound.

III. REDUCTION WITH IRON IN ACID OR NEUTRAL SOLUTIONS

Theory and Mechanism of the Reaction.—Béchamp's discovery in 1854 that nitro compounds could be reduced in the presence of iron and acetic acid and Perkin's subsequent application in 1857 of this reaction for the commercial preparation of aniline were events of great significance for the development of the dye industry. Technical progress in the application of this reaction was first made by substituting hydrochloric acid for the acetic acid originally employed. Subsequently, it was discovered that the ferrous salt of the acid functioned catalytically, so that the reduction could be effected with less than the theoretical quantity of acid.

Considerable discussion has taken place in explaining the consumption of less acid than the quantity theoretically required, when the reduction is represented as taking place as follows.

$$C_6H_5NO_2 + 2Fe + 6HCl \rightarrow C_6H_5NH_2 + 2H_2O + 2FeCl_3$$

Mol. wts.   123   2(55.84)   6(36.45)

In industrial practice, less than 2 per cent of the amount indicated above is actually used. Operating experience has shown that 3.0 lb. of hydrochloric acid (10 lb. of 30 per cent solution) is required to bring about a satisfactory reduction of 100 lb. of nitrobenzene to aniline.

The presence of free acid, which was long considered essential to the reduction process, has furthermore been shown to be no longer necessary. In 1894, Wohl[1] revealed that nitrobenzene could be reduced with iron powder, in alcoholic or aqueous solutions, in the presence of calcium or magnesium chloride and stated that the absence of free acid is advantageous. In 1914, von Girsewald[2] showed that ferrous chloride could be used as the catalytic agent in the reduction process. Moore[3] sub-

---

[1] Wohl, *Ber.*, **27**, 1432, 1815 (1894).

[2] Girsewald, Ger. 281,100 (1914).

[3] Moore, Brit. 155,319 (1919).

sequently demonstrated that sodium chloride could be employed in the reduction of nitrosophenols and p-nitroacetanilide to the corresponding amino and amido derivatives. This investigator found also that sodium chloride was not nearly so active as calcium chloride for this purpose.

Within recent years, it has been demonstrated that aniline hydrochloride, aluminum chloride, sodium bisulfate, or other salts derived from strong acids can be successfully employed. It is merely essential to use such salts which in the presence of metals are hydrolyzed in aqueous solutions resulting in the formation of hydrogen ions. The introduction of salts for the technical preparation of amino compounds has been a notable achievement. It has made possible a more sanitary environment in the reducer building and has furthermore resulted in the elimination of acid pots and hard rubber and lead-lined equipment, which previously were considered essential to commercial reduction processes.

Theory of Reaction.—A number of investigators have advanced theories to explain the catalytic iron-salt reduction process. To appreciate better these explanations, it is interesting first to follow the rôle that iron plays in providing the active hydrogen for the reduction process.

Alexander and Byers[1] have established that hydrogen is generated when a mill containing iron balls and water is rotated at room temperatures. Bergius[2] has shown that pure hydrogen can be continuously generated from iron and water at 200 to 300°C. He has also found that common salt, iron chloride, or small quantities of hydrochloric acid greatly accelerate the reaction and that the iron is converted almost entirely to ferroso-ferric oxide.

$$3Fe + 4H_2O \rightarrow Fe_3O_4 + 4H_2$$

Magnetic iron oxide is the final product of oxidation, the intermediate products being presumably ferrous and ferric hydroxides.

Whitney[3] has suggested that the initial step in the oxidation process is the direct combination of iron with the hydroxyl ions of the water. At elevated temperatures, this reaction is quite rapid. The ferrous hydroxide [$Fe(OH)_2$] formed is a powerful reducing agent. It will reduce nitrates to ammonia. Neutral or acid solutions of ferrous salts absorb oxygen with the formation of the ferric salt, part of which is precipitated as a basic salt when there is no excess of acid present. Colloidal ferric hydroxide is also readily precipitated by the addition of an electrolyte such as sodium chloride or ferrous chloride.

[1] ALEXANDER and BYERS, *J. Chem. Education*, **9**, 916 (1932).
[2] Bergius, U. S. 1,059,818 (1913).
[3] WHITNEY, *J. Am. Chem. Soc.*, **25**, 394 (1903).

In considering the behavior of the amines, it is found that these compounds dissociate on solvation only to a slight extent, thereby forming a weak base.

$$C_6H_5NH_2 + HOH \leftrightarrows (C_6H_5NH_3)OH \leftrightarrows (C_6H_5NH_3)^+OH^-$$

The salts of aniline, like those of all primary benzenoid amines, are easily hydrolyzed. Since the amines are comparatively weak bases, their salts with mineral acids are acidic.

In the following equations, an attempt is made to present an outline of the reduction process based on facts relating to the oxidation of the iron, the hydrolysis of neutral salts, and the dissociation of amines. The representation is obviously incomplete in many of the details, particularly with respect to the steps involved in the progressive oxidation of the iron:

$$(FeCl_2)Fe + 2H_2O \rightarrow (FeCl_2) + Fe(OH)_2 + H_2 \tag{0}$$
$$R \cdot NO_2 + (FeCl_2) + 3Fe + 4H_2O \rightarrow R \cdot NH_2 + (FeCl_2) + 3Fe(OH)_2 \tag{1}$$
$$R \cdot NH_2 + H_2O \rightarrow (R \cdot NH_3)OH \rightarrow (R \cdot NH_3)^+OH^- \tag{2}$$
$$2R \cdot NH_3^+ + 2OH^- + Fe^{++} + 2Cl^- \rightarrow 2R \cdot NH_3Cl + \underset{\text{Limited Solubility}}{Fe(OH)_2} \tag{3}$$
$$2R \cdot NH_3^+ + 2Cl^- + 2Fe(OH)_2 + 2Fe \rightarrow 2R \cdot NH_2 + FeCl_2 + \underset{\substack{\text{Completely} \\ \text{Insoluble}}}{Fe_3O_4} + 3H_2 \tag{4}$$

Formula (0) merely expresses the preliminary action between iron powder and water in the presence of an acid or salts derived from strong acids. This activity, as Bergius has shown, is accelerated at higher temperatures and pressures. When a nitro compound is introduced (1), the active hydrogen does work in the reduction process. Equation (2) represents the formation of the weak base through solvation. The intermediate catalytic step is expressed by Eq. (3). The reactions indicated by the second and third equations show that aniline behaves similar to ammonia. It unites with water to form the weakly dissociated base phenylammonium hydroxide, which, like ammonium hydroxide, precipitates the hydroxides of the heavy metals from solutions of their salts.

The reaction products in Eq. (3) are $R \cdot NH_3Cl$ and $Fe(OH)_2$. Continuation and completion of the process depend on the hydrolysis of the phenylammonium chloride, which is a salt derived from a weak base. The hydrolysis of such salts is known to take place very readily in the presence of metals. The introduction of a slight excess over the theoretical quantity of iron brings about this result.

It is interesting to note that the ferrous ion which is essential to the reduction process is not present in the products of Eq. (3). In this connection, it has been observed that only a faint test for soluble iron can be obtained by spotting on filter paper with sodium sulfide solution directly after feeding considerable nitro compound to the reducer. When, however, reduction is complete, qualitative or spot tests show very distinctly the presence of soluble iron. From Eqs. (3) and (4), it may reasonably be implied that the quantity of ferrous chloride catalyst should be proportional to the amount of amine that is dissociated, a slight excess being necessary in order to insure an acid reaction. This is a matter of considerable practical importance in order that maximum yields and purity of product may be obtained. It has previously been shown that nitrobenzene may yield directly hydrazobenzene, phenylhydroxylamine, or aniline, depending on the hydrogen ion concentration of the solution. The production of primary amines in this type of reduction necessitates a slight but definite acidity. Since the utilization of acid-reacting salts as catalysts at no time provides a solution which is strongly acid, it is essential that the feeding and temperature control be regulated to insure an active state of reduction so that there is no accumulation of phenylammonium chloride and ferrous hydroxide.

The final reaction, Eq. (4), yields end products in accordance with those observed under actual operating conditions. The ferrous chloride is regenerated and is again ready for further activity. The iron is in a large measure oxidized to Fe_3O_4, and the amine is set free. It is obvious that a slight excess of iron is necessary to complete the reaction. Without the presence of active hydrogen or reducto-active ferrous compounds, the formation of intermediate reduction products would take place.

The liberation of hydrogen generated by the action of water on finely ground cast iron in the presence of iron salts may be observed quite distinctly long after the reduction is complete. It is a matter of record that fires have started with explosive violence when a spark was accidentally brought over a recently emptied open reducer vessel.

Eliminating the intermediate catalytic reaction, a condensed picture of the reduction process may be obtained from the first and final products, as presented in the following equation:

$$2R \cdot NO_2 + (FeCl_2) + 5Fe + 4H_2O \rightarrow 2R \cdot NH_2 + (FeCl_2) + Fe_3O_4 + 2Fe(OH)_2$$

In works practice, it is customary to use only slightly over 2 moles Fe per mole of nitro compound to carry out the reduction process. Under such circumstances, not all of the iron is converted to the ferroso-ferric oxide, some reducto-active ferrous hydroxide also being present. Iron sludge obtained from the reduction of nitrobenzene gave the analysis shown in Table I. Since magnetic iron oxide consists of 1 part FeO + 1 part Fe_2O_3, if all the iron were converted to the ferroso-ferric oxide, the ferric content would be about 66 per cent Fe^{III}.

The following sludge analyses show that slight fluctuations in the ratio or quality of iron will produce magnified differences in its chemical composition.

Industrial experience has shown that it is practicable to operate using a ratio of 2 moles of iron per mole of nitrobenzene as a low limit and 2.5 moles as an upper limit.   Undue economy in the use of iron is a faulty

TABLE I

Expt. No.	Sludge analysis			Iron to Nitrobenzene	
	Metallic iron, %	Ferrous iron, %	Ferric iron, %	Weight ratio	Molar ratio
1	None	11.05	50.16	1:1	2.24:1
2	None	8.44	54.47	1:1	2.24:1
3	1	46.81	13.50	1.1:1	2.45:1

Nitrobenzene, 4,000 lb.; FeCl₃, 139 lb.

practice, as it may lead to side reactions with consequent lowering of the yield.

In works practice, it has been found that when insufficient iron is present, the addition of heat or acid is not effective in carrying the reduction to completion.   The introduction of some finely divided iron under such circumstances brings about a vigorous reaction which results in the complete reduction of the nitro compound.   Some operators prefer to use very finely divided iron to finish a reduction, and this practice is particularly advisable when the bulk of the iron turnings are not of a good quality.

Chemical Factors in Iron-acid Reduction.—The more important of the physico-chemical factors that merit consideration here are the following:

1. Size and physical condition of the iron particles.
2. Homogeneity of the reaction mass.
3. Concentration of the catalyst.
4. Reaction temperature.
5. Heat of reaction.

Physical Condition of Iron.—From a study of the equations outlining the reduction process, it is obvious that the iron fed into the reducer not only supplies the metal adsorption surface but enters into the reactions by providing the iron for the regeneration of the ferrous chloride upon the hydrolysis of the (aniline hydrochloride) phenylammonium chloride and also acts as an oxygen carrier.   An analysis of the residual sludge reveals that the bulk of the iron is converted to iron oxides, the degree of oxidation depending on the quantity of iron employed.   Experiments have shown that a clean, finely divided, soft, gray cast iron yields the best results.   The rate of reduction depends in part on the fineness and porosity of the iron particles, the homogeneity of the charge in the reducer, and the degree of etching imparted to the iron by the preliminary acid treatment. To insure a thoroughly etched iron, it is customary to boil the iron-acid suspension before adding any nitro compound. When this precaution is observed, the reaction proceeds very readily, with no danger of a violent deferred reaction.

Size of Particles.—When coarse particles are used, the oxidation of the iron is retarded and an excess of it must be provided. Furthermore, an accumulation of partially oxidized iron, as $Fe(OH)_2$ and $Fe(OH)_3$, oftentimes throws such a load on the stirring mechanism as to bring it to a stop. Since the reaction velocity for nitro compound reduction is a function of the rate of iron oxidation, it is clear that the use of finely divided iron shortens the time of reaction. This fact is brought out in the following table from the work of Lyons and Smith:[1]

TABLE II.—EFFECT OF SIZE OF IRON PARTICLES IN REDUCTION OF NITROBENZENE
Nitrobenzene, 100 gm.; iron, 123 gm.; water, 45.5 cc.; FeCl₃ solution, 7.5 cc. (0.035 gm. Cl as FeCl₃ per cc. of solution)

Expt. No.	Time, hours	Iron fineness, mesh/sq. cm.	Yield aniline, %
1	1.5	80	100.0
2	7.0	40	96.7
3	9.0	20	78.0
4	2.5	13	66.0
5	9	13	45.6
6	9	20	44.2
7	9	40	78.8
8	2	80	100.2

In experiments 5 to 8, inclusive, 2.90 gm. of *sodium chloride* with 50 cc. of water was used as catalyst. Speed of agitation 34 r.p.m. in all experiments.

Effect of Agitation.—Since the reduction process under consideration is a catalytic reaction, it is clear that the best results are obtainable only when the nitro compound, iron, and water-soluble catalyst are in intimate contact. A stirrer that merely pushes the iron around the bottom of the vessel and permits the charge to separate out into layers cannot function efficiently. It is apparent, therefore, that a sturdy sleeve-and-propeller or double-impeller type of stirrer will in this case be superior to the slow-moving plow type. Furthermore, most aromatic nitro compounds are practically insoluble in faintly acid solution, and thorough mixing is consequently a factor of major importance. Lyons and Smith[2]

[1] LYONS and SMITH, *Ber.*, **60**, 173 (1927).
[2] LYONS and SMITH, *loc. cit.*

obtained the following results (Table III) in determining the effect of rate of agitation in the reduction of nitrobenzene:

TABLE III.—EFFECT OF AGITATION REDUCTION OF NITROBENZENE TO ANILINE

Nitrobenzene, 100 gm.; H_2O, 325 gm.; 20-mesh iron, 224 gm.; $FeCl_3$ solution, 50 cc. (0.00319 gm. Cl as $FeCl_3$ per cc.)

Expt. No.	Time, hours	Speed of agitators, r.p.m.	Yield aniline, %
1	2	0	66.0
2	1	34	93.2
3	2	34	95.4
4	2	76	93.8

Failure to get improved results at the highest speed of agitation is susceptible to explanation. An improvement in the type of stirrer or the use of a finer iron instead of the 20-mesh material would probably have altered the results. The two factors—homogeneity and iron fineness—must be harmonized. When the rate of reduction is limited by the quality of the iron used, an increased agitation will not, of course, show a corresponding improvement in operations. It is, of course, clear that a rate of agitation beyond that necessary throws an extra burden on the driving mechanism.

Effect of Concentration of Catalyst.—Theoretical considerations involving the progressive oxidation of the iron indicate the desirability of using 4 to 5 moles of water per mole of nitro compound treated. This approximation is based on the assumption that the iron employed is converted first to ferrous and then to ferric hydroxides as intermediate products during its oxidation to the oxide, thus:

$$2R \cdot NO_2 + 4Fe + 8H_2O \rightarrow 2R \cdot NH_2 + 4Fe(OH)_3$$
$$2R \cdot NO_2 + 5Fe + 11H_2O \rightarrow 2R \cdot NH_2 + 5Fe(OH)_3 + 1.5H_2$$

Owing to the fact that part of the iron hydroxides formed loses water to form the ferroso-ferric oxide during the course of the reaction, it is entirely possible that the reduction may be made with less than 4 moles of water, provided, however, that a uniform reaction mass can be maintained by effective agitation (see Expt. 15, Table IV). Practical problems relating to (1) the agitation of the reaction mass, (2) the promotion of a smooth active reaction, and (3) the conservation of the heat of reduction frequently make it advisable to employ a slight excess over this proportionality. Some reductions require a much larger water ratio, particularly when a mild reaction is required. Unnecessary dilution, however, not only places undesirable restrictions on the productivity of each reducer but also reduces the concentration of the catalyst so that it is less effective.

According to Lyons and Smith,[1] a concentration of 0.035 gm. of Cl per cubic centimeter as FeCl$_3$ gives the best results in the preparation of

TABLE IV.—INFLUENCE OF IRON CHLORIDE CONCENTRATION
Nitrobenzene, 100 gm.; 80-mesh iron, 123 gm.

Expt. No.	Time, hours	H$_2$O, cc.	FeCl$_3$, cc. of solution (0.2315 gm. Cl per cc.)	Gm. Cl as FeCl$_3$ per cc. of solution	Yield C$_6$H$_5$NH$_2$, %
1	2	325	50	0.0319	95.4
2	1	325	50	0.0319	93.2
3	1	315	60	0.0360	94.3
4	1.5	325	50	0.0319	96.1
5	1	315	60	0.0316	95.1
6	1.5	151	22	0.0314	93.0
7	2	151	22	0.0314	98.5
8	2	67	11	0.0354	94.1
9	2	69	5.5	0.0174	93.6
10	2	16.5	2.5	0.0313	80.0
11	2	33	2.5	0.0165	88.0
12	2	33	3	0.0197	90.0
13	2	50	2.5	0.0111	86.0
14	2	47.5	4	0.0184	95.0
15	1.5	45.5	7.5	0.035	100.0

aniline from nitrobenzene. From the data (Table IV), it can be seen that no benefits were derived from the use of a larger quantity of ferric chloride. As is to be expected the important factor is the concentration of the catalyst. It is interesting to observe that the Cl$^-$ content is only about 1 per cent of the amount theoretically required by the equation

$$C_6H_5NO_2 + 3Fe + 6HCl \rightarrow C_6H_5NH_2 + 3FeCl_2 + 2H_2O$$

When non-jacketed reducers are used and considerable water as live steam is introduced, it is clear that the concentration of the water-soluble catalyst is continuously being lowered and, consequently, it becomes less effective. Furthermore, with increasing volume, it becomes more difficult to maintain a homogeneous reaction mass. It is obvious that the reaction velocity cannot be at a maximum when the iron, water-soluble catalyst, and nitro compound are not thoroughly mixed.

Ferric chloride reacts more actively than sodium chloride in the catalytic iron–salt reduction of nitro compounds. The comparative data relating to the preparation of aniline are given in Table V.

Reaction Temperature.—It has been found that the use of a high catalyst concentration (3 or more per cent compared to nitrobenzene taken) during reduction results in a finely divided iron sludge of proba-

[1] LYONS and SMITH, *loc. cit.*

ble commercial value. This result can be obtained by limiting the quantity of water introduced into the jacketed reducer and utilizing the heat of reaction to carry on the reaction. An obvious advantage arising from operating with such concentrated solutions is the fact that the charge is easily maintained at the boiling temperature. The vigorous reflux

TABLE V.—COMPARATIVE ACTIVITY OF FeCl₃ AND NaCl, IN THE REDUCTION OF NITROBENZENE[1]

Nitrobenzene, 100 gm.; iron, 123 gm.; r.p.m., 34

Expt. No.	Time, hours	Iron fineness through mesh	Chloride used	H₂O, cc.	Total chloride	Cl per cc. solution, gm.	Yield C₆H₅NH₂, %
1	2	80	NaCl	50	1.523 gm.	0.0183	88.0
2	2	80	FeCl₃	47.5	4.0 cc.	0.0184	95.0
3	2	80	NaCl	50	2.90 gm.	0.035	100.2
4	1.5	80	FeCl₃	45.5	7.5 cc.	0.035	100.0
5	7	40	FeCl₃	45.5	7.5 cc.	0.035	96.7
6	9	20	FeCl₃	45.5	7.5 cc.	0.035	78.0
7	9	13	NaCl	50	2.90 gm.	0.035	45.6
8	9	40	NaCl	50	2.90 gm.	0.035	78.8
9	9	20	NaCl	50	2.90 gm.	0.035	43.0

[1] Lyons and Smith conclude from these results that sodium chloride is about 84 per cent as efficient as ferric chloride.

that characterizes such a reduction insures against the formation of intermediate products of reaction. The reaction is not only rapid and efficient but is economical on account of the lower consumption of steam.

Heat of Reaction.—A study of the thermal factors relating to the reduction of nitrobenzene shows that the reaction is distinctly exothermic. It is necessary, therefore, to remove the surplus heat generated while maintaining the reduction at the optimum reaction temperature. When nonvolatile materials are treated, as in the conversion of *p*-nitroaniline to *p*-phenylenediamine, flumes of suitable diameter and height are sufficient. When volatile nitro compounds are used, an efficient tubulous condenser gives eminently satisfactory results.

The data below show the heat in B.t.u. generated during the "feed" and reduction of a 1,200 lb. charge of nitrobenzene.

Operation	Heat Generated, B.t.u.
Feed	1,805,000
Reduction	488,000
Total heat liberated	2,293,000
Heat of conversion per pound nitrobenzene	1,911

Ferrous Sulfate as Catalyst.—It has long been known that sulfuric acid could be substituted for hydrochloric acid in the reduction process. As a rule, the amino compounds obtained from its use, particularly in the case of solid products, are darker and the yields lower. These disadvantages appear to be minimized when the sulfuric acid is introduced as sodium acid sulfate. When used alone or preferably in conjunction with a calculated quantity of sodium chloride, a very economical and satisfactory promotor is obtained. The acid sulfate ($NaHSO_4$) may be considered as having 40.8 per cent available H_2SO_4, but as a rule the niter cake of commerce averages about 31 per cent acidity. When used in conjunction with sodium chloride, Davis[1] claims it to be an excellent promotor of the catalytic action. This is apparently due to the formation of hydrochloric acid at the start of the process and the formation of ferrous chloride as a secondary reaction. Davis suggests the use of 2 lb. of H_2SO_4 as 6 lb. of niter cake per 100 lb. of nitrobenzene. When employed in conjunction with sodium chloride, sufficient NaCl must be added to use up the acidity of the niter cake. Thus, 2.4 lb. of sodium chloride with 6 lb. of niter cake per 100 lb. of nitro compound give satisfactory results. The niter cake is first ground and added, along with the sodium chloride, to the water and finely divided iron in the reducer.

Recovery of the Catalyst.—In the technical preparation of amines by catalytic reduction with iron and a soluble salt, it is not customary to recover and utilize the dissolved catalyst. This step is not always feasible, particularly when the amino compound is also soluble in aqueous solutions. In many instances, however, such a step could be made part of the chemical engineering operations employed in separating the amine from the aqueous suspension of iron compounds. Utilization of the aqueous portion in subsequent reductions appears to be an excellent method of introducing the catalyst in an active form. In this connection, it is known that the impure mother liquors from the aniline hydrochloride crystallizing pans can be used advantageously.

IV. TIN AND HYDROCHLORIC ACID REDUCTION

The reduction of aromatic nitro compounds with tin and hydrochloric acid may be represented by the following equation:

$$2R \cdot NO_2 + 3Sn + 12HCl \rightarrow 2R \cdot NH_2 + 3SnCl_4 + 4H_2O$$

Owing to the comparatively high cost of tin, this method of effecting reductions has not achieved significant commercial importance. In place of tin and hydrochloric acid, a solution of stannous chloride in hydrochloric acid can be employed; but there is little advantage, in general, in this procedure, as double the amount of tin must be used to effect the reduction.

[1] Davis, U. S. 1,663,473 (1928).

There are, however, occasional uses for stannous chloride reductions on account of the mildness of the reaction. It can be employed in the reduction of 4, 4′-dinitrodiphenylamine which accompanies *p*-nitroaniline as an impurity when the latter is prepared by the ammonolysis of *p*-nitrochlorobenzene. Stannous chloride is also employed when it is desired to reduce one nitro group of two originally present. In alcoholic solution, this reduction proceeds very smoothly, yielding excellent products.

Stannous chloride in hydrochloric acid can also be employed for the reduction of the nitroparaffins. Ordinarily, however, this procedure results in the formation of the related hydroxylamine in addition to the primary alkylamine:

$$R \cdot CH_2NO_2 \xrightarrow{\ 2H_2\ } R \cdot CH_2NHOH \xrightarrow{\ H_2\ } R \cdot CH_2NH_2$$

When, however, a large excess of stannous chloride and fuming hydrochloric acid are used, primary and secondary nitro compounds are reduced to the corresponding oximes. Thus, by adding an aqueous solution of the alkali salt of the acinitro compound to about 2.5 times the theoretical quantity of $SnCl_2$—HCl, as required by the equations below, the oxime is formed.

$$R \cdot CH : N {\overset{O}{\underset{OK}{\Big\langle}}} \xrightarrow{\ SnCl_2\ } R \cdot CH : NOH \xrightarrow{\ H_2O\ } R \cdot C {\overset{H}{\underset{O}{\Big\langle}}} + NH_2OH$$

$$\underset{R}{\overset{R}{\Big\rangle}} C : N {\overset{O}{\underset{OK}{\Big\langle}}} \xrightarrow{\ SnCl_2\ } \underset{R}{\overset{R}{\Big\rangle}} C : NOH \xrightarrow{\ H_2O\ } \underset{R}{\overset{R}{\Big\rangle}} C{=}O + NH_2OH$$

If the charge is neutralized and live steam introduced, the oxime will be distilled over. By passing steam into the acid charge, however, hydrolysis occurs with the formation of a ketone or aldehyde and hydroxylamine. The carbonyl compound will distill over while the hydroxylamine hydrochloride remains in solution.

Stannous Chloride as a Reducing (and Chlorinating) Agent.—Under anhydrous conditions in the presence of acetic acid, stannous chloride may be used for the reduction of aromatic nitro compounds, acetylating the base and in many cases chlorinating the resultant anilide *in situ.*[1] The concomitant reduction and chlorinating of nitrobenzene may be indicated as follows:

$$C_6H_5 \cdot NO_2 \rightarrow C_6H_5 \cdot NH_2 \rightarrow C_6H_5 \cdot NH \cdot COCH_3 \rightarrow C_6H_4Cl \cdot NH \cdot COCH_3$$

Generally, monochlorination takes place in the para position to the original nitro group. In para substituted nitro compounds, no chlorination takes place except in the case of *p*-chloronitrobenzene, which, only if hydrogen chloride is present during the reduction, gives 2, 4-di-

[1] KIEWIET and STEPHEN, *J. Chem. Soc.*, **1931**, 82.

chloroacetanilide; in the absence of hydrogen chloride, the product is p-chloroacetanilide.

Vₐ. REDUCTION WITH ZINC OR IRON IN STRONG ALKALINE SOLUTION

When nitrobenzene or its homologues are treated in alkaline solution in the presence of finely divided zinc or iron, they can be reduced step by step to the hydrazo stage. Such hydrazo compounds—hydrazobenzene, hydrazotoluene, hydrazoanisole—may be converted readily to benzidine, tolidine, and dianisidine by intramolecular rearrangement in cold concentrated hydrochloric acid.

The several steps in the reduction of nitrobenzene are represented by the following graphic formulas:

$$
\begin{array}{cccccc}
C_6H_5NO_2 & C_6H_5N\!\diagdown & C_6H_5N & C_6H_5NH & C_6H_5NH_2 \\
 & & \!\!\!\!\!\!>\!O & \| & | \\
C_6H_5NO_2 & C_6H_5N\!\diagup & C_6H_5N & C_6H_5NH & C_6H_5NH_2 \\
\text{Nitrobenzene} & \text{Azoxybenzene} & \text{Azobenzene} & \text{Hydrazobenzene} & \text{Aniline}
\end{array}
$$

Ethanol and methanol are usually employed in the zinc-alkali reduction, in order to moderate the reducing activity of the system which tends toward the production of some aniline in the final stages. The use of zinc in alcoholic caustic soda, which was the first procedure for the technical preparation of hydrazobenzene, has to a considerable extent been replaced by iron in alkaline solution. Although the materials involved in the former process are more costly, the method is still employed on account of the comparative simplicity of the operation. Numerous modifications have, however, been made so that the residual zinc, alkali, and alcohol are recovered. This improved technic is described later in this chapter under technical operation.

When zinc is employed, some of it is dissolved in the alkaline solution with the evolution of hydrogen, the zinc hydroxide first formed dissolving in the excess of alkali:

$$Zn + 2H^+ + 2OH^- \rightarrow Zn^{++} + 2OH^- + H_2\!\uparrow \rightarrow Zn(OH)_2$$
$$Zn(OH)_2 + 2NaOH \rightarrow Na_2ZnO_2 + 2H_2O$$

Zinc hydroxide is weakly basic and gives salts with acids, but with respect to strong bases it is weakly acidic. Zinc hydroxide is very soluble in an excess of alkali, zinc oxide acting as an acid-forming oxide toward the strong alkalis, and it is upon this fact that the solution of zinc in alkalis with evolution of hydrogen depends. Freshly precipitated zinc hydroxide requires nearly seven molecular proportions of caustic soda in concentrated solution to dissolve it completely, and the solution thus formed is not permanent, zinc hydroxide being gradually precipitated from it in a less soluble form. Only a very small amount of sodium zincate is ever present in solution, the greater part of the dissolved hydroxide being probably present in the colloidal state.[1] The equilibrium may be expressed by the following equation, zinc hydroxide being represented as a weak acid H_2ZnO_2:

$$H_2ZnO_2 + 2NaOH \rightleftarrows Na_2ZnO_2 + 2HOH$$

The reduction of the nitro compound to the hydrazo stage may be represented by the following equation:

$$10NaOH + 5Zn + 2R\cdot NO_2 \rightarrow R\cdot \underset{H}{N}\cdot \underset{H}{N}\cdot R + 5Na_2ZnO_2 + 4H_2O$$

In technical operations, an excess of 15 to 50 per cent of zinc (based on the preceding equation) is used. The quantity of alkali employed is, however, only about 2 to 3 per cent of the theoretical. Here, as in the case of acid reductions, there is a hydrolysis of the intermediate soluble catalytic agent which the presence of metals encourages. In this process, the sodium zincate is hydrolyzed with the regeneration of sodium hydroxide, the zinc hydroxide being ultimately converted to the oxide:

$$Na_2ZnO_2 + 2H_2O \overset{Zn}{\rightleftarrows} Zn(OH)_2 + 2NaOH$$

In spite of the fact that the atomic weight of iron is less than that of zinc and that iron furthermore can be oxidized to Fe_2O_3, the excess of ordinary iron that must be actually employed in this reduction (when it replaces zinc) is very much greater. This circumstance is attributed to the lower activity of iron. It is necessary, therefore, to facilitate the catalytic and hydrolytic reactions by employing a fine quality of iron, which gives a maximum surface and is free from oil.[2] In works practice, it is expedient to etch the iron before using, by treating it with a strong alkali solution, whereupon the metal assumes the appearance of damp sand. Dreyfus[3] has found that the ratio of both iron and alkali with respect to nitrobenzene can be substantially lowered by using iron which has been prepared by the reduction of the oxides. Such iron is obtained in a very finely divided condition and has an extended active surface with respect to its mass. Compared with alkali-etched iron turnings, only about 65 to 75 per cent of the quantity need be used; the molar ratio of nitrobenzene to iron and alkali respectively here being approximately 2:4:8. This indicates that the oxidation of the iron will occur closely as follows:

$$4Fe + 10H_2O \rightarrow 2Fe(OH)_2 + 2Fe(OH)_3 + 5H_2$$

The iron-alkali reduction, like the zinc-alkali process, is subject to numerous modifications. The following example[3] illustrates the procedure in carrying out such reductions:

[1] Goudriaan, *Proc. Acad. Sci. Amsterdam,* **22,** 179 (1919).

[2] Meer, Ger. 138,496 (1900).

[3] Dreyfus, U. S. 2,010,067 (1935).

Progressive Reduction of Nitrobenzene to Hydrazobenzene.—*a.*
Fifty parts of finely divided iron, obtained by reducing iron oxide with
hydrogen, or by the thermal decomposition of iron carbonyl, is added to
100 parts of nitrobenzene contained in a reducer fitted with an efficient
stirrer. The suspension is heated to 90°C. and 80 parts of 60 per cent
sodium hydroxide are gradually added. The mixture is then stirred at
100°C., the temperature being maintained by supplying steam or cooling
water to the jacket of the reducer. The course of the reaction may

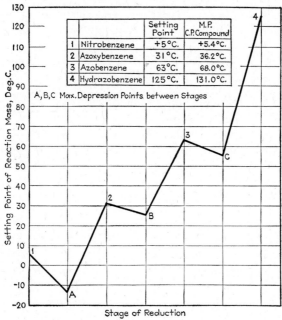

		Setting Point	M.P. C.P.Compound
1	Nitrobenzene	+5°C.	+5.4°C.
2	Azoxybenzene	31°C.	36.2°C.
3	Azobenzene	63°C.	68.0°C.
4	Hydrazobenzene	125°C.	131.0°C.

A,B,C Max.Depression Points between Stages

Fig. 2.—Alkali-iron reduction of nitrobenzene.

be observed by the change of color and the disappearance of the odor of
nitrobenzene. A more exact indication may be obtained by determining
the setting point on a sample of the charge (Fig. 2), since this changes
with each phase of the reaction. As the reduction proceeds, the setting
point drops from about 5 (corresponding to nitrobenzene) to a minimum
of −13°C., at which time about 40 per cent of the nitro compound is
converted to azoxybenzene. The setting point then gradually rises to
31°C., at which time the odor of nitrobenzene has disappeared and the
azoxy compound can be discharged.

b. Azobenzene can be obtained upon further reduction of the azoxy
compound by adding a paste consisting of 16 parts iron and 40 parts of
60 per cent caustic soda and heating at 110 to 120°C. The setting point
of the reduction mass first sinks to a minimum of 25°C. and then rises to

about 63°C.   The apparatus may then be stopped and the azobenzene discharged.

c. In order to proceed to the next stage of reduction, *i.e.*, to hydrazobenzene, it is necessary again to add a paste consisting of 16 parts iron and 40 parts of 60 per cent caustic soda solution.   The setting point of the mass sinks to a minimum of 55°C. and then rises to 122 to 125°C.   In order to prevent the reduction mass from solidifying, it is necessary either to raise the temperature to 130°C. or add some solvent *e.g.*, benzene, to the reaction mixture.   The introduction of benzene in sufficient quantities also affords a convenient means of separating and decanting the hydrazobenzene from the iron-alkali residues.

It is difficult to remove the hydrazobenzene from the iron sludge at this point, and a number of modifications of this process have consequently been advocated.   A practical suggestion involves the removal of azobenzene and reducing this compound by zinc in alcoholic alkaline solution at 60°C.   The reduction mass is filtered, and the zinc residues are boiled up with fresh alcohol.   The filtrate separates into two layers, of which the lower contains aqueous sodium zincate, while the upper is an alcoholic solution of hydrazobenzene.   The alcoholic layer is separated and saturated with carbon dioxide to precipitate the alkali.   After filtering, the alcoholic solution is evaporated to obtain the hydrazobenzene, for which Fierz[1] claims practically quantitative yields.

Vʙ. REDUCTION WITH ZINC IN WEAKLY ALKALINE SOLUTIONS

In the preceding pages, it was shown that the mechanism of reduction with zinc and strongly alkaline solutions led to the formation of azoxybenzene as the first step in the reduction of nitrobenzene.   Brand and his coworkers have shown that when faintly alkaline systems are employed, the principal initial product of reduction is β-phenylhydroxylamine. The systems—zinc + calcium chloride; and zinc + ammonium chloride —are not neutral but quite alkaline to phenolphthalein.   Employing the hydrogen electrode and indicators, it was found that in the preparation of β-phenylhydroxylamine from nitrobenzene by means of zinc dust and aqueous calcium chloride, the reduction liquid has a pH between 10.5 and 11.7, which corresponds to the alkalinity of 0.01 N alkali.   When NH_4Cl was substituted for $CaCl_2$ in the reducing system, the pH was between 8 and 9.   Brand and Modersohn[2] advanced the following scheme in the reduction of nitrobenzene to phenylhydroxylamine:

$$C_6H_5NO_2 + 2H^+ + 2OH^- + Zn \rightarrow C_6H_5NO + H_2O + Zn^{++} + 2OH^- \qquad (a)$$

$$C_6H_5NO + 2H^+ + 2OH^- + Zn \rightarrow C_6H_5N\begin{smallmatrix} H \\ \diagdown \\ OH \end{smallmatrix} + Zn^{++} + 2OH^- \qquad (b)$$

[1] Fierz-David, *op. cit.*
[2] Brand and Modersohn, *J. prakt. Chem.*, **120**, 160 (1928).

$C_6H_5NO_2 + 4H^+ + 4OH^- + 2Zn \rightarrow$

$$C_6H_5N \begin{smallmatrix} H \\ \diagdown \\ \diagup \\ OH \end{smallmatrix} + 2Zn^{++} + 4OH^- + H_2O \quad (a + b)$$

$$2Zn^{++} + 4OH^- \rightleftarrows 2Zn(OH)_2$$

Zinc and ammonium chloride can also be used advantageously for the reduction of nitroparaffins to alkylhydroxylamines:

$$CH_3 \cdot NO_2 \xrightarrow{\quad Zn + NH_4Cl \quad} CH_3NHOH$$

Brand and Mahr[1] showed that the formation of azoxybenzene in the reduction of nitrobenzene is brought about by the condensation of nitrosobenzene and phenylhydroxylamine, the latter being intermediate products of reduction.

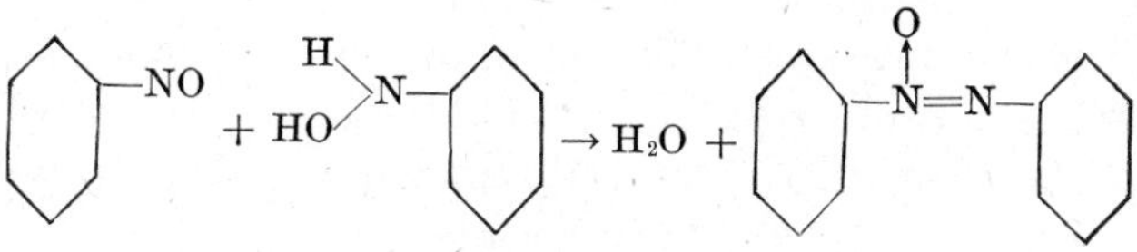

VI. REDUCTION OF NITRO COMPOUNDS WITH ALKALI OR METAL SULFIDES

Alkaline reductions are milder than the iron-acid reductions, and for this reason modifications of this process find extensive use in technical operations. By utilizing alkali or metal sulfides, it is possible to control better the rate and degree of reduction. Although ammonium sulfide is sometimes used, sodium sulfide or sodium disulfide are most frequently employed. The sulfides of iron and manganese[2] have also been found of value in reduction processes but thus far have not found widespread industrial applications.

The more important uses of alkali or metal sulfides are (1) preparation of nitroamines from dinitro compounds; (2) reduction of nitrophenols; (3) reduction of aromatic nitro compounds containing a halogen substituent; (4) preparation of aminoazo compounds from the corresponding nitro derivatives.

The following brief descriptions will serve to illustrate each of the preceding alkaline reductions:

1a. Preparation of *m*-Nitroaniline.—One hundred and sixty-eight parts of *m*-dinitrobenzene and 1,600 parts of water are placed in a tub and thoroughly agitated while the temperature of the mixture is brought to 85°C. To this suspension is gradually added a concentrated solution

[1] BRAND and MAHR, *J. prakt. Chem.*, **131**, 119 (1931).
[2] Dawes, U. S., 1,765,660 (1930).

containing 128 parts of sodium sulfide and 140 parts of sodium acid carbonate. The stirring is continued at 80 to 85°C. until the reduction to nitroamine is complete. This point may be recognized by the fact that a drop of the solution on a filter paper gives a streak of metallic sulfide with a solution of iron sulfate. The whole reduction mixture is poured on ice and stirred. The *m*-nitroaniline is then filtered off and washed with cold water. The yields by this procedure, according to Vorontzov,[1] are stated to be 87 per cent of the theoretical.

For works operations, this crude product is dissolved in hydrochloric acid, the sulfur filtered off, and the solution used directly. A distinct loss in yield is obtained when the *m*-nitroaniline is recrystallized from hydrochloric acid solution, it being only 71 to 73 per cent. The mother liquors may, however, be employed in subsequent purification operations.

1b. Preparation of 5-Nitro-1-Naphthylamine.—When naphthalene is dinitrated, a mixture of 1, 5- and 1, 8-dinitronaphthalenes is obtained. Upon reduction under controlled conditions with sodium sulfide, the 1, 5-isomer is partially reduced selectively, while the 1, 8-derivative remains substantially unaltered.[2] Thus, a suspension of 55 parts of the mixture of isomerides in 400 parts of water is heated to 90°C., and a solution containing 23.2 parts sodium sulfide crystals and 6.2 parts of sulfur in 80 parts of water is added. The mixture is stirred for 15 min., and then cooled and filtered. The residue on the filter is washed with water and then is treated with dilute hydrochloric acid to dissolve any nitroamino compound. The acid mixture is filtered and the residue which is relatively pure 1, 8-dinitronaphthalene is washed with water. The filtrate contains the hydrochloride of 5-nitro-1-naphthylamine.

2. Preparation of 2, 4-Aminonitrophenol from 2, 4-Dinitrophenol.— This reduction[3] is made by adding 90 parts of an aqueous solution containing 17 parts of sodium sulfide to a solution of 60 parts ferrous sulfate dissolved in 80 parts of water. The mixture is thoroughly stirred until a suspension of freshly precipitated ferrous sulfide is obtained. There is then added 20.6 parts of the sodium salt of 2, 4-dinitrophenol dissolved in 160 parts of water, and the mixture is heated gradually to approximately 60 to 80°C. until the reduction of one nitro group is complete.

The charge is then filtered and the filtrate exactly neutralized by the addition of hydrochloric acid. The precipitated 4-nitro-2-aminophenol is then filtered off.

3. Preparation of 2-Amino-7-Chloroanthraquinone.—The procedure recommended by Gubelmann[4] shows that 2-nitro-7-chloroanthraquinone

[1] Vorontzov, *Jour. Chem. Ind.* (*Moscow*), **7,** 2145 (1930).
[2] Hodgson, U. S. 1,988,493 (1935).
[3] Dieterle, U. S. 1,689,014 (1928).
[4] Gubelmann, U. S. 1,810,012 (1931).

can be reduced satisfactorily in alkaline sulfide solutions without appreciable replacement of the chloro substituent. This procedure is of interest in view of the fact that the halogen substituent is loosely bound by virtue of the presence of the $-NO_2$ and $>CO$ groups. The reduction is carried out by suspending 287 parts of 2-nitro-7-chloroanthraquinone in 5,000 parts of water containing 40 parts of caustic soda and 625 parts of sodium sulfide ($9H_2O$). The mass is heated to the boiling point and boiled for 1 to 2 hr. The amino compound is then filtered off and washed with hot water.

4. Reduction of Nitroazo Compounds.—When *p*-nitroaniline is diazotized and coupled with an amine or a phenol, a nitroazo compound is formed, thus:

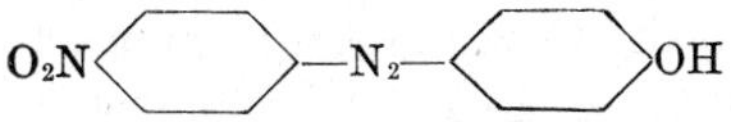

Strong reducing agents will reduce not only the nitro group but the azo group as well, with the production of *p*-phenylenediamine and *p*-aminophenol. The nitroazo compound is therefore dissolved in a weak alkaline solution, and at a temperature of 40 to 50°C. 2 moles of sodium sulfide as 30 per cent crystals are slowly added. The charge is thoroughly stirred until spot tests show a change of color, thus indicating that the selective reduction is complete. The aminophenyl-azo compound is then separated by either salting out or neutralizing the solution with dilute mineral acid.

Sulfides in the Reduction Process.—Despite its low heat of formation, hydrogen sulfide is very stable.

$$H_2 + S \text{ gas} \rightarrow H_2S + 4.82 \text{ cal.}$$

At 400°, dissociation of the gas begins, and it is complete at 1700°C. Its activity apparently depends on the fact that here sulfur has a valence of -2 and consequently enters readily into reactions involving oxidation and reduction. The gas is useful, therefore, as an active reducing agent. Even at room temperature, hydrogen sulfide reduces sulfur dioxide with the precipitation of sulfur.

The activity of alkali sulfides in the reduction of nitro compounds is due to the ease with which the former take up oxygen.

$$4R \cdot NO_2 + 6Na_2S + 7H_2O \rightarrow 4R \cdot NH_2 + 3Na_2S_2O_3 + 6NaOH \qquad (1)$$
$$R \cdot NO_2 + Na_2S_2 + H_2O \rightarrow R \cdot NH_2 + Na_2S_2O_3 \qquad (2)$$

At one time, an appreciable proportion of the aniline production was made according to Eq. (2). This process[1] runs very satisfactorily and is

[1] Ger. 144,809 (1902).

devoid of problems relating to the separation and disposal of iron sludge. It would, indeed, be a very attractive procedure if a profitable use or outlet were found for the by-product sodium thiosulfate to offset the comparatively higher cost of the sulfide reducing agent.

Concentration of Sulfide.—Whereas some agreement appears to exist regarding the optimum concentration of the catalyst in acid reductions, there seems to be no such condition for alkali sulfide reductions. This situation is, of course, brought about by the fact that most alkaline reductions are employed when only a limited reduction is desired. Conditions in the reduction system must consequently be adjusted with respect to each type of nitro compound and the degree of reduction required. In the reduction of *m*-dinitrobenzene to *m*-nitroaniline, there is considerable variation in the type and concentration of the alkaline reducing agent. Thus, in the reduction of 100 parts of *m*-dinitrobenzene, the conditions shown below have been recommended.

REDUCTION OF *m*-DINITROBENZENE

H_2O, parts	Reducing agent, parts	S/H_2O, %	$S/R \cdot NO_2$, %	Authority
880	Na_2S, 62	2.7	23.8	Fierz, Farbenchemie
2,300	{ Na_2S, 25	1.5	35.0	Cobenzl, *Chem. Ztg.*, **37**, 1913
1,200	{ S, 20 MnS, 105	3.2	38.7	Dawes, U. S., 1,765,660

VII. FERROUS SULFATE IN ALKALINE SOLUTION AS A REDUCING AGENT[1]

Although ferrous sulfate in alkaline solutions acts as a strong reducing agent, the system has only a limited usefulness in the commercial reduction of nitro compounds. The amount of ferrous sulfate used is slightly in excess of that required by theory, which is 6 moles of ferrous sulfate to 1 mole of the nitro compound.

$$R \cdot NO_2 + 6FeSO_4 + H_2O \rightarrow R \cdot NH_2 + 2Fe_2(SO_4)_3 + Fe_2O_3$$

m-Nitrobenzaldehyde can be converted to the amino compound utilizing this procedure, by putting it into solution as a bisulfite compound with double its weight of a 30 per cent solution of sodium bisulfite. This solution is slowly delivered to a vat containing the required quantity of ferrous sulfate in 3 parts of water, and to which one-third of its weight of calcium carbonate has been added. The mixture is boiled with stirring. Carbon dioxide is given off with effervescence, and reduction takes place rapidly. The amino compound can be extracted from the solution after first acidifying with hydrochloric acid to expel the sulfur dioxide.

[1] U. S. 1,765,660 (1930).

VIII. REDUCTION OF NITRO COMPOUNDS WITH HYDROGENATED QUINOLINE BASES

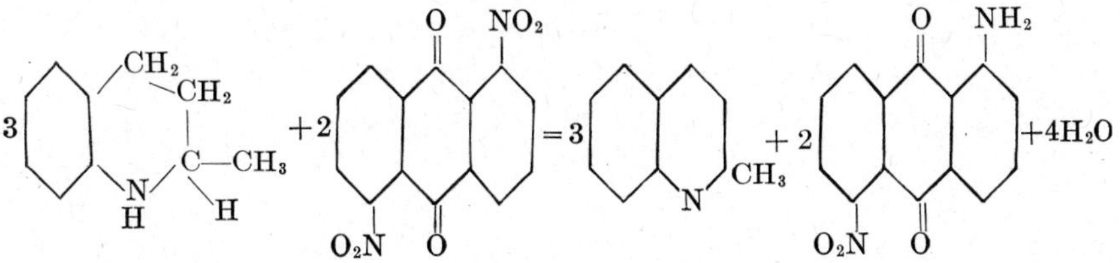

Berthold[1] has shown that nitroanthraquinones and their nuclear substituted products can be reduced by means of hydrogenated bases of the quinoline series. Employing 1, 2, 3, 4-tetrahydro-2-methyl-quinoline, the reduction runs smoothly. The reduction can be made to take place in the presence of diluent solvents such as *o*-dichlorobenzene, pyridine, glacial acetic acid, or, preferably, 2-methylquinoline. The reaction proceeds at moderate temperatures without catalysts; and when 2-methylquinoline is employed as the diluent, the mixture of the latter and the unoxidized hydromethylquinoline can again be catalytically hydrogenated. The regenerated hydrogenated quinoline base is again used in the process. It is apparent, therefore, that hydrogen is the real reducing agent, while the base acts as a carrier only.

The following example will illustrate the principles of this reduction process:

Partial Reduction of 1, 5-Dinitroanthraquinone.—One part by weight of 1, 5-dinitroanthraquinone is heated with 1 part by weight of 2-methyl-quinoline, 1 part by weight of 1, 2, 3, 4-tetrahydro-2-methylquinoline (b.p., 252 to 279°C.), and 2 parts by weight of glacial acetic acid for 8 hr. at the boiling point. On cooling, pure 1-amino-5-nitroanthraquinone separates out in reddish-brown crystals. On adding caustic soda solution to the filtrate, the mixture of 2-methylquinoline and its hydrogenated compounds can be separated and, after distillation, again catalytically hydrogenated.

IX. SODIUM HYPOSULFITE (HYDROSULFITE) IN ALKALINE SOLUTIONS AS A REDUCING AGENT

Sodium hydrosulfite ($Na_2S_2O_4$) in alkaline solutions has come to play an important part in the reduction of anthraquinone and indigoid deriva-tives to the leuco compounds. Although it is an active reducing agent, it finds only a limited use in the reduction of nitro compounds because of the comparatively greater cost attached to its use.

Sodium hydrosulfite can be used as the white crystalline product of commerce, or it can be prepared in the course of the reaction by adding

[1] Berthold, U. S. 1,691,428 (1928).

zinc dust to a solution of sodium bisulfite. The latter procedure is employed by Rogers[1] for the reduction of indigo and by Sidgwick and Callow[2] for the preparation of *o*-aminophenol from the corresponding nitro derivative. The reaction involved is as follows:

$$2NaHSO_3 + SO_2 + Zn \rightarrow Na_2S_2O_4 + ZnSO_3 + H_2O$$

The required SO_2 is obtained by the introduction of a mineral acid to the reaction mixture during reduction.

According to Sidgwick and Callow, aminophenol is prepared by mixing *o*-nitrophenol with 4.5 molecular proportions of sodium bisulfite as a 25 per cent solution. The charge is warmed, and zinc dust added at such a rate that the liquid keeps boiling. Completion of the reaction is indicated by the disappearance of the yellow color when spotting on filter paper. The *o*-aminophenol is obtained by filtering the hot solution and permitting the filtrate to cool, whereupon the amino compound crystallizes out.

X. REDUCTION BY HYDROGEN WITH THE AID OF A CATALYST

Developments in the catalytic hydrogenation of vegetable and mineral oils have resulted in similar advances in the field of aromatic chemistry. These activities are, of course, a natural outgrowth of the progress in the field of catalysis as well as in the art of producing and using gaseous hydrogen.

In the reduction of nitro compounds, it is not essential to use pure hydrogen, since a mixture of it with reducto-active, or inert gases, has been found to serve most economically for this purpose.

Some of the principal technical methods for the production of hydrogen are the following:[3]

1. Passing steam over incandescent carbonaceous material.

$$C + H_2O \rightarrow CO + H_2 \text{ (water gas)}$$

2. Passing carbon monoxide and steam over a (Cu-Zn-Cr) catalyst.

$$CO + H_2O \rightarrow H_2 + CO_2$$

3. Passing methane and steam under pressure over a nickel-magnesia catalyst.

$$CH_4 + H_2O \rightarrow CO + 3H_2$$

4. Electrolysis of water.

$$2H_2O \rightarrow 2H_2 + O_2$$

5. Passing steam over iron.

$$4H_2O + 3Fe \rightarrow 4H_2 + Fe_3O_4$$

---

[1] Rogers, U. S. 1,721,319 (1929).

[2] SIDGWICK and CALLOW, *J. Chem. Soc.*, **125**, 2452 (1924).

[3] See chapter on Hydrogenation for a more detailed discussion of hydrogen production and hydrogenation processes.

The reduction of nitro compounds with hydrogen or hydrogen-containing gases can be carried out in either the liquid or the vapor phase. Furthermore, aminations brought about by gaseous hydrogen in the presence of a catalyst can be carried out in a continuous manner, and when the amino compound is readily susceptible to purification by physical means, such processes are economical and attractive. Brief descriptive examples of each of these methods are given below.

Nord[1] has shown that the reduction of nitrobenzene by hydrogen gas in the presence of colloidal platinum gives rise to the same intermediate compounds that are obtained by electrolytic reduction or by reduction with metals in acid or neutral solutions. The following shows the course of the reaction:

$$C_6H_5NO_2 \rightarrow C_6H_5NO \rightarrow C_6H_5NH\cdot OH \rightarrow C_6H_5NH_2$$

$$C_6H_5\cdot N$$
$$\diagdown$$
$$O + H_2O$$
$$\diagup$$
$$C_6H_5\cdot N$$

LIQUID-PHASE REDUCTIONS

Hydrogen in the Presence of Iron.—According to Von Girsewald,[2] nitrobenzene and water are charged into an autoclave containing finely divided iron and a pressure of 30 atmos. carbon dioxide and 60 atmos. hydrogen is applied. The reduction is carried out at 300 to 350°C., at which temperature a rapid absorption of hydrogen occurs.

Herold and Koppe[3] show that milder temperature conditions can be used in liquid-phase reductions with hydrogen in the presence of iron if a spongy iron containing natural or added sulfur is used. By way of example, 300 parts of nitrobenzene are stirred with 100 parts of Swedish spongy iron for 6 hr. in an iron autoclave at a temperature of 180°C. and under a pressure of 140 atmos. of hydrogen. Approximately 220 parts (97.0 per cent of the theoretical) of aniline are thus obtained. Small quantities of sulfur or ammonium sulfide may be added to the reaction system to accelerate the reduction.

Reduction with Hydrogen in Alkaline Solution.—It is not necessary to employ the calculated quantity of sulfide when an alkaline reduction is carried out under pressure in the presence of hydrogen. It has been found[4] that by means of readily soluble sulfides the reaction can be carried out under hydrogen or water-gas pressure and at an elevated temperature using only one-twentieth to one-sixtieth of the quantity of sulfide required in the absence of reducing gases. Under such circum-

[1] Nord, F. F., *Ber.* **52**, 1705 (1919).   [3] Herold and Koppe, U. S. 1,854,258 (1932).
[2] Girsewald, Ger. 281,100 (1914).   [4] U. S. 1,662,421 (1928).

stances, the small sulfide concentration is sufficient to effect complete reduction of the nitro compound, inasmuch as the polysulfide or thiosulfate formed is continuously reduced again to the sulfide by the action of the hydrogen. The sulfide solution is therefore able to convert any desired quantity of the nitro compound to the amino derivative.

Solutions of polysulfides and thiosulfates may also be used. It has been found that in this reaction the whole of the thiosulfate is not continuously reduced to sulfide by hydrogen, a small portion being converted to sulfate. Under the conditions used in this operation, *viz.*, 150°C., under a pressure of 100 atmos. of hydrogen, the sulfate cannot be reduced by hydrogen. The regenerated sulfide is, however, the active catalytic agent.

The quantity of sulfide or polysulfide introduced with the nitro compound into the process may be so chosen that the sulfur is practically all present as sulfate at the completion of the reduction process. The possibilities of this method of obtaining amines may be seen from the following example:

Nitrobenzene to Aniline.—Five hundred parts of nitrobenzene, 100 parts of a 10 per cent solution of ammonium sulfide, and 10 parts of ferrous sulfide are heated to 150°C., while stirring, in an autoclave under a pressure of 100 atmos. of hydrogen. As the pressure drops, it is restored by forcing in more hydrogen at intervals. The reaction will be completed at the end of 12 hr. The yield is 370 parts of aniline, free of nitrobenzene. This yield corresponds with the best industrial practice in which iron and ferrous chloride are employed.

VAPOR-PHASE REDUCTION

A large number of patents have been issued covering the vapor-phase reduction of nitrobenzene by hydrogen-containing gases in the presence of metal catalysts.[1] Such a process has many attractive features. Some

[1] *Reduction with Nickel.*—Brochet (Brit. 16,936, 22,523 of 1913) passes hydrogen into a thoroughly stirred mixture of nitrobenzene and reduced nickel at 100 to 120°C. Meister, Lucius, and Brüning (Ger., 282,492) pass steam and hydrogen through nitrobenzene at 120°C. The gases then pass through a long tube containing finely divided nickel.

With Iron Oxides.—Weiler ter Meer (Fr. 462,006) passes a mixture of nitrobenzene vapor and hydrogen over finely divided ferrous oxide or magnetic oxide, which is mixed with asbestos or kieselguhr.

With Tin.—Brown and Henke (U. S. 1,456,969) pass nitrobenzene or nitrotoluene vapors with hydrogen gas over a tin catalyst at 200 to 350°C.

With Copper.—Senderens (Fr. 312,615) and Schmidt (U. S. 1,237,828) employ hydrogen-containing gases or carbon monoxide gases with a copper catalyst to reduce nitrobenzene in the vapor phase.

With Silver or Gold.—The Badische Aniline und Soda-Fabrik (Ger. 263,396) passes a mixture of nitrobenzene vapor and hydrogen over silver or gold or a mixture of these two precious metals at 230 to 250°C.

of these are: (1) continuous conversion of reactants to finished amine, (2) minimum operating labor requirements, (3) low steam and power costs by utilizing the heat in vapors leaving the catalytic chamber, and (4) absence of industrial waste problems, *e.g.*, disposal of iron oxide sludge. Such a process is particularly suited for works having a water-gas plant and where carbon monoxide is required for the synthesis of alcohols and other compounds.

No specific conclusions can be drawn regarding the groups of metals that are most effective. Although nickel and copper are considered the most active catalysts for a large number of hydrogenation processes, it is not always advisable in the reduction of nitro compounds to employ the most active catalysts. In fact, as will be shown later, it is known that

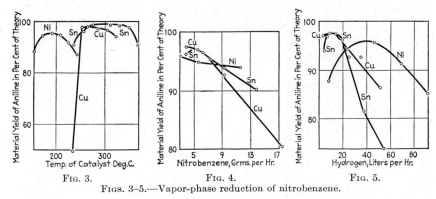

Fig. 3.   Fig. 4.   Fig. 5.
Figs. 3–5.—Vapor-phase reduction of nitrobenzene.

different aromatic nitro compounds react with different intensity on the same catalyst. It has been found that the metals both preceding and following hydrogen in the electrochemical series can be used as catalysts. Thus, nickel, iron, tin, copper, silver, and gold are are all mentioned in the patent literature.

An impressive study on the vapor-phase catalytic reduction of nitro compounds has been made by O. W. Brown and his associates.[1]

Working under favorable conditions with a *nickel catalyst*, Brown and Henke obtained a 95 per cent yield of aniline from nitrobenzene. With a constant rate of flow of nitrobenzene the yields drop off with too much or too little hydrogen. This fluctuation has been ascribed to over- or underreduction. Since nickel is such an active catalyst for this purpose, reduction of the aniline to cyclohexane and ammonia is known to take place.

When a catalyst prepared from precipitated *copper oxide* was used, the reaction was more moderate, and the yields under optimum conditions were uniformly good.

[1] Reports of these investigations have been published in *J. Phys. Chem.*, **26**, 161, 273, 715 (1922); **27**, 739 (1923).

When *tin* was employed as a catalyst, excellent results were obtained in the reduction of nitrobenzene to aniline. The catalyst made from the hydroxide prepared by precipitation with sodium carbonate from a stannous chloride solution was the best.

The relative activity of some of the metal catalysts employed by Brown and Henke are shown in Figs. 3, 4, and 5. In Fig. 4, showing the effects of "rate of feed" for nitrobenzene, it can be seen that at only one point is the curve for tin below that of copper; in most places, the values for tin are above those for copper. Tin is likewise superior to nickel at all but the highest rates of feed; while at the lower rates, the yields with tin are far superior to those for nickel.

The effect of "flow of hydrogen" in the presence of the same catalysts is shown in Fig. 5. It will be noted that the curve for tin has a shape different from that of the other two curves. Thus, the decrease in yield with too much or too little hydrogen is more rapid for tin than with nickel or copper. However, the region within which high yields are secured is as wide or wider with tin than with other catalysts.

On comparing the curves for tin with those of copper and nickel (in Figs. 3, 4, 5), one is led to believe that for producing aniline a tin catalyst from stannous hydroxide would be better than one from precipitated copper oxide or ignited nickel oxide. Thus, in Fig. 3, the curves show that tin will give high yields over a wider range of temperature than either nickel or copper. As a result, a tin catalyst would not necessitate such close temperature control as copper or nickel.

XI. DESIGN AND CONSTRUCTION OF EQUIPMENT

Materials of Construction.—Liquid-phase reductions are usually carried out in cast-iron vessels of various sizes. The larger ones (1,600 gal. capacity) are favored by plant engineers, because of the possibilities of more economical operation. The standard machines made by a number of equipment manufacturers resemble one another quite closely. Each manufacturer has, however, introduced one or more accessories or refinements calculated to appeal to the experienced chemical engineer.

The iron reducers for iron-acid reductions are sometimes equipped with side and bottom cast-iron lining plates, which may be reversed or replaced in order to protect the vessel against the continuous erosive action of the iron borings. Alternatively, the reducers may be lined to a limited extent with acid-resisting brick or tile. Such a protective coating lasts almost indefinitely and performs satisfactorily in service.

The vessel is equipped with a nozzle at the base so that the iron oxide sludge or entire charge may be run out upon completion of the reaction. A wooden plug faced with iron disks and operated by a screw device fills the nozzle so that it is flush with the inside of the machine and makes an effective seal.

Wooden equipment is also used, particularly for the reduction of solid nitro compounds such as *p*-nitroaniline. These vessels are made of

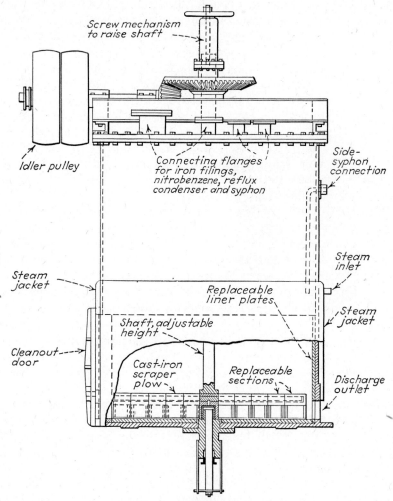

Fig. 6.—Jacketed reducer.

staves 2 to 3 in. in thickness, and the base is constructed of a double layer of 2-in. boards. Such tubs may range from 6 to 12 ft. in diameter and up to a height of 12 ft. They are equipped with wooden exhaust stacks to vent the vapors and gases liberated during the reaction. The top of such a reducer contains a large opening, through which the solid nitro body, iron, and acid are delivered, and it is provided with a removable cover.

Bronze pipes are employed for the introduction of steam to such reducers.

Agitation.—In some reducers, a vertical shaft carries a set of cast-iron plows which can be removed through the side door to the reactor (Fig. 6). These plows travel at the rate of 30 to 50 r.p.m. and serve merely to keep the iron particles in suspension in the lower part of the vessel. On the whole, such a type of agitation is not entirely satisfactory. It will be recalled that the reduction process is a three-component system, *e.g.*, reducible organic compound, acid, or metal salts and metal. Obviously, the best results in such a catalytic process can be obtained only when all three components are in intimate contact. If, in the reduction of nitro-

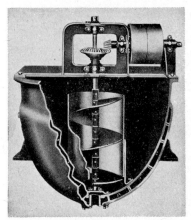

FIG. 7.—Sleeve-and-conveyor agitator.

benzene or similar compounds, the agitation is poor, most of the iron will be at the base, while the aqueous portion containing the acid or soluble metal salt will be at the top. It appears that an agitator of the type shown in Fig. 7 is more satisfactory, since it will be instrumental in bringing the iron particles to the upper portion of the reactor. It is recognized that such a sleeve-and-conveyor agitator needs to be made of material that will resist both the corrosion and erosion incidental to such reactions. A further advantage of this type of stirrer is the fact that the increased agitation assists in the diffusion of the amino compound away from the surface of the metal and thereby makes possible a more extensive contact between nitro body and catalytic surface.

Advantages of Jacketed Reducers.—Practically all the iron reducers employed for the reduction of liquid nitro compounds are equipped with jackets. Although the reduction process is distinctly exothermic, the reaction proceeds best at slightly elevated temperatures, and it is customary therefore to warm the reactants at the start. Sometimes it is found necessary to add heat to maintain an active reaction, and it is generally necessary to do so to complete the reduction.

When jacketed reducers are employed, the heat is applied indirectly and no dilution of the charge occurs. Under such circumstances, the optimum quantity of water can be delivered during the "feeding" stage, and the reaction is kept active by regulating the introduction of the reactants. When unjacketed vessels are used and live steam is introduced to maintain the reaction temperature, the charge becomes unduly diluted and reduces the concentration of the water-soluble catalyst below the optimum. Furthermore, the liberated heat alone may not then be able to keep the system sufficiently hot. Such conditions lead to poor yields.

It is apparent that the introduction of excessive water also entails an increased cost in subsequent operations. It is immaterial whether the

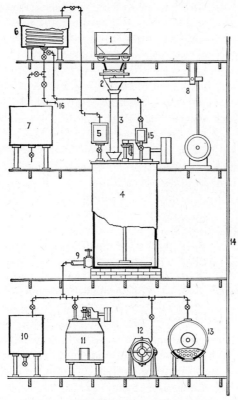

Fig. 8.—Plant assembly: reducer house.

1, delivery car for iron borings; 2, hopper and automatic feeder; 3, iron borings delivery line; 4, reducer; 5, baffle box; 6, condenser (note connections at base for refluxing or for distilling into); 7, crude receivers; 8, weighing apparatus for iron borings; 9, outlet valve to reducer leading to either; 10, ordinary receiver used in syphon system; 11, vacuum distilling kettle; 12, filter press; or 13, horizontal vacuum still; 14, elevator shaft; 15, sight box on reflux line; 16, safety drip which is kept open during reflux period to prevent contamination of system with nitrobenzene.

amine is a liquid or a solid or is recovered by fractional distillation or removal of water in a vacuum dryer; any excess of water introduced during the reduction proper later requires a proportional amount of heat to effect its removal.

Reducer Accessories.—The reducer (Fig. 6) is, of course, equipped with a suitable feeding device, which will deliver the iron borings as required. The borings bin is frequently attached to a scale so that the charge entering the reducer is being weighed continuously and accurately

(Fig. 8). Suitable flanged or screwed openings are provided for the introduction of the liquid nitro compound and catalyst solution. Steam connections are made in accordance with specific requirements, depending on whether or not the vessel is jacketed and whether or not the resulting amine is to be distilled with steam. A sight box is placed directly over the reducer to enable the operator to watch the progress of the reduction. By means of a valve or gooseneck under this mechanism, a heel of condensate is retained to prevent fumes from escaping through this return line from the condenser. A vent connection on top of the sight box leads to an absorber and condenser.

A very efficient and compact heat exchanger for condensing the vapors from the reducer consists of a closed tank completely filled with concentric layers of lead coils. Water at a high velocity circulates through the coils, entering at the top and discharging at the base. The vapors are distributed by a cylinder in the center of the condenser. The advantages of this heat exchanger are that it offers a maximum of surface to the vapors, no deposit or bubbles cover the outside of the coils to cut down the heat transfer, and the flow of cooling liquid is countercurrent to the ascending vapors. The condensed liquid collects in a lower cast-iron sleeve from which it flows back either to the reducer or to the distilling tanks (aniline receivers) in the event that the reaction is completed and the amine is being distilled with steam.

XII. TECHNICAL PREPARATION OF AMINES

THE MANUFACTURE OF ANILINE

An accurately weighed charge of nitrobenzene is delivered to the reducer from a lower floor level to avoid the danger of contamination, which is inherent in gravity-flow systems. About 10 to 20 per cent of the total iron, water, and catalyst is added, and the charge warmed to the reflux temperature, maintaining a constant effective agitation. The rate of reflux as observed in the sight glass must be quite vigorous, and the condensate fairly hot. If the reaction temperature is too low, intermediate compounds are formed, and these are later reduced to aniline only with great difficulty.

From an operating viewpoint, the process of feeding the reducer is a comparatively simple matter. A smooth reaction devoid of pressure peaks is obtained when the iron is uniform in quality and of a good physical character. It should preferably be delivered in small quantities to the boiling charge. The frequent delivery of small batches of iron minimizes the possibility of "sticking" the stirrers, due to the presence of an abnormal proportion of iron hydroxides. When a solid catalyst, such as ferrous chloride, sodium chloride, or sodium acid sulfate, is used, it is customary to feed it along with the iron, although theoretical considerations would suggest its complete introduction at the start. Such a practice, although simplifying the operation, may lead to excessive pressures. The water required for the hydrolytic reactions may be introduced in a number of ways. It may consist of (1) aniline-waters recovered from certain steps in the operation; (2) dilute aniline-salt mother liquors when such a catalyst is available; (3) the aqueous solution containing the soluble active catalyst from a previous reduction; or (4), finally, it may be tap water that is used to wash down each addition of iron borings.

During the addition of iron, no external heat is required to carry on the reaction, as the reduction process is distinctly exothermic, about 1,900 B.t.u. being liberated per pound of nitro compound that is converted. It is necessary, therefore, to provide the most efficient type of condenser to maintain a rapid rate of reduction and to avoid excessive operating pressures.

Obviously, the preceding outline relating to the feeding of materials to the reducer is susceptible to many modifications. It is entirely feasible to add all the water, iron, and soluble catalyst at the start. This mass is then thoroughly heated and agitated to etch the iron. The aromatic nitro compounds can thereupon be introduced at definite time intervals, the precaution being taken that each portion is completely reduced before continuing with further addition. This technic gives satisfactory results in the reduction of many nitro compounds.

After all the reactants have been introduced, external heat is required to maintain a lively reflux. Steam may be introduced directly into the reducer charge, or it may be circulated through the jacket of the reducer. The condenser water is throttled down in order to avoid overcooling of the condensate, as this should be only slightly below the boiling point. As the reduction nears completion, the color of the distillate changes from orange to yellow and finally becomes colorless.

From an inspection of the equations representing the reduction process, the presence of combined aniline ($C_6H_5NH_3Cl$) in appreciable quantities would not be expected at the close of the reduction. The use of alkali to neutralize the charge, when small proportions of a chloride salt are used as catalyst, is then largely a precautionary measure, for it can be shown that the base has been set free almost in entirety by the hydrolytic action. The more highly dissociated ferrous chloride is, of course, concomitantly regenerated at the close of the reduction, and the test for soluble iron with sodium sulfide solution is very distinct. It is clear that the reaction represented below proceeds to the right most readily in the presence of metallic iron. In its absence, the weak base would be almost completely converted to the salt of the amine by the strong acid.

$$2R\cdot NH_3Cl + 2H_2O \underset{Fe}{\rightleftharpoons} 2R\cdot NH_3OH + 2HCl$$
$$2HCl + Fe \rightarrow FeCl_2 + H_2$$

The introduction of alkali does, however, break up soluble iron aromatic compounds, such as hydroxylamine derivatives. Furthermore, it makes possible a more rapid distillation of the amine, as the introduction of the common ion OH⁻ reduces the solubility of aniline in water. In the preparation of water-soluble amines, neutralization of the charge is desirable only when the crude product is to be dehydrated and purified

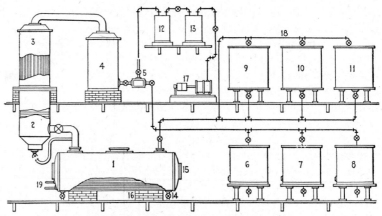

Fig. 9.—Aniline distillation: plant assembly.

1, horizontal still, completely lagged; 2, dephlegmator; 3, dephlegmator condenser; 4, condenser; 5, sight box with connection leading to 6, 7, 8, receivers for pure aniline; 9, 10, 11, crude aniline reservoirs; 12, 13, catch-all tanks for aniline vapors; 14, bottom outlet to still; 15, clean-out hole; 16, horizontal steam coils in still; 17, vacuum pump; 18, vacuum feed line from crude aniline reservoirs to still; 19, outside steam connections to still.

by distillation. The preparation of p-phenylenediamine is such an example. When the soluble amine is recovered by partial dehydration and crystallization, the faintly acid mother liquors, containing the active catalyst, can be used in subsequent reductions.

IMPORTANCE OF CHEMICAL ENGINEERING IN LOWERING COSTS

The most important problem in the preparation of aniline relates to its separation from the reducer charge. The problem is essentially one of chemical engineering. The engineer's goal is to provide for the continuous mechanical separation of the aniline and water from the iron oxide sludge and to recover the latter as a finely divided dry powder of commercial value. The aniline oil should then be separated from the water in a reasonably pure state, the amine going to the storage for final distillation (Fig. 9), while the aqueous solution containing dissolved catalyst and some amine is returned to the reducer. Groggins,[1] in a survey of the processes for the manufacture of aniline, shows that a great economic advantage accompanies the choice of an efficient separating scheme. In the work just referred to, the following criteria are suggested as a guide in the selection of equipment:

1. *Simplicity.* Minimum handling of material.
2. *Yields.* Reduction to a minimum of the known sources of loss.
3. *Productivity.* Discharging the batch immediately after reduction is complete.
4. *Water Balance.* Elimination of methods that cause an accumulation of aniline-water, as this involves a great loss in yield and an increase in power costs.
5. *Power Load.* The consumption of steam, water, and electricity is an important factor in determining the cost.
6. *By-product Sludge.* In some localities, a market can be obtained for a dry, clean, finely divided, aniline-free iron oxide.

The above criteria will be better appreciated by reviewing some of the methods for separating the aniline from the reducer charge. These will be presented very briefly, giving due attention to the underlying economic factors.

Method I. Steam Distillation of Aniline from the Charge and Treatment of Aniline-water in Stills.—This is one of the first and most costly systems. After reduction is complete, the reflux from the reducer condensers is directed to a receiving tank, and live steam is introduced to carry on the distillation. It is obvious that a large quantity of water is thus introduced into the system. The distillate in the receiving tank is permitted to cool, and the heavier oil is drawn off and delivered to the rectifier. The aniline-water, containing from 3.5 to 5.0 per cent amine (Figs. 10, 11) is drawn from an upper valve and pumped to storage tanks. It is usually made slightly alkaline prior to its being delivered to the aniline-water stills. The latter are usually long horizontal tanks provided with steam coils. When half of the charge is distilled, the residual liquor shows only a trace of aniline. The distillate is cooled and settled, and the aniline which separates out owing to its increased concentration, is removed. The aniline-water is again returned to the system and treated again. It is evident that in this steam-distillation process, the material must be handled considerably. The method is, furthermore, objectionable, as it curtails production because the reducer is used as a still.

Steam Distillation from Jacketed Reducers.—When the reduction takes place in a jacketed reducer, a slight improvement is realized. This is due to the fact that the jacket cuts down the dilution during the reduction

---

[1] GROGGINS, "Aniline and Its Derivatives," D. Van Nostrand Company.

period. Furthermore, some of the ensuing distillate is fortunately consumed in the reduction of the next charge. Finally, less steam is required

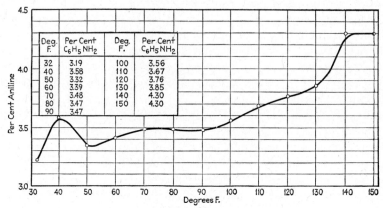

Deg. F.	Per Cent $C_6H_5NH_2$	Deg. F.	Per Cent $C_6H_5NH_2$
32	3.19	100	3.56
40	3.58	110	3.67
50	3.32	120	3.76
60	3.39	130	3.85
70	3.48	140	4.30
80	3.47	150	4.30
90	3.47		

FIG. 10.—Solubility of aniline in water.

during the distillation period, owing to the increased aniline concentration in the reducer charge.

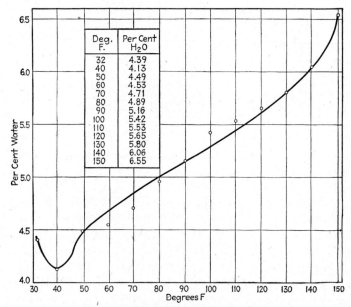

Deg. F.	Per Cent H_2O
32	4.39
40	4.13
50	4.49
60	4.53
70	4.71
80	4.89
90	5.16
100	5.42
110	5.53
120	5.65
130	5.80
140	6.06
150	6.55

FIG. 11.—Solubility of water in aniline.

Steam Distillation and Nitrobenzene Extraction of Aniline-waters.—
The procedure in this system is identical with the preceding up to the point where the aniline oil is drawn off from the settling tanks. The supernatant water is now treated with nitrobenzene intended for

the reducer house. Two extractions are made on each batch of aniline according to the flow sheet shown in Fig. 12, after which the water is practically free of both aniline and nitrobenzene.

Steam Distillation in Conjunction with Aniline Boiler.—The practice of using the surplus aniline-water in a boiler to generate steam for use in the reducers is one that formerly found considerable favor in Europe. The operation calls for a large aniline-water reservoir to which all the

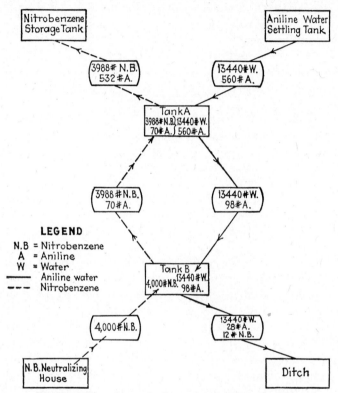

FIG. 12.—Flow sheet: nitrobenzene extraction of aniline.

water from the settling tanks is delivered. From a side valve considerably above the base of the tank the water is drawn off and delivered under pressure to the boiler. The steam line from the boiler is led to the reducers and is connected separately, so that "pure" steam can be used to complete the reduction and distillation. It is apparent that this is a fairly economical method of treating distillation waters. Precautions must be taken to neutralize the aniline-waters in order to minimize boiler-tube troubles, which are one of the disturbing features of this system.

Method II. Jacket Reduction and Vacuum Still.—This system involves the use of a large cast-iron vacuum still into which the reducer charge runs by gravity.   As soon as delivery is complete, the reducer is prepared for the next run, and the distillation of the finished charge started.   Inasmuch as the distillation is carried on *in vacuo*, the aniline-water comes over first, and then a mixture containing increasing proportions of aniline, until all the water is removed.   The aniline content is about half distilled by the time water-free aniline is obtained.   This fraction continues only for a short time, when the distillate is darkened by contamination with the residual sludge.   The installation of an auxiliary dephlegmator makes possible a better separation, but this, of course, entails an additional cost.

The system works fairly satisfactorily, the greatest difficulty being the reduction of the aniline content of the iron oxide sludge.   When the residual amino content is about 10 per cent, the charge becomes gummy, and a tremendous load is put on the stirring mechanism.   This condition prevails until the oxide granulates and falls over the plows.   Approximately half the operating time is consumed in recovering the last 10 per cent of the yield.   When the distillate is reduced to negligible proportions, the dry sludge is discharged into industrial cars.

An analysis of the hot residue, which is very fine and dusty, shows that it is practically all magnetic iron oxide.   As it is hot, the surface material sets up an oxidation with the formation of the red Fe_2O_3.   Analytical tests show that considerable aniline remains behind unless long drying periods are provided.

A modification of the preceding method is carried out as follows: The reducer charge is dropped into a large horizontal vacuum tank that is fitted with a large number of welded, seamless, extra-heavy steam pipes. Heat is applied as before, and the distillation proceeds even more rapidly on account of the greater heating surface.   At the close of the distillation, the manhead to the vacuum tank is removed, and the dry iron oxide flushed out at the base by means of a powerful stream of water.

The vacuum-distillation system may be further modified by distilling with live steam the final 10 per cent of aniline.   Such a practice does not introduce a large quantity of water into the system and saves considerable time.   The vacuum-distillation system apparently doubles the productivity of the reducers; but since the cost of the stills is quite as great, the saving is more apparent than real.

Method III.   Filtration of Reducer Charge.—In this system, the entire charge from the reducer is delivered to a large filter box.   Since the sludge retains considerable aniline, the cake is first washed with a stock solution of aniline-water, then with fresh boiling water, and then blown with hot air or steam.   This procedure leaves about 8 per cent aniline-water of 5 per cent aniline content with the sludge and constitutes a loss of less than 1 per cent of the total yield. Some of the advantages of filtration separation are:

1. Simplicity of operation.
2. Low operating cost.
3. Increase in productive capacity of reducers.
4. Elimination of cooling water and lowering of steam and power costs.
5. Compact system, making for good yields.

The success of this procedure depends on the solution of the unit operation —filtration. The reducer charge contains iron hydroxides and filters very poorly. It is necessary, therefore, to effect the filtration in stages through metal screens, preferably after the introduction of an electrolyte to expedite the precipitation of colloidal iron compounds. The filtrate can be settled for the separation and decantation of aniline. The sludge can be washed on the screens with some aniline-water and then dropped into a vessel where final traces of amine are removed by distillation with steam.

Method IV. Syphon Separation.—The introduction of a syphon into the reducer at the completion of the reduction stage to draw off the

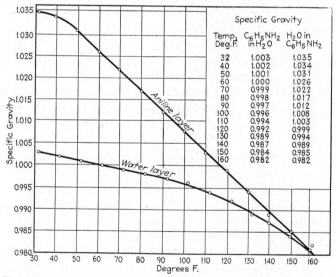

Temp. Deg. F.	$C_6H_5NH_2$ in H_2O	H_2O in $C_6H_5NH_2$
32	1.003	1.035
40	1.002	1.034
50	1.001	1.031
60	1.000	1.026
70	0.999	1.022
80	0.998	1.017
90	0.997	1.012
100	0.996	1.008
110	0.994	1.003
120	0.992	0.999
130	0.989	0.994
140	0.987	0.989
150	0.984	0.985
160	0.982	0.982

Fig. 13.—Temperature-specific gravity curves: Aniline-Water System.

supernatant oil from the lower aqueous layer is a convenient and inexpensive method of effecting the separation. A glance at the specific gravity curves (Fig. 13) reveals that the aniline oil layer becomes lighter than water above 71°C. (160°F.). The separation is accelerated and made sharper by the addition of salt, which further increases the density of the aqueous layer.

Jacketed reducers are used in this system, and reduction is effected by the use of external heat. Owing to the fact that there is a slight loss of water during the reduction process, it is necessary to provide sufficient at the start to insure fluidity. An excessive water content, however, distinctly slows up the reduction on account of the lower concentration of soluble catalyst.

The syphon is usually an inverted funnel operated by a worm drive and enters the vessel through a tight stuffing box. During the operation, it is worked up toward the top of the reducer so as to clear the paddles or other type of stirring mechanism. An alternate scheme utilizes a bent tube for withdrawing the aniline. A 2-in. pipe penetrates the side of the reducer through a stuffing box above the jacket line, and an improvised gage on the outside of the reducer indicates the position of the bend on the inside. By this means, it is possible to lower the syphon end accurately to the desired level and later raise it out of the sphere of agitation. This scheme avoids almost completely any stoppage and breaks in the draw-off line, difficulties that are encountered when the syphon is suspended from the top cover of the reducer.

After reduction is completed, 5 to 10 per cent by weight of salt (compared with nitrobenzene used) is added, and the agitation continued until the sodium chloride is completely dissolved. Agitation is then stopped, the plows are raised above the sludge, and the charge allowed to settle. Steam is kept on the jacket to maintain a temperature of 85 to 90°C. in the reducer. The introduction of a demulsifying agent along with the salt has been suggested for expediting the separation of the layers.

After settling about 1 hr., a slight vacuum is put on the receiving tank and the syphon mechanism lowered to the desired level. A sight glass on the delivery line indicates the rate of delivery and the quality of the aniline. If too great a vacuum is used, considerable turbidity results. The tube is lowered slowly until the sight glass indicates that the aniline is being contaminated with considerable water.

The remainder of the charge consists of aniline-water and iron oxides. With continued stirring, live steam is admitted until the batch is free of aniline. The final distillation may be made in a separate still when production requirements justify such an installation. In view of the fact that only a small quantity of aniline remains after the separation, very little time and steam are consumed in the final operation. In fact, the aqueous layer may be returned to the reducer for the next charge and thus save the bulk of the soluble catalyst. Still another use for the aqueous layer is its utilization in washing the nitrobenzene intended for the reducer house. These alternative methods save the expense of steam distillation and, incidentally, serve a useful purpose in the scheme of operations.

The syphon system is indeed attractive, as it is easily adapted to existing plants. It is compact, economical, and devoid of aniline-water problems. The cost of salt, the use of which may be dispensed with, is quite insignificant when compared to the cost of steam necessary to distill the aniline from the reducer charge. A filter box can be used to advantage in order to eliminate the fine iron oxide that is drawn over with the aniline. These boxes are constructed so that they can be opened and cleaned in a few minutes, and if necessary a new filter plate may be installed. In all cases, it is advisable to clarify the aniline by some method before submitting it to final distillation.

In the syphon system of aniline oil separation, the cost of installation and maintenance is very low, less machinery being used than in any of the other systems. There is also a minimum of handling of the amine, which is reflected in better operating yields.

Owing to the fact that the sludge has to settle out to effect a satisfactory separation, a mechanical problem is presented in providing a proper type of transmission to permit resumption of agitation after the aromatic compound is drawn off. When fine iron borings are used and these are fed in small portions, the resultant sludge should not cause any transmission trouble. In fact, in some reductions (*p*-nitroaniline to *p*-phenylenediamine), it is quite customary to permit the reduced charges to stand overnight. When, however, the transmission apparatus is designed to permit the raising of the stirrer (see Fig. 6), no difficulty is experienced in restarting.

TABLE VI.—MANUFACTURE OF ANILINE. ECONOMIC SURVEY

Type of separation	Cost per 1,000 lb. of aniline
Steam distillation of aniline in non-jacketed reducer	$12.81
Steam distillation of aniline in jacketed reducer	10.26
Steam distillation of aniline: nitrobenzene extraction of aniline-water: Non-jacketed reducers	8.16
Steam distillation of aniline: nitrobenzene extraction of aniline-water: Jacketed reducer	6.15
Use of aniline boiler to generate steam from aniline-water	4.11
Jacket reduction, accompanied by vacuum still	3.11
Filtration of reducer charges	1.20
Syphon separation, according to modifications	1.00 to 4.25

Economic Summary.—It would be misleading to draw conclusions solely from the data just presented regarding the known sources of loss in the various methods of separating the aniline from the charge. A number of other factors enter into the preparation of the cost sheet besides the tabulation of comparative losses and power charges. The figures do present, however, the known possible efficiencies that may be expected from the several modifications of this unit process. Disregarding for the moment the variable of operating efficiencies, the apparent comparative charges for separating the crude aniline from the reducer charge are as shown on page 105.

COST FACTORS IN PRODUCTION OF ANILINE

Reduction of nitrobenzene to aniline:

Molecular weight benzene (C_6H_6)	78
Molecular weight nitrobenzene ($C_6H_5NO_2$)	123
Molecular weight aniline ($C_6H_5NH_2$)	93
Theoretical yield of aniline per 100 lb. benzene	119.2
Standard yield of aniline per 100 lb. benzene	109.75
Theoretical yield of aniline per 100 lb. nitrobenzene	75.6
Standard yield of aniline per 100 lb. nitrobenzene	71.5

Materials to produce 100 lb. aniline from nitrobenzene:

140 lb. nitrobenzene, at $0.0562	$7.87
160 lb. iron borings, at $0.0075	1.20
15 lb. HCl (or equivalent) at $0.01	0.15
Total material costs	$9.22

Operating costs $\begin{cases} \text{Labor operating} \\ \text{Repairs} \\ \text{Supplies} \\ \text{Direct supervision} \end{cases}$ $1.00

Power costs $\begin{cases} \text{Electricity} \\ \text{Steam} \\ \text{Air} \\ \text{Water} \end{cases}$ 0.80

Overhead $\begin{cases} \text{Administration} \\ \text{Depreciation} \\ \text{Insurance} \\ \text{Fixed charges} \end{cases}$ 0.50

Plant cost per 100 lb. aniline $11.52

ANILINE COST DATA ANALYSIS[1]

$$\text{Operating costs} = \frac{1.00}{11.52} = 8.68\% \text{ total cost}$$

$$\text{Power costs} = \frac{0.80}{11.52} = 6.96\% \text{ total cost}$$

$$\text{Overhead} = \frac{0.50}{11.52} = 4.36\% \text{ total cost}$$

$$\text{Raw materials} = \frac{9.22}{11.52} = 80.04\% \text{ total cost}$$

[1] Numerator = cost of each phase of production.
Denominator = total net cost.

The Manufacture of Paraphenylenediamine

Reduction of Paranitroaniline with Iron and an Acid

$$O_2N\langle\hspace{1cm}\rangle NH_2 + 6H \rightarrow H_2N\langle\hspace{1cm}\rangle NH_2 + 2H_2O$$

p-Phenylenediamine is manufactured commercially by the reduction of p-nitroaniline. This reduction is quite similar to that of aniline, and its technic is subject to some of its numerous modifications.

The process may be conveniently divided into four steps, which are as follows:

1. Reduction of the p-nitroaniline to p-phenylenediamine.
2. Filtration of the reduction batch.
3. Dehydration of filtered liquor.
4. Vacuum distillation of crude p-phenylenediamine.

The Reduction.—A large wood vat is used to carry on this operation (Fig. 14). The batch is stirred by means of a steel shaft which carries

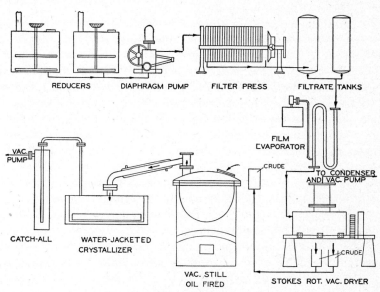

Fig. 14.—p-Phenylenediamine plant.

two or more sets of plows. A heavy-duty motor is provided to take care of the heavy initial reduction load and also when starting up tubs that have been left quiescent overnight. Two tubs are required for plant operations. One is used for preparing a new batch, while the other is delivering the reduced charge to the filter.

The operation is started by pumping up sufficient wash-water from previous charges to cover the paddles of the agitator. The stirrers operating at 40 r.p.m. are then started, and 1,000 lb. of iron borings are slowly put into the tub. One hundred pounds of 20°Bé. hydrochloric acid is then added, and the mixture agitated and heated until the iron is etched and a good paste of ferrous chloride is made. It should react immediately and distinctly when spotted with a weak sodium sulfide solution. Either dry or moist p-nitroaniline is then introduced, about 50 lb. at a time. After each addition, sufficient time must elapse to insure the presence of ferrous chloride, for it will be noticed that the spot test for soluble iron fails immediately after the addition of nitro compound. The charge must be kept sufficiently warm so that a foaming reaction prevails. It has been found that a ratio of 1.20 lb. of iron to 1 lb. of p-nitroaniline (molar ratio $3:1$) gives the best results, although it is possible as in the production of aniline slightly to lower this ratio. Toward the close of the feeding operation, the balance of iron necessary for reduction is introduced. Thus, when 750 lb. out of a total of 1,200 lb. of nitro compound have been fed into the vat, the balance of approximately 500 lb. of fine iron is added.

Toward the end of the run, the reaction slows down, and it is necessary to introduce steam to carry on and complete the reduction. The test for soluble iron also becomes less distinct. As long as there is any p-nitroaniline present, a yellow spot test will be obtained on filter paper. p-Phenylenediamine yields a purple spot with a perfectly clear ring around the sludge spot. It is always advisable to test for soluble iron with sodium sulfide to insure completeness of reduction. If the reduction is not carried on at the boiling temperature, intermediate azo and hydrazo products are sure to be formed. These are not so easily reduced and cause a lowering of the yield.

In order to prevent any oxidation of the p-phenylenediamine liquor prior to filtration, it is advisable not to neutralize the charge until this phase of the process begins. An excess of soda ash is used, and a test for alkalinity with phenolphthalein is required. Two pounds of sodium bisulfite and 3 lb. of sodium sulfide (30 per cent crystals) are then added to precipitate soluble iron salts and to insure against subsequent oxidation. About 12 hr. are required to feed the nitro compound into the reducer.

Filtration of Reduction Batch.—A large plate-and-frame filter is customarily used to separate the residual iron sludge from the p-phenylenediamine liquor. The press is fitted up with a pump for delivering the charge from the tubs. Air and water lines and an ejector for delivering hot water during the washing period complete its accessories. The press is first warmed by passing in live steam, and the delivery pump started.

The filtrate is tested for completeness of reduction and for clarity. A spot on filter paper should be very light purple with no traces of yellow. The presence of a blue tint indicates the formation of indulines.

As soon as the batch is on the filter, it is washed with wash-water from previous batches. This liquid follows the rest of the batch into one of two storage tanks which are placed below the press level, so that the filtrate flows into them by gravity. Hot water is then introduced into the press, and this filtrate runs into a large tank. Sufficient hot water is used to maintain a water balance, *i.e.*, to have sufficient to provide a heel for the reducer tub and to replace the original mother liquor on the filter. The filter is then blown with air until the cake is dry. The cake is dropped into a pan underneath the press and removed. It is analyzed regularly for amino content.

Dehydration of Diamine Liquor.—The filtrate from the press is a dilute solution of p-phenylenediamine containing a small amount of iron oxide in suspension. Since only 936 lb. of p-phenylenediamine can be theoretically obtained from 1,200 lb. of p-nitroaniline and about 9,000 to 10,000 lb. of water is used during the reduction, it is manifest that a 10 per cent solution of phenylenediamine is delivered to the liquor-storage tank. Although it is feasible and practicable to deliver a solution of such strength directly to the dryer, it is more economical from the standpoint of both yield and steam consumption first to concentrate this liquor. Two-stage vertical evaporators and film evaporators have been used successfully for this purpose. A steam-jacketed vacuum dryer of suitable dimensions can be used for effecting the final dehydration. On top of the dryer is an upright steel shell 2 ft. in diameter and 4 ft. high. This is packed with suitable material to prevent any entrainment and leads to a tubular condenser. A sight box at the base of the condenser permits the operator to inspect the condensate. This should not contain more than a trace of color; otherwise, a loss of p-phenylenediamine is indicated. When the sight box indicates that most of the water has been distilled off, the jacket steam pressure is reduced from 15 to 5 lb. and after 1 hr. turned off completely. If the batch in the dryer is now further agitated for 1 hr., it will be ready for dumping. A sample must always be first taken to insure absolute dryness. The crude product must be black with a purplish tinge. A gray tinge indicates moisture. The presence of 1 per cent of water in the crude product is detrimental to the production of a good p-phenylenediamine.

The material in the dryer is discharged into large steel cans and weighed. From this weight, the yield of crude p-phenylenediamine is obtained, and the charges for the vacuum still are made up. It is advisable to analyze the crude p-phenylenediamine for salt and iron at regular intervals, as these figures give valuable information regarding the operations. About 82 lb. of crude product are obtained for every 100 lb. of p-nitroaniline reduced.

Vacuum Distillation of Crude p-Phenylenediamine.—A cast-iron still (Fig. 15) capable of holding 1,000 lb. of crude p-phenylenediamine is placed on a masonry setting, and a solid arch built underneath it so that it runs back within 10 in. of the rear wall. In this way, the heat furnished

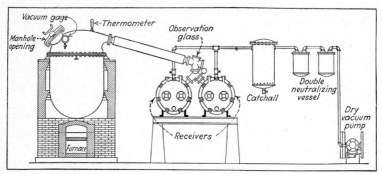

Fig. 15.—Vacuum distillation plant for p-phenylenediamine.

either by gas or by fuel oil reaches the still mainly by radiation. When optimum conditions prevail, the temperature of the batch in the still will be 230 to 250°C., and the temperature of the vapors in the line leaving the still will be 180 to 190°C. It is essential that an efficient vacuum pump be installed on this system in order to obtain a very attractive crystalline product. The crystallizing pans which receive the condensed vapors from the still are placed into water-cooled castings. At the close of each run, the pans are allowed to stand and cool for several hours and then pulled out. It is necessary to cool the distilled product about 36 hr. before breaking it up, as it remains molten on the inside for a long time. It is also true that its color deteriorates if the fused cake is broken prematurely.

If the crude is moist, the final product will be very poor and sometimes be sloppy. A distinct red coloration of the finished product indicates either moisture or acidity in the crude product.

Yields.—The yields obtained by the process outlined above should be about 90 per cent of theory or slightly over 70 lb. of finished p-phenylenediamine per 100 lb. of p-nitroaniline used. The sources of loss in the system are

	%
Reduction	3
Filtration	1½
Dehydration	1½
Distillation	3
Total	9

Cost of Materials Used in Reduction

Reduction {
p-Nitroaniline	1,200 lb. at $0.40	=	$480.00
Iron borings	1,460 lb. at 0.013	=	18.98
Hydrochloric acid	115 lb. at 0.01	=	1.15

Neutralization {
Sodium carbonate	60 lb. at 0.012	=	0.72
Sodium sulfide	4 lb. at 0.02	=	0.08
Sodium bisulfite	2 lb. at 0.05	=	0.10

Cost of raw materials.. $501.03

Cost of raw materials per 100 lb. *p*-phenylenediamine
based on yield of 70.1 lb. per 100 lb. *p*-nitroaniline
used.. $59.56

Based on a monthly production of approximately 20,000 lb. of *p*-phenylenediamine, the factory cost data per 100 lb. of product will be close to the following:

Raw materials	$59.56
Operating charges	4.30
Power charges	4.20
Plant overhead	3.54

Plant cost per 100 lb. *p*-phenylenediamine, exclusive of package,
storing, and sales expense.............................. $71.60

An analysis of the cost elements again reveals the importance of obtaining high operating efficiencies:

$$\text{Percentage cost of raw materials} \quad \frac{\$59.56}{\$71.60} = 83.2\%$$

$$\text{Percentage cost of operation} \quad \frac{\$4.30}{\$71.60} = 6.0\%$$

$$\text{Percentage cost of power} \quad \frac{\$4.20}{\$71.60} = 5.9\%$$

$$\text{Percentage cost of plant overhead} \quad \frac{\$3.54}{\$71.60} = 4.9\%$$

m-Nitroaniline from *m*-Dinitrobenzene

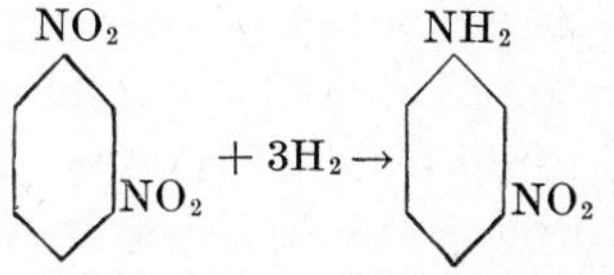

Alkali-Sulfide Reduction.—One hundred parts of *m*-dinitrobenzene is added to 1,000 parts of water at 90°C. contained in a reducer fitted with a reflux condenser and a propeller-type stirrer. Upon emulsification, 245 parts of sodium sulfide ($9H_2O$), dissolved in a minimum of water, is gradually run in. The dinitro compound is gradually reduced to *m*-nitroaniline, the end point being determined by the formation of a definite black streak when ferrous sulfate solution is added to filter paper spotted with some of the reducer liquor.

The preceding process has been modified by Lyford,[1] who uses an organic solvent, which is immiscible with water, for the m-dinitrobenzene. Accordingly, 100 parts of technical dinitrobenzene, 90 per cent purity, and 160 parts of either solvent naphtha or toluene are put into the reducer, and the mixture is warmed to 60°C. to effect solution. Then, 4,000 parts of hot water is added and the m-dinitrobenzene solution is stirred and heated to 95°C. A hot polysulfide (Na_2S_3) solution—made by heating 720 parts of 7 per cent Na_2S with 40 parts of flowers of sulfur—is then added rather rapidly. The reaction of the polysulfide is distinctly exothermic, and the charge boils vigorously, but overheating is avoided because of the vaporization of the solvent. Reduction of the dinitrobenzene to m-nitroaniline is found to take place very quickly under such conditions.

The hot reduction mass is first filtered to remove any free sulfur, and the solvent naphtha in the filtrate is distilled with steam. The dissolved m-nitroaniline crystallizes out in the form of bright yellow crystals when the residual liquor is cooled. After washing, the product has a melting point of about 113°C. (c.p. = 114°C.), and can be used directly in the manufacture of azo dyes. A yield of approximately 90 to 92 per cent of theory is attainable, and the process is applicable to other m-dinitro compounds, e.g., the m-dinitro derivatives of toluene and xylene.

PREPARATION OF HYDRAZOANISOLE

Reduction of o-Nitroanisole with Zinc in Alkaline Solution

The following process[2] for the preparation of hydrazoanisole involves the reduction of the nitro compound in the presence of alcohol by the intermittent addition of zinc and caustic alkali, the subsequent direct distillation and recovery of the alcohol, and the extraction of the hydrazo compound from the resulting reduction mass by means of an immiscible solvent so that the hydrazo compound is obtained as a solution that is essentially free of the zinc residue which remains behind.

Reduction of o-Nitroanisole.—One hundred fifty pounds of o-nitroanisole and 15 gal. of ethanol are mixed together in a steam-jacketed iron kettle provided with a reflux condenser and brought to a boil. The mixture is maintained in vigorous agitation, and the reduction is effected by the intermittent and progressive addition of zinc dust and caustic

[1] Lyford, U. S. 1,878,950 (1932).
[2] U. S. 1,644,483 (1927).

soda, adding one or the other as needed at such a rate as to keep up a steady reflux action, the total amount of caustic being about 16 lb. of 35 to 40°Bé. solution, and the total amount of zinc dust being about 190 lb. The amount of caustic soda corresponds to about 2 to 2.6 per cent of the theoretical amount of caustic alkali necessary to transform the zinc from the metallic state to a zincate.

The caustic soda acts as an accelerator, particularly in continuing the reaction from the azoxy to the azo stage, after which further additions of caustic have relatively little effect. The reduction can be followed to and through the azoxy and azo stages and then to the hydrazo stage (see Fig. 2). During the last stage of the reduction, the remaining zinc is added more slowly, and the reflux is maintained by means of steam delivered to the jacket of the kettle; the reduction as a whole appears to progress more slowly during this stage. It is of advantage, therefore, when the hydrazo crystals begin to separate out from test samples, to hasten the completion of the reduction by adding about 15 lb. of zinc dust in small portions at short intervals. The progress of the reaction or reduction can be followed by taking samples of the reduction mass and spotting them on paper. As the reduction nears completion, the crystals become larger, are more yellow in color, and crystallize out rapidly. They remain yellow until the reduction to hydrazoanisole is complete, when they suddenly become almost colorless. At this stage, the mass may tend to foam somewhat, in which case the foaming may be checked by cooling of the reaction kettle. The avoidance of any large excess of zinc dust also tends to prevent excessive foaming.

After complete reduction, the mixture is of a light-gray color and relatively thick, so that the zinc oxide does not separate readily from the solution. The alcohol is then distilled off by direct heating, *e.g.*, with the steam jacket, and recovered in a highly concentrated state so that it is directly available for reuse. The direct distillation of the alcohol in this manner leaves a residue which is thick and granular and from which the hydrazoanisole can be extracted with facility by means of a solvent.

Extraction of Hydrazoanisole.—After the removal of the alcohol by distillation, the residue, consisting mainly of the hydrazoanisole with some small amounts of anisidine and of the zinc oxide residue admixed with some caustic soda or sodium zincate, is cooled to about 50°C. About 40 gal. of benzene is then added. This mixture is agitated for a period of about 1 hr. until a concentrated solution of the hydrazoanisole in benzene is obtained. It is then transferred to a settling tank, the zinc permitted to settle, and the benzene solution decanted. The zinc residue is further extracted by the addition of further amounts of benzene until all the hydrazoanisole has been extracted, leaving the zinc residue in a relatively pure state.

The total amount of benzene used may amount to 80 gal. or more. After the completion of the extraction, the remaining benzene held by the zinc residue can be recovered by distillation. The zinc oxide residue is substantially free from organic matter. By crystallization from the solvent, or by distillation of the benzene, the hydrazoanisole can be obtained in an isolated state.

According to Wieland[1] it is not necessary to remove the aqueous alcohol prior to extraction of the hydrazoanisole with benzene. The controlled addition of water to the reducer charge effects the coagulation and settling of the zinc oxide, thus facilitating the subsequent decantation of the benzene-alcohol solution of hydrazoanisole.

PREPARATION OF α-NAPHTHYLAMINE

When solid nitro compounds such as α-nitronaphthalene are being reduced, Miller[2] recommends the use of a horizontal rotating reducer. An apparatus of this type, which in some respects is similar to a rod mill, obviates the difficulties in obtaining positive agitation which characterize operations with the ordinary type of vertical reducer.

The reduction operation is carried out as follows: 200 lb. of hydrochloric acid, 2,800 lb. of iron borings, and 500 gal. of water are introduced into a horizontal rotating reactor, and it is started revolving. α-Nitronaphthalene is then introduced at the rate of 10 lb. per minute until 2,500 lb. has been added, and the reaction is permitted to continue until reduction of the nitro compound is complete.

[1] Wieland, U. S., 2,012,234 (1935).
[2] Miller, U. S. 1,845,759 (1932).

CHAPTER III

DIAZOTIZATION AND COUPLING

By Harold E. Woodward

I. INTRODUCTION

Diazotization is the reaction by which a diazo compound is obtained from a primary aromatic amine. The reaction is usually carried out by treating a salt of an amine with nitrous acid in aqueous solution.

$$R—NH_2 + HCl + HNO_2 \rightarrow R—N_2Cl + 2H_2O$$

The class of diazo compounds was discovered in 1858 by J. Peter Griess. It was known at that time that an amino group on an aliphatic compound could be replaced by a hydroxyl group by treatment with nitrous acid. It had also been found that some aromatic amines could be converted into phenols in this way. Omitting intermediate steps, the reaction may be shown as follows:

$$R—NH_2 + HNO_2 \rightarrow R—OH + H_2O + N_2$$

When Griess attempted to prepare 1, 2-dihydroxy-4, 6-dinitrobenzene by the action of nitrous acid on 2-amino-4, 6-dinitrophenol (picramic acid), he obtained a new type of compound to which he gave the name *diazo*, because he believed that it contained two nitrogen atoms in place of two hydrogen atoms of the benzene ring.[1] This discovery was in a measure due to the fact that in experimenting with picramic acid he obtained a stable diazo oxide which is not easily decomposed. By using lower temperatures than were previously employed in this reaction, he then obtained diazo compounds from many other amines and thus opened up an important field from which many valuable commercial products have been obtained.

II. USES AND REACTIONS OF DIAZO COMPOUNDS

Among the practical uses of diazo compounds which make diazotization an important reaction are the following:

1. Some diazo compounds, being stable in the dark but decomposed in the light, are used for the preparation of light-sensitive printing papers. After exposure to light under a film, the undecomposed diazo compound is developed with a suitable solution of a compound, such as resorcinol,

[1] Griess, *Ann.*, **106**, 123 (1858).

which combines with it to give an insoluble azo color. This type of paper is used for printing from positive films, such as ink drawings, rather than from negatives, because the color is developed only under the dark part of the film where the diazo is not decomposed by the light. Among the amines the diazo compounds of which have been used for printing papers are dianisidine, 3-aminocarbazole,[1] 1-amino-2-naphthol-4-sulfonic acid,[2] and *p*-aminophenyl-diisopropylamine.[3]

2. Many stabilized diazonium compounds are produced by dyestuff manufacturers and used by dyers for dyeing or printing cotton goods that have been impregnated with a coupling component such as beta naphthol or an anilide of 2-hydroxy-3-naphthoic acid. Some of these stabilized diazonium compounds are also mixed with the coupling component in an alkaline printing paste, and after this is printed on the cotton cloth the color is developed by making it slightly acid. For example, Rapid Fast Red GL printing paste[4] is an alkaline aqueous paste consisting of a mixture of equivalent parts of the nitrosamine made from 3-nitro-4-aminotoluene and 2-hydroxy-3-naphthoic acid anilide. The azo dyes thus formed in or on the fiber are generally much less soluble in water than those which can be applied in ordinary dyeing processes, and they have unusually good fastness properties. Among the stabilized compounds in use are the following:

a. Diazonium Salts.—Some of the most stable diazonium salts may be dried and diluted with an inorganic salt to make sufficiently stable preparations. The dried diazonium sulfate obtained from *p*-nitroaniline was a commercial product before the development of the nitrosamines. Diazonium chlorides of the following type may be salted out and dried:[5]

b. Diazonium Salts of Sulfonic Acids.—These are obtained by treating a solution of a soluble diazonium salt with a solution of certain naphthalene- or benzenesulfonic acids, which form slightly soluble salts of the diazonium compound. For example, the calcium salt of benzenedisulfonic acid may be used.[6]

[1] RUFF and STEIN, *Ber.*, **34**, 1668 (1901).

[2] SCHMIDT and MAIER, *Ber.*, **64**, 767 (1931).

[3] Grinten, Brit. 294,972 (1928).

[4] Colour Index, No. 70.

[5] Schnitzspahn, U. S. 1,846,150 (1932).

[6] Johner, U. S. 1,846,113 (1932).

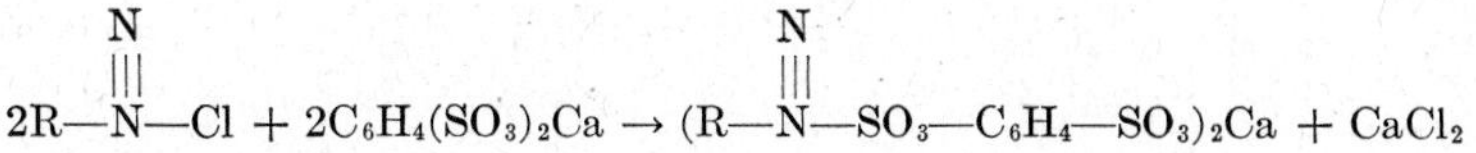

$$2R-\overset{\overset{N}{|||}}{N}-Cl + 2C_6H_4(SO_3)_2Ca \rightarrow (R-\overset{\overset{N}{|||}}{N}-SO_3-C_6H_4-SO_3)_2Ca + CaCl_2$$

c. Double Salts.—Some inorganic salts form rather insoluble addition products with diazonium salts. There are two kinds of double salts—the stable diazonium double salts, which are colorless; and the unstable *syn*-diazo double salts, which are colored.[1] They are represented by the mercuric chloride and the cuprous chloride double salts of benzene-diazonium chloride.

$$C_6H_5-\overset{\overset{}{|||}}{\underset{N}{N}}-Cl\cdot HgCl_2 \qquad\qquad C_6H_5-\overset{\overset{}{||}}{\underset{Cl-N}{N}}\cdot Cu_2Cl_2$$

Zinc chloride, stannic chloride, sodium borofluoride, and cadmium chloride have been used for the preparation of stable double salts.

d. Nitrosamines.—These are obtained by adding a solution of a diazonium salt to a solution of sodium hydroxide. Diazonium salts containing negative groups are converted to nitrosamines at low temperatures, but others require a high temperature for the conversion. For example, *p*-nitrobenzenediazonium chloride is converted at 0°C., while benzenediazonium chloride requires a temperature of 130°C. Positive groups make the conversion even more difficult.

The first step in the conversion of diazonium salts to nitrosamines is the formation of a diazonium hydroxide which is partly ionized. The un-ionized part is probably hydrated and reacts like a diazo hydroxide.[2]

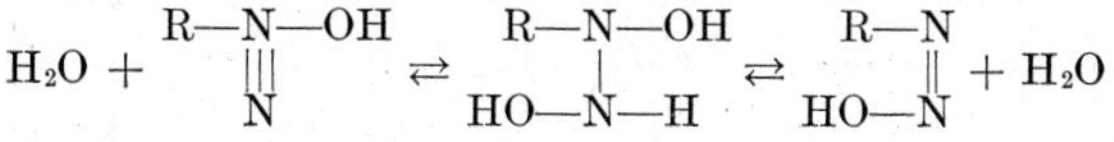

$$H_2O + \overset{\overset{R-N-OH}{}}{\underset{N}{|||}} \rightleftarrows \overset{R-N-OH}{\underset{HO-N-H}{|}} \rightleftarrows \overset{R-N}{\underset{HO-N}{||}} + H_2O$$

With alkalis, the diazo hydroxide forms salts called *diazotates*. The diazotate obtained at very low temperatures is active and unstable, but at higher temperatures it is transformed into an isomeric form that is inactive and stable. While the possibility of structural isomerism has been advocated by several authors, it is rather generally believed that Hantzsch's theory of stereoisomerism is the best explanation of this transformation. By this theory, the active form has the *syn* structure, and the inactive form has the *anti* structure.

$$\overset{\overset{R-N}{||}}{\underset{NaO-N}{}} \qquad\qquad \overset{\overset{R-N}{||}}{\underset{N-ONa}{}}$$

$$\textit{syn}\text{-Diazotate} \qquad\qquad \textit{anti}\text{-Diazotate}$$

[1] HANTZSCH, *Ber.*, **28**, 1734 (1895).
[2] DAVIDSON and HANTZSCH, *Ber.*, **31**, 1612 (1898).

When a sodium *anti*-diazotate is treated with one equivalent of hydrochloric acid, a neutral solution of a nitrosamine is obtained.

$$\underset{\underset{\text{N—ONa}}{\|}}{\text{R—N}} + \text{HCl} \rightarrow \underset{\underset{\text{N—OH}}{\|}}{\text{R—N}} \rightarrow \underset{\underset{\text{NO}}{|}}{\text{R—NH}} + \text{NaCl}$$

On treatment with another equivalent of acid, the nitrosamine is slowly changed to a diazonium salt.

$$\underset{\underset{\text{NO}}{|}}{\text{R—NH}} + \text{HCl} \rightarrow \underset{\underset{\text{N}}{\||}}{\text{R—NCl}} + \text{H}_2\text{O}$$

e. Diazoamino Compounds.—These are obtained by reaction between diazonium salts and some amino compounds that do not easily couple to form azo dyes. For example, 4-sulfoanthranilic acid may be used for this purpose.[1]

$$\underset{\underset{\text{Cl}}{|}}{\text{R—N}\equiv\text{N}} + \text{NH}_2\text{—}\underset{\text{SO}_3\text{H}}{\overset{\text{CO}_2\text{H}}{\bigcirc}} \rightleftarrows \text{R—N}=\text{N—N—}\underset{\text{SO}_3\text{H}}{\overset{\text{CO}_2\text{H}}{\underset{\overset{|}{\text{H}}}{\bigcirc}}} + \text{HCl}$$

The reaction goes to the right when the hydrochloric acid is neutralized with a buffer such as sodium acetate. These diazoamino compounds are stable in alkaline solution; but in acid solution, the diazonium salt is regenerated.

3. The largest and most varied use of diazo compounds is for coupling with amino or hydroxy aromatic compounds to produce azo dyes, containing one or more azo groups.[2] The spectral absorption curve of a simple azo dye like aminoazobenzene shows a maximum absorption at about the shortest visible wave length. Since it absorbs some violet light and transmits the rest of the visible spectrum, the color of its solution appears to be yellow. By the substitution in the benzene rings of various groups, such as hydroxyl, amino, alkyl, nitro, or sulfonic groups; by the use of naphthalene compounds instead of benzene; and by lengthening the chain of azo groups, the spectral absorption curve may be moved to longer wave lengths. The most complex azo dyes in this sense have a

[1] Hentrich, Tietze *et al.*, U. S. 1,858,623 (1932).

[2] The Colour Index lists 623 commercial azo dyes of known composition. The Census of Dyes of the U. S. Tariff Commission for the year ending June 30, 1936, showed the production of 37,599,000 lb. of azo dyes in this country for that year. In one color alone Direct Black E. W. the production for that year of nearly 8,174,000 lb. contained about 320,000 lb. of azo nitrogen.

maximum absorption of light at about 600 mμ and are therefore green. It is thus possible, through countless variations in the structure of azo compounds, to obtain the whole range of spectral colors of different degrees of brilliance, either soluble or insoluble in water or other solvents; having affinity for a wide variety of textile fibers and other materials; and of different degrees of fastness to light, washing, and many other common destructive agents.

4. By means of a number of different reactions, the diazonium group can be replaced by certain elements or groups.[1] The most important of these reactions are the following:

a. The hydroxyl group replaces the diazonium group on heating with dilute sulfuric acid.

$$R—N_2Cl + H_2O \rightarrow R—OH + HCl + N_2$$

b. When the double salt formed with cuprous halides is heated, the diazonium group is replaced with a halogen.

$$R—N_2Cl·Cu_2Cl_2 \rightarrow R—Cl + Cu_2Cl_2 + N_2$$

The same result is often obtained by using copper powder or a large excess of a halide of zinc or potassium instead of a cuprous halide.

c. A nitrile is formed when a solution of a diazonium salt is heated with potassium cyanide and copper sulfate or copper powder.

$$R—N_2Cl + KCN \rightarrow R—CN + KCl + N_2$$

d. The diazonium group is replaced with hydrogen by treatment with aliphatic alcohols in alkaline solution.

$$R—N_2Cl + C_2H_5OH \rightarrow R—H + CH_3CHO + HCl + N_2$$

e. Ethers are sometimes formed when a diazonium salt is heated with an alcohol in neutral solution.

$$R—N_2Cl + CH_3OH \rightarrow R—OCH_3 + HCl + N_2$$

f. Hydrazines are obtained by reduction with potassium bisulfite.

$$R—N_2Cl + 2KHSO_3 + 2H_2O \rightarrow R—NH—NH_2·HCl + 2KHSO_4$$

III. PROPERTIES AND REACTIONS OF DIAZONIUM SALTS

The essential feature of the diazotization reaction is the replacement of three hydrogen atoms of a salt of a primary aromatic amine by one nitrogen atom. The reaction takes place between equivalent parts of a salt of the amine and nitrous acid, with the elimination of 2 molecules

---

[1] For a complete discussion of these reactions see Saunders "The Aromatic Diazo Compounds," Longmans, Green & Co., New York, Chap. 8 (1937).

of water.　It may be graphically represented as follows, taking aniline hydrochloride as an example:

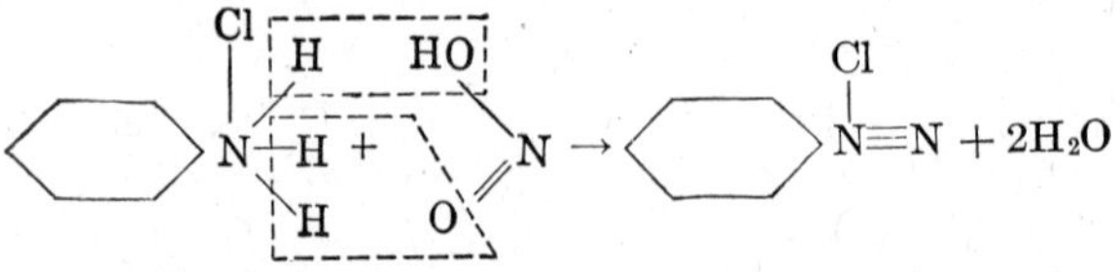

$$\langle\ \rangle\!-\!N\!\begin{array}{c} Cl \\ | \\ H \\ | \\ H \end{array}\!+\begin{array}{c} HO \\ O \end{array}\!N\ \rightarrow\ \langle\ \rangle\!-\!\begin{array}{c} Cl \\ | \\ N\!\equiv\!N \end{array}+2H_2O$$

The above formula, first proposed by Bloomstrand[1] in 1869, and the name benzenediazonium chloride, suggested by Hantzsch in 1895, have been generally accepted as best explaining the properties of these compounds.　There is a possibility of the preceding reaction's taking place in two steps, and an intermediate product has been isolated in the diazotization of 1-amino-2-naphthol-4-sulfonic acid.[2]

These diazonium salts are obtainable from all primary amines of the benzene and naphthalene series that do not contain in addition a hydroxyl, sulfonic, or carboxylic group.　They are also obtainable in general from unsaturated isocyclic and heterocyclic compounds in which the amino group is attached to a doubly bound carbon atom of the ring.[3]　There has been no published information on the formation of diazonium compounds from acyclic amines, but when such aliphatic diazonium compounds are discovered they will probably be obtained from amines in which the amino group is attached to a doubly bound carbon atom with some other unsaturation in the compound.　Among the diazotizable amino derivatives of cyclic compounds are aminoanthraquinone, -benzanthrone, -pyrene, -furane, -pyrrole, -pyridine, -pyrazole, -isoöxazole, -thiazole, and -carbazole.

The diazonium salts of hydrochloric, sulfuric, and nitric acids are very soluble in water and very reactive when treated with alkaline solutions of phenols or naphthols.　For example, benzenediazonium chloride reacts rapidly with sodium 2-naphthol-6-sulfonate (Schaeffer salt) in alkaline solution to give an orange azo dye.[4]

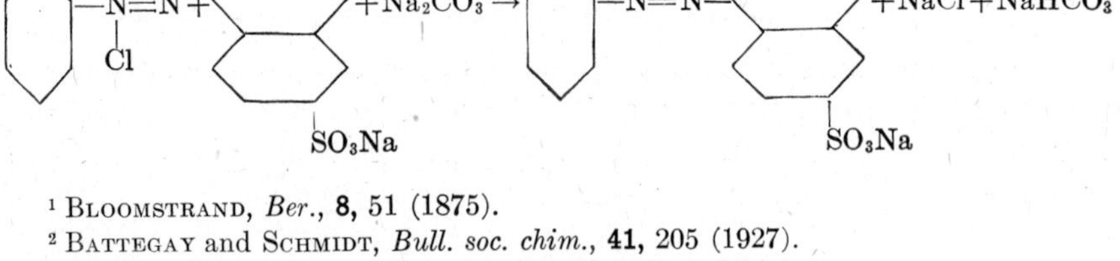

$$\langle\ \rangle\!-\!\begin{array}{c}N\!=\!N \\ | \\ Cl\end{array}\!+\!\begin{array}{c}OH \\ | \\ \langle\ \rangle\end{array}\!+\!Na_2CO_3\ \rightarrow\ \langle\ \rangle\!-\!N\!=\!N\!-\!\begin{array}{c}OH \\ | \\ \langle\ \rangle\end{array}\!+\!NaCl+NaHCO_3$$

SO₃Na　　　　　　　　　SO₃Na

[1] Bloomstrand, *Ber.*, **8**, 51 (1875).

[2] Battegay and Schmidt, *Bull. soc. chim.*, **41**, 205 (1927).

[3] Morgan and Burgess, *Chem. News*, **123**, 186 (1921).

[4] Croceine Orange, Colour Index, No. 26.

Benzenediazonium hydroxide is a stronger base than ammonium hydroxide. As determined by saponification and by conductivity this base is ionized about 35 per cent at 0°C. in a concentration of $N/128$. The undissociated part is in equilibrium with the weakly acid *syn*-diazo hydroxide.

$$C_6H_5—N \equiv N \rightleftarrows C_6H_5—N$$
$$\underset{OH}{|} \qquad\qquad \underset{HO—N}{\|}$$

When treated with one equivalent of sodium hydroxide, the sodium salt is formed to the extent of 80 per cent in a concentration of $N/64$.[1] The dry salts are somewhat explosive, and in solution they decompose, especially when heated or exposed to light, with the evolution of nitrogen and the formation of a phenol, as shown on page 119. The rate of decomposition is not affected by the amount of acid in solution. At fixed temperatures, the following formula applies to this decomposition reaction:

$$\frac{1}{t} \log \frac{a}{a - x} = \text{constant}$$

In this formula, t is time in minutes, a is the original amount of diazonium salt, and x is the amount of decomposed diazonium salt.

The amount of decomposition may be determined by measurement of the volume of nitrogen evolved, this being more accurate than the titration of undecomposed diazonium salt with a standard solution of a naphthol. The following values determined for this constant by Cain and Nicoll[2] show the variation in the stability of diazonium salts at different temperatures and the effect of some substituent groups on the benzene ring:

Diazotized amine	20°C.	40°C.	60°C.	80°C.	100°C.
Aniline..................	0.00072	0.00877	0.107		
o-Toluidine................	0.000187	0.0238			
m-Toluidine...............	0.00208	0.0257			
p-Toluidine................	....	0.0010	0.012		
p-Sulfanilic acid...........	....	....	0.00633	0.0709	
o-Nitroaniline.............	....	....	....	....	0.00546
m-Nitroaniline.............	....	....	....	0.00312	0.0325
p-Nitroaniline.............	....	....	....	0.00734	

Yamamoto[3] determined the decomposition constant for a number of diazonium compounds and calculated the time required to decompose 1 per cent of the diazo at 0°C.

[1] DAVIDSON and HANTZSCH, *Ber.*, **31**, 1612 (1898).

[2] CAIN and NICOLL, *J. Chem. Soc.*, **81**, 1412 (1902); **83**, 470 (1903).

[3] YAMAMOTO, *J. Soc. Chem. Ind. Japan*, Suppl., **36**, 59B (1933); **38**, 275B (1935).

DECOMPOSITION OF DIAZONIUM COMPOUNDS: 1 % DECOMPOSED AT 0°C.

Diazotized Amine	Time		Diazotized Amine	Time	
m-Toluidine	40	min.	2-Amino-4-nitroanisole	31	hr.
o-Toluidine	45	min.	o-Chloroaniline	44	hr.
Aniline	211	min.	4-Amino-3-nitrotoluene	48.5	hr.
α-Naphthylamine	460	min.	2-Amino-4-nitrotoluene	107	hr.
β-Naphthylamine	700	min.	Sulfanilic acid	158	hr.
Metanilic acid	16.5 hr.		p-Nitroaniline	1,053	hr.
p-Toluidine	21.5 hr.		p-Chloroaniline	1,294	hr.
m-Chloroaniline	25.2 hr.		m-Nitroaniline	1 817	hr.
o-Anisidine	25.2 hr.		o-Nitroaniline	3,820	days

Substituent groups which may be present on the benzene or naphthalene ring have a considerable effect on the properties of diazonium salts. Either negative groups, such as chlorine or nitro, or positive ones, such as alkoxy, increase the stability to decomposition by water. Negative groups decrease the stability to decomposition by light.[1] The rate of coupling with hydroxy or amino compounds to form azo dyes is increased by negative groups and decreased by positive groups. This reduction in the coupling activity may be connected with the fact that diazonium salts containing positive groups are ionized to a greater extent than those without such groups.

Solutions of many diazonium salts are colorless, but spectral analysis shows an absorption band in the ultra-violet.[2] The absorption band is shifted to the violet part of the spectrum in the naphthalenediazonium salts and in some substituted benzenediazonium salts, especially those containing nitro groups or substituted amino groups, so that the solutions are yellow. It has been observed[3] that in the dry state, diazonium iodides are more deeply colored and more explosive than the corresponding chlorides or bromides. Hantzsch assumed that the dry salts consist of an equilibrium mixture of diazonium halide and *syn*-diazo halide.

$$\underset{X}{R-N{\equiv}N} \rightleftarrows \underset{X-N}{R-N}$$

Factors that increase the proportion of diazonium salt in the dry mixtures are positive groups on R, lower temperature, and lower atomic weight of the halogen.

Some diazonium salts that contain negative groups in the aromatic nucleus are subject to molecular rearrangement. Hantzsch[4] observed that brominated diazonium chlorides are transformed to chlorinated diazonium bromides when bromine atoms are ortho or para to the

[1] SEYEWETZ and MOUNIER, *Compt. rend.*, **186**, 953 (1928).

[2] HANTZSCH and LIFSCHITS, *Ber.*, **45**, 3011 (1912).

[3] HANTZSCH, *Ber.*, **33**, 2179 (1900).

[4] HANTZSCH, *ibid.*, **30**, 2334 (1897); **33**, 505 (1900).

diazonium group. The transformation is more rapid at higher temperatures and in alcohol.

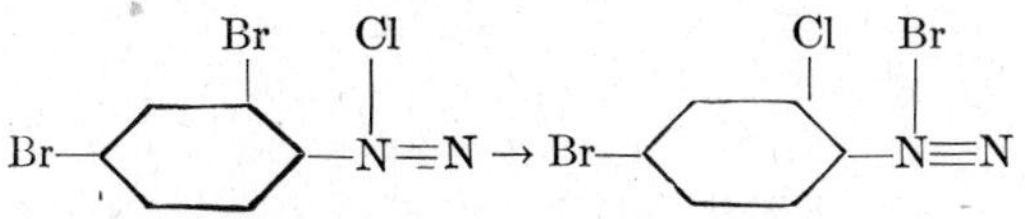

In many cases a nitro, halogen, sulfonic, or methoxyl group ortho or para to a diazonium group is easily hydrolyzed in alkaline or slightly acid solution to form a diazo oxide. This is explained as being due to the strong negative character of the diazonium group, which Schoutissen[1] found to be equal to two nitro groups in this respect. The hydrolysis of the nitro group liberates nitrous acid.

IV. PROPERTIES AND REACTIONS OF DIAZONIUM SULFONATES

The reaction by which diazo compounds are obtained from aminosulfonic acids is seen to be the same as that used to explain the formation of the diazonium chlorides if we assume that in the aminosulfonic acids there is a salt formation between the amino group and the sulfonic group.[2] Using such a formula for sulfanilic acid, the reaction with nitrous acid may be explained in the same way as for aniline hydrochloride.

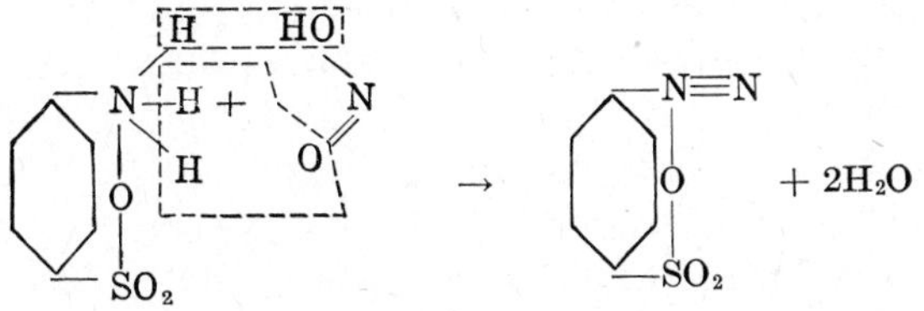

These diazonium compounds have been variously named, but they are probably best described as diazonium sulfonates, and the above compound is benzenediazonium 4-sulfonate. The formula of Strecker[3] and the above name and explanation of the reaction all show the close relationship between these compounds and the diazonium salts obtained from unsulfonated amines.

The properties and reactions of the diazonium sulfonates are, in general, the same as for the diazonium chlorides, except that they are probably not ionized. They are considerably less soluble, so that they may be isolated as crystalline products in fairly good yields. Some of them have been reported to be explosive when dry. The color of diazonium sulfonates is the same as that of corresponding diazonium salts from unsulfonated amines.

[1] SCHOUTISSEN, *Rec. trav. chim.*, **40**, 763 (1921).

[2] SIDGWICK, "The Organic Chemistry of Nitrogen," Clarendon Press, Oxford, p. 55 (1910).

[3] STRECKER, *Ber.*, **4**, 786 (1871).

With one equivalent of sodium hydroxide, the diazonium sulfonate ring is opened to form a more soluble sodium sulfonate of a normal diazo hydroxide. Since the diazo group is more strongly chromophoric than the diazonium group, there is a slight deepening of the color, which is confirmed by the spectral absorption value.[1]

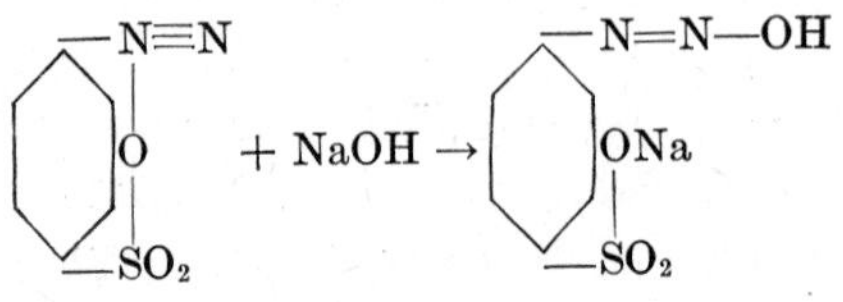

By further treatment with alkali, isomeric normal and stable diazotates are formed. Azo coupling probably does not depend on the hydrolysis of this ring, as the diazonium sulfonates are very reactive in neutral or acid solutions.

From aniline and naphthylaminedisulfonic acids are obtained diazonium sulfonates containing a sodium sulfonate group which makes them more soluble. For example, 2-naphthylamine-4, 8-disulfonic acid, commonly known as *C acid*, reacts with nitrous acid as follows:

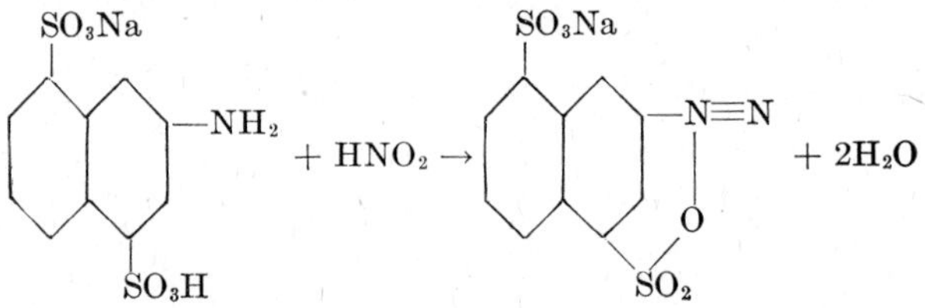

Aminophenol- or aminonaphtholsulfonic acids yield diazonium sulfonates except when the amino and hydroxy groups are ortho to each other. The diazonium sulfonates obtained from some aminophenol-sulfonic acids have been described by Morgan and Tomlins,[2] and the diazonium sulfonate formula has been assigned to the diazo compound of 2-amino-5-naphthol-7-sulfonic acid (J acid) by Battegay and Wolff.[3]

The hydroxynaphthalenediazonium sulfonates immediately form blue azo compounds when made alkaline. This is usually explained as an internal coupling of one molecule or as a disazo color formed by coupling between two molecules.

The hydroxyl group of the diazonium sulfonate obtained from 1-amino-8-naphthol-3, 6-disulfonic acid (H acid) can be acetylated to give the following compound:[4]

[1] HANTZSCH and LIFSCHITZ, *loc. cit.*

[2] MORGAN and TOMLINS, *J. Chem. Soc.*, **111**, 497 (1917).

[3] BATTEGAY and WOLFF, *Bull. soc. chim.*, **33**, 1481 (1923).

[4] Jordan, Ger. 206,455 (1909).

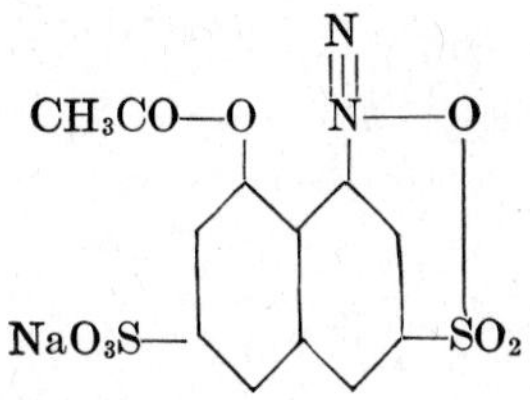

$$\text{CH}_3\text{CO—O} \quad \overset{\overset{\overset{\text{N}}{|||}}{\text{N}}}{} \text{—O}$$

$$\text{NaO}_3\text{S—} \qquad \text{—SO}_2$$

When this is made slightly alkaline at a low temperature, it does not immediately give a blue azo color like that obtained from the unacetylated compound.

V. PROPERTIES AND REACTIONS OF DIAZONIUM CARBOXYLATES

Aminocarboxylic acids, which do not contain in addition a hydroxyl group, yield diazo compounds similar to those obtained from aminosulfonic acids. Thus, 2-aminobenzoic acid (anthranilic acid) gives benzene-2-diazonium carboxylate when treated with nitrous acid.

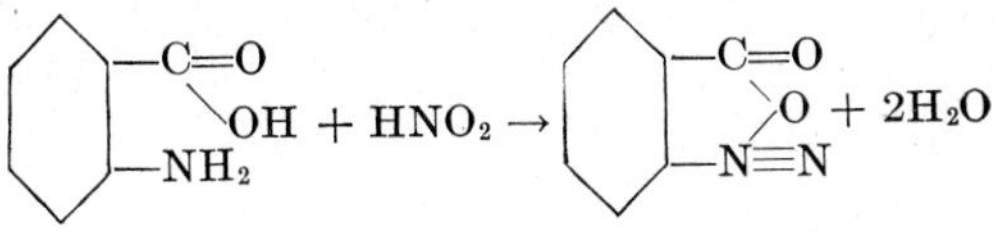

$$\begin{array}{c}\text{—C=O}\\\text{\quad OH}\\\text{—NH}_2\end{array} + \text{HNO}_2 \rightarrow \begin{array}{c}\text{—C=O}\\\text{\quad O}\\\text{—N≡N}\end{array} + 2\text{H}_2\text{O}$$

Some of the aminocarboxylic acids are soluble in water as hydrochlorides; but if diazonium chlorides are formed during the reaction, they quickly change to the less soluble diazonium carboxylates. They have the same general properties as the diazonium sulfonates.

The diazonium carboxylates obtained from aminodicarboxylic acids do not usually form a soluble sodium salt of the free carboxylic group in acid solution as do the corresponding disulfonic acid derivatives. Some of the aminosulfobenzoic acids, however, give soluble diazonium sulfonates containing a sodium carboxylate group in neutral or slightly acid solution, but hydrochloric acid precipitates the free carboxylic acid. These facts require consideration in determining the amount of acid necessary in diazotization.

VI. PROPERTIES AND REACTIONS OF DIAZO OXIDES

Nitrous acid reacts with aminophenols and aminonaphthols to replace three hydrogen atoms with one nitrogen atom, giving a different type of diazo compound. These are known as diazo oxides, and the formula proposed by Kekulé is generally considered to be satisfactory. For example, 4, 6-dinitrobenzene-2, 1-diazo oxide is obtained from picramic acid.

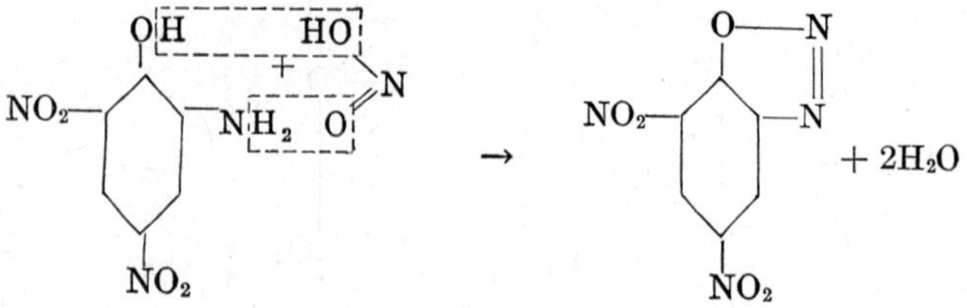

No diazo oxide has been obtained from *m*-aminophenol, but only an unstable diazonium salt. This has seemed to lend support to the theory that diazo oxides have a quinone diazide formula, as proposed by Wolff.

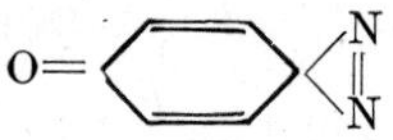

Diazo oxides are obtained from substituted aminophenols and aminonaphthols. However, diazonium sulfonates are obtained from sulfonic acids of aminophenols and aminonaphthols, except when the amino and hydroxy groups are adjacent to each other, in which case diazo oxides are obtained. Diazo oxides are obtained from aminophenol-carboxylic acids whether the amino group is ortho or para to the hydroxyl group.

In comparison with the diazonium salts, the diazo oxides are less soluble, less reactive, and more stable. In some cases, it is recognized that the diazo ring is opened in alkaline solution to give a diazotate. Coupling probably does not take place until the ring is hydrolyzed in this way. Another explanation of the above facts is that the induced polarization in ortho and para hydroxy diazo compounds results in a highly ionized acid hydroxyl group and a highly ionized basic diazonium group, while the meta hydroxyl group induces a polarization which results in a weakly acid *syn*-diazo group.

The stability of the diazo oxides is well illustrated by the one obtained from 1-amino-2-naphthol-4-sulfonic acid, which is used in large amounts in the manufacture of several azo dyes. This diazo oxide may be isolated either as the free sulfonic acid or as a salt (sodium, zinc, etc.) and dried or recrystallized from hot water.[1] It may be nitrated[2] or brominated.[3] It is however quantitatively decomposed by light.[4]

VII. FACTORS AFFECTING DIAZOTIZATION

Diazotization is a bimolecular reaction between equivalent quantities of un-ionized nitrous acid and a primary aromatic amine which contains

[1] BATTEGAY and SCHMIDT, *loc. cit.*
[2] RUGGLI, KNAPP, *et al.*, *Helv. Chim. Acta*, **12**, 1034 (1929).
[3] RUGGLI and MICHELS, *Helv. Chim. Acta*, **14**, 779 (1931).
[4] SCHMIDT and MAIER, *Ber.*, **64**, 778 (1931).

an acid hydrogen. The constants of the reaction in very dilute solutions have been determined by several investigators,[1] but the reaction is too rapid at ordinary concentrations for a determination of the constant. It is agreed that the reaction proceeds very quickly at temperatures from 0 to 20°C. in concentrations of about molar to 0.2 molar, and it is probable that under these conditions all soluble salts of aromatic amines are diazotized at approximately the same rate.

Solvent.—Diazotizations are usually carried out in water solution, which is a suitable solvent in most cases. Other solvents may be used and are sometimes necessary.

When it is desired to isolate and dry the pure diazonium salts, a salt of the amine is dissolved in alcohol or glacial acetic acid and diazotized with amyl nitrite. The diazonium salts are soluble in these solvents but are precipitated by adding ether.

Salts of very weakly basic amines are almost completely hydrolyzed in water at low temperature and therefore cannot be diazotized in this solvent, except at high temperatures which are usually not suitable. Such amines are soluble enough in glacial acetic acid or concentrated sulfuric acid to result in the formation of a sufficient amount of the salt to react with nitrous acid at a reasonable rate.

Concentration.—In concentrations below 0.01 M, the reaction is rather slow; but at the usual concentrations, the reaction may be considered practically complete in 10 min. Ordinarily, the concentration of a diazonium salt at the completion of the reaction is about 0.5 M, but this may vary from a high concentration of 2 M to a low concentration of 0.2 M. When it is impossible to avoid a greater dilution than this, a longer time up to 30 min. or even 1 hr. is allowed for the reaction to go to approximate completion.

Temperature.—The rate of the reaction is increased at higher temperatures; but since the rate is rapid at ordinary temperatures, this is not important. Generally, a temperature above 20°C. is to be avoided, because the rate of decomposition is also greatly increased at higher temperatures. However, temperatures of 30 to 60°C. are sometimes used in the diazotization of weakly basic amines in order to increase the amount of salt formed in the reaction

$$\text{Amine} + \text{acid} \rightleftarrows \text{salt}$$

This reaction goes more completely to the right at higher temperatures; and since the formation of a salt of the amine is necessary for diazotization, elevated temperatures are sometimes employed.

[1] Schümann, *Ber.*, **33**, 527 (1900); Tassilly, *Compt. rend.*, **157**, 1148 (1913); **158**, 335, 489 (1914); Tassilly, *Bull. soc. chim.*, **27**, 19 (1920); Boeseken, Brandsma, and Schoutissen, *Proc. Acad. Sci. Amsterdam*, **23**, 249 (1920); Willard, *Textile Colorist*, **46**, 22, 164 (1924); Ueno and Suzuki, *J. Soc. Chem. Ind. Japan*, Suppl., **36**, 615B (1933).

The necessity for high temperatures for salt formation may often be avoided by the use of larger amounts of acid to force the above reaction to the right or by preparing the amine in a physical form which reacts more readily with dilute acids.

It is, in general, true that the amines which require a high temperature for the formation of a salt are those whose diazonium compounds are more stable to the effect of high temperature. Oddo and Ampola[1] and Snow[2] have reported the possibility of obtaining satisfactory yields of some diazonium salts above 60°C. Elevated temperatures are also necessary in the diazotization of some very insoluble monosulfonic acids of amino or aminoazo compounds from which very insoluble diazonium sulfonates are obtained.

The temperatures at which different amines may be diazotized to give the same stability as aniline diazotized at 0°C. (1 per cent decomposed in 211 min.) were calculated by Yamamoto.[3]

DIAZOTIZATION TEMPERATURE OF AMINES
DECOMPOSITION OF 1 PER CENT IN 211 MIN.

Diazotized Amine	Temp.	Diazotized Amine	Temp.
m-Toluidine	−10	Sulfanilic acid	21
o-Toluidine	−10	m-Nitro-p-toluidine	22
Aniline	0	p-Nitroaniline	34
Alpha-naphthylamine	4	m-Nitroaniline	37
Beta-naphthylamine	7	p-Chloroaniline	38
Metanilic acid	9	o-Anisidine	40
p-Toluidine	12	o-Chloroaniline	42
m-Chloroaniline	14	o-Nitroaniline	58
p-Nitro-o-anisidine	17		

Acid.—The function of the acid used in diazotization is threefold, as follows:

1. To supply one of the three hydrogen atoms to be replaced by nitrogen. In the case of the simple amines, this is accomplished by the formation of a salt. In the case of sodium salts of aminosulfonic acids, it is accomplished by the formation of one free sulfonic group. In either case, one equivalent of acid is required, but a slight excess is often necessary to reduce the hydrolytic dissociation of the salt.

Reilly and Drumm found that without excess acid amines diazotize at different rates depending on their basicity, and they believed that the rate is not affected by more acid than is necessary to prevent hydrolysis of the amine salt.[4] However, Schoutissen found that the influence of small amounts of hydrochloric acid is more than can be accounted for by

[1] ODDO and AMPOLA, *Gaz. Chim. tal.*, **26**, II 541 (1897).

[2] SNOW, *Ind. Eng. Chem.*, **24**, 1420 (1932).

[3] YAMAMOTO, *loc. cit.*

[4] REILLY and DRUMM, *J. Chem. Soc.*, **1935**, 871.

decreasing hydrolysis.[1] This added influence of a small excess of acid is probably accounted for by the second function of acid.

2. To react with sodium nitrite and thus furnish the necessary nitrous acid. Since ionized nitrous acid does not take part in the diazotization reaction, a slight excess over the theoretical 1 mole of acid is desirable in order to repress this ionization.

3. To supply hydrogen ions sufficient to prevent reaction between the diazonium compound and any undiazotized amine in solution, as in the equation

$$R—N_2Cl + R—NH_2 \rightarrow R—N=N—NH—R + HCl$$

A slight excess of acid is generally enough to prevent this reaction from going to the right, except with nitro or halogenated diazonium salts, but the nitro and halogenated amines are so slightly soluble in dilute acid that this reaction is easily avoided by keeping an excess of nitrous acid in the solution. Usually, from 0.2 to 0.5 equivalent of a strong acid is a sufficient excess to take care of all these requirements, provided the amine salt is in solution.

Mineral acids are usually necessary for the complete formation of the salt and the prevention of the diazoamino coupling. Organic acids, such as acetic, are generally not suitable, unless used in considerable excess (10 to 20 moles), because the formation of the salt is incomplete, so that the diazotization is slowed up, and in such weaker acids the formation of the diazoamino compound is more rapid. Of the mineral acids, hydrochloric and sulfuric are most often used on account of their low cost. The sulfates of some amines are less soluble than the hydrochlorides, and therefore hydrochloric acid seems to be more generally suitable. As shown above, the amount of acid to be used in preparing diazonium compounds is 2.2 to 2.5 equivalents for each amino group, either in the simple amines or in the sodium salts of aminosulfonic or aminocarboxylic acids.

It has been reported[2] that the velocity of diazotization using hydrobromic acid is about 50 times greater than when hydrochloric acid is used, and with the latter it is considerably more rapid than with nitric or sulfuric acids. This difference is of practical importance only when the concentration of the diazotization is much less than 0.1 N.

In the diazotization of most aminophenols and aminonaphthols, it is not necessary to add acid for the formation of a salt, since the three hydrogen atoms to be replaced by nitrogen are already present in the amino and hydroxyl groups. Neither is acid necessary for the prevention of diazoamino coupling, for such compounds are not readily

---

[1] Schoutissen, *J. Am. Chem. Soc.*, **58**, 259 (1936).

[2] Ueno and Suzuki, *loc. cit.*

formed from aminophenols. Mineral acids are, therefore, not always used in the preparation of diazo oxides. In fact, in some cases, the use of mineral acids results in oxidation instead of diazotization.

Time.—In concentrations above 0.2 M, soluble amines react with almost the theoretical quantity of nitrous acid in 5 min. or less. A slight excess of nitrous acid is usually maintained for 5 to 10 min. longer. A longer time may be necessary in lower concentrations or for very insoluble amino compounds; but if a high enough temperature is used, it is not necessary to take more than 1 hr. for any diazotization.

Since the rate of decomposition of most diazonium compounds is appreciable at temperatures suitable for the diazotization, they are not kept beyond the time necessary for approximate completion of the diazotization but are used at once.

Light.—Since many diazo compounds are decomposed by light as well as by heat, it is advisable to avoid exposure to strong light. Commercial production in closed equipment is safe from this harmful action, but laboratory experiments in glass should be protected from direct sunlight.

VIII. DESIGN AND CONSTRUCTION OF EQUIPMENT

Materials of Construction.—Small laboratory preparations are of course made in glassware, with vacuum filtrations made on porcelain funnels. For larger amounts, enameled or stoneware containers are used. Motor-driven agitators are made of bent glass rods or wooden paddles.

In commercial-scale production, the materials used for the construction of the equipment are selected from those which withstand the action of dilute acids and in addition do not have a reducing action on diazo compounds. They include cypress, stoneware, glazed tile, rubber, enamel-lined iron, and lead. Valves of some stainless alloys are used, after being subjected to laboratory tests in solutions of diazonium salts. Lead is ordinarily the only metal used in contact with diazo compounds, as its reducing action is very slight at low temperatures.

Description of Equipment.—For commercial production on a scale of 0.2 to 2.0 pound mole, the diazotization reaction is carried out in wooden tubs or tile-lined iron tanks of approximately equal height and diameter, which may have a capacity as high as 20,000 liters or 40,000 lb. or 5,000 gal. On the inside of the tank are several vertical ribs or baffle plates of wood or tile, projecting inward a few inches, to reduce swirling motion and improve agitation. The contents of the tub are kept in a homogeneous condition by a wooden agitator, which may be any one of several designs and is suspended in the center of the tub and geared to an electric motor in such a way that the r.p.m. may be varied from about 20 to about 40. The contents of the tank are drained through a hole at the edge of the bottom, closed on the inside with a rubber plug on a stick and on the outside by a clamp on a rubber hose or by a valve of acid-resistant metal in a lead line. The temperature of the solution in the tub may be raised by means of an open steam line of wood, lead, or rubber-covered iron reaching to the bottom. Low temperatures are attained by the addition of cracked ice. The 30 per cent solutions of the reagents are measured in calibrated tanks, those for sodium nitrite and sodium hydroxide being of iron but that for hydrochloric acid being rubber lined.

Diazotizations in concentrated sulfuric acid are made in a jacketed iron kettle with an iron agitator. The sulfuric acid solution of the

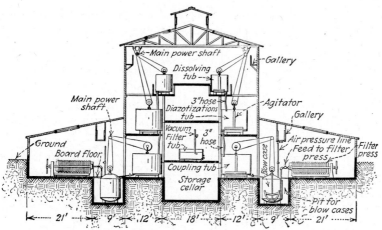

Fig. 1.—Equipment for commercial production of diazo compounds and of azo colors. (*Courtesy of O'Brien, "Factory Practice in Manufacture of Azo Dyes."*)

diazonium sulfate is allowed to flow on to ice in one of the above-described tubs, or is run directly into a solution of a coupling component.

The solution or suspension of the diazo compound is generally used directly as prepared, either in the same tub or in another similar one below it. In special cases, solutions of diazo compounds are filtered with a purified charcoal through a small wooden filter press, under pressure from a lead-lined centrifugal pump or from a lead- or tile-lined iron blow case. Sometimes, insoluble diazo compounds are purified by filtration on a wooden nutsch or a wooden filter press or by letting the crystals settle and removing the supernatant mother liquor with a syphon.

IX. TECHNICAL DIAZOTIZATIONS

Examples are given below of the usual methods of diazotization of different types of amino compounds, together with a discussion of the general application of these methods. The methods here given are for preparations of 1 mole in pounds, but any unit down to centigrams may be used equally well. Volumes are expressed in pounds, since plant equipment can be calibrated in pounds of water as easily as in gallons, and this scheme has the advantage of the metric system in making calculation of percentage concentration simpler. It also makes possible quick and accurate conversions between laboratory- and plant-scale processes, which is very valuable in maintaining a close control of plant operation.

In plant operations, cooling is usually accomplished by addition of flake ice or crushed ice and heating by use of live steam, as the slight dilution resulting from these additions is not harmful. The amount of ice to use may be roughly estimated by the formula $\dfrac{1.1 \text{ vol. } (T_1 - T_2)}{80 + T_2}$. For example, to cool a volume of 5,000 lb. from 30 to 5°C. requires about $\dfrac{5,500 \times 25}{80 + 5}$, or 1,618 lb. of ice. The factor 1.1 varies somewhat in different equipment, depending on its heat capacity. Since the heat of the diazotization reaction, due to the substitution of 1 atom of nitrogen for 3 atoms of hydrogen and the formation of 2 molecules of water, is about 20,000 cal., there is a rise of about 10°C. in temperature in the diazotization of a 0.5 N solution of an amine salt. This requires about 250 lb. of ice for 1 pound mole of the amine to keep the temperature of the solution at 0°C. The increase in volume to be expected from the condensation of dry steam is approximately $\dfrac{1.1 \text{ vol. } (T_2 - T_1)}{537 + (100 - T_2)}$. For example, in raising the temperature of a charge measuring 5,000 lb. from 20 to 80°C., the volume will be increased about $\dfrac{5,500 \times 60}{537 + 20}$, or 592 lb.

The reagents used in large-scale operation are 30 per cent solutions of hydrochloric acid, sodium hydroxide, and sodium nitrite. In laboratory experimental work, a considerable amount of calculation may be avoided by using solutions made on a molar basis. Hydrochloric acid and sodium hydroxide may be used as 10 N solutions and sodium nitrite as 5 N solution in preparations of 0.1 gram mole or more. For smaller preparations, it is more convenient to use 2 N solutions; but in this case, external cooling and heating must be used in order to avoid dilution.

Diazotization of Simple Amines.—In 500 lb. of water, 93 lb. of aniline is dissolved as hydrochloride with 1 mole of hydrochloric acid (120 lb. of 30 per cent solution). Then 1.5 moles more acid (180 lb. of 30 per cent) is added, together with about 650 lb. of ice, this being about the amount required not only to cool all the solutions to 0°C. but also to absorb the heat of the diazotization reaction. While the solution is well agitated, 1 mole of sodium nitrite (230 lb. of 30 per cent solution) is gradually poured in, keeping the temperature below 5°C. The solution must show an acid reaction on Congo Red paper, and it is tested for nitrous acid with starch-potassium iodide paper. The sodium nitrite is added until the test shows the presence of a slight excess of nitrous acid for 10 min. When there has been an excess for this length of time, the reaction is complete. A clear solution of benzenediazonium chloride is obtained, the volume of which is not over 2,000 lb.

Benzenediazonium Chloride

The foregoing method is used for any amines of the benzene or naphthalene series which do not contain negative groups. In some cases, it is necessary to use a larger volume of water and a higher temperature to dissolve the salt of a base. For example, for α-naphthylamine it is necessary to use about 2,500 lb. of water at 70°C. to dissolve 143 lb. of the base as hydrochloride. If the solution of the diazonium salt is dark colored or turbid, it may be clarified by filtering with a purified charcoal, which has practically no harmful effect on the diazonium salt in a short time at a low temperature.

Diazotization of Nitroamines.—p-Nitroaniline is most easily diazotized if obtained as crystals which pass through a 40-mesh sieve. Larger crystals do not react completely in cold dilute acid, and very small ones dissolve too easily, so that it is difficult to avoid some diazoamino's coupling during the addition of the nitrite. One hundred thirty-eight pounds of p-nitroaniline is stirred in 1,000 lb. of water and 300 lb. of 30 per cent hydrochloric acid at 15°C. for a few minutes until the crystals are wet. Then 230 lb. of 30 per cent sodium nitrite solution is added rapidly with good agitation. It is advisable to reserve about 2 per cent of the nitrite solution for the final adjustment. The solution is tested frequently with starch-iodide paper, and a slight excess of nitrous acid must be maintained until the reaction is complete. In case of a deficiency of nitrous acid, any undiazotized amine in solution couples to form a diazoamino compound which is not easily hydrolyzed. The diazotization is complete in about 10 min., and, if it is not exposed to strong light, a clear solution is obtained with a volume of about 1,500 lb. at 25°C.

p-Nitrobenzenediazonium Chloride

Many other nitroamines may be diazotized in the same way, but those which are less soluble must be ground to a powder fine enough to pass through a 100-mesh sieve, and it may take 1 hr. to complete the reaction.

Some of the chloro- and nitroamines may be dissolved in about 5 moles of normal hydrochloric acid at 90°C.; and on rapidly cooling the solutions with ice, the bases are precipitated in a crystalline form which diazotize easily. They may likewise be dissolved in concentrated sulfuric acid and poured into ice and water to precipitate the base. For example, 138 lb. of *p*-nitroaniline is stirred in 400 lb. of water, and 200 lb. of sulfuric acid is added. The temperature rises to about 55°C., and the base is dissolved. This solution is poured in to 1,000 lb. of water and 1,000 lb. of ice and then diazotized as above.

The dinitro- and trihalogenoamines of the benzene series, mononitro- or halogenoamines of the naphthalene series, and the aminoanthraquinones are generally too weakly basic to be diazotized in water solutions. They may be diazotized in concentrated nitric, sulfuric or glacial acetic acid, or suitable mixtures of these acids.

Many of these weakly basic amines may be diazotized in about 10 moles of glacial acetic acid with 2.5 moles of hydrochloric acid and 1 mole of sodium nitrite. Though the amine may not be completely dissolved in this volume of acetic acid, it is in most cases sufficiently soluble for fairly rapid diazotization. With different amines, more or less acetic acid may be required, and it may be considerably diluted in some cases.

A satisfactory method of diazotizing these weakly basic amines is with nitrosylsulfuric acid, as follows: With good agitation 69 lb. of sodium nitrite (about 71 lb. of the commercial product) is added to 1,000 lb. of sulfuric acid (sp. gr., 1.84) at 30°C., allowing the temperature to rise to 60°C. in order to obtain a clear solution. The solution is cooled to 25°C. by external means, and 1 pound mole of the amine is added. After stirring about 1 hr., the sulfuric acid solution is poured on about 2,500 lb. of ice. The cold solution is stirred a few minutes and filtered. The large excess of sulfuric acid in the solution of the diazonium sulfate prepared in this way does not generally interfere with its use in the preparation of azo dyes, since diazonium salts containing several negative groups couple even in strongly acid solutions.

Schoutissen concluded that nitrosylsulfuric acid requires dilution in order to diazotize some amines, and he modified the above method by adding to the sulfuric acid, after the amine, two volumes of phosphoric acid (sp. gr., 1.70).[1]

Hodgson and Walker have diazotized mono- and dinitro-α-naphthylamine by dissolving in glacial acetic acid and pouring this solution

[1] SCHOUTISSEN, *J. Am. Chem. Soc.*, **55**, 4531–4534 (1933).

into nitrosylsulfuric acid. This is probably the best method for diazotizing amines which dissolve neither in water nor in concentrated sulfuric acid.[1]

Solutions of diazonium salts of most nitroamines, by whatever method obtained, must usually be filtered with charcoal in order to obtain pure products. Water solutions of those containing two or more nitro groups are not very stable on account of hydrolysis of a nitro group (see page 123).

Diazotization of Aminosulfonic Acids.—A solution is prepared of 245 lb. of sodium naphthionate in 2,000 lb. of water at room temperature, and 2.5 moles of hydrochloric acid (300 lb. of 30 per cent solution) is added. The precipitated naphthionic acid is stirred for about 15 min. in order that it may become crystalline, as it will then react more rapidly. It is cooled with ice to about 12°C., and 230 lb. of a 30 per cent solution of sodium nitrite is added. A slight excess of nitrous acid is maintained for 15 min. at about 20°C., and the reaction is then practically complete. This diazonium sulfonate is light yellow in color, and it is very insoluble.

$$\text{---N}\!\equiv\!\text{N}$$
$$|$$
$$\text{O}$$
$$|$$
$$\text{---SO}_2$$

Naphthalene-1-diazonium 4-Sulfonate

Other mono- or disulfonic acids of amino compounds of the benzene or naphthalene series are diazotized in a similar way. Those less soluble may be dissolved at a higher temperature, or in some cases they may be dissolved as a more soluble salt, such as the ammonium salt. The solution is not cooled until the free sulfonic acid is precipitated, as they are obtained in a more reactive form if precipitated from solution than if the salt is allowed to crystallize before it is acidified.

In this reaction, many of the diazonium sulfonates go into solution and then crystallize out almost immediately. The insoluble sulfonates are crystalline products which may be filtered or decanted. Some of them, like that derived from 2-naphthylamine-1-sulfonic acid (Tobias acid), may be obtained in either of two crystalline forms, depending on the purity of the product and modifications of the process. Although these crystalline diazo compounds can be easily isolated in fairly good yields and a high state of purity, it is rarely necessary to purify them in this way. They are not dried, as some of them are explosive.

Diazotization of Aminocarboxylic Acids.—These may be treated in the same way as the aminosulfonic acids, but it is not necessary to dis-

---

[1] HODGSON and WALKER, *J. Chem. Soc.*, **1933**, 1620.

solve some of them as sodium salts, as they are basic enough to form hydrochlorides. One hundred thirty-seven pounds of anthranilic acid is dissolved in 2,500 lb. of water with 1.5 moles of hydrochloric acid (180 lb. of 30 per cent). The solution is cooled to 10°C. with ice, and then 230 lb. of 30 per cent solution of sodium nitrite is added. A slight excess of nitrous acid is maintained for 10 min. at 10°C.

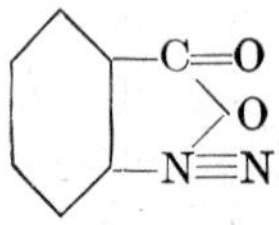

Benzene-2-diazonium Carboxylate

Diazotization of Aminophenols and Aminonaphthols.—No general method can be given for the preparation of the diazo oxides. Some of the aminophenols and aminonaphthols are basic enough to dissolve as hydrochlorides, and they may be diazotized like the unsubstituted amines but using 1.5 moles of acid instead of 2.5 moles. Some of those containing negative groups, like picramic acid, may be dissolved as the sodium or ammonium salt and treated with 2.5 moles of acid and 1 mole of sodium nitrite the same as the aminosulfonic acids. Some o-aminonaphthols are easily oxidized to naphthoquinones, and so they are not diazotized in acid solution. The free sulfonic acid group is the only acid necessary in the diazotization of the important 1-amino-2-naphthol-4-sulfonic acid. A small amount of copper sulfate is used as a catalyst in this reaction. The method in general use for the diazotization of this amino compound is as follows:

A mixture of 239 lb. of 1-amino-2-naphthol-4-sulfonic acid and 1,000 lb. of water is stirred at 20°C., and a solution of 2 lb. of copper sulfate crystals in 20 lb. of water is added. Then 230 lb. of 30 per cent solution of sodium nitrite is poured in, and in a few minutes the temperature rises to about 35°C. After stirring 15 min. more, the yellow-brown solution is filtered and either used directly, or the diazo oxide may be isolated. It may be precipitated as the sodium salt by adding about 300 lb. of sodium chloride or as the free sulfonic acid by adding 150 lb. of 30 per cent hydrochloric acid.

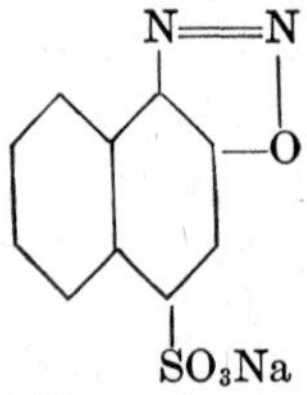

Naphthalene-1. 2-Diazooxide-4-Sodium Sulfonate

Diazotization of Diamino Compounds.—When some diamino compounds of the benzene or naphthalene series are treated with nitrous acid, both amino groups are diazotized; but in others, only one amino group reacts with nitrous acid. When ortho diamines are treated with nitrous acid, one amino group is diazotized, and this immediately reacts with the other amino group to form an azimino compound.[1]

When *m*-diamines are treated with nitrous acid, there is usually a considerable amount of coupling to produce azo dyes of the type of Bismarck Brown.[2] Both amino groups of *m*-phenylenediamine may be diazotized by dissolving it together with 2 moles of sodium nitrite in water and pouring this solution gradually into 5 moles of cold $\frac{1}{2}$ N hydrochloric acid. Many *m*-diamines with negative substituents do not show such a tendency to couple during the diazotization, and bisdiazonium salts are more easily obtained.

A film apparatus has been developed which permits diazotization to proceed without coupling. In this apparatus equivalent amounts of solutions of sodium nitrite and of *m*-phenylenediamine with excess acid are allowed to come in contact as thin films, so that the diazotization reaction takes place between relatively few molecules, and coupling with undiazotized amine is avoided.[3]

Ordinarily, only one amino group of a *p*-diamine is diazotizable, because the basicity of the second amino group is reduced so much by the diazonium group in the para position. The second amino group sometimes reacts in more concentrated acid. Schoutissen[4] has shown that both amino groups of ortho-, meta-, and para-phenylene diamines are diazotized in concentrated sulfuric acid with nitrosyl sulfuric acid and phosphoric acid.

Diamino compounds in which the amino groups are on different rings of diphenyl compounds such as biphenyl, dibenzyl, stilbene, diphenylamine, diphenyl ether, diphenyl urea, diphenyl sulfide, and diphenyl or triphenyl methane are generally tetrazotized without difficulty in a manner similar to that used for diazotizing monoamino compounds. Many such diamines are used for making azo dyes, and the method used for tetrazotizing dianisidine will be given as an example.

---

[1] LADENBURG, *Ber.*, **9**, 219 (1876).

[2] Colour Index, No. 331.

[3] HEERTJES, KOLB, and WATERMAN, *J. Soc. Chem. Ind.*, **56**, 173 (1937).

[4] Schoutissen, *Chem. Weekblad*, **34**, 506 (1937).

In 8,000 lb. of water, 244 lb. of dianisidine is dissolved with 240 lb. of 30 per cent hydrochloric acid at about 20°C. When solution is complete, 360 lb. of 30 per cent hydrochloric acid is added and then 460 lb. of 30 per cent sodium nitrite solution is gradually poured in during a period of about 5 min. A slight excess of nitrous acid is maintained for 10 min. at 20 to 25°C. The volume of the solution is about 9,500 lb. The solution is rather dark colored unless it is clarified with charcoal, when a yellow solution is obtained.

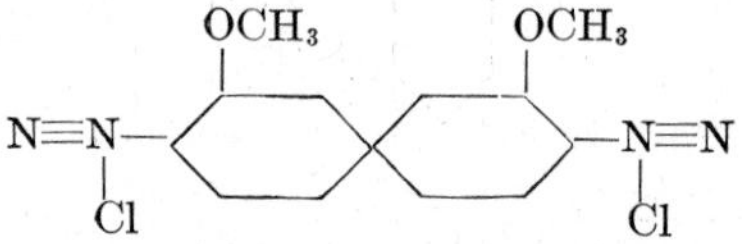

3, 3'-Dimethoxydiphenyl-4, 4'-tetrazonium Dichloride

Diazotization of Aminoazo Compounds.—In the preparation of many polyazo dyes, it is necessary to diazotize a *p*-aminoazo compound, which may have been obtained by coupling a diazo compound with an amine of the benzene or naphthalene series. Those which do not contain acid groups give fairly soluble diazonium chlorides. Some of these aminoazo compounds form soluble hydrochlorides, but whether they are soluble in acid solution or not they usually diazotize easily under about the same conditions as the simple amines, except that, on account of the lower solubility and a slower rate of reaction, the temperature should be held at 20°C. or higher. Of course, good agitation is necessary in diazotizing insoluble compounds. Aminoazotoluene may be taken as an example of this type of amine. Two hundred twenty-five pounds of aminoazotoluene is stirred in 1,000 lb. of water at 12°C. with 300 lb. of 30 per cent hydrochloric acid, and 230 lb. of 30 per cent nitrite solution is added during an interval of about 2 min. The temperature rises to about 20°C., and a slight excess of nitrous acid is maintained at this temperature for about 5 min. The solution may be clarified with charcoal at 10 to 15°C.; but at lower temperatures, the diazonium chloride crystallizes out of solution.

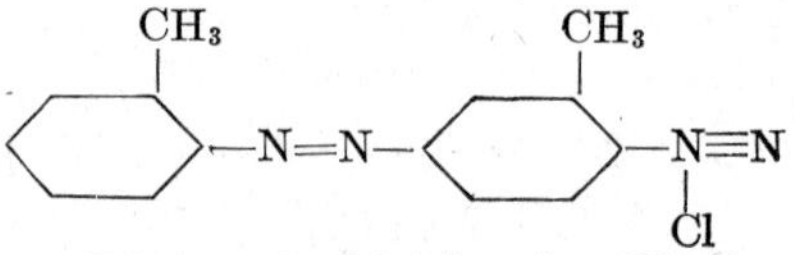

2-Tolueneazo-3-tolyl-4-diazonium Chloride

There is such a variety of aminoazo compounds with sulfonic or carboxylic groups that they are diazotized in various ways. Some of them, with several sulfonic groups, are soluble in dilute acid and form soluble diazonium compounds. Others, with only one or two sulfonic or carboxylic groups, are more or less soluble in neutral or alkaline solution but insoluble in acid solution. These are generally prepared for diazotization by dissolving as the sodium or ammonium salt and allowing it to crystallize out, sometimes with the addition of sodium chloride. A sufficient amount of acid is then added followed by the sodium nitrite. For monosulfonic acids, a temperature above 25°C. is usually necessary; but for more soluble compounds, a temperature below 20°C. is to be preferred. The amount of acid necessary to use with the neutral sodium salts is usually 2.5 moles when there is a sulfonic group on the radical which contains the amino group and 3.5 moles when there is no sulfonic group on this radical. A diazonium sulfonate is obtained in the former case and a diazonium chloride in the latter. The reaction is usually complete in 30 to 45 min. A variation of the above general procedure is to dissolve the sodium nitrite in the neutral solution of the aminoazo compound and then add the acid to this or run it into the acid. However, this reverse method rarely offers any advantage over the ordinary direct method. The above method is illustrated by the diazotization of the aminoazo compound obtained by coupling diazotized metanilic acid with α-naphthylamine.

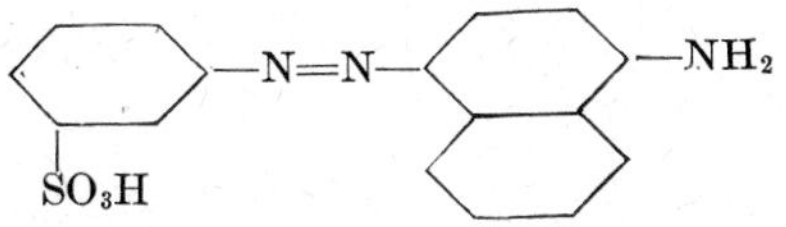

One pound mole of this is dissolved in 2,000 lb. of water at 20°C. with 40 lb. of sodium hydroxide. Since the solution is strongly colored, it cannot be tested directly with indicator papers to show when it is slightly alkaline. It is tested by putting a few drops of the solution on some crystals of ammonium sulfate and then suspending over these crystals a strip of moistened red litmus paper or of Brilliant Yellow paper. The dye is crystallized out of solution by the gradual addition of 300 lb. of sodium chloride. Then 3.5 moles of hydrochloric acid (430 lb. of 30 per cent solution) is added, followed by 230 lb. of 30 per cent solution of sodium nitrite, which is poured in during about 5 min. At 25 to 30°C., the nitrous acid is used up in 15 to 30 min., and enough more sodium nitrite is added to keep a slight excess for 10 min. longer at 25°C. This diazonium chloride is insoluble in the 10 per cent salt solution in which it is prepared; and for the preparation of some dyes, it is cooled below 10°C. and filtered.

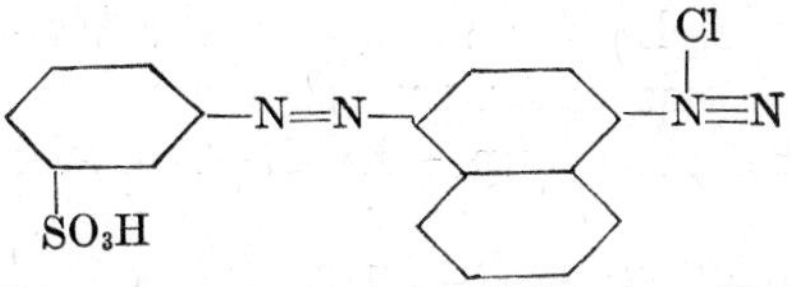

3-Sulfobenzeneazo-1-naphthalene-4-diazonium Chloride

While the course of the reaction can generally be followed by adding the last 5 per cent of the sodium nitrite only as fast as the test with starch-iodide paper shows it is used, it is sometimes desirable to check this observation by testing for undiazotized amine. Small amounts of many sulfonated aminomonoazo compounds can be detected by the change in color when a test portion is made alkaline and then immediately made acid on a piece of white filter paper. In alkaline solution, these compounds are yellow or orange; while in acid solution, they are red or violet. In other cases, a small amount of undiazotized sulfonated aminoazo compound can be detected in a large amount of the diazo compound by adding a few drops to an alkaline solution of H acid and dipping the end of a strip of soft filter paper in it for a few minutes. The blue azo dye formed with H acid rises in the filter paper by capillary action, but the undiazotized amine, being of lower molecular weight, rises a little higher and is easily seen.

X. ANALYSIS OF DIAZO COMPOUNDS

Methods of quantitative estimation of diazonium salts may be briefly summarized as follows:

1. Measurement of the nitrogen evolved in decomposition.

a. By hydrolysis. The acid solution or suspension of the diazonium salt is heated until the evolution of gas ceases.

b. By reduction. Nitrogen is quickly removed from diazo compounds, except diazo oxides, by treatment with *p*-phenylenediamine, and it is claimed that a determination can be made in 5 to 10 min.[1]

2. Coupling with an excess of a standard solution of a coupling component, such as β-naphthol or 1-phenyl-3-methyl-5-pyrazolone and titration of the excess with a standard solution of a diazonium salt.

3. Coupling with an excess of a coupling component and determination of the azo nitrogen by titration with standard titanium trichloride solution.

XI. COUPLING

Use of Diazo Compounds in the Manufacture of Azo Dyes.—The preparation of diazo compounds by the unit process diazotization is, for all practical purposes, a means to an important end. Diazonium compounds as a class react practically quantitatively in aqueous solution with certain amines and phenols and their derivatives. A reaction termed *coupling* takes place, and new compounds are formed which contain the groups of atoms that were formerly diazo and the added *component*, united by the azo group —N=N—. The coupling process was

---

[1] GOLESSENKO, *Chem. Zentr.*, **1937**, II, 112.

illustrated by the formation of the dyestuff Croceine Orange from benzenediazonium chloride and Schaeffer salt on page 120.

The reactants in this coupling reaction comprise on one side the class of diazo compounds, and on the other side a wide variety of compounds commonly called *coupling components*. Among the coupling components commercially used are:

1. Hydroxybenzenes and naphthalenes such as phenol, cresols, resorcinol, salicyclic acid, naphthols, naphtholsulfonic acids and hydroxynaphthoic acids. The diazo compound reacts to replace the hydrogen on the carbon ortho or para to the hydroxyl group and in some cases 2 or 3 molecules of a diazo couple with 1 molecule of a phenol.

2. Aminobenzenes and naphthalenes, such as *m*-toluidine, dimethylaniline, *m*-phenylenediamine, naphthylamines, and naphthylaminesulfonic acids. The amino compounds are less reactive than the hydroxy compounds, and usually couple only in the position para to the amino group. Although phenol couples easily with one or more equivalents of diazo compounds, aniline scarcely couples at all but does condense in the amino group. However, secondary and tertiary amino compounds couple more easily than the primary amines. A method of obtaining azo compounds in which aniline and other rather inactive amines are the coupling components is to form the secondary amino compound by treating with the formaldehyde bisulfite addition compound.

$$R—NH·CH_2SO_3Na$$

This derivative couples fairly well and the primary amino group can then be regenerated by acid or alkaline hydrolysis.

3. Aminohydroxy compounds, such as *m*-aminophenol, aminonaphthols and aminonaphtholsulfonic acids. These coupling components couple ortho or para to the amino group in acid solution and ortho or para to the hydroxy group in alkaline solution, and some of them couple in both positions, provided the acid coupling is made first. The best known example of such a double coupling component is H acid (1-amino-8-naphthol-3, 6-disulfonic acid) from which disazo dyes are obtained.

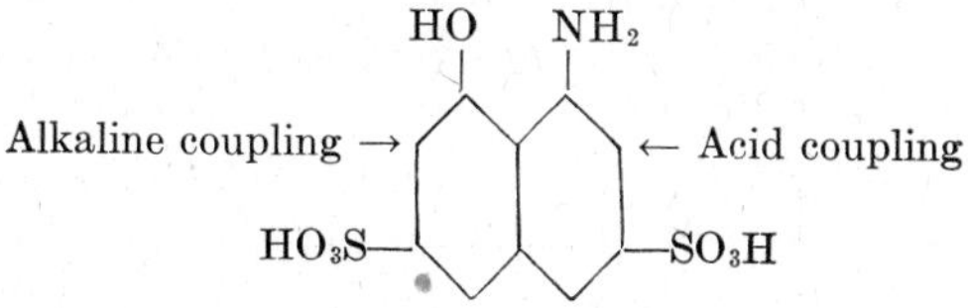

4. Beta diketo aliphatic or cyclic compounds such as aceto-acetyl aromatic amides, and barbituric acid. These compounds couple on the carbon between the keto groups, but only under conditions such that the enol form is present.[1]

[1] DIMROTH, *Ber.*, **40**, 2404 (1907).

5. Other compounds with a so-called active methylene group such as pyrazolone, especially 1-phenyl-3-methyl-5-pyrazolone.

In the azo compounds formed by the coupling reaction the azo nitrogens are joined to carbon atoms of the diazo component and of the coupling component. Stereoisomerism is possible, but the stable form of azo compounds is the *trans* form.[1]

Structure of the Diazo Compound.—Opinion has been divided on the question of whether it is the diazonium or the *syn*-diazo form of the diazo compound which takes part in the coupling reaction. This has been partly due to the lack of information on the state of the equilibrium,

$$\text{Diazonium} \qquad \begin{matrix} \text{R—N—X} \rightarrow \text{R—N} \\ \vertiii{} \qquad \Vert \\ \text{N} \quad \leftarrow \text{X—N} \end{matrix} \qquad syn\text{-Diazo}$$

for different diazo compounds. The equilibrium is affected by the character of the cyclic compound R and the groups connected to it, and by the pH of the solution, and it is further complicated by the fact that the diazonium compound is a strong base and the *syn*-diazo compound is a weak acid. Spectral-absorption methods should be of assistance in the study of this question.

The generally accepted opinion at present is that the *syn*-diazo compound is the active form in coupling. This is in agreement with the fact that coupling is more rapid as the pH is increased. It is supported by the principle of induced alternate polarities, for the very active diazo compounds, such as those containing nitro groups ortho and para to the diazo group, are those in which the induced positive pole is transferred to the second nitrogen atom.[2]

Does not Couple in Acid Solution   Couples in Strong Acid Solution

This effect of negative groups on the reactivity is shown in the following list of amines arranged in the order of increasing coupling reactivity of their diazo compounds.[3]

Aniline
2, 4, 6-Trichloraniline
3, 5-Dinitroaniline
p-Nitroaniline
2, 6-Dichloro-4-nitroaniline
2, 4-Dinitroaniline
2, 4, 6-Trinitroaniline

Increasing reactivity ↓

[1] BERGMANN, ENGEL, and SANDOR, *Ber.*, **63**, 2572 (1930).
[2] WALKER, T. K., *J. Soc. Dyers Colourists*, **39**, 293 (1923).
[3] SCHOUTISSEN, *J. Am. Chem. Soc.*, **55**, 4541 (1933).

Structure of the Coupling Component.—In addition to the coupling components listed above as being used commercially, many other unsaturated compounds couple to give azo compounds. Meyer[1] found that even hydrocarbons couple, and he prepared azo compounds from 2, 3-dimethylbutadiene and *p*-nitrobenzenediazonium chloride, from isoprene and 2, 4-dinitrobenzenediazonium sulfate and from mesitylene and 2, 4, 6-trinitrobenzenediazonium sulfate.

From the studies of Meyer, in particular, it appears that the characteristic of a coupling component is that it contains a double bond between two carbons and some other unsaturation in the compound. The coupling reactivity is increased by the presence on one of the doubly bound carbon atoms of a positive group, such as hydroxy; primary, secondary, or tertiary amino; ether; or methyl groups. The effect of the substituents (commonly called auxochrome groups) which increase the coupling activity is to polarize the double bond or make one of the carbons more positive than the other.

If positive groups induce a polarization which makes a compound react more easily with diazo compounds, it would be expected, according to the principle of alternate induced polarities, that additional positive groups on alternate carbons would increase the polarization and make the compound more reactive. This is actually the case, and the following examples illustrate the point:

1. The benzene hydrocarbons which have been coupled with 2, 4, 6-trinitrobenzenediazonium sulfate are those containing three methyl groups on alternate carbons, such as mesitylene, isodurene and pentamethylbenzene, while other methyl substituted benzenes show little or no coupling activity.[2]

Mesitylene and Isodurene Couple

Because coupling tends to go para or ortho to existing substituents, it is clear that in the case of mesitylene there are three positive forces making for coupling, *i.e.*, polarization with expulsion of an ortho hydrogen atom; in the case of isodurene there is one opposing force.

2. The order of coupling ability of phenols, as found by Meyer[3] and by Goldschmidt,[4] is

[1] MEYER, *Ber.*, **52**, 1468 (1919); MEYER and TOCHTEMANN, *Ber.*, **54**, 2283 (1921).

[2] MEYER, *loc. cit.;* SMITH and PADEN, *J. Am. Chem. Soc.*, **56**, 2169 (1934).

[3] MEYER, IRSCHICK, and SCHLÖSSER, *Ber.*, **47**, 1741 (1914).

[4] GOLDSCHMIDT and WERZ, *Ber.*, **30**, 670 (1897).

Phloroglucinol > Resorcinol > *m*-Cresol > Phenol > Hydroquinone >
o-Nitrophenol, etc.

Here negative substituents make coupling more difficult and frequently
prevent it. The coupling ability of the ethers is in the same order, but
they couple more slowly.

3. Among the naphthalene compounds, also, coupling takes place
more easily if the hydroxy or amino groups are on alternate carbons.

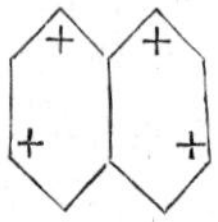

This effect is most easily seen when it is attempted to couple two diazo
compounds to the same coupling component. In the case of 1, 5-dihy-
droxynaphthalene where the effect of the hydroxy groups is opposed it is
difficult to couple a second diazo group, while 1, 6-dihydroxynaphthalene,
in which the inductive effect is additive, couples easily with 2 or 3
molecules of a diazo compound.[1] In the case of 6-amino-1-naphthol-
3-sulfonic acid (J acid) it is possible to couple one diazo compound in acid
solution and another in alkaline solution, while if 7-amino-1-naphthol-3-
sulfonic acid (Gamma acid) is coupled with a diazo compound in acid
solution it does not then couple again in alkaline solution:[2]

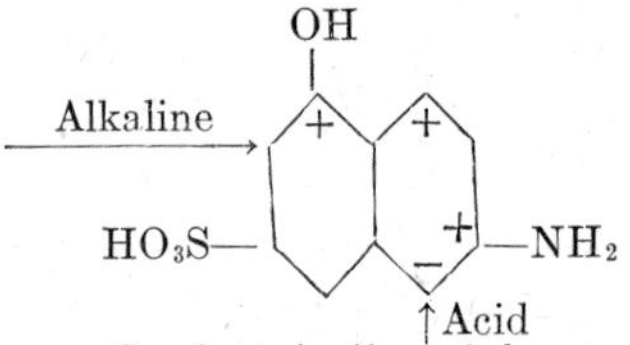

Couples twice if coupled
first in acid solution

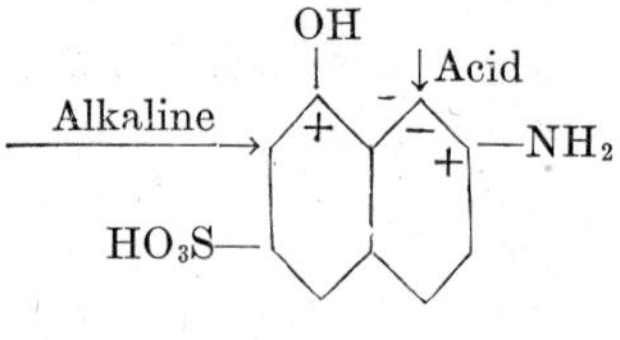

Couples only once, either
in acid or in alkaline solution

XII. MECHANISM OF THE COUPLING REACTION

It was shown above that the diazo compound is probably in the form
of a *syn*-diazo hydroxide, and that the coupling component has a double
bond between two carbons which are polarized. Meyer[3] believed that
the coupling reaction consisted in an addition to this double bond to form
an intermediate product from which water was eliminated to form the
azo compound.

[1] Fischer, *J. prakt. Chem.*, **94**, 1, 13 (1916).

[2] Fierz-David, "Kunstliche Organische Farbstoffe," Julius Springer, Berlin,
p. 135 (1926).

[3] Meyer, *Ber.*, **52**, 1468 (1919).

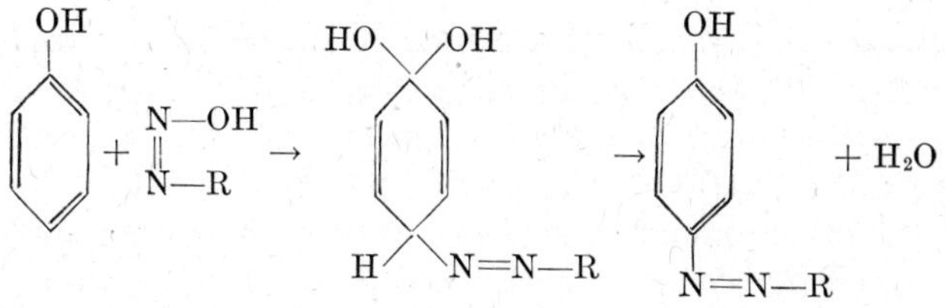

The theory of an intermediate addition product is also supported by Wizinger,[1] who obtained such addition products by coupling diazo compounds with substituted ethylene. He stated that the formation of the intermediate product and the azo dye proceeds more easily the more positive the carbon atom to which the anion is added. Although such intermediate addition compounds may exist, the reaction may also be considered as the direct replacement of the hydrogen on a negatively polarized carbon atom.

XIII. FACTORS AFFECTING COUPLING

The coupling reaction is bimolecular,[2] and with the reactants in equivalent amounts the rate of reaction at constant temperature and constant pH is shown by the formula

$$k = \frac{1}{t} \frac{x}{a(a - x)}$$

where k = a constant.

a = the initial concentration.

t = time in minutes.

x = concentration of reacted material.

Concentration.—From the equation it is seen that the rate of reaction is proportional to the concentration. For reactions which are rather slow it is therefore important to keep the concentration of reactants as near the saturation point as possible. In commercial production of azo colors, it is not always necessary to use a volume of solvent sufficient to dissolve both reactants at the temperature and pH used for the coupling, and one of them may be present as a freshly precipitated solid. It is desirable that at least one of the reactants be completely dissolved. The volume of the coupling reaction for a monazo color ordinarily is from 3,000 to 6,000 parts per mole. However, the coupling reaction is often carried out in volumes several times as great, especially in the last couplings of some polyazo colors.

Temperature.—Raising the temperature increases the rate of coupling, but since the decomposition of diazo compounds is also more rapid at

[1] Wizinger, *Z. angew. Chem.*, **46**, 756 (1933); Brit. 435, 449 (1934).

[2] Goldschmidt, *Ber.*, **35**, 3634 (1902); Conant and Peterson, *J. Am. Chem. Soc.*, **52**, 1220 (1930).

higher temperatures, couplings are usually made at low temperatures. For coupling in alkaline solution, the temperature is generally below 15°C. For couplings in acid solution, the temperature is usually above 10°C. and may be at 60°C. or higher.[1]

Hydrogen Ion Concentration.—Since the diazo compound is an equilibrium mixture of active and inactive forms, the concentration of active form of any particular diazo compound depends on the pH of the solution, and the rate of reaction will be greatest at the pH at which the highest ratio of active to inactive diazo exists.

The forms of the diazo compound may be plotted against the hydrogen ion concentration as follows:

$$\uparrow \quad \begin{array}{l} anti\text{-Diazotate} \\ syn\text{-Diazotate} \\ syn\text{-Diazo hydroxide} \\ \text{Diazonium hydroxide} \\ \text{Diazonium salt} \end{array}$$

(pH on vertical axis)

As pointed out above, there is little published information regarding the range of this equilibrium for different diazo compounds. Based on the conditions ordinarily used in making couplings it appears that approximate values of the pH for maximum ratios of *syn* diazo in substituted benzene compounds is as follows:

MAXIMUM COUPLING ACTIVITY

Substituent	pH
Ether	13
Alkyl	12
Unsubstituted	11
Sulfonic or halogen	8
Nitro	5
Dinitro	2

However the above values depend not only on the substituent present on the ring, but on its position relative to the diazo group. Generally a substituent has less effect in the meta position than in the ortho or para position.

Conant and Peterson[2] found for several couplings that

$$\log k - \log k_0 = \text{pH}$$

so that the coupling rate is ten times faster with an increase of one unit in pH.

The hydrogen ion concentration also affects the position of coupling in some compounds, especially those containing both amino and hydroxy groups, such as aminonaphthols. In these compounds the amino group has the greatest effect on polarization of the conjugated double bonds in

---

[1] In U. S. 1,811,576 (1931), a temperature of 70 to 95°C. is used.
[2] *Loc. cit.*

acid solution, and the coupling then takes place ortho or para to the amino group, while in alkaline solution the coupling takes place ortho or para to the hydroxy group, since it is then the most effective in causing an induced polarization. The pH at which the coupling position changes varies with different aminonaphtholsulfonic acids from about pH 4 to pH 8.

Another way in which the pH influences the coupling is its effect on the solubility of the coupling component. Some naphthols, *e.g.*, 2-hydroxy-3-naphthoic acid anilide, require a high alkalinity, such as that of sodium hydroxide, for solubility in water, and at lower alkalinity the concentration of the coupling component in solution is almost negligible at a low temperature.

The hydrogen ion concentration is maintained in the desirable range by the use of buffer salts, such as sodium carbonate and sodium acetate.

Couplings are usually not made at a constant pH, because the diazonium compound containing an excess of acid is gradually added to the coupling component containing an excess of buffer.

Time.—From the preceding equation it is seen that the time for completion of the reaction is inversely proportional to the concentration and the constant. Conditions of concentration and pH are usually chosen so that couplings are completed in a short time. Alkaline couplings of hydroxy compounds are generally very rapid, but acid couplings of amino compounds may take from a few minutes to several hours.

Solvent.—The diazo compounds are usually sufficiently soluble in water to allow the reaction to take place. Coupling components are also usually soluble enough, but in some cases other solvents are required, *e.g.*, alcohol or acetic acid. Since the rate of coupling depends on the concentration of reactants in solution it is desirable for the solvent to keep the reactants in solution or to dissolve them rapidly during the coupling. In the case of reactants of rather low solubility at the temperature or pH of the coupling, it is necessary that they be precipitated or prepared in a form which dissolves easily.

In some couplings, *e.g.*,

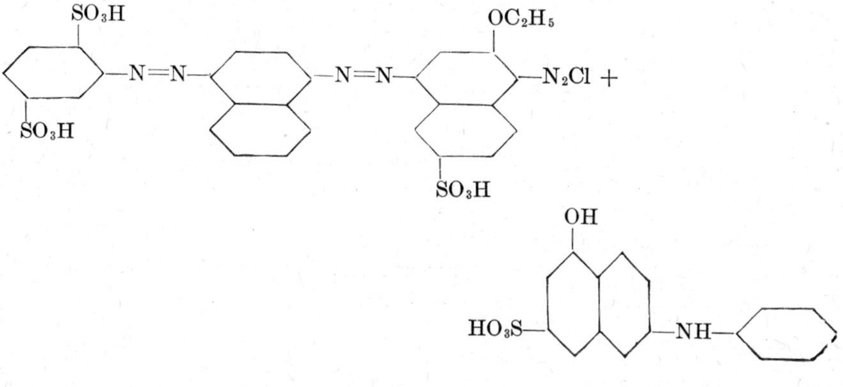

it is necessary to use a mixture of water and pyridine as the reaction medium.[1] The use of pyridine in such cases is not because of low solubility of the reactants in water but because of a low coupling rate in water. It seems probable that the advantage in the use of pyridine is due to an increase in the polarization of the coupling component, making it more reactive.

XIV. TECHNICAL COUPLINGS

Many hundreds of different coupling reactions are made on a commercial scale. They are of two main classes; those which produce marketable dyes or pigments and those made on textiles by dyers.

Azo dyes made on textile fibers are of three types:

1. Those in which the coupling component is absorbed on the fiber (usually cotton), which is then immersed in a solution of a diazonium salt. These are often called *ice colors*.

2. Those in which the amino compound or amino azo compound is absorbed on the fiber, which is then immersed in a solution of nitrous acid and later in a solution of the coupling component. These are known as *diazo colors* or *ingrain colors*.

3. Those in which a stabilized diazo compound and the coupling component are applied together as a printing paste, the printed cloth then being subjected to treatment which causes the diazo compound to become active and couple. These are the *printing colors*.

Couplings made on the fiber are complicated by the problems of application and handling of the textiles, and they will not be considered here.

Azo compounds made in substance may be classified as those in which the coupling component is a hydroxy compound, such as a phenol, a naphthol, or a keto compound (in its enol form), and those in which the coupling component is an amino compound, such as a primary, secondary, or tertiary amine.

Coupling Hydroxy Compounds in Alkaline Solution.

Chicago acid ← Tolidine → Chicago acid*

Tolidine (212 lb.) is tetrazotized according to the method for dianisidine, described on page 138, in which the upper tub of a unit like that of Fig. 1, page 131, is used. In the lower tub a paste is made from 716 lb. (2.1 moles) of the monosodium salt of 1-amino-8-naphthol-2, 4-disulfonic acid (Chicago acid) and 5,000 lb. of water, and solution is effected by the addition of 267 lb. of 30 per cent sodium hydroxide, the solution being tested with litmus, in order to leave the reaction still acid. The solution

---

[1] Schweitzer, U. S. 1,602,991 (1926).

* This method adapted from Hartwell and Fieser, "Organic Syntheses," John Wiley & Sons, Inc., New York, vol. 16, pp. 12–17 (1936).

is cooled to 18°C. by the addition of ice, and, just before the coupling, 370 lb. (3.5 moles) of anhydrous sodium carbonate is added.

With vigorous mechanical agitation the diazonium salt solution is run into the Chicago acid solution rather rapidly. The blue dye which separates at first gradually dissolves on further stirring. A portion of

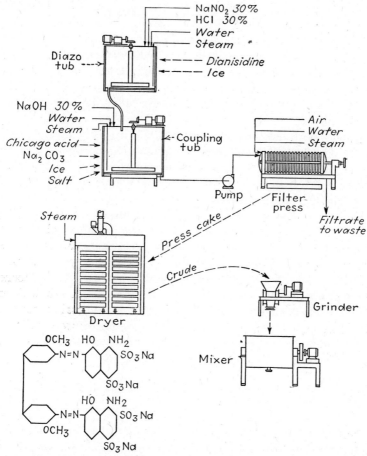

Fig. 2.—Flow sheet. Preparation of Diamine Sky Blue FF. Colour Index No. 518. Couple tetrazotized dianisidine with 2 molecular proportions of 1-amino-8-naphthol-2.4-disulfonic acid (Na salt) in alkaline solution.

the solution is saturated with salt and tested for alkalinity on litmus paper. The salted-out sample is then poured on filter paper, and the clear rim of the spot is tested for excess Chicago acid with a solution of diazotized sulfanilic acid. A red-violet color at the meeting of the two solutions shows the presence of Chicago acid.

After stirring for a total of 2 hr., the mixture is heated to 85°C. and the volume estimated. For each 1,000 lb. of the solution, 250 lb. of sodium chloride (about 4,500 lb. in all) is added slowly, with vigorous stirring, in four or five portions. The dye is thus caused to separate in an easily filtrable form. When a drop of the mixture is allowed to fall on filter paper, the dye forms a dark-blue mass in the center of a violet rim. While still warm, the mixture is filtered in a plate-and-frame press with pressure from a blow case or from a centrifugal pump. The press cake (of about 40 per cent solids) is dried on pans placed in racks in an air dryer, and the crude product is standardized by grinding and mixing with salt in order to equal the commercial standard which is about 25 per cent dye. Analysis shows a yield of about 85 per cent of the theoretical amount. The flow diagram for the similar preparation of Diamine Sky Blue FF. is shown in Fig. 2.

Couplings with most hydroxy compounds are carried out in a similar manner. The coupling component is dissolved, usually as the sodium salt, the concentration being about one-quarter normal. In order to keep the pH at a high enough value for rapid coupling, sodium carbonate was used in this example, but in some couplings other alkalis may be used, such as ammonium hydroxide, or sodium bicarbonate. The pH used for a coupling depends mainly on the coupling ability of the two reactants, but sometimes on other factors. For example, some 1-hydroxynaphthalene compounds couple in the 2 or 4 position depending on the pH. The coupling reaction is usually not carried out at constant concentration or at constant pH, since the diazonium salt with excess acid is gradually added to a solution containing the total amount of the coupling component and the buffer. The temperature of the above coupling is about as high as is used for alkaline couplings.

Coupling Hydroxy Compounds in Acid Solution.

m-Nitro-p-toluidine → β-naphthol[1]

m-Nitro-p-toluidine (152 lb.) is diazotized according to the method for p-nitroaniline on page 133, but since it is a weaker base it must be ground to about 200 mesh. The solution of the diazonium chloride is filtered with charcoal and treated with some agent to remove excess nitrous acid, such as urea or sulfamic acid.

In 2,000 lb. of water, 151 lb. of β-naphthol is dissolved with 143 lb. of 30 per cent sodium hydroxide solution, and 220 lb. of sodium acetate crystals are added to it. The β-naphthol is then precipitated by adding about 138 lb. of 30 per cent hydrochloric acid, or enough to make the suspension slightly acid to litmus. The clarified solution of diazonium

---

[1] Colour Index, No. 69. For other examples of acid couplings see U. S. 921,546 (1909), 1,947,028 (1934), and 2,016,495 (1935).

chloride, free from excess nitrous acid, is then run into this suspension during about 45 min. at a temperature of 25 to 30°C. Testing of spots on filter paper shows the presence of β-naphthol in solution, but no excess diazo. The solution remains acid to litmus but neutral to Congo Red papers. The insoluble color is filtered and washed until the wash-water is no longer acid to litmus paper.

This method of coupling is used for couplings of nitrodiazonium compounds with many hydroxy compounds which couple easily, such as β-naphthol and β-diketones. It is especially used for making azo compounds to be used as pigments for paints and inks to avoid the formation of slight amounts of impurities which might be formed in alkaline solution. It is necessary to avoid an excess of nitrous acid in the solution of the diazonium salt, as it would form a nitroso compound with β-naphthol. The hydroxy coupling component is first dissolved and then reprecipitated in order that it may easily dissolve as the coupling proceeds, but this step may be omitted if the coupling component is in a physical form which easily dissolves in water. When the diazonium compound contains two nitro groups (ortho or para) it couples at a low pH, and buffers are not necessary. The common buffers for acid couplings are sodium acetate and sodium formate but others are used. The temperature for acid couplings is around 20 to 30°C. Higher temperatures are used for coupling components of low solubility.

A slightly acid coupling solution is also used for coupling any diazo compound with a coupling component which easily couples more than once, as in this way the coupling may be limited to one position.

Coupling Amino Compounds in Acid Solution.

Metanilic Acid → α-naphthylamine

The diazonium sulfonate is prepared from 173 lb. of aniline-*m*-sulfonic acid according to the method for naphthionic acid on page 135. There should be no excess of nitrous acid in the solution.

In 2,500 lb. of water at 75°C., 143 lb. of α-naphthylamine is dissolved as the hydrochloride with 126 lb. of 30 per cent hydrochloric acid. It is then cooled to 30°C. with about 1,200 lb. of ice. The resulting crystalline suspension is run into the diazonium sulfonate reserving about 2 per cent for the final balance. The coupling mixture, having a volume of about 8,000 lb. and a temperature of 25°C., becomes rather thick, and good agitation is required. In order to complete the coupling in a reasonable time, the mineral acidity is neutralized with 200 lb. of 30 per cent sodium hydroxide. The progress of the coupling is observed by spotting on filter paper and testing the clear rim of the spot for diazo and for coupling component. Enough α-naphthylamine is added to exactly balance the diazo and leave no excess of either component. The reaction should be complete within 1 hr.   This amino azo compound may be filtered as the free acid, or it may be converted to the sodium salt and salted out.   However, it is not often isolated but is diazotized and used in the production of disazo or trisazo colors.[1]   The method of diazotizing it was given on page 139.

Amino compounds are usually coupled in slightly acid solution, as the amino group has more effect on the reactivity in acid solution than in alkaline solution.   Since amino compounds are generally less reactive than hydroxy compounds, and since they are coupled at a lower pH, higher temperatures are used.

The yield obtained in the coupling reaction is very nearly 100 per cent when the components are very reactive and the azo compound is insoluble.   When the components are less active or when side reactions take place, the yield of isolated color may be around 80 per cent.

Azo dyes made commercially are subjected to numerous tests to determine that they are equal to the standards in use.   As with any colored compound, the freedom from colored and colorless impurities is best determined by means of the spectral-absorption curve of a solution of the dye.   Such a curve is easily, quickly, and accurately obtained by means of an automatic recording spectrograph, and it is a specific property of a colored compound, equal in diagnostic value to any other single property or test.   Individual batches of color are tested for dyeing and fastness properties, and a number of them are mixed together into a lot which may be as much as 5,000 or 10,000 lb.

Azo compounds used to color inks, paints, gasoline, and other solvents are often manufactured in a purity of about 99 per cent, but water-soluble dyes for textiles are not easily prepared of such purity, and they are generally standardized to a purity of 25 to 50 per cent with an inert material such as sodium chloride.   Many water-soluble azo dyes may be prepared in a pure condition by precipitating with acid, or by the method of Lubs,[2] which consists in repeated salting out of the color by sodium acetate and removal of the sodium acetate by extraction with alcohol.

Most soluble azo compounds are easily analyzed by titration with $TiCl_3$ solution,[3] and this method is used for a determination of the theoretical yield.   However, routine analysis of manufactured color is usually accomplished by a dye test or by a spectral-absorption determination against the standard color.

[1] Such as Colour Index, No. 289, metanilic acid → α-naphthylamine → 1-*p*-tolyl-naphthylamine-8-sulfonic acid.

[2] LUBS, *Ind. Eng. Chem.*, **11**, 456 (1919).

[3] KNECHT and HIBBERT "New Reduction Methods in Volumetric Analysis," Longmans, Green & Company, London, 1925.

CHAPTER IV

HALOGENATION

By P. H. Groggins and H. P. Newton

I. INTRODUCTION

Halogenation may be defined as the process whereby one or more halogen atoms are introduced into an organic compound.

The preparation of organic compounds containing fluorine, chlorine, bromine, and iodine can be accomplished by a variety of methods. The conditions and procedures differ, not only for each member of the halogen family but also with the type and structure of the compound undergoing treatment.

The chlorine derivatives, because of the greater economy in effecting their preparation, are by far the most important of the technical halogen compounds and for this reason are given primary consideration. The bromine derivative, however, sometimes has certain advantages because of the greater ease in effecting the replacement of this halogen in subsequent reactions or because it possesses certain pharmaceutical or dyeing properties.

As may be observed from the following examples, halogenations may involve reactions of (1) addition; (2) substitution, *i.e.*, of hydrogen; (3) replacement, *i.e.*, of groups, *e.g.*, the hydroxyl or sulfonic acid group.

$$HC{\equiv}CH + 2Br_2 \xrightarrow{\text{Alkali}} Br_2HC{-}CHBr_2 \qquad (I)$$

$$CH_3COOH + Cl_2 \xrightarrow{\text{I + P}} CH_2ClCOOH + HCl \qquad (II)$$

$$C_2H_5{\cdot}OH + HCl \xrightarrow{\text{FeCl}_3} C_2H_5Cl + H_2O \qquad (III)$$

From the preceding formulations, it becomes clear that each type of reaction may involve not only a specific halogenating agent but also a suitable catalyst. The catalysts, with the exception of carbon and the activating agent actinic light, are characterized by the fact that they are halogen carriers. Thus, iron, antimony, and phosphorus, which are able to exist in two valences as halogen compounds, are used to a large extent, for they are less stable at the higher valence and give up part of their chlorine during the process. In the presence of free chlorine, such compounds alternately add on and give up halogen to carry on the reaction. Iodine and bromine, which are capable of forming mixed halogens with chlorine, are also frequently employed as catalysts in chlorinating processes.

Chlorination.—A number of methods are available for organizing the material relating to halogenation processes, all of which are necessarily complex. Here, as in other chapters, the principal classification is based on the (halogenating) agents employed. The most important methods for preparing chlorine compounds are the following:

The Direct Action of Chlorine Gas.

$$H_2C{=}CH_2 + Cl_2 \xrightarrow{Br_2 \text{ or } Pb} ClH_2C{\cdot}CH_2Cl \qquad (a)$$

$$CH_4 + Cl_2 \xrightarrow{400 \text{ to } 500°C.} CH_3Cl + HCl \qquad (b)$$

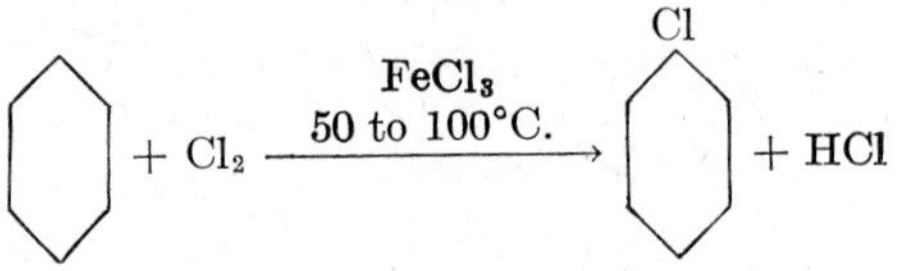

Cl
FeCl3
50 to 100°C.
+ Cl2
+ HCl

(c)

CH3
+ Cl2
Actinic rays
Vapor phase
CH2Cl
+ HCl

(d)

CH3
+ Cl2
PCl3
Liquid phase
CH2Cl
+ HCl

(e)

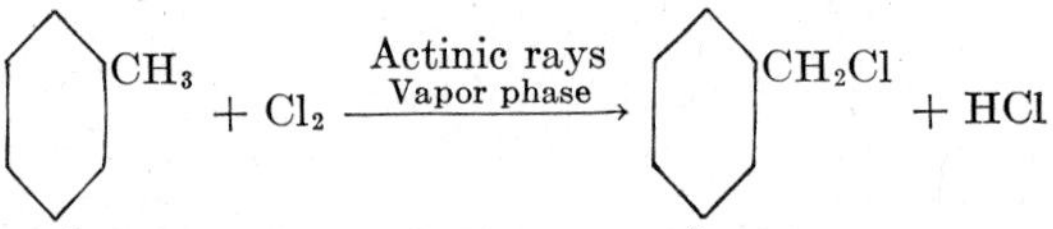

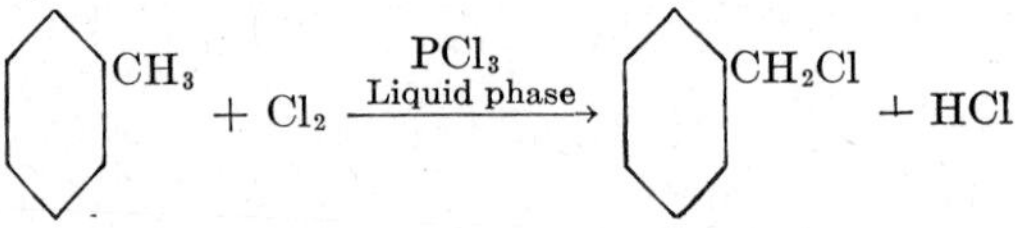

Hydrochloric Acid as the Chlorinating Agent.

a. Addition reaction, direct action:

$$HC{\equiv}CH + HCl \xrightarrow[NH_4Cl]{Cu_2Cl_2} H_2C{=}CHCl$$

b. Substitution reactions, indirect action:

$$2CH_4 + 2HCl + O_2 \xrightarrow[400 \text{ to } 500°C.]{\text{Oxidant}} 2CH_3Cl + 2H_2O$$

c. Replacement reactions:

$$C_2H_5{\cdot}OH + HCl \xrightarrow{FeCl_3} C_2H_5Cl + H_2O$$

O
NaO3S
3
NO2
+ 6HCl
NaClO3
Cl
3
O
NO2
+4NaCl + 3H2SO4
O
O

Sodium Hypochlorite as Chlorinating Agent.

OH
NaOCl
Alkaline Solution
Cl

(a)

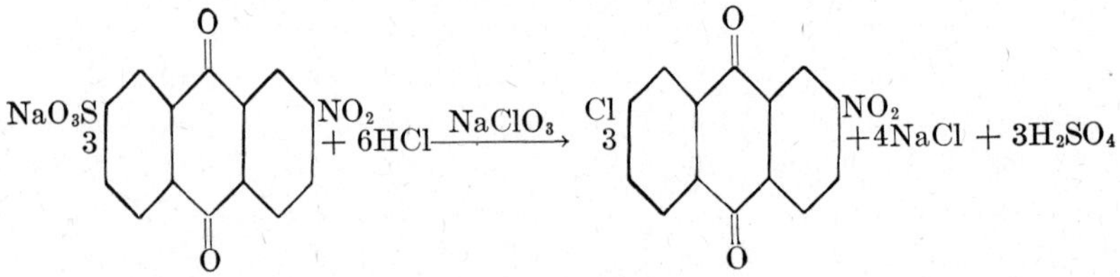

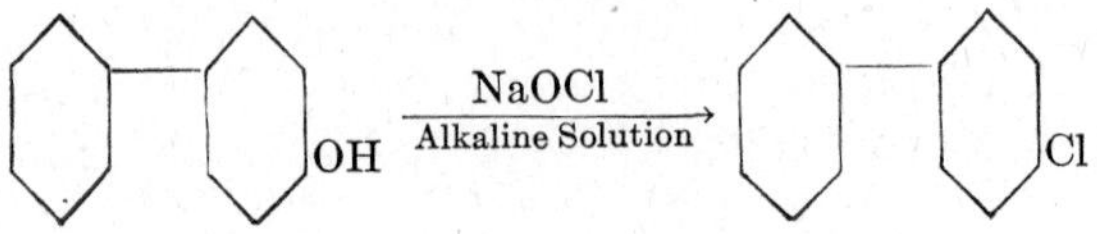

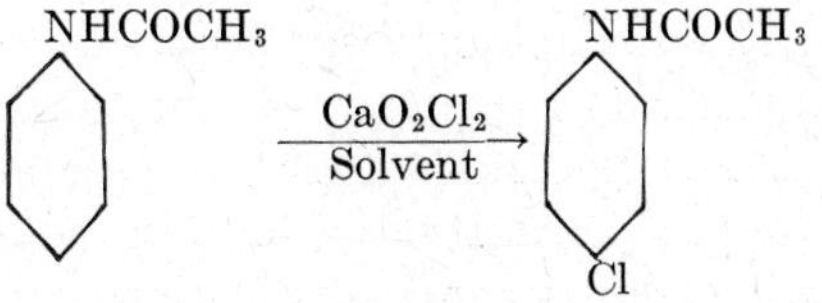

$$(b)$$

Chlorination with Phosgene $(COCl_2)$.

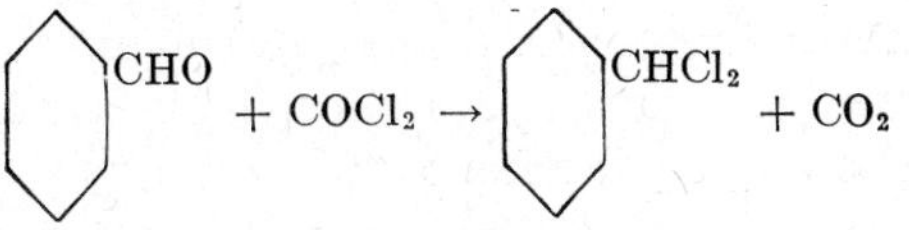

$$(a)$$

$$CH_3 \cdot COOH + COCl_2 \rightarrow CH_3 \cdot CO \cdot Cl + CO_2 + HCl \qquad (b)$$

Chlorination with Sulfuryl Chloride (SO_2Cl_2).

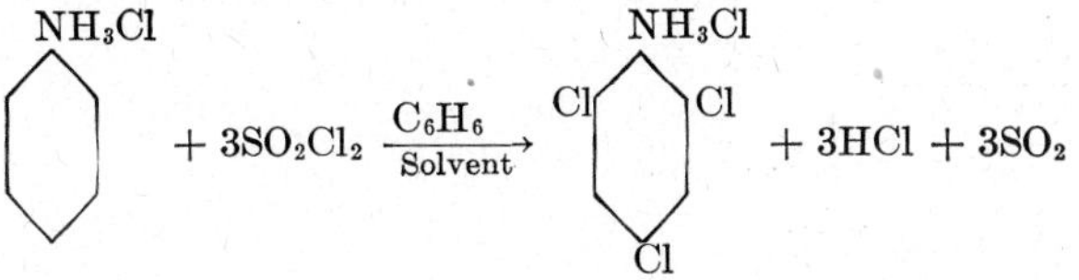

$$(a)$$

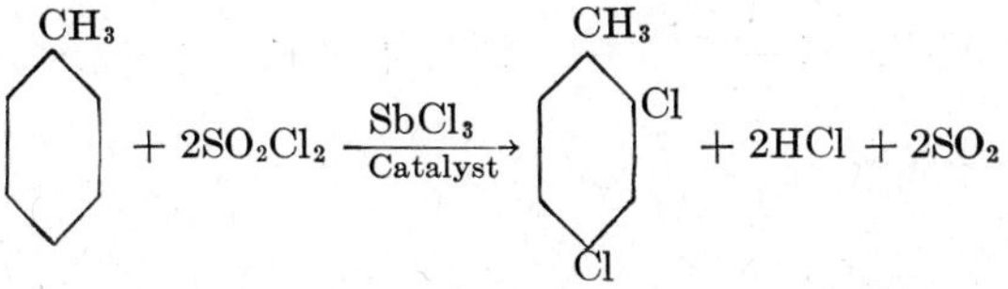

$$(b)$$

Action of Metal and Non-metal Halides.

Chlorination with Ferric and Phosphorus Chlorides:

$$3C_2H_5OH + FeCl_3 \xrightarrow{\;HCl\;} 3C_2H_5Cl + Fe(OH)_3 \qquad (a)$$
$$3R \cdot COOH + PCl_3 \rightarrow 3R \cdot COCl + H_3PO_3 \qquad (b)$$
$$3R \cdot COONa + PCl_5 \rightarrow 3R \cdot COCl + NaPO_3 + 2NaCl \qquad (c)$$

Preparation of Chlorine Derivatives by the Sandmeyer and Gattermann Reactions.

$$R \cdot N_2 \cdot Cl + Cu_2Cl_2 \xrightarrow{\;HCl\;} R \cdot Cl + N_2 + Cu_2Cl_2 \quad \text{(Sandmeyer)}$$
$$R \cdot N_2 \cdot Cl \xrightarrow{\;\frac{HCl}{Cu}\;} R \cdot Cl + N_2 \quad \text{(Gattermann)}$$

Electrochemical Preparation of Halogeno Compounds.

$$C_2H_6 + Cl_2 \xrightarrow[\text{discharge}]{\text{Silent electric}} C_2H_5Cl + HCl$$

Bromination.—In many instances, brominations may be carried out in a manner similar to that employed for the preparation of chlorine derivatives. Thus, bromine, bromides, bromates, and alkaline hypobromites may be employed instead of the corresponding chlorine compounds. The Sandmeyer and Gattermann reactions also may advantageously be used for the preparation of bromine compounds.

Reactions involving addition and substitution are common. Bromine dissolved in water is frequently employed, particularly in the bromination of phenols. Potassium bromide is generally added to aqueous bromine solutions to increase the concentration of soluble molecular halogen. Concentrated bromine solutions are thus made available, presumably because of the following equilibrium:

$$Br_2 + KBr \rightleftarrows KBr_3*$$

Bromine, hydrobromic acid, and alkali hypobromites, like the corresponding chlorine compounds, find employment in technical brominations.

   a. Addition reaction:

$$H_2C:CH_2 + Br_2 \rightarrow BrH_2C \cdot CH_2Br$$

   b. Replacement reaction:

$$C_2H_5 \cdot OH \xrightarrow[H_2SO_4]{KBr} C_2H_5Br + KHSO_4 + H_2O$$

   c. Substitution reaction:

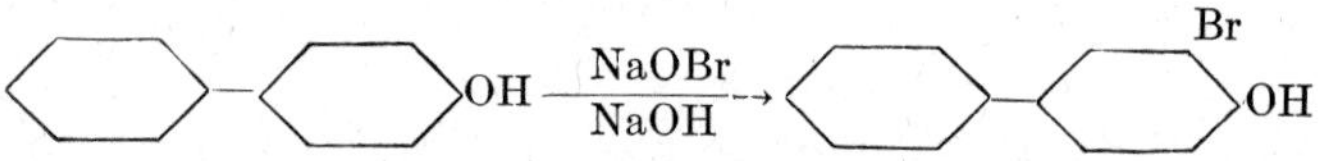

Iodination.—The methods employed in iodination differ somewhat from those for chlorination or bromination. The relatively weak C-I bond, which is indicated by the low heat of reaction, and which distinguishes iodine from other halogens, makes permanent, direct union of carbon to iodine by the replacement of hydrogen possible only in exceptional cases. Such iodinations are reversible in character, as, for instance, the iodination of acetic acid:

$$CH_3 \cdot COOH + 2I \rightleftarrows CH_2ICOOH + HI$$

* The quantity of iodine (or bromine) which dissolves in aqueous solution increases with increasing concentration of alkali halide. It must not, however, be assumed that compounds with higher iodine content are formed; for the polyiodides contain such a high percentage that they tend to behave somewhat similarly to the element itself. Substances that are chemically similar always tend to form mixtures, such as solid solutions or mixed crystals, or to increase the solubility of each other in a given solvent. In a concentrated solution of potassium iodide, quantities of iodine up to 8 or more atoms per molecule can be dissolved, and still higher iodides can be made by melting KI_3 with iodine. [EPHRAIM, "Inorganic Chemistry," p. 200, Gurney and Jackson (1926).]

and are governed largely by the conditions employed. The hydrogen iodide tends to effect deiodination of the halogenated compounds and, indeed, is sometimes thus employed. The removal of the hydrogen iodide by such means as oxidation or absorption in alkali is consequently essential for successful iodination. When nitric acid is employed as the oxidant, practically all the iodine enters the organic compound. In the ordinary direct halogenation in the absence of an oxidizing agent, half of the reacting halogen is converted to the hydrogen halide.

Catalysts are only infrequently employed in iodination, phosphorus being the principal accelerator. Iodine monochloride,[1] because of its

$$\underset{126.92}{\text{I}} + \underset{35.46}{\text{Cl}} \rightleftarrows \underset{162.38}{\text{I.Cl}}$$

activity under mild operating conditions is a useful catalyst for the iodination of amino compounds:

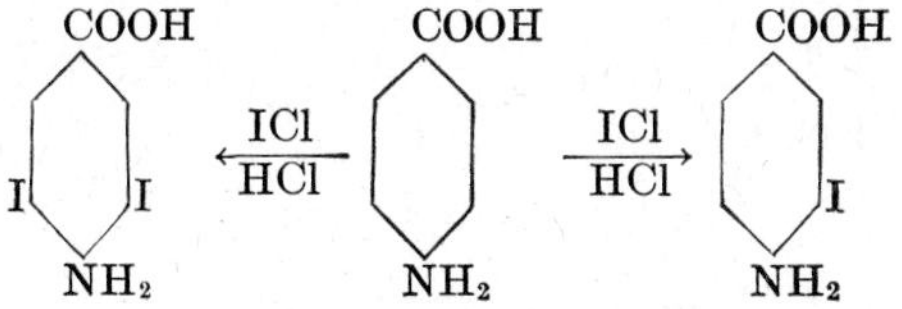

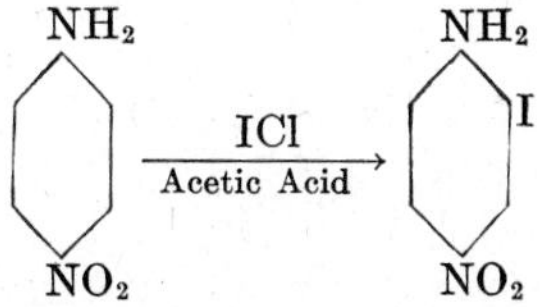

Hydriodic acid and alkali hypoiodites, like the corresponding chlorine and bromine compounds, find employment in iodinations:

$$H_2C:CH_2 + HI \rightarrow CH_2I\cdot CH_3 \qquad (a)$$

$$CH_3\cdot CO\cdot CH_3 + 3KOI \xrightarrow{\text{Alkali}} CH_3\cdot CO\cdot CI_3 + 3KOH \qquad (b1)$$

$$CH_3\cdot CO\cdot CI_3 + KOH \rightarrow CH_3\cdot COOK + CHI_3 \qquad (b2)$$

Fluorination.—Fluorine acts directly upon hydrocarbons to produce fluorides, either by substitution or by addition, but the element fluorine is troublesome to handle. The bonds holding the atoms in the fluorine molecule are stronger than in the other halogens, but once the reaction is initiated and fluorine atoms are available, they combine more readily with hydrogen and hydrocarbons than do the halogens of higher molecular weight. Furthermore, the new bonds which are formed are so strong and the heat liberated is so great that precautions must be taken to moderate the reaction so as to keep it under control. For this reason, fluorides are usually prepared by indirect methods.

[1] Prepared by passing dry chlorine gas over iodine until the increase in weight approaches the theoretical.

1. Just as chlorine will displace bromine in hydrocarbon combinations, so fluorine will displace chlorine. The reaction is as follows:

$$RCl_n + \frac{n}{2}F_2 \rightarrow RF_n + \frac{n}{2}Cl_2$$

in which R represents the hydrocarbon radical. In the case of polychlorides, fluorine displaces the chlorine progressively, the order of displacement depending upon the structure of the polychloride. For example, trichloro-trifluorobenzene and tetrachloro-difluorobenzene have been prepared by the interaction of fluorine with hexachlorobenzene.

2. A convenient method of preparation is the reaction between sodium or potassium fluoride and alkyl hydrogen sulfate:

$$R \cdot H \cdot SO_4 + NaF \rightarrow RF + NaHSO_4$$

Methyl and ethyl fluorides may be prepared in this manner.

3. Alkyl chlorides may be made to react with silver fluoride to form the hydrocarbon fluorides:

$$RCl_n + nAgF \rightarrow RF_n + nAgCl$$

Methyl fluoride, methylene fluoride, and fluoroform may be prepared in this manner.

4. The hydrochlorides of amines may be made to react with sodium fluoride to form the organic fluorides with the elimination of ammonia:

$$R \cdot NH_2 \cdot HCl + NaF \rightarrow RF + NH_3 + NaCl$$

In this manner, fluoronaphthalene may be prepared from naphthylamine.

5. The polychlorinated alkanes will react with hydrogen fluoride in the presence of antimony pentachloride.

$$CCl_4 + 2HF \rightarrow CCl_2F_2 + 2HCl$$
$$C_2H_2Cl_4 + 2HF \rightarrow C_2H_2Cl_2F_2 + 2HCl$$
$$CCl_3F + HF \rightarrow CCl_2F_2 + HCl$$

Other chlorinated and brominated acyclic compounds such as hexachloroethane, trichloroethylene, ethylene dibromide, tetrabromobutane, bromoform, etc., can be used for the preparation of the corresponding fluorine derivatives.

6. Diazo compounds react with hydrogen fluoride and borontrifluoride to form organic fluorides with the liberation of nitrogen:

$$R \cdot N : N \cdot Cl + HF \rightarrow RF + N_2 + HCl$$

3, 4-Dichlorofluorobenzene has been prepared by diazotizing the sulfate of 3, 4-dichloroaniline and digesting the diazonium sulfate with hydrofluoric acid.

7. Tetraalkylammonium fluorides may be heated to produce alkyl fluorides and tertiary amines:

$$R_4 \cdot N \cdot F \cdot \xrightarrow{\text{heat}} RF + N \cdot R_3$$

8. Acetyl fluoride may be prepared by reacting acetic acid with phosphorus trifluoride:

$$3CH_3 \cdot COOH + 2PF_3 \rightarrow 3CH_3 \cdot COF + P_2O_3 + 3HF$$

9. Acetyl fluoride will react with benzaldehyde to form triphenyl fluoromethane:

$$3C_6H_5 \cdot CHO + CH_3 \cdot COF \rightarrow C \cdot (C_6H_5)_3F + C_2H_4(COOH)_2$$

Hydrogen fluoride does not possess the capacity to form addition compounds with unsaturated hydrocarbons, a characteristic that becomes more pronounced with increased molecular weight and diminished heat of formation of the hydrogen halide. This is to be expected, since the high dielectric constant indicates that liquid hydrogen fluoride consists of long chains of molecules in which the bond between H and F in $(HF)x$ is very strong. The formation of hydrogen fluoride salts of amines, which contain 4 molecules of HF attached to the base, *e.g.*, $R \cdot NH_2(HF)_4$, is evidence of such a high state of association.[1] Furthermore, vapor-pressure measurements and vapor-density determinations[2] can be explained only on the basis of an equilibrium

$$6HF \rightleftarrows (HF)_6$$

II. THE THEORETICAL BASIS OF HALOGENATION REACTIONS

By A. Sherman[3] and R. H. Ewell[4]

General Discussion.[5]—The reactivities of the halogens with hydrogen, aliphatic halides, and hydrocarbons may best be understood by considering the variation in bond strengths for the different halogen bonds. These energies, together with some additional relevant bond values, have been calculated from the data in Bichowsky and Rossini[6] and are given in Table I.

[1] Berliner and Hann, *J. Phys. Chem.*, **32**, 1142 (1928).

[2] Yost and Hatcher, *J. Chem. Ed.*, **10**, 330 (1933).

[3] A. Sherman, University of Cincinnati.

[4] R. H. Ewell, Purdue University.

[5] The editor is also greatly indebted to F. D. Rossini, National Bureau of Standards, for valuable suggestions as to the scope and content of this section of the chapter.

[6] Bichowsky and Rossini, "Thermochemistry of Chemical Substances," Reinhold Publishing Corporation, New York, 1936. It is assumed that the best value for the heat of sublimation of carbon is probably 125 kg. cal. See Rossini, *Ind. Eng. Chem.*, **29**, 1424 (1936); and Herzberg, *Chem. Rev.*, **20**, 145 (1937).

TABLE I.—NET BOND ENERGIES AT 18°C. IN KG. CAL.

Type of bond	F	Cl	Br	I
X—X	63.5	57.8	46.1	36.3
H—X	147.6	102.9	87.4	71.6
C—X	103.8	66.6	53.0	38.7

C—C	56.2	I—Br	42.9
C=C	95.8	I—Cl	51.0
C≡C	124.5	Br—Cl	52.7
C—H	87.7	Cl—F	86.4
H—H	103.8		

The activation energy of a reaction is found experimentally from the Arrhenius equation

$$dlnk/dT = A/RT^2$$

where k is the specific reaction rate constant, *i.e.*, the rate of the reaction when the concentration of reactants is unity, and A is the activation energy. A is a complex function of the energies of the bonds *broken* and *formed* in the reaction.[1] In general, it is to be expected that for similar reactions the activation energy will be greater the stronger the bonds broken, and less the stronger the bonds formed in the reaction, so that qualitatively the non-catalytic reactions of fluorine derivatives would be expected to occur at higher temperatures and involve a higher activation energy than the corresponding chlorine, bromine, or iodine compounds. Iodine derivatives, for example, should react under comparatively mild conditions. These expectations are confirmed by experiment.

Reactions of the Halogens with Hydrogen.—Let us first consider the reactions of the halogens with hydrogen. Two possible mechanisms suggest themselves:

I. $H_2 + X_2 \rightarrow 2HX$

II. $\begin{cases} X_2 \rightleftharpoons 2X & (1) \\ X + H_2 \rightarrow HX + H & (2) \\ H + X_2 \rightarrow HX + X & (3) \end{cases}$

The first mechanism is simply a bimolecular collision between the two molecules concerned, and the second a chain reaction initiated by the thermal dissociation of halogen molecules. The apparent activation energy for the second mechanism will be approximately equal to the

[1] The activation energy is determined by the energy of the activated complex. In the complex the new bonds can be thought of as partially formed and the old ones as partially broken.

activation energy of reaction (2), plus one-half the heat of dissociation of the halogen molecule into atoms.[1]

Eyring[2] has calculated activation energies for the bimolecular reaction, and Morris and Pease[3] have evaluated these energies for reaction (2) from the available experimental data. The results, together with the over-all activation energy for the chain mechanism, are given in Table II. The experimental value for the bimolecular reaction between H_2 and I_2 is also given.

TABLE II.—ACTIVATION ENERGIES IN KG. CAL. FOR THE REACTION $H_2 + X_2 \rightarrow 2HX$ IN THE GAS PHASE

		F	Cl	Br	I	
I	A_{bi}	79	75	62	40*	
II $\begin{cases} \\ \\ \end{cases}$	$\frac{1}{2}X_2 \rightarrow X \qquad \Delta H_0$	31.3	28.5	22.6	17.7	(1)
	$X + H_2 \rightarrow HX + H$	0	6.0	17.7	33	(2)
	$A_{ch} = A_{(2)} + \Delta H_0$	31.3	34.5	40.3	50.7	(3) ,

* BODENSTEIN, *Z. physik. Chem.*, **13**, 56 (1894); **22**, 1 (1897); **29**, 295 (1898).

In the preceding table A_{bi} is the calculated activation energy for bimolecular mechanism (I), $A_{(2)}$ is the activation energy for reaction (2) as determined by Morris and Pease and A_{ch} is the over-all activation energy for the chain mechanism (vide supra).

From the values given in Table I it is seen that reaction (3) is in all cases exothermic, since one HX bond is stronger than one X-X bond. The energy of the H-H bond is 103.8 kg. cal. at 18°C. It is also seen that reaction (2) is 43.8 kg. cal. exothermic for F, 0.9 kg. cal. endothermic for Cl, 16.4 kg. cal. endothermic for Br, and 32.2 kg. cal. endothermic for I. Hence it is evident that the values given by Morris and Pease[4] are in accord with the general qualitative rule that for *atomic* reactions the activation energy is nearly zero in the exothermic direction, and approximately equal to the endothermicity in the endothermic direction.

The Activation Energy for the Reactions of the Halogens with Hydrogen.—A reaction will occur by that mechanism which involves the lowest over-all activation energy, since the rate at which it would proceed by another mechanism having an appreciably higher activation energy would be negligible in comparison. The values given in Table II, therefore, lead us to expect that, whereas F_2, Cl_2, and Br_2 will react with H_2 via an atomic chain, I_2 will do so via a molecular mechanism. The experimental results are in agreement with these conclusions.

[1] VAN VLECK and SHERMAN, *Rev. Modern Phys.*, **1**, 167, 210 (1935).

[2] EYRING, *J. Am. Chem. Soc.*, **53**, 2537 (1931).

[3] MORRIS and PEASE, *J. Chem. Phys.*, **3**, 796 (1935).

[4] *Loc. cit.*

The homogeneous combination of H_2 and F_2 would not be expected to proceed at room temperatures or below since an activation energy of 31.3 cal. corresponds to a conveniently measurable rate around 100 to 200°C. Eyring and Kassel[1] experimentally confirmed the non-reactivity of the mixture of H_2 and F_2 at ordinary temperatures. The reaction is quite sensitive to impurities and is very apt to explode. In view of the large exothermic nature of the reaction $F + H_2 \rightarrow HF + H$, the most reasonable explanation is that the 43.8 kg. cal. of energy cannot be dissipated fast enough and, therefore, a thermal explosion results.

The thermal reaction of H_2 and Cl_2 has been studied by a number of authors at about 200°C., which is quite reasonable for an activation energy of 34.5 kg. cal. Nernst[2] suggested the atomic chain given above. The chains may be initiated by light,[3] H atoms,[4] and Na or K vapor.[5] In the case of Na or K vapor, chlorine atoms are produced by the reaction

$$Na + Cl_2 \rightarrow NaCl + Cl$$

The thermal formation of HBr from H_2 and Br_2 has been studied by Bodenstein and Lind[6] in the temperature range 230 to 300°C. Christiansen, Herzfeld, and Polanyi[7] explained the experimental results in terms of the chain mechanism given above, the reverse of reaction (2) and the chain-breaking step $Br + Br \rightarrow Br_2$ also being considered.

The thermal reaction between H_2 and I_2 is one of the best known bimolecular reactions and was studied extensively by Bodenstein[8] in the temperature region 200 to 500°C.

Reactions of Halogens with Hydrocarbons.—One might expect analogous reactions between the hydrocarbons and the halogens. The two corresponding mechanisms would be:

I. $CH_4 + X_2 \rightarrow CH_3X + HX$

$$\text{II.} \quad \begin{cases} X_2 \rightarrow 2X & (4) \\ X + CH_4 \rightarrow CH_3X + H & (5) \\ H + X_2 \rightarrow HX + X & (6) \end{cases}$$

[1] EYRING and KASSEL, *J. Am. Chem. Soc.*, **55**, 2796 (1933).

[2] NERNST, *Z. Elektrochem.*, **24**, 335 (1918).

[3] COEHN and JUNG, *Z. physik. Chem.*, **110**, 705 (1924); COEHN and HEYMER, *Naturwissenschaften*, **14**, 299 (1926); ALLMAND and BEESLEY, *J. Chem. Soc.*, 2693, 2709 (1930); KORNFELD and MÜLLER, *Z. physik. Chem.*, **117**, 242 (1925); BODENSTEIN and UNGER, *ibid*, **11B**, 253 (1930).

[4] MARSHALL, *J. Phys. Chem.*, **29**, 842 (1925).

[5] BOGDANDY and POLANYI, *Z. Elektrochem.*, **33**, 554 (1927).

[6] BODENSTEIN and LIND, *Z. physik. Chem.*, **57**, 168 (1906).

[7] CHRISTIANSEN, K. *Danske Videnskab. Selskab.*, *Math.-fys. Medd.*, **1**, 14 (1919); HERZFELD, *Z. Elektrochem.*, **25**, 301 (1919); *Ann. Physik*, **59**, 635 (1919); POLANYI, *Z. Elektrochem.*, **26**, 50 (1920).

[8] *Ibid.*

Just as in the previous case, the over-all activation energy for the chain mechanism A_{ch} is equal to the activation energy for reaction (5) $[A_{(5)}]$ plus one-half of the energy of dissociation of the halogen molecule into atoms. The corresponding bimolecular activation energies have not as yet been calculated.

If we assume that the heat of reaction (5) is given approximately by the difference between the energy of one C-X and one C-H bond, then it follows from the values in Table I that (5) will be 16.1 kg. cal. exothermic for F, 21.1 kg. cal. endothermic for Cl, 34.7 kg. cal. endothermic for Br, and 49.0 kg. cal. endothermic for I. The reaction between CH_4 and Br_2, and CH_4 and I_2, would definitely not be expected to occur via the postulated chain mechanism, whereas the reaction between CH_4 and Cl_2 would hardly be expected to involve an intermediate atomic reaction endothermic to the extent of 21.1 kg. cal.

Another alternative reaction scheme to that of II above is the following:

$$\text{III.} \begin{cases} X_2 \rightleftharpoons 2X & (7) \\ X + CH_4 \rightarrow CH_3 + HX & (8) \\ CH_3 + X_2 \rightarrow CH_3X + X & (9) \end{cases}$$

If we assume the heat of reaction (8) is given by the difference between the energy of a H-X and a C-H bond, the values in Table I show that (8) will be 59.9 kg. cal. exothermic for F, 15.2 kg. cal. exothermic for Cl, 0.3 kg. cal. endothermic for Br, and 16.1 kg. cal. endothermic for I.

The over-all activation energy for scheme III is

$$A_{ch} = \frac{1}{2}\Delta H_{(7)} + A_{(8)}$$

If we make the additional assumption that $A_{(8)}$ is zero when reaction (8) is exothermic, it follows that $A_{ch} = 31.8$ for F, 28.9 for Cl, 23.4 for Br, and 34.3 for I.

The experimental data for these homogeneous, non-catalytic, gas-phase reactions are relatively meager. Pease and Walz[1] studied the gas-phase reaction between CH_4 and Cl_2 and concluded that the reaction must involve a chain mechanism, since at 250°C., a mixture of $2CH_4$ with 1 Cl_2 reacted ten times more slowly in the presence of 0.25 per cent oxygen. This is, of course, strong evidence for chains.

Addition of Halogen and Halogen Hydrides.—Activation energies for the addition of the halogens to ethylene have been calculated by Sherman and Sun.[2] Although they did not use the same bond energies as given in Table I, the relative values for Cl_2, Br_2, and I_2 are probably

---

[1] Pease and Walz, *J. Am. Chem. Soc.*, **53**, 3728 (1931).

[2] Sherman and Sun, *J. Am. Chem. Soc.*, **56**, 1096 (1934).

significant. The differences are not very great, however, the calculated values being 25.2, 24.4, and 22.4 kg. cal., respectively. One might have expected the activation energy for Cl_2 to be much larger than for Br_2, and this, in turn, much larger than that for I_2, since the heats of dissociation of Cl_2, Br_2, and I_2 are 57.8, 46.1, and 36.3 kg. cal. respectively. But the activation energy is a function of the bonds formed as well as those broken (vide supra), and if one compares the differences between C-X and X-X it is found that they do not vary greatly, namely, 8.8, 6.9, and 2.4 kg. cal. for Cl, Br, and I, respectively.

Stewart and Edlung[1] found the homogeneous gas-phase addition of Br_2 to C_2H_4 to occur rapidly at 200°C.

Considering, now, the addition of the hydrogen halides to ethylene, Sherman, Quimby, and Sutherland[2] calculated activation energies for the addition of HX to the corresponding vinyl compounds (CH_2=CHX). If it be assumed that the same relative values hold for CH_2=CH_2, it enables us to understand why HI and HBr add to ethylene readily but HCl requires a catalyst, since the corresponding calculated activation energies to the vinyl halide are 27.7, 29.0, and 39.3 kg. cal. respectively.

It is interesting to note that Sherman, Quimby, and Sutherland (loc. cit.) calculate, in agreement with experiment; that whereas $C_2H_4I_2$ and $C_2H_4Br_2$ will decompose to give C_2H_4 and the corresponding halogen, $C_2H_4Cl_2$ will give CH_2=CHCl and HCl. This difference in behavior is due to the fact that the energy of one H-Cl bond is much stronger than one C-H bond, whereas H-Br and H-I bonds are not.

Chlorine tends to displace bromine, and bromine, in turn, iodine, from organic molecules. The explanation is probably to be sought in

TABLE III.—HEATS OF REACTIONS INVOLVING THE HALOGENS (18°C.)
(All Atoms or Molecules in the Gaseous State)

$I + Cl_2 \rightarrow ICl + Cl - 6.8$ kg. cal.	$CH_4 + I_2 \rightarrow CH_3I + HI - 13.7$ kg. cal.
$I + Br_2 \rightarrow IBr + Br - 3.2$ kg. cal.	$C_2H_4 + Cl_2 \rightarrow C_2H_4Cl_2 + 40.3$ kg. cal.
$Br + Cl_2 \rightarrow BrCl + Cl - 5.1$ kg. cal.	$C_2H_4 + Br_2 \rightarrow C_2H_4Br_2 + 29.3$ kg. cal.
$Br + I_2 \rightarrow IBr + I + 6.6$ kg. cal.	$C_2H_4 + I_2 \rightarrow C_2H_4I_2 + 9.9$ kg. cal.
$Cl + Br_2 \rightarrow BrCl + Br + 6.6$ kg. cal.	$C_2H_4 + HCl \rightarrow C_2H_5Cl + 14.6$ kg. cal.
$Cl + I_2 \rightarrow ICl + I + 14.8$ kg. cal.	$C_2H_4 + HBr \rightarrow C_2H_5Br + 17.9$ kg. cal.
$Cl + F_2 \rightarrow ClF + F + 22.9$ kg. cal.	$C_2H_4 + HI \rightarrow C_2H_5I + 17.9$ kg. cal.
$F + Cl_2 \rightarrow ClF + Cl + 28.6$ kg. cal.	$\frac{1}{2}Cl_2 + C_2H_5Br \rightarrow C_2H_5Cl + \frac{1}{2}Br_2 +$ 6.3 kg. cal.
$CH_4 + Cl_2 \rightarrow CH_3Cl + HCl + 23.9$ kg. cal.	$\frac{1}{2}Cl_2 + C_2H_5I \rightarrow C_2H_5Cl + \frac{1}{2}I_2 +$ 17.2 kg. cal.
$CH_4 + Br_2 \rightarrow CH_3Br + HBr + 6.6$ kg. cal.	$\frac{1}{2}Br_2 + C_2H_5I \rightarrow C_2H_5Br + \frac{1}{2}I_2 +$ 10.9 kg. cal.

[1] STEWART and EDLUNG, J. Am. Chem. Soc., 45, 1014 (1923).

[2] SHERMAN, QUIMBY, and SUTHERLAND, J. Chem. Phys., 4, 732 (1936).

terms of equilibriums rather than rates, since the calculated activation energies do not differ appreciably.[1] These reactions are exothermic and insofar as the entropy change can be neglected are, therefore, accompanied by a decrease of free energy.

The heats of some reactions involving the halogens are given in Table III. These values have been computed from the data in Bichowsky and Rossini's book (*loc. cit.*). In all cases the heats calculated from the bond energies given in Table I are in approximate agreement with the values given in Table III.

III. SURVEY OF HALOGENATIONS

CHLORINATION

Chlorination of Paraffins.—It is difficult to overestimate the economic importance of the compounds obtained by the halogenation of the saturated and unsaturated lower paraffins.[2] To a considerable extent these halogeno derivatives are used per se as cleaning fluids ($CHCl\!=\!CCl_2$); refrigerants (CCl_2F_2); plant stimulants ($CH_2Cl\cdot CH_2Cl$); anesthetics ($CHCl_3$); general solvents (CCl_4) etc. By and large, however, the saturated and unsaturated halogeno paraffins are used as the raw materials for an exceedingly large number of syntheses, *e.g.*, the preparation of alcohols, alkylene oxides, ethers, amines, hydrocarbons, alkaryl compounds, etc. Because the paraffinic hydrocarbons and chlorine are widely available and cheap, this segment of chemical activity is destined to expand.

1. Halogenation with Chlorine Gas

Chlorination Rules, Paraffins.—On the basis of extensive research, Hass and coworkers[3] have postulated the following rules regarding the chlorination of paraffins. Such operations can be carried out in the apparatus shown diagrammatically in Figs. 13 and 22.

CHLORINATION RULES

1. Carbon skeleton rearrangements do not occur during either photochemical or thermal chlorinations if pyrolysis temperatures are avoided; every possible monochloride derivable without such rearrangement is always formed. As far as is known this generalization extends also to

---

[1] SHERMAN, COVET, and MAGEE (forthcoming publication).

[2] In 1936 the total United States production of *all* aromatic compounds including dyestuffs was approximately 336,000,000 lb.; whereas the output of halogenated paraffins was about 450,000,000 lb.

[3] HASS and MARSHALL, *Ind. Eng. Chem.*, **23**, 352 (1931); HASS, McBEF, and WEBER, *Ind. Eng. Chem.*, **27**, 1190 (1935); **28**, 333 (1936). HASS and WEBER, *Ind. Eng. Chem., Anal. Ed.*, **7**, 231 (1935); HASS, McBEE, and HATCH, *Ind. Eng. Chem.*, **29**, 1335 (1937).

the polychlorides.   The boiling-point data for the lower paraffin monochlorides are given in Table IV.

TABLE IV.—BOILING-POINT DATA, CHLOROALKANES*

Compound	B.p. or range, °C.	B.p. of corresponding alcohol, °C.
2-Chloropropane	34.8	82.26
1-Chloropropane	46.60	97.18
2-Chloroisobutane	51.0	82.86
2-Chlorobutane	68.25	99.53
1-Chloroisobutane	68.85	107.89
1-Chlorobutane	78.50	117.71
1-Chloro-2, 2-dimethylpropane	84.4	114.0
2-Chloro-2-methylbutane	85.7	101.8
2-Chloro-3-methylbutane	92.9–93.0*	110.0–111.5
3-Chloropentane	97.1–97.4	115.40
2-Chloropentane	96.6–96.8	119.28
1-Chloro-2-methylbutane	99.9	128.0
1-Chloro-3-methylbutane	98.8	132.00
1-Chloropentane	108.35	138.00

* Corrected to 760 mm.; value in literature is 91.8 to 91.9°C. at 736 mm.

2. The hydrogen atoms are always substituted at rates which are in
the order primary < secondary < tertiary.   At 300°C. with reaction
in vapor phase these relative rates are 1.00:3.25:4.43.   The data in
Table V present the evidence for this rule, the experimental results serving
as a basis for the calculation of the empirical constants noted above.   The
method of computation will readily be comprehended by using a specific
example, in this case isopentane:

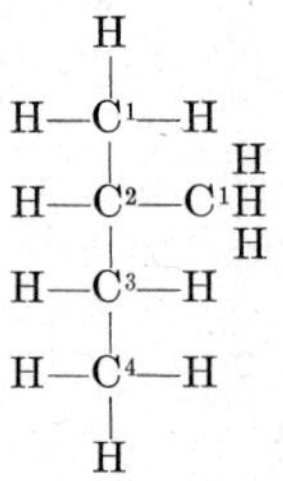

$$6 \times 1.00 = 6.00; \quad \frac{6.00 \times 100}{19.93} = 30.1\%$$

1-Chloro-2-methylbutane

$$1 \times 4.43 = 4.43; \quad \frac{4.43 \times 100}{19.93} = 22.2\%$$

2-Chloro-2-methylbutane

$$2 \times 3.25 = 6.50; \quad \frac{6.50 \times 100}{19.93} = 32.6\%$$

3-Chloro-2-methylbutane

$$3 \times 1.00 = \frac{3.00}{19.93}; \quad \frac{3.00 \times 100}{19.93} = 15.1\%$$

4-Chloro-2-methylbutane

There are six hydrogen atoms attached to carbon atoms in the positions
numbered 1 in the formula.   These are primary hydrogen atoms, and
their relative reaction rate is arbitrarily taken as 1.00.   The product
of the number of hydrogen atoms in this position multiplied by the rela-

tive reaction rate gives the chance of the chlorine substituting in this position to yield 1-chloro-2-methylbutane. The sum of all such products for isopentane under these conditions is 19.93, so 6 × 100/19.93 gives the percentage of 1-chloro-2-methylbutane in the monochlorides. A reversal of this calculation enables us to obtain the relative reaction rates from the composition of the monochloride mixtures. It is understood in applying the rule that conditions must be selected so that pyrolysis is substantially eliminated, and only a very small amount of monochloride is carried to a higher state of chlorination.

TABLE V.—CHLORINATION OF PARAFFINS, OBSERVED AND CALCULATED ISOMETRIC RATIOS AT 300°C.

Hydrocarbon	Isomeric Monochloride, %							
	-1-Chloro		-2-Chloro		-3-Chloro		-4-Chloro	
	Found	Calcd.	Found	Calcd.	Found	Calcd.	Found	Calcd.
Propane................	48	48	52	52				
2-Methylpropane........	67	67	33	33				
Butane................, ...	32	32	68	68				
2-Methylbutane.........	33.5	30	22	22	28	33	16.5	15
n-Pentane..............	23.8	23.5	48.8	51	27.4	25.5		

3. At increasing temperatures there is increasingly close approach to relative rates of 1:1:1 in both liquid and vapor phase.

Evidence for this generalization is given in Fig. 1, where the relative rates of secondary and tertiary hydrogen atoms are shown to vary with temperature in both vapor and liquid phases. The relative substitution rate of a primary hydrogen atom is taken as 1.

By the use of these graphs one can find the relative reaction rates which may be used as shown previously to obtain the isomeric ratios. With this information available it is easy to estimate from the structural formula of any paraffin hydrocarbon the relative proportions of the various isomeric monochlorides which can be obtained by chlorination under any of the conditions covered by the graph.

Certain precautions must be observed in applying these curves. The different monochlorides may chlorinate to dichlorides, trichlorides, etc., at different rates. This would change their ratios in the monochloride fraction so that results are most accurate when not more than a small proportion of monochloride is converted to dichloride. This is the condition always used in commercial operations for obtaining monochlorides, for reasons of economy. At low temperatures, where substantially no olefin formation occurs, results are not complicated by selective pyrolysis, but, when operating at temperatures above 300°C., one can easily get the impression that a non-selective chlorination is taking place, whereas actually the tertiary and/or secondary chlorides are being preferentially decomposed. When pyrolysis becomes appreciable, (*a*) the organic chlorine fails to balance the chlorine present as hydrochloric acid; (*b*) olefins appear in the recovered hydrocarbon; and (*c*) especially if recycling is used, chloroolefins appear in the organic chloride fractions.

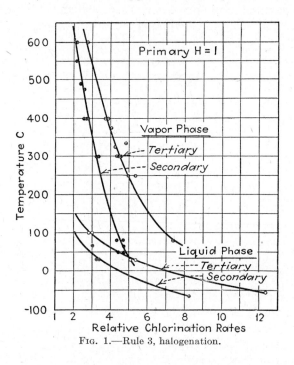

Fig. 1.—Rule 3, halogenation.

4. Liquid-phase chlorination gives relative rates of primary, secondary, and tertiary substitution which are obtainable only at much higher temperature in vapor phase. This is obvious from an inspection of Fig. 1.

A given temperature change produces a much greater difference in relative reaction rates of primary, secondary, and tertiary hydrogens when one is operating in liquid phase than when the chlorination takes place in gaseous phase. This means that the isomeric ratios are much more readily controllable in liquid than in vapor phase. Maximum yields of either primary isomers (at high temperatures) or secondary or tertiary isomers (at low temperatures) can be obtained by operating with the reagents in liquid form. In case the critical temperature of the hydrocarbon is inconveniently low, the chlorination may be carried out using carbon tetrachloride as a solvent.

5. The presence or absence of the following factors does not affect appreciably the relative rates of primary, secondary, and tertiary substitution: (*a*) moisture; (*b*) carbon surfaces; and (*c*) light.

6. Excessive temperatures and/or reaction times result in appreciable pyrolysis of the chlorides in the order primary < secondary < tertiary. This has already been commented on in connection with rule 3 in so far as excessive temperatures are concerned, but it may be added that the extent of the pyrolysis is more than would be predicted from data obtained by passing the pure chlorides through a hot reactor in the absence of chlorine. This result would be expected on the basis of free radical formation, since the radicals may decompose as follows:

$$C_nH_{2n+1} \rightarrow C_nH_{2n} + H$$

The free hydrogen atoms would continue the chlorination chain as follows:

$$H + Cl_2 \rightarrow HCl + Cl$$

Excessive polychloride formation is presumably caused by the following type reactions:

$$C_5H_{11}Cl \quad \rightarrow C_5H_{10} + HCl$$
$$C_5H_{10} + Cl_2 \rightarrow C_5H_{10}Cl_2, \text{ etc.}$$

7. If a molar excess of hydrocarbon is used and the chlorination conditions are maintained constant, the yield of monochlorides *vs.* polychlorides may be obtained from the equation:

$$X = KY$$

where X = weight ratio of monochlorides over polychlorides.

Y = ratio of moles of hydrocarbon over moles of chlorine.

K = a constant peculiar to the hydrocarbon and the conditions. As evidence, Fig. 2 is presented. In applying this graph, conditions are chosen so that all the chlorine reacts.

The practical import of rule 7 is that the yield of overchlorinated material may be suppressed to any desired degree if only a small percentage of the material to be chlorinated is allowed to react at each pass through the chlorinator. This applies to any stage of chlorination. An economic balance must be struck between the advantages of the higher yields of monochlorides which are caused by the lower chlorine concentrations in the reacting hydrocarbon, and the increased cost of additional recycling. When chlorination is achieved thermally, recycling involves the expense of heating and cooling large quantities of materials. In the case of the further thermal chlorination of the homologous alkyl chlorides, too many passes through the hot reactor may increase the amount of pyrolysis unduly, so that too much recycling is undesirable from that standpoint also.

One of the advantages of liquid-phase thermal chlorination is that, because of the lower temperatures involved, the pyrolysis is almost completely eliminated and the amount of heat put into the reacting materials and removed from the reaction products is lessened.

8. Dichlorination proceeds by two mechanisms: (*a*) loss of hydrogen chloride followed by addition of chlorine to the resulting olefin and (*b*) progressive substitution. Slow, thermal chlorination favors mechanism 1, whereas with rapid, liquid-phase or vapor-phase, single-pass thermal

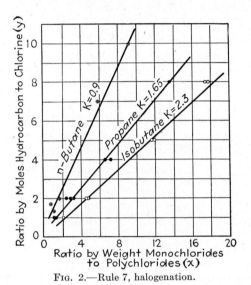

Fig. 2.—Rule 7, halogenation.

reaction, or low-temperature photo-chemical conditions, mechanism 1 is substantially eliminated.

In view of the large amount of work which has been performed on the addition of chlorine to olefin bonds, it is evident that conditions conducive to the formation of unsaturates must result in at least some union of chlorine with these products, unless the temperature is too high. Thus, a prolonged vapor-phase thermal chlorination of *n*-pentane at 100°C. in the absence of light yields a much higher ratio of polychlorides to monochlorides than if the reaction is carried out rapidly at the same temperature in the presence of light. This is due to the pyrolysis of the secondary chlorides, which, though very slow, is appreciable at this temperature, followed by saturation of the double bonds with chlorine.

Conclusive evidence that dichlorination occurs also by progressive substitution is available in the formation of large quantities of 1, 3-disubstitution products which cannot be produced by the addition, under these conditions, of either hydrogen chloride or chlorine to any olefin or chloroolefin.

9. In vapor-phase chlorination the presence of a chlorine atom on a carbon atom tends to hinder further reaction upon that carbon atom during the second substitution.

The data obtained in the dichlorination of propane and isobutane show that only small amounts of dichlorides containing both chlorine atoms on the same carbon atom are found to be present. In the case of propane the boiling points of the dichlorides are as follows: 2, 2-dichloride, 69.7°C.; 1, 1-dichloride, 86°C.; 1, 2-dichloride, 96.8°C.; 1, 3-dichloride, 120.4°C. A rectification analysis, (Fig. 5, page 174) is therefore conclusive and relatively easy.

10. In vapor-phase chlorination of saturated hydrocarbons, increased pressure causes increased relative rates of primary substitution. The influence of pressure, in the chlorination of propane in the vapor phase, is shown by the curve of Fig. 3.

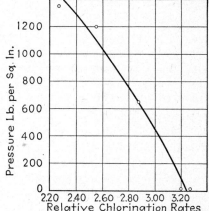

FIG. 3.—Chlorination of propane, at 300°C. Effect of pressure upon relative chlorination rates of primary and secondary hydrogen atoms.

Substitution Reactions.—The reaction of chlorine gas with vapors of paraffin hydrocarbons is so vigorous that precautions must be taken to avoid the sudden development of excessive temperatures and pressures. Consequently, numerous procedures have been devised to avoid decomposition and diminished yield of the desired product. The following are some of the methods that have been proposed for moderating and controlling the reaction:

1. Employing a considerable excess of the hydrocarbon vapors.

2. Carrying out the reaction in the presence of diluent gases such as nitrogen, steam, or the hydrogen chloride that is liberated.

3. Introducing the reacting gases into a liquid cosolvent.

4. Employing a halogen gas that reacts mildly and then replacing the combined halogen with chlorine.

5. Effecting chlorination in successive stages by mixing only part of the chlorine with the hydrocarbon.

Treatment of Gaseous Aliphatic Compounds. Chlorination of Methane. The chlorination of methane can be accomplished by treating a mixture of chlorine with an excess of the hydrocarbon. Actinic rays, iodine, and the chlorides of copper, iron, and antimony have been found useful in catalyzing this reaction.

When inorganic compounds capable of forming higher and lower chlorides are employed as the catalyst, the reaction proceeds very smoothly. The efficacy of such halides is based on the following type reaction:

$$SbCl_3 + Cl_2 \rightleftarrows SbCl_5$$

At ordinary temperatures in the presence of molecular chlorine, the lower chloride has a great tendency to add on chlorine. With increasing temperature, the reverse is true, and the pentachloride loses chlorine. The dissociation of the antimony pentachloride starts at about 140°C. and is practically complete at a temperature slightly above 200°C.[1]

These cyclic processes of association and dissociation result in a continuous transformation of molecular chlorine into an activated atomic chlorine. Whereas, in plant practice, molecular chlorine alone does not readily chlorinate methane below a temperature of about 300°C., in the presence of antimony trichloride in about equimolecular amounts, it reacts rapidly at a temperature as low as 230°C.

When antimony trichloride is employed as the catalyst for the chlorination of methane, the reaction is carried out entirely in the gaseous phase by maintaining an atmosphere of vapors of antimony chlorides.[2] A still is charged with antimony trichloride, and the contents brought to a boil at approximately 223°C. A superimposed reaction tower is heated by hot gases to a temperature of 265°C. and maintained at approximately that temperature while a large amount of antimony trichloride is kept refluxing through it. The whole system is kept under a pressure of 5 to 6 cm. of mercury. Methane, 1.875 moles; and chlorine, 0.305 mole, are then introduced. The reaction proceeds smoothly, and the products obtained consist of methyl chloride, 0.061 mole; methylene chloride, 0.032 mole; and chloroform, 0.034 mole. The corresponding amount of hydrogen chloride obtained is 0.381 mole. The actual conversion of chlorine is, therefore, 99 per cent, based on the following equations:

$$CH_4 + Cl_2 \rightarrow CH_3Cl + HCl$$
$$CH_4 + 2Cl_2 \rightarrow CH_2Cl_2 + 2HCl$$
$$CH_4 + 3Cl_2 \rightarrow CHCl_3 + 3HCl$$

By increasing the ratio of chlorine to methane, larger percentages of dichloromethane and chloroform are obviously formed. When the latter are preferred as final products, any methyl chloride obtained from the reaction can be fractionated and returned to the system.

[1] Martin, U. S. 1,801,873 (1931).
[2] Ibid.

Chlorination of Methane in the Presence of Oxygen and a Copper Catalyst. In the chlorination of methane and its homologues, the principles of the Deacon process may be utilized in order to obtain a maximum efficiency based on chlorine consumed.[1] When a copper catalyst and air are present, the hydrogen chloride liberated is decomposed

$$(4HCl + O_2 \rightarrow 2H_2O + 2Cl_2),$$

and the chlorine thus set free reacts with more hydrocarbon.[2]

Methane can also be chlorinated in the presence of partly reduced copper, using nitrogen as a diluent to avoid explosive reactions.[3] A gaseous mixture comprising chlorine and steam at 400 to 500°C.; or chlorine and part of the liberated hydrogen chloride can also be used to advantage.[4]

Chlorination of Propane.—When propane is chlorinated under conditions which avoid excessive pyrolysis, every possible monochloride and polychloride derivable without carbon-skeleton rearrangement is always formed in accordance with Hass's[5] rule. According to this generalization, the chlorination of propane to the dichloride stage occurs according to the following diagram.[6]

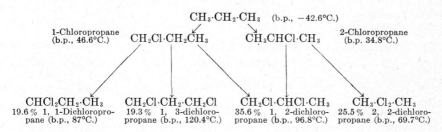

The chlorination may be carried out in apparatus shown diagrammatically in Fig. 4.

By means of flowmeters F a molar excess of material to be chlorinated (propane and monochlorides) over chlorine, of approximately 10:1 is maintained in the gases flowing to the chlorinator. This excess, in

[1] U. S. 1,654,821 (1928); Ger. 478,083 (1929).

[2] The following reactions may also occur:

$$CH_4 + O_2 \xrightarrow{\text{Cu}_2\text{ Cl}_2} H\cdot CHO + H_2O \tag{1}$$
$$H\cdot CHO + 2HCl \rightarrow CH_2Cl_2 + H_2O \tag{2}$$

[3] BOSWELL and MCLAUGHLIN, *Can. J. Research*, **1**, 240 (1929).
[4] U. S. 1,889,157 (1932).
[5] HASS, MCBEE, and WEBER, *Ind. Eng. Chem.*, **27**, 1190 (1935).
[6] HASS, MCBEE, and HATCH, *Ind. Eng. Chem.*, **28**, 1178 (1936).

combination with complete removal of dichlorides from the recycled gas by means of the continuous rectifying column, ensures a low concentration of trichlorides in the crude dichloride mixture. The chlorine is allowed to react completely in the chlorinator, and the material flowing

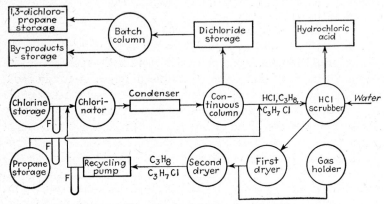

Fig. 4.—Flow diagram, chlorination of propane.

to the condenser and hence to the continuous rectifying column consists essentially of propane, both monochloropropanes, all four dichloropropanes, and hydrogen chloride. The effluent from the base of the continuous column consists of dichloropropanes with minor amounts of more highly chlorinated material. The hydrogen chloride, propane, and monochlorides pass up through the column in which a sufficient monochloride reflux is maintained to remove the dichlorides efficiently from the overhead product. The make-up propane is introduced immediately after the continuous column and assists in preventing condensation of monochlorides in the hydrochloric acid scrubber, in which the hydrogen chloride is removed. The moist gases from the hydrochloric acid scrubber must be dried in order to prevent corrosion in other parts of the plant. This is accomplished in two sulfuric acid scrubbing towers which also remove olefins and chloroolefins which are formed in traces in the chlorinator. The gas holder serves as a guide to the rate of flow in the make-up propane, which is adjusted to keep the gas holder about half full.

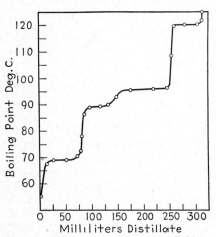

Fig. 5.—Rectification curve for dichloropropanes.

The crude dichlorides are fractionated in the batch rectifying column. When 1, 3-dichloropropane is wanted for the preparation of the anesthetic cyclopropane, it is separated from all other chlorinated products except 1, 2, 2-trichloropropane. This trichloride (boiling at 123°C.) boils only 1.6°C. higher than the 1, 3-dichloride, and its removal by distillation is therefore impractical. Since only about 8 per cent of the crude dichloride mixture consists of trichlorides, and the 1, 2, 2-trichloropropane is the only one of the five isomers present which is difficultly separable, it occurs in only minor amounts in the rectified 1, 3-dichloropropane. The final elimination of this impurity occurs in the ring-closure reaction where it is converted to 2-chloro-1-propene (boiling at 22.68°C.) which is removed in the rectification of the crude cyclopropane.

Addition Reactions.—The olefins combine readily with chlorine and bromine. In these reactions the characterizing double bond is replaced by a single bond, and two halogen atoms become attached to the adjacent carbon atoms which were previously united by a double bond:

$$CH_3 \cdot CH {=\!=} CH_2 + Cl_2 \rightarrow CH_3 \cdot CHCl \cdot CH_2Cl$$
$$CH_3 \cdot CH {=\!=} CCl_2 + Cl_2 \rightarrow CH_3 \cdot CHCl \cdot CCl_3$$
$$HC {\equiv} CH \xrightarrow{\ Cl_2\ } (ClHC {=\!=} CHCl) \xrightarrow{\ Cl_2\ } Cl_2HC {-\!\!-} CHCl_2$$

The addition reactions are usually carried out in the presence of a solvent which may be some of the finished product or unwanted higher chlorinated derivatives. Any of the lesser active polychlorinated compounds such as CCl_4 and $C_2H_2Cl_4$ may also be used.

When the hydrogen halides are similarly allowed to react with olefinic hydrocarbons, the halogen, in accordance with Markownikow's rule, ordinarily attaches itself preponderantly to that carbon with which are combined the least number of hydrogen atoms, while the hydrogen adds on to the terminal carbon atom.

$$CH_3 \cdot CH {=\!=} CH_2 + HCl \rightarrow CH_3 \cdot CHCl \cdot CH_3$$
$$CH_3 \cdot CH_2 \cdot CH {=\!=} CH_2 + HCl \rightarrow CH_3 \cdot CH_2 \cdot CHCl \cdot CH_3$$

If this reaction were universally true, only secondary and tertiary halogeno compounds could be obtained from the higher olefins. Kharasch[1] has, however, shown (see page 201) that the addition of HBr to the double bonds of olefinic hydrocarbons is influenced by the presence of either peroxides or antioxidants, the former serving to produce primary and the latter secondary or tertiary halogen derivatives.

Treatment of Unsaturated Paraffin Hydrocarbons. *Preparation of Ethylene Dichloride. Bromine and Bromides as Catalysts.*—By employing aliphatic bromides or iodides possessing higher boiling points than the

[1] KHARASCH, *J. Am. Chem. Soc.*, **55**, 2468, 2521, 2531 (1933); **56**, 244, 712, 1212, 1643, 1782 (1934); **57**, 2463 (1935); **59**, 195 (1937).

corresponding chlorine derivative, it is practicable to carry out the chlorination of ethylene to ethylene dichloride under comparatively mild conditions.[1] The advantages of such a procedure are that it permits an easy and fairly complete separation of the more volatile and desired chlorine derivative. Since the less volatile bromide or iodide is condensed and returned to the system, only a small quantity of it need be employed. The process may be carried out as follows: Chlorine gas is introduced under moderate pressure beneath the surface of ethylene dibromide in the vessel 2 (Fig. 6). A steam coil is provided for maintaining the temperature of the ethylene dibromide at a point to give a sufficient concentration of its vapors during the chlorination. The chlorine gas bubbles

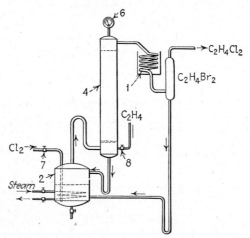

FIG. 6.—Chlorination of ethylene: bromine as catalyst.

up through the ethylene dibromide and becomes saturated with the vapor of the latter and then passes into the base of the chlorinator 4. Ethylene is introduced into the base of the chlorinator through the pipe 8, and the two gases diffuse and pass upward through the tower, which is filled with a suitable packing of porous material such as coke or pumice. The reaction between chlorine and ethylene dibromide or ethylene chlorobromide takes place smoothly. The heat developed is sufficient to maintain the reaction products as vapors within the chlorinator. By means of thermoelectric equipment 6, the inlet valves 7 and 8 for the reactants are regulated so that the reaction temperature is maintained between 40 to 50°C. The ethylene dibromide which is condensed in the coils 1 is returned to the vessel 2. The vapors of ethylene dichloride containing some dibromide and unreacted gases leave the system and are cooled and condensed. The crude ethylene dichloride is purified by

[1] U. S. 1,841,279 (1932).

fractional distillation and separated from any residual dibromide, the latter being returned to the system.

When bromine is substituted for a liquid organic bromide in vessel 2, a mixture of chlorine saturated with bromine vapor passes to the chlorinator. The catalytic function of the bromine depends on the formation and activity of the unstable BrCl, requiring a low activation energy [Eq. (1)], rather than on the preliminary addition and subsequent displacement of bromine from the organic compound [Eq. (2)].

$$C_2H_4 \xrightarrow{\text{BrCl}} C_2H_4BrCl \xrightarrow{\text{Cl}_2} \underset{\substack{+ \\ (\text{BrCl})}}{C_2H_4Cl_2} \tag{1}$$

$$C_2H_4 \xrightarrow{\text{Br}_2} C_2H_4Br_2 \xrightarrow{\text{Cl}_2} \underset{\substack{\text{Br} \\ +}}{C_2H_4BrCl} \xrightarrow{\text{Cl}_2} \underset{\substack{\text{Br} \\ +}}{C_2H_4Cl_2} \tag{2}$$

When equal parts of Cl_2 and Br_2 are distilled slowly, a compound of higher vapor pressure than bromine is formed, and the fraction obtained at 90°C. shows a ratio of $Cl:Br = 1:1$.[1] Studies on the mixture of these two gases indicate that the equilibrium is on the right-hand side and may be expressed quantitatively as follows:[2]

$$\underset{10\%}{Br_2} + \underset{10\%}{Cl_2} \rightarrow \underset{80\%}{2BrCl}$$

It is entirely probable, therefore, that BrCl and not Br_2 is the active halogenating agent, for the former reacts more rapidly than either bromine or chlorine. The supposition that C_2H_4 in the presence of both bromine and chlorine combines first with bromine and that chlorine displaces part of the bromine in $C_2H_4Br_2$ is not in accord with the facts.[3]

Bromine chloride[4] can be employed as a technical method of separating unsaturated aliphatic hydrocarbons from the saturated alkanes. The BrCl is prepared by passing chlorine into a vessel containing a concentrated aqueous solution of an alkali bromide. At first, the bromine that is liberated settles

$$NaBr + Cl_2 \rightarrow NaCl + BrCl$$

and forms a layer at the bottom of the vessel. With continued introduction of chlorine, the bromine layer disappears and merges with the brine solution. Although Br_2 and Cl_2 are soluble in their saturated salt solutions only to about 4 per cent, 40 parts by weight of bromine (as NaBr) when treated with chlorine will dissolve in 75 parts of a saturated

[1] Lux, *Ber.*, **63B**, 1156 (1930).

[2] Taylor and Forscey, *J. Chem. Soc.*, **1930**, 2272.

[3] Delepine and Ville, *Compt. rend.*, **170**, 1390 (1920).

[4] Nafash, U. S. 2,086,473 (1937).

sodium chloride solution.[1] The feasibility of obtaining high concentrations of BrCl in solution makes it practical to use such a system for the treatment of large volumes of cracked hydrocarbon gases for the separation of the unsaturated components; *e.g.*, ethylene and propylene. The olefins form bromochloro derivatives at normal temperatures and pressures and these can be separated subsequently by fractional distillation.[2] The analysis of a gas mixture before and after being passed

TABLE VI.—SEPARATION OF OLEFINS WITH BROMINE CHLORIDE

Component	Analysis of cracked gas, %	Analysis of treated gas, %
Unsaturates.............................	32.65	Nil
Carbon dioxide..........................	0.20	Nil
Air.....................................	Nil	Nil
Methane and lighter.....................	44.70	75.01
Ethane..................................	17.25	21.36
Propane.................................	3.87	2.75
Butanes.................................	1.04	0.27
Pentane and heavier.....................	0.28	0.61
Total...............................	100.00	100.00

through a saline BrCl solution is presented in Table VI.

Halogenated Olefins.—Halogenated olefins can be made by the addition of a halogen or a hydrogen halide to acetylene, or by pyrolysis of the chloroparaffins, but most frequently they are made by halogenating the olefins by addition and then dehydrohalogenating by hydrolysis. Alcoholic KOH is most frequently used for low-temperature reactions, but the alkali hydroxides alone can be employed at elevated temperatures. The preparation of vinyl chloride, 1, 1-dichloroethylene and perchloroethylene may be represented by the following equations:

$$CH_2{=}CH_2 \ + Cl_2 \rightarrow CH_2Cl{\cdot}CH_2Cl \xrightarrow{\ KOH\ } CH_2{=}CHCl + HCl$$
$$CH_2{=}CHCl + Cl_2 \rightarrow CH_2Cl{\cdot}CHCl_2 \xrightarrow{\ KOH\ } CH_2{=}CCl_2 + HCl$$
$$CHCl{=}CCl_2 + Cl_2 \rightarrow CHCl_2{\cdot}CCl_3 \xrightarrow{\ KOH\ } CCl_2{=}CCl_2 + HCl$$

When ethylene dichloride (b.p., 84°C.) is used for the preparation of vinyl chloride, it is reacted with dilute potassium or sodium hydroxide at approximately 150°C. in a pressure vessel provided with an agitator.   By

[1] Nafash, U. S. 2,075,825; 2,078,582 (1937).

[2] The student should refer to the chapter on Ammonolysis for the discussion relating to the utilization of these halides, as well as the cyclic recovery of the NaBr. He should also compare this method of separating olefins with the acid hydration methods described in Chap. XI, Hydrolysis.

means of a suitable fractional condensing system, the vapors of dichloro-ethane are condensed and returned to the reactor, the water of reaction is removed, and the volatile vinyl chloride (b.p., 13.9°) is withdrawn and liquefied in a low-temperature condenser. Vinyl chloride polymerizes readily under the influence of light and is used extensively in the preparation of vinylite plastics.

When propylene dichloride is treated with an alcoholic solution of potassium hydroxide at ordinary temperatures, propenyl chloride will be formed, but when reacted with alkali hydroxides at relatively high temperatures, the product consists largely of isopropenyl chloride.

$$CH_3 \cdot CHCl \cdot CH_2Cl \left\langle \begin{array}{c} \xrightarrow{\text{Alcoholic KOH @ 25°C.}} CH_3CH{=}CHCl \\ \xrightarrow{\text{Aqueous KOH @ 150°C.}} CH_3CCl{=}CH_2 \end{array} \right.$$

It is not essential to isolate the halogeno compounds prior to dehydro-halogenation when the chlorination is carried out at high temperatures. Under such conditions hydrogen chloride is split out with the formation of olefins. Indeed, a hydrocarbon or chlorinated hydrocarbon containing more carbon atoms than the desired olefin may be used because of the deep-seated pyrolytic reactions which occur. The following equations indicate the reactions which take place when preheated saturated compounds at 180°C. are mixed with chlorine and then subjected to reaction in a molten metal bath at about 400°C.[1]

$$C_2H_4Cl_2 + 3Cl_2 \rightarrow CCl_2{=}CCl_2 + 4HCl \tag{1}$$
$$C_3H_6Cl_2 + 6Cl_2 \rightarrow CCl_2{=}CCl_2 + CCl_4 + 6HCl \tag{2}$$
$$C_3H_8 \quad\;\; + 8Cl_2 \rightarrow CCl_2{=}CCl_2 + CCl_4 + 8HCl \tag{3}$$

Under certain conditions, it appears that the chlorinated olefin can be obtained directly by substitutive methods; *e.g.*, methallyl chloride is obtained when isobutylene (2-methyl-1-propene) is reacted with an insufficient quantity of chlorine for less than 1 sec., and the hot reaction gases at about 300°C. are then passed into a scrubbing tower containing dilute hydrochloric acid. The initial and final products are

$$\begin{array}{c} CH_3 \\ {>}C{=}CH_2 \rightarrow CH_2{=}C{-}CH_2Cl + HCl \\ CH_3 \qquad\qquad\;\; | \\ \qquad\qquad CH_3 \end{array}$$

There is no evidence for the formation of the expected intermediate dichloride although it is known that the bromine adds on in a normal fashion to give a yield of 75 per cent isobutylene dibromide which would yield the methallyl bromide on dehydrohalogenation.

[1] U. S. 2,034,292 (1936).

$$\begin{array}{c}CH_3\\CH_3\end{array}\!\!\!\!>\!\!C\!\!=\!\!CH_2 + Br_2 \rightarrow \left[\begin{array}{c}Br\\|\\CH_3\cdot C\!-\!CH_2Br\\|\\CH_3\end{array}\right] \rightarrow CH_2\!\!=\!\!\underset{\underset{CH_3}{|}}{C}\!\!-\!\!CH_2Br + HBr$$

It is also known that methallyl chloride adds HCl in the expected manner to give isobutylene dichloride, thus:

$$CH_2\!\!=\!\!\underset{\underset{CH_3}{|}}{C}\!\!-\!\!CH_2Cl + HCl \rightarrow CH_3\!\!-\!\!\underset{\underset{CH_3}{|}}{CCl}\!\!-\!\!CH_2Cl$$

Preparation of Chloroacetic Acid.—The chlorination of liquid aliphatic compounds other than hydrocarbons generally takes place at temperatures lower than are necessary for the paraffins. Iodine, sulfur, phosphorus, and their halides have been employed as catalysts.

The preparation of monochloroacetic acid may be carried out as follows:[1] Two hundred parts of acetic acid, 1 part of iodine, 5 parts of phosphorus pentachloride, and 5 parts of red phosphorus are placed in a jacketed, agitated kettle. The charge is heated to 100°C., while gaseous chlorine is gradually introduced. The consumption of chlorine is practically quantitative, the termination of the reaction being indicated by the presence of chlorine in the effluent gas. The hot solution is drawn off from the settled phosphorus compounds and is diluted by the addition of 25 parts of glacial acetic acid. The monochloroacetic acid, which crystallizes out on cooling, is removed by filtration and washed with a small quantity of acetic acid. A yield of 220 parts (70 per cent of theory) of technical chloroacetic acid is thus obtained. The mother liquors and wash-waters, which contain the balance of the halogen compound, and the settled catalysts (except the red phosphorus) can be added in entirety to subsequent chlorinations.

Strosacker[2] has shown that by elevating the temperature to 160°C., it is possible to increase the absorption of chlorine so that a preponderance of trichloroacetic acid is obtained.

Tetra- and pentachloroethanes can also be employed for the preparation of mono- and dichloroacetic acids respectively. The hydrolytic reactions, which are carried out in sulfuric acid may be represented as follows:[3]

$$CH_2Cl\cdot CCl_3 + 2H_2O \xrightarrow{\;H_2SO_4\;} CH_2Cl\cdot COOH + 3HCl$$

$$CHCl_2\cdot CCl_3 + 2H_2O \xrightarrow{\;H_2SO_4\;} CHCl_2\cdot COOH + 3HCl$$

The water is supplied by sulfuric acid of 90 to 95 per cent strength. The preparation of dichloroacetic acid is accomplished by intimately

[1] Ger. 506,280 (1927).
[2] U. S. 1,757,100 (1930).
[3] U. S. 2,036,137 (1936).

mixing 1,400 parts of pentachloroethane and 1,000 parts of 93 per cent sulfuric acid at 168°C. A regular evolution of hydrogen chloride occurs particularly when additional dilute sulfuric acid is introduced to compensate for the loss of water entering into reaction. The reaction mixture is distilled *in vacuo;* whereby the unreacted pentachloroethane is first removed and this is followed by the fraction consisting of relatively pure concentrated dichloroacetic acid.

Preparation of Chloropropionic Acids.—By the action of phosphorus pentachloride on lactic acid, α-chloropropionyl chloride is obtained, and this on hydrolysis yields α-chloropropionic acid.

$$CH_3 \cdot CHOH \cdot COOH + 2PCl_5 \rightarrow 2POCl_3 + 2HCl + CH_3 \cdot CHCl \cdot COCl$$
$$CH_3 \cdot CHCl \cdot COCl \quad + H_2O \quad \rightarrow CH_3 \cdot CHCl \cdot COOH + HCl$$

When propionic acid is photo-chemically chlorinated in the presence of propionyl chloride and then hydrolyzed, the product consists of approximately equal quantities of α- and β-chloropropionic acids.[1] In all probability the acyl halide is first converted into a mixture of α- and β-chloropropionyl chlorides which react with propionic acid to form the corresponding chloropropionic acids with the regeneration of the acyl halide.

$$CH_3 \cdot CHClCOCl + CH_3CH_2COOH \rightleftharpoons CH_3CHClCOOH + CH_3CH_2COCl$$
$$CH_2Cl \cdot CH_2COCl + CH_3CH_2COOH \rightleftharpoons CH_2ClCH_2COOH + CH_3CH_2COCl$$

Preparation of Acetyl Chloride.[2]—When hydrogen chloride reacts upon a mixed anhydride such as monochloroacetic anhydride, the latter is resolved into chloroacetic acid and acetyl chloride. The regulation of the reaction temperature to keep the acetyl chloride (b.p., 55°C.) as a vapor drives the mechanism of the following equilibrium to the right:

$$ClCH_2 \cdot CO \cdot O \cdot COCH_3 + HCl \rightarrow ClCH_2 \cdot COOH + CH_3 \cdot COCl \qquad (1)$$

When the chloroacetic acid (b.p., 189°C.) is brought into contact with chlorine in the presence of sulfur chloride, at 40 to 50°C., chloroacetyl chloride is formed. When 1 mole of chloroacetyl chloride (b.p., 105°C.) reacts with 1 mole of glacial acetic acid (b.p., 118°C.), a mixed anhydride is produced—monochloroacetic anhydride.

$$2Cl \cdot CH_2CO \cdot OH + SCl_2 + Cl_2 \rightarrow 2Cl \cdot CH_2 \cdot CO \cdot Cl + 2HCl + SO_2 \qquad (2)$$
$$Cl \cdot CH_2 \cdot CO \cdot Cl + HO \cdot CO \cdot CH_3 \rightarrow ClCH_2 \cdot CO \cdot O \cdot CO \cdot CH_3 + HCl \qquad (3)$$
$$Cl \cdot CH_2 \cdot CO \cdot O \cdot CO \cdot CH_3 + HCl \rightarrow ClCH_2 \cdot COOH + CH_3 \cdot COCl \qquad (4)$$

To carry out the preparation of the acetyl chloride as a cyclic reaction,[3] two chambers are required: (I) the chlorination chamber for the

---

[1] U. S. 1,993,713 (1935).

[2] The usual methods of preparing acid chlorides with phosphorus chlorides and phosgene are discussed later.

[3] U. S. 1,850,205 (1932).

preparation of chloroacetyl chloride according to Eq. (2); and (II) a reaction chamber for the preparation of the isolatable intermediate mixed anhydride, which reacts with hydrogen chloride to form chloroacetic acid and acetyl chloride according to Eqs. (3) and (4). It is obvious that, should it be desired to isolate the mixed anhydride, the greatest care must be exercised in removing the hydrogen chloride from vessel 2. To encourage the formation of acetyl chloride, it is desirable to insure the presence of an excess of hydrogen chloride and carry out the operation at approximately 51°C., the boiling point of the acid chloride.

Chlorination in the Side Chain of Aromatic Compounds.—When chlorine is passed into boiling toluene in the presence of natural or artificial light, a mixture of different chlorine products is obtained. The degree of halogenation will depend on the quantity of chlorine consumed, the principal products being those in which chlorine is substituted in the side chain; but compounds containing chlorine in the ring are also present.

Generally, a higher temperature of chlorination favors substitution in the side chain, while chlorination at a lower temperature in the presence of a catalyst, *e.g.*, iron, favors the replacement of nuclear hydrogen. On mixing gaseous toluene in excess, with chlorine gas in the presence of light, only a portion of the hydrocarbon is converted. Benzyl chloride, benzal chloride, and benzotrichloride, as well as chlorotoluene and chlorobenzyl chloride, etc., are produced.

When chlorine gas and vapors of toluene in definite stoichiometric proportions are permitted to react in the presence of ultra-violet rays, the formation of side-chain compounds in a comparatively pure condition is favored. One mole of chlorine (35.5 × 2) is required for the substitution of each hydrogen atom, the formation of benzyl chloride taking place according to the following reaction:

$$C_6H_5 \cdot CH_3 + Cl_2 \rightarrow C_6H_5 \cdot CH_2Cl + HCl$$

For the formation of benzal chloride and benzotrichloride, two and three moles, respectively, will obviously be required.

The preparation of these side-chain halides can be carried out in the vapor phase as follows:[1] A reaction chamber, lined with bonded lead, is provided with a quartz mercury lamp, which emits ultra-violet rays. Liquid toluene is delivered to a vaporizer, and the gaseous hydrocarbon is drawn into the reaction chamber. The chlorine, in calculated quantities based on the toluene used, is delivered through a measuring apparatus directly into the reaction chamber by means of a tube concentric with that employed for delivering the toluene vapors. The product of the reaction collects at the bottom of the chlorination chamber and is drawn

[1] Gibbs and Geiger, U. S. 1,246,739 (1917).

off in such a manner as to prevent the introduction of air. The hydrogen chloride formed is drawn off through the top of the chamber. This operation is preferably performed at 130 to 140°C., a temperature below the boiling point of the side-chain halide.[1] In this way, the halide benzyl chloride (b.p., 179°C.) is removed from the gaseous reaction sphere, and its further chlorination is inhibited.

By allowing hot toluene at 80 to 100°C. to trickle through a tall vitreous tower packed with glass rings, countercurrent to the supply of chlorine, the chlorination to benzyl chloride can be made to take place in the liquid phase.[2] The reaction is carried out in a glass tower which is equipped with mercury lamps spaced every 4 ft. to insure uniform illumination. Hot toluene is introduced continuously and in a regulated flow into the top of the tower, and dry chlorine is delivered at the bottom. The rate of feed is adjusted to keep the temperature below the boiling point of toluene (111°C.). The benzyl chloride is withdrawn at the base, while the hydrogen chloride, along with some hydrocarbon vapors, is removed at the top. By introducing a cooler and scrubber, the toluene can be condensed and returned with fresh material.

Chlorination in the Nucleus of Aromatic Compounds.—Substitution of chlorine for hydrogen in the benzene ring takes place readily. The reaction is greatly facilitated by the presence of a halogen carrier, such as iron, aluminum, or iodine. Previously, it has been shown that side-chain chlorination occurs with the alkylbenzenes when chlorination is carried out at comparatively elevated temperatures and in the presence of light. At low temperatures and in the presence of a halogen carrier, if reaction takes place, the halogen replaces hydrogen atoms in the ring.

Chlorination of Benzene.—The chlorination of benzene is carried out in iron vessels which may be lined with lead or coated with glass. Steel or wrought-iron particles which are gradually converted to anhydrous ferric chloride are generally used as the halogen carrier. The reaction vessel is provided with an efficient stirrer and a reflux condenser. Benzene takes up chlorine readily in the presence of a carrier, and the heat of the reaction brings the charge to boil, making it necessary to employ a cooling or refluxing system to control the temperature. When only monochlorobenzene is desired, it is advisable to maintain the temperature at 40°C. and use only about 60 per cent of the chlorine necessary for chlorination. When chlorine is passed in until the increase in weight indicates that the theoretical quantity of chlorine, calculated for mono-chlorination, has been consumed, some dichlorination takes place, and the charge will give approximately the following fractions when rectified in a column:

[1] Ger. 478,084 (1929).
[2] Conklin, U. S. 1,828,858 (1931).

Distillation products	%	Boiling range, °C.
Benzene...............................	3	79 to 81
Benzene and chlorobenzene...............	10	81 to 125
Chlorobenzene...........................	75	126 to 133
Chlorobenzene and dichlorobenzenes........	10	133 to 180
Resinous materials and loss...............	2	

The yield of monochlorobenzene decreases slightly as the temperature of chlorination is raised. In the vicinity of ordinary temperatures (18 to 35°C.) for every 10° rise, the temperature coefficient of the velocity of transformation of the mono- to dichlorobenzenes is about 8.5 per cent higher than that of the transformation of benzene to chlorobenzenes.[1] Hass[2] has made similar observations with respect to the vapor-phase chlorination of paraffins and reasonably attributes the phenomenon to

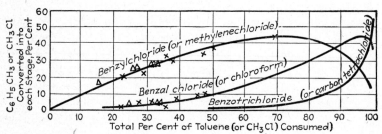

Fig. 7.—Vapor-phase chlorination of toluene. Continuous curves = theoretical curves for three-stage reaction. Points marked x = experimental values, chlorination of toluene. Points marked Δ = experimental values, chlorination of methyl chloride.

the tendency of the energy-rich freshly formed monochloride to react with more chlorine when it is present in high concentrations.

Chlorination of Benzene in the Presence of Sulfuric Acid.—Benzene can be chlorinated at low temperatures in the presence of 10 per cent by weight of sulfuric acid.[3] The reaction product is separated from the sulfuric acid and submitted to fractional distillation. The sulfuric acid is employed in subsequent chlorinations.

Vapor-phase Chlorination of Toluene and Benzene. *Discussion of Factors.*—Chlorine reacts smoothly with an excess of toluene vapors at temperatures above 250°C. in the absence of specific chlorine carriers,

---

[1] BOURION, *Compt. rend.*, **170**, 1319 (1920).

[2] HASS, *Ind. Eng. Chem.* **29**, 1338 (1937).

[3] Battegay, Fr. 641,102 (1928).

the chlorination products being chiefly benzyl and benzal chlorides.[1] The results thus obtained are satisfactorily expressed by the kinetic formulas of Martin and Fuchs[2] for a three-stage (possible bimolecular reactions involved) reaction. The experimental data are shown not to differ appreciably from the theoretical curves (Fig. 7) relating to the chlorination of either toluene or methyl chloride. In the presence of a carrier, substitution in the nucleus also occurs.

Iodine, ammonia to a lesser extent, ferric chloride, and sulfur promote chlorination in the nucleus. Chloroform and water tend only to increase the proportion of benzyl chloride.

The Action of Chlorine on Benzene.—Chlorine reacts similarly with excess of benzene at temperatures above 400°C. to yield mono- and

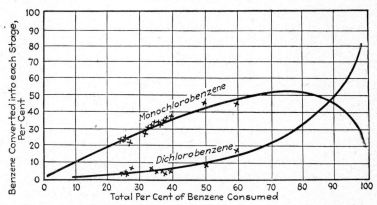

Fig. 8.—Vapor-phase chlorination of benzene. Continuous curves = theoretical curves for two-stage reaction. Points marked x = experimental values.

dichlorobenzenes, with little or no trichlorobenzene. When the molecular proportion of benzene to chlorine falls below 1:1, inflammation occurs at the entrance to the reaction tube but can be stopped by momentarily increasing the flow of benzene.

The data in Table VII show that there is little change in the proportion of isomers with change in the temperature of reaction. It is evident that for a given space velocity, there is a critical temperature below which the amount of chlorine passing through unreacted increases rapidly. Above certain temperatures, pyrolysis sets in and carbon is deposited. In Fig. 8 are compared the experimental results with the theoretical curves for a two-stage process. It is apparent that the experimental and calculated results are in close agreement.

[1] MASON *et al., J. Chem. Soc.*, **1931**, 3150.
[2] MARTIN and FUCHS, *Z. Elektrochem.*, **27**, 150 (1921).

TABLE VII.—EFFECT OF VARYING TEMPERATURE: VAPOR-PHASE CHLORINATION OF
BENZENE

Molar Ratio, $Cl_2 : C_6H_6 = 1 : 2.2$
Tube Diameter, 2.0 cm.   Space Velocity, 10 per minute†

°C.	Percentage of benzene introduced converted into			Unreacted chlorine, % of input
	C_6H_5Cl	$C_6H_4Cl_2$	$C_6H_3Cl_3$	
500	31.3	2.7	Nil	Nil*
475	32.6	3.5	Nil	Nil*
450	34.5	3.2	Nil	Nil
425	32.9	3.9	Nil	0.1
400	32.5	3.9	Nil	1.0
375	24.1	2.1	1.0	20.1

* Carbon deposited.
† Space velocity, *i.e.*, the number of volumes of gas, at the reaction-tube temperature, passing through the heated volume per minute.

Nuclear Chlorination of Nitrotoluene.

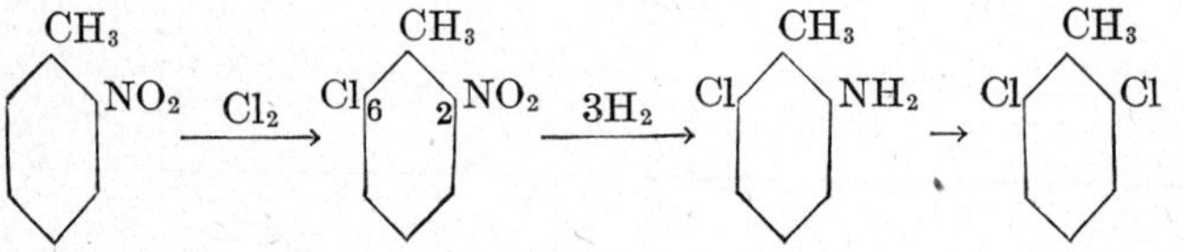

When *o*-nitrotoluene reacts with chlorine in the presence of steel turnings at a temperature of 40°C., substitution takes place principally in the ring. When sufficient chlorine has been added to correspond to monochlorination, the principal product is 2-nitro-6-chlorotoluene. On reduction, this product yields 2, 6-chlorotoluidine; and on subsequent chlorination, according to the Sandmeyer reaction (see pages 198, 200), 2, 6-dichlorotoluene is obtained. Other polychlorinated toluene derivatives may be obtained in a similar manner.

Chlorination of Naphthalene and Biphenyl in Presence of a Solvent.— In organic synthesis, it is often necessary in carrying out reactions to employ inert solvents, or solvents which, although normally reactive, will, under the conditions of reaction employed, remain substantially inert. Thus, Britton has shown that benzene can advantageously be employed as a solvent in the chlorination of naphthalene and biphenyl.[1]

α-Chloronaphthalene can thus be prepared by taking 150 parts by weight of naphthalene, 300 parts of benzene, and passing in chlorine in the presence of iron, until about 0.8 mole of chlorine is absorbed. The hydrogen chloride remaining in solution is neutralized by adding soda ash, and any excess of the latter together with the resulting sodium

[1] Britton, U. S. 1,784,267 (1930); U. S. 1,835,754 (1931).

chloride is separated by filtration or decantation. On distillation of the filtrate, about 95 per cent of the benzene employed is recovered. A yield of about 85 per cent technical α-chloronaphthalene based on naphthalene consumed is obtained.

Chlorinated biphenyl derivatives can be obtained by a similar procedure.[1] Chlorine is introduced into a vessel containing 700 gm. of biphenyl dissolved in 1,500 cc. of benzene, 0.7 gm. of iron turnings, and 0.8 gm. iodine. The charge is stirred while the temperature of reaction is maintained by cooling devices at −10 to 0°C. The introduction of chlorine is stopped when 80 per cent of the theoretical amount required for converting all of the biphenyl to the monochloro derivatives has been added, the time required being about 4 hr.

Upon filtration and fractional distillation under reduced pressure, the following yield of materials, in terms of biphenyl, is obtained:

	%
Unchanged biphenyl	30
o-Chlorobiphenyl (b.p., 210 to 211° at 150 mm.)	27
p-Chlorobiphenyl (b.p., 224 to 226° at 150 mm.)	34
Polychlorinated products, chiefly dichloro compounds	17

When 94 per cent of the chlorine required for monochlorination is added the fractions are as follows:

	%
o-Chlorobiphenyl	37
4, 4′-Dichlorobiphenyl (b.p., 327 to 329° at 750 mm.)	31
Isomeric dichlorobiphenyl derivatives (b.p., 240 to 242°)	30

At lower temperatures—below 0°C.—the tendency is greater toward the formation of p-chlorobiphenyl; while at 25°C., there is a greater tendency toward the formation of the ortho derivative. It has also been observed that when monochloro are converted to dichloro derivatives by continued chlorination, there is a distinct tendency for p-chlorobiphenyl to be further chlorinated before there is any substantial further chlorination of the ortho isomer.

Chlorination of o-Phthalic Acid.—By introducing an acid-absorbing agent, o-phthalic acid can be chlorinated in alkaline aqueous solution.[2] In 200 parts of water containing 41.4 parts of potassium carbonate, 29.6 parts of phthalic anhydride is dissolved, and chlorine is passed in slowly. When the required quantity has been absorbed, the precipitated acid potassium salt of 4-chloro-o-phthalic acid is filtered off. The addition of concentrated sulfuric acid to the mother liquor until the strength of the acid is 20 to 30 per cent H_2SO_4 will cause a further quantity of the product to be precipitated.

[1] U. S. 1,822,982 (1931).

[2] Brit. 348,632 (1930).

By treating the alkali metal salt of 4-chloro-*o*-phthalic acid with hot 100 per cent sulfuric acid first at 100°C. and then at 200°C., the anhydride is obtained.

Halogenation of Anthraquinones.—Ordinarily, the halogenated anthraquinones are derived from the corresponding keto acids, which in turn are prepared according to the Friedel and Crafts reaction. Thus, not only chlorobenzene but also *o*- and *m*-dichlorobenzenes have been utilized in the synthesis of halogenated keto acids by condensing with phthalic anhydride as well as its halogen derivatives. Under certain conditions, particularly when halogeno-amino derivatives are required, it is desirable to chlorinate the anthraquinone compounds directly in order to obtain a specific intermediate for vat dye manufacture.

The chlorination of 2-aminoanthraquinone can be carried out by suspending 10 parts of the amine in 100 parts of nitrobenzene and then passing in chlorine until the increase in weight indicates monochlorination.[1] With constant agitation, the mixture is boiled vigorously for ½ hr. and then permitted to stand overnight. The 2-amino-3-chloroanthraquinone that crystallizes out is filtered off and washed with nitrobenzene, alcohol, and finally water. When 20 parts of 2-amino-3-chloroanthraquinone is suspended in 180 parts of nitrobenzene containing 10 parts of sodium carbonate and treated with 21 parts of bromine dissolved in 60 parts by weight of nitrobenzene, the bromine enters the alpha position. The 1-bromo-2-amino-3-chloroanthraquinone thus obtained is isolated by the procedure previously used.

An aminoanthraquinone can also be chlorinated in nitrobenzene solution if it is first converted to the leuco compound. Upon oxidation, the chlorinated aminoanthraquinone is obtained.

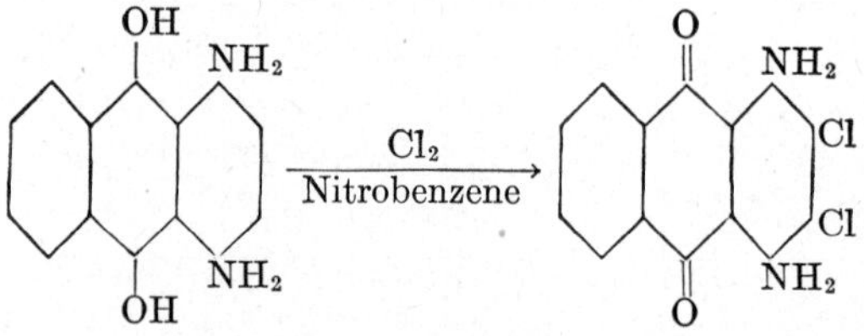

2. Chlorination by the Action of Hydrochloric Acid with and without Oxidants

Reactions in this group include chlorination with (1) hydrochloric acid and (2) chlorides and chlorates in the presence of mineral acids. The syntheses made possible by the action of liberated chlorine comprise reactions involving addition, substitution, and replacement.

[1] U. S. 1,452,774 (1923).

Addition Reactions. *Preparation of Alkyl Halides from Olefins.*—There are two general methods for the synthesis of alkyl halides: (1) by the interaction of an alcohol with a halogen hydride. This procedure may reasonably be discussed under esterification or halogenation and, also, under the Friedel and Crafts synthesis when a metal halide is used to catalyze the reaction; (2) by the addition of a halogen hydride to an unsaturated hydrocarbon. This reaction may be catalyzed by metal halides and by sulfuric acid. In the latter instance, the ethylsulfuric acid first formed is converted to the halide by gaseous chlorine or chlorine[1] liberated *in situ* by the action of sulfuric acid on a halide.

It has long been known to students of the Friedel and Crafts reaction that olefins could be employed instead of the corresponding alkyl halides in alkylation reactions, since they were transformed into the alkyl halide by the added or liberated halogen hydride. The preparation of the alkyl halide may be presented as follows:

$$R—HC\!=\!CH_2 + HCl \xrightarrow[\text{Catalyst}]{\text{Friedel and Crafts}} R—CH_2 \cdot CH_2 Cl$$

Aluminum chloride,[2] ferric chloride,[3] bismuth trichloride,[4] zinc chloride,[5,6] and stannic chloride[7] have been variously employed to catalyze the reaction.

The synthesis may be carried out as a batch process by bringing the olefin and halogen hydride together, in a pressure vessel containing the catalyst (*a*) suitably distributed over an absorbent material, or (*b*) dissolved in an inert solvent. The synthesis may also be effected by passing the reactants as vapors over a solid catalyst; *e.g.*, zinc chloride on charcoal at approximately 100°C.

In general, the ease of synthesis of alkyl halides from olefins is dependent on the molecular weights of the hydrocarbons and the particular hydrogen halide. Thus, as was explained earlier in this chapter, the reaction becomes more difficult in passing from iodides through bromides to chlorides. Likewise, olefins containing several carbon atoms react much more readily than those of a lower order.

Substitution Reactions. *Chlorination of Methane with Hydrogen Chloride in the Presence of Oxygen.*—It has been shown that the introduction of air or oxygen into the reaction chamber containing chlorine and methane makes possible the conversion of the liberated hydrogen

[1] U. S. 2,016,072 (1935).
[2] U. S. 1,518,182 (1924).
[3] U. S. 1,637,972 (1927).
[4] U. S. 1,591,151 (1926).
[5] U. S. 2,094,064 (1937).
[6] U. S. 2,097,750 (1937).
[7] U. S. 2,099,480 (1937).

chloride to active chlorine. By taking advantage of the principles of the Deacon reaction, it is feasible to chlorinate methane employing hydrogen chloride in the presence of air and a copper catalyst.

$$2CH_4 + 2Cl_2 \rightarrow 2CH_3Cl + 2HCl$$

$$2CH_4 + 2HCl + O_2 \xrightarrow[400°C.]{Cu_2Cl_2} 2CH_3Cl + 2H_2O$$

The process may be carried out as follows:[1] A mixture of two volumes of methane and one of hydrogen chloride is led into a tube containing pumice impregnated with cupric chloride and brought to a temperature of 400°C. The reaction tube is of sufficient length to insure a practically complete transformation of the hydrogen chloride. The exit gases from the catalytic chamber are cooled to remove water and hydrochloric acid. The chlorinated methane is washed to remove any residual acid and then recovered either by absorption in a high-boiling solvent or by cooling and employing pressure.

The residual gases, comprising methane and oxygen, may be returned to the catalytic chamber along with more hydrogen chloride, oxygen, and methane. When air is employed instead of oxygen, the reaction proceeds more slowly on account of the presence of such a comparatively large volume of nitrogen. Under such circumstances, it is advisable to employ a second catalytic chamber into which additional air and hydrogen chloride are added to combine with the unchlorinated methane.

Benzene may be chlorinated by an entirely similar procedure.[2] Vapors of benzene and hydrogen chloride in the ratio of 600 to 300 parts by volume are mixed with 170,000 volumes of air and led into the catalytic chamber containing pumice impregnated with cupric chloride or preferably a mixture of cupric and ferric chlorides at 180°C. The condensed reaction gases separate out into a two-layer liquid system, comprising dilute hydrochloric acid and chlorobenzene. The chlorobenzene layer is washed free of acid and then submitted to fractional distillation. Only a small quantity of benzene and higher chlorinated compounds is found to accompany the principal product. For the practical application of this procedure as the first step in the technical production of phenol, see Chap. XI, Hydrolysis.

Manganese dioxide may be used as the oxidant when the chlorination of benzene takes place in the liquid phase. Under such circumstances, the hydrogen chloride may be liberated *in situ* by the action of sulfuric acid on sodium chloride. The reactions involved are

$$C_6H_6 + MnO_2 + 3HCl \rightarrow C_6H_5Cl + MnCl_2 + 2H_2O$$

$$C_6H_6 + MnO_2 + 2H_2SO_4 + NaCl \rightarrow C_6H_5Cl + MnSO_4 + NaHSO_4 + 2H_2O$$

[1] U. S. 1,654,821 (1928); Ger. 486,952 (1929)

[2] Ger. 487,596 (1929); U. S. 1,935,648 (1933); U. S. 1,963,761 (1933).

Utilization of Liberated Hydrogen Chloride in Preparation of Alkyl Halides.—By causing the hydrogen chloride split off in direct chlorinations to react with compatible alcohols, it is not necessary to employ oxidants to obtain a maximum utilization of the chlorine introduced. Thus, methanol can be introduced into the chamber containing hydrogen chloride, hydrocarbon, and chlorinated hydrocarbon and is converted (esterified) to methyl chloride.[1] The principal reactions involved may be represented as follows:

$$CH_4 + Cl_2 \rightarrow CH_3Cl + HCl$$
$$HCl + CH_3OH \rightarrow CH_3Cl + H_2O$$

When methylene chloride is desired, the reactions are

$$CH_3Cl + Cl_2 \rightarrow CH_2Cl_2 + HCl$$
$$HCl + CH_3OH \rightarrow CH_3Cl + H_2O$$

For the preparation of methylene chloride, the process may be carried out as follows: A mixture of 3 parts by volume of CH_3Cl and 1 part by volume of Cl_2 is conducted at the rate of 1.20 liters per hour through a chamber of 750 to 800 cc. capacity, which is heated to 360 to 380°C. The chlorination product leaving the chamber consists approximately of 2 parts by volume of CH_3Cl, 1 part CH_2Cl_2, and 1 part HCl. These gases are subjected to reaction with methanol in a second chamber in which a catalyst comprising silica gel impregnated with zinc chloride is provided. The methanol and hydrogen chloride react to form methyl chloride and water. The water is separated from the gaseous mixture, which contains by volume 3 parts of CH_3Cl (b.p., -23.7°C.) and 1 part of CH_2Cl_2 (b.p., 42°C.). After these constituents have been separated, the methyl chloride is again treated with chlorine, and the process repeated.

Replacement Reactions. *Chlorination with Hydrochloric Acid. Esterification of Alcohols. Preparation of Alkyl Chlorides from Alcohols.*— The reactions between alcohols and hydrochloric acid may be represented by the following equation:

$$R \cdot OH + HCl \rightarrow R \cdot Cl + H_2O$$

It is apparent that the preparation of alkyl chlorides by this method is indeed a process of esterification. The following brief remarks merely present the operation in its relationship to other halogenations: Such reactions are catalyzed by dehydrating agents such as strong sulfuric acid, copper sulfate, magnesium chloride, and polyvalent metals between chromium and bismuth in the electrochemical series which form water-soluble chlorides. Such salts as ferric chloride, cuprous chloride, stannous chloride, in aqueous solution, are capable of preventing the vaporization

[1] Brit. 283,877 (1928).

of the alcohols at temperatures well above their respective boiling points. This may be attributed to (1) a lowering of the vapor pressure of the reaction mass; (2) the formation of loose addition products of the metals with alcohols; or (3) the formation of ternary complexes involving the metal, alcohol, and hydracid.

Preparation of Chloroanthraquinones. *Replacement of Sulfonic Acid Groups.*—The sulfonic acid groups of anthraquinone compounds can readily be replaced by chlorine. Hydrochloric acid or liberated hydrogen chloride may be used as the source of chlorine. The reaction is generally carried out in the presence of compatible oxidants such as chlorates and chlorites.

The preparation of 1-chloroanthraquinone from the corresponding sodium α-sulfonate is accomplished in the following manner: 170 lb. of sodium anthraquinone-1-sulfonate as a 50 per cent paste is added to a solution of 42 lb. of 36 per cent hydrochloric acid in 200 lb. of water. The suspension is stirred thoroughly, then brought to a boil, and refluxed for 3 to 5 hr. Sodium chlorate is added slowly until 70 lb. is introduced, and the charge is boiled vigorously for an additional period of 5 hr. The resultant 1-chloroanthraquinone is separated by filtration and washed with hot water.

When 2-nitroanthraquinone-7-sulfonic acid is similarly treated, the β-sulfonic acid group is replaced. The following equation probably best represents the reaction:[1]

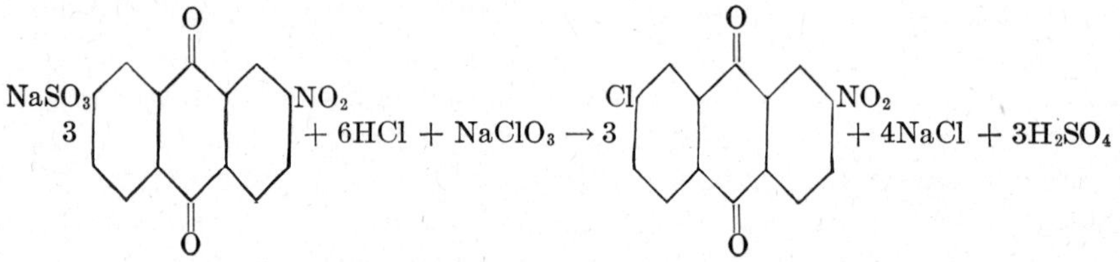

$$3\ \text{NaSO}_3 \diagup\!\!\diagdown \text{NO}_2 + 6HCl + NaClO_3 \rightarrow 3\ Cl \diagup\!\!\diagdown \text{NO}_2 + 4NaCl + 3H_2SO_4$$

Instead of hydrochloric acid, it is feasible to employ sodium chloride and sulfuric acid in the presence of chlorates. The required chlorine is thereby liberated *in situ*. It is possible, furthermore, to utilize the sulfuric acid solution resulting from the preparation of the sulfonic acid derivatives. Such a procedure provides a convenient and economical method for recovering and utilizing any disulfonates that remain in solution after the less soluble and comparatively pure monosulfonate has been isolated by salting out and filtering.[2]

---

[1] U. S. 1,810,011 (1931).

[2] U. S. 1,761,620 (1930). The reverse procedure whereby halogen atoms are replaced by the sulfonic acid group through the medium of sulfites is discussed in Chap. V, Sulfonation.

3. Chlorination with Hypochlorites

Hypohalites in alkaline solution are employed to effect halogenations. Such solutions are particularly effective in preparing halogen addition compounds of acetylene. Ethylene chlorhydrin is also customarily made by reacting gaseous ethylene with hypochlorous acid in aqueous solution. Preferably, the gas is introduced under pressure into a solution of hypochlorite containing a weak acid, boric, or carbonic acid. Such weak acids give so low a concentration of H^+ that union of this ion with OCl^- to form $HOCl$ is the predominant reaction. In the presence of strong acids, the following equilibrium:

$$HCl + HOCl \rightleftarrows H_2O + Cl_2$$

is shifted to the right, and chlorine water is produced.

a. Addition Reactions. *Preparation of Ethylene Chlorhydrin.*—When ethylene is brought into contact with a hypochlorous acid solution, the principal reaction product is ethylene chlorhydrin:

$$HOCl + H_2C{=}CH_2 \rightarrow CH_2OH{\cdot}CH_2Cl$$

Owing to the slight solubility of ethylene in such aqueous solutions at ordinary pressure, some of the undissolved hydrocarbon reacts with the chlorine gas which is present to form ethylene dichloride. To prevent extensive dichloride formation, it is necessary to maintain an excess of ethylene or to increase the solubility of the hydrocarbon by the employment of pressure.

The solubility of ethylene[1] can be increased about two hundredfold by increasing the pressure from atmospheric to 200 atmospheres. When this property is utilized in the preparation of ethylene chlorhydrin, it is necessary only to bring ethylene gas dissolved in water under high pressure into contact with hypochlorous acid (see page 227).

Preparation of Dichloroethylene CHCl:CHCl.—The addition of chlorine or bromine to acetylene may be accomplished by introducing the unsaturated hydrocarbon gas into an alkaline hypohalite solution whereby two atoms of halogen are fixed. Chlorine gas is bubbled into an aqueous solution comprising 12 parts of potassium hydroxide in 80 parts of water, until litmus is bleached, and to this is added a solution of 48 parts of potassium hydroxide in 160 parts of water. Acetylene gas (diluted with nitrogen) is introduced into the cooled solution; and, as the reaction proceeds, dichloroethylene separates out as a colorless oil. By elevating the temperature to 25 to 30°C. and introducing a stream of nitrogen, the halogen compound can be driven over and then condensed.

[1] Youtz, U. S. 1,875,309 (1932).

b. Substitution Reaction. *Chlorination of Hydroxy- or Methoxybiphenyls.*

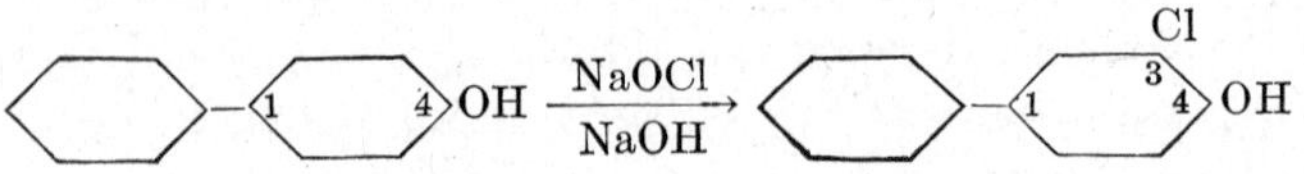

Alkali hypochlorite solutions can be employed in chlorinating hydroxy- or methoxybiphenyl.[1] One mole of 4-hydroxybiphenyl is dissolved in 1 mole of caustic soda and 6 liters of water. The solution is cooled, and 1 mole of sodium hypochlorite in solution is added slowly, with constant stirring. The reaction mixture is allowed to stand for about 1 hr. and then warmed to 40°C. After filtration and cooling, 3-chloro-4-hydroxy-biphenyl is precipitated by the addition of hydrochloric acid.

4. Phosgene (COCl$_2$) and Thionyl Chloride (SOCl$_2$) as Chlorinating Agents

Phosgene finds an important use in the preparation of acid chlorides.[2] When vapors of organic acids are mixed with phosgene in the presence of charcoal, these react readily and provide a continuous and comparatively cheap method of preparing acid chlorides. Chloroacetyl chloride is prepared by admitting gaseous phosgene at the rate of 200 liters per hour and liquid chloroacetic acid at the rate of 900 gm. per hour into a reaction chamber packed with charcoal and maintained at 200°C. The effluent vapors are led to a reflux condenser, and the chloroacetyl chloride (b.p., 106°C.) passes through, while the chloroacetic acid (b.p., 187°C.) is returned to the reactor. Approximately 900 gm. of chloroacetyl chloride per hour is thus obtained.

Thionyl chloride serves as a useful chlorinating agent for replacing the hydroxyl groups in alcohols and carboxylic acids by chlorine. Compared with phosphorus pentachloride, it has the advantage of forming only volatile reaction products.

$$SOCl_2 + HO\cdot C_6H_4\cdot COOH \rightarrow SO_2 + HCl + HO\cdot C_6H_4\cdot COCl$$

When 16 parts of sodium salicylate is treated with 20 parts of thionyl chloride, a vigorous reaction ensues with the liberation of SO$_2$ and HCl. The reaction is carried out in the cold and with constant agitation, while the thionyl chloride is added in small portions. The reaction mass is heated gently *in vacuo* to remove any remaining thionyl chloride, and the salicyl chloride is taken up with a low-boiling solvent.[3]

[1] U. S. 1,832,484 (1931).
[2] Ger. 283,896 (1913).
[3] Ger. 277,659; 284,161 (1913).

5. Sulfuryl Chloride (SO$_2$Cl$_2$) as a Chlorinating Agent

Treatment of Paraffin Hydrocarbons.—Sulfuryl chloride reacts readily with unsaturated paraffins to form the halogen derivatives. It can also be employed to advantage in the chlorination of saturated hydrocarbons, such as methane and ethane.

Previously, it has been shown that the direct chlorination of saturated paraffins is accomplished with considerable difficulty, owing to the tendency to explosions, unless special precautions are taken. The advantage of using sulfuryl chloride for chlorinating saturated hydrocarbons resides primarily in the fact that no great amount of heat is evolved when it is used. The dissociation of sulfuryl chloride results in the formation of sulfur dioxide and chlorine, heat being absorbed during the process. The halogen enters into reaction with the hydrocarbon that is present. Approximately two-thirds of the amount of heat evolved by the chlorination of methane or other hydrocarbons is absorbed in effecting the progressive dissociation of sulfuryl chloride. For this reason, it is difficult to cause an explosion when saturated paraffins are mixed with sulfuryl chloride, regardless of the proportions in which the reactants are present.

By regulating the quantity of sulfuryl chloride, it is possible, in the chlorination of methane, to obtain a yield of 50 per cent of chloroform.[1] When a lesser quantity of sulfuryl chloride is used, it is obvious that a larger proportion of mono- and dichloromethanes is formed. The reaction is promoted by the presence of ionizing agents such as light, heat, metallic chlorides, and activated carbon. The heat of reaction is slightly greater than the quantity absorbed by the decomposition of sulfuryl chloride. The excess of heat is sufficient to keep the temperature of the hydrocarbon gas at the optimum reaction temperature, without the application of heat after the reaction has started.

The chlorination of methane can be carried out by bubbling the hydrocarbon gas through sulfuryl chloride (b.p., 69°C.) at a predetermined temperature. The higher the temperature the larger the ratio of sulfuryl chloride vapor to hydrocarbon. The mixture of gases is passed through a tube filled with inert material and maintained at about 350°C. The flow is sufficiently rapid to constitute turbulent flow. It is necessary to use only a small quantity of catalyst, *e.g.*, carbon; otherwise, the decomposition of sulfuryl chloride will be too rapid, and the rate of formation of chlorine will then be greater than the reaction between chlorine and methane.

Treatment of Aromatic Compounds with SO$_2$Cl$_2$.—In the absence of a catalyst, sulfuryl chloride (SO$_2$Cl$_2$) does not react readily with such

[1] U. S. 1,765,601 (1930).

compounds as benzene or halogenated benzene, it being necessary to operate in closed vessels at 150°C. In the presence of aluminum chloride and sulfur or sulfur chloride, chlorination of benzene occurs with vigor at ordinary temperatures. Dichlorobenzene can thus be converted substantially to the tetrachloro derivative.[1]

Sulfuryl chloride can be employed in conjunction with numerous chlorine carriers to effect substitution in either the ring or side chain.[2] The chlorides of antimony, iron, molybdenum, and aluminum are valuable with sulfuryl chloride in effecting substitution in the ring. The chlorides of phosphorus and, to a lesser extent, manganese, arsenic, and bromine favor side-chain substitution. Sulfur accelerates both types of substitution.

Reed[3] has found that substitutive chlorinations can be induced by introducing SO_2 into a vapor-phase reaction system. This is to be expected because sulfuryl chloride is readily formed by the interaction of sulfur dioxide and chlorine.

6. Chlorination with Metal and Non-metal Chlorides

Ferric Chloride.—In the chapter on the Friedel and Crafts reaction, it is pointed out that aluminum chloride and ferric chloride can exercise a chlorinating action in addition to serving as a condensing agent. Ferric chloride is particularly valuable in the preparation of alkyl chlorides from their respective alcohols. The metal halide serves, therefore, as an esterification agent, but in such reactions it functions best in the presence of hydrochloric acid.

Chlorination with Antimony Pentachloride.—In addition to serving as a halogen carrier for direct chlorinations, antimony pentachloride itself can be employed as a chlorinating agent. The addition of chlorine to acetylene can be effected by introducing acetylene into the liquid antimony halide and then decomposing the addition compound which is formed. Saturated gaseous paraffins can be chlorinated similarly by passing the hydrocarbon vapors through a column at 300°C. filled with quartz impregnated with cuprous chloride and over which liquid antimony pentachloride is permitted to flow. The antimony trichloride recovered from the operation is treated with chlorine gas to regenerate the pentahalide. The chlorinated products of methane comprise CH_3Cl, CH_2Cl_2, and $CHCl_3$, the monochloro derivative predominating.

When the chlorination is carried out below 100°C., saturated paraffins are practically unaffected by antimony pentachloride. It is thus feasible and economical to treat unsaturated hydrocarbons of the ethylene series

[1] Brit. 193,200 (1923).
[2] Brit. 259,329 (1926).
[3] U. S. 2,046,090 (1936).

containing saturated hydrocarbons as impurities.[1] The reactions may be represented by the following equation:

$$C_nH_{2n} + SbCl_5 \rightarrow C_nH_{2n}Cl_2 + SbCl_3$$

The reactions proceed rapidly and completely, with the production exclusively of dichloro addition compounds, no chlorination taking place by substitution.

Phosphorus Chlorides as Chlorinating Agents.—At moderate temperatures, PCl_5, is almost as powerful a chlorinating agent as chlorine; and at higher temperatures, its behavior is approximately of the same order. The liberation of chlorine from PCl_5 takes place according to the law of mass action, as can be seen from a consideration of the following system, all of the components

$$PCl_5 \rightleftarrows PCl_3 + Cl_2 \qquad \frac{(PCl_3) \cdot (Cl_2)}{(PCl_5)} = K$$

being in the vapor phase. The formation of PCl_5 is favored by the application of pressure, whereby PCl_3 and Cl_2 combine; the liberation of chlorine is favored by an increase in temperature and an opportunity for the free movement of the vapors. The dissociation of PCl_5 at various temperatures is as follows:

Temperature, °C	182	200	250	300
Percentage decomposition	41.7	48.5	80	97.3

Phosphorus pentachloride is employed as an esterification agent in the treatment of alcohols, the halide becoming hydrolyzed during the reaction:

Acid Chlorides.—Acid chlorides are usually made from the corresponding fatty acids by treatment with phosphorus halides. When liquid carboxylic acids are reacted, the phosphorus halide, PCl_3 or $POCl_3$, may be added gradually. If the acid does not react energetically, as in the case of the higher members of the acetic acid series or with aromatic acids, phosphorus pentachloride is used. The reactions may be represented as follows:

$$\begin{aligned}
&R \cdot COOH &+ PCl_5 &\rightarrow R \cdot COCl + POCl_3 + HCl &(1) \\
&3R \cdot COOH &+ 2PCl_3 &\rightarrow 3R \cdot COCl + P_2O_3 + 3HCl &(2) \\
&2R \cdot COONa &+ POCl_3 &\rightarrow 2R \cdot COCl + NaPO_3 + NaCl &(3)
\end{aligned}$$

Phosphorus oxychloride is used ordinarily when treating salts of the carboxylic acids. This reaction [(Eq. (3)] may be used to advantage in order to utilize more of the chlorine of PCl_5 than is the case when the latter acts upon the free acids. When the pentachloride reacts with the sodium salt, as above, $POCl_3$ is formed as an intermediate compound and

[1] U. S. 1,754,656 (1930).

while this no longer has the capacity to act on free fatty acid, it can convert two other molecules of the salt into the acid chloride:

$$3CH_3COONa + PCl_5 \rightarrow 3CH_3COCl + NaPO_3 + 2NaCl$$

When acetyl chloride is desired, it can be readily made according to Eq. (2) above by adding phosphorus trichloride to boiling acetic acid. The acetyl chloride (b.p., 55°) is condensed while the hydrogen chloride is led to an absorption system.

7. Halogenation by the Sandmeyer Reaction

Replacement of Diazonium Group.

$$C_6H_5 \cdot N_2 \cdot Cl + Cu_2Cl_2 \xrightarrow{HCl} C_6H_5 \cdot Cl + N_2 + Cu_2Cl_2 \qquad (a)$$

$$2C_6H_5 \cdot N_2 \cdot Cl + Cu_2Br_2 \xrightarrow{HBr} 2C_6H_5 \cdot Br + 2N_2 + Cu_2Cl_2 \qquad (b)$$

$$C_6H_5 \cdot N_2 \cdot SO_4H + KI \xrightarrow{HI} C_6H_5I + N_2 + KHSO_4 \qquad (c)$$

The Sandmeyer reaction is a valuable procedure for the preparation of halogen derivatives which generally cannot be made by other more direct methods. When diazonium salts, which are unstable and unsaturated bodies, react with halogen hydracids alone or, preferably, in the presence of the corresponding cuprous salt, nuclear halogen derivatives are formed, and nitrogen is evolved. Although this procedure is comparatively costly, it makes possible obtaining specific halogenated derivatives in a high state of purity. In a number of syntheses, the Sandmeyer reaction is used in conjunction with other methods of halogenation to secure polyhalogenated derivatives.

The reaction involves the preparation of a solution of the diazonium halide and gradually adding it to a solution of the corresponding cuprous halide. In the preparation of compounds that are volatile, it is essential to employ a reflux condenser. In some cases, the diazo solution is prepared in the presence of the cuprous halide. Under such circumstances, a solution of sodium nitrite is added to a heated acid solution of the amine and copper salt. The diazotization and replacement of the diazo group then take place in one operation.

The reaction scheme for the conversion of benzenediazonium chloride to chlorobenzene, as formulated by Sandmeyer, is as follows:

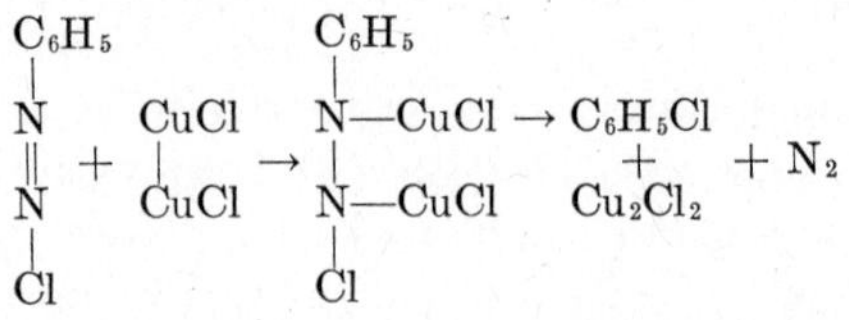

$$
\begin{array}{ccc}
C_6H_5 & C_6H_5 \\
| & | \\
N & CuCl & N-CuCl \rightarrow C_6H_5Cl \\
|| \;+\; | \;\rightarrow\; | & + \; + N_2 \\
N & CuCl & N-CuCl \quad Cu_2Cl_2 \\
| & | \\
Cl & Cl
\end{array}
$$

A more general formulation based on the known formation of colored intermediate addition compounds, which takes into consideration the preparation of other halides, the nitrile, and other derivatives, has been proposed.[1]

$$
\begin{matrix}
\text{R} & \text{X} & \text{R} \; \text{X} & \text{R} \;\; \text{X} & \text{RX} \\
| & | & |\;\; | & |\;\;\; | & + \\
\text{N}\equiv\text{N} + & | & \text{N}\!-\!\text{N} & \text{N}\!=\!\text{N} & \text{N}_2 \\
| & | & |\;\; | & + & + \\
\text{Cl} & \text{Cu} & \text{Cl} \; \text{Cu} & \text{ClCu} & \text{CuCl}
\end{matrix}
$$

Diazonium Halide → Addition → *Syn*-diazo → Aromatic Halide
or Cyanide, Cyanate,   Complex   Compound   or Cyanide, etc.
etc.

In the Gattermann reaction, the identical processes are carried out in the presence of pure, finely divided copper. For the preparation of nitriles, however, the Sandmeyer reaction gives uniformly better results.

Copper is not the only metal that can advantageously be employed for the replacement of the diazo group by halogen. When the precaution is taken to insure a maximum concentration of chloride ions, saturated solutions of calcium chloride, zinc chloride, and zinc-ammonio chloride often give equally good results.

Eichenberger[2] holds two factors of decisive importance in considering the dynamics of the Sandmeyer reaction: (1) the activation energy required to discharge the chloride ions; and (2) the operation of the law of mass action. It is evident that in solutions containing hydroxyl as well as halogen ions, the former will move with a greater velocity and react more readily and therefore play a prominent rôle in the formation of phenols. But, on the other hand, from the law of mass action, it would be expected that in a solution containing different ions, each will react in proportion to its concentration. From the consideration of molecular or ionic concentration alone, practically theoretical yields of aryl halide would be expected when maximum concentrations of HCl and $ZnCl_2$ are used in the Sandmeyer reaction.

The mechanism of the Sandmeyer reaction may consequently be explained as follows: The aryldiazonium compound first forms an addition compound with cuprous salts, resulting in a complex cation which subsequently undergoes decomposition. In this process, it is not the halogen inherent in the diazonium compound or the free halogen ions of the reaction solution but the halogen of the copper halide by virtue of its closer proximity to the aryl radical that enters the nucleus. That quantitative yields are never obtained in carrying out this reaction (see technical section) is explicable on the hypothesis that the diazonium salt reacts with OH^- ions before the addition complex is formed.

Progressive Halogenation by Different Methods.—In some syntheses, it is necessary to employ two or more methods of halogenation in order

[1] HANTZSCH, *Ber.*, **27**, 1702 (1894); EICHENBERGER, Dissertation E. T. H., Zurich (1929).

[2] EICHENBERGER, Dissertation E. T. H., Zurich (1929).

to obtain the desired halogen compound.   An interesting example is the preparation of 2, 6-dichlorobenzaldehyde from *o*-nitrotoluene.   The reactions involved are shown in the following graphic representation:

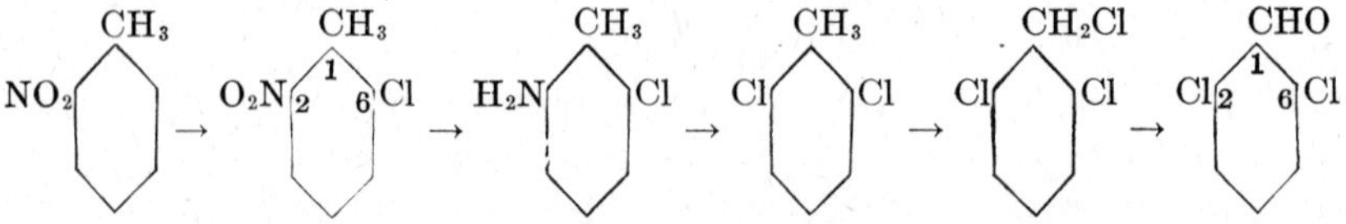

I		II	III	IV	V
Direct nuclear chlorination			Chlorination, Sandmeyer reaction	Side-chain photo-chlorination	

1. The nuclear chlorination of toluene is carried out with gaseous chlorine at 20 to 40°C., using steel turnings as catalyst.

2. The reduction of the nitro group is accomplished by the usual iron-acid method.   The reduction charge is made alkaline with soda ash, and the 6-chloro-*o*-toluidine is distilled with steam.

3. The amino group is replaced by chlorine through the Sandmeyer reaction, and 2, 6-dichlorotoluene is thus obtained.   The diazonium solution, which is prepared separately, is delivered slowly to the copper chloride solution at 70 to 80°C.   The dichlorotoluene is distilled with steam and then purified by washing with caustic soda solutions and distilling *in vacuo*.

4. The side-chain chlorination of 2, 6-dichlorotoluene to form 2, 6-dichlorobenzal chloride is carried out in glass apparatus provided with a reflux condenser.   Mercury quartz lamps are used to catalyze the chlorination, chlorine gas being admitted until the increase in weight corresponds to the formation of the benzal chloride derivative.   The product is distilled *in vacuo*, since higher chlorinated products and resins are formed.

5. The hydrolysis of 2, 6-dichlorobenzaldehyde is accomplished with 93 per cent sulfuric acid by heating at 50 to 60°C.   The reaction mass is diluted, and the corresponding benzaldehyde distilled with steam.

Bromination

In general, methods similar to chlorination with chlorine and chlorides can be employed in the preparation of bromine derivatives.   Because the reaction is milder, the bromination of the paraffin hydrocarbons does not, however, proceed so rapidly or to so great a degree; and with the lower permissible operating temperature, the formation of polybromine compounds occurs to a lesser extent.

In brominations, it is generally advisable to employ a compatible solvent, not only for the organic compound but also for the bromine. Water, dilute alkali, glacial acetic acid, concentrated sulfuric acid, methanol, chloroform, carbon disulfide, and carbon tetrachloride can thus be employed. The use of such cosolvents serves to ameliorate the reaction and thus subjects it to closer control.

The choice of the solvent will, of course, depend on the reactants employed and their specific reactivity in various solvents. Thus, benzaldehyde takes up bromine in carbon tetrachloride about a thousand times as rapidly as it does in chloroform or carbon disulfide.[1] The bromination leads to the formation of bromobenzyl benzoate according to the following reactions:

$$C_6H_5 \cdot CHO + Br_2 \rightarrow C_6H_5 \cdot COBr + HBr \tag{I}$$
$$C_6H_5 \cdot COBr + C_6H_5 \cdot CHO \rightarrow C_6H_5 \cdot COO \cdot CHBr \cdot C_6H_5 \tag{II}$$

The reactivity of aromatic side-chain compounds toward brominating agents is also influenced by the nature of the solvent. Under comparable conditions, the percentage formation of benzyl bromide from bromine and toluene in various solvents is as follows:[2]

$$CS_2 = 85.2; \quad CCl_4 = 56.6; \quad CH_3COOH = 4.0; \quad C_6H_5NO_2 = 2.0.$$

This same influence is exhibited not only in the dark, but also in photo-brominations. From the preceding data, Bruner has concluded that solvents such as nitrobenzene and acetic acid, which have strong ionizing (dissociating) powers, favor substitution in the nucleus.

Addition Reactions with Bromine.—Bromine in aqueous solution forms addition compounds readily with unsaturated organic compounds. This reaction is of considerable interest, since it provides an analytical method for the detection and estimation of double bonds.

Allyl alcohol on bromination takes on two atoms of bromine, one of which is hydrolyzed when the reaction is carried out in aqueous solutions. In the presence of an excess of alkali, the second bromine is split off with the formation of glycerol.[3]

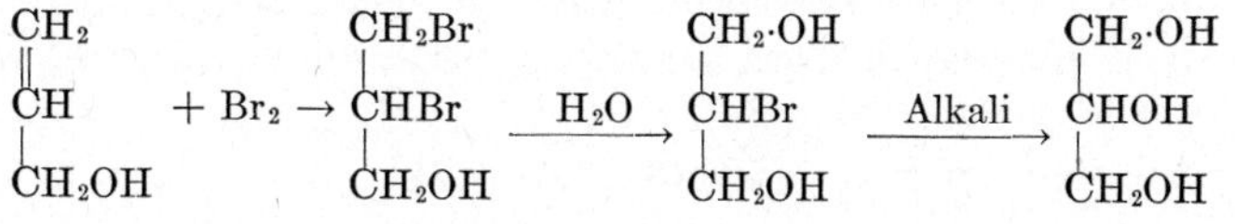

$$
\begin{array}{cccc}
CH_2 & CH_2Br & CH_2 \cdot OH & CH_2 \cdot OH \\
\parallel & \mid & \mid & \mid \\
CH & +Br_2 \rightarrow \ CHBr & \xrightarrow{H_2O} \ CHBr & \xrightarrow{\text{Alkali}} \ CHOH \\
\mid & \mid & \mid & \mid \\
CH_2OH & CH_2OH & CH_2OH & CH_2OH
\end{array}
$$

Addition of HBr.—Kharasch and coworkers have shown that the addition of HBr to the double bonds of olefinic hydrocarbons or substituted olefinic hydrocarbons is influenced by the presence of either peroxides or antioxidants. Normal additions occur in the absence of peroxides and in practice this condition can be brought about by working

[1] HERZ and DICK, *Ber.*, **41**, 2645 (1908).
[2] BRUNER and VORBRODT, *Chem. Zentr.*, **33**, 557 (1909).
[3] STRITAR, *Chem. Ztg.*, **43**, 23 (1919).

under carefully controlled conditions, or by the addition of antioxidants to the reaction mixture.   Among the antioxidants found to be effective, are diphenylamine, thiophenol and thiocresol, the first being the least effective of the three.   Benzoyl peroxide and ascaridole (Δ-2, p-men-thene-1, 4-dioxide) are useful in insuring a peroxide-catalyzed addition of HBr and HI to olefins.

In Table VIII are presented typical data illustrating the influence of peroxides and antioxidants.

TABLE VIII.—INFLUENCE OF PEROXIDES AND ANTIOXIDANTS

Compound treated	Addition agent	Normal product	Addition agent	Catalyzed product
$CH_2=CHBr$	Diphenylamine	$CH_3 \cdot CHBr_2$	Air	$CH_2Br \cdot CH_2Br$
$CH_3CH=CH_2$	Thiocresol	$CH_3CHBrCH_3$	Benzoyl peroxide	$CH_3CH_2CH_2Br$
$CH_3CH_2CH=CH_2$	None	$CH_3CH_2CHBrCH_3$	Ascaridole	$CH_3CH_2CH_2CH_2Br$
$CH_3—C=CH_2$	Diphenylamine	CH_3CBrCH_3	Ascaridole	$CH_3 \cdot CH \cdot CH_2Br$
$\quad\quad \vert$		$\quad\quad \vert$		$\quad\quad \vert$
$\quad CH_3$		$\quad CH_3$		$\quad CH_3$
$CH_3(CH_2)_{10}CH=CH_2$	Antioxidant	2-Bromotridecane	Peroxide	1-Bromotridecane

It is clear from the above data that the addition of HBr to the alkenes containing terminal double bonds results in the formation of primary bromides whenever "peroxides" are present in the reaction mixture. Secondary and tertiary bromides are formed during the normal addition in the presence of "antioxidants" in accordance with Markownikow's rule.   In general, the yields of the alkyl halides are high and the formation of the specific product is almost quantitative.

Some olefins, e.g., vinyl bromide and allyl bromide, are very sensitive to peroxides; whereas, others, e.g., butene-1, are comparatively insensitive.   Kharasch has found that external conditions such as solvents, light, and temperature have a very powerful effect on those systems which are sensitive to peroxides, but practically no effect on those which are comparatively insensitive.   Peroxides are the most important single factor governing the direction of addition and in all probability this is due to their action on the hydrogen bromide or the unsaturated compound or both before addition actually takes place.   The physical and chemical agencies such as light, solvent, temperature, etc., exert their peculiar influence on the peroxide molecules or in activating the oxygen liberated by the decomposition of the peroxides.

IODINATION

Although chlorine and bromine react with methane and other saturated hydrocarbons, iodine enters into combination only under exceptional circumstances. Chlorine and bromine react with hydrogen with the evolution of heat, whereas under the same conditions (400°C.) hydrogen iodide is formed with the absorption of heat. Since the heat of formation is a measure of the strength of the bond, then, compared to the halogens of lower molecular weight, iodine exhibits a stronger tendency to combine only loosely and to enter into reversible reactions.

Treatment of Aliphatic Compounds. *Addition.*—Iodine and hydriodic acid combine readily with unsaturated paraffin hydrocarbons. When ethylene gas is passed into a warm solution of iodine in alcohol, the two substances unite:

$$H_2C:CH_2 + I_2 \rightarrow IH_2C \cdot CH_2I \text{ Ethylene diiodide}$$

With hydriodic acid, the reaction takes place with the formation of ethyl iodide.

Replacement.—1. Chlorine and bromine may be replaced by iodine in many compounds by heating the derivative with an alkali iodide:

$$CH_3 \cdot CH_2Cl + KI \rightarrow CH_3 \cdot CH_2I + KCl$$

2. Alkyl iodides may be prepared (*a*) by the reaction of PI_3 with an alcohol. In practice, this is generally accomplished by digesting red phosphorus with an anhydrous alcohol and then adding iodine. The mixture is heated under a reflux condenser and finally distilled:

$$3C_2H_5OH + PI_3 \rightarrow 3C_2H_5I + P(OH)_3$$

(*b*) By treating an alcohol with hydriodic acid, the reaction taking place according to the following equation:

$$CH_3OH + HI \rightarrow CH_3I + H_2O$$

The process may be made continuous, by adding the alcohol gradually and keeping the temperature sufficiently high so that the water distills over as it is formed. Methyl iodide is prepared by heating methyl alcohol with sodium iodide and sulfuric acid.

3. The action of iodine on either acetone or alcohol, in a mildly alkaline solution, will yield iodoform

$$C_2H_5OH + 8I + 6KOH \rightarrow CHI_3 + HCOOK + 5KI + 5H_2O$$

Industrially, iodoform is prepared by electrolysis, at 60 to 65°C. of a solution of 60 kg. of KI, 20 kg. of Na_2CO_3, and 80 liters of ethanol per 400 liters of solution. The iodine set free by the current converts the ethanol and the sodium carbonate into iodoform and sodium iodide. In practice, part of the iodine reacts with the caustic alkali formed at the cathode and forms an iodate. Prevention of this reaction by surrounding the cathode with a porous cup brings the yield of iodoform up to about 90 per cent of the theoretical.

Aromatic Compounds. *Substitution.*—Direct substitution of iodine into the benzene nucleus is feasible only in the presence of an oxidizing agent. The hydrogen iodide formed simultaneously with the iodo compound is unstable, the iodine in the benzene nucleus is loosely bound; and conditions must therefore be provided to avoid reversibility.

$$2C_6H_6 + I_2 + (O) \rightarrow 2C_6H_5I + H_2O$$

1. Benzene treated in a sealed tube with iodine and iodic acid under suitable conditions will yield iodobenzene. The iodic acid oxidizes the hydrogen iodide as it is formed, thus preventing the reduction of the iodobenzene to benzene.

2. The method of Varma and Panickar,[1] which involves the use of sodium nitrite and fuming sulfuric acid, may be employed for the iodination of aromatic compounds. Nitric acid[2] can be used advantageously as the oxidant for the liberated hydriodic acid. The procedure as applied to the production of iodobenzene[3] involves the reaction of 1.5 moles of iodine with 5.1 moles of benzene in the presence of 6.15 moles of nitric acid. The yield is in excess of 85 per cent of the theoretical. Other benzenoid compounds are iodinated in a similar manner. It should be noted that, in this reaction, all the halogen enters into the benzene compound, unlike ordinary direct halogenations in which half of the halogen used is given off as halogen hydride.

3. Phenols may be iodinated by treatment with iodine in the presence of strong ammonia. 2, 4, 6-Triiodophenol is prepared quantitatively by treatment of phenol in concentrated aqueous ammonia with iodine until the color of iodine persists. Phenolic compounds, in general, are susceptible to the foregoing method.

FLUORINATION

Under atmospheric conditions, fluorine attacks with violence all organic compounds; ether, benzene, and turpentine take fire immediately on contact with it. The fluorine derivatives of organic compounds are consequently made by indirect methods from materials that have been rigorously dried. Of the nine indirect methods shown on page 158 for the preparation of fluorine derivatives, the displacement process is undoubtedly the one most widely used. Whereas the direct fluorination of hydrocarbons proceeds with such vigor as to cause carbonization, the

[1] VARMA and PANICKAR, *Quart. J. Indian Chem. Soc.*, **3**, 342 (1926).

[2] DATTA and CHATTERJEE, *J. Am. Chem. Soc.*, **39**, 437 (1917).

[3] DAINS and BREWSTER, "Organic Synthesis," Collective vol. I, p. 316, John Wiley & Sons, Inc., New York (1932).

replacement of Cl by F in polyhalogenated compounds can be accomplished smoothly by the use of fluorides at ordinary temperatures. Hydrofluoric acid, antimony trifluoride, and boron trifluoride are the fluorinating agents most frequently employed. A catalyst is necessary, and ordinarily either iodine, bromine, or a metal pentachloride is used.

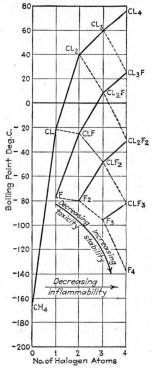

Fig. 9.—Properties of chloro-fluoromethanes.

When fluorine gas is led into a flask containing carbon tetrachloride, practically no fluorination takes place up to 40 to 50°C. At 77°C., the boiling point of CCl_4, the introduction of fluorine results in an explosive reaction.[1] If, in a similar reaction, 5 per cent by weight of iodine is added to the charge, the introduction of fluorine results in the formation of a flame at the tip of the fluorine inlet, and the presence of iodine chlorides is observed in the vapors leaving the reaction chamber. Analysis of the condensed reaction products shows the presence of all four stages of fluorinated methane—CCl_3F to CF_4.

In general, it may be stated[2] that fluorides of the less positive metals, *e.g.*, Ag, Hg, and Sb, are useful in replacing other halogens by fluorine. Thus, Swarts found that antimony trifluoride in the presence of bromine[3] could be used for the fluorination of a large number of organic compounds. Chlorides may also be employed instead of bromine to catalyze such fluorinations.

The reaction involved in the manufacture of dichlorodifluoromethane, which is used widely as a refrigerant, is as follows:

$$CCl_4 + 2HF \xrightarrow{\text{SbCl}_5} CCl_2F_2 + 2HCl$$

Since the introduction of each atom of fluorine lowers the boiling point of the resulting compound by about 52°C. (Fig. 9), it is a relatively simple matter to extract any desired substitution product by fractional distillation.[4] By regulating the temperature of the dephlegmating column, which is an integral part of the reaction system, the desired product is

[1] Ruff and Keim, *Z. anorg. allgem. Chem.*, **201**, 245 (1931).
[2] Swarts, *Bull. Soc. Chem.*, **35**, 1533 (1924).
[3] *Ibid.*
[4] Midgley and Henne, *Ind. Eng. Chem.*, **22**, 542 (1930).

removed as it is formed.   Small amounts of excessively or insufficiently fluorinated compounds will accompany the principal product, but yields of 88 to 94 per cent of dichlorodifluoromethane are obtained directly.

The reaction may be carried out at atmospheric pressure; but if dichlorodifluoromethane is the desired product, a large amount of refrigeration will be necessary for dephlegmation.   Therefore, it is more economical to run at 60 lb. pressure and to use water to maintain the dephlegmator at 15°C.   The technical application of this reaction may be carried out as a batch operation or in a continuous manner.[1]

Treatment of Diazonium Compounds with Borofluorides.—When aryldiazonium sulfates are treated with a large excess of hydrofluoric acid, the corresponding aryl fluorides are obtained.   A better and more practical method involves the use of borofluoric acid HBF_4 or its sodium salt.   Aryldiazonium chlorides are readily converted by means of sodium borofluoride to the aryldiazonium borofluorides, and these compounds are converted to aryl fluorides by thermal decomposition.   The following equations, in which aniline is used as a typical amine, may be employed to represent the several reactions involved:

$$C_6H_5NH_2 \cdot HCl + NaNO_2 + HCl \rightarrow C_6H_5N_2Cl + NaCl + H_2O \qquad (1)$$
$$C_6H_5N_2Cl + NaBF_4 \rightarrow C_6H_5N_2BF_4 + NaCl \qquad (2)$$
$$C_6H_5N_2BF_4 \rightarrow C_6H_5F + BF_3 + N_2 \qquad (3)$$

The control of the hydrogen ion concentration during the formation of the aryldiazonium borofluoride is an important matter, for when this is excessive the yields are not so satisfactory.   For this reason, sodium borofluoride is used in part at least to precipitate the diazonium borofluoride.   When borofluoric acid is used as the precipitant, the free acid formed by double decomposition builds up during the reaction and exerts a deleterious effect.[2]

IV. CHLORINATION IN THE PRESENCE OF A CATALYST

The catalytic agents most frequently employed in chlorinations are metallic iron, cupric oxide, bromine, iodine, sulfur, the halides of iron, antimony, tin, arsenic, phosphorus, aluminum and copper, and vegetable and animal carbons.

Aside from the carbons, practically all the catalysts function as chlorine carriers, ferric chloride, for example, liberating chlorine and being itself converted to ferrous chloride.   The chlorine thus freed combines with the organic compound, presumably because it is already intimately associated with it as an addition complex; then the ferrous chloride in the presence of an excess of chlorine is oxidized to ferric chloride.

---

[1] Fr. 720,474 (1932); 701,324 (1931); Ger. 552,919 (1932).
[2] U. S. 1,916,327 (1933).

Although the halogen carriers exert a powerful influence in promoting ring substitution in the chlorination of aromatic side-chain compounds and also markedly affect the ratio of disubstituted isomers,[1] they have no considerable effect upon the relative reaction rates of primary and secondary hydrogen atoms in paraffin molecules.[2]

Iron Salts as Catalysts.—The preparation of chlorobenzene is the classical example of chlorination in the presence of iron. Of considerable interest also is the chlorination of nitrobenzenes, since this leads to meta derivatives, whereas the nitration of the chloro derivatives leads to para and ortho compounds.

The preparation of carbon tetrachloride from carbon disulfide is also frequently brought about through the catalytic intervention of iron. The operation is carried out in two steps:

$$CS_2 + 3Cl_2 \xrightarrow{Fe} S_2Cl_2 + CCl_4 \tag{1}$$

The products are separated by distillation, and the sulfur chloride is subsequently reacted with fresh carbon disulfide.

$$CS_2 + 2S_2Cl_2 \rightarrow CCl_4 + 4S \tag{2}$$

On cooling, most of the sulfur is precipitated and the supernatant liquid is drawn off and fractionated. The recovered sulfur is reconverted to carbon disulfide.

Antimony pentachloride is an excellent chlorine carrier which has been used extensively for the manufacture of tetrachloroethane, ethylene dichloride, tetrachlorophthalic anhydride, and aliphatic hydrocarbons in general. When used for the manufacture of tetrachloroethane $Cl_2HC \cdot CHCl_2$ from acetylene,[3] an equimolecular double compound of acetylene and antimony pentachloride is formed, and this may be chlorinated without danger of explosive reactions:

$$2Cl_2 + SbCl_5 \cdot C_2H_2 \rightarrow C_2H_2Cl_4 + SbCl_5$$

To insure a smooth reaction, a mixture of tetrachloroethane and antimony trichloride is first placed in the chlorinating vessel, and the chlorine and acetylene are delivered into the charge through separate lines T_1T_2 (Fig. 10). The gases and liquid are brought into intimate contact by means of an efficient agitator and circulated through the gates L. The reaction mass is kept cool by cold water circulating through lead coils.

Bromine and iodine, because of their capacity to form mixed halogens, e.g., BrCl and ICl which have a low energy of activation, are excellent

[1] Stoesser and Smith, U. S. 1,946,040 (1934).

[2] HASS, McBEE, and HATCH, *Ind. Eng. Chem.*, **29**, 1337 (1937).

[3] Ger. 154,657 (1903); Fr. 346,652 (1903).

chlorinating catalysts. In general, it can be stated that small quantities of iodine and bromine are frequently added along with other less costly chlorine carriers, and the literature records numerous examples of such halogenations.

Sulfur and sulfur chloride (S_2Cl_2) are important and efficacious catalysts. They are used for the conversion of glacial acetic acid into monochloroacetic acid, the latter compound being employed for the synthesis of ω-chloroacetophenone (tear gas), and indigo.   It is necessary to carry out this chlorination at the boiling point of glacial acetic acid, for, in the cold, acetyl chloride is obtained.

In the presence of sulfur or antimony pentasulfide, CS_2 is transformed into CCl_4.   This reaction may be carried out simply by bubbling chlorine gas through boiling carbon disulfide containing free sulfur.

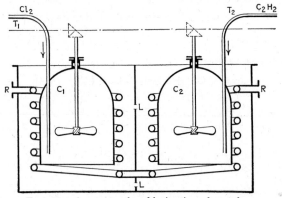

Fig. 10.—Apparatus for chlorination of acetylene.

Valence and Catalytic Activity.—The catalytic activity of metal halides or mixed halogens which can exist in two valences in chlorination is probably comparable to the activity of some of such compounds in oxidation processes. Thus, it is known that HOCl, which forms an addition compound by adding on at an ethylenic linkage, can enter into reactions involving either oxidation or chlorination. The factors that determine the course of the subsequent rearragement and dissociation are principally (1) the concentration of the reactants; (2) the nature of the material undergoing treatment; and (3) the temperature of the reaction.

The reactivity of HOCl is related to the analogous activity of the compounds, which occur as unstable intermediate compounds in organic synthesis. Thus, HOCl is a stronger oxidizing agent than $HClO_3$, although the latter contains more oxygen. This behavior is quite a general phenomenon.[1]   When compounds intermediate in state of oxidation decompose spontaneously into higher and lower state, they are more

[1] LUTHER, *Z. physik. Chem.*, **36**, 385 (1901).

powerful oxidizing agents than the higher compound and more powerful reducing agents than the lower one.

Chlorinations Catalyzed by Porous Carbons.—When organic compounds, *e.g.*, the vapors of saturated hydrocarbons, are introduced into a system containing chlorine and a porous carbon, a reaction occurs which leads to the formation of hydrogen chloride and a chlorine derivative of the organic compound. The activity of coke, graphite, and activated carbons depends essentially on their contact surface and appears to be due in part to the influence of capillary forces on the reaction velocities.

In the presence of porous substances such as charcoal, gases or vapors are condensed as a result of capillary forces and pass by adsorption into the liquid state. When two gases capable of slow reaction are brought into contact with a porous carbon, if adsorption occurs, this will increase their concentrations and augment the rate of reaction accordingly.

When gases or vapors are adsorbed at atmospheric pressure in porous carbons, it is found that they occupy only a fraction of their original volume, and it is presumed that some of the vapors must have been compressed into the liquid state. It may be supposed, therefore, that in such porous bodies, layers of adherent molecules are strongly compressed, as a result of which local increases in concentration, pressure, and temperature occur. Such conditions are favorable to the formation of active molecules and to their encounter with one another. Whether these collisions lead to the preliminary formation of addition compounds which undergo dissociation cannot be definitely stated, although this appears probable.

It is known that in the presence of carbon and moisture, molecular chlorine is readily transformed into hydrochloric acid and that in the presence of oxidants, chlorine is liberated from hydrochloric acid. Presumably, a common active intermediate compound is formed in such oxidation-reduction reactions—because both methods are useful in carrying out chlorinations.

$$Cl_2 \quad \begin{array}{c} \xrightarrow{C} \\[-2pt] \overline{H_2O} \\[2pt] \xleftarrow[O_2]{} \end{array} \quad \begin{array}{ccc} H & & H \\ & O & \\ Cl & & Cl \end{array} \quad \begin{array}{c} \xleftarrow{O_2} \\[-2pt] \overline{H_2O} \\[2pt] \xrightarrow[C]{} \end{array} \quad HCl$$

V. PHOTO-CATALYTIC CHLORINATIONS

The influence that light can exert on the progress of a chlorination is of great technical importance, especially when this influence is selective. Whereas nuclear hydrogen is not affected by light, the substitution of side-chain hydrogen by chlorine is strongly influenced, and this phenomenon is utilized industrially for the preparation of side-chain halides from toluene.

The effects of photo-catalysis depend on two quite distinct factors, the quantity of light present and the quality of this light, factors directly influenced by the absorption of the medium. This absorption is evidently not the same for all radiations. The intensity of any radiation decreases geometrically as the thickness of the absorbent layer increases arithmetically. Thus, with a layer x mm. thick, the intensity of a radiation i, after penetration of the surface, is I/n^x, where I is the initial intensity and n is a factor dependent both on the medium and on the original radiation, for the rapidity with which a radiation is absorbed by any medium depends upon the nature of the radiation. For solids, n is generally of considerable magnitude; it decreases greatly in the case of liquids and becomes very small in the case of gases. If the thickness traversed be very great, the intensity of the radiation may be reduced practically to zero.

The excitation produced by light on chlorination reactions is sometimes so violent that the reaction becomes explosive, as in the classical example of hydrogen and chlorine. Similarly, if chlorine gas be saturated with vapors of methyl formate in the darkness, and the mixture be kept in a stoppered flask for some time in a black box, when the flask is brought out into the light a violent detonation ensues. This remarkable phenomenon takes place in any sort of weather, even in the total absence of ultra-violet rays.

The violence of certain exothermic chlorinations may be explained by the facility of the medium to transmit with extreme rapidity the heat evolved when the equilibrium is disturbed by luminous excitation. This phenomenon occurs only in the case of gases. The gaseous state is, in fact, the only one capable of aiding the explosion phenomenon, because of the very high velocity of the molecules in the gas and the great numbers of collisions per second between these molecules, a number that increases with pressure.

In contrast with the photo-chlorination of toluene and its homologues, Hass[1] has found that in the chlorination of paraffins, the ratios of the isomeric compounds are unaffected by the presence or absence of light. Light, however, causes an accelerated reaction rate at lower temperatures showing that most of the chlorination is caused by the absorption of photons. These results would seem to indicate that the reaction mechanism is the same whether the chains are initiated by some catalytic effect at the carbon surfaces, inside the reactor, by the reaction

$$Cl_2 + h\nu \rightarrow 2Cl$$

or by the simple thermal dissociation of chlorine molecules.[2]

[1] HASS, McBEE, and WEBER, *Ind. Eng. Chem.*, **28**, 335 (1936).
[2] COEHN and WASSILJEWA, *Ber.*, **42**, 3183 (1909).

A reaction mechanism[1] which is consistent with the available data is the following.

$$Cl_2 \rightarrow 2Cl$$
$$R{\cdot}H + Cl \rightarrow R— + HCl$$
$$R + Cl_2 \rightarrow RCl + Cl$$

In thermal chlorination, the chlorine atoms are produced by some wall reaction; whereas, in photo-chemical chlorination, the chlorine molecules are decomposed by absorbing a quantum of blue light, and the reaction chains are thus initiated.

VI. DESIGN AND CONSTRUCTION OF EQUIPMENT FOR HALOGENATION

From the preceding survey of halogenations, it is obvious that no general rules can be formulated for the design and construction of the plant. Conditions vary so greatly, not only as regards continuous or batch operations but also with the chemical and physical characteristics of the organic compound undergoing treatment. Reactions in the vapor phase, particularly those that are accelerated by light (Fig. 11), require equipment which differs markedly from that which is suitable for the liquid-phase chlorination of naphthalene or anthraquinone derivatives.

The materials of construction are, however, limited, because of the inability of most products to withstand the corrosive action of hydrogen chloride or hydrochloric acid. With non-aqueous media, apparatus constructed of iron, iron or other alloys, copper or

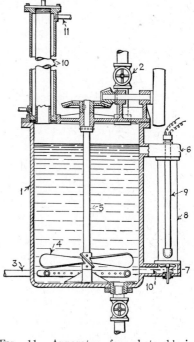

FIG. 11.—Apparatus for photo-chlorinations.

1. Vessel for chlorinated hydrocarbon.
2. Inlet for hydrocarbon.
3. Inlet for chlorine.
4, 5. Shaft and propeller
6, 7. Circulating tunnels
8. Glass reaction vessel.
9. Mercury vapor lamp.
10. Reflux condenser.
11. Vent for hydrogen chloride.

autogenously welded lead are the most suitable, though chemical stoneware, fused quartz, glass, or glass-lined equipment can be used either for the whole plant or for specific apparatus. In aqueous media when hydrochloric acid is present in either the liquid or vapor phase, and particularly when under pressure, tantalum is undoubtedly the most

[1] PEASE and WALZ, *J. Am. Chem. Soc.*, **53**, 3728 (1931).

resistant material of construction.   Reactors and catalytic tubes lined with this metal give satisfactory service for prolonged periods.

Resinous woods, in particular red or pitch pine, are satisfactory materials for constructing reaction vats.   All hoops and tie rods should be covered with lead or else coated with a mixture of tar and silicates (prodorite) or tar and pitch, to minimize corrosion and dislocation.

Large apparatus of enameled cast iron is not suitable for chlorinations in which the hydrochloric acid is not immediately absorbed or removed. Experience with such apparatus has given evidence that the enamel may be attacked at a weak point of such a large surface.   Once the enamel has been completely penetrated at any point, a rapid attack on the whole vessel follows.

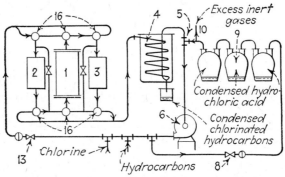

Fig. 12.—Use of liberated hydrogen chloride as a diluent in chlorinations.

1. Reaction vessel.	6. Circulating fan.
2, 3. Heat exchangers.	8. Line to hydrogen chloride absorbers.
4. Condenser.	9. Absorbers.
5. Vent for excess hydrogen chloride.	13, 16. Circulating lines.

When a chlorination has to be carried out at a low temperature, it is more convenient and economical to circulate the cooling water through a lead coil within the chlorinator or circulate the charge through an outside cooling system, rather than to make use of an external jacket.   When the temperature is to be maintained at 0°C. or below, a calcium chloride brine, cooled by a refrigerating machine, is employed.   When the chlorination necessitates the use of light, flanged joints on the lid, closed by glass 8 to 12 mm. thick, permit satisfactory illumination under gas-tight conditions.

Chlorinators should be provided with sight glasses to permit observations on the progress of the reaction.   These observation tubes are interposed in the gas-exit pipe and are illuminated by an electric lamp.   The longer the tube the more delicate are the observations made with it, and the escape of very small amounts of chlorine can be detected by the color of the gas.

When inert diluent gases are employed in the chlorination of hydrocarbons, a plant similar to that shown in Fig. 12 may be used.[1] Here part of the liberated hydrogen chloride resulting from the chlorinating operation is recirculated and fortified with chlorine gas. This gaseous mixture and a gaseous hydrocarbon, such as methane, are led into the reactor 1, and the products of chlorination separated by cooling. The residual gases, containing hydrogen chloride and hydrocarbon mist, may be preheated by passing through heat exchangers, thus utilizing the heat of reaction.

VII. TECHNICAL HALOGENATIONS

Chlorination of Pentanes.—An important and timely contribution to the chemistry of solvents was made by Ayres[2] in developing the process for the manufacture of amyl alcohols from pentanes. The source of pentane is natural gas gasoline the lower fractions of which yield the following pentanes:

	B.p., °C.
Normal pentane ($CH_3 \cdot CH_2 \cdot CH_2 \cdot CH_2 \cdot CH_3$)	36.0
Isopentane $\begin{matrix} CH_3 \cdot CH \cdot CH_2 \cdot CH_3 \\ \vert \\ CH_3 \end{matrix}$	28.0
Tetramethylmethane $\begin{matrix} CH_3 \\ \vert \\ CH_3 \cdot C \cdot CH_3 \\ \vert \\ CH_3 \end{matrix}$	9.5

The reactions involved in this procedure may be simply expressed as follows:

$$C_5H_{12} + Cl_2 \rightarrow C_5H_{11}Cl + HCl$$
$$C_5H_{11}Cl + NaOH \rightarrow C_5H_{11}OH + NaCl$$

Since there are three pentanes, eight possible amyl chlorides, and therefore eight arrangements of the alcohol $C_5H_{11}OH$, the process is not so simple as indicated in the equations above. In the commercial synthesis, normal pentane and isopentane (2-methyl-butane) are submitted to chlorination and subsequent hydrolysis. The vapors from the hydrolyzed material may be separated by a train of fractionating columns into five components, *viz.*, (1) amyl chloride, which is returned for hydrolysis; (2) amylene, which is later hydrated to amyl alcohol; (3) diamyl ether; (4) amyl alcohol fractions that are used for special purposes; and (5) the mixture of amyl alcohols marketed under the name of "Pentasol" for use as a solvent in the preparation of pyroxylin lacquers.

[1] U. S. 1,889,157 (1932).
[2] AYRES, *Ind. Eng. Chem.*, **21**, 899 (1929); U. S. 1,741,393 (1929); 1,835,202 (1931).

Previously in this chapter, emphasis has been placed upon the fact that chlorine does not readily attack the paraffin hydrocarbons unless considerable external energy in the form of heat—200 to 300°C.—is applied. Once initiated, however, the reaction is so vigorous that it is difficult to control unless special precautions are taken. When chlorine is added to an excess of pentane vapor flowing at the rate of 10 miles per hour, there is no tendency to ignite at temperatures up to 100°C., provided the ratio of pentane to chlorine is not less than 10:1. At lower ratios, ignition will be spontaneous, the combustion yielding carbon in the form of soot and hydrogen chloride:

$$C_5H_{12} + 6Cl_2 \rightarrow 5C + 12HCl$$

If the velocity of the admixed pentane is now increased to 30 miles per hour, the chlorine flame can be blown out. These phenomena are advantageously used in the process to be described.[1]

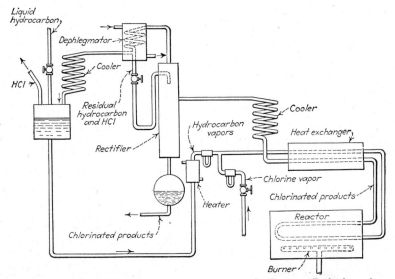

Fig. 13.—Plant layout for chlorination of pentane and other paraffin hydrocarbons.

The chlorination of pentane is accomplished in equipment represented diagrammatically in Fig. 13, as follows: Pentane (normal or iso) is introduced into the system and is saturated with hydrogen chloride from the cycle of operations. The hydrocarbon is pumped at 75 lb. gage pressure through a heater and vaporized at 85°C. It then passes into a venturi throat where it comes into contact with chlorine vapors which are supplied at 50°C. and 60 lb. pressure. At this point, the velocity of the pentane vapors should be above 60 miles per hour, and the volume ratio of hydro-

[1] U. S. 1,741,393 (1929); 1,831,474 (1931); 1,835,202 (1931).

carbon to chlorine about 15:1. When these conditions are observed, there is no danger of ignition when the combined vapors are led through the heat exchanger and the reactor. The reaction vessel is controlled at 250 to 300°C. The chlorine-free reaction gases pass through the heat exchanger and a cooler before entering a rectifying tower. The rectifier is supplied with a large body of refluxing pentane and chlorinated pentane from the dephlegmator. The refluxing mixture serves to condense most of the organic compounds but permits the hydrogen chloride and some uncondensed pentane to pass on. These residual gases are cooled and bubbled through pentane entering the system. The hydrogen chloride combines with any moisture in the paraffin hydrocarbon and is separated as hydrochloric acid by agglomerization and decantation.

Any amyl chloride returned to the reaction zone immediately becomes an amylene dichloride. The reactions are quantitative, because the amyl chlorides are in equilibrium with amylenes and hydrogen chloride, and the fixation of the amylenes with chlorine causes the decomposition of amyl chlorides to be rapid and complete:

$$C_5H_{11}Cl \rightleftarrows C_5H_{10} + HCl$$
$$C_5H_{10} + Cl_2 \rightarrow C_5H_{10}Cl_2$$

Even with a 15:1 hydrocarbon-to-chlorine ratio, about 5 per cent dichloride is formed.

According to Hass,[1] chlorination of the pentanes yields all possible isomers, and when the reaction is carried out at 300°C. the following ratios are obtained.

From *n*-pentane: 24 per cent primary, 76 per cent secondary.

From isopentane: 50 per cent primary, 28 per cent secondary, 22 per cent tertiary.

Preparation of Monochloroacetic Acid.—Monochloroacetic acid is prepared by passing chlorine through glacial acetic acid heated to 100°C., using red phosphorus as a catalyst.

The plant assembly may be arranged in the manner shown in Fig. 14. The acetic acid is stored in lead-lined tanks of any suitable size and is delivered as required to jacketed preheaters. The heated acid is run into a scale tank prior to delivery to the chlorinator. The chlorinator is a large, steam-jacketed vessel lined with heavy lead. The top of the vessel is equipped with connections for acetic acid, chlorine, air, effluent gases, condensate, discharge, and thermometer well. The jacket of the chlorinator is connected to both water and steam lines. The condensing system comprises a vertical reflux cooler through which the vapors rise, and a return condenser to complete the condensation. The non-condensable

---

[1] HASS, MCBEE, and WEBER, *Ind. Eng. Chem.*, **28**, 333 (1936).

gases are trapped out while the condensate is returned to the chlorinator below the surface of the reaction mixture.

A charge consisting of 350 lb. of glacial acetic acid at 75°C. and 14 lb. of red phosphorus in 15 lb. of acetic acid is delivered to the chlorinator. The quantity of red phosphorus necessary for reaction diminishes with succeeding runs, so that 12 and 10 lb. may subsequently be employed. Chlorine is now admitted at the rate of 20 lb. per hour. At the end of the first hour, the rate is increased to 40; and at the end of this period, it is raised to 60 lb. per hour and thus maintained throughout the remainder of the run. The heat of reaction brings the temperature of the charge up to 95 to 105°, at which range it is held by the use of either water or steam in the jacket of the chlorinator.

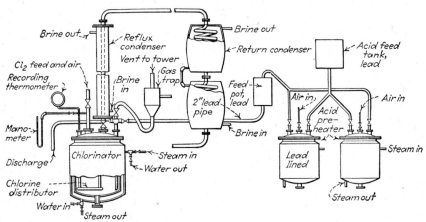

Fig. 14.—Plant assembly, preparation of chloroacetic acid.

During the first part of the run, the circulation of brine through the reflux condenser system must be limited to avoid crystallizing the acetic acid. As chlorination proceeds, the quantity of acetic acid distilling off decreases, and the circulation of brine can be increased accordingly. Since the reflux condenser prevents the passage of any considerable quantity of acetic acid vapors from reaching the return condenser, the latter may be kept at approximately 0°C. to insure the condensation of acetylchloride.

The results of operations, according to the preceding method, are shown in Table IX.

From the preceding data, it is evident that the best yields are obtained in those runs in which a liberal excess of chlorine is introduced over a longer period of time.

Chloroacetyl Chloride.—Chloroacetyl chloride is prepared by passing chlorine through a mixture of chloroacetic acid and sulfur monochloride

TABLE IX.—PREPARATION OF CHLOROACETIC ACID

Run	Acetic acid, lb.	Cl₂, lb.	Time of chlorination, hr.	Weight of chlorination mass, lb.	Yield based on acetic acid, %
1	350	425	11	472	85.7
2	350	480	9	503	91.1
3	350	485	12¼	512	93.0
4	350	425	8⅓	448	81.5
5	350	430	7¾	448	81.5
6	350	425	8	462	84.0
7	350	485	8	487	88.5
8	350	435	7	459	83.5

at 45°C. Anhydrous zinc chloride is used as a catalyst. After the chlorination is complete, the chloroacetyl chloride (b.p., 105 to 106°C., at 760 mm.) is distilled from the mass as a colorless liquid.

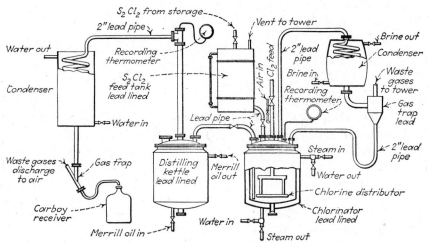

FIG. 15.—Plant assembly: preparation of chloroacetyl chloride.

The complete reaction involved in the preparation of chloroacetyl chloride is expressed by the following equation:

$$4CH_2Cl \cdot COOH + 3Cl_2 + S_2Cl_2 \xrightarrow{ZnCl_2} 4CH_2ClCOCl + 2SO_2 + 4HCl$$

When chloroacetyl chloride is condensed with benzene according to the Friedel and Crafts reaction (see Chap. XII), the valuable lachrymator ω-chloroacetophenone is obtained.

The plant assembly may be arranged in the manner shown in Fig. 15. The chlorinator used in this operation is preferably tall and narrow. This type of vessel is conducive to more efficient chlorination, because the time of contact between the chlorine and chloroacetic acid is increased. The chlorinator is lined with heavy lead and may be provided with a lead coil inside the reactor, connected to both steam and water to control the temperature. When jacketed vessels are employed, the lower heat transfer necessitates the maintenance of a considerable temperature gradient. Here, however, there is no danger of water entering the reaction and ruining the charge because of a faulty coil.

The top of the chlorinator is equipped with connections for chlorine and air, chloroacetic acid and zinc chloride, sulfur monochloride, effluent gases, return line for condensate, and a thermometer well. At the base of the vessel is a flanged opening for cleaning purposes.

The chloroacetic acid (448 lb.) and zinc chloride (15 lb.) are put into the kettle through a large-flanged opening, and the required quantity of sulfur chloride (200 lb.) is then introduced. The chlorinator is closed, and steam is turned into the jacket or internal coil. When the temperature of the mass reaches 40°C., chlorine is introduced at the rate of 40 lb. per hour. The heat of reaction brings the temperature up to 45°C., and it is maintained at this point by circulating steam or water through the heat-transfer medium. At the end of the first hour, the rate of flow of chlorine is increased to 60 lb. per hour, and this rate is maintained until chlorination is complete. When the run is finished, the charge is transferred to a still.

The still is a lead-lined, jacketed vessel, the jacket being connected for high-pressure steam or a circulating fluid. The cover is provided with openings for charging, for effluent gases, a manhole for inspection purposes, and a well for a recording thermometer. A bottom flanged outlet is used when cleaning out the still. The distilled gases travel through a vertical dephlegmating column to effect a sharp separation of the fractions. The condensate is led to several receivers, and the uncondensed gases may be recovered in a suitable absorption system.

The first stages of distillation should be carried on slowly in order to get a satisfactory fractionation. The distillate obtained up to 90°C. (column temperature) is, after an analysis has been made for sulfur monochloride and dichloride, used again in the chlorination process. The second fraction, distilling between 90 and 102°C., is reserved for redistillation. The bulk of the charge, which distills between 102 and 110°C., is principally chloroacetyl chloride.

The presence of acetic acid to any appreciable extent has a tendency to lower the yields. The presence of sulfur as sulfur chlorides may be found in the chloroacetyl chloride, particularly when the fractionation is not satisfactory. The sulfur later exercises a deleterious effect if the chloroacetyl chloride is condensed with benzene to form chloroacetophenone.

TABLE X.—PREPARATION OF CHLOROACETYL CHLORIDE

Run	Monochloro-acetic acid, lb.	Acetic in chloroacetic acid, %	ZnCl$_2$, lb.	S$_2$Cl$_2$, lb.	1st and 2d fractions, lb.	Chloroacetyl chloride, lb.
1	448	0	15	190	55	378
2	446	0	15	199	103	380
3	448	0.31	15	190	45	385
4	449	Trace	15	200	110	395
5	444	0.33	15	200	75	375
6	447	0	15	200	91	379
7	443	0.30	30	210	68	382[1]
8	448	0.09	30	200	80	393

[1] The quantity of ZnCl$_2$ employed is generally increased in the first run following the cleaning of the chlorinator.

In Table X are shown data relating to the preparation of chloroacetyl chloride.

Preparation of Chloroprene (2-Chloro-1, 3-butadiene).[1]—Chloroprene is obtained by passing monovinylacetylene into a cold aqueous solution containing hydrogen chloride and a cuprous chloride-ammonium chloride catalyst. The reactions for the preparation of vinyl acetylene and chloroprene may be represented as follows:

$$2CH\equiv CH \xrightarrow[NH_4Cl]{Cu_2Cl_2} HC\equiv C-CH=CH_2 \tag{1}$$
Vinylacetylene

$$HC\equiv C-CH=CH_2 + HCl \xrightarrow[NH_4Cl]{Cu_2Cl_2} CH_2=C-CH=CH_2 \tag{2}$$
$$\underset{\text{Chloroprene}}{\overset{|}{Cl}}$$

Vinylacetylene, which has a vapor pressure of 621 mm. at 0°C. is removed along with some acetylene and vinylchloride by distillation at low temperatures. When reaction (1) is permitted to continue, particularly at temperatures above 30°C., a number of condensation products, especially divinylacetylene, are obtained. The latter on polymerization gives the synthetic drying oil, "S.D.O."

Chloroprene can be prepared[2] by adding 50 parts of cold vinylacetylene to a chilled mixture composed of 175 parts of concentrated hydrochloric acid (sp. gr. 1.19), 25 parts of cuprous chloride, and 10 parts of

[1] The literature on this subject is important and voluminous, and the student is particularly referred to: NIEUWLAND, CALCOTT, DOWNING, and CARTER, *J. Am. Chem. Soc.*, **53**, 4197 (1931); CAROTHERS, WILLIAMS, COLLINS, and KIRBY, *J. Am. Chem. Soc.*, **53**, 4204 (1931); BRIDGWATER, *Ind. Eng. Chem.*, **28**, 396 (1936); U. S. 1,811,959, 1,812,541, 1,812,542, 1,812,544, 1,812,849 (1931); 1,896,159, 1,896,160, 1,896,162 (1933); 1,950,430 to 1,950,442 (1934).

[2] CAROTHERS, WILLIAMS, COLLINS, and KIRBY, *loc. cit.*

ammonium chloride.   The reaction mass is warmed to 30°C. and stirred for a period of 2 hr.   The chloroprene which is formed is obtained by distilling the reaction mixture by steam in partial vacuum (100 to 250 mm.).

Chloroprene is a colorless liquid (b.p., 59.4°C. at 760 mm.).   It polymerizes spontaneously even in the absence of light, and it is consequently essential to incorporate stabilizing agents, *e.g.*, phenyl-β-naphthylamine, catechol, etc. to keep polymerization conditions under control. At first the chloroprene is converted to a stiff, colorless transparent jelly which contains a considerable amount of unpolymerized 2-chloro-1, 3-butadiene.   As polymerization proceeds, the jelly contracts in volume and becomes a resilient elastic mass resembling a completely vulcanized soft rubber.

The condensation of vinylacetylene with hydrogen chloride may also be carried out in the vapor phase.[1]   A gas consisting mainly of hydrogen and containing about 10 per cent of vinylacetylene (obtained by leading electric arc acetylene over a cuprous catalyst), together with 3 liters of hydrogen chloride, is passed over a catalyst consisting of active carbon laden with mercurous chloride which is maintained at 120°C.   The gas mixture leaves the reaction chamber with a vinylacetylene content of about 3 per cent.   In the course of 24 hr., 190 gm. of chloroprene and 5 gm. dichlorobutene are obtained.   The unconverted vinylacetylene is condensed with the 2-chloro-1, 3-butadiene and is returned to the reaction chamber after distilling it off from the condensate.

The 3, 4-dichloro-1-butene formed in the preceding operation can be converted to chloroprene by dehydrochlorination with solid potassium hydroxide.[2]   The reaction may be represented as follows:

$$CH_2Cl\cdot CHCl\cdot CH=CH_2 \xrightarrow{\text{KOH}} CH_2=CH-CH=CH_2$$
$$\underset{\displaystyle Cl}{|}$$

Preparation of Chlorobenzenes.—The technical chlorination of benzene is carried out in glass-lined, lead-lined, or iron vessels.   Wrought-iron particles or scrap pipe fittings are generally employed as the catalyst.   When some anhydrous iron or aluminum chloride is added, the chlorination takes place more smoothly and without appreciable increase in the reaction temperature.

In the chlorination of benzene, the isomeric *o*- and *p*-dichlorobenzenes are found to accompany the principal monochloro compound.   The reaction rate of benzene to chlorobenzene is approximately 8.5 times as great as that for chlorobenzene to dichlorobenzenes.[3]   The relative

[1] U. S. 2,098,089 (1937).

[2] U. S. 2,038,538 (1936).

[3] BOURION, *Compt. rend.*, **170**, 1309 (1920).

yield of chlorobenzene improves with the speed or increase in rate of chlorination. Thus, when similar batches are treated at 25°C. for 3.5 and 5 hr., respectively, the former will contain about 6.51 per cent and the latter 8.05 per cent polychloro compounds at 74 to 75 per cent chlorination. Since the market and uses for dichlorobenzenes are limited, practical considerations sometimes decree the employment of less than the required molecular quantities of chlorine. Under such conditions, some benzene remains unreacted and is subsequently recovered upon distillation of the reaction mass.

Of the two isomeric dichlorobenzenes, the more valuable crystalline para compound (m.p., 53°C.) is formed in the largest quantities, the ratio of para to ortho being approximately 8:1. In most technical operations, the chlorination is continued until the benzene is all converted to the chloro derivatives. The composition of the charge will vary somewhat, depending on the temperature employed, the catalyst used, and the rate and degree of chlorination. The composition will be approximately as follows: chlorobenzene, 80 per cent; p-dichlorobenzene, 17 per cent; and o-dichlorobenzene, including polychloro compounds, 3 per cent.

p-Dichlorobenzene has found considerable use as an insecticide, moth repellant, and deodorant, whereas the ortho isomer has been used principally to combat termites and as a solvent. Nitration of the dichlorobenzenes followed by amination by ammonolysis leads to the formation

o-Nitro-p-dichloro-benzene ; p-Chloro-o-nitro-aniline ; 1.2-Dichloro-4-nitrobenzene ; o-Chloro-p-nitroaniline

of useful dye intermediates. When these compounds are submitted to amination by reduction, diamino compounds are obtained.

Procedure.—The chlorination of benzene is generally carried out in tall cast-iron or steel tanks which preferably have been lined with a bonded lining of pure lead. The chlorinators are provided with a reflux condenser or an outside cooling system through which the charge may be circulated. When circulation of the chlorinated charge is effected by an external pumping system, it is not necessary to have an agitator in the reactor. All the auxiliary apparatus for stirring, cooling, and pumping should be lined with lead.

The chlorine is delivered through a distributor near the base of the reactor. The distributor may consist of a fused silica tube suitably perforated, or it may be made of a heavy-walled, seamless tubing which is inserted from a convenient opening in the top of the vessel. It may also be attached to a hollow, glass-lined shaft which serves as a stirrer as well as the inlet for chlorine.   When an iron distributor is used, it offers a contact surface for catalysis and is readily attacked, and it therefore needs to be replaced periodically.

Approximately 12,000 lb. of dry benzene is delivered to the chlorinator.   A small quantity of finely divided iron may be added, the amount depending on the quantity of catalyst retained in the chlorinator.   In most technical operations, the bulk of the iron is retained in the system,

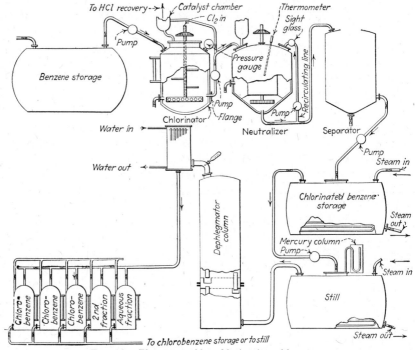

FIG. 16.—Plant assembly: chlorination of benzene.

either in the dished bottom of the chlorinator or in the shelves of the catalyst chamber superimposed on the chlorinator (Fig. 16).   The former procedure permits operating at slightly higher temperatures, since the condenser and dephlegmator return any condensable vapors to the chlorinator.   When the chlorinated benzene is circulated through a condenser located on the outside, the temperature of the solution when in contact with the catalyst must obviously be lower.

Chlorine is bubbled into the charge, the rate of feed being controlled so as to keep the temperature at the desired point.   With outside circulation, the temperature of the chlorinated benzene is kept at 55 to 60°C. When a sample shows the required density, the current of chlorine is stopped. When all the benzene is to be chlorinated, the operation ceases when the density is 1.280 at 15°C. The time consumed is approximately 6 hr.

The hydrogen chloride which escapes through a vent in the dephlegmating or condensing system is washed with chloro- or *o*-dichlorobenzene to remove any organic spray that has been carried away.[1] The scrubbed gas is absorbed in a suitable absorption system.

Neutralization.—The chlorinated benzene is permitted to settle and then drawn off from a side outlet and delivered to the neutralizer. This may be a vertical, jacketed, steel tank equipped with a reflux or condenser and a vent. A solution of caustic soda is added to the chlorinated benzene as it enters the neutralizer to insure a distinct alkaline reaction to litmus. It is necessary to mix the charge thoroughly to insure neutrality, and agitation with a corrosion-resistant propeller or turbine type of stirrer is preferred. The charge is kept warm by jacket steam during the neutralizing treatment.

When repeated tests indicate a faintly alkaline reaction, the chlorinated benzene is delivered to a settling tank and permitted to stand for several hours. The sludge that settles out at the conical base is rich in dichlorobenzenes. The bulk of the charge is withdrawn through a side outlet and pumped to a storage tank, which is heated to prevent crystallization of the charge.

The purification system comprises a horizontal still along with a dephlegmating and condensing apparatus. The chlorinated benzene is heated by steam coils and refluxed until the system is warm. The vapors are then drawn through a tall Kubierschky column to the condenser by a vacuum pump. The first fraction consists of benzene and water. The second fraction (sp. gr., 1.090 to 1.108 at 15°C.) is impure chlorobenzene and is added to the batch next to be distilled. The chlorobenzene fraction (sp. gr., 1.108 at 15°C.) is then run into separate containers. The presence of *p*-dichlorobenzene in the distillate is indicated by a sudden increase in the density of the distillate. The point is watched closely to prevent contamination of the principal product.

The residue in the still is principally dichlorobenzenes. This may be withdrawn after each charge or mixed with subsequent batches of chlorinated benzene until a sufficient quantity of it is accumulated. The para isomer, which has a slightly lower boiling point, can be recovered in a fairly pure state by fractional distillation. The residual ortho compound is contaminated with the para isomer and polychloro derivatives, principally 1, 2, 4-trichlorobenzene.

When the market for dichlorobenzenes is so restricted that it is not desirable to chlorinate all the benzene, the chlorination may be carried

[1] U. S. 1,858,521 (1932).

out as follows:[1] To reduce the formation of higher chlorinated products to a minimum, it is necessary to employ a large excess of benzene, and it is advisable, in order to avoid the handling of large volumes, to combine the chlorinating with a fractionating apparatus (Fig. 17). By this means, the monochlorobenzene is isolated as rapidly as it is formed, and only fresh benzene is exposed to the action of the chlorine. A portion of the benzene is introduced into the heating chamber of a fractional distillation unit *B.C.D.* This plant is completely lined with lead and has its column filled with Raschig rings. A second portion of benzene is delivered into the lead-lined chlorinating vessel *A*, which is provided with a circular

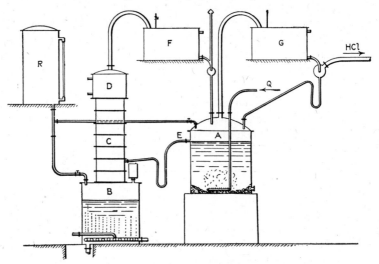

Fig. 17.—Plant layout: continuous chlorination of benzene.

A. Chlorinating vessel.
B. Heating chamber.
C, D. Fractionating column.
E. Overflow from chlorinator.

F. Condenser.
G. Scrubber.
Q. Chlorine inlet.
R. Benzene reservoir.

perforated pipe for the distribution of the chlorine. About 1 per cent by weight of iron turnings is used as the catalyst. The benzene in the chlorinator is brought to a boil by means of a closed steam coil. The condensed vapors return to the vessel, and then the partially chlorinated material runs through an overflow pipe *E* into the heating chambers of the distillation unit, where it is fractionated, the benzene returning to the chlorinator.

The operation is continuous and is considered completed when the material in the fractionating still boils at 118 to 120°C. The material is then transferred to a vat containing a 10 per cent aqueous solution of caustic soda. The mixture is agitated mechanically for some time and then allowed to settle for a few hours. The aqueous portion is removed

[1] BARTHELMY, *Rev. prod. chim.*, **25**, 693 (1922).

by decantation, and the crude chlorinated benzene rectified. The fraction between 80 to 90°C. is returned to the chlorination plant; the portion between 90 and 132°C. is redistilled with the next charge. The distillate coming over between 132 and 133°C., which constitutes about 70 per cent of the whole, is monochlorobenzene.

Production of Chlorinated Biphenyls.—Biphenyl in the liquid state is chlorinated readily by gaseous chlorine in the presence of iron as a catalyst. By regulating the temperature of the reaction, the quantity of chlorine admitted, and by varying the size, quantity, and distribution of the catalyst, the degree of chlorination may be controlled so as to obtain a series of products ranging from the isomeric 2-chloro- and 4-chlorobiphenyls to polychlorinated products containing over 66 per cent of chlorine.[1]

The operation may be conducted in the chlorinator shown in Fig. 18. This comprises a cylindrical iron body 10, closed at both ends by flanged plates. The body is provided with an inlet for chlorine gas and an outlet for the liberated hydrogen chloride. An annular coil 17, for the circulation of the heat-transfer medium, surrounds an internal container 18, which contains the chlorine-inlet pipe 22 and the distributor plate 23, the latter

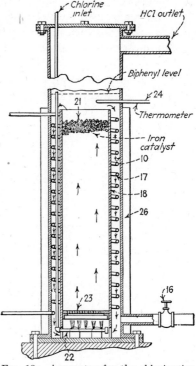

FIG. 18.—Apparatus for the chlorination of biphenyl.

10. Iron casing surrounding apparatus.
16. Outlet for chlorinated biphenyl.
17. Annular heating or cooling coil.
18. Inner wall of chlorinator.
21. Iron particles.
22. Chlorine feed.
23. Distributor plate.
24. Thermometer well.
26. Insulation.

serving also as a support for short sections of iron pipe, which constitute the catalyst.

Molten biphenyl is delivered into the chlorinator until the catalytic mass is covered, and the flow of chlorine is then started. Chlorination proceeds rapidly with the evolution of heat, and water must be circulated through the heat-transfer coil to keep the temperature at approximately 80°C. The rising gases, *i.e.*, Cl and HCl, together with the heat of reaction are instrumental in creating a circulation of the liquid reaction mass, first upward through the catalytic mass and then downward through

[1] Jenkins, U. S. 1,892,397 (1932).

the annular space between the container and the body. By means of the heat-transfer coil, heat may be introduced or removed as desired. The progress of the reaction is readily followed by determining the specific gravity of samples of the chlorinated liquid at frequent intervals.

In the chart (Fig. 19) is shown the increase in weight of the reaction mixture (pounds of chlorine per pound of biphenyl), at progressively increasing percentages of monochlorination, together with the correspond-

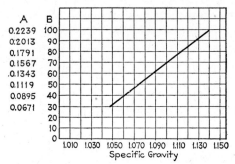

FIG. 19.—Specific gravity chart for chlorinated biphenyl.
A. Increase in weight of reaction mixture in units per unit of biphenyl.
B. Per cent chlorination.

ing density measurements. By ascertaining the characteristics of a sample and comparing the observations with the data in Fig. 18, it is possible to gage quickly the completeness of the reaction. When the monochlorinated product is desired, the flow of chlorine is stopped when the increase in weight indicates 80 to 85 per cent completion. The

TABLE XI.—PROPERTIES OF CHLORINATED BIPHENYL[1]

Expt. No.	% chlorine	Properties at room temperature
1	18.30	Very light, mobile liquid
2	27.19	Light oil, less mobile than 1
3	42.11	Light oil, (density = 1.375 @ 29°C.)
4	42.86	Oil, slightly heavier than 3
5	52.15	Viscous oil
6	57.19	Semisolid, consistency of pitch
7	59.73	Semisolid, slightly heavier than 6; softening point 49.5°C.
8	65.26[2]	Non-crystalline solid, conchoidal fracture, softening point 61.5°C.; bends if slowly deformed and breaks if rapidly deformed
9	65.40	Semi-conchoidal fracture partly crystalline, softens at 63.5°C.
10	66.21	Crystalline fracture

[1] U. S. 1,892,397 (1932).
[2] The production of non-crystalline polychlorinated compounds is promoted by incorporating some of the less volatile still residues obtained in the preparation of biphenyl, along with biphenyl in the chlorination process. These resinous materials find use in the preparation of varnishes.

mass is then discharged from the chlorinator, washed with water to remove ferric chloride, and finally distilled *in vacuo*.

The production of higher chlorinated products can be obtained by continuing the chlorination and allowing the temperature of the reaction mass to rise to 175 to 200°C. Some of the more highly chlorinated biphenyls are crystalline, while mixtures of the lower chlorinated biphenyls are liquid. The properties of a series of such chlorinated mixtures are given in Table XI.

Preparation of Ethylene Chlorhydrin.—The preparation of ethylene chlorhydrin[1] may be carried out continuously in the apparatus shown in Fig. 20. The tower is first charged with ethylene under a pressure of 200 atmospheres at 20°C. A solution of hydrated lime is then introduced

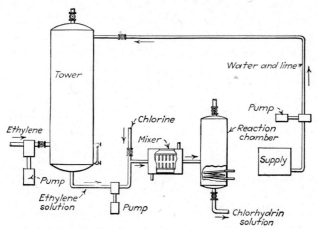

Fig. 20.—Plant assembly: preparation of ethylene chlorhydrin.

until the desired quantity collects at the base of the tower, compressed ethylene being admitted simultaneously in order to maintain the desired pressure. The alkaline solution of ethylene is then transferred at such a rate as to keep the solution level in the tower about constant. Under such operating conditions of temperature and pressure, about 28 gm. of ethylene per liter is in solution, compared with 0.14 gm. at normal temperatures and pressures. As the solution enters the mixer, chlorine is introduced at the rate of 1 mole (70.9 gm.) per liter. The quantity of lime in suspension in the tower is regulated at approximately half the molal concentration of the ethylene in solution leaving the tower—in this case, 0.5 mole, or 28 gm., of CaO per liter. In the mixer, the chlorine reacts with the hydrated lime to form calcium oxychloride. This compound is at once decomposed to form hypochlorous acid and calcium chloride.

[1] Youtz, U. S. 1,875,309 (1932).

$$CaO + Cl_2 \rightarrow CaCl \cdot OCl$$
$$CaCl \cdot OCl + Cl_2 + H_2O \rightarrow CaCl_2 + 2HOCl$$

The hypochlorous acid reacts with ethylene as the mixture traverses the reactor, forming ethylene chlorhydrin.

$$HOCl + H_2C = CH_2 \rightarrow CH_2OH \cdot CH_2Cl$$

The ethylene chlorhydrin-calcium chloride solution is withdrawn from the reaction chamber. Such solutions may be treated directly with alkaline reagents for the preparation of glycol. Alternatively, the ethylene chlorhydrin may be recovered by distillation and subsequent salting out.

Application of Sandmeyer Reaction.—The preparation of halogeno-anthraquinones according to the Sandmeyer reaction necessitates some slight modifications in the usual procedure because of the insolubility of the diazonium halide. The preparation of alpha mono- and dihalogenoanthraquinones may be carried out according to the procedure that follows:

Preparation of 1-*Bromoanthraquinone.*—Of 1-aminoanthraquinone 40 parts is dissolved in 400 parts of 66°Bé. sulfuric acid. Diazotization is carried out by the addition of sodium nitrite solution at 10 to 20°C. The temperature of the diazonium solution is lowered by the addition of ice until the yellow crystals start to separate out. In about two hours, the precipitation of the diazo compound is complete. The product is filtered off and then treated with 400 parts of hydrobromic acid (15°Bé.), until a fine slurry is obtained. This is added to a solution of 15 parts of cuprous bromide in 400 parts of hydrobromic acid. 1-Bromoanthraquinone separates out as fine yellow crystals, while nitrogen is evolved. The product can be purified by recrystallizing from nitrobenzene.

The 1, 5- and 1, 8-diaminoanthraquinones can be treated similarly to obtain the corresponding halogen derivatives. It will be remembered that in the nitration of anthraquinone, the alpha dinitro compounds are formed along with 1-nitroanthraquinone. By subsequent reduction, these dinitro compounds are converted to amino derivatives and then, by the Sandmeyer reaction, are transformed to the corresponding halogen derivatives. In the preparation of 2-anthraquinonesulfonic acid, some 2, 6- and 2, 7-anthraquinonedisulfonic acids are formed. These compounds also can be converted to halogen derivatives by treatment with halogen hydracids and halogenates. Alternatively, the disulfonic acids may be converted to dihydroxy compounds by hydrolysis with strongly alkaline solutions. The advantageous utilization of such by-products is recognized to be an important factor in maintaining the economic stability of dye plants.

Fluorination of Carbon Tetrachloride.—The preparation of difluoro-dichloromethane by the fluorination of carbon tetrachloride can be carried out in the apparatus shown diagrammatically in Fig. 21.[1] The operation is started by adding about 600 parts of antimony pentachloride

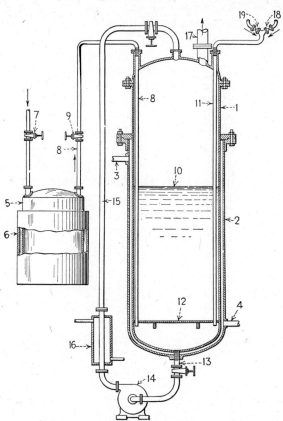

Fɪɢ. 21.—Apparatus for fluorination of CCl₄.

1, 2. Reaction vessel with jacket.
3, 4. Inlet and outlet to jacket.
5, 6. Hydrogen fluoride vaporizer with jacket.
7, 9. Control valves on inlet and outlet lines for HF.
8. Delivery line for HF.
10. SbCl₅ catalyst.
11. Internal delivery line for CCl₄.
12. Distributor plate.
13, 14, 15. Circulating line and pump.
16. Heat exchanger for steam.
17. Outlet for gaseous products.
19. 18, Control lines for fresh and recovered CCl₄.

to the cast-iron reaction vessel, which is maintained at 60°C. Over a period of 24 hr., 500 parts of dry hydrogen fluoride is delivered from the vaporizer through the steel line 8, while concurrently 1,925 parts of fresh carbon tetrachloride is introduced through lines 18 and 11. After the

[1] U. S. 2,058,453 (1936).

reaction is under way, the recovered CCl_4 from steel scrubbers is returned by way of line 19.   During the reaction the catalyst-containing reaction mixture is continuously circulated through the heat exchanger 16, maintained at 110°C., and is returned to the vapor space above the charge.

The vaporized products are hydrochloric acid, fluorotrichloromethane and difluorodichloromethane, together with some unreacted hydrogen fluoride and carbon tetrachloride.   These vapors are passed first to a warm and then to a cold carbon tetrachloride scrubber—the second

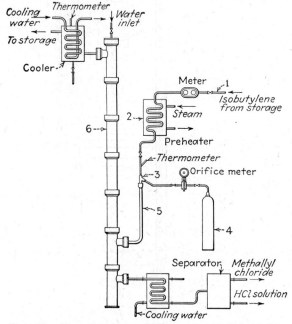

Fig. 22.—Flow diagram, preparation of methallyl chloride.

refluxing back to the first.   The residual gases are further purified by passing them through water, aqueous sodium hydroxide, concentrated sulfuric acid, and then subjecting them to condensation.   Difluorodichloromethane is thus obtained in good yields.

Preparation of Methallyl Chloride.[1]

$$\begin{array}{c} CH_3 \\ {}_{} \hspace{-0.5em}\diagdown \\ CH_3 \diagup \end{array}\hspace{-0.7em} C{=}CH_2 \xrightarrow[300°C.]{Cl_2} CH_2{=}\underset{\underset{CH_3}{|}}{C}{-}CH_2Cl$$

The operation is conducted in the apparatus shown diagrammatically in Fig. 22.   Isobutylene is delivered from a storage tank through a meter to a preheater 2, and thence to a branched mixing tube 3, where

[1] Engs and Redmond, U. S. 2,077,382 (1937).

it comes in contact with chlorine gas delivered from cylinder 4. The flow of chlorine is controlled by valves so that about ⅔ mole is introduced per mole of isobutylene. The mixed reactants pass through a reaction tube 5, at such a rate that the time spent in this zone at 300°C. is less than 1 sec. The reaction products are conducted directly to the base of a hydrochloric acid scrubbing tower 6, which is packed with ceramic rings. Water or dilute hydrochloric acid is admitted at a rate sufficient to form a

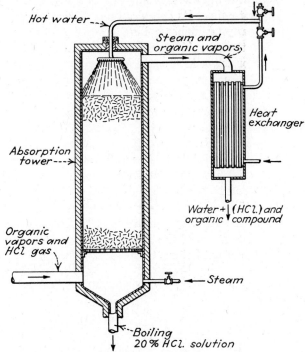

Fig. 23.—Apparatus for the recovery and purification of hydrochloric acid.

5 to 10 per cent HCl solution at the bottom of the column. The unre-acted isobutylene, together with other hydrocarbons and some methylallyl chloride, pass to the top of the tower and thence through the cooler, where the methallyl chloride separates out. The methallyl chloride and dilute hydrochloric acid run from the bottom of the tower through a cooler to a separator. Here, the crude methallyl chloride, which is contaminated by isocrotyl chloride $\begin{matrix} CH_3 \\ \diagdown \\ CH_3 \diagup \end{matrix} C{=}CHCl$ is separated and then purified.

Recovery of Hydrochloric Acid.—Because of the diversity in the char-acter of organic impurities that accompany the hydrochloric acid vapors leaving the chlorination system, it is obviously necessary to make modifications in the somewhat standardized recovery systems.   When relatively low-boiling organic vapors (b.p. < 10°C.) which are insoluble in water are encountered, these may be cooled and condensed by pressure after the removal of the hydrogen chloride in a water-absorption system. In the case of volatile high-boiling liquids (b.p. > 10°C.), the chlorinated compound can usually be removed by cooling and dephlegmating the effluent vapors and then passing the uncondensed gases through water or relatively nonvolatile organic solvents or through the compound to be chlorinated in order to effect its dehydration.   The halogeno compound itself or an accompanying higher-boiling polyhalogeno compound may also be employed as the scrubbing agent, this operation being carried out in a suitable vessel or tower interposed between the chlorinator and the absorption system.   Such a polyhalogeno compound (*e.g.*, *o*-dichlorobenzene) or other high-boiling compatible solvents can be submitted to fractional distillation at convenient intervals to effect the recovery of the desired halogeno compound.

When the apparatus shown in Fig. 23 is employed for the recovery of hydrogen chloride, it is possible to free the resultant acid of undesired organic materials which impart color and odor.   The process hydrogen chloride is delivered near the bottom of a suitably packed absorption tower containing boiling water whereby a 20 per cent solution of hydrochloric acid is formed.   The absorption process is exothermic and tends to maintain the temperature of the scrubbing solution at 110°C., which corresponds to the constant boiling temperature of this binary mixture.[1]

[1] U. S. 2,047,611 (1936).

CHAPTER V

SULFONATION

By P. H. Groggins and W. A. Simpson

I. INTRODUCTION

Definition.—Sulfonation may be defined as the process whereby the union of the group

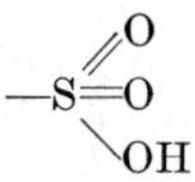

$$-S\overset{\displaystyle O}{\underset{\displaystyle OH}{\Vert}}O$$

to carbon or nitrogen of an organic compound is effected. In the aliphatic series, three sulfonic groups may be attached to the same carbon atom, as in methanetrisulfonic acid [$CH(SO_3H)_3$]. In the aromatic series, however, no sulfonic acid is known that has two such groups attached to the same carbon atom. In the aliphatic series, mono-, di- and tri-sulfonic acids can be obtained; and in the aromatic series, even tetra-sulfonic acids have been prepared. Combinations of aliphatic sulfonic acids attached to an aromatic nucleus also occur, as in toluene-ω-sulfonic acid.

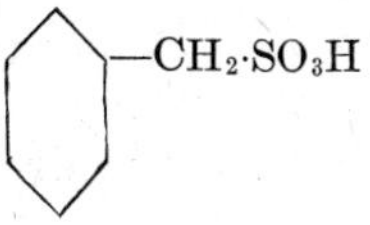

The sulfonic acids of aromatic compounds are of much greater commercial importance than the aliphatic sulfonic acids. One of the distinguishing characteristics between aliphatic and aromatic compounds is the ease with which the aromatic unsubstituted hydrocarbons form sulfonic acids with moderately concentrated sulfuric acid, in contrast to the difficulty experienced with the lower saturated paraffin hydrocarbons. The latter require sulfuric acid containing free SO_3 (oleum) to effect substitution of the sulfonic acid group. Unsaturated aliphatic compounds, however, readily add on sulfuric acid, and this reaction is employed extensively in the commercial separation of olefines from the saturated components of petroleum.

The sulfonic acids are not to be confused with the esters of sulfuric acid, or alkyl sulfuric acids, of the general formula $RO\cdot SO_2\cdot OH$, as for example ethyl sulfuric acid (ethyl hydrogen sulfate) $C_2H_5O \cdot SO_2 \cdot OH$, wherein SO_3H is linked to oxygen and not to carbon, as in ethylsulfonic acid ($CH_3 \cdot CH_2 \cdot SO_3 \cdot H$). A general distinguishing characteristic of the sulfuric acid esters is the ease with which they are hydrolyzed when boiled with dilute aqueous solutions of acids or alkalis; the sulfonic acids are ordinarily relatively stable under these conditions. Because of the extensive industrial utilization of the sulfuric acid esters of the higher fatty acid alcohols and their similar mode of preparation, such *sulfations* are discussed very briefly in this chapter.

Uses of Sulfonic Acids.—By far the most important uses of sulfonic acids relate to their employment in the synthesis of intermediates for dyestuffs. By replacing the sulfonic acid group in aromatic compounds, it is possible to effect the preparation of hydroxy, nitro, amino, and halogeno compounds.' A particular advantage of the sulfonic acid group is its property of conferring increased solubility of the compound in aqueous solutions, and it is this characteristic which facilitates the subsequent conversion or direct application of such compounds. In the chapter on amination by ammonolysis, it is shown that the replacement of —SO_3H by —NH_2 takes place more readily than the similar replacement of —Cl.

Sulfonated castor oil, olive oil, and other vegetable oils have long been used in the textile, leather, paper, glue, and other industries. Certain sulfonic acids find special uses as follows:

1. As aids in leather treatment—employing the sulfonation products of phenol-aldehyde condensations.

2. As a constituent of soaps—using the alkali salts of sulfonated mineral oils.

3. As wetting or emulsifying agents—introducing small quantities of sulfonated tetrahydrobenzene, propylene, trichloroethylene, butyl-naphthalene, stearic, oleic or palmitic acids, etc.

4. As an aid in dyeing.

5. As detergents—derivatives of isethionic acid (hydroxyethyl-sulfonic acid) with oleic acid or its derivatives.

Of great importance also, and related to sulfonic acids, are the sulfuric acid esters of cetyl, stearyl, and palmityl alcohols which are used as detergents.

II. SULFONATING AGENTS AND THEIR PRINCIPAL APPLICATIONS

In the following paragraphs, a survey is made of the principal sulfonating agents and some of their technical applications. These agents may be listed as follows:

1. Sulfuric acid.
2. Oleum (solution of SO_3 in 100% H_2SO_4).
3. Sulfur trioxide alone.

4. Acid sulfates and polysulfates.
5. Chlorosulfonic acids.
6. Sulfur dioxide.
7. Sulfites and acid sulfites.
8. Hydrosulfites.
9. N-pyridiniumsulfonic acid.
10. Aminosulfonic acids.

The choice of the agent and the technic employed will be governed by such factors as the chemical and physical properties of the organic compound as well as by the economics of competitive methods.

SULFURIC ACID

Properties.—In the sulfonation process, the chemical behavior of sulfuric acid is conditioned largely by its power for withdrawing water. Sulfur trioxide forms a number of well-defined hydrates with water. The principal hydrates coming within the category of sulfonating agents are the following:

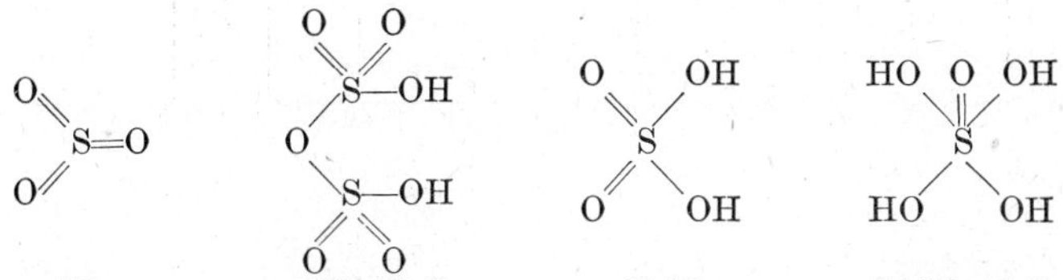

$$\underset{\substack{SO_3 \\ \text{Anhydride}}}{O{=}S{<}\!\!\begin{smallmatrix}O\\O\end{smallmatrix}} \qquad \underset{\substack{2SO_3 \cdot H_2O \\ \text{Pyrosulfuric Acid}}}{\begin{smallmatrix}O\\\|\\O{-}S{-}OH\\\|\\O\end{smallmatrix}} \qquad \underset{\substack{H_2SO_4 \\ \text{Monohydrate}}}{\begin{smallmatrix}O\\\|\\S\\O\end{smallmatrix}\!\!\begin{smallmatrix}OH\\ \\OH\end{smallmatrix}} \qquad \underset{\substack{H_2SO_4 \cdot H_2O \\ \text{Dihydrate}}}{\begin{smallmatrix}HO\ \ O\ \ OH\\\|\\S\\HO\ \ \ \ OH\end{smallmatrix}}$$

Tri- and pentahydrates of sulfur trioxide are also known, and this great affinity for water is evidenced by its hygroscopicity and its efficacy as a dehydrating agent in removing the elements of water from inorganic and organic substances.

The hydrates of sulfuric acid exist at low temperatures as definite crystalline compounds, and with rising temperature they all decompose with more or less ease with the disengagement of either sulfur trioxide or water. In their ordinary form, they present all the properties of simple solutions, and it is permissible to presume that between SO_3 and H_2O exists a consecutive series of homogeneous liquids or solutions among which are distinguished definite hydrates. In other words, the term *sulfuric acid* is the generic name of a series of solutions of sulfur trioxide in water, some of which are chemical hydrates of SO_3 and most of which are merely solutions of the gas of convenient strength for use in the arts.

When sulfuric acid and water are mixed, a considerable rise of temperature occurs (see Fig. 1). Experience has shown that the activity of sulfuric acid as a sulfonating agent is directly related to its concentration, and this governs the heat of solution and the capacity to withdraw the elements of water from other chemical compounds.

The vapor of sulfuric acid is completely dissociated into water and sulfur trioxide at 450°C. At ordinary temperatures, however, the gas is more or less bound up as hydrates; this union becomes weaker with increasing temperature. These properties of sulfuric acid thus lead to the belief that SO_3 dissolved in, or combined with, sulfuric acid may be the true sulfonating agent. It is known that sulfur trioxide, liquid or

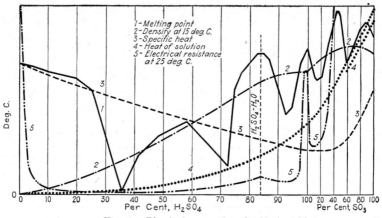

Fig. 1.—Physical properties of sulfuric acid.

gaseous, can be employed for the preparation of sulfonic acids, the process being essentially one of addition, thus:

$$R \cdot H + SO_3 \rightarrow R \cdot SO_3H$$

The sulfonating action of sulfuric acid may be represented by the following equation:

$$R \cdot H + \begin{matrix} HO \\ \\ HO \end{matrix} \hspace{-0.5em} \diagup \hspace{-1em} \diagdown \hspace{-0.5em} SO_2 \rightarrow R \cdot SO_2 \cdot OH + H_2O$$

Water is therefore a by-product, and it is known that with increasing H_2O concentration the rate of sulfonation is decelerated. The critical acid concentration is not the same for all sulfonations, for this depends on the reactivity of the organic compound with sulfuric acid; and this characteristic is related to the type, structure, and substituents present in the compound undergoing treatment.

Treatment of Aliphatic Compounds with Sulfuric Acid.—Sulfuric acid does not react with the saturated paraffin hydrocarbons, and only by using oleum can the compounds containing 6 to 8 carbon atoms be converted directly to sulfonic acids.

$$C_6H_{14} \xrightarrow{\text{Oleum}} C_6H_{13} \cdot SO_3H + H_2O$$

Sulfuric acid does, however, combine with olefinic compounds to form sulfates, and this reaction is employed in the preparation of alcohols

$$H_2C:CH_2 + H_2SO_4 \rightarrow \quad \begin{matrix} C_2H_5O \\ HO \end{matrix} \Big\rangle S \begin{matrix} O \\ O \end{matrix}$$

and in the technical separation of unsaturated hydrocarbons derived from petroleum cracking operations. This procedure, like the treatment of ethanol with sulfuric acid, results in the formation of alkyl sulfates or esters wherein a hydrogen atom rather than the hydroxyl group of the sulfuric acid is replaced. The following formulations serve to bring out this distinction:

$$\begin{matrix} HO \\ HO \end{matrix} \Big\rangle S \begin{matrix} O \\ O \end{matrix} \qquad \begin{matrix} C_2H_5O \\ HO \end{matrix} \Big\rangle S \begin{matrix} O \\ O \end{matrix} \qquad \begin{matrix} C_2H_5 \\ HO \end{matrix} \Big\rangle S \begin{matrix} O \\ O \end{matrix}$$

Sulfuric Acid   Ethyl Sulfuric Acid   Ethylsulfonic Acid

Treatment of Aromatic Compounds with Sulfuric Acid. *Benzene Derivatives.*—The ease with which aromatic hydrocarbons react with sulfuric acid to form sulfonic acids is one of the characteristics that differentiate them from the paraffin hydrocarbons. Benzene, for example, can be sulfonated by adding to it 2.5 times its weight of 98 per cent sulfuric acid, heating at 80°C. until refluxing stops, and finally heating at 100°C. Completion of the reaction is indicated by the absence of benzene in a diluted sample of the reaction mass. The product can be converted to the calcium sulfonate by treatment with lime and filtering off the precipitated gypsum. The sodium sulfonate is obtained by treat-

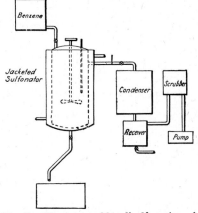

FIG. 2.—Plant assembly: disulfonation of benzene.

ing a hot suspension of the calcium salt with the calculated quantity of soda ash or treating the sulfonation mass directly with sodium sulfite, when the latter is available as a by-product from the alkali fusion operations in the production of sodium phenolate.[1]

To prepare benzenedisulfonic acid, it is necessary to sulfonate at 220 to 260°C. When a considerable excess of sulfuric acid is employed, *i.e.*, about 300 per cent, a yield of about 90 per cent of the theoretical is obtained. The excess of acid required can be reduced greatly by carrying

[1] HOTSON, *Chem. & Met. Eng.*, **19**, 540 (1918); Levinstein, Brit. 2300 (1883).

out the sulfonation under reduced pressures.[1] Under such conditions, the water of reaction is removed, and the concentration of the sulfonating acid maintained at the desired point. The reaction may be carried out in the apparatus shown in Fig. 2 by delivering benzenesulfonic acid to the jacketed sulfonator and then introducing sulfuric acid at a temperature of 200 to 220°C. to effect disulfonation.

The production of *sulfanilic acid* (1-aminobenzene-4-sulfonic acid) is generally carried out as a two-stage process. The sulfuric acid salt is made first, and this is "baked" at 200°C. *in vacuo* (12 to 15 mm. pressure) to bring about the dehydration and intramolecular rearrangement.

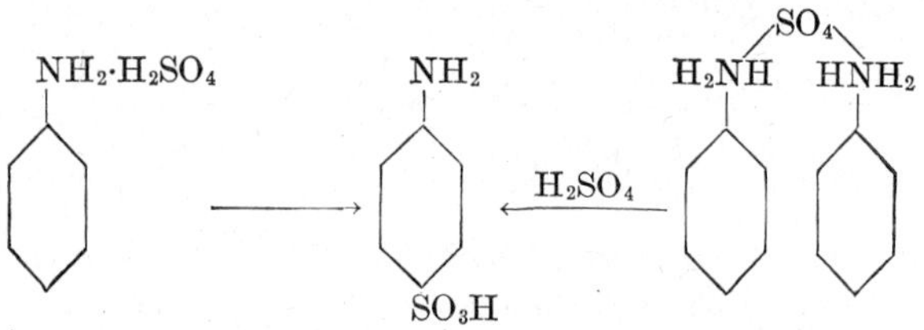

Alternatively, dianiline sulfate may first be prepared by mixing approximately the combining proportions of the materials and then carrying out the sulfonation directly by heating with an excess of strong sulfuric acid.

The isomeric toluidines and xylidines, as well as α-naphthylamine and 1-aminoanthraquinone, can be sulfonated in a similar manner. The —SO_3H group generally enters para to the —NH_2 group, unless this position is occupied.[2] 1-Aminoanthraquinone, however, forms the orthosulfonic acid.

Naphthalenesulfonic Acids.—The sulfonic acids of naphthalene, naphthol, and naphthylamine are numerous and important. In the course of years, these compounds have acquired a wide technical application and are among the most important intermediates in the preparation of azo dyes. The literature[3] pertaining to these compounds is so voluminous and specialized that only a bare outline can be presented here.

In the sulfonation of naphthalene, two isomeric monosulfonic acids are obtained. The proportion of each isomer formed depends on the temperature of sulfonation, but under no conditions is either isomer obtained as the sole product. When the reaction is carried out at 40°C., the α-monosulfonate predominates,

---

[1] Downs, U. S. 1,279,295 (1918); 1,301,785 (1919).

[2] HUBER, *Helv. Chim. Acta*, **15**, 1372 (1932).

[3] WITT, *Ber.*, **48**, 743 (1915); FIERZ-DAVID, "Grundlegende Operations der Farbenchemie" (1924).

SO₃H diagram with naphthalene structures:

SO_3H ... $\xleftarrow[40°C.]{H_2SO_4}$ ... $\xrightarrow[160°C.]{H_2SO_4}$ ... SO_3H

96% ... 85%

the ratio of the alpha to beta compound being closely 96:4. When sulfonation is effected at 160°C., the beta compound constitutes 85 per cent of the monosulfonic acids formed. The number of isomers that are possible on continued sulfonation is large, and their separation is often very difficult. The isolation of the individual sulfonic acids is the operation that has presented the most interesting and difficult problems in the sulfonation process.

In the further sulfonation of naphthalene, Armstrong and Wynne[1] found that the second —SO₃H group never enters the ortho, para, or peri position to the first. It has also been established that when two sulfonic acid groups are introduced, they enter different nuclei in the naphthalene molecule. At low temperatures, the second sulfo group enters the most remote alpha position and the most remote beta position at high temperatures. Thus, 1-naphthalenesulfonic acid, on further sulfonation in the cold, gives 70 per cent 1, 5-disulfonic acid and 25 per cent of the 1, 6-isomer. At higher temperatures the 1, 6-disulfonic acid is formed predominantly. A schematic representation of the naphthalenesulfonic acids is shown in Fig. 3.

The monosulfonation of naphthalene is practically always carried out with a 25 to 40 per cent excess of sulfuric acid of 93 to 98 per cent strength. In the preparation of the alpha compound, naphthalene is added to the acid below 60°C.; while in the production of the beta derivative, the naphthalene is first melted, and the acid run into the melted hydrocarbon at 160 to 165°C. When a sample is distilled with steam and naphthalene is absent, the reaction is considered complete.

In the production of naphthalene-2-sulfonic acid, any unconverted naphthalene along with the 15 per cent of naphthalene-1-sulfonic acid can be removed by passing dry steam into the sulfonation mixture at 150 to 160°C. The alpha compound is desulfonated or hydrolyzed, and the resulting naphthalene is distilled off.

SO_3H ... $\xrightarrow{\text{Steam}}$ ... $+ H_2SO_4$

[1] Armstrong and Wynne, *Ber.*, **25**, 226 (1892); **32**, 1136, 3186 (1899); *Ann.*, **361**, 170 (1908).

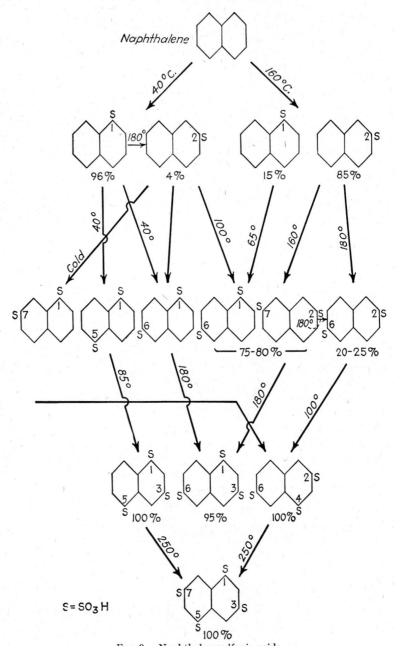

Fig. 3.—Naphthalenesulfonic acids.

Naphthalene-2-sulfonic acid is almost always converted to the sodium salt, but the methods to this end vary considerably. Frequently, the sulfonation mass is diluted by running into 2 parts of cold water and then neutralizing by the addition of dilute hot hydrated lime. The total volume of water added is approximately 5.5 times the original weight of

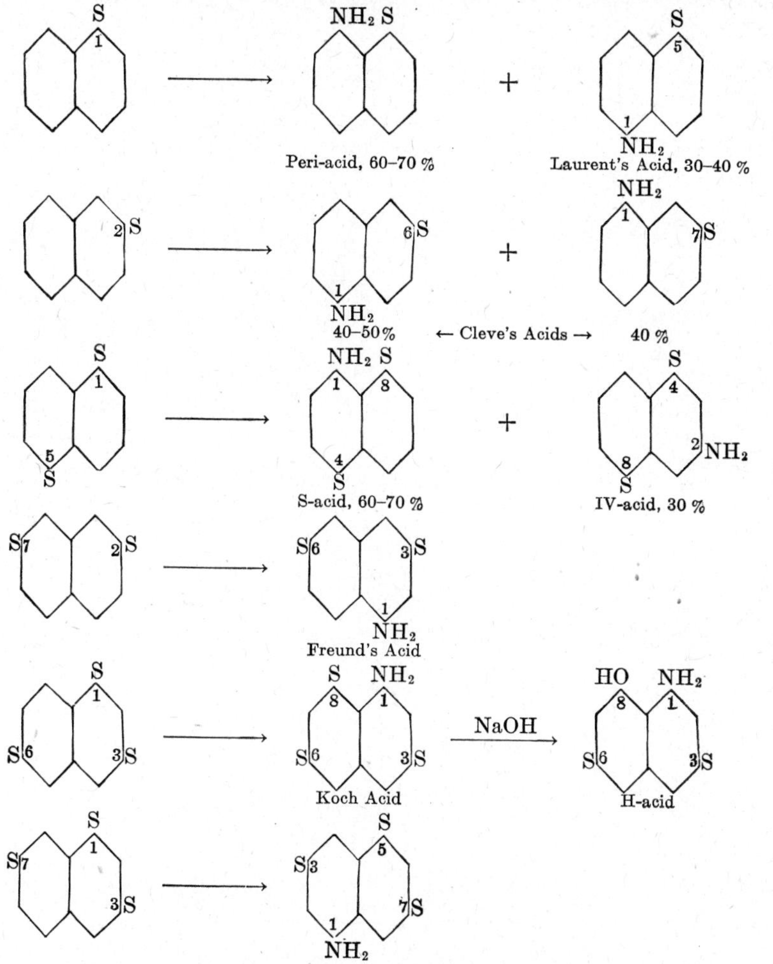

FIG. 4.—Naphthylaminesulfonic acids derived by nitration and reduction of sulfonic acids.

the reactants. The mass is filtered hot, and the calcium naphthalenesulfonates separated from the gypsum. The filtrate is cooled to 30°C., and the calcium sulfonates that separate out are filtered and washed. By treating the press cake with the calculated amount of soda ash in boiling water, the solution of sodium sulfonates is obtained. This is filtered from the calcium carbonate and allowed to cool. The crystallized

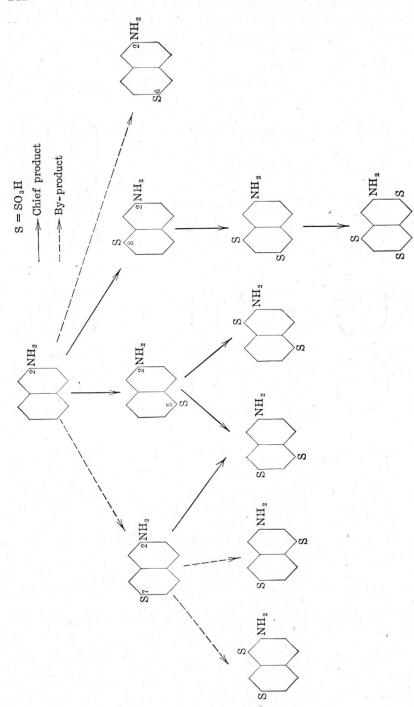

FIG. 5.—Sulfonic acids derived from β-naphthylamine by sulfonation.

sodium naphthalene-2-sulfonate is separated from the mother liquor containing the alpha isomer.

The sulfonation mass may also be treated with sodium sulfite containing some sodium hydroxide and naphthol, which is obtained as a by-product in the subsequent fusion of sodium naphthalene-2-sulfonate.[1] In a further modification, a slight excess over the calculated quantity of Glauber's salt is added to the diluted sulfonic acid to form the sodium sulfonate, while the sulfuric acid produced by metathesis is neutralized

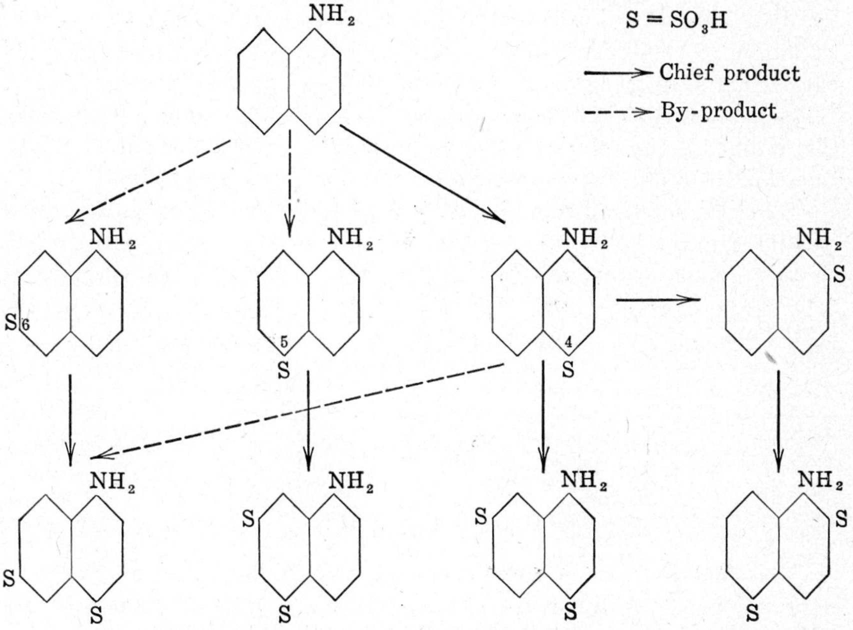

FIG. 6.—Sulfonic acids derived from α-naphthylamine by sulfonation.

with lime or chalk. The soluble sodium naphthalene-2-sulfonate is then filtered from the gypsum.

Naphthylaminesulfonic Acids.—Of greater technical importance than the naphthalenesulfonic acids are the naphthylaminesulfonic acids. These compounds are derived by three general methods:

1. Nitrating a sulfonic acid and then reducing. The products obtained by this procedure are set forth in Fig. 4.[2]

2. Sulfonating a nitro compound and then reducing.

3. Sulfonating an amino compound, which leads to the naphthylamine sulfonic acids shown in Figs. 5 and 6.

[1] Levinstein, Brit. 2300 (1883).
[2] Moore, Diss. E. T. H., Zurich (1925).

Naphthionic acid, 1-aminonaphthalene-4-sulfonic acid is prepared from α-naphthylamine by the baking process (see Sulfanilic Acid, pages 287–288). One thousand pounds of α-naphthylamine is melted and delivered slowly to 750 lb. of 66°Bé. sulfuric acid, the mass being thoroughly mixed. The charge is heated to 170 to 180°C., and 50 lb. of oxalic acid is added cautiously, a uniform porous mass thus being obtained. The mixture is then run into trays which are resistant to sulfuric acid, put into a vacuum oven, and heated at 180°C. for 8 hr.

The porous gray mass is cooled and powdered and then neutralized by dissolving in dilute alkali. To remove the unconverted α-naphthylamine (5 to 10 per cent), the solution of the sodium salt is extracted with benzene in an extraction apparatus. As indicated in Fig. 6, some 1, 5-acid (Laurent's acid) accompanies the naphthionic acid. To remove this impurity, the solution of sodium naphthionate is concentrated and then cooled to effect the crystallization of the principal product.

1-Naphthylamine-2-sulfonic acid is prepared by heating the dried sodium naphthionate obtained from the previous operation with two to three parts of naphthalene at 217°C., the conversion taking place in 3 hr. The excess of naphthalene is recovered by adding water to the cooled charge and blowing steam through the reaction mass.

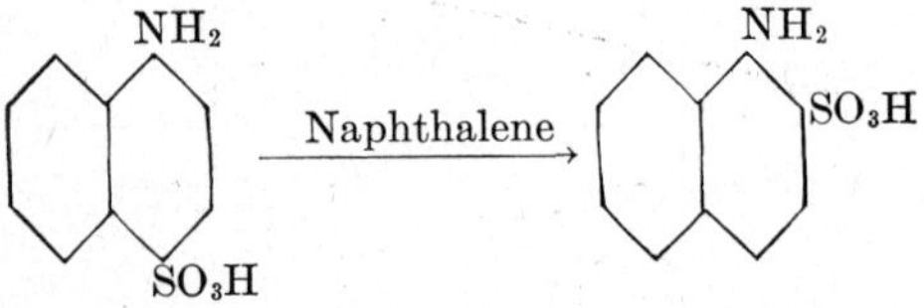

This reaction is of interest in showing the influence of an excess of naphthalene or sulfuric acid on the migration of the sulfonic acid group. The course of the reaction is probably as follows:

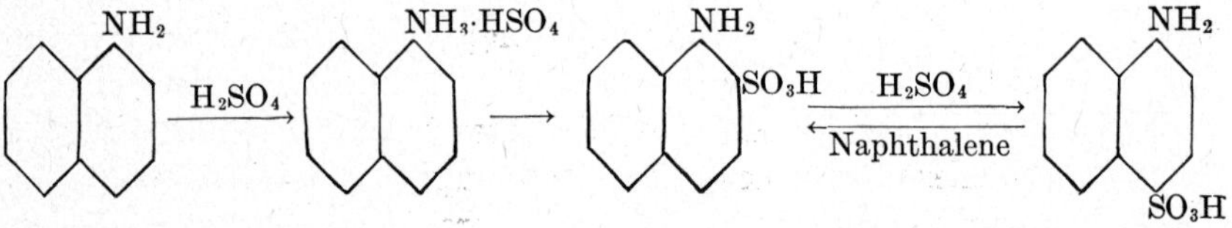

In the monosulfonation of β-naphthol leading to the formation of Crocein and Schäffer acids (see below), there is a similar migration of the sulfonic acid group to the most stable positions in the presence of an excess of sulfuric acid and at comparatively high temperatures.

2-Naphtholsulfonic Acids.—By sulfonating β-naphthol with approximately two parts of sulfuric acid (93 per cent), a mixture of two monosulfonic acids is obtained, *viz.*, Crocein acid and Schäffer acid.

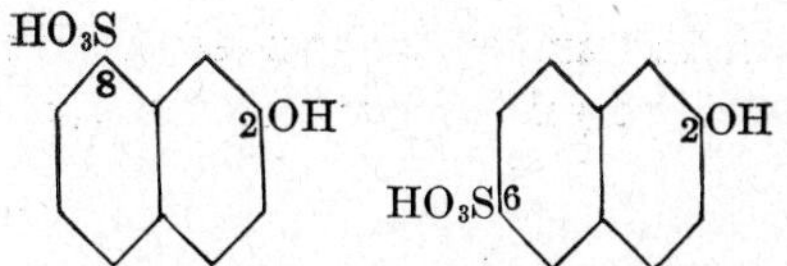

Crocein Acid   Schäffer Acid

At low temperatures, *i.e.*, 20°C., the former predominates; but at higher temperatures (100 to 110°C.), the latter is the principal product.

It is known that the initial product of reaction is the 2-naphthol-1-sulfonic acid II presumably derived from the sulfuric acid ester I at 20 to 40°C. and transformed to the isomeric Crocein acid III at slightly higher temperatures. The most stable of the monosulfonic acids, obtained either by the direct sulfonation of β-naphthol at 100°C. or by

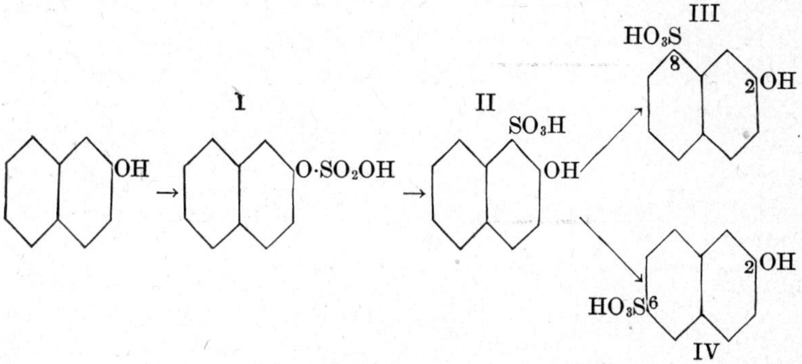

further heating of Crocein acid, is 2-naphthol-6-sulfonic acid (Schäffer acid).

When the quantity of sulfuric acid is increased, two disulfonic acids are formed, the proportion of each isomer again depending on the sulfonation temperature employed. When operating at 30 to 35°C., G-acid (2-naphthol-6, 8-disulfonic acid) predominates; and at 60°C., R-acid (2-naphthol-3, 6-disulfonic acid) is the principal product.

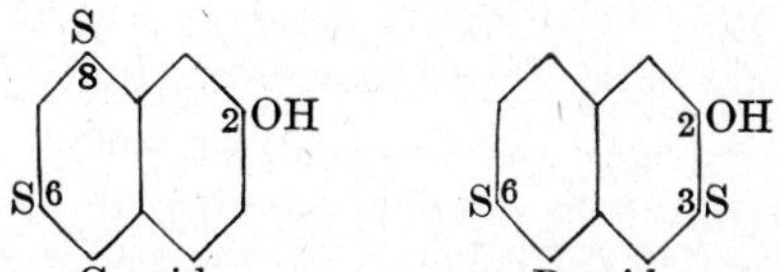

G-acid   R-acid

Naphtholsulfonic acids may also be obtained by the alkali fusion of naphthalenedisulfonic acids. Thus, 2-naphthol-7-sulfonic acid (F-acid) is obtained by causticizing naphthalene-2, 7-disulfonic acid. Only one sulfonic acid group is attacked by proper regulation of the fusion temperature and the proportions of the reactants.

Some of the important amino derivatives obtained from 2-naphtholsulfonic acids by ammonolysis according to the Bucherer reaction are shown in Fig. 7.

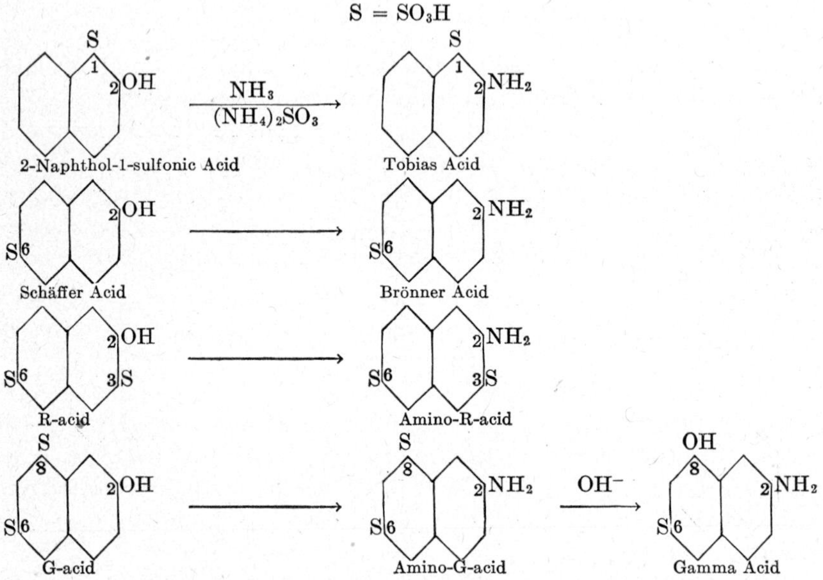

$S = SO_3H$

2-Naphthol-1-sulfonic Acid → Tobias Acid

Schäffer Acid → Brönner Acid

R-acid → Amino-R-acid

G-acid → Amino-G-acid → Gamma Acid

Fig. 7.—Amino derivatives obtained from 2-naphtholsulfonic acids by Bucherer reaction.

Oleum as a Sulfonating Agent

Introduction.—It has been pointed out that sulfuric acid comprises a series of hydrates of sulfur trioxide, some of which are very unstable,[1] and experience has shown that the activity of sulfuric acid as a sulfonating agent is directly related to its SO_3 concentration.

From our present knowledge of the sulfonation process, it appears that aqueous sulfuric acid may be conceived as a solvent for the active sulfonating agent, *viz.*, free or combined sulfur trioxide. Water does, of course, ameliorate the intensity of the reaction and in many sulfonations inhibits the formation of oxidation products and to that extent performs a beneficial service. Current developments indicate that sulfur trioxide alone or as 40 to 50 per cent oleum[2] is being advantageously employed to obviate the decelerating influence of water.[3] A number of simple expedients are being employed, *e.g.*, (1) adding oleum to the reaction mass comprising all the organic compound dissolved or suspended in cycle sulfuric acid; (2) adding oleum and organic compound con-

---

[1] Baumgarten, *Ber.*, **64B**, 1502 (1931).
[2] Percentage of oleum $= (\%H_2SO_4 - 100) \times (80 \div 18)$.
[3] (This trend was predicted in the first edition.)

currently to a large mass of reacting material at equilibrium in so far as sulfonation is concerned; and (3) using part of the residual acid from disulfonation to effect monosulfonation and then introducing oleum for the disulfonation step. Such procedures make possible the presence of only a small excess of SO_3 at any stage of the reaction and thus inhibit the tendency to disulfonation and are also conducive to economies in the amount of SO_3 that must be employed.

When water or sulfuric acid is the solvent the organic compound will remove the combined SO_3 until a point is reached when the affinity of SO_3 for $(H_2O)_x$ under the conditions of operation is equal to that of SO_3 for the organic compound. An equilibrium then exists. Naphthalene, which readily forms addition compounds with SO_3, is sulfonated at comparatively low temperatures with comparatively weak acids. Benzene, however, requires a more concentrated acid; for when the hydrate $SO_3 \cdot 3H_2O$ corresponding to 73 per cent H_2SO_4 is formed, it will no longer give up SO_3 to benzene to form the sulfonic acid.

Oleum (100 per cent sulfuric acid containing dissolved sulfur trioxide) is used instead of sulfuric acid for sulfonation in cases where the reaction proceeds with difficulty even with the application of heat. It finds extensive use in the preparation of polysulfonic acids the formation of which necessitates the presence of either free SO_3 or minimal quantities of water. The reaction for monosulfonation is as follows:

$$R \cdot H + SO_3 \rightarrow R \cdot SO_2 \cdot OH$$

No water is produced, the free SO_3 concentration of the sulfuric acid merely decreases, and for this reason its use is often more economical than that of sulfuric acid.

Treatment of Aliphatic Compounds with Oleum.—Whereas methane is not attacked by oleum, all its homologues beginning with hexane can be sulfonated. Oleum reacts with ethanol and with ether to form ethanedisulfonate.

$$\underset{\text{Ethanol}}{\overset{\displaystyle CH_2 \cdot OH}{\underset{\displaystyle CH_3}{|}}} \xrightarrow{\text{Oleum}} \underset{\text{Ethanedisulfonic Acid}}{\overset{\displaystyle CH_2 \cdot SO_3H}{\underset{\displaystyle CH_2 \cdot SO_3H}{|}}}$$

Aliphatic aldehydes and ketones yield di- and trisulfonic acids when treated with oleum. The reaction with acetaldehyde may be represented as follows:

$$\overset{\displaystyle CH_3}{\underset{\displaystyle CHO}{|}} \xrightarrow{\text{Oleum}} \overset{\displaystyle CH(SO_3H)_2}{\underset{\displaystyle CHO}{|}}$$

The sulfonic acid thus formed may be considered as being a derivative of glyoxal.

$$\begin{matrix} \text{CHO} \\ | \\ \text{CHO} \end{matrix} \quad \text{Glyoxal}$$

Treatment of Aromatic Compounds with Oleum.—The use of oleum for the sulfonation of nitrobenzene typifies its use in the aromatic series. In this instance, nitrobenzene is not appreciably sulfonated by sulfuric acid, and the use of oleum is therefore a necessity. In other cases, where it is desired to prepare polysulfonic acids, the entrance of the first sulfonic group may be effected by means of sulfuric acid, further sulfonation being conditioned on the introduction of oleum. The preparation of naphthalenetrisulfonic and anthraquinonedisulfonic acids is an example of such usage.

The dependence of velocity of sulfonation on the SO_3 concentration is brought out in a striking manner in the treatment of *p*-nitrotoluene with sulfuric acid and oleum. The introduction of only slight amounts of water greatly retards the reaction rate, particularly when the sulfonating acid is weaker than 100 per cent H_2SO_4. At 25°C., the velocity coefficients (in reciprocal minutes) are[1]

> In oleum, 2.4 % SO_3 .... 0.003
> In 100 % H_2SO_4 .... 0.0004
> In 99.4 % H_2SO_4 .... 0.0000005

The velocity increases 2 to 2.5 times for each rise of 10°C. in temperature.

The trisulfonation of naphthalene incident to the preparation of Koch acid (1-aminonaphthalene-3, 6, 8-trisulfonic acid) provides an example illustrating the use of concentrated sulfuric acid for effecting monosulfonation, this step then being followed by the introduction of oleum to insure the formation of the trisulfonic acid. The reactions involved may be represented as follows:

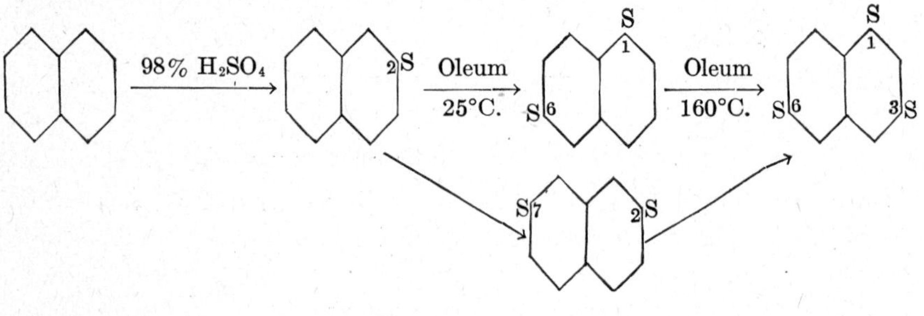

Sulfonation of Anthraquinone. General Remarks.—Of the numerous anthraquinonesulfonic acids theoretically possible, only two mono acids and six disulfonic acids are known.

[1] MARTINSEN, *Z. physik. Chem.*, **62**, 713 (1908).

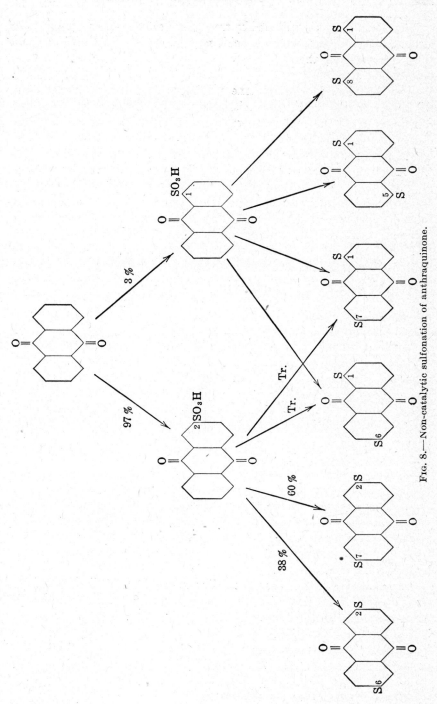

Fig. 8.—Non-catalytic sulfonation of anthraquinone.

In general, they are prepared by the action of oleum on anthraquinone, although anthraquinonesulfonic acids may be made from α-nitro derivatives by replacing the —NO$_2$ by —SO$_3$H, and by oxidizing anthracenesulfonic acids.

The behavior of anthraquinone on direct sulfonation is simpler than the corresponding naphthalene chemistry. Unlike the latter, acid concentration and time and temperature of reaction determine only the degree of sulfonation and not the orientation—which is influenced only by the presence or absence of a catalyst. As in the case of naphthalene, the monosulfonation of anthraquinone does not result in a uniform product—more or less disulfonic acids always being present, the quantity being dependent on the conditions employed. The monosulfonic acid formed appears to undergo sulfonation just as readily as does anthraquinone, resulting in an equilibrium between the anthraquinone mono- and disulfonic acids.[1] Because of the easy formation of disulfonic acids in monosulfonation, an excess of anthraquinone is employed; or, in other words, the quantity of SO$_3$ used is sufficient to convert only part (50 per cent) of the anthraquinone. In the absence of a catalyst, the sulfonic acid groups enter almost exclusively in beta positions. When a mercury catalyst is employed, alpha substitution takes place.

Anthraquinone-β-sulfonic Acids.—The sulfonation of anthraquinone to form the β-monosulfonic acid can be accomplished by employing 2.5 parts of concentrated sulfuric acid and heating at 250 to 260°C. The reaction can be carried out more readily, however, by using oleum at 120 to 140°C. The production of disulfonic acids (Fig. 8) approximately parallels the formation of the monosulfonic acid, the relative quantities of each being dependent principally on the SO$_3$ ratio and the temperature and time of reaction. To avoid excessive disulfonation, it is customary to use only about 70 per cent of the quantity of free SO$_3$ required by theory. Under such conditions, about 50 per cent of the anthraquinone treated remains unconverted (Table I), and about 16 per cent of the converted material is found as the 2, 6- and 2, 7-anthraquinonedisulfonic acids.[2] About 5 per cent of other acids are formed simultaneously, and these include 2 to 3 per cent of the α-monosulfonic acid, the rest being hydroxysulfonic acids.

Disulfonation ceases when the SO$_3$ concentration of the sulfonating acid drops to 2 per cent, for the monosulfonic acid remains unaltered when treated with 2 per cent oleum at 140°C. The isomeric 2, 6- and 2, 7-anthraquinonedisulfonic acids are formed in practically the same quantities. The curves in Fig. 9 show the effect of various factors in the preparation of anthraquinone-2-sulfonic acid. When anthraquinone is

---

[1] Krebser, Diss. E.T.H., Zurich (1915).
[2] LAUER, *J. prakt. Chem.*, **130**, 198 (1931).

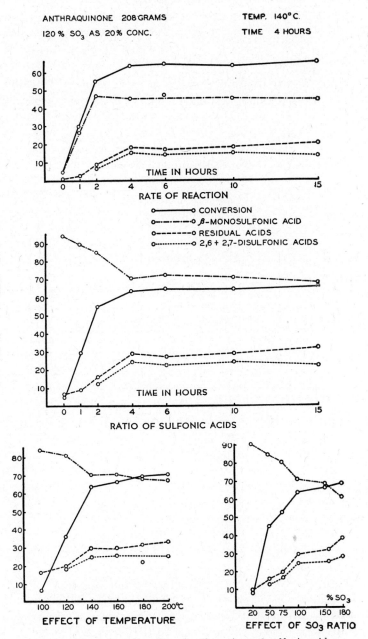

ANTHRAQUINONE 208 GRAMS

120 % SO$_3$ AS 20% CONC.

TEMP. 140°C.

TIME 4 HOURS

RATE OF REACTION

o———o CONVERSION
o—·—·—o β-MONOSULFONIC ACID
o———o RESIDUAL ACIDS
o········o 2,6 + 2,7-DISULFONIC ACIDS

TIME IN HOURS

RATIO OF SULFONIC ACIDS

EFFECT OF TEMPERATURE

EFFECT OF SO$_3$ RATIO

FIG. 9.—Factors: preparation of anthraquinone-2-sulfonic acid.
Each of the charts above contains one variable.   Per cent yield is plotted against variable.

completely sulfonated with 120 per cent of the theoretical quantity of 40 per cent oleum, the results shown in the curves of Fig. 10 are obtained.[1] Sulfonation at 190°C. with 40 per cent oleum (110 per cent of theory) results in a yield of 85 per cent 2, 6- and 2, 7-anthraquinonedisulfonic acids, the ratio of the isomers being 1:1.15. As the temperature of sulfonation is lowered, the relative proportion of the 2, 7-disulfonic acid increases.

TABLE I.—SULFONATION OF ANTHRAQUINONE[1]
Effect of SO$_3$ Ratio
Anthraquinone, 104 gm.; oleum, 20 per cent SO$_3$; temperature, 140°C.; reaction time, 4 hr.

% of theory, SO$_3$	Unconverted anthraquinone		Con-version	Silver salt		2, 6-Salt (Na)		2, 7-Salt (Na)		Residual acids
	Grams	%	%	Grams	% of conversion	Grams	%	Grams	%	%
20	95.5	91.9	8.1	11.5	90.8	....	....	....	....	9.2
50	57.1	55.0	45.0	58.9	84.3	5.6	6.1	6.0	6.5	3.1
75	49.1	47.3	52.7	66.2	80.4	8.7	8.0	9.2	8.5	3.1
75	50.1	48.1	51.9	64.1	79.8	7.9	7.4	8.5	8.0	4.8
100	38.5	37.0	63.0	69.3	70.9	13.4	10.3	14.1	10.9	7.9
150	35.4	34.1	65.9	69.4	67.9	16.3	12.0	17.7	13.1	7.0
150	35.2	33.8	66.2	68.7	67.0	15.5	11.4	16.9	12.4	9.2
180	32.7	31.5	68.5	65.6	61.7	19.4	13.8	20.0	14.2	10.3
180	31.3	30.1	69.9	65.3	60.3	19.3	13.4	20.1	13.9	12.4

[1] LAUER, *J. prakt. Chem.*, **130** (1931).

In addition to the two principal easily isolatable disulfonic acids, there are also present in the mother liquor (1) hydroxysulfonic acids, 3 per cent; (2) α, β-disulfonic acids, 3 per cent; (3) β, β-disulfonic acids, 10 per cent.

Anthraquinone-1-sulfonic Acid.—The sulfonation of anthraquinone in the presence of mercury or a mercury salt causes substitution to take place almost exclusively in alpha positions.

Catalytic Sulfonation of Anthraquinone.—Approximately 1 per cent by weight of mercury to anthraquinone used is required if 20 to 30 per cent oleum is used. An increase in the concentration of the catalyst above this ratio does not, as can be seen from the data in Table II, appreciably alter the character of the results. When the strength of the oleum is reduced from 20 to 5 per cent SO$_3$, an increased proportion of the catalyst displays a definite hindrance to the formation of beta sulfonic acids. The data in Table V (page 272) show that the mercury salt anion is without effect, since any of the salts give similar results.

[1] LAUER, *loc. cit.*

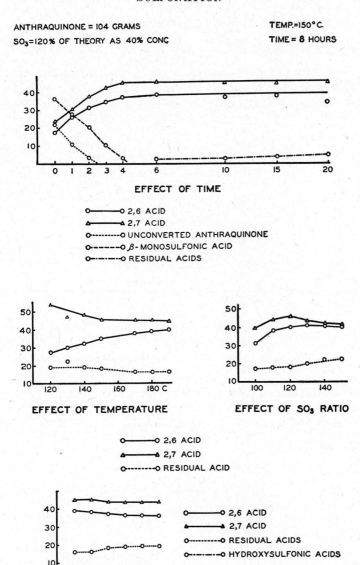

ANTHRAQUINONE = 104 GRAMS
SO₃=120% OF THEORY AS 40% CONC

TEMP.=150°C.
TIME = 8 HOURS

EFFECT OF TIME

○————○ 2,6 ACID
△————△ 2,7 ACID
○·········○ UNCONVERTED ANTHRAQUINONE
○— — —○ β- MONOSULFONIC ACID
○—·—·—○ RESIDUAL ACIDS

EFFECT OF TEMPERATURE

EFFECT OF SO₃ RATIO

○————○ 2,6 ACID
△————△ 2,7 ACID
○·········○ RESIDUAL ACID

EFFECT OF SO₃ CONC.

○————○ 2,6 ACID
△————△ 2,7 ACID
○·········○ RESIDUAL ACIDS
○—·—·—○ HYDROXYSULFONIC ACIDS

Fɪɢ. 10.—Factors: preparation of anthraquinone-β, β-disulfonic acids.
Each of the charts above contains one variable.   Per cent yield is plotted against variable.

TABLE II.—PREPARATION OF ANTHRAQUINONE-1-SULFONIC ACID*
Effect of Catalyst Ratio
Anthraquinone, 104 gm.; SO_3, 100 per cent of theory; time of reaction, 3 hr.;
temperature, 140°C.

Strength of oleum, % SO_3	Volume, cc.	Hg, %	Alpha acids, %	Beta acids, %
20	110	1.0	92.8	7.2
20	110	2.0	91.3	8.7
20	110	3.0	92.1	7.9
10	220	1.0	90.8	9.2
10	220	2.0	93.1	6.9
10	220	3.0	93.7	6.3
5	440	1.0	91.6	8.4
5	440	2.0	94.0	6.0
5	440	3.0	95.4	4.6
5	440	4.0	98.3	1.7
5	440	4.5	98.7	1.3
5	440	5.0	99.1	0.9

* LAUER, *J. prakt. Chem.*, **135**, 174 (1932).

The curves in Fig. 11 show the effect of various factors in the preparation of anthraquinone-1-sulfonic acid. Here the acid was precipitated as the potassium salt, a second fraction being obtained from the first filtrate.

α-Anthraquinonedisulfonic Acids.—The principal products obtained by the catalytic disulfonation of anthraquinone are the 1, 5- and 1, 8-acids. According to Krebser,[1] these are formed to the extent of 45 to 50 per cent and 27 per cent, respectively.

SULFONATION WITH SO_3 ALONE

Sulfur trioxide finds use in the sulfonation of both aliphatic and aromatic compounds.

The reaction of sulfur trioxide with absolute ethanol results in the formation of carbyl sulfate,

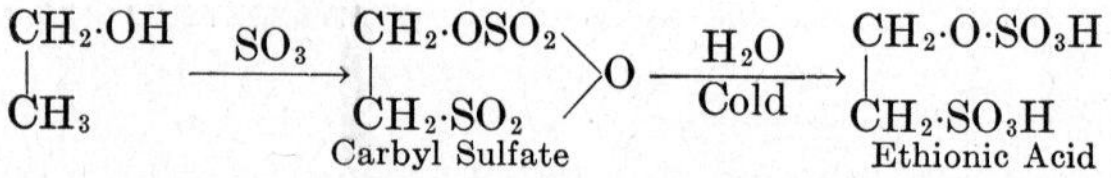

$$\begin{array}{ccccc} CH_2 \cdot OH & \xrightarrow{SO_3} & \begin{matrix} CH_2 \cdot OSO_2 \\ | \\ CH_2 \cdot SO_2 \end{matrix} \Big\rangle O & \xrightarrow[\text{Cold}]{H_2O} & \begin{matrix} CH_2 \cdot O \cdot SO_3H \\ | \\ CH_2 \cdot SO_3H \end{matrix} \\ CH_3 & & \text{Carbyl Sulfate} & & \text{Ethionic Acid} \end{array}$$

which, on hydrolysis in the cold, yields ethionic acid. The constitution of this acid indicates it to be both a sulfonic acid and a sulfuric acid ester. This observation appears correct, since carbyl sulfate is converted to isethionic acid $(HO \cdot CH_2 \cdot CH_2 \cdot SO_3H)$[2] upon warming with water.

[1] KREBSER, Diss. E. T. H., Zurich (1925).
[2] This is converted to taurine $(CH_2 \cdot NH_2 \cdot CH_2SO_3H)$ by ammonolysis.

On sulfonating fumaric acid with SO₃, maleic anhydride is formed first, rearrangement and dehydration taking place, thus:

$$\begin{array}{ccc} \text{HOOC·CH} & & \text{H·C—CO} \\ \| & \rightarrow & \| \hspace{1.2em} \text{>O} \\ \text{HC·COOH} & & \text{H·C—CO} \end{array}$$

When 3 moles of SO₃ per mole of maleic or fumaric acids is employed at 60 or 70°C., respectively, a yield of 87 per cent of sulfomaleic acid as $(C_4HO_7S)_2Ba_3$ is obtained.[1]

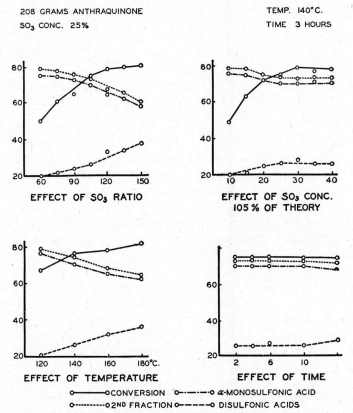

Fig. 11.—Factors: preparation of anthraquinone-1-sulfonic acid. Each of the charts above contains only one variable. Per cent yield is plotted against variable.

In the aromatic series, sulfur trioxide has been used for the sulfonation of *p*-dichlorobenzene and *m*-chlorobenzoic acid,[2] gaseous SO₃ being passed directly into the melted substances.

[1] BACKER and ZANDEN, *Rec. trav. chim.*, **49**, 735 (1930).
[2] OTTO, *Ann.*, **123**, 216 (1862).

A comparatively inert solvent may be employed for the sulfonation of compounds that react readily with sulfur trioxide. When β-naphthol is suspended in nitrobenzene containing SO_3 at 16°C., 2-naphthol-1-sulfonic acid is obtained. Tetrachlorethane ($C_2H_2Cl_4$) is used[1] as a solvent in the sulfonation of amines such as m-xylidine, and β-naphthylamine with sulfur trioxide. This method is employed advantageously when the ortho sulfonic acid is desired instead of the para isomer. The mechanism of addition and intramolecular rearrangement with respect to the preparation of 2-naphthol-1-sulfonic acid (and 2-naphthylamine-1-sulfonic acid) is probably as follows:

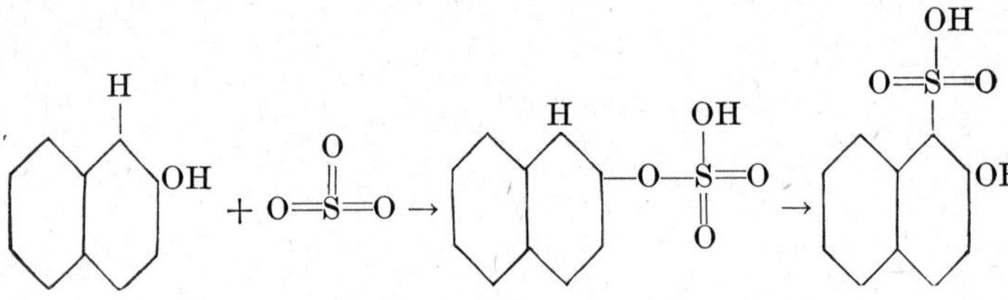

An interesting application of SO_3 in the production of sulfonic acids relates to the preparation of sulfophthalic anhydride. Sulfur trioxide is introduced into molten phthalic anhydride[2] at 190 to 210°C. Some of the anhydride sublimes on the walls of the sulfonator during the early stages of the reaction, but after 23 hr. sublimation is no longer visible. The reaction is completed after 66 hr., and a light-brown syrup is obtained. Dry air at 200°C. is employed to remove any free SO_3, and a high yield of 4-sulfophthalic anhydride is obtained.

The 3, 5-disulfophthalic anhydride is formed by carrying out the sulfonation in the presence of a mercury salt. The reaction in this instance takes place more rapidly than the formation of the 4-sulfo acid.

Lauer[3] has found that the presence of water plays an important role in the orientation of the sulfonic acid group. The substituents already present have only a limited directing influence when H_2SO_4 is the sulfonating agent and exclusively meta or ortho-para acids are not usually obtained. When, however, SO_3 is used, either as a gas or in the presence of an organic solvent, and the reactants are free of moisture, only ortho-para or only meta compounds are formed, as is evident from the data in Table III. What appears as an exception to this rule is the sulfonation of toluene with SO_3 but this can be explained by the presence of water in the reaction mass as a result of sulfone formation, thus:

$$2C_6H_5CH_3 + SO_3 \rightarrow (C_6H_4CH_3)_2SO_2 + H_2O$$

[1] U. S. 1,794,861 (1931).
[2] SCHWENK, *Ann.*, **487**, 287 (1931).
[3] LAUER, *J. Für. prakt. chemie*, **143**, 127 (1935).

When this reaction is carried out in the presence of acetic anhydride or phosphorus pentoxide only ortho and para sulfonic acids are obtained.

TABLE III.—INFLUENCE OF SUBSTITUENTS SULFONATION OF BENZENOID COMPOUNDS

Substituent	With H_2SO_4 % composition			With SO_3 % composition		
	Ortho	Para	Meta	Ortho	Para	Meta
NO_2	..	3	97	..	...	100
SO_3H	..	5	95	..	...	100
CHO	..	...	100	..	...	100
COOH	..	14	86	..	...	100
CO	..	...	100			
CCl_3	..	...	...	..	...	100
$CHCl_2$	10	60	30			
CH_3	15	80	5	20	80	
Br	4	96	...	..	100	
I	2	98	...	..	100	
Cl	..	100	...	..	100	
NHAc	..	100				
OH	..	15	85			

SULFONATION WITH ACID SULFATES

Bisulfates, *e.g.*, $NaHSO_4$, and trihydrosulfates, *e.g.*, $NaHSO_4 \cdot H_2SO_4$, of the alkali metals may be employed as sulfonating agents, but their use is distinctly limited. The activity of the acid sulfates may be considered as a modification of the action of concentrated sulfuric acid, since the salts contain no water. The trihydrosulfate $KH_3(SO_4)_2$ melts at approximately 100°C. and can therefore be used more advantageously than the acid sulfate $KHSO_4$, which melts at 210°C. When the acid sulfates are obtained as by-products from the manufacture of nitric acid, they may be employed to advantage in the preparation of 1-aminoanthraquinone-2-sulfonic acid. Here the reaction is carried out by treating 1-aminoanthraquinone at 210 to 240°C. under reduced pressure.[1]

Benzene, toluene, and naphthalene are sulfonated only with indifferent success by trihydrosulfates. Using two parts of $NaH_3(SO_4)_2$ per part of benzenesulfonic acid and heating at 240°C. Gebler[2] obtained the disodium salt of benzene-1, 3-disulfonic acid with practically quantitative yields. Naphthalene is converted to sodium β-naphthalenesulfonate when similarly treated at 180°C. for 8 hr.

[1] Ger. 530,135 (1930).
[2] GEBLER, *J. Chem. Ind. (Moscow)*, **2**, 984 (1926).

CHLOROSULFONIC ACID $\left(O_2S\!\!\begin{array}{c}\diagup OH \\ \diagdown Cl\end{array}\right)$ AS A SULFONATING AGENT

Chlorosulfonic acid reacts with hydrocarbons, both aliphatic and aromatic, and the reaction may be represented by the following equations:

$$R{\cdot}H + Cl{\cdot}SO_2{\cdot}OH \rightarrow R{\cdot}SO_2{\cdot}OH + HCl$$
$$R{\cdot}SO_2{\cdot}OH + Cl{\cdot}SO_2{\cdot}OH \rightarrow R{\cdot}SO_2{\cdot}Cl + H_2SO_4$$

The first reaction results in the formation of the sulfonic acid of the hydrocarbon and hydrogen chloride; while the second produces the sulfonylchloride of the hydrocarbon and sulfuric acid. The ordinary method of carrying out the first reaction is to dissolve or suspend the hydrocarbon in an inert solvent, such as CS_2, $CHCl_3$, CCl_4, etc., and to add the required quantity of chlorosulfonic acid gradually, heating if necessary. Hydrogen chloride is liberated, and the reaction is considered finished when the evolution of gas ceases. Mono- and disulfonic acids of benzene and naphthalene can be obtained by this procedure, but the product contains varying amounts of the sulfonylchloride because of the unavoidable secondary reaction previously indicated.[1]

Corbellini[2] found that when 1 mole of naphthalene is treated at 15 to 45°C. with 2 moles of chlorosulfonic acid, 1, 5-naphthalenedisulfonic acid is formed, together with varying proportions of the corresponding disulfonylchloride. When CCl_4 is used as a solvent, and naphthalene is treated with either 2 or 4 moles of chlorosulfonic acid, sulfonylchlorides are always formed in addition to the mono- and disulfonic acids. In all cases, naphthalene is attacked only in the 1 and 5 positions. The final yields of the various products depend on the velocities of the different concurrent reactions, which, in turn, are governed by the conditions employed. The reaction leading to the formation of chlorosulfonic acids is favored by low temperatures.

In the aliphatic series, the use of chlorosulfonic acid is illustrated by the following sulfonations: Sulfoacetic acid $\left(\begin{array}{c}\diagup COOH \\ CH_2 \\ \diagdown SO_3H\end{array}\right)$ is obtained by heating acetic and chlorosulfonic acids together. A sulfopropionic acid $CH_3{\cdot}CH(SO_3H)COOH$ is formed by the similar action of chlorosulfonic acid on propionic acid.[3]

Chlorosulfonic acid is employed to advantage in the preparation of *o*-toluenesulfonyl chloride, an intermediate in the preparation of benzo-

[1] ARMSTRONG, *J. Chem. Soc.*, **24**, 173 (1891).

[2] CORBELLINI, *Giorn. chim. ind. applicata*, **9**, 118 (1927).

[3] KURBATOW, *Ann.*, **173**, 6 (1874).

sulfimide, *i.e.*, saccharin.   The use of chlorosulfonic, while more expen-

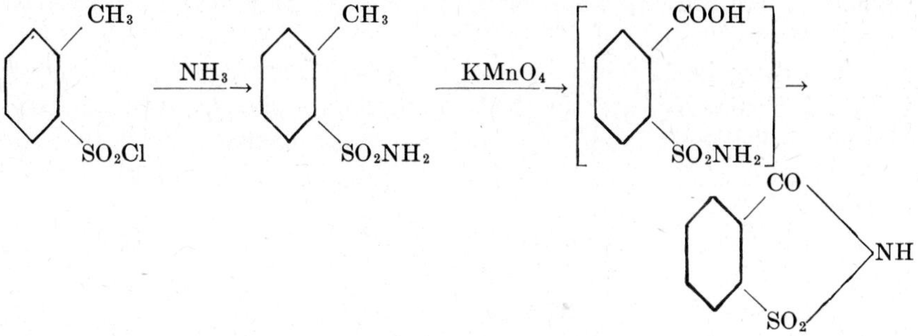

sive than sulfuric acid, gives a higher yield (40 per cent of the ortho
isomer) and at the same time eliminates the costly conversion of the
sulfonic acid to sulfonyl chloride by phosphorus pentachloride that
would otherwise be necessary.   The para isomer, which is a solid, is
readily separated from the desired ortho compound, which is then
submitted to further purification.

Chlorosulfonic acid forms sulfamic acids with amines of both
the aliphatic and aromatic series.   The reaction is carried out in a
solvent, *e.g.*, chloroform and acids of the following types are formed:

$$C_2H_5N\begin{cases}H\\SO_3H\end{cases} \qquad (I)$$

$$C_6H_5N\begin{cases}H\\SO_3H\end{cases} \qquad (II)$$

This reaction is used in the preparation of *o*-anilinesulfonic acid, which is
derived through rearrangement of the sulfamic acid (II) by heating
in the presence of sulfuric acid.   *o*-Sulfonic acids of naphthylamines can
be prepared in a similar manner.

SULFONATION WITH SULFUR DIOXIDE

The action of SO_2 on aqueous solutions of quinones results in reduction
as well as sulfonation.

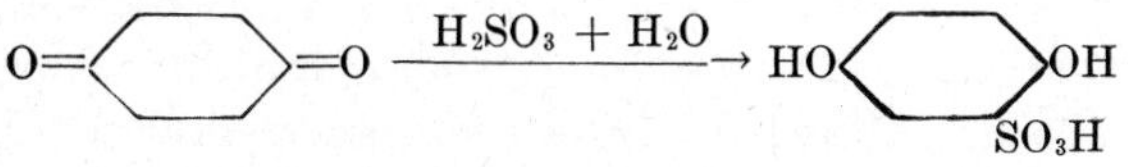

In the treatment of chloroquinones, there is a tendency to form disulfonic
acids because of the replacement of a chlorine atom by a sulfonic acid
group.[1]

$$C_6H_2Cl_2O_2 + 2H_2SO_3 \rightarrow C_6HCl(OH)_2(SO_3H)_2 + HCl$$

[1] DODGSON, *J. Chem. Soc.*, **1930**, 2498.

A similar reducing and sulfonating action is observed when 1-nitroso-2-naphthol reacts with sulfurous acid in a boiling alcoholic solution, 1-amino-2-naphthol-4-sulfonic acid being formed.

When diazotized amines in alcoholic solution are treated with sulfur dioxide, sulfonic acids are obtained through the replacement of the diazo group.[1] *m*-Toluenesulfonic as well as *m*-sulfobenzoic acid may be obtained from the corresponding diazotized amines by this procedure.[2]

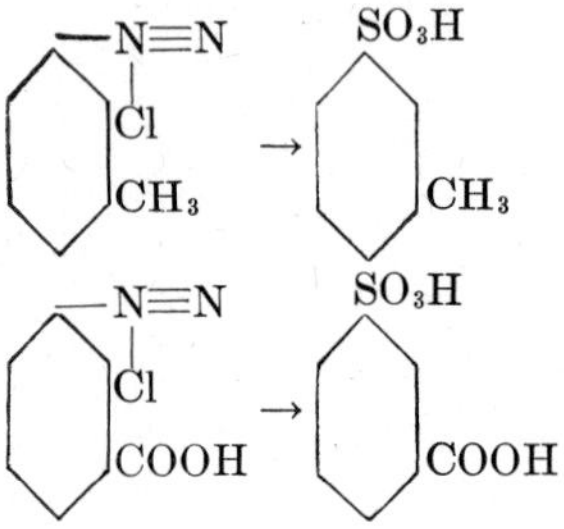

SULFITES AND BISULFITES AS SULFONATING AGENTS

Sulfurous acid has two possible structures:

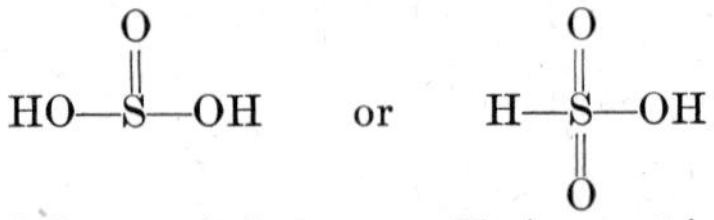

I. Symmetrical　　II. Asymmetrical

The soluble sulfites possibly exist in both forms but in their reaction with alkyl halides yield sulfonates.

$$KSO_2 \cdot OK + C_2H_5I \rightarrow C_2H_5SO_2OK + KI$$

The sulfonic acids and their esters may therefore be considered as derivatives of unsymmetrical sulfurous acid. When, however, SO_2 is passed into a solution of an alkali alcoholate, an unstable salt of alkyl sulfurous acid is obtained,

$$SO_2 + C_2H_5OK \rightarrow C_2H_5O \cdot SO_2K$$

which easily loses SO_2 and which is isomeric with the stable alkylsulfonate previously mentioned. On heating in the presence of potassium iodide, in alcoholic solution, this unstable salt is converted to the double salt of potassium ethylsulfonate and potassium iodide.

Treatment of Aliphatic Compounds.—It will be recalled that one of the characteristics distinguishing aliphatic from aromatic compounds is their inability to react with sulfuric acid. The formation of aliphatic

[1] MÜLLER, *Ber.*, **12**, 1348 (1879).

[2] HÜBNER. *Ber.*, **10**, 1715 (1877).

sulfonic acids is generally accomplished by heating the alkyl halides with alkali sulfites, methane- and ethanesulfonic acids being prepared in this manner.

Treatment of Aromatic Compounds.—The use of sulfites as a sulfonating agent in aromatic chemistry sometimes offers certain advantages when the compound to be treated contains the nitro group, a halogen atom, a hydroxyl group, or when it is a quinone. When 1-nitronaphthalene reacts with a boiling aqueous-alcoholic solution of ammonium sulfite, 1-aminonaphthalene-4-sulfonic acid is obtained along with some α-naphthylsulfamic acid. To prepare 1-aminonaphthalene-2, 4-disulfonic acid,[1] the nitronaphthalene is heated with a sodium bisulfite solution at 100°C.

The nitroanilides and nitroaniline are converted to sulfamic acid derivatives when acted on by sodium bisulfite:[2]

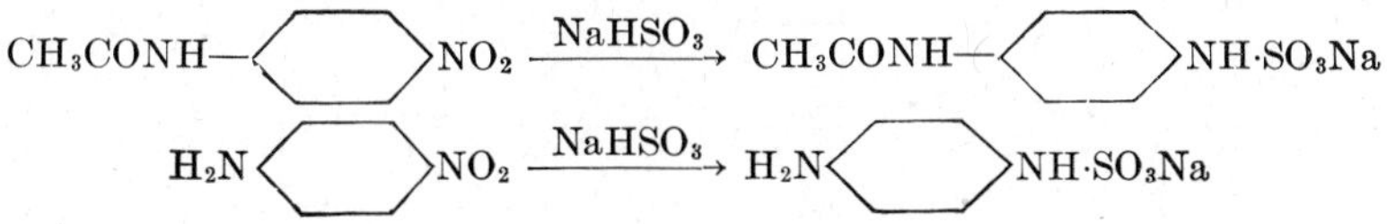

An industrially important application of sulfites relates to the replacement of the chlorine atom of 4′-chloro-2-benzoylbenzoic acid by the sulfonic acid group. The reaction is carried out by treating the keto acid with an excess of aqueous 20 per cent sodium sulfite at 170°C. for 16 hr.[3] The resultant sodium 4′-sulfo-2-benzoylbenzoate is readily cyclized to anthraquinone-2-sulfonic acid.

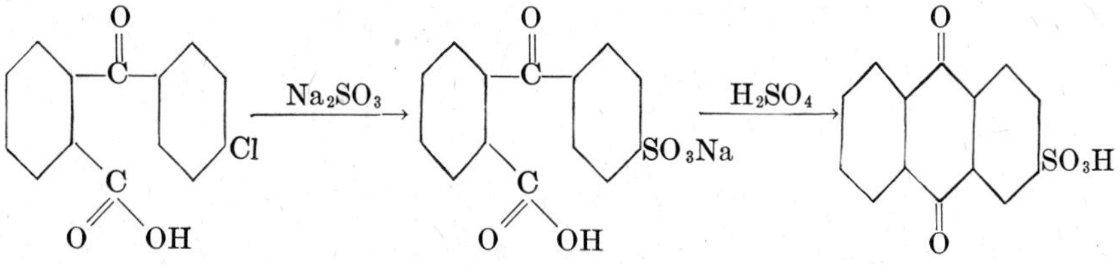

It will be recalled that direct sulfonation of anthraquinone results in the formation of disulfonic acids and hydroxy impurities when all the anthraquinone undergoes reaction. The 2-aminoanthraquinone obtained by the ammonolysis of the corresponding sodium sulfonate runs uniformly over 99 per cent purity.

The halogen atom in *p*-bromotoluene is replaced by the sulfonic acid group at 180 to 200°C. by reaction with a 15 per cent solution of sodium sulfite containing a trace of copper sulfate. The chlorine in the side

[1] Ger. 92,081 (1895).

[2] WEIL and WASSERMANN, *Ber.*, **55**, 2533 (1922).

[3] U. S. 1,779,221 (1930).

chain can also be replaced, as is evidenced by the formation of toluene-ω-sulfonic acid from benzyl chloride and a concentrated boiling solution of sodium sulfite.[1]

When a nitro group is ortho or para to a halogen atom in the aromatic nucleus, the replacement of the halogen atom takes place much more readily than in the previous examples wherein high temperatures and pressures are required. This reaction may be represented as follows:

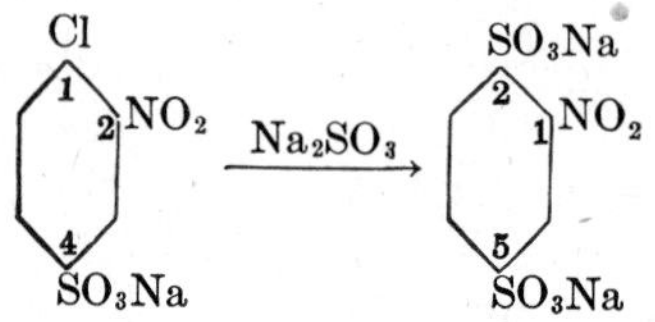

Sometimes, the nitro compounds are reduced to amines concurrently with the replacement of the halogen atom by the sulfonic acid group.

HYPOSULFITES (HYDROSULFITES) AS SULFONATING AGENTS

Sodium hyposulfite ($Na_2S_2O_4$)—frequently called sodium hydrosulfite—may be used for the formation of ω-sulfonic and sulfamic acids from either nitro or chloro substituted aromatic compounds. When nitrobenzene is treated with aqueous sodium hyposulfite in the presence of sodium phosphate at 65°C., benzenesulfamic acid is formed according to the following reaction:

$$C_6H_5NO_2 + Na_2S_2O_4 + H_2O \rightarrow C_6H_5NH\cdot SO_3Na + NaHSO_4$$

For the production of toluene-ω-sulfonic acid, benzyl chloride is treated with an alkaline solution of sodium hyposulfite in the presence of zinc dust. Dibenzylsulfone is also formed during the reaction.[2]

N-PYRIDINIUMSULFONIC ACID AS A SULFONATING AGENT

Pyridine reacts with sulfur trioxide and chlorosulfonic acid to form N-pyridiniumsulfonic acid, having the following structural formula:

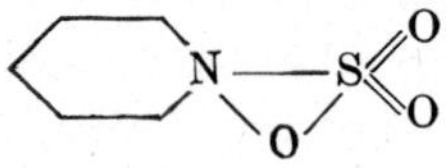

This compound may be employed for the sulfonation of methylamine, phenol, and naphthalene, pyridine being recovered and reconverted to the sulfonic acid for further use.[3] When p-aminophenol is heated with this

---

[1] BÖHLER, *Ann. Chem. Pharm.*, **154**, 50 (1870). MOHR, *Ann.*, **221**, 216 (1883).

[2] FROMM, DE SEIXAS PALMA, *Ber.*, **39**, 3319 (1906).

[3] Baumgarten, Ger. 499,571; 514,821 (1926).

agent, the sulfamic acid is obtained as the alkali salt upon hydrolysis of the reaction mass. The reaction may be represented as follows:

$$C_6H_4(OH)NH_2 \xrightarrow{C_5H_5N \cdot SO_3} C_6H_4(OH)NH \cdot SO_3Na$$

USE OF AMINOSULFONIC ACIDS

Aminosulfonic acid ($NH_2 \cdot SO_3H$) has been used as a sulfonating agent in the treatment of aromatic hydroxy and unsaturated compounds. Styrene may thus be converted when the reaction takes place at 150°C. for one hour.[1]

$$C_6H_5CH=CH_2 \xrightarrow{NH_2 \cdot SO_3H} C_6H_5CH=CHSO_3H$$

Sulfanilic acid ($NH_2 \cdot C_6H_4 \cdot SO_3H$) has also been employed for the conversion of α-naphthylamine to 1-naphthylamine-2-sulfonic acid.[2]

III. SEPARATION OF SULFONIC ACIDS

An important problem in sulfonation operations is the isolation or separation of the desired products. When only one sulfonic acid derivative is produced, it can generally be isolated as the alkali or alkaline earth salt with good yields and in a high state of purity. When isomers are present, the process of separating the components is often tedious and difficult. In a few cases, the sulfonic acid, because of its low solubility in the residual sulfuric acid, separates out in the reaction mixture. The sulfonic acid derivative of salicylic acid can thus be isolated.[3]

A number of general methods are available for recovering the sulfonic acids from the reaction mixture, and these procedures are susceptible to numerous modifications. Some of the more common methods are the following:

Method I. Dilution of Sulfonation Mixture.—Some isomeric sulfonic acids can be separated by pouring the reaction mass into water and cooling; p-toluenesulfonic acid can thus be separated from the ortho isomer.[4] The process is often facilitated by the addition of concentrated hydrochloric acid.

Method II. Neutralization of Reaction Mass.—*a.* When only one sulfonic acid is produced, as in the preparation of benzenesulfonic acid, the charge may be completely neutralized with either marble dust or hydrated lime. In each case, the solution of the sulfonate is removed by filtration. The calcium benzenesulfonate may be converted to the sodium salt by treatment with soda ash.

[1] QUILICO, *Atti accad. Lincei*, [6] **7**, 141, 1050 (1928).
[2] Ger. 75,319 (1894).
[3] MELDRUM and SHAH, *J. Chem. Soc.*, **123**, 1986 (1923).
[4] DORSSEN, *Rec. trav. chim.*, **29**, 371 (1910).

b. A mixture of sodium and calcium salts may be employed, the former being added in slight excess of the quantity necessary to form the soluble sodium sulfonate, while the latter insures the conversion of the sulfuric acid to the insoluble calcium sulfate.

c. When isomers are present, advantage may sometimes be taken of the difference in solubility of the calcium salts. Thus, after the removal of the gypsum, the calcium salt of naphthalene-2-sulfonic acid, which is less soluble than the alpha isomer, separates out from the filtrate.

d. Sometimes, an alkaline earth salt of a sulfonic acid can be separated from a mixture of the sodium salts. By adding the correct quantity of barium chloride to a solution containing sodium phenanthrenesulfonates, the barium salt of phenanthrene-2-sulfonic acid is precipitated.[1]

Method III. Fractional Precipitation.—*a.* The precipitation of sodium sulfonates from the reaction mass by the addition of sodium chloride is due, in most cases, to their slight solubility in the excess of sulfuric acid. In many instances, the addition of equivalent quantities of sodium sulfate, nitrate, or acetate serves equally well for the precipitation of the sodium salt. When soluble metallic salts of Cu, Zn, Ni, etc., are employed, almost theoretical yields of the insoluble metal sulfonate can be obtained.

b. In the production of 1, 5-naphthalenedisulfonic acid, the isomeric 1, 6-disulfonic acid is also formed. By adding sodium chloride to the mixture of acids, the difficultly soluble acid sodium salt of 1, 5-naphthalene disulfonic acid separates out. The acid sodium salts of benzoic-3-sulfonic and salicylic-5-sulfonic acids can similarly be precipitated because of their meager solubility in the residual sulfuric acid.

c. Sodium chloride may be added to a solution containing isomeric sodium sulfonates, and the introduction of the common ion so diminishes the solubility that one of the isomers is thrown out. β-naphthalenesulfonic acid can thus be separated from the alpha isomer.

Method IV. Formation of Basic Salts.—In some cases, it is advisable to use a relatively insoluble basic salt for the separation of a sulfonic acid. This method is applicable to sulfonic acids containing hydroxyl groups. A mixture of R- and G-acids, *i.e.*, 2-naphthol-3, 6 and 6, 8-disulfonic acids, respectively, is treated with lime to permit the separation of the calcium disulfonates from the gypsum. The filtrate of calcium naphtholdisulfonates is treated with a base, *e.g.*, NH$_4$OH, to convert the neutral into basic salts, and the less soluble basic calcium salt of R-acid crystallizes out. The mother liquor is then treated with ammonium sulfate. The calcium sulfate is removed by filtration, and the ammonium salt of 2-

---

[1] FIESER, *J. Am. Chem. Soc.*, **51**, 2460 (1929).

naphthol-6, 8-disulfonic acid is obtained after concentrating the filtrate to effect crystallization.

Method V. Formation of Sulfonchlorides.—In some cases where fractional precipitations fail, it is feasible to form the sulfonchlorides and then separate these by fractional crystallization. The sulfonchlorides may then be reconverted to the corresponding acids by boiling with water. Toluene-2, 5-disulfonic acid can be separated from the 3, 5-isomer in this manner. The barium disulfonates are treated with phosphorus pentachloride, and the sulfonchlorides are separated by recrystallization from carbon disulfide.

It must be understood that none of the above methods is general in its application. Many specific procedures have been devised for individual operations; the Dennis process for extracting benzenesulfonic acid with benzene (page 280) constitutes an important example of such special methods of separation.

IV. PHYSICAL AND CHEMICAL FACTORS IN SULFONATION

The preceding survey has indicated that the products resulting from sulfonation depend upon a number of factors and that these may affect not only the degree but also the course of the reaction. Some of the more important of these factors for a particular sulfonation are

Concentration of the sulfonating agent.

Temperature of the reaction.

Time of reaction.

Catalysts and sulfonation aids.

Agitation.

Relation of SO$_3$ Concentration to Sulfonation.—When sulfuric acid is employed, it is known that the sulfonation reaction stops at a definite SO$_3$ concentration, different for each compound undergoing treatment. Guyot[1] designated the limiting SO$_3$ concentration by the Greek letter π; and he found that in the preparation of benzenesulfonic acid, sulfonation stopped regardless of temperature, agitation, or catalysts when the value of π is 64 per cent corresponding to the hydrate $H_2SO_4 \cdot 1.5H_2O$. In practice, no action takes place after the acidity reaches 66.4 per cent SO$_3$. Considerable acid is thus obviously wasted by ordinary methods of sulfonation. When 100 per cent sulfuric acid is used, only 55 per cent of the available sulfur trioxide is utilized in the reaction, this value being reduced to 40 per cent with the employment of 94 per cent H_2SO_4.

This situation has led to the use of stronger acids, which, however, result in the formation of disulfonic acids. Novel procedures have therefore been devised and employed to eliminate the water of reaction as

[1] Guyot, *Chimie & industrie*, **2**, 879 (1919).

it is formed, and some of these methods are discussed later on pages 277 *et seq.*

In the sulfonation of naphthalene, Regnault[1] found that sulfonation ceases at a definite residual acidity. The values for π for naphthalene mono-, di-, and trisulfonation, as determined by Courtot,[2] are as follows:

For naphthalene monosulfonation at 55 to 60°C. = 53 % SO_3
For naphthalene monosulfonation at 160°   = 52 % SO_3
For naphthalene disulfonation at 10°   = 82 % SO_3
For naphthalene disulfonation at 80 to 90°   = 80 % SO_3
For naphthalene disulfonation at 160°   = 66.5 % SO_3
For naphthalene trisulfonation at 160°   = 79.8 % SO_3

The value of π is here shown to be a function of the reaction temperature. Courtot demonstrated further that naphthalenedisulfonic acids form addition compounds with sulfur trioxide, these being capable of giving up SO_3 slowly to naphthalenemonosulfonic acid which is present. Therefore, for some sulfonations π depends also on the sulfur trioxide fixed in a labile state, and calculations for complete sulfonation should take into account the formation of the addition compound.

The ease with which different compounds are sulfonated varies considerably. Benzene can be sulfonated with acids stronger than 64 per cent $SO_3 \backsimeq 78.4$ per cent H_2SO_4; naphthalene, with acids stronger than 52 per cent $SO_3 \backsimeq 63.7$ per cent H_2SO_4; and anthracene is readily converted to the monosulfonic acid with sulfuric acid containing 43 per cent $SO_3 \backsimeq 53$ per cent H_2SO_4. For the sulfonation of anthraquinone, however, practical considerations dictate the use of oleum, because the employment of concentrated sulfuric acid at 200 to 250°C. entails difficulties in operation as well as losses in yield due to oxidation. In the preparation of anthraquinonedisulfonic acids from the monosulfonic acid, the reaction does not proceed satisfactorily unless the concentration of free SO_3 is in excess of 3 per cent. The effect of SO_3 concentration on the rate and degree of sulfonation in the treatment of anthraquinone is shown[3] by the appropriate curves of Figs. 10 and 11.

In general, disulfonation and trisulfonation require increasingly greater concentrations of sulfur trioxide. Not only must the acid concentration be greater, but the acid ratio must be larger and the operating temperature higher.

When only the monosulfonic acid is desired, and the equilibrium between the mono- and disulfonic acid is such that large proportions of the latter are obtained, it is customary to resort to partial sulfonation. Thus, in the sulfonation of anthraquinone, 16 per cent of disulfonic acids

[1] REGNAULT, *Ann. chim. phys.*, [2] **65**, 87 (1837).
[2] COURTOT, *Compt. rend.*, **182**, 855 (1926).
[3] LAUER, *J. prakt. Chem*, **130**, 185 (1931).

is obtained when 75 per cent of the acid theoretically necessary for complete monosulfonation is employed, and 21 per cent of disulfonic acids is obtained with the stoichiometric quantity of acid. Practical considerations therefore dictate the most suitable ratio of reactants, since the unconverted anthraquinone must be recovered.

Since the value of π is greater for disulfonations than for the formation of the monosulfonic acid, it is often good practice to feed the sulfonating acid gradually throughout the run. This technic provides a medium wherein the SO_3 concentration is sufficiently low to inhibit to a considerable extent the formation of disulfonic acids.

Evidence that the orientation of sulfonic acids is to some extent influenced by the acid concentration has been obtained by Holleman and Polak.[1] When barium *m*-benzenedisulfonate is heated at 209°C. with oleum containing 12.5 per cent SO_3, 2 per cent of the product is converted to the para isomer; similar treatment with 98 per cent sulfuric acid results in the formation of 11.1 per cent of *p*-benzenedisulfonic acid.

Effect of the Reaction Temperature.—An increase in the sulfonation temperature accelerates both the rate and degree of reaction. Since the tendency to polysulfonation is increased with a rise in temperature, practical considerations dictate the use of thermal conditions and proportions of the reactants which produce a minimum of undesirable reaction products. The temperature of sulfonation may also play an important rôle in the orientation of the sulfonic acid groups. In the preparation of *m*-benzenedisulfonic acid or anthraquinonemono- or disulfonic acids, the orientation of the substituents is practically unaffected by the reaction temperature, but this factor does play an important rôle in the sulfonation of toluene and naphthalene derivatives.

In the monosulfonation of toluene, all three isomers are formed, but a rise in the reaction temperature favors the formation of the para acid at the expense of the ortho isomer. The data of Holleman and Caland[2]

TABLE IV.—EFFECT OF TEMPERATURE ON SULFONATION OF TOLUENE

Isomer	0° %	35° %	75° %	100° %
Ortho	42.7	31.9	20.0	13.3
Meta	3.8	6.1	7.9	8.0
Para	53.5	62.0	72.1	78.7

are given in Table IV. The meta acid undergoes practically no change; but in the presence of a large excess of sulfuric acid at 100°C., the ortho

[1] HOLLEMAN and POLAK, *Rec. trav. chim.*, **29**, 416 (1910).
[2] HOLLEMAN and CALAND, *Ber.*, **44**, 2504 (1921).

acid is transformed in part to the para isomer.   A further illustration
of the orientating influence of temperature in the toluene series is the
sulfonation of 6-chloro-o-toluidine.   At 140 to 200°C., the formation of
the 5-sulfonic acid is favored; while a temperature of 100°C. or under is
conducive to the formation of the 3-sulfonic acid.

The orientating influence of the reaction temperature is brought out
in a striking manner in the formation of naphthalene-, naphthol-, and
naphthylaminesulfonic acids.   In the monosulfonation of naphthalene,
the proportions of alpha and beta acids formed at different temperatures
are the following:[1]

Tempera-ture, °C.	Alpha, %	Beta, %
40	96.0	4.0 (Fierz-David)*
80	96.5	3.5
90	90.00	10.0
100	83.0	17.0
110.5	72.6	27.4
124	52.4	47.6
129	44.4	55.6
138.5	28.4	71.6
150.0	18.3	81.7
161.0	18.4	81.6
160.0	15.0	85.0 (Fierz-David)*

Naphthalene and 100 per cent sulfuric acid in equimolecular proportions were heated at the temperatures noted for a period of 8 hr.

* Fierz-David, "Grundlegende Operations der Farbenchemie" (1924).

The data of Euwes indicate that α-naphthalenesulfonic acid is the
primary product, this being transformed to the more stable beta isomer
at higher temperatures.

According to Fierz-David and Hasler, the following conclusions may
be drawn from experimental data[2] on the disulfonation of naphthalene:
Under 40°C., about 70 per cent of naphthalene-1, 5-disulfonic acid and
25 per cent of the 1, 6-isomer are formed in practically constant proportions, together with traces of the 2, 7-acid.   As the temperature of
sulfonation is raised, the proportion of the 1, 5-acid diminishes, owing to
replacement by 1, 6- and 2, 7-acids; and at 135°C., the 1, 5-acid is no
longer present in the reaction mixture.   At 140°C., the 2, 6-acid begins
to appear; and at 165°C., the reaction mixture contains about 25 per cent
of the 2, 6-acid, 65 per cent of the 2, 7-acid, and 10 per cent of the 1,
6-acid.

[1] Euwes, *Rec. trav. chim.*, **28**, 298 (1909).

[2] Fierz and Hasler, *Helv. Chim. Acta*, **6**, 1133 (1923).

These temperature orientation relationships are brought out in Fig. 3, which includes also the course of the reactions leading to the formation of naphthalenetrisulfonic acids.

On sulfonating β-naphthol, the reaction temperature again plays an important rôle. Below 15°C., Crocein acid (2-naphthol-8-sulfonic acid) is the principal product; but at 80°C., this is transformed to Schäffer acid (2-naphthol-6-sulfonic acid). Similarly, when Schäffer acid is further sulfonated, R- and G-acids, *i.e.*, the 2, 3, 6- and 2, 6, 8-naphtholdisulfonic acids, are obtained, the proportions of R-acid being greater when the sulfonation is carried out at 100°C. G-acid predominates if the reaction is conducted under 35°C.

β-Naphthylamine on sulfonation with three parts of sulfuric acid monohydrate yields a mixture of monosulfonic acids the composition of which varies with the reaction temperature.[1] At temperatures under 100°C., a mixture comprising 60 per cent of 2-naphthylamine-5-sulfonic acid and 40 per cent of the 2, 8-isomer is obtained, along with traces of the 6- and 7-sulfonic acids. A sulfonation temperature of 150°C. leads to the formation of about equal quantities of 2-naphthylamine-6- and 7-sulfonic acids.

In the anthraquinone series, the temperature of sulfonation is without influence on the position taken by the first sulfonic acid group, but it does exercise a slight orientating influence in the preparation of the 2, 6- and 2, 7-anthraquinonedisulfonic acids. At 120°C., the proportions are 26 per cent of the former and 52 per cent of the latter; but at 180°C., the proportions are approximately 40:45. These relationships are brought out graphically by the temperature curves of Fig. 10, page 253.

Although migrations of the sulfonic acid group with rising temperature are common in the naphthalene series, no such action has been observed with respect to the anthraquinonesulfonic acids. Without the presence of a mercury catalyst, substitution takes place practically exclusively in the beta positions, and an increase in the reaction temperature leads to the formation of disulfonic acids and oxidation compounds.

Relations of Temperature, Hydrolysis, and Sulfonation.—When naphthalene-1, 6-disulfonic acid is heated with sulfuric acid under conditions of temperature and acid concentration that are too low for hydrolysis of the α-sulfonic acid group, no change takes place. If both of these factors are sufficiently great to hydrolyze the sulfonic acid but insufficient for the sulfonation of naphthalene, hydrolysis (desulfonation) occurs but not sulfonation. When the temperature is high enough and the SO_3 concentration sufficient for sulfonation, then new sulfonic acids are formed.[2]

[1] GREEN and VAKIL, *J. Chem. Soc.*, **113**, 35 (1918).

[2] HODGSON, *Z. Farben-Ind.*, **20**, 124 (1929).

Oxidation and Its Relation to the Sulfonation Temperature.—Because concentrated sulfuric acid and sulfur trioxide exercise an oxidizing action, and since this characteristic is accentuated at higher temperatures, it is advantageous to carry out sulfonations at the lowest practical temperature.

The sulfonation of aromatic amines, as, *e.g.*, the preparation of sulfanilic and naphthionic acid, always gives evidence of oxidation through the presence of free carbon in the diluted reaction mass. In the disulfonation of anthraquinone from 2 to 5 per cent hydroxyanthraquinonesulfonic acids are formed,[1] the lesser quantity being obtained by heating slowly at the start and gradually raising the temperature to 120 to 130°C.

Influence of Reaction Time.—The influence of reaction time is probably best indicated by the curves relating to the sulfonation of anthraquinone (Figs. 9 to 11). In general, it can be stated that prolonging the reaction beyond the conversion period results in the formation of impurities which although small in quantity may be difficult to remove. Where polysulfonation is possible, the disulfonic acids will be formed at the expense of the monosulfonic acids; and when only the latter are desired, it is necessary to stop the reaction at some point before equilibrium has been reached.

When rearrangements or migrations are possible, a prolonged reaction period will favor the completion of such intramolecular changes. Thus, in the preparation of 2, 7- and 2, 6-naphthalenedisulfonic acids, it is known that the proportion of the 2, 6-acid is increased when the period of sulfonation is prolonged beyond 2 hr. at 165°C.

Effect of Catalysts and Sulfonation Aids.—In the sulfonation process, certain substances such as mercury compounds may catalyze the formation of specific products; *i.e.*, they exercise an orientating effect, or, in the case of vanadium compounds, they may merely accelerate the normal reaction without having influence on the positions taken by the sulfonic acid groups. Thus, in some sulfonations, the presence of a catalyst is absolutely essential, whereas in others its value may range from a convenience to an economic advantage.

Some of the substances that have been employed to catalyze sulfonations are the following:

1. Mercury and its salts.
2. Vanadium, its oxides and salts.
3. Alkali carbonates and sulfates.
4. Boric acid.

Use of Mercury.—The ordinary sulfonation of anthraquinone results in almost the exclusive formation of beta derivatives. In the presence

[1] LAUER, *J. prakt. Chem.*, **130**, 213 (1931).

of mercury or its salts, the alpha derivatives are formed almost wholly. The products of sulfonation by these two procedures are shown on pages 249 and 293. Krebser[1] attributes this catalytic activity to the preliminary formation of a mercury sulfate compound with anthraquinone, thus:

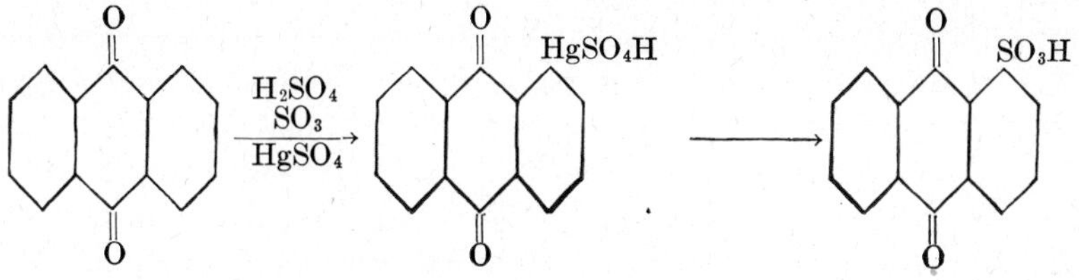

Lauer[2] confirmed this view experimentally by showing that the unconverted anthraquinone from catalytic monosulfonation contained organically bound mercury and further demonstrated that this material would on further treatment with oleum yield anthraquinone-1-sulfonic acid as the principal product.

When the α-monosulfonic acid is further sulfonated in the presence of mercury, the 1, 5- and 1, 8-disulfonic acids are obtained.

The further sulfonation of anthraquinone-2-sulfonic acid in the presence of mercury results in the formation of α, β-disulfonic acids, thus:

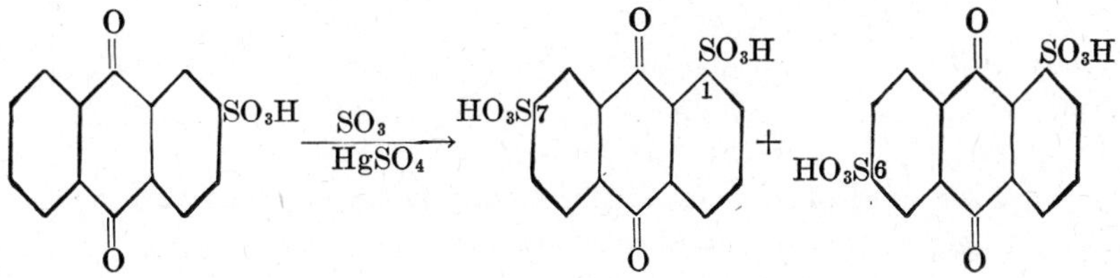

Similarly, the treatment of mercury-free anthraquinone-1-sulfonic acid leads principally to the 1, 6- and 1, 7-disulfonic acids. These observations lead to the conclusion that only one of the alpha positions in the anthraquinone nucleus is affected during each stage of the sulfonation.

The data in Table V show that it is immaterial what mercury compound is employed, all the salts giving substantially the same results when the equivalent of 1 per cent by weight of mercury is employed. An increase over this proportion of mercury does not appreciably repress the formation of the beta isomer unless the SO_3 concentration of the sulfonating acid is reduced to 5 per cent (Table II), page 254.

Stimulated by the discovery[3] of the catalytic activity of mercury in the sulfonation of anthraquinone, its use was investigated in many other

[1] KREBSER, Diss. E.T.H., Zurich (1923).
[2] LAUER, *J. prakt. Chem.*, **130**, 231 (1931).
[3] ILJINSKY, *Ber.*, **36**, 4194 (1903); SCHMIDT, *Ber.*, **37**, 66 (1904); Ger. 228,876 (1910).

TABLE V.—PREPARATION OF ANTHRAQUINONE-1-SULFONIC ACID. EFFECT OF MERCURY SALT

Anthraquinone, 208 gm. oleum, 25 per cent SO_2 (105 per cent of theory); temperature, 140°C.; time, 3 hr. at operating temperature

Expt. No.	Catalyst = 1 % Hg	Conversion, %	Fraction I		Fraction II		Residual acids, %
			Grams[1]	%[2]	Grams	%	
1	Hg metal..........	74.8	180.5	55.4	9.8	3.0	16.4
2	Sulfate............	75.3	178.4	54.8	9.3	2.8	17.7
3	Sulfate............	74.4	181.8	55.7	8.8	2.7	16.0
4	Chloride″(ic).......	74.6	179.8	55.2	9.2	2.8	16.6
5	Chloride′(ous)......	74.8	181.4	55.6	9.9	3.0	16.2

[1] Grams of K salt.
[2] Based on anthraquinone used.

reactions. It is known that many organic compounds may be mercurated, and in the aromatic series the mercury generally takes a position *ortho* to a substituent already present. During subsequent treatment with concentrated sulfuric acid, the mercury is replaced by the sulfonic acid group, thus:

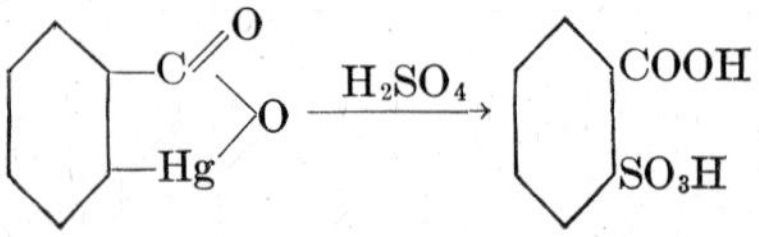

When the presence of mercury is practically without effect, it is assumed that sulfonation occurs more readily than mercuration.

α-Naphthol sulfonated in the presence of 20 per cent by weight of mercury sulfate[1] gives 1-naphthol-2-sulfonic acid as the principal product. Ordinary sulfonation of phthalic anhydride with sulfur trioxide yields 4-sulfophthalic anhydride; while in the presence of mercury sulfate, the 3-sulfo- and 3, 5-disulfophthalic anhydrides are obtained.

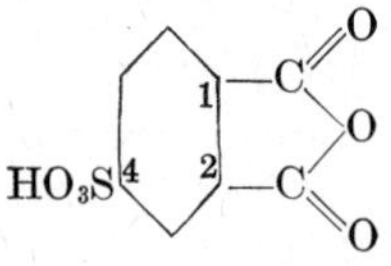

Normal Sulfonation 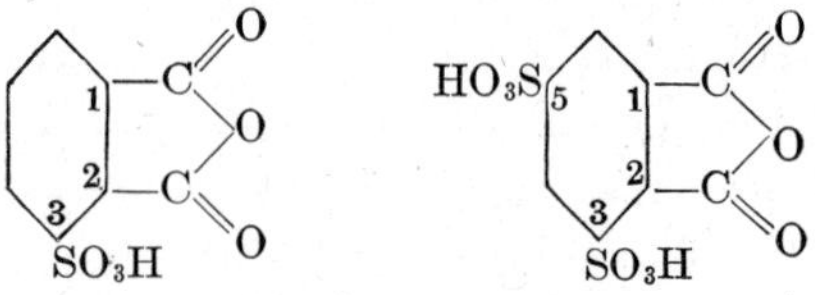   Catalytic Sulfonation

The orientating influence of mercury in the sulfonation of aromatic compounds has been summarized by Lauer[2] as follows:

[1] HOLDERMANN, *Ber.*, **39**, 1266 (1906).
[2] LAUER, *J. prakt. Chem.*, **138**, 81 (1933).

1. Mercury and its salts, especially the sulfate, which is known to be effective, dissolve only slowly in concentrated sulfuric acid and in oleum.

2. Mercury sulfate combines slowly with the organic components to form an intermediate addition product of sulfonation.

3. In the presence of aqueous sulfuric acid, the organic mercury compound either does not form or is not stable.

4. Normal as well as abnormal products of sulfonation are formed in the presence of mercury, as can be seen from the data below:

Compound sulfonated	Concentration oleum %	Temp., °C.	Hg, %	Yield, %		
				Ortho	Para	Meta
Nitrobenzene.............	20	90	0	..	3	97
Nitrobenzene.............	20	90	5	..	25	75
Benzoic acid.............	10	150	0	..	14	86
Benzoic acid.............	10	150	5	5	26	69
Benzenesulfonic acid........	20	200	0	..	5	95
Benzenesulfonic acid........	20	200	5	..	31	69

The remarkable orientating influence of the acid concentration when sulfonating in the presence of mercurous chloride is evident from the following data:

HgCl,[1] addition compound of	Concentration of sulfuric acid	Sulfonic acids obtained, %		
		Ortho	Para	Meta
Nitrobenzene....................	92	..	5	95
Nitrobenzene....................	20 % SO₃	94	..	6
Benzoic acid....................	92	..	8	92
Benzoic acid....................	10 % SO₃	97	..	3

[1] Obtained by treating organic compound in 100 per cent H_2SO_4 with 5 per cent its weight of mercury as chloride.

Use of Vanadium.—In the disulfonation of benzene with concentrated sulfuric acid, vanadium pentoxide accelerates the rate of reaction[1] but does not alter the position of the substituents. Anderau[2] likewise ascertained that the sulfonation of anthraquinone proceeded somewhat more rapidly in the presence of vanadium sulfate.

Use of Alkali Salts.—In the disulfonation of benzene, it was found that sodium carbonate catalyzed the rate of reaction.[3] Fierz points out,

[1] Senseman, *Ind. Eng. Chem.*, **13**, 1124 (1921).

[2] Anderau, Diss. E.T.H., Zurich (1923).

[3] Senseman, *loc. cit.*

however, that the addition of soda ash to the substance to be sulfonated is made solely for the purpose of preventing lump formation on mixing with sulfuric acid; the mixture is broken up by the carbonic acid liberated and very small quantities of sodium carbonate suffice.[1]

Lauer has found that the introduction of sodium sulfate in the sulfonation of anthraquinone increases the ratio of monosulfonic acid to disulfonic acid and decreases the percentage conversion of anthraquinone to sulfonic acids.

Boric acid has been used as a catalyst in the sulfonation of β-naphthol.[2] Here the presence of boric acid causes no changes in the usual substitution products obtained but does contribute to higher yields of 2-naphthol-1-sulfonic acid and 2-naphthol 1, 6-disulfonic acids at the expense of the 2-naphthol-8- and 2-naphthol-6-sulfonic acids.

Sulfonation Aids.—Acetic and phosphoric anhydrides have been used advantageously as sulfonation aids. When the mono- and dihydric phenols and their ethers are treated with a mixture containing acetic acid, acetic anhydride, and molecular proportions of sulfuric acid, the sulfonic acids are formed almost quantitatively.[3]

Effect of Agitation.—Experience has demonstrated that efficient agitation is one of the principal requisites of good sulfonation practice. For example, in the sulfonation of benzene, there is a tendency for the benzene and sulfuric acid to separate into layers, and it is obvious that satisfactory results cannot be obtained unless a means is provided to obtain an intimate mixture of the reactants. Even in reactions where solutions or emulsions are more or less readily formed, as for example, naphthalene in concentrated sulfuric acid and nitrobenzene in oleum, it is necessary to provide a practically homogeneous reaction mass, because local differences in temperature or acid concentration may give rise to the formation of undesirable isomers, polysulfonic acids, sulfones, and charred material.

V. FORMATION OF ADDITION COMPOUNDS IN SULFONATION

The treatment of organic substances with sulfuric acid appears to proceed through the preliminary formation of addition compounds before reaction resulting in the production of sulfonic acids takes place. The experimental evidence[4] of compound formation is largely limited to substances containing oxygen, and here the addition reaction is practically

---

[1] FIERZ-DAVID, "*Dye Chemistry*," D. Van Nostrand Company, p. 39 (1921 trans.).

[2] U. S. 1,570,046 (1926); ENGEL, *J. Am. Chem. Soc.*, **52**, 2837 (1930).

[3] FRIESE, *Ber.*, **64B**, 2103 (1931).

[4] KENDALL and CARPENTER, *J. Am. Chem. Soc.*, **36**, 2498 (1914); HOOGEWERFF and VAN DORP, *Rec. trav. chim.*, **18**, 211 (1899); **21**, 353 (1902).

instantaneous, even at temperatures of 0 to 100°C.   Some of the addition compounds can be isolated; thus, *p*-cresol with sulfuric acid (molar ratio, 1:2) forms a white crystalline isolable mass which melts at 93.5°C.

Kendall[1] has made a systematic survey of addition compound formation in the systems

$$H_2SO_4 + \begin{cases} \text{Organic acids} \\ \text{Aromatic aldehydes} \\ \text{Aromatic ketones} \\ \text{Aromatic phenols} \end{cases}$$

Evidence for the existence of compounds in solution was obtained from freezing-point measurements.   The principle involved is as follows:

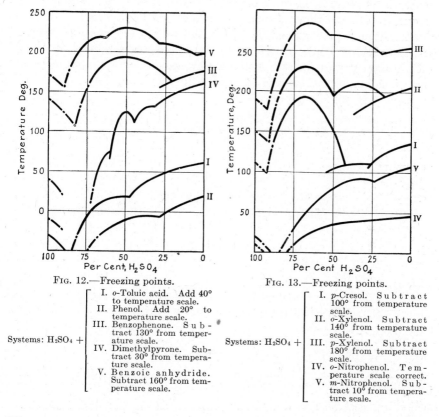

FIG. 12.—Freezing points.

Systems: H₂SO₄ +

I. *o*-Toluic acid.   Add 40° to temperature scale.
II. Phenol.   Add   20°   to temperature scale.
III. Benzophenone.   Subtract 130° from temperature scale.
IV. Dimethylpyrone.   Subtract 30° from temperature scale.
V. Benzoic anhydride.   Subtract 160° from temperature scale.

FIG. 13.—Freezing points.

Systems: H₂SO₄ +

I. *p*-Cresol.   Subtract 100° from temperature scale.
II. *o*-Xylenol.   Subtract 140° from temperature scale.
III. *p*-Xylenol.   Subtract 180° from temperature scale.
IV. *o*-Nitrophenol.   Temperature scale correct.
V. *m*-Nitrophenol.   Subtract 10° from temperature scale.

When a pure substance A is added to a second pure substance B, the freezing point of the latter is lowered; similarly, the addition of B lowers

[1] KENDALL, *J. Am. Chem. Soc.*, **36**, 1722 (1914); KENDALL and BOOGE, *J. Am. Chem. Soc.*, **38**, 1712 (1916).

the freezing point of A.   Plotting temperature against concentration gives two curves that intersect at the eutectic point.   If, however, a compound AB is formed, this also acts as a pure substance, and its freezing point is lowered by the addition of either A or B.

The freezing-point curves exhibit therefore a maximum or a series of maxima which, when referred to the axis of molecular concentration, indicate the composition of the addition compounds formed.   From the shape of the curves at the maximum point, it is possible to judge very approximately the amount of compound formed, since a rapid decrease in the temperature of fusion of a compound on addition of either component indicates extensive compound formation in solution.

In Figs. 12 and 13 are shown some of the curves obtained with systems comprising phenols, ketones, carboxylic acids, and H_2SO_4, and it can be seen that some of these possess well-defined maxima.

Addition compounds of the type A_2B, (A being the organic substance; B, the sulfuric acid), AB (or A_2B_2), A_2B_3, and A_2B_4 can be obtained.[1] It is apparent that the compounds form a regular series in four steps and are explained on the basis of oxonium salt formation, thus:

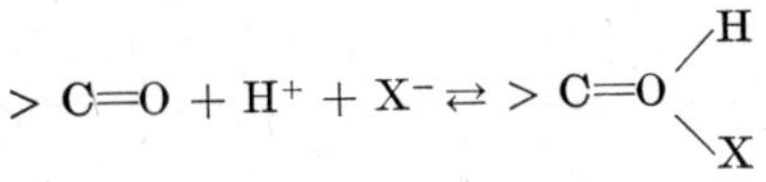

$$> C{=}O + H^+ + X^- \rightleftarrows\ > C{=}O\diagup^{H}_{\diagdown X}$$

or, more specifically,

$$R{\cdot}C{=}O^{\pm}_{\underset{OH}{|}} + H^+ + HSO_4^- \rightleftarrows R{\cdot}C{=}O\underset{\underset{OH}{|}}{\diagup}^{H}_{\diagdown O(SO_2)OH}$$

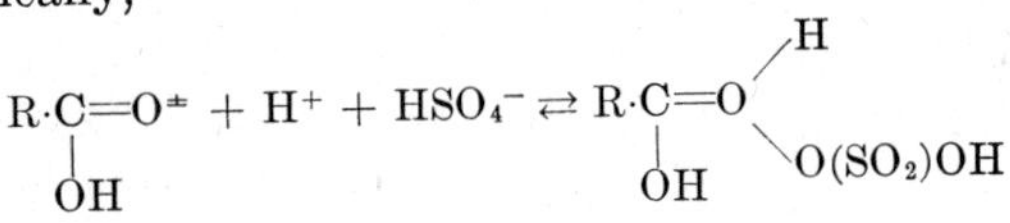

Kendall and Carpenter concluded that "sulfonation is preceded by the formation of addition compounds of the nature of oxonium salts and the reaction is ionic and instantaneous."

Although the preceding experiments were made with pure 100 per cent H_2SO_4, it is not certain whether the sulfuric acid or its more active dissolved SO_3 is responsible for the formation of the addition compounds. It is known that at sulfonation temperatures, concentrated sulfuric acid is a system comprising SO_3, H_2SO_4, and H_2O.   It is also known that sulfur trioxide readily forms stable addition compounds with substances containing atoms capable of existing in a higher and lower valence.   The formation of pyridinium sulfonic acid is an example of such addition.

It is, therefore, entirely reasonable to believe that the dissolved or combined (as in pyrosulfuric acid) SO_3 may add on as follows:

---

[1] KENDALL and CARPENTER, *loc. cit.*

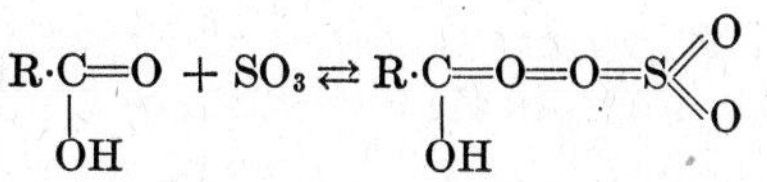

$$R \cdot C = O + SO_3 \rightleftarrows R \cdot C = O = O = S \overset{O}{\underset{O}{\diagdown}} \quad \left(\begin{matrix} \text{Addition} \\ \text{of } SO_3 \end{matrix} \right)$$
$$\underset{OH}{|} \qquad\qquad \underset{OH}{|}$$

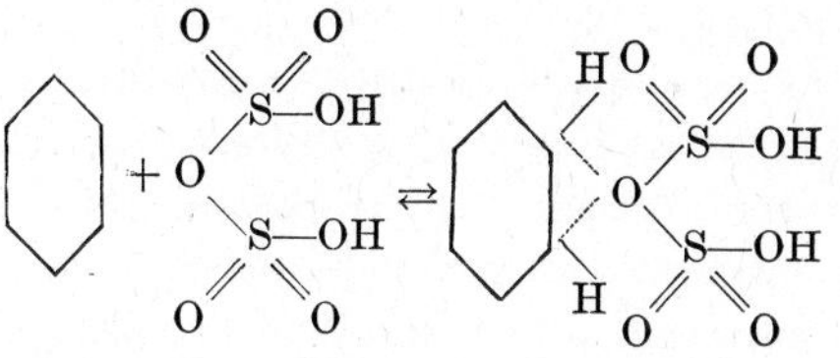

$$\left(\begin{matrix} \text{Addition of} \\ \text{pyrosulfuric acid} \end{matrix} \right)$$

It is emphasized that this is merely a hypothesis, presented to stimulate a closer examination of our concepts regarding organic synthesis. In the sulfonation of aromatic hydrocarbons, addition may take place by means of the unsatisfied carbon valences of the benzene ring. This is supported by the fact that the saturated aliphatic compounds do not form sulfonic acids when treated with sulfuric acid and by the observation that naphthalenedisulfonic acids can loosely bind sulfur trioxide[1] and relinquish it for the further sulfonation of naphthalenemonosulfonic acid.

VI. TECHNICAL METHODS OF SULFONATION

Substances sulfonated by sulfuric acid, oleum, etc., can be divided into two general classes: (1) those that can be volatilized, *e.g.*, benzene, naphthalene, etc.; and (2) those that cannot be easily vaporized, *e.g.*, α-nitronaphthalene and anthraquinone. Usually, the material being sulfonated is in the liquid phase at the temperature of sulfonation, but there are notable exceptions, as, for example, the sulfonation of sodium 2-naphthol-7-sulfonate to 2-naphthol-1, 3, 7-trisulfonic acid.[2] The substances of both classes can be sulfonated by the batch method, but only those of the first class lend themselves advantageously to the process of continuous sulfonation.

Batch Sulfonations. *Introducing Reactants.*—In batch or discontinuous sulfonation, the introduction of the reactants into the sulfonator varies with the physical and chemical properties of the materials undergoing treatment. It is customary to add anthraquinone compounds to fuming sulfuric acid, but concentrated sulfuric acid is generally added to the more volatile benzene. In sulfonating naphthalene, the aromatic hydrocarbon is generally melted in the kettle prior to the introduction of acid, although a number of operators prefer to introduce the reactants alternately in regulated portions.

Removing Water of Reaction.—From a study of the relationship between SO_3 concentration and sulfonation activity, it is apparent that

---

[1] COURTOT, *Rev. gén. mat. color.*, **33**, 177 (1929).
[2] DRESSEL and KOTHE, *Ber.*, **27**, 1207 (1894).

unless a method is devised to prevent excessive dilution because of water formed during the reaction, the rate of sulfonation will undergo gradual deceleration.   Finally, the reaction will be stopped at a definite H_2SO_4 or SO_3 concentration—different for each organic compound undergoing sulfonation.   With respect to economy in sulfuric acid consumption, it is advantageous physically to remove or chemically combine this water, and various methods have been devised for accomplishing this purpose.

Use of Oleum.—The use of oleum for maintaining the necessary SO_3 concentration of a sulfonation mixture is a practical procedure that can

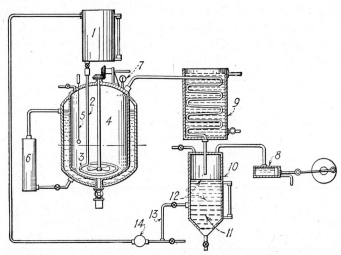

FIG. 14.—Apparatus for the sulfonation of benzene.

1. Benzene supply.
2. Benzene feed line.
3. Perforated distributor for benzene.
4. Sulfonator. '
5. Thermometer.
6. Oil heating mechanism.
7. Pressure gage.

8. Vacuum pump.
9. Cooling coil.
10. Condensed liquor tank.
11–12. Water and benzene layers, respectively.
13. Recovered benzene-return line.
14. Circulating pump.

be employed for the disulfonation of benzene and naphthalene.   Preferably, the oleum and organic compound should be added gradually and concurrently to a large volume of cycle acid so as to take up the water as rapidly as it is formed by the reaction.

Use of Vacuum.—The use of reduced pressure for removing the water of reaction has some technical advantages in the sulfonation of phenol[1] and of benzene.[2]   According to Downs, the disulfonation of benzene may be carried out under an absolute pressure of 0.5 to 1.0 in. of mercury at 260°C., with a lower ratio of oleum than is otherwise feasible.   Under such conditions, sulfuric acid itself can be distilled from the reaction mass.

[1] Hazard-Flamand, Ger., 141,751 (1903).

[2] Downs, U. S. 1,279,295 (1918).   1,301,785 (1919).   Bender, U. S. 1,301,360 (1919).

Bender produced benzenesulfonic acid in the apparatus shown in Fig. 14 by carrying out the sulfonation in the ordinary manner to obtain the maximum absorption of benzene in sulfuric acid and then removing the excess of benzene and water under reduced pressures at 150 to 180°C. to reduce the ratio of water to sulfuric acid at the close of the reaction to less than 22:78.

Special Sulfonating Processes: Discontinuous. *Guyot or Tyrer Process.*[1]—Here advantage is taken of the low boiling point of some aromatic hydrocarbons to remove the water formed during sulfonation. The method is applicable to compounds boiling below 200°C. Benzene may accordingly be sulfonated as follows: Sulfuric acid of 90 to 92 per cent strength is warmed to 100°C. in a closed vessel, and benzene vapors from a special boiler are introduced into the heated acid through a pipe extending below a perforated cast-iron plate located at the bottom of the sulfonator. Provision is made for the condensation of the benzene and water vapors emerging from the kettle. While the benzene vapor is being delivered into the acid, the temperature of the latter is raised at the rate of 1°C. per minute until it reaches 185°C., at which point it is maintained for half an hour. The condensate, comprising benzene and water. is allowed to separate into layers and the benzene is again returned to the system. Disulfonic acids are formed when the temperature or acid concentration is high at the beginning of the operation.

In industrial operations, the benzene vapors are supplied to a series of sulfonators operating at 10 to 12 lb. pressure and at a gradually increasing temperature up to 180°C. The hydrocarbon is fed in at a rate to insure the presence of some unreacted benzene in the distillate. The course of the reaction is followed by specific-gravity measurements on samples from the reactor; when density falls to 39°Bé., the process is considered complete. About 95 per cent of the sulfuric acid is used.

This process can be employed with volatile organic compounds such as toluene, xylenes, and chlorobenzene, which are capable of being sulfonated directly by sulfuric acid not containing free sulfur trioxide.

Instead of passing benzene vapors into the heated sulfuric acid, liquid benzene under pressure can be introduced. The vapors leaving the system are passed through a water separator, and the condensed benzene is automatically and continuously returned to the system.[2] Operating at 130 to 135°C. with 100 per cent H_2SO_4, only 3.05 per cent of the acid remains after 8 hr. A typical analysis of a sample taken when the sulfuric acid content is reduced to 4.0 to 4.5 per cent is as follows:

[1] Tyrer U. S. 1,210,725 (1917); GUYOT, *Chimie & Industrie*, **2**, 879 (1919).

[2] ZAKHAROV, *J. Chem. Ind. (Moscow)*, **6**, 1648 (1929).

	%	
$C_6H_5·SO_3H$	93	to 94
H_2SO_4	4.0 to	4.5
H_2O	1.5 to	2.0
$(C_6H_5)_2SO_2$	0.5	

Gay, Aumeras, and Mion Process.[1]—The Guyot process cannot be used successfully with naphthalene, because a temperature in excess of 200°C. is required to remove the water of reaction, and this condition results in a charred sulfonic acid. The liberated water may, however, be removed by the use of an auxiliary liquid or an inert gas. The auxiliary liquids, such as carbon tetrachloride or ligroin, are characterized by the fact that their vapors are practically insoluble in the reaction mixture at sulfonation temperatures. These liquids, when circulated through the charge at 170°C., remove the water of reaction. The condensed vapors are subsequently separated, and the auxiliary liquid returned to the sulfonator.

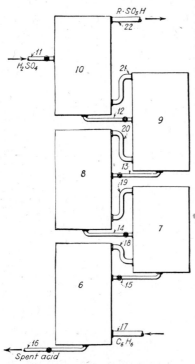

Fig. 15.—Plant assembly. Dennis-Bull process for the sulfonation of benzene.

Continuous Sulfonation. *Dennis and Bull Process.*—A process for the continuous sulfonation of aromatic hydrocarbons is based on the discovery by Dennis[2] that, although the solubility of pure benzenesulfonic acid in benzene is negligible, in the presence of free sulfuric acid benzene will take up between 2 and 3 per cent of its own volume of the sulfonic acid. Bull[3] applied this principle in the technical sulfonation of benzene, the salient features of the procedure being shown in Fig. 15.

The vessels (6 to 10) are filled with benzene through the pipe 17. Sulfuric acid or preferably oleum is then introduced into the upper reaction vessel through the pipe 11. Owing to its greater density, the acid flows downward through the series of reactors and comes into intimate contact with the ascending aromatic hydrocarbon. Because of the large

[1] GAY, AUMERAS and MION, *Chimie & industrie*, **19**, 387 (1928).

[2] Dennis, U. S. 1,211,923; 1,212,612 (1917).

[3] Bull, U. S. 1,247,499 (1917).

excess of benzene used, the benzenesulfonic acid is extracted and leaves the system by the top outlet 22 as a 2 per cent solution. The residual sulfuric acid of approximately 77 per cent H_2SO_4 leaves the system at the lower outlet pipe 16 and is then concentrated for reuse.[1] It is also feasible to circulate the spent acid through a SO_3 absorption system and thus effect its concentration.

The benzene-benzenesulfonic acid mixture may be sent to washers to remove the sulfonic acid and liberate the benzene. The aqueous solution of the acid then may be utilized to neutralize the sodium phenolate produced by alkali fusion of the sodium benzenesulfonate, thus providing an economical procedure for the preparation of phenol.[2]

VII. DESIGN AND CONSTRUCTION OF APPARATUS

Cast-iron apparatus is suitable for sulfonations with concentrated sulfuric acid of 88 to 98 per cent strength. When oleum or when mixtures containing free SO_3 are used, it is advisable to employ steel equipment. It is known that sulfur trioxide sometimes causes faults to develop in castings, and this is attributed to the action of the acid anhydride on the slag left in the pores of the cast iron.

Sulfuric acid (85 per cent, which is too weak for most sulfonations) has a specific conductance of only 0.1, while the value of the specific conductance of pure sulfuric acid is practically zero. Whereas dilute sulfuric acid, which is appreciably dissociated into $2H^+$ and SO_4^-, attacks iron, forming ferrous sulfate, sulfuric acid stronger than the dihydrate $SO_3 \cdot 2H_2O$ (85 per cent H_2SO_4) does not appreciably attack the iron vessels that are employed in synthetical processes.

When the sulfonation involves no special characteristics such as have been discussed previously, the operation can be carried out conveniently in most of the available commercial vessels designed for this unit process. Typical industrial apparatus is shown in Fig. 16. Two factors are of importance in the design and construction of sulfonators, *viz.*, heat transfer and agitation. Although the problem of dissipating the heat of reaction is not so important as in nitration, operations at distinctly higher temperatures (200 to 280°C.) are necessary for certain sulfonations. Consideration must also be given to the stirring of viscous mixtures in order to avoid surface overheating.

Heat Transfer.—Although sulfonation is an exothermal reaction, heat is frequently desirable to accelerate the initial reaction, and generally it is necessary to continue the heating during the final stages. Sulfonators are consequently provided with devices for effecting heat transfer, and these may be classified broadly as (1) jacket; (2) coils imbedded in

[1] PETERKIN, *Chem. & Met. Eng.*, **19**, 255 (1918).
[2] U. S. 1,227,894 (1917).

castings (Thermocoil and Frederking construction); and (3) vertical cast-iron tubes. Obviously, a combination of the preceding methods may oftentimes be employed advantageously.

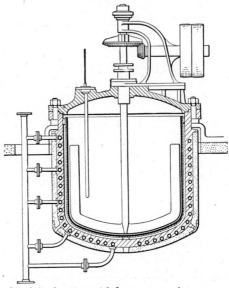

Fig. 16.—Sulfonator fitted for heating with hot water or low-pressure steam (Frederking system).

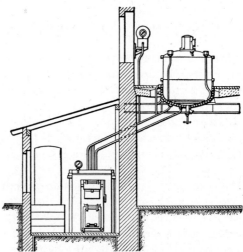

Fig. 17.—Thermocoil hot-water system.

A typical installation. Hot water, under pressure, circulates without pump or other mechanical device and, once properly adjusted, requires no attention other than to the furnace or heater.

Heating Agents.—Hot water, steam, heated oils, and hot gases find employment in sulfonation operations. Hot water automatically controlled at the desired temperatures oftentimes provides a satisfactory method of heating. In the Frederking or Thermocoil apparatus (Figs. 16, 17), the hot water or steam can be circulated under high pressures, and this makes possible obtaining relatively high temperatures, *i.e.*, 170 to 300°C. (Fig. 18). Steam is generally the most economical and efficient and therefore the most common means of heating a jacketed kettle. When high temperatures are required, steam is not generally employed in jacketed vessels because of the accompanying high pressures.

Heating by the use of hot oil is frequently resorted to for operations requiring a temperature range of 200 to 250°C. The oil is generally

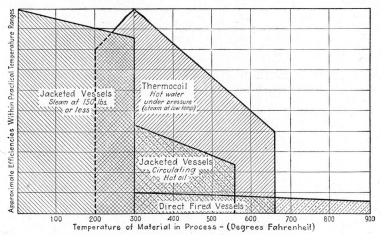

FIG. 18.—Thermal classification of processing systems.

heated in a separate tubular boiler and delivered to the jacket of the reactor by means of pumps. The rate of flow to the jacket is regulated automatically. It has the advantage over steam in that no great jacket pressures are involved but suffers in comparison since heat conduction through an oil film is considerably less than from a condensing vapor. Consequently, thermal efficiency must be sacrificed for the advantage gained in apparatus construction.

VIII. TECHNICAL PREPARATION OF SULFONIC ACIDS

Sources of Loss.—In sulfonation operations, there are several known sources of loss, some of which can be determined analytically. These are (1) tar formation; (2) sulfone formation; (3) unreacted crude material; (4) undesirable sulfonic acids; (5) solubility losses in mother liquors; and (6) mechanical losses. Wherever possible, these sources of loss should be checked regularly, and methods devised to control such losses to the lowest possible limits. These losses may be illustrated by considering the sulfonation of naphthalene to naphthalene-2-sulfonic acid.

It is known that (1) is small (less than 1 per cent); (2) can be limited to 0.5 to 1.0 per cent; (3) can be limited to less than 1.0 per cent; (4) and (5) amount to about 15 to 20 per cent; and (6) should be less than 0.5 per cent and varies with each sulfonation. It comprises sulfonic acid lost in discarded press cakes, spilling, etc.

Preparation of Carbylsulfate and Ethionic Acid.   *Carbylsulfate.*

$$\begin{matrix} CH_2 \\ \| \\ CH_2 \end{matrix} + 2SO_3 \xrightarrow{\quad SO_2 \quad} \begin{matrix} CH_2 \cdot OSO_2 \\ | \\ CH_2 \cdot SO_2 \end{matrix} \Big\rangle O$$

Two hundred forty parts of sulfur trioxide is dissolved in 480 parts of liquid sulfur dioxide. Into this solution 28 parts of ethylene is introduced in a slow current. The SO_2 is eliminated by distillation, and the crystalline residue, after cooling to 0°C., is separated on a suction filter. Carbylsulfate is obtained in crystalline form in a yield of 90 per cent of theory.

Ethionic Acid.

$$CH_3CH_2OH + 2SO_3 \xrightarrow{\quad SO_2 \quad} \begin{matrix} CH_2 \cdot OSO_3H \\ | \\ CH_2 \cdot SO_3H \end{matrix}$$

Ethyl alcohol (480 parts) is dissolved in 500 parts of liquid SO_2, which is instrumental in maintaining a low reaction temperature. Into this solution there is run during a 6-hr. interval, a mixture of 1,600 parts of SO_2 and 1,600 parts of SO_3. The reaction mass is stirred for about 10 hr. at 0°C. and then warmed to 10 to 15°C. to drive off most of the SO_2. The product consists of crude ethionic acid. Carbylsulfate also leads to ethionic acid by hydration in the cold.

$$\begin{matrix} CH_2OSO_2 \\ | \\ CH_2SO_2 \end{matrix} \Big\rangle O + H_2O \rightarrow \begin{matrix} CH_2OSO_3H \\ | \\ CH_2SO_3H \end{matrix}$$

Benzenesulfonic Acid.—For the production of benzenesulfonic acid, the sulfonator should be equipped with an efficient propeller and a reflux condenser. The operation is started by running 1,000 lb. of benzene into the sulfonator. Then, during a period of 6 to 8 hr., 2,050 lb. of 5 per cent oleum is delivered, and the temperature controlled at 35 to 40°C. by means of circulating water. After all of the oleum has been added, the water is drained from the jacket and the temperature brought up to 100 to 110°C. by jacket steam. The unreacted benzene starts to reflux as the temperature is raised, and the reaction is complete in 2 to 3 hr. A sample of the sulfonation mixture is diluted with water to determine the presence of free benzene; and if the reaction is incomplete, additional concentrated sulfuric acid is introduced, and the process continued.

The sulfonated mass may be treated by diverse methods. A simple procedure is to run the charge into 4,000 lb. of water, neutralizing with hydrated lime and then filtering the calcium benzenesulfonate from the gypsum. The sodium salt is obtained by boiling the solution of the calcium salt with soda ash and filtering to remove the calcium carbonate. The solution of sodium benzenesulfonate may be evaporated or employed directly in subsequent reactions.

When the benzenesulfonic acid is to be employed in the synthesis of phenol, the sodium salt can be made by the addition of by-product sodium sulfite, that is obtained from the subsequent caustic fusion operations. The sulfite is put into solution with any available wash waters containing sodium benzenesulfonate, and the charge containing benzenesulfonic acid is then slowly introduced. The sulfur dioxide that is liberated is delivered to another vessel or absorption tower containing sodium phenolate, thus accomplishing the useful purpose of liberating the phenol. The last traces of sulfur dioxide are removed by boiling with live steam. This economic utilization of materials is similar to the method of preparing β-naphthylamine, from sodium β-naphthalenesulfonate.[1]

Continuous Sulfonation of Benzene.—The sulfonation of benzene can also be carried out continuously and economically by the method of Barbet.[2]

The process is carried out as follows:[3] Sulfuric acid of 98 per cent strength is heated in the coil *D* (Fig. 19) and delivered to the top of a cast-iron reaction tower *A*, which is provided with baffle plates and a suitable stoneware packing. By means of heat provided by steam coils located on the baffles, a temperature of 150°C. is maintained within the tower. Benzene is heated in the heat exchanger *B* by the descending benzenesulfonic acid and is vaporized in the vessel *C*. The benzene vapors enter at the bottom of the reaction tower and on ascending come in contact and react with sulfuric acid of increasing strength. The hydrocarbon is finally completely converted to benzenesulfonic acid, which, with the excess of mineral acid, flows out at the base and passes through the heat exchanger.

Water and acid vapors as well as other gaseous impurities will pass to the cooler *E* and then to the scrubber *H*, where the sulfurous acid is removed by washing. The benzenesulfonic acid may be worked up according to the procedures previously described or may be used to neutralize a solution of sodium phenolate,[4] thus producing phenol and sodium benzenesulfonate.

[1] CAMPBELL, *J. Soc. Dyers Colourists*, **38**, 114 (1922).

[2] Barbet, U. S. 1,459,081 (1923).

[3] This process was developed independently at the Color Laboratory by Ambler and Gibbs [U. S. 1,300,228 (1919)].

[4] Dennis, U. S. 1,227,894 (1917).

Benzene-1, 3-Disulfonic Acid.—The calcium salt of benzenesulfonic acid may be used for the preparation of the disulfonic acid. Because of the high temperatures and heavy load, it is necessary to employ a Thermocoil system or heat with circulating oil and to use an efficient stirrer. In this process, 1,670 lb. of powdered anhydrous calcium benzenesulfonate and 1.25 lb. of sodium carbonate (to prevent formation of lumps) are added to 2,600 lb. of 95 per cent sulfuric acid at 200°C. in a cast-iron sulfonator. The temperature is raised to 250°C. over a period of 6 hr., and held at this point for 1 hr. The batch is then dropped into 800 gal. of water and neutralized by the addition of milk of lime.

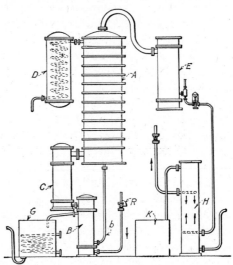

Fig. 19.—Sulfonation of benzene: Barbet process.

A. Reaction column.	*G*. Outlet for benzenesulfonic acid.
B. Heat exchanger to preheat benzene.	*H*. Scrubber.
b. Hot benzenesulfonic acid line.	*K*. Reservoir for unsulfonatable volatile hydro-
C. Benzene vaporizer.	carbons.
D. H₂SO₄ inlet.	*R*. Benzene inlet.
E. Cooler for water vapors.	

The suspension is heated to boiling with live steam and filtered from the gypsum. The calcium benzenedisulfonate is converted to the sodium salt by treating with a hot solution of sodium carbonate.

The disulfonic acid may be prepared at much lower temperatures, *e.g.*, 70 to 120°C., and with greater economy with respect to the sulfuric acid by using a cyclic system of sulfonation. Here the concentrated sulfuric acid which is present at the termination of disulfonation (cycle acid) is used to prepare the monosulfonic acid. The process may be carried out as follows:[1]

Monosulfonation.—Into a mixture of 213.6 parts of sulfuric acidmonohydrate (approximately 2 moles) and 476 parts of benzene disulfonic

[1] U. S. 1,956,571 (1934).

acid (2 moles) there are added gradually over a period of about 4 to
5 hr. 78 parts (one mole) of benzene. The temperature which is kept at
about 70°C. during the feeding operations is raised to 120°C. and maintained at that point for about 1 hr. During this phase of the operation
the residual acid resulting from disulfonation is used for the monosulfonation of benzene.

Disulfonation.—The charge is cooled to 70°C., and 266 parts of 60 per
cent oleum (containing 2 moles SO_3 and 1.09 moles of sulfuric acid) is run
in over a period of 4 hr. Toward the end of this operation the temperature is permitted to rise to 100°C. and is then further raised to 120°C.
within a period of about $\frac{1}{2}$ hr. After maintaining this temperature for
3 hr., disulfonation is substantially complete. One-third of the charge is
then removed for treatment with lime. The residue—which is identical
with the cycle acid used at the beginning of the operation—is cooled to
70°C. and the operation is repeated.

Sulfanilic Acid. *Preparation by Baking Process.*

The contents of one drum of aniline, *i.e.*, about 900 lb., are emptied
into a shallow mixing pot or mixing machine, which preferably is made
of an acid-resistant alloy; 1,050 lb. of 66°Bé. (93.2 per cent) of water-
white sulfuric acid is then fed in very slowly, with constant and thorough
agitation. A thick paste is obtained, which is removed while warm and
placed in trays in a vacuum oven. Heat is supplied to the oven by superheated steam or a circulating oil system.

The paste is heated at 200°C. for 6 hr. The dry cake is discharged
into a lead-lined mixing kettle provided with a cover and vent. The
material is now slightly gray in color and is upward of 90 per cent pure.
In this crude form, it contains from 0.3 to 3.0 per cent unchanged aniline
and some carbonaceous impurities. The "bake" is put into solution
with dilute sodium carbonate, precaution being taken to insure a strong
blue coloration with litmus. Live steam is then passed into the charge
to remove all traces of aniline. Some decolorizing carbon is added, and
the solution passed through a pressure filter. The filtrate is suitable
for making certain azo dyes and in some plants is thus employed. The
sodium salt is often made by treating the crude sulfanilic acid with milk
of lime, reacting the calcium salt with sodium carbonate, and then filtering
to remove the calcium carbonate. When this solution is acidified with

sulfuric acid, a good quality of free acid is obtained.   The purified material is put on a filter, washed, and then dried in a vacuum oven.   The yield of purified sulfanilic acid should be over 90 per cent of theory or in excess of 165 lb. based on 100 lb. of aniline used.[1]

Naphthalene-2-Sulfonic Acid.

When naphthalene is sulfonated at 165°C., the principal product is naphthalene-2-sulfonic acid, and about 15 per cent of the alpha isomer is formed simultaneously.   Of powdered naphthalene 5,000 lb. is charged into a jacketed cast-iron sulfonation kettle, melted, and heated to 165°C. Then 5,400 lb. of 98 per cent sulfuric acid is run into the molten naphthalene at such a rate that the temperature does not rise above 165°C.   This takes about 3 hr.   The heating and stirring are continued for an additional hour, and the reaction mass is then dropped into 1,760 gal. of water contained in a lead-lined vat, fitted with a stirrer.   The batch is neutralized with milk of lime at the boiling temperature.   The volume at the end of this operation should be about 5,630 gal.   The calcium naphthalene-2-sulfonate in solution is filtered from the gypsum and cooled to 20°C. in a tank provided with cooling coils.   The calcium salt of the acid crystallizes out and is separated by filtration from the alpha isomer and disulfonates that are in the mother liquor.   The calcium salt may be converted to the sodium salt by treatment with a solution of soda ash. The sodium salt may be made directly by completely neutralizing the sulfonation charge with soda ash, adding sufficient sodium chloride to give a solution of 17°Bé., and allowing to crystallize overnight.

The product may be tested for completeness of sulfonation by distilling with steam.   A typical analysis reveals the presence of 0.6 per cent free naphthalene and 0.9 per cent sulfone.   The latter remains in suspension in the acid solution and may be removed by filtration.   The percentage of alpha isomer may be determined by converting the dried calcium salts to the sulfonchlorides with phosphorus pentachloride and estimating the components from melting point-composition curves, the

[1] HUBER, *Helv. Chim. Acta*, **15**, 1372 (1932).

melting point of the alpha and beta derivatives being 67 and 77°C., respectively.

Naphthalene-2-sulfonic Acid: Alternative Procedure.—The preparation of β-naphthalenesulfonic acid with respect to its utilization in the manufacture of β-naphthol is advantageously carried out as follows:[1] 3,350 lb. of naphthalene is charged into a 1,500-gal. sulfonator, and the hydrocarbon melted by warming to 90°C. With rapid agitation, 3,350 lb. of sulfuric acid (93.0 per cent) is run in, permitting the temperature to rise to 160°C. The charge is heated at 160 to 165°C. for several hours. During this period, some of the naphthalene distills off and is cooled in condensers kept at 90°C. by means of hot water. The naphthalene thus condensed and recovered is subsequently dried and reused.

The reaction product contains 85 per cent of the β-sulfonic acid and 15 per cent of the alpha isomer. The latter is now removed by blowing dry steam into the charge whereby the naphthalene-1-sulfonic acid is desulfonated (hydrolyzed) and the liberated naphthalene is distilled off

and recovered. It is essential to employ dry steam to avoid foaming and to maintain a temperature of 160 to 165°C. to expedite the hydrolytic reaction. About 18 per cent, or 542 lb. of the original naphthalene employed, is recovered, leaving the residual β-naphthalenesulfonic acid contaminated with about 0.1 per cent alpha isomer.

The "hydrolyzed" sulfonation mixture is discharged into 1,600 gal. of water (13,400 lb., or 4 lb. of water per pound of naphthalene originally used) under vigorous agitation. This diluted solution is then run into a previously prepared solution of 4,750 lb. of salt in 14,100 lb. of water (1,760 gal. of solution), whereby the formation of the sodium-2-naphthalenesulfonate is effected. The mixture is agitated for a period of about 10 hr., or until the charge has cooled to 30°C., and is then filtered.

The filtration is accomplished by pumping or blowing the sodium sulfonate suspension into a pressure filter containing wooden plate filters and rubber-coated frames. The shell of the filter is coated with tar to minimize corrosion. The filtrate is permitted to stand and more salt added if necessary and then refiltered to collect any additional sulfonate that has crystallized out. The second crop of sodium sulfonate is not so pure as the first. The filter cakes are generally washed with a mini-

[1] SHREVE, *Color Trade J. Textile Chem.*, **14**, 42 (1924); *cf.* U. S. 1,922,813 (1933), which is practically identical.

mum of water, and these washings are employed to advantage as part of the liquor in the sulfonation dilution tank.

The filter cake of sodium naphthalene-2-sulfonate containing about 70 per cent of water is packed into the trays of hydraulic presses and subjected to pressure until the water content is approximately 30 per cent. The press cakes are disintegrated and then delivered to the fusion kettles for the preparation of β-naphthol.

When the naphthalenesulfonic acid is to be converted to β-naphthol, the sulfonic acid may be treated with the alkali fusion mass obtained in the ensuing operation. The reactions that take place are as follows:

$$C_{10}H_7SO_3Na + 2NaOH(Fusion) \rightarrow C_{10}H_7ONa + Na_2SO_3 + H_2O \qquad (I)$$
$$C_{10}H_7ONa + C_{10}H_7SO_3H \rightarrow C_{10}H_7OH + C_{10}H_7SO_3Na \qquad (II)$$

Preparation of 2-Naphthol-1-Sulfonic Acid. *Sulfonation with Chlorosulfonic Acid.*—Chlorosulfonic acid is employed to sulfonate β-naphthol when the 1-sulfonic acid is desired. The sulfonation is carried out in a jacketed cast-iron vessel provided with a brine coil and a propeller stirrer. The liberated hydrogen chloride escapes through a vent and is advantageously absorbed in water to produce the halogen acid.

The reactor is charged with 500 lb. of *o*-nitrotoluene and 144 lb. of β-naphthol. The solution obtained is cooled to 0°C., and 140 lb. of chlorosulfonic acid is then run in at such a rate that the addition of acid requires about 3 hr. The charge is stirred for 3 hr. longer, maintaining the temperature below 10°C.

When hydrogen chloride ceases to be liberated, the reaction mass is dropped into a conical wooden tank containing 2,200 lb. of water, whereupon the *o*-nitrotoluene separates and the 2-naphthol-1-sulfonic acid is dissolved in the water. The nitrotoluene is drawn off, and the aqueous solution neutralized with potassium carbonate. The potassium salt of 2-naphthol-1-sulfonic acid is salted out with potassium chloride and is then filtered off.

Preparation of 1-Amino-2-Naphthol-4-Sulfonic Acid. *Sulfonation with Sodium Bisulfite.*—In the preparation of 1-amino-2-naphthol-4-sulfonic acid, 1,000 lb. of water, 28 lb. of caustic soda, and 100 lb. of β-naphthol are charged into a wooden tank provided with a wooden stirrer. A solution of 50 lb. of sodium nitrite (96 per cent) dissolved in 1,000 lb. of water is then added. About 1,000 lb. of crushed ice is added to reduce the temperature to 0 to 5°C., whereupon a mixture of 1,260 lb.

of water. 1.000 lb. of ice, and 140 lb. of sulfuric acid (98 per cent) is added. After stirring for 2 hr., the mixture is filtered and the press cake is washed with a moderate amount of water. The nitrosonaphthol is obtained in the form of a cake containing about 80 per cent water.

The wet nitrosonaphthol from the preceding operation is mixed in another wooden tub with 1,500 lb. of water and 206 lb. of sodium bisulfite. The nitrosonaphthol dissolves, and, when solution is complete, the charge is filtered into another tank. The clear solution is heated to 40°C., and 230 lb. of hydrochloric acid run in. The mixture is then kept at 40°C. overnight while stirring. The 1-amino-2-naphthol-4-sulfonic acid separates out as a pinkish flaky solid which is easily filtered and washed. The yield of sulfonic acid is about 235 lb. of moist, or 112 lb. of dry product, equivalent to 77 per cent of theory.

Sulfonation of β-Naphthol.—When β-naphthol is sulfonated at 100°C. with 98 per cent sulfuric acid, 2-naphthol-6-sulfonic acid (Schäffer acid) is obtained as the principal product. 2-Naphthol-3, 6-disulfonic acid (R-acid) is also formed to the extent of 20 to 30 per cent, and this is found in the mother liquor after separating the monosulfonate.

To prepare the monosulfonic acid, 144 parts of powdered naphthol is added to 216 parts of 98 per cent sulfuric acid at 60°C. The temperature is then raised to 100 to 105°C. and thus maintained for 2.5 hr. or until a sample dissolves completely in water. The charge is then run into 1,000 parts of water, and 200 parts of salt is added. Upon cooling, with stirring, the Schäffer salt separates out practically completely during the course of a day. It is filtered off and washed with a minimum of brine. About 200 parts of product averaging 75 per cent pure Schäffer salt is thus obtained. This corresponds to a yield of approximately 67 per cent based on the quantity of monosulfonate theoretically possible. The mother liquor is treated with sodium sulfate and evaporated to precipitate out the disulfonate, R-salt.

The Disulfonic Acids of 2-Naphthol.

When 2-naphthol is sulfonated with an excess of sulfuric acid, both 3, 6- and 6, 8-disulfonic acids (R- and G-acids), respectively, are produced at all temperatures and with all acid concentrations. At temperatures below 100°C., G-acid is preponderant; while above 100°C., the quantity of R-acid increases with an increase in operating temperature until, at 160°C., it is the principal constituent in the sulfonation mass.

The sulfonator is charged with 720 lb. of 98 per cent sulfuric acid, and 144 lb. of β-naphthol is added. The charge is kept at 50°C. for 50 to 60 hr. until the decrease in acidity indicates that disulfonation has taken place. The reaction mass is dropped into water and treated with hydrated lime and filtered hot from the precipitated gypsum. The calcium salt may be converted to the potassium salt by treatment with potassium sulfate and filtering. The solution is evaporated and acidified with hydrochloric acid, and, on cooling, the G-acid, *i.e.*, 2-naphthol-6, 8-disulfonic acid, separates out as a technically pure product. After standing one to two days, it is filtered and washed with a potassium chloride solution. The filtrate and washings, on evaporation, yield R-acid.

Anthraquinonesulfonic Acids. *Preparation of Anthraquinone-2-Sulfonic Acid.*—The sulfonation of anthraquinone is carried out in large steel vessels provided with an efficient stirrer and a jacket for heating. Technical anthraquinone 2,400 lb. (purity 99 per cent) is added slowly to 2,500 lb. of 25 per cent fuming sulfuric acid at room temperature. The reaction mass is stirred thoroughly while the temperature is raised to 135°C. over a period of 1.5 hr. It is maintained at this temperature for 3 hr., and during this period 1,000 lb. of 40 per cent oleum is added. The charge is heated finally at 140°C. for 1 hr.

After cooling, the contents of the sulfonator are run into a large vat, lined with lead, which contains 2,000 gal. of cold water. Live steam is passed into the suspension until the unchanged anthraquinone becomes coarse grained and easy to filter. The charge is then filtered, and the retained anthraquinone is washed with water. The filtrate is always deep brown and contains the soluble, free acids.

The neutralization by lime which is often suggested is not satisfactory. All salts of anthraquinone-2-sulfonic acid are so moderately soluble (see Table VII) that they precipitate readily in strong acid solutions. Immense quantities of water would consequently be necessary to keep the calcium salt in solution.

Seven thousand pounds of sodium chloride is added to the warm filtrate, which is stirred while cooling. It is then permitted to stand for 10 hr. The sodium anthraquinone-2-sulfonate separates out as yellow mother-of-pearl leaves. It may be colored brown to gray according to the increased purity of the sulfonate. In the latter case, the pressed cake has the appearance of a silver bar—whence the popular synonym *silver salt.*

The sodium salt is filtered off and washed with a saline solution and when air dried contains a molecule of water of crystallization. The technical product employed in subsequent syntheses usually averages about 90 per cent in purity, the contaminants being principally water, inorganic salts, and small amounts (1 per cent) of disulfonates. By concentrating the mother liquor from 2,000 to 1,000 gal. and then cooling, part of the isomeric sodium disulfonates separate out. These are filtered off and washed with a saturated salt solution; the mother liquor and washings are discarded. The yield of β-anthraquinonesulfonic acid by this method of operation fluctuates within narrow limits but on the whole closely checks laboratory data, as can be observed by a study of the following two tables, VIA and VIB:

TABLE VIA.—TECHNICAL SULFONATION OF ANTHRAQUINONE

	Yield Products, %	Acids, %
2,400 lb. of anthraquinone sulfonated		
1,200 lb. of anthraquinone recovered	50	
1,400 lb. of anhydrous silver salt	39.2	78.4
200 lb. of 2, 6- and 2, 7-disulfonates	4.1	8.3
Loss by solubility, etc	6.7	

The mother liquor and washings contain most of the 2, 7-disulfonate, since at 20°C. its sodium salt is about ten times more soluble than the 2, 6-isomer.

With only slight modifications of the process and with complete precipitation of the sulfonic acids, Lauer[1] obtained the data shown in Table VIB.

TABLE VIB.—SULFONATION OF ANTHRAQUINONE
Anthraquinone, 104 Gm.; SO_3 introduced as 20 per cent Oleum. Time, 4 Hr.

Expt. No.	Temp., °C.	SO_3 % of theory	Anthraquinone recovered, %	β-monosulfonic acid, %	β-disulfonic acids, %	α-sulfonic acids, %
1	120	100	62.8	81.4	16.5	2.1
2	130	100	56.2	78.4	19.2	2.4
3	140	100	38.5	73.6	24.4	2.0
4	160	100	36.3	72.4	24.9	2.7
5	180	100	33.8	70.9	26.6	2.5
6	140	60	58.2	83.6	13.6	2.8
7[1]	140	80	49.6[1]	80.2[1]	17.3	2.5
8	140	120	34.4	70.6	27.3	2.1
9	140	150	34.0	66.4	30.7	2.9

[1] Compare with results in Table VIA.

Data relative to the solubility of salts of anthraquinonemonosulfonic acids are shown in the following table:

[1] LAUER, *J. prakt. Chem.*, **135**, 166 (1932).

Table VII.—Comparison of Solubility of α- and β-Anthraquinonemonosulfonic Acids[1]

Cation	α-Anthraquinonemono-sulfonic acid		β-Anthraquinonemono-sulfonic acid	
	18°C.	100°C.	18°C.	100°C.
NH₄	1:60	Very soluble	1:20	1:2
K	1:100	1:25	1:110	1:10
Na	1:100	1:20	1:120	1:5
Mg	1:100	1:20	1:300	1:100
Ca	1:250	1:50	1:800	1:200
Sr	1:1,000	1:140	1:1,100	1:200
Ba	1:2,500	1:1,000	1:3,000	1:500

[1] According to Anderau, Diss. E.T.H., Zurich (1925).

Preparation of Anthraquinone-1-Sulfonic Acid. *In the presence of a catalyst.*—When approximately 1 per cent of mercury as the sulfate or oxide is added to the oleum employed for sulfonation and the operation is conducted in a manner similar to that used previously, anthraquinone-1-sulfonic acid is the principal product obtained.

Two thousand eighty pounds of anthraquinone is triturated with 30 to 40 lb. of mercuric oxide or sulfate and then gradually delivered into 2,000 lb. of 20 per cent oleum. The temperature rises during the feeding operation to approximately 50°C., and, with the aid of external heat, this is brought up to 130 to 135°C. in a period of 1 hr. During the next 2 hr., 750 lb. of 40 per cent oleum is added, and the reaction completed by heating for an additional hour. The charge is cooled and run into 2,000 gal. of cold water, and, after heating with live steam, the coarse-grained unconverted anthraquinone is filtered off. The filtrate is light brown and contains the very soluble α-sulfonic acid, which is precipitated as the potassium salt by the addition of 1,000 lb. of potassium chloride to the boiling and thoroughly agitated solution. Since potassium anthraquinone-1-sulfonate separates out almost immediately, it is advantageous to add the potassium chloride as a hot solution. The suspension is cooled to 60°C. while stirring.

At this temperature, the 1, 5-disulfonate is very soluble compared with the monosulfonate, whereas, at 18°C., both are sparingly soluble. Adoption of this technic provides a simple way of obtaining the potassium anthraquinone-1-sulfonate with minimal quantities of disulfonic derivatives.

By recrystallizing from hot water, the traces of the more soluble beta derivative that may be present in the principal alpha sulfonate are removed.

According to Lauer,[1] it is best to adjust the operating conditions to obtain a conversion of 75 per cent of the anthraquinone employed. Under such circumstances, the yield of α-monosulfonic acid is approximately 55 per cent, based on anthraquinone used or 70 per cent of that theoretically obtainable. These relationships are brought out by the data in Table V (page 272), which also show the effect of the type of mercury catalyst.

Sulfonation of Fatty Acids.—The sulfated oils and fats have long been used as wetting and emulsifying agents in the textile industry. The

$$\overset{\text{OH}}{\underset{|}{}}$$

sulfonation of ricinoleic acid $C_6H_{13}CHCH_2CH{=}CH(CH_2)_7COOH$, which is a constituent of castor oil, may be accomplished in the following manner: 300 parts of ricinoleic acid is mixed with 100 parts of acetic anhydride and sulfonated at 0 to 5°C. with 450 parts of concentrated sulfuric acid. The crude sulfuric acid ester is allowed to flow into a cooled and agitated solution of Glauber's salt. The mixture is then settled, the salt solution separated, and the remainder neutralized with a caustic soda solution of 40°Bé. After a few hours, sodium sulfate solution is again separated by decantation or filtration.

The neutralized sulfate is treated with 600 parts of water and then thoroughly stirred with 500 parts of trichloroethylene. The mixture is allowed to settle, and the aqueous solution of the ester separates out as an upper layer; while the trichloroethylene, containing unsulfonated oil or fat, forms a lower one. The lower solvent portion is separated, leaving a completely sulfated product behind.[2]

The removal of the unsulfated products constitutes an important problem in such sulfonations. Even when an excess of strong sulfuric acid or chlorosulfonic acid is used, some unsulfonated material is found in the reaction product along with a mixture of sulfated products, *e.g.*,

$$C_6H_{13}{\cdot}CH{\cdot}CH_2{\cdot}CH{=}CH{\cdot}C_7H_{14}COOH \quad \text{(ricinoleylsulfuric acid), and}$$
$$\underset{|}{OSO_3H}$$

$$C_6H_{13}{\cdot}CH{\cdot}CH_2{\cdot}CHOH{\cdot}C_8H_{15}COOH \quad \text{(dihydroxystearylsulfuric acid).}$$
$$\underset{|}{OSO_3H}$$

Since it is desirable to have a maximum of sulfuric acid in organic combination, it has also been found convenient to decompose the more readily hydrolyzable sulfuric acid esters after sulfonation. Partial saponification of the acid sulfonate with the aid of water, or dilute acid, results in the

[1] LAUER, *J. prakt. Chem.*, **130**, 216 (1931).
[2] U. S. 1,906,924 (1933).

regeneration of the fatty acids, which can then be separated from the more stable sulfuric acid esters.

In more recent years numerous sulfuric acid esters of straight- and branched-chain fatty alcohols have been synthesized and these are finding wide use as wetting and dispersing agents. It is also possible to obtain true sulfonic acid derivatives which have these valuable characteristics, and the sulfonation of oleic acid will be described to illustrate the procedure.[1]

Of oleic acid, 300 parts by weight are mixed with 100 parts of acetic anhydride and 300 parts of concentrated sulfuric acid are gradually added to the stirred mass at about 0°C. After the mixture has become soluble in water, the excess of sulfuric acid is washed out with a solution of sodium sulfate. The resultant sulfonic acid which is clearly soluble in water may be used as such or in the form of the sodium salt obtained on neutralization.

The following formulas (1) and (2) indicate the probable reactions which occur:

$$CH_3(CH_2)_7CH{=}CH(CH_2)_7COOH + H_2SO_4 \xrightarrow{\;(CH_3CO)_2O\;}$$

$$CH_3(CH_2)_7CH{=}CHCH(CH_2)_6COOH \quad (1)$$
$$\underset{SO_3H}{|}$$

$$CH_3(CH_2)_7CH{=}CHCH_2(CH_2)_6COOH + 2H_2SO_4 \xrightarrow{\;(CH_3CO)_2O\;}$$

$$CH_3(CH_2)_7CH_2{\cdot}CHCH(CH_2)_6COOH \quad (2)$$
$$\overset{|}{O} \;\; \overset{|}{SO_3H}$$
$$\underset{SO_3H}{|}$$

Unlike the turkey red oils obtained by the sulfation of castor oil or ricinoleic acid, these sulfonated products do not readily split off a sulfuric acid radical on boiling with water, or with boiling acids, or even on treatment with alkalis.

Chlorosulfonic ethyl ester can also be employed for the sulfonation of oleic acid and other unsaturated fatty acids.[2] Thus, 70 parts of oleic acid is stirred at 80°C. with 72 parts of chlorosulfonic ethyl ester, prepared from sulfuryl chloride and alcohol or from ethylene and chlorosulfonic acid. The reaction is continued for 2 hr., and the charge is then diluted with water. About 10 parts of sulfuric acid is added, and the charge is boiled under a reflux condenser until the product dissolves to a clear solution in water. The reaction apparently proceeds according to the following equations:

[1] U. S. 1,923,608 (1933).
[2] U. S. 1,931,491 (1933).

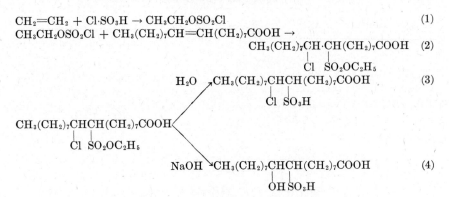

$$CH_2{=}CH_2 + Cl{\cdot}SO_3H \rightarrow CH_3CH_2OSO_2Cl \tag{1}$$

$$CH_3CH_2OSO_2Cl + CH_3(CH_2)_7CH{=}CH(CH_2)_7COOH \rightarrow$$

$$\underset{\substack{| \quad | \\ Cl \quad SO_2OC_2H_5}}{CH_3(CH_2)_7CH{\cdot}CH(CH_2)_7COOH} \tag{2}$$

$$H_2O \quad \underset{\substack{| \quad | \\ Cl \quad SO_3H}}{CH_3(CH_2)_7CHCH(CH_2)_7COOH} \tag{3}$$

$$\underset{\substack{| \quad | \\ Cl \quad SO_2OC_2H_5}}{CH_3(CH_2)_7CHCH(CH_2)_7COOH}\Big\langle$$

$$NaOH \quad \underset{\substack{| \quad | \\ OH \quad SO_3H}}{CH_3(CH_2)_7CHCH(CH_2)_7COOH} \tag{4}$$

IX. CONCENTRATION OF SPENT SULFURIC ACID

An unavoidable by-product of nitration and sulfonation operations is large amounts of dilute sulfuric acid. Such spent acids, being contaminated with dissolved organic materials, have little value in organic synthesis and must be concentrated for reuse. During this operation, the organic impurities are carbonized and later removed by settling. The removal of water from the dilute acid requires a concentrating plant and the application of heat. The efficiency of the system must be measured, therefore, by its low fuel consumption and its serviceability in concentrating this highly corrosive liquid.

In Fig. 20 is shown a modern plant for concentrating dilute sulfuric acid.[1]

The principal apparatus of this concentrator consists of a combustion chamber, a concentrating pan flue, concentrating tower, filter, and scrubbing tower, all of which are constructed of acid-proof masonry, well braced with steel framing and supported on concrete or brick foundations at a suitable height above the ground level. On top of the concrete foundations, masonry-lined lead pans are used on which are built the masonry walls. The concentrating tower is packed with checkered brick, and the filter tower with rings of quartz.

The weak acid is sprayed in at the top of the tower. The upper portion of the tower does the preheating, and the lower portion the preliminary concentration. The acid trickles over the packing materials before falling into a long horizontal flue containing a bath of acid over which the hot gases pass. The combustion gases enter the flue at the acid outlet end and pass along the surface of the acid to the foot of the tower and then pass up the interstices of the tower packing meeting the downcoming weak acid. The tower is of sufficient height and size to utilize the remaining sensible heat of the combustion gases. The greater part of the concentration is done in the pan flue, where the acid is brought

[1] GILCHRIST, *Trans. Am. Inst. Chem. Eng.*, **14**, 13 (1921).

to a maximum strength.   The bath of acid is about 9 in. deep; and as the
hot gases are brought into immediate contact with the acid surface, the
acid takes up the heat much better than when the acid and heat are
separated by metal or siliceous plates, as is the case with cascade or pan
systems, which were formerly used.   Evaporation is greatly assisted by
the direct heat over the acid, as the draft quickly removes the vapors that
are formed.   The finished acid leaves the concentrator at the furnace

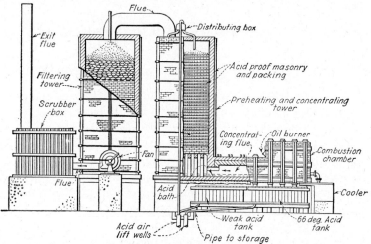

Fig. 20.—Combination surface evaporation and tower type for concentrating sulfuric acid.

end, its temperature being much below the actual boiling point of the
acid.   From the illustration of the system (Fig. 20), it may be seen that
the combustion takes place in a separate chamber; because of this design,
the gases reaching the tower are not sufficiently hot to cause a rapid
deterioration, and this apparatus therefore has a very long life.

The thermal efficiency of this type of acid concentrator is approximately 86 per cent—a performance which far surpasses that obtained in
systems wherein no direct contact between hot gases and acid is provided.

CHAPTER VI

AMINATION BY AMMONOLYSIS

By P. H. Groggins and A. J. Stirton

I. GENERAL DISCUSSION

Classification of Reactions

In organic synthesis, amination by ammonolysis relates to those reactions wherein an amino compound is formed as a result of the action of ammonia. To a limited extent, such agents as ammonium carbamate and urea, which during the course of the reaction undergo decomposition with the liberation of NH_3, may be employed. When an organic ammonia derivative, e.g., an alkyl- or arylamine is used as the reactant, the product will be the corresponding substituted secondary or tertiary amine. Most frequently, a univalent substituent; —Cl, —OH, —SO_3H is replaced by the —NH_2 group during ammonolysis, but reactions involving simple addition and the replacement of oxygen are known, and some of these are economically important.

For convenience, the compounds that are susceptible to ammonolysis may be divided into four classes:

1. Halogeno compounds.
2. Sulfonic acids.
3. Oxygen-containing compounds.
   a. Phenols and alcohols.
   b. Aldehydes and intranuclear ketones.
   c. Aliphatic ring oxides.
   d. Carbon dioxide.
4. Compounds possessing a labile nitro group.

Although the preponderant number of reactions are carried out in the liquid phase with aqueous ammonia, the ammonolysis of alcohols, aldehydes, and oxides may often be carried out most advantageously in the vapor phase.

The following type reactions are illustrative of the four classes of compounds previously mentioned.

Class I. Replacement of Halogen.

1. Aniline from chlorobenzene.

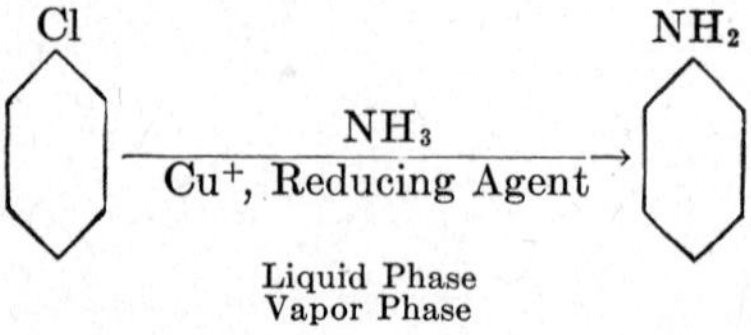

Liquid Phase
Vapor Phase

2. 2, 3-Diaminoanthraquinone from 2, 3-dichloroanthraquinone.

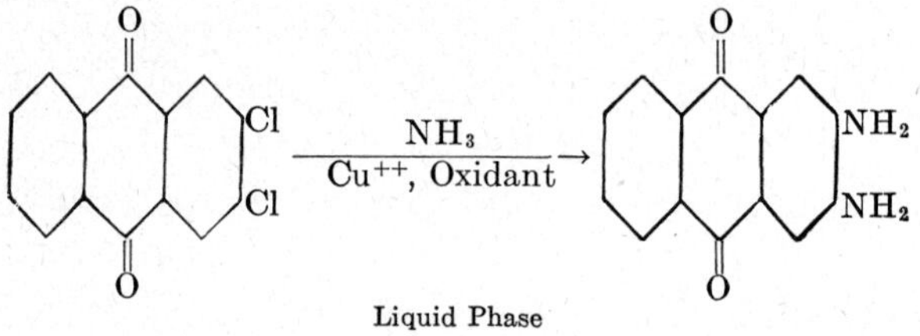

Liquid Phase

3. 2-Aminoanthraquinone from 2-chloroanthraquinone.

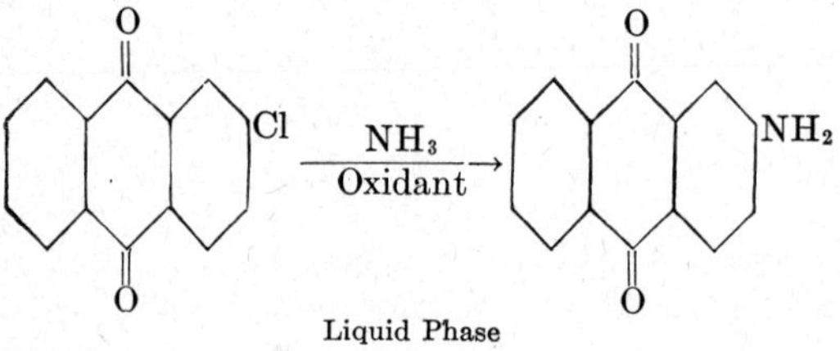

Liquid Phase

4. *p*-Nitroaniline from *p*-nitrochlorobenzene.

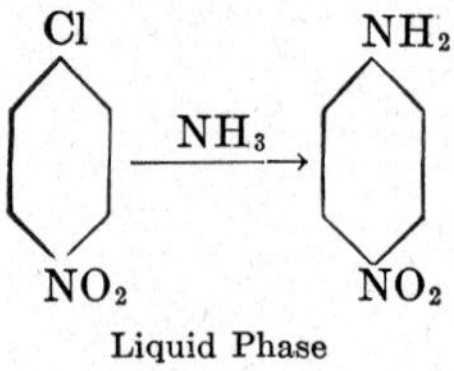

Liquid Phase

5. 4-Chloro-(N-methyl-)aniline from 4-chlorobromobenzene.

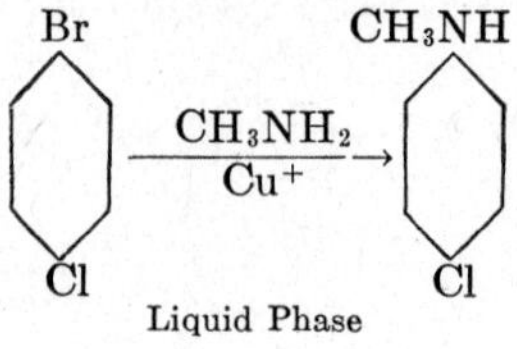

Liquid Phase

6. Ethylenediamine and diethylenetriamine from ethylene dichloride.

$$ClH_2C \cdot CH_2Cl \xrightarrow[?Cu^+]{NH_3} \begin{cases} NH_2H_2C \cdot CH_2NH_2 \\ \\ NH_2H_2C \cdot CH_2 \\ NH \\ NH_2H_2C \cdot CH_2 \end{cases}$$

Liquid Phase and Vapor Phase

7. Morpholine from *sym*-dichloroethyl ether.

$$O \begin{cases} CH_2 \cdot CH_2Cl \\ CH_2 \cdot CH_2Cl \end{cases} \xrightarrow{NH_3} O \begin{cases} CH_2 \cdot CH_2 \\ CH_2 \cdot CH_2 \end{cases} NH$$

Liquid Phase

8. 1, 3-Diaminopropanol from 1, 3-dichloropropanol-2.

$$\begin{matrix} CH_2Cl \\ | \\ CHOH \\ | \\ CH_2Cl \end{matrix} \xrightarrow{NH_3} \begin{matrix} CH_2NH_2 \\ | \\ CHOH \\ | \\ CH_2NH_2 \end{matrix}$$

Liquid Phase

9. Glycine from chloroacetic acid.

$$\begin{matrix} CH_2 \cdot COOH \\ | \\ Cl \end{matrix} \xrightarrow{NH_3} \begin{matrix} CH_2 \cdot COOH \\ | \\ NH_2 \end{matrix}$$

Liquid Phase

Class II. Replacement of Sulfonic Acid Radicals.

2-Aminoanthraquinone from sodium anthraquinonesulfonate.

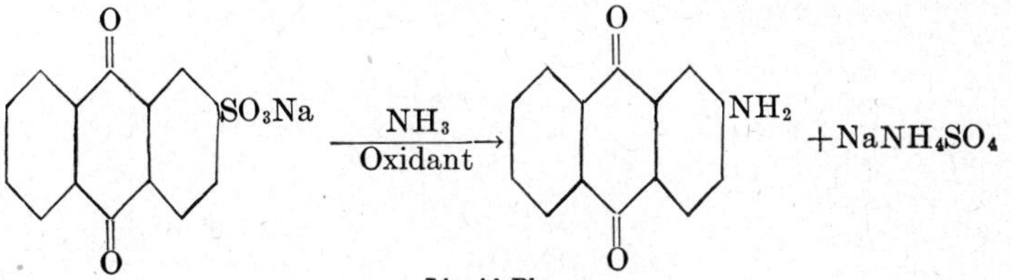

$$\xrightarrow[\text{Oxidant}]{NH_3}$$

$$+ NaNH_4SO_4$$

Liquid Phase

Class III. Ammonolysis of Oxygen-containing Compounds.

A. *Conversion of Phenols and Alcohols.*

1. *Sym*-xylidine from *sym*-xylenol.

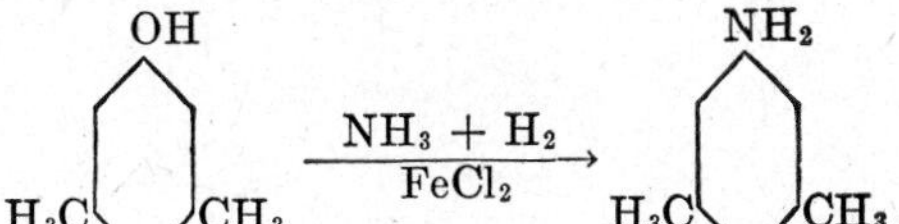

$$\xrightarrow[\text{FeCl}_2]{NH_3 + H_2}$$

Liquid Phase

2. β-Naphthylamine from β-naphthol.

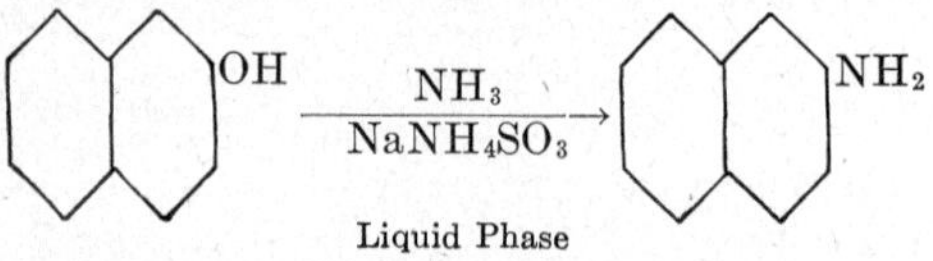

$$\text{(naphthalene)-OH} \xrightarrow[\text{NaNH}_4\text{SO}_3]{\text{NH}_3} \text{(naphthalene)-NH}_2$$

Liquid Phase

3. Methylamines from methanol.

$$\text{CH}_3\text{OH} \xrightarrow[\text{AlPO}_4]{\text{NH}_3} \begin{cases} \text{CH}_3\cdot\text{NH}_2 \\ (\text{CH}_3)_2\text{NH} \\ (\text{CH}_3)_3\text{N} \end{cases}$$

Vapor Phase

4. Butylamine from butanol.

$$\text{CH}_3\cdot\text{CH}_2\cdot\text{CH}_2\cdot\text{CH}_2\text{OH} \xrightarrow[\text{Al}_2\text{O}_3]{\text{NH}_3} \text{CH}_3\cdot\text{CH}_2\cdot\text{CH}_2\cdot\text{CH}_2\text{NH}_2$$

Vapor Phase

5. Methyloctadecylamine from *n*-octadecyl alcohol.

$$\text{CH}_3(\text{CH}_2)_{16}\text{CH}_2\text{OH} \xrightarrow[\text{Alumina Gel}]{\text{CH}_3\cdot\text{NH}_2} \text{CH}_3(\text{CH}_2)_{16}\text{CH}_2\cdot\text{NHCH}_3$$

Liquid Phase

B. *Conversion of Aldehydes and Ketones.*

1. Acetaldehydeammonia by addition.

$$\underset{\text{CH}_3\cdot\overset{\text{H}}{\text{C}}=\text{O}}{} \xrightarrow{\text{NH}_3} \text{CH}_3\cdot\overset{\text{H}}{\underset{\text{NH}_2}{\text{C}}}\text{OH}$$

2. *n*-Propylamine from acrolein.

$$\text{CH}_2{=}\text{CH}\cdot\text{C}\overset{\text{O}}{\underset{\text{H}}{\diagdown}} \xrightarrow[\substack{\text{Hydrogenation} \\ \text{Catalyst} \\ \text{Vapor Phase}}]{\text{NH}_3 + \text{H}_2} \text{CH}_3\cdot\text{CH}_2\cdot\text{CH}_2\cdot\text{NH}_2$$

3. Glucamine from glucose.

$$\text{CH}_2\text{OH}(\text{CHOH})_4\cdot\text{C}\overset{\text{O}}{\underset{\text{H}}{\diagdown}} \xrightarrow[\substack{\text{Ni Catalyst} \\ \text{Liquid Phase}}]{\text{NH}_3 + \text{H}_2} \text{CH}_2\text{OH}(\text{CHOH})_4\text{CH}_2\text{NH}_2$$

4. Cyclohexylamine from cyclohexanone.

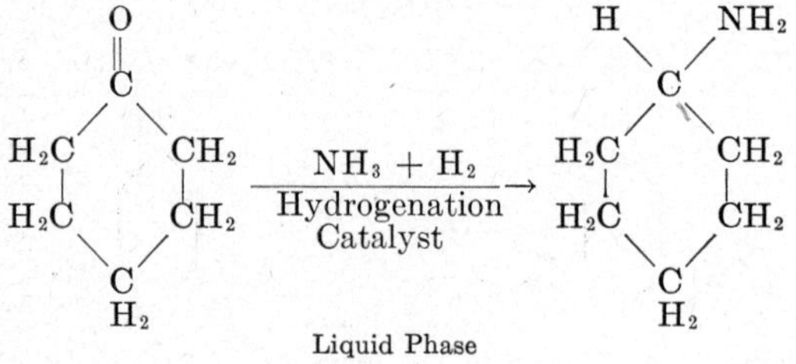

$$\xrightarrow[\substack{\text{Hydrogenation} \\ \text{Catalyst}}]{\text{NH}_3 + \text{H}_2}$$

Liquid Phase

C. Alkanolamines from Alkylene Oxides.

1. Ethanolamines from ethylene oxide.

$$\text{H}_2\text{C}-\text{CH}_2 \xrightarrow{\text{NH}_3}$$

$$\longrightarrow \text{CH}_2\text{OHCH}_2\text{NH}_2 \quad \text{Ethanolamine}$$

$$\longrightarrow \begin{array}{c} \text{CH}_2\text{OHCH}_2 \\ \text{CH}_2\text{OHCH}_2 \end{array}\!\!\!\!\bigg\rangle \text{NH} \quad \text{Diethanolamine}$$

$$\longrightarrow \begin{array}{c} \text{CH}_2\text{OHCH}_2 \\ \text{CH}_2\text{OHCH}_2 \\ \text{CH}_2\text{OHCH}_2 \end{array}\!\!\!\!\text{N} \quad \text{Triethanolamine}$$

Liquid Phase

2. 1, 3-Diaminopropanol from epichlorohydrin.

$$\begin{array}{c}\text{CH}_2\text{Cl}\\ |\\ \text{CHOH}\\ |\\ \text{CH}_2\text{Cl}\end{array} \xrightarrow{\text{NaOH}} \begin{array}{c}\text{CH}_2\\ |\\ \text{CH}\\ |\\ \text{CH}_2\text{Cl}\end{array}\!\!\!\!\rangle\text{O} \xrightarrow{\text{NH}_3} \begin{array}{c}\text{CH}_2\text{NH}_2\\ |\\ \text{CHOH}\\ |\\ \text{CH}_2\text{Cl}\end{array} \xrightarrow{\text{NaOH}} \begin{array}{c}\text{CH}_2\text{NH}_2\\ |\\ \text{CH}\\ |\\ \text{CH}_2\end{array}\!\!\!\!\rangle\text{O} \xrightarrow{\text{NH}_3} \begin{array}{c}\text{CH}_2\cdot\text{NH}_2\\ |\\ \text{CHOH}\\ |\\ \text{CH}_2\cdot\text{NH}_2\end{array}$$

Liquid Phase

D. Replacement of Oxygen.

Urea from carbon dioxide.

$$\text{O}=\text{C}=\text{O} \xrightarrow{\text{NH}_3} \text{O}=\text{C}\!\!\bigg\langle\begin{array}{c}\text{ONH}_4\\ \text{NH}_2\end{array} \xrightarrow{\text{NH}_3} \text{O}=\text{C}\!\!\bigg\langle\begin{array}{c}\text{NH}_2\\ \text{NH}_2\end{array}$$

Vapor Phase

Class IV. Replacement of Labile Nitro Groups.

6-Chloro-3-nitro-o-toluidine from 5, 6-dinitro-o-chlorotoluene.

Liquid Phase

II. REACTIONS AND PROPERTIES OF AQUEOUS AMMONIA

Reactions of Aqueous Ammonia.—Although aqueous ammonia is generally employed in liquid-phase ammonolysis, it is known that anhydrous ammonia can also be used for this purpose. In the latter instance, it is almost always necessary to incorporate an organic solvent such as an

TABLE I.—PROPERTIES OF AMMONIA AND WATER

Properties	Liquid ammonia	Water
Melting point	−77.7°C.	0°C.
Boiling point (760 mm.)	−33.35°C.	100°C.
Specific heat	1.13	1.0
Specific gravity at 20°C.	0.607	0.9982
Critical temperature	131°C.	365°C.
Critical pressure	112 atmos.	195 atmos.

alcohol, so that ammonolysis is in reality effected with a solution of ammonia in a comparatively inert solvent.   In the vapor-phase conversion of aliphatic alcohols and aldehydes, anhydrous NH_3 is used.

As will be shown later, when water is used as a solvent for ammonia, ammonolysis should be interpreted as being brought about by the activity of NH_3 and not by the base NH_4OH.   In fact, the presence of hydroxyl ions from the dissociation of ammonium hydroxide, arylammonium hydroxide, or water is responsible for the simultaneous formation of hydroxy compounds.   Thus, in the amination of chlorobenzene and chloroanthraquinones by this unit process, phenol and hydroxyanthraquinones, respectively, are found accompanying the amino compounds in the reaction product:

$$C_6H_5 \cdot Cl \xrightarrow{\;NH_3\;aq.\;} C_6H_5 \cdot NH_2 + Some\ C_6H_5 \cdot OH + NH_4Cl$$

The presence of hydroxyl ions must not always be considered deleterious.   In some technical operations involving the ammonolysis of halogeno compounds, the hydroxyl-ion concentration is purposely increased in order to hydrolyze some of the ammonium halide or arylammonium halide formed during the reaction.   The decomposition of such reaction products is believed to account for the increased degree of conversion of the halogen compound.   Furthermore, the formation of secondary amines by condensation in the presence of ammonium halide is largely inhibited.

The reactions relating to the formation of secondary amines are presumably as follows:

$$R \cdot Cl + R \cdot NH_2 \rightarrow \overset{R}{\underset{R}{>}}NH + HCl = intermediate\ product \qquad (1)[1]$$

$$2R \cdot NH_2 \underset{NH_3}{\overset{HCl}{\rightleftharpoons}} \overset{R}{\underset{R}{>}}NH + NH_3 = equilibrium\ product \qquad (2)$$

The first equation represents Ullmann's interpretation,[2] the formation of the dialkyl or diarylamine being an intermediate step in the preparation

---

[1] Reaction (1) is accelerated by the removal of HCl from the reaction medium; reaction (2) is aided by the removal of NH_3.   Since secondary amines are such weak bases, the added HCl presumably combines almost instantaneously with the primary amine to carry on its catalytic activity.   The reaction of amines with phenols likewise leads to secondary amines:

$$R-OH + R \cdot NH_2 \rightleftharpoons R-\overset{\overset{\textstyle H}{|}}{N}-R + H_2O$$

and the H_2O must be removed to complete the reaction.

[2] ULLMANN, "Enzyklopädie der technischen Chemie," **1**, 440 (1914); Urban and Schwarzenberg, Berlin.

of primary amines. Secondary and tertiary amines are almost always formed during the ammonolysis of halogeno and hydroxy compounds, the quantity depending on the specific reactants, the NH_3 ratio, and other conditions employed. By reintroducing these intermediate products in subsequent charges, their further formation is inhibited.[1,2,3,4] This is probably explained by the reversible character of Eq. (2), which does not go to completion even when precautions are taken continuously to remove the liberated ammonia.

When the objective of ammonolysis is the formation of a primary amine, the removal of the associated product of reaction; i.e., HCl, NH_4Cl, or H_2O definitely aids the completion of the reaction, insofar as the utilization of the reactants is concerned. When copper or other oxides, which introduce hydroxyl ions, are used to decompose the ammonium chloride, the products of reaction show a distinct increase in the quantity of hydroxy compound and a diminution in the yield or purity of the amino derivative. When the product of hydrolysis has a value comparable to the product of ammonolysis, then there is no serious objection to the employment of compounds that introduce hydroxyl ions. In the preparation of aniline, the concomitant formation of phenol is not always objectionable; the situation is entirely different in the preparation of compounds such as 2-aminoanthraquinone and other solid amines which cannot be purified by inexpensive physical or chemical means.

To obtain the best results in the amination process, it appears necessary to provide a system that is continuously neutral and in which the activity of NH_3 is practically the sole activity.

pH of Aqueous Ammonia Solutions.—It is of considerable importance to trace the causes contributing to the formation of hydroxy derivatives and secondary amines in the ammonolysis of halogeno compounds. Some knowledge regarding the change in alkalinity of aqueous ammonia with change in temperature and ammonium chloride content is therefore obviously necessary in order to control such side reactions.

Colorometric studies[5] in sealed glass tubes indicate that ammonia combines with water, above the critical temperature of NH_3, to form the ionogen NH_4OH. The curves in Fig. 1 show that the pH of 28 per cent aqueous ammonia decreases, however, with rising temperature from 11.8 at room temperature to only 8.2 at 175°C., under approximately 500 lb. pressure per square inch. The pH drops off more rapidly when

[1] Williams, U. S. 1,775,360 (1930); Hale, U. S. 1,932,518 (1933).
[2] Swallen, U. S. 1,926,691 (1933).
[3] Herold and Smeykal, U. S. 2,068,132 (1937).
[4] Arnold, U. S. 1,799,722; Reissue 19,632 (1935).
[5] GROGGINS and STIRTON, Ind. Eng. Chem., 25, 42 (1933).

hydrogen chloride or its ammonium salt is introduced corresponding to conditions prevailing during ammonolysis.   At 175°C. the pH of neutrality is 5.7.

Physical Properties of Aqueous Ammonia. *Vapor Pressures.*— Wilson[1] has investigated the partial pressures of aqueous ammonia over a wide range of both concentration and temperature.   Some of his data are presented in Figs. 2 and 3.   The curves (Fig. 2) show that the partial pressures of the water vapor in the vapor phase are not strictly propor-

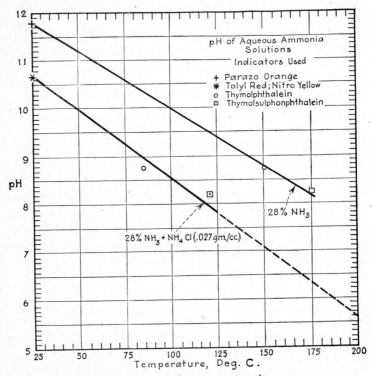

Fig. 1.—pH of aqueous ammonia.

tional to the water content of the solution phase.   There is a slight, consistent negative deviation from the ideal value entirely in harmony with the idea that, below the critical temperature of NH_3, solutions of ammonia are not completely physical mixtures of two components.

Perman[2] also observed a similar deviation with respect to Henry's law, but on account of the slightness of the deviation he concluded that an aqueous solution of ammonia behaves as a mixture of two liquids the boiling points of which are far removed from each other.   The lowering

[1] WILSON, *Bull.* 146, *Univ. Ill. Eng. Expt. Sta.* (1925).
[2] PERMAN, *J. Chem. Soc.,* **79,** 718 (1901); **83,** 1168 (1903).

of the vapor pressure of water by the ammonia follows Raoult's law closely, showing that the molecular weight of NH_3 in solution is normal and no large quantity of hydrate is formed.

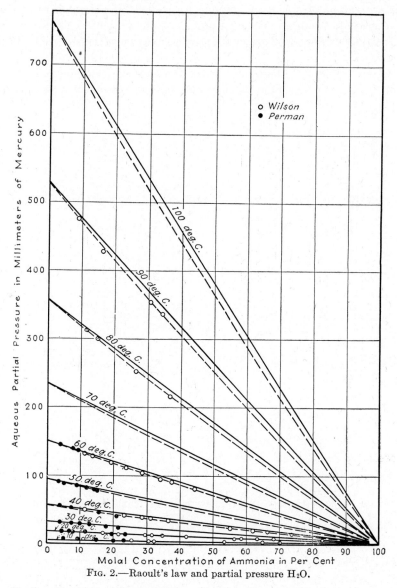

Fig. 2.—Raoult's law and partial pressure H_2O.

Surface Tension.—King, Hall, and Ware,[1] in studying the properties of the ammonia-water system, concluded that "It is evident from the

[1] KING, HALL, and WARE, *J. Am. Chem. Soc.*, **52**, 5128 (1930).

surface tension and thermodynamic standpoint that the system does not deviate radically from what is to be expected of a *perfect mixture.*"

It appears, therefore, that ammonolysis with aqueous ammonia is similar to ammonolysis with ammonia gas dissolved in any comparatively inert solvent. Indeed, the pH studies and the review of the properties and reactions of aqueous ammonia practically compel the adoption of this viewpoint.

Comparative NH_3 and H_2O Vapor Pressures.—The effects of operating with aqueous NH_3 solutions of various concentrations may be

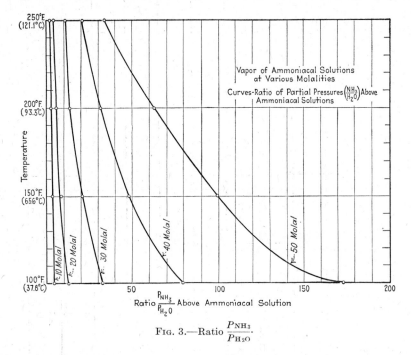

FIG. 3.—Ratio $\dfrac{P_{NH_3}}{P_{H_2O}}$.

appreciated by a study of the curves of Fig. 3, which relate to the proportionality $\dfrac{P_{NH_3}}{P_{H_2O}}$.

From these data,[1] it can be observed that with increasing NH_3 concentration, there is a comparative acceleration in the quotient $\dfrac{P_{NH_3}}{P_{H_2O}}$. For a definite concentration, however, the partial pressure of ammonia does not increase so rapidly as the water-vapor pressure when the temperature of the solution is increased. From this, it may be predicted that there is a proportionally increased activity of water vapor at increasing temperatures. Thus, in order to obtain the best results during ammonolysis,

[1] WILSON, *op. cit.*

it is advisable to employ the lowest possible temperature that produces the necessary energy intensity factor. This condition is, in a measure, realized by increasing the molal concentration of NH_3 in the ammonia employed.

III. SURVEY OF AMINATION REACTIONS

CLASS 1. CONVERSION OF HALOGENO COMPOUNDS

The halogen of alkyl halides is generally readily susceptible to replacement by the $—NH_2$ group but aromatically bound halogen usually requires more drastic treatment. Because of economic considerations, the chlorine derivatives are ordinarily employed, but bromine-substituted compounds are sometimes used because they usually lead to the formation of primary amines of higher purity under milder operating conditions.

When a catalyst is essential, copper, its oxides, and salts are preferred, and these are almost always used in the ammonolysis of compounds wherein the halogen is attached to an otherwise unsubstituted phenyl nucleus; e.g., chlorobenzene, chloroxenene, and chloronaphthalene. In the treatment of alkylene, nitrophenyl, and anthraquinone halides, copper catalysts are not essential, but may be used to accelerate the reaction.

The following brief survey is merely a presentation of typical syntheses. The factors governing these reactions, as well as an insight into the details of technical operations in the manufacture of some of the more important amino compounds, will be discussed later in this chapter.

Aniline from Chlorobenzene.—Although it has been known since 1893 that aniline could be produced by the interaction of chlorobenzene with an excess of ammonia under pressure, the process has only within recent years achieved commercial success. This has been brought about by (1) a better understanding of the problems involved in what will be shown to be a complex reaction system; (2) improvements in the chemical engineering technic relating to the treatment of the reaction mass;[1] and (3) improvements in the design, construction, and control of chemical engineering equipment for operations involving high pressures.

Briefly, the process consists in treating chlorobenzene with aqueous ammonia in the presence of cuprous oxide. Amination proceeds slowly under 160°C. and very rapidly at 210°C. At still higher temperatures there is a distinct tendency to phenol formation and decomposition; and the increased pressure on the system makes gas-tight operations more difficult of attainment. A temperature range of 200 to 210°C. gives satisfactory results. At this temperature, with a 6:1 ammonia ratio of

---

[1] Patents assigned to the Dow Chemical Co.: U. S. 1,607,824 (1926); 1,726,170; 1,726,171; 1,726,172; 1,726,173; 1,729,775 (1929); 1,775,360 (1930); 1,823,025; 1,823,026 (1931); 1,840,760; 1,885,625 (1932); 1,932,518 (1933); 2,016,962 (1935).

28 per cent aqueous ammonia, the pressure on the system will be about 850 to 950 lb. per square inch. At the conclusion of the reaction, the vapors leaving the pressure system are expanded and cooled below 100°C. in a suitable pipe condenser or dephlegmating column. Most of the ammonia continues to an absorption system in which the gas is recovered and concentrated for reuse.

Although only 2 moles of NH_3 are required theoretically per mole of chlorobenzene treated, experience has shown that better results are obtained with higher ratios. In plant practice, a ratio of only 4 to 6 moles is employed, for it is necessary to exercise the strictest economy in the preparation of such a low-priced intermediate. In the two competitive methods of producing aniline,

$$\text{Benzene} \overset{Cl_2}{\nearrow} \text{Chlorobenzene} \overset{NH_3}{\searrow} \text{Aniline}$$
$$\overset{HNO_3}{\searrow} \text{Nitrobenzene} \overset{H_2}{\nearrow}$$

the cost of introducing the nitrogen-containing group is the most important item of expense. Since the price of nitric acid is now generally dependent on the cost of synthetic ammonia, neither process has any pronounced advantage in material or processing costs.

Aniline can also be prepared by the vapor-phase ammonolysis of chlorobenzene.[1] A catalyst prepared from a copper salt and the ammonium salt of vanadic, tungstic, or phosphoric acid has been found to be somewhat effective. The vapors of chlorobenzene are passed over such a catalyst maintained at 400°C. and a per pass conversion to aniline of 10 per cent is obtained.

Preparation of Chloroanilines.—The comparative ease in replacing the bromine atom of 4-chlorobromobenzene can be taken advantage of in the preparation of 4-chloroaniline as well as 4-chloro-(N-methyl-)aniline.[2]

$$\text{Cl}\langle\text{}\rangle\text{Br} \xrightarrow[\text{Cu}^+]{\text{CH}_3\text{NH}_2} \text{Cl}\langle\text{}\rangle\text{N}\underset{\text{H}}{\overset{\text{CH}_3}{\langle}}$$

For the preparation of the substituted amine, 19.2 parts by weight of 4-chlorobromobenzene is reacted with 45 parts of aqueous monomethylamine (33 per cent) in the presence of 2 parts of cuprous chloride for 5 hr. at 110°C.

The replacement of both chlorine atoms from *o*-dichlorobenzene is very difficult, and a satisfactory process has not as yet been developed. A high ammonia ratio and 40 to 50 per cent ammonia is desirable. The presence of cuprous copper in quantities sufficient to form an organo

[1] Mathes and Prahl, U. S. 2,001,281 (1935).
[2] Mills, U. S. 1,935,515 (1933).

copper complex is helpful. To precipitate the copper and to avoid oxidation of the *o*-phenylenediamine, it is necessary to add a reducing agent such as sodium sulfide with caustic soda to the vented and cooled autoclave charge before any attempt is made to recover the diamine.

Preparation of Aliphatic Amines.—In the amination of aliphatic halides, it is comparatively easy to replace the halogen by the amino group. The alkyl chlorides are readily converted to the corresponding amines by treatment with aqueous ammonia under pressure. The separation of the primary, secondary, and tertiary amines thus formed is made by taking advantage of slight differences in their physical constants.

In the aromatic series, the replacement of two chlorine atoms in the phenyl or anthraquinone nucleus is generally very difficult, even when a nitro group is present. In contrast, however, ethylenediamine can readily be obtained from the dihalide by a number of similar procedures.

Preparation of Ethylenediamines.—Ethylenediamine and the polyamines obtained concomitantly through condensation can readily be prepared by treating the dichloride with aqueous ammonia under pressure at 100° to 180°C. To secure a preponderance of primary amine, it is necessary to employ concentrated ammonia in large excess. The process may be carried out in a continuous manner (see page 342) and can also be adapted for use with anhydrous ammonia. When ethylene dichloride is injected under pressure into a pressure system containing anhydrous ammonia at 150°C., needles of ethylenediamine hydrochloride are obtained, which on hydrolysis with alkali yield the free amine.[1]

When dilute aqueous ammonia is employed, the expected mixture of primary and polyamines is obtained. Thus, when 1,600 gm. of water, 340 gm. of ammonia liquor, and 200 gm. of ethylene dichloride, are heated at 140 to 150°C. for approximately 1 hr., all the halide has entered into reaction. The product consists approximately of the following:

Substance	B.p., °C.	Formula	%
Ethylenediamine	118	$H_2N \cdot CH_2 \cdot CH_2NH_2$	40
Diethylenetriamine	208	$\begin{array}{c} H_2N \cdot CH_2 \cdot CH_2 \\ \diagdown \\ \quad\quad\quad NH \\ \diagup \\ H_2N \cdot CH_2 \cdot CH_2 \end{array}$	30
Triethylenetetramine	266	$\begin{array}{c} H_2N \cdot CH_2 \cdot CH_2 \\ \diagdown \\ \quad\quad NH \\ \diagup \\ CH_2 \cdot CH_2 \\ NH \\ \diagdown \\ CH_2 \cdot CH_2NH_2 \end{array}$	20
Higher polyamines	...	....	10

[1] Bersworth, U. S. 2,028,041 (1936).

Nafash[1] has developed a cyclic process for the preparation of ethylenediamine and other primary alkylamines from the corresponding bromine derivatives. A combination of well-known chemical reactions is employed, and these are indicated by the following equations:

1. $C_2H_4Br_2 \xrightarrow{NH_3} C_2H_4(NH_2)_2 \cdot 2HBr$
2. $C_2H_4(NH_2)_2 \cdot 2HBr + 2NaOH \rightarrow C_2H_4(NH_2)_2 + 2NaBr + 2H_2O$
3. $2NaBr\ aq. + Cl_2 \rightarrow 2NaCl + Br_2$
3a. $NaBr\ aq. + Cl_2 \rightarrow NaCl + BrCl$

4. $C_2H_4 \diagup^{\xrightarrow{Br_2} C_2H_4Br_2}_{\xrightarrow{BrCl} C_2H_4BrCl}$

The alkyl bromides are more costly than the corresponding chlorine derivatives and their use necessitates additional operating steps. These economic handicaps are to a substantial extent offset by certain advantages as follows: (*a*) the practicability of using weaker ammonia liquor; (*b*) the feasibility of operating at lower temperatures and pressures; and (*c*) the production of comparatively pure primary amines as the principal product.

For the preparation of ethylenediamine, the following procedure may be employed: Ethylene dibromide, preferably as a vapor, is introduced into a vertical autoclave partly filled with aqueous ammonia at 180°C. Reaction apparently occurs in the vapor phase with the formation of the solid dihydrobromide of ethylenediamine. During the course of the amination, the solid particles fall into the ammonia liquor, creating a slurry which is periodically removed. The solid ethylenediamine dihydrohalide is then treated with sodium hydroxide, whereupon the base is liberated and is recovered by subjecting the alkaline mass to distillation. The residue which is essentially an unsaturated solution of sodium bromide is treated with chlorine gas, and the bromine is set free. The continued bubbling of chlorine into the solution apparently effects the solution of bromine, presumably as BrCl. Although Br_2 and Cl_2 are soluble in their saturated salt solutions only to about 4 per cent by weight, 40 parts by weight of bromine when treated with chlorine will dissolve in 75 parts of saturated sodium chloride solution. When ethylene is introduced into the vessel containing the liberated bromine, ethylene dibromide is immediately formed admixed with some of the corresponding bromochloride or dichloride.

Morpholine from β, β'-dichlorodiethyl ether.

$$O\diagup^{CH_2CH_2Cl}_{CH_2CH_2Cl} \xrightarrow{NH_3} O\diagup^{CH_2 \cdot CH_2}_{CH_2 \cdot CH_2}\diagdown NH$$

[1] Nafash, U. S. 2,075,825; 2,078,582 (1937).

When the two chlorine atoms of *sym*-dichlorodiethyl ether are replaced by the imino group through the action of anhydrous ammonia, morpholine is obtained.[1]   The synthesis is carried out as follows: 400 parts by weight of *sym*-dichlorodiethyl ether dissolved in 500 parts of benzene is introduced into a nickel-lined autoclave, and 286 parts of liquid anhydrous ammonia is added.   The total pressure is increased to about 1,500 lb. per square inch by the addition of nitrogen gas.   The temperature of the charge is brought to 50°C., corresponding to a pressure of 1,750 lb. and thus maintained for 24 hr.   The ammonia is vented and reliquefied. The benzene and unreacted β, β'-dichlorodiethyl ether remain in the autoclave along with aliphatic amines and ammonium chloride.   After filtering off the ammonium chloride, the constituents of the liquid are separated by fractional distillation.   Based on dichlorodiethyl ether consumed, the yield of morpholine is 80 per cent.

1, 3-Diaminopropanol-2 from Glycerol Dichlorohydrin.

$$
\begin{array}{ccc}
CH_2Cl & & CH_2NH_2 \\
| & NH_3 & | \\
CHOH & \xrightarrow{\quad} & CHOH \\
| & NH_4Cl & | \\
CH_2Cl & & CH_2NH_2
\end{array}
$$

According to Bottoms[2] the principal precautions to observe in this synthesis are: (*a*) use of methanol or ethanol as a solvent for the 1, 3-dichloropropanol-2; (*b*) use of a large excess of concentrated (50–60 per cent) aqueous ammonia; (*c*) the introduction of ammonium chloride; and (*d*) the gradual introduction of the dichlorohydrin into the reaction vessel containing the ammoniacal solution.   Under such conditions the formation of secondary and tertiary amines and 1-amino-2, 3-dihydroxypropane is largely inhibited.

Preparation of Amino Acids.—When β-halogen acids are reacted with aqueous ammonia, unsaturated acids are formed and very little amination occurs.   The similar treatment of α-halogen acids leads not only to the corresponding primary amino acids, but also to secondary and tertiary derivatives.   In the ammonolysis of chloroacetic acid, the following products are obtained, the proportions depending largely on the ratio of aqueous ammonia:

Glycine	$H_2N \cdot CH_2COOH$
Diglycine	$HN{<}^{CH_2COOH}_{CH_2COOH}$
Triglycine	$N{<}^{CH_2COOH}_{CH_2COOH}{}_{CH_2COOH}$

[1] Campbell, U. S. 2,034,427 (1937)
[2] Bottoms, U. S. 2,065,113 (1936).

To diminish the quantity of secondary and tertiary amines to less than 30 per cent, it is necessary to use a molar ratio $NH_3:CH_2ClCOOH$ of 60:1.

Cheronis[1] has found that 4 moles of ammonium carbonate give as good results as 60 moles of NH_3 *aq.* in the preparation of glycine. The efficacy of these two agents is compared in Fig. 4. The difference between conversion and ammonolysis to primary amine indicates the extent of formation of di- and triglycine and glycolic acid—$CH_2OHCOOH$. The results obtained when the secondary and tertiary amines are reintroduced in subsequent batches have not been reported.

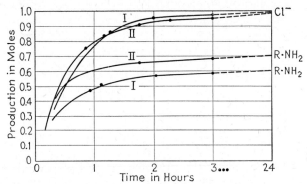

FIG. 4.—Ammonolysis of one mole chloroacetic acid.   (*According to Cheronis.*)
I. Sixty moles of ammonia (aqueous) at 25°C.
II. Four moles of ammonium carbonate at 60°C.

The conclusions[2] which may be drawn from reaction-rate studies in the ammonolysis of halogen fatty acids are:

1. The reaction of most bromo acids with NH_3 *aq.* proceeds rapidly. Branched chains show a decrease in reactivity.

2. Ammonolysis of chloro acids with the exception of chloroacetic is not practical even with a 60 molar NH_3 ratio.

3. The rate of ammonolysis is increased by raising the temperature, and, as is to be expected, this results in an increase in the amounts of secondary and tertiary amino derivatives as well as hydroxy compounds.

CLASS II.   CONVERSION OF SULFONIC ACIDS

Ammonolysis of Anthraquinonesulfonic Acids.—The need of oxidants in the ammonolysis of anthraquinonesulfonic acids has long been recognized.[3] If it is not oxidized, the sulfurous acid which is split off gives rise to the formation of soluble reduction-products. The yield of

---

[1] CHERONIS, Private communication re forthcoming publication.

[2] CHERONIS, *loc cit.*

[3] Ger. 256,515 (1911); 391,073 (1921).

2-aminoanthraquinone, according to the following reaction, is consequently only about 60 per cent of the theoretical.

$$C_{14}H_7O_2 \cdot SO_3H + NH_3 \rightarrow C_{14}H_7O_2 \cdot NH_2 + H_2SO_3$$

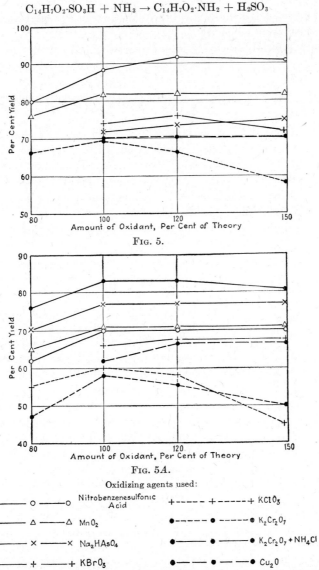

FIG. 5.

FIG. 5A.

Oxidizing agents used:

o————o————o Nitrobenzenesulfonic Acid	+————+————+ KClO₃
△————△————△ MnO₂	●————●————● K₂Cr₂O₇
×————×————× Na₂HAsO₄	●————●————● K₂Cr₂O₇+NH₄Cl
+————+————+ KBrO₃	●————●————● Cu₂O

FIG. 5.—Effect of oxidants; ammonolysis of anthraquinone-1-sulfonic acid.
FIG. 5A.—Effect of oxidants; ammonolysis of anthraquinone-2-sulfonic acid.

Lauer[1] has found that inorganic oxidants have a specific value, depending on the particular anthraquinonesulfonic acid undergoing treatment

[1] LAUER, *J. prakt. Chem.*, **135**, 7 (1932).

as well as on the operating conditions employed.   Certain oxidants give rise to impurities that are not entirely removed by simple technical purification.   When present even in traces, the impurities may interfere with the use of the amine in dyestuffs, this, in the final analysis, being the best criterion of purity.

The results obtained by Lauer are indicated by the curves in Figs. 5 and 5*A*.

Class III.   Conversion of Oxygen-containing Compounds

The amines derived from alcohols, aldehydes, alkylene, and other oxides have wide technical application.   By and large, the aliphatic amines are (1) relatively strong bases; (2) readily soluble in water; and (3) stable over wide ranges of temperature.   Because of these properties, they find many uses in the textile, rubber, and plastics industries and as absorbents for acidic gases.

In the ammonolysis of halogeno compounds, the formation of the corresponding hydracid or its salts gives rise to a number of operating problems.   In the amination of oxygen-containing compounds, water is split out, and, as is to be expected, the operating technic is in many respects modified because of this characteristic.

The catalytic ammonolysis of phenols, alcohols, aldehydes, and ketones differs from the treatment of halogeno compounds in several respects.   The oxygen-containing compounds are best aminated in the presence of metals preceding hydrogen in the electrochemical series. These active metals are, however, either ineffective or deleterious in the treatment of halogeno compounds.   Whereas the catalytic conversion of halogeno compounds depends on the formation of copper-ammonia complexes, the oxy compounds offer a convenient point of addition for the NH_3 in the phenolic, ketonic, and aldehydic groups.

The pertinent type reactions at the beginning of this chapter indicate that the treatment of oxy compounds may involve (1) esterification; (2) dehydration; and (3) reduction; *i.e.*, the elimination of oxygen.

Conversion of Phenols to Amines.—When phenol and ammonia are heated under pressure in the presence of ferric chloride,[1] aluminum hydroxide or ferrous hydroxide, aniline is obtained as the principal product[2] of amination, together with small proportions of diphenylamine. Ortho and para cresols can be treated similarly; but, as is well known, the corresponding amines can be obtained more economically by the direct reduction of nitrobenzene or appropriate nitrotoluenes.

---

[1] Brit. 355,715 (1931).
[2] Brit. 386,375 (1932).

Sym-Xylenol (5-hydroxy-1, 3-dimethylbenzene) heated under pressure with ammonia yields the primary base as the main product, and this procedure is undoubtedly the best method of arriving at *sym*-xylidine. When this xylenol is heated under pressure to 320°C. with ammonium chloride, two products are obtained in approximately equal amounts. One is *sym*-xylidine (1-amino-3,-5-dimethylbenzene), and the other is *sym*-dixylylamine or 5-imino-bis-1,3-dimethylbenzene:

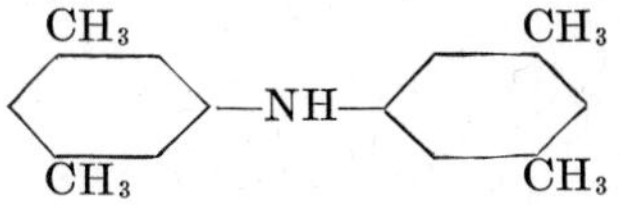

Conversion of Naphthols to Naphthylamines. *Sulfurous Acid Salts as Catalysts (Bucherer Process).*—The most general method for the replacement of —OH by —NH$_2$ groups in naphthols is the use of ammoniacal solutions containing salts of sulfurous acid. The alkali metal bisulfites are ordinarily employed in the preparation of primary amines; but other compounds, such as the sulfite of methylamine (CH_3-$NH_3)_2SO_3$, can be used in making substituted amines. The equations underlying these reactions may be represented as follows:

$$\text{Hydroxy Compound} \underset{\underset{\longleftarrow}{\text{Alkali}}}{\overset{\text{Bisulfite}}{\longrightarrow}} \text{Sulfurous Acid Ester} \underset{\underset{\longleftarrow}{\text{Bisulfite}}}{\overset{\text{Ammonia}}{\longrightarrow}} \text{Amino Compound} \tag{1}$$

$$\text{R·OH} \underset{\underset{\longleftarrow}{\text{Alkali}}}{\overset{\text{Sulfite}}{\longrightarrow}} \text{Sulfurous Acid Ester} \underset{\underset{\longleftarrow}{\text{Sulfite}}}{\overset{HN{\overset{R_1}{\underset{R_2}{}}}}{\longrightarrow}} RN{\overset{R_1}{\underset{R_2}{}}} \tag{2}$$

The intermediate product of the reaction is the ester R·O·SOOM, where R is an aromatic nucleus such as naphthalene and M is an alkali metal. These are comparatively stable and, by adjusting the subsequent conditions of reaction, can be converted to either naphthols or naphthylamines. Compared with the corresponding naphthols, these esters are more readily soluble in water. Those of monohydroxy compounds do not combine with diazo or tetrazo solutions, while those derived from some dihydroxy- and aminohydroxynaphthalenes still possess the power of combination, although in a lesser degree than do the dihydroxynaphthalenes and aminonaphthols themselves. Some of the aminonaphthol esters can be diazotized and the diazo compounds used in the manufacture of azo colors. The esters are, in general, fairly stable against the action of dilute hydrochloric acid and sulfuric acid. They are hydrolyzed, however, on heating with concentrated sulfuric acid, yielding the corresponding hydroxy compounds. By heating with ammonia, they are converted into the amino derivatives.

The methods for producing these aromatic esters and the compounds that are obtained by subsequent hydrolysis or ammonolysis are as follows:[1]

Preparation of an Amine from the Sulfurous Acid Ester.—In a reflux apparatus are heated 100 parts of 1-naphthol-7-sulfonic acid with 250 parts of sodium bisulfite solution (containing about 40% $NaHSO_3$) and 250 parts of water, until the formation of the sulfurous acid ester is finished. This, being very soluble in water, remains in solution. The reaction product is saturated with ammonia either directly or after having first decomposed the excess of bisulfite with acid and then heated in a closed vessel at 100 to 110°C. until the conversion to the 1-naphthylamine-7-sulfonic acid is practically completed. The sulfonic acid is then precipitated in crystalline form by the addition of hydrochloric acid to the solution.

Preparation of a Diamine from an Aminonaphthol.—In a closed vessel are heated 159 parts of 1-amino-5-naphthol with 116 parts of ammonium sulfite, 280 parts of water, and 100 parts of 20 per cent aqueous ammonia. The reaction is conducted at 125°C., until the formation of the 1, 5-diaminonaphthalene is completed. The reaction product separates out in crystalline form and can be filtered off.

It is, of course, unnecessary to prepare the intermediate addition compound first in order to prepare amino derivatives from the corresponding hydroxy compounds. By adding the reacting proportions of ammonium sulfite and providing sufficient ammonia, it is indeed entirely practical to go directly from hydroxy compound to amino derivatives, or *vice versa*.

Sodium bisulfite may be substituted for the more costly ammonium salt without decreasing the yields of β-naphthylamine obtained by the Bucherer reaction.[2] In the course of the reaction, this is converted to the sodium ammonium salt in the presence of an excess of ammonia.

TABLE II.—AMINATION OF β-NAPHTHOL

	1	2	3	4	5
Total H_2O in system, gm	475	475	475	475	475
Total NH_3 used, gm	28.4	31.8	35.2	37.8	44.55
NH_3 for amination, gm	25	25	25	25	25
NH_3 to form $NaNH_4SO_3$, gm	3.4	6.8	10.2	12.8	19.55
$NaNH_4SO_3$ used, moles	.2	.4	.6	.75	1.15
Yield of β-naphthylamine,* %	37	37	84	84	84

* Average results.

[1] Brit. 1,387 (1900).
[2] BEZZUBEZ, *J. Chem. Ind. (Moscow)*, **7**, 908 (1932).

About 0.6 mole of sodium ammonium sulfite is necessary per mole of naphthol. The data[1] on page 318 (Table II) relate to experiments wherein one mole (144 gm.) of β-naphthol was treated at 150°C. for 8 hr.

Preparation of 2-Aminonaphthalene-3-carboxylic Acid.—The ammonolysis of 2-hydroxynaphthalene-3-carboxylic acid affords an interesting study in the conversion of hydroxy compounds to amines, for it reveals a failure to appreciate and protect the fundamental factors involved in this synthesis.

Fierz and Tobler[2] recognized the advantages to be derived from the use of soluble salts of the more active metals—particularly zinc chloride because of its property of adding on ammonia—which had long been used in the amination of β-naphthol. These salts are employed in quantities sufficient to form addition compounds or esters with the aromatic compounds. Instead of using zinc chloride, Schweitzer[3] employs the zinc salt of the hydroxynaphthoic acid in the presence of ammonium chloride. Henle[4] subsequently conceived the idea of incorporating zinc chloride-ammonia as the catalyst; while Hotz[5] resorted to the use of ferrous sulfate. The operating details of the Fierz process are presented later in the technical section of this chapter.

Ammonolysis of Hydroxyanthraquinones.—The advantages of carrying out the ammonolysis of hydroxyanthraquinones in a reducing medium are illustrated in the following preparation of 1, 4-diaminoanthraquinone from quinizarin.[6] The mono- and dialkylaminoanthraquinones are similarly prepared by employing an alkylamine instead of ammonia as the reactant.

Preparation of Leuco 1, 4-*Diaminoanthraquinone Directly from Quinizarin.*—An autoclave is charged with 100 parts of quinizarin, 108 parts of sodium hydrosulfite (85 per cent), and 450 parts of aqueous ammonia (sp. gr., 0.92 to 0.88), and the whole warmed at a temperature of from 70 to 90°C. for 6 hr. The charge is then cooled, filtered, and

[1] Bezzubez, *loc. cit.*

[2] Fierz and Tobler, *Helv. Chim. Acta*, **5,** 557 (1922); U. S. 1,629,894 (1925).

[3] Schweitzer, U. S. 1,806,714 (1931).

[4] Henle, U. S. 1,871,990 (1932).

[5] Hotz, U. S. 1,690,785 (1928).

[6] U. S. 1,828,262 (1931).

washed with warm water. The product, which is obtained in the form of green or brown crystals, consists of practically pure leuco 1, 4-diaminoanthraquinone.

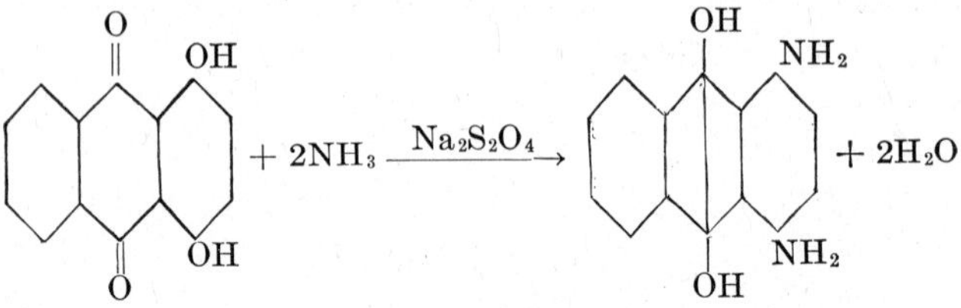

Conversion of Alcohols.—Practically the whole range of primary alcohols from methanol and butanol to cetyl and stearyl alcohols has been investigated. The synthesis of low-molecular-weight alkylamines from alcohols is almost always carried out in the vapor phase, according to the method of Sabatier and Mailhe[1] in which the reacting alcohol and ammonia are passed over a dehydrating catalyst. Compounds of aluminum or phosphorus; *e.g.*, alumina,[2] aluminum silicate,[3] aluminum phosphate,[4] and diammonium phosphate are most frequently employed for this purpose. As in the amination of alkyl halides, the product of reaction may comprise primary, secondary, and tertiary amines, depending on the specific alcohol, the NH_3 ratio, and other conditions employed. The net reaction may be expressed thus:

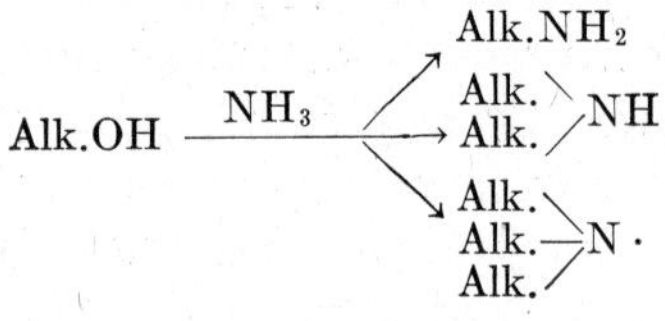

The amines of the high-molecular-weight fatty acids are best prepared in a pressure system. Cetylamine is thus obtained by conducting cetyl alcohol and ammonia through a catalytic reaction chamber containing aluminum oxide which is kept at 380 to 400°C.[5] and under a pressure of 125 atmos. The vented vapors are condensed and yield an oily liquid containing some water. Upon distillation of the oil, cetylamine is obtained. Oleyl and stearyl alcohols react in a similar fashion. When alkylamines are employed instead of ammonia, the corresponding

---

[1] Sabatier, and Mailhe, *Compt. rend.*, **148**, 898 (1909).

[2] Arnold, U. S. 1,799,722 (1931); Reissue 19,632 (1935); Smolenski, *Roczniki Chem.*, **1**, 232 (1921).

[3] Arnold, U. S. 1,799,722 (1931); Reissue 19,632 (1935); Martin and Swallen, U. S. 1,875,747 (1932).

[4] Andrews, U. S. 2,073,671 (1937).

[5] Smeykal, U. S. 2,043,965 (1936).

alkylamino compounds are formed. Thus, monoisobutyldodecylamine is prepared from 1 part *n*-dodecyl alcohol and 10 parts monoisobutylamine.[1] It is also possible to carry out the ammonolysis of the higher fatty alcohols in the vapor phase.[2] A mixture of primary, secondary, and tertiary alcohols is usually obtained.

Taurine from Hydroxyethanesulfonic Acid (Isethionic Acid).

$$OH \cdot CH_2 \cdot CH_2 \cdot SO_3Na \xrightarrow[Na_2SO_3]{NH_3} H_2N \cdot CH_2 \cdot CH_2 \cdot SO_3Na$$

Taurine along with some ditaurine can be obtained by reacting 256 parts by weight of sodium hydroxyethanesulfonate with 800 parts of 25 per cent ammonia liquor at 210°C. for 3 hr. The addition of 10 parts of sodium sulfite aids materially in increasing the conversion, which falls off as the quantity of sodium sulfite is reduced. The synthesis is of particular interest, because it shows that, in aliphatic compounds containing both sulfonic and hydroxyl groups, the —OH group can be replaced preferentially by —NH_2[3] and —$N\begin{smallmatrix}Alk^4\\H\end{smallmatrix}$ In addition to sodium sulfite, other salts such as sodium carbonate can be used. In the preparation of the alkylamino derivatives, *e.g.*, methyltaurine, the introduction of caustic potash is found to be advantageous.

Ammonolysis of Aldehydes.—The conversion of aldehydes to amines is generally carried out in the presence of a hydrogenation catalyst, *e.g.*, nickel, for here the reduction of the aldehydic group necessitates the presence of hydrogen. When unsaturated aldehydes, such as acrolein, are reacted, saturation as well as amination takes place, and a normal primary amine, *viz.*, propylamine, will be obtained.

Preparation of Glucamine and Related Products from Monosaccharides.

$$CH_2OH(CHOH)_4CHO \xrightarrow[Ni]{NH_3 + H_2} CH_2OH(CHOH)_4CH_2NH_2$$

Stable hydroxyamino compounds can be prepared readily by reacting ammonia or an aliphatic amine with monosaccharides in the presence of hydrogen and a suitable reducing catalyst. These reactions are exemplified by the following synthesis of glucamine:[5] Twenty-five hundred grams

---

[1] Smeykal, U. S. 2,043,965 (1936).

[2] Arnold, U. S. 2,078,922 (1937).

[3] Nicodemus and Schmidt, U. S. 1,999,614 (1935).

[4] Nicodemus and Schmidt, U. S. 1,932,907 (1933).

[5] Flint and Salzberg, U. S. 2,016,962 (1935).

of commercial glucose is charged into an autoclave containing 2,500 grams of 21 per cent aqueous ammonia and 250 grams of a reduced nickel catalyst. Hydrogen is then introduced until a pressure of about 100 atmos. is obtained, and the charge is stirred rapidly without heating for $\frac{1}{2}$ hr. to effect solution of the glucose. With the application of heat hydrogen absorption begins at 63 to 65°C., and the temperature is brought up to 95°C. Hydrogen is introduced periodically during a $\frac{1}{2}$-hr. period to replenish that consumed in the reaction. The charge, which is then free from reducing sugars, is filtered and concentrated. Glucamine is obtained in good yields as a viscous noncrystalline syrup. From the anhydrous syrup, glucamine can be crystallized out of methanol as a white crystalline compound melting at 127°C.

By treating glucose, xylose, fructose, and other monosaccharides with monomethylamine, the corresponding methylamino sugars are obtained. Of course, any alkylamine with a replaceable hydrogen can be substituted for the methylamine to give a wide variety of alkylaminomonosaccharides.[1]

Conversion of Aldehydes.—Saturated and unsaturated aliphatic and aromatic aldehydes and intranuclear ketones can be converted to amines in the vapor phase by passing their vapors along with equal volumes of ammonia and hydrogen over a heated nickel catalyst.[2] A reaction temperature of 125 to 150°C. has been found satisfactory. To avoid resinification of unstable unsaturated aldehydes or ketones before their contact with the catalyst, they are preferably vaporized separately, and their vapors, admixed with fresh hydrogen, are led into the reaction system where they are mixed with the circulated, preheated mixture of ammonia and hydrogen. The ammonolysis of acrolein, crotonaldehyde, and cyclohexanone respectively is as follows:

$$CH_2:CH\cdot CHO \xrightarrow[H_2]{NH_3} CH_3\cdot CH_2\cdot CH_2NH_2$$
n-Propylamine

$$CH_3\cdot CH:CH\cdot CHO \xrightarrow[H_2]{NH_3} CH_3\cdot CH_2\cdot CH_2\cdot CH_2NH_2$$
n-Butylamine

$$\begin{matrix} CH_2-CH_2 \\ CH_2 \qquad CO \\ CH_2-CH_2 \end{matrix} \xrightarrow[H_2]{NH_3} \begin{matrix} CH_2-CH_2 \\ CH_2 \qquad CHNH_2 \\ CH_2-CH_2 \end{matrix}$$
Cyclohexylamine

The Conversion of Alkylene Oxides to Alkanolamines.—The alkylene oxides, *e.g.*, ethylene,[2] isopropylene[2,3] and isobutylene[2] oxides can readily be converted to alkanolamines.

---

[1] Flint and Salzberg, U. S. 1,994,467; 2,016,963 (1935).

[2] Kauter, U. S. 2,051,486 (1936).

[3] Wickert, U. S. 1,988,225 (1935).

CH₂OH·CH₂NH₂
Ethanolamine

$$H_2C\!\!-\!\!CH_2 \quad \xrightarrow{NH_3}$$

CH₂OH·CH₂
                    NH
CH₂OH·CH₂
Diethanolamine

CH₂OH·CH₂
CH₂OH·CH₂——N
CH₂OH·CH₂
Triethanolamine

CH₃·CHOH·CH₂NH₂
Isopropanolamine

$$CH_3CH\!\!-\!\!CH_2 \quad \xrightarrow{NH_3}$$

CH₃·CHOH·CH₂
                    NH
CH₃·CHOH·CH₂
Diisopropanolamine

CH₃·CHOH·CH₂
CH₃·CHOH·CH₂——N
CH₃·CHOH·CH₂
Triisopropanolamine

These reactions are exothermic, and an operating temperature of 50° to 60°C. usually suffices. When ordinary 28 per cent aqueous ammonia

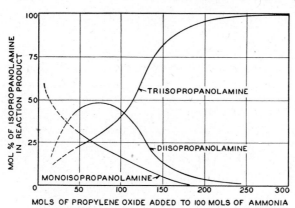

Fig. 6.—Preparation of propanolamines; influence of NH₃ ratio.

is employed, primary, secondary, and tertiary amines are obtained—the proportions being dependent on the NH₃ ratio.

When propylene oxide is bubbled into aqueous ammonia at 40 to 50°C. in a sealed agitated vessel, the isopropanolamines are formed, and these can be separated by fractional distillation. Wickert[1] has shown that it is feasible to control the proportions of the various amines by adjusting the relative concentration of the reactants. The curves in Fig. 6 show clearly the relation of the reactants to the products. The physical properties of the ethanol- and propanolamines which find employment as wetting agents, rubber accelerators, and as absorbents for acidic gases, are given below.[1]

[1] Wickert, U. S. 1,988,225 (1935).

Substance	Sp. gr., 20°/20°C.	B.p. at 5 mm., °C.	Freezing point, °C.	1% solution, alkalinity pH
Monoisopropanolamine............	0.981	45	−5	11.4
Diisopropanolamine........⸱........	1.0089	116	32	11.1
Triisopropanolamine....⸱........	1.0196	144	45	10.2
Monoethanolamine...............	1.0180	58	10.5	11.50
Diethanolamine..................	1.0984	156	28.0	11.75
Triethanolamine.................	1.1258	201	21.2	11.30

Although the alkylene oxides on ammonolysis give rise to amines with one to three alkanol groups, the epichlorohydrins derived from glycerol yield mono- and diaminopropanols. When one mole of glycerol dichlorohydrin is added to 2 liters of aqueous ammonia containing 2 moles of NaOH at 30 to 50°C., the conversion to diamine takes place according to the following scheme.[1]

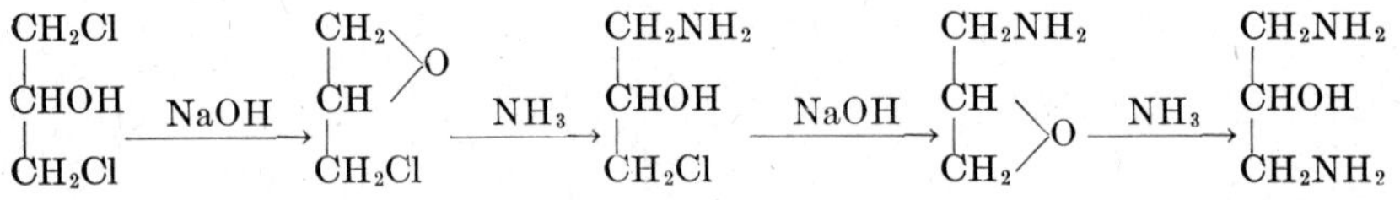

$$
\begin{array}{ccccccccc}
CH_2Cl & & CH_2 & & CH_2NH_2 & & CH_2NH_2 & & CH_2NH_2 \\
| & NaOH & | \!\!\diagdown\!\! O & NH_3 & | & NaOH & | \!\!\diagdown & NH_3 & | \\
CHOH & \longrightarrow & CH \diagup & \longrightarrow & CHOH & \longrightarrow & CH \;\; O & \longrightarrow & CHOH \\
| & & | & & | & & | \diagup & & | \\
CH_2Cl & & CH_2Cl & & CH_2Cl & & CH_2 & & CH_2NH_2
\end{array}
$$

The first reaction that takes place probably is one between the dichlorohydrin and the caustic soda in which one chlorine atom is removed with the formation of epichlorohydrin. This immediately reacts with a molecule of ammonia to form a glyceryl aminochlorhydrin, which then reacts with caustic soda forming sodium chloride, releasing water and producing epiaminohydrin. The epiaminohydrin forthwith reacts with a further quantity of ammonia to produce the 1, 3-diaminopropanol-2. The intermediate formation of epihydrins makes it necessary to have ammonia present in large excess and at the operating temperature (50°C.) in order to prevent the amino derivatives which are first formed from reacting with further quantities of the chlorhydrin and producing undesirable secondary and tertiary reaction products and complex polymers.

The Synthesis of Urea from CO_2.—Although urea was the first of the organic compounds to be formed synthetically, its commercial production had to await the development of the synthetic ammonia process. Here the principal product, NH_3, and a by-product, CO_2, which constitute the raw materials for urea production, are prepared cheaply.

[1] Bottoms, U. S. 1,985,885 (1935); 2,065,113 (1936); Eisleb, U. S. 1,790,042 (1931).

The reactions involved in the formation of urea from carbon dioxide and ammonia are as follows:[1,2]

$$2NH_3 + CO_2 \rightleftharpoons CO \begin{smallmatrix} NH_2 \\ \\ ONH_4 \end{smallmatrix}$$

Ammonium
Carbamate

At elevated temperatures urea is formed from ammonium carbamate by a series of reactions:

$$CO \begin{smallmatrix} NH_2 \\ \\ ONH_4 \end{smallmatrix} \rightarrow CO \begin{smallmatrix} NH_2 \\ \\ OH \end{smallmatrix} + NH_3 \tag{1}$$

Ammonium   Carbamic
Carbamate   Acid

$$CO \begin{smallmatrix} NH_2 \\ \\ OH \end{smallmatrix} \rightarrow (HO \cdot CN \rightleftharpoons HN:CO) + H_2O \tag{2}$$

Cyanic Acid
(Enol form)   (Keto form)

$$HN:CO + NH_3 \rightarrow HN:C \begin{smallmatrix} NH_3 \\ | \\ O \end{smallmatrix} \qquad O:C \begin{smallmatrix} NH_2 \\ \\ NH_2 \end{smallmatrix} \tag{3}$$

Cyanic Acid   Urea   Urea
                 (Solution)   (Crystalline)[3]

Although the transformation of ammonium carbamate to urea is not a direct dehydration, the presence of water is, however, a limiting factor with respect to the extent that the reaction occurs. It has been found that at any temperature a definite equilibrium is established which can be approached from either direction.[4] Krase and Gaddy[5] have shown that a real shift in the carbamate-urea-water equilibrium is obtained by employing an excess of anhydrous ammonia, which functions as a strong dehydration agent. The employment of ammonia, up to 280 per cent of that combined as carbamate, gives conversions to urea between 81 and 85 per cent of the carbamate ammonia. These results are shown in the curve (Fig. 7), page 326.

Class IV. Replacement of Labile Nitro Groups

Before giving concrete examples of the type reactions of this group, it is advisable to draw attention to a peculiar but important property that attaches to the arrangements of nitro groups in cyclic compounds.

[1] Mixter, *Amer. Chem. J.* **4**, 35 (1882).
[2] Werner, "The Chemistry of Urea," Longmans, Green & Company (1923).
[3] Hendricks, *J. Am. Chem. Soc.*, **52**, 3088 (1930).
[4] Clark, Gaddy, and Rist, *Ind. Eng. Chem.*, **25**, 1092 (1933).
[5] Krase and Gaddy, *J. Am. Chem. Soc.*, **52**, 3088 (1930).

Whenever a nitro group is found ortho or para to another nitro radical, it is rendered labile or very susceptible to chemical action. This mobility offers a convenient method of making transformations otherwise very difficult. Thus, Kenner and Parkin[1] obtained 3-nitro-*o*-toluidine from 2, 3-dinitrotoluene by treating the latter with alcoholic ammonia for 15 hr. at 150 to 160°C.

When 5, 6-dinitro-*o*-chlorotoluene is treated with alcoholic ammonia under pressure, the reaction product obtained is 6-chloro-3-nitro-*o*-

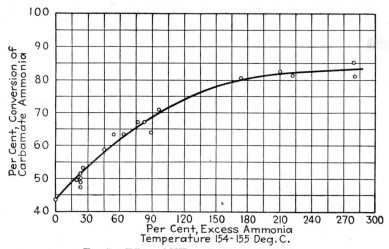

FIG. 7.—Effect of NH₃ ratio on urea formation.

toluidine. If, however, 3, 5-dinitro-*o*-chlorotoluene is thus treated, the halogen is replaced and 3, 5-dinitro-*o*-toluidine is produced. The group ortho to the nitro substituent is in each case the one entering into the

reaction. In fact, the replacement of the labile nitro group takes place so readily[2] that it can be replaced quantitatively by bases. Thus, when 2-chloro-3, 4-dinitrotoluene is treated with ammonia or aniline, the following substituted toluidines are obtained:

[1] KENNER and PARKIN, *J. Chem. Soc.* **117,** 852 (1920).
[2] MORGAN and GLOVER, *J. Chem. Soc.,* **119,** 1700 (1921).

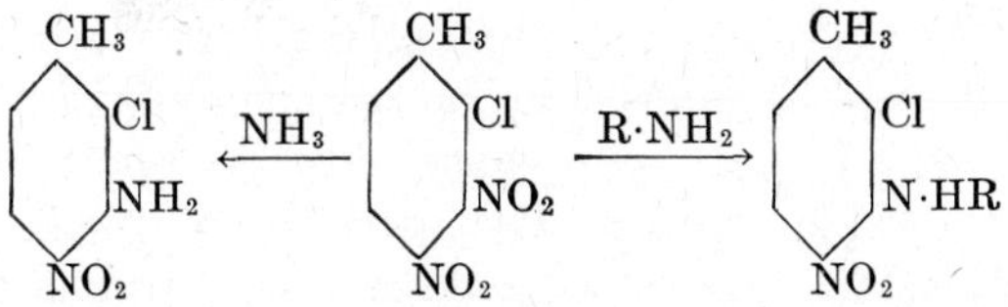

It is noteworthy that the two consecutively substituted isomerides 2-chloro-5, 6-dinitrotoluene and 2-chloro-3, 4-dinitrotoluene having the two contiguous nitro groups at one end or the other of the consecutive series of substituents each lost the interior (3- or 6-) nitro group only and gave rise to the corresponding amine when treated with ammonia or aniline. Burton and Kenner further ascertained[1] that the nitro group that suffers replacement under the influence of alcoholic ammonia would be more resistant to the action of reducing agents. They found that the replacement of —NO_2 groups by —NH_2 in dinitro compounds is dependent upon the reagent employed. Thus, 3, 4-dinitro-*o*-xylene gives 3-nitro-*o*-4-xylidine when treated with alcoholic ammonia, whereas 4-nitro-*o*-3-xylidine was obtained by reduction with stannous chloride.

IV. PHYSICAL AND CHEMICAL FACTORS AFFECTING AMMONOLYSIS

A number of factors accelerate or retard the replacement of atoms or radicals by the amino group. These will be discussed in the following order: (1) solubility; (2) agitation; (3) halogen derivative treated; (4) presence of nitro groups; (5) temperature of amination and NH_3 concentration; and (6) free space in autoclaves.

Solubility.—The soluble anthraquinonesulfonic acids are more readily converted to amines than the insoluble halogeno compounds. A similar comparison cannot be drawn, however, between 4'-chloro-2-benzoyl-benzoic acid and the 2-chloroanthraquinone derived from it upon ring closure. In the soluble keto acid, the halogen is attached to the benzene nucleus and it is consequently more difficult to replace than the chlorine atom linked to the anthraquinone nucleus. It is thus absolutely necessary to employ a metal catalyst in the ammonolysis of the halogeno keto acid, whereas its use in the conversion of the anthraquinone derivative is not essential.

When a compound such as 2-chloroanthraquinone is being aminated, solution is facilitated by increasing either the NH_3 concentration or the temperature. Both of these factors incidentally increase the partial pressure or activity of the dissolved ammonia.

From Fig. 8, showing the vapor pressure (extrapolated) of ammoniacal solutions at various molalities, it can be seen that an ammonia partial pressure of 800 lb. per square inch can be obtained at 200°C. with a

[1] BURTON and KENNER, *J. Ch m. Soc.*, **119**, 1047 (1921).

30 molal solution, at 165°C. with a 40 molal solution, and at 140°C. with a 50 molal solution.   Experience in the ammonolysis of halogenoanthraquinones has shown that lower temperatures suffice when the NH_3 concentrations are increased.   The permissible diminution in operating temperature is not, however, so great as one would expect from the vapor-pressure curves.

When more dilute NH_3 solutions are employed, the results obviously suffer from the increased activity of the solvent—water.   Experience in the preparation of aniline, *p*-nitroaniline, aminoanthraquinones, and ethylenediamine from the corresponding halogeno compounds demon-

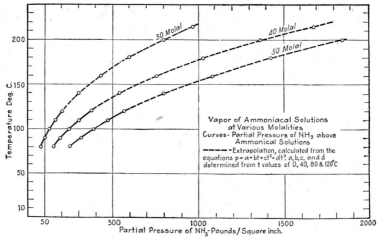

Fig. 8.—Extrapolation NH_3 vapor pressure.

strates that the yields and purity of primary amine are invariably favored by the utilization of the highest practical concentrations of ammonia.

Effect of Agitation.—In liquid-phase ammonolysis the rate of amination depends upon the homogeneity of the reaction mass.   Without agitation, some insoluble compounds would on account of their greater density settle to the bottom of the autoclave while the ammonia liquor remained as a distinct layer above it.   Reaction would then take place only at the interface, and a complete conversion of the compound to the amino derivative would not be feasible.

Such a problem exists in the ammonolysis of 2-chloroanthraquinone. In this instance, the aromatic compound does not wet out and has a tendency to remain on the surface of the ammoniacal solution.   Since this amination apparently takes place in the liquid phase, it is impossible to obtain satisfactory results in this operation unless the type of agitation provides a practically homogeneous reaction mass.

In some operations, where no stirrers are provided, the mixing of the reacting materials depends on the convection currents produced by a flame at the base of the autoclave or on forced circulation through a tubular system. The influence of speed of stirring on the reaction velocity of a number of unit processes has been worked out by Huber and Reid,[1] who found that three classes existed:

. . . (1) those in which the rate of reaction is a linear function of the speed of stirring; (2) those in which this relation becomes linear only after a certain speed is attained, it being very slow without stirring, the rate increasing at first far more rapidly than the speed of stirring; and (3) those in which the rate is independent of the speed of stirring.

Ammonolysis of sparsely soluble substances in aqueous ammonia is largely included in the second class—without agitation practically no reaction taking place. A slight stirring brings about a substantial increase in the reaction velocity, but a proportionate increase in the rate of reaction is not produced by a more vigorous agitation.

Effect of Halogen Derivative.—From the known activity of the halogens and the heats of formation of the halides, it would be expected that replacement of bromine atoms could be accomplished more readily than that of chlorine atoms. This has been found to be true in the treatment of the respective halogenoanthraquinones. Thus, without the employment of catalysts, bromoanthraquinone is approximately twice as reactive as the chloro derivative. When a copper catalyst is used, 2-aminoanthraquinone of 97 to 98 per cent purity can be obtained with a 28.5 per cent NH_3 solution, whereas the maximum purity of product from the chloro derivative under the same conditions is only 93 per cent.

The comparative ease in replacing —Br by —NH_2 is brought out in the conversion of 4-bromochlorobenzene to 4-chloroaniline. By heating with aqueous ammonia at 120°C. for 10 hr., only the bromine atom is replaced by the amino group.[2]

Effect of Nitro Substituents.—The conversion of chlorobenzene to aniline requires a comparatively high temperature—200°C. or above— and the presence of a catalyst. When certain negative groups such as the —NO_2 or —COOH are introduced in the phenyl nucleus, the replacement of the halogen atom takes place more readily. Thus, it is a comparatively easy procedure to produce the nitroanilines from their respective nitrophenyl halides. No catalyst is required in this operation, and a temperature of 170°C. suffices.

The labilizing influence of the nitro group is demonstrated by the work of McMaster and Steiner[3] in the amination of nitro-*p*-dichloro-benzene. Whereas *p*-dichlorobenzene cannot readily be aminated,

---

[1] HUBER and REID, *Ind. Eng. Chem.*, **18**, 535 (1926).

[2] Mills, U. S. 1,935,515 (1933).

[3] McMASTER and STEINER, *Ind. Eng. Chem.*, **22**, 547 (1930).

the introduction of the nitro group makes possible the replacement of the ortho halogen at 150°C. without the assistance of a catalyst.

Sprung,[1] in studying the reactivities of the chloro- and bromonitro-benzenes with alcoholic sodium sulfite to form nitrophenylsulfonates, also found that the introduction of more than one nitro group greatly increases the activity of the halogen atom.

The ease in replacing halogen in nitrophenyl compounds is in all probability due to the activity of the nitro group in forming addition complexes. Garner and Gillbe[2] have shown that dinitrobenzene forms addition complexes with ammonia that show measurable conductivities. It is logical to assume that the point of contact is the oxygen of the nitro group. Here each oxygen has only two of its six available electrons saturated as bond energy, and the remaining atomic energy is available in part for auxiliary attachments.

Energy Factors in Ammonolysis. *Effect of Temperature.*—The generally accepted explanation for the temperature coefficient of reactions is essentially the Arrhenius hypothesis of activated molecules. Tolman[3] has elaborated this principle in a comprehensive manner on the assumption that there is a whole series of active molecules in statistical equilibrium with the inactive ones and that the active molecules differ from the inactive only in their energy content; each of these active molecules has a finite probability of reacting, which depends upon this energy content. On this hypothesis, the energy of activation is the difference of the mean energy of the molecules that react and the mean energy of all the molecules.

An increase in the temperature of amination increases not only the solubility and internal energy of the compound that is being treated but also the partial pressure of the ammonia. Since the activity of the ammonia is a function of this partial pressure, the probabilities of reacting are increased in proportion to the temperature. The validity of these expectations is borne out by the data in Table IV, relating to the non-catalytic preparation of *p*-nitroaniline, and in Table VI, relating to the catalytic ammonolysis of chloronaphthalene.

Effect of NH₃ Concentration.—It is necessary to distinguish between the terms *ammonia ratio* and *ammonia concentration*. The first relates to the capacity factor of the system; the second, to the intensity factor. Aside from economic considerations, there are no disadvantages in using a large ratio of aqueous ammonia (25 to 35 per cent NH_3 solution) with respect to the compound being treated. Within reasonable limits, an increase in this ratio promotes both the yield and purity of primary amine

[1] SPRUNG, *J. Am. Chem. Soc.*, **52**, 1650 (1930).
[2] GARNER and GILLBE, *J. Chem. Soc.*, **1928**, 2889.
[3] TOLMAN, *J. Am. Chem. Soc.*, **47**, 2652 (1925).

obtained. The larger volume of concentrated aqueous ammonia promotes solubility and therefore causes the reaction to take place more
readily.

Furthermore, the use of a large ammonia ratio serves to reduce the
concentration of H^+ or RNH_3^+ ions, thus resulting in a diminution of

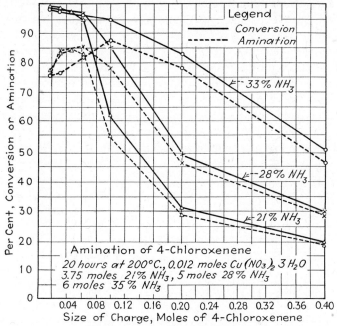

FIG. 9.—Amination of 4-chloroxenene.

secondary and tertiary amines. This phenomenon is particularly noticeable in the preparation of amino acids from the corresponding halogeno
compounds. The data relating to the preparation of glycine from chloroacetic acid are as follows:

TABLE III.—EFFECT OF NH_3 RATIO: AMMONOLYSIS OF CHLOROACETIC ACID[1]
Temp., 60°C., NH_3 Conc., 28%

Molar ratio, NH_3:Acid	Time, hr.	Yield	
		Cl⁻, %	R·NH₂, %
4	0.5	98.3	30.4
8	1.1	99.4	36.4
8	3.0	99.8	34.7
8	0.25	98.3	41.0
60	0.5	96.2	48.5
60	1.0	99.0	50.1
110	0.25	99.6	65.0

[1] According to Cheronis.

Extensive investigations in the ammonolysis of halogeno compounds have shown that the practical advantages to be obtained by utilizing a more concentrated NH_3 solution for non-catalytic aminations may be summed up as follows: (1) amination is more rapid; (2) conversion of reacting compound to amine is more complete; (3) formation of secondary and tertiary amines and hydroxy compounds is inhibited; (4) lower reaction temperatures can be used; and (5) since larger batches can be treated with the same quantity of liquor, economies in the number of pieces of equipment can be effected. To a large extent these observations are confirmed by the data in Table IV relating to the preparation of *p*-nitroaniline, and the curves of Fig. 9 relating to xenylamine.

The effect of NH_3 concentration in catalytic ammonolysis has been investigated by Vorozhtzov and Kobelev,[1] and by Groggins and Stirton.[2] The practical benefits of employing higher ammonia concentrations are brought out clearly by the data in Table V. In these experiments, as in

TABLE IV.—NON-CATALYTIC AMMONOLYSIS OF *p*-CHLORONITROBENZENE[1]
Influence of NH_3 concentration, NH_3 ratio, and temp.

Expt. no.	Temp., °C.	Time, hr.	NH_3 conc., %	ClC_6H_4-NO_2, mole	Cl^-, %	*p*-Nitro-aniline, %	Mole ratio, $NH_3/ClC_6H_4NO_2$
1	140	4	21	0.4	1.63	1.31	9.375
2	140	4	35	0.4	3.52	3.09	9.375
3	140	4	21	0.1	4.71	3.64	37.5
4	140	4	35	0.1	6.81	6.26	37.5
5	180	4	21	0.1	82.73	78.67	37.5
6	180	4	35	0.1	91.88	89.16	37.5
7	200	4	21	0.1	97.71	93.47	37.5
8	200	4	35	0.1	98.80	95.56	37.5
9	200	1	21	0.025	36.19	31.74	150.0
10	200	1	28	0.025	36.81	33.98	150.0
11	200	1	35	0.025	36.80	35.68	150.0
12	200	1	21	0.025	36.19	31.74	150.0
13	200	1	28	0.025	35.36	32.82	200.0
14	200	1	35	0.025	30.12	28.26	240.0

[1] See technical section for description of industrial procedure. Molar NH_3 ratios in excess of 37.5 are impractical.

plant practice, a constant ratio of ammonia and copper to 4-chloroxenene was provided. From the tabulated data it can be concluded: (1) for any particular ammonia concentration, within limits, the rate of conversion is a function of the copper-ammonia concentration; (2) most of the generalizations relating to the non-catalytic ammonolysis of halogeno

[1] VOROZHTZOV and KOBELEV, *J. Chem. Soc. (U.S.S.R.)*, **4**, 310 (1934).
[2] GROGGINS and STIRTON, *Ind. Eng. Chem.*, **28**, 1051 (1936).

compounds are equally valid; (3) The difference between conversion; *i.e.*, decomposition of halogeno compound, as determined by chloride ion, and amination, for 18 per cent copper, is approximately twice as great as that for 12 per cent copper; and (4) as the ammonia concentration is increased this "difference" becomes less despite the fact that the reaction has proceeded farther.

TABLE V.—INFLUENCE OF AMMONIA CONCENTRATION IN PREPARATION OF
XENYLAMINE
(16 hr. at 200°C.)

Expt. no.	NH_3 conc., %	Aqueous NH_3, gm.	4-Chloroxenene, mole	Cu $(NO_3)_2 \cdot$ $3H_2O$, mole	Catalyst conc., gr. atom copper per liter	Conversion, A, %	Amination B, %	$100 \times$ mole ratio, Cu: R·Cl	Mole ratio NH_3: R·Cl	Difference, A − B
1	14	304	⅙	0.03	0.0932	55.31	45.14	18	15	10.17
2	21	304	¼	0.045	0.1360	66.20	57.68	18	15	8.52
3	28	304	⅓	0.06	0.1770	86.35	80.15	18	15	6.20
4	35	292	⅖	0.072	0.2169	93.26	88.77	18	15	4.49
5	21	304	¼	0.072	0.2175	85.56	73.82	28.8	15	11.74
6	14	304	⅙	0.02	0.0621	41.20	35.73	12	15	5.47
7	21	304	¼	0.03	0.0906	58.38	53.44	12	15	4.94
8	28	304	⅓	0.04	0.1180	74.10	71.35	12	15	2.75
9	35	292	⅖	0.048	0.1446	87.02	84.41	12	15	2.61
10	35	292	¼	0.048	0.1446	98.92	88.99	19.2	24	9.93
11	21	304	¼	0.048	0.1450	73.38	64.06	19.2	15	9.32

According to Groggins and Stirton.

Reaction-rate studies showed that the effect of NH_3 concentration on the rate of conversion in catalytic ammonolysis depends upon (1) the ammonia ratio; (2) the reaction temperature; and (3) the halogeno compound.[1]

The results in Table VI relating to the preparation of 1-naphthylamine show that at 180°C. an increase in conversion and amination rates is brought about by the use of stronger ammonia. When the reaction temperature is raised to 200°C., the conversion rate for 28 per cent aqueous ammonia is still better than that for 21 per cent ammonia, but the 35 per cent solution no longer has an advantage. The amination rates are, however, better with increased ammonia concentration.

Effect of Free Space in Autoclaves.—Associated with the factor of NH_3 concentration is the influence of *freeboard*, or the free space in the

[1] GROGGINS and STIRTON, *Ind. Eng. Chem.*, **28**, 1051 (1936).

TABLE VI.—REACTION-RATE STUDIES IN AMINATION OF 1-CHLORONAPHTHALENE*

Expt. no.	NH₃ conc., %	Cl⁻, %	1-Naphthylamine, %

Temp., 180°C.; Chloronaphthalene Taken, 0.2 Mole; Mole Ratio NH_3/Chloronaphthalene, 18.75; b = Gram Atom Cu/Liter = 0.12085

Expt. no.	NH₃ conc., %	Cl⁻, %	1-Naphthylamine, %
1†	28	0.21	0
2	21	5.54	2.32
3	28	7.84	4.90
4	35	8.62	5.66

Temp., 200°C.; Chloronaphthalene Taken, 0.3 Mole; Mole Ratio NH_3/Chloronaphthalene, 12.5

Expt. no.	NH₃ conc., %	Cl⁻, %	1-Naphthylamine, %
5	21	12.02	10.91
6	28	14.43	12.38
7‡	28	14.59	12.93
8	35	14.44	13.16

* Time, 5 hr.; catalyst, CuCl.
† No catalyst.
‡ Cu(NO₃)₂·3H₂O as catalyst.

autoclave. This is a matter of importance which must be taken into careful consideration in carrying out operations involving ammonolysis. It is obviously advantageous to fill the autoclave up to its maximum safe capacity. Such conditions permit a larger production and generally give a better yield and purity of product. When aminations involving insoluble halides such as halogenoanthraquinones are carried out in glass tubes, it will be observed that the reaction takes place in the liquid phase. The solid material remaining above the surface of the liquid does not appear to react, despite the fact that it is in contact with vapors that are essentially gaseous ammonia.

When an excess of freeboard is left in the autoclaves, this space will be filled with vapors in equilibrium with the aqueous solution. The greater the free space the greater will be the quantity of aqueous ammonia that goes from the liquid to the vapor state, thus actually lowering the active NH_3 ratio and concentration. Since ammonolysis of sulfonic acid and halogeno compounds takes place in the liquid phase, it is obvious that the best results can be obtained only by introducing the maximum-size charge into the autoclave.

V. METAL CATALYSTS IN AMMONOLYSIS OF HALOGENO COMPOUNDS

Compounds of metals following hydrogen in the electrochemical series; e.g., arsenic, copper, and silver, can advantageously be employed in the conversion of certain halogeno compounds to amino derivatives.[1] Their efficacy in a number of aminations has been somewhat exaggerated in the patent literature, where apparently many of the claims are inserted merely for protective purposes. This is particularly true in the amination of aromatic compounds containing a nitro group. Thus, in the conversion of *p*-nitrochlorobenzene to *p*-nitroaniline, it has been found that the use of copper and its salts is actually detrimental. McMaster and Steiner[2] have reported the same observations in the preparation of *p*-chloro-*o*-nitroaniline from nitro-*p*-dichlorobenzene; while Grether and Keener[3] use no catalyst in the ammonolysis of 1, 2-dichloro-4-nitrobenzene.

Copper and Its Salts as Catalysts.—From studies on aniline, it has been presumed that cuprous salts alone are satisfactory, whereas cupric salts are practically ineffective. Such general conclusions are, however, not justified. It is probable that certain practical factors; *i.e.*, susceptibility of amine to oxidation, inherent in the ammonolysis of chlorobenzene make the presence of metallic copper, along with a cuprous salt, desirable. The fact that cupric nitrate serves as well as cuprous salts in the ammonolysis of chloroxenene, chloronaphthalene, and chloroanthraquinones indicates that no generalization can be made with respect to the advantages of univalent copper.

The anion accompanying the copper is not without influence, since the introduction of hydroxyl or nitrate ions also affects the known reactions. The more favorable action of cuprous salts in the preparation of aniline and *p*-phenylenediamine may be explained by assuming that these amines are readily susceptible to catalytic oxidation by the anion of the cupric salt. The concentration of copper for the conversion of chlorobenzene is, consequently, reduced because some of it enters into the second catalytic reactions; *viz.*, the oxidation of aniline. In support of the oxidation theory it is known[4] (1) cupric and cuprous compounds are about equally active in the preparation of amines which are not readily susceptible to oxidation; (2) in the preparation of easily oxidizable amines, low catalyst concentration results in a smaller difference in the reaction rates when cuprous and cupric compounds are compared; and (3) the treatment of aniline with cupric nitrate leads to a much greater oxidation of amine than with cuprous chloride. The preceding observations explain why cupric compounds and oxidants may be used to advantage in the preparation of aminoanthraquinone and must be avoided in the preparation of aniline.

[1] Groggins, Stirton, and Newton, *Ind. Eng. Chem.*, **23**, 893 (1931).
[2] McMaster and Steiner, *loc. cit.*
[3] Grether and Keener, U. S. 1,882,811 (1932).
[4] Groggins, *Ind. Eng. Chem.*, **28**, 1051 (1936).

In Table VI, page 334, the data show that the ammonolysis of 1-chloro-naphthalene is not practical unless a copper catalyst is used. The results also reveal that cupric nitrate serves as well as cuprous chloride, and that only small quantities are required. It appears necessary, therefore, in those aminations that require copper, to assume that copper-ammonio cations serve as cyclic catalysts forming ternary addition compounds comprising halogeno compound, ammonia, and copper which subsequently undergo metamorphosis during the course of the reaction.

The action of aqueous ammonia on copper, particularly in the presence of ammonium salts, indicates quite clearly that the pressure system could not be constructed from this metal.

VI. CORROSION AND THE pH OF THE AUTOCLAVE CHARGE

Groggins and Stirton[1] showed that the pH of aqueous ammonia decreases with rising temperature and more rapidly under such conditions when ammonium salts are introduced. During the course of the reaction in the liquid-phase treatment of halogeno compounds, the concentration of NH_3 in the charge diminishes while that of the hydrohalide increases. It is important to remember that during ammonolysis the molar concentration of the hydracid must be *at least* equivalent to the molar concentration of the amino compound, because of the concomitant formation of hydroxy compounds and secondary and polyamines. The hydrohalide may be distributed as free acid, as ammonium halide in solution, and as the salt of the newly formed amino compound. These are all acidic compounds (proton donors), and, unless their activity is neutralized, they will corrode steel vessels. The pH of the molar solutions of such compounds at 25°C. is closely as follows: NH_4Cl, 4.7; $CH_3NH_2 \cdot HCl$, 5.5; $C_2H_5NH_2 \cdot HCl$, 6.0; $C_6H_5NH_2 \cdot HCl$, 2.3.

In closed systems containing an excess of aqueous ammonia in addition to corresponding molal concentrations of hydrochloric acid and primary amine, the equilibriums involved may be represented as follows:

$$NH_4Cl\ aq. \rightleftharpoons NH_4^+ \quad + Cl^- : Cl^- + R \cdot NH_3^+ \quad \rightleftharpoons R \cdot NH_3Cl$$
$$+ \qquad\qquad + \ : + \qquad +$$
$$OH^- \qquad\quad H^+ : H^+ \quad OH^-$$
$$\Updownarrow \qquad\qquad \Updownarrow : \Updownarrow \qquad \Updownarrow$$
$$Excess\ NH_3 + H_2O \rightleftharpoons NH_4OH \quad HCl:HCl \quad R \cdot NH_3OH \rightleftharpoons H_2O + R \cdot NH_2$$

The available information regarding these reactions at high temperatures is inadequate, and our knowledge relates only to certain segments of the whole. There is little doubt, however, that the principal factors which affect the equilibriums are: (1) the temperature of the system; (2) the relative basicity of the amine; and (3) the solubility of the amine.

[1] GROGGINS and STIRTON, *Ind. Eng. Chem.,* **25,** 42 (1933).

Because of its volatility, NH_3 can be displaced from $(H(NH_3))Cl$ by basic substances of higher boiling point. The rate at which such displacement occurs, however, obviously depends on the strength of the base, *e.g.*, $Ca(OH)_2$, $Alk.NH_2$, etc.; the reaction temperature and the counter influence of free NH_3. It is known, however, that with increasing temperature NH_3 has a diminishing capacity to form the ionogen NH_4OH, and at 290°C. the union of NH_3 to HCl in aqueous $(H(NH_3))Cl$ is so weak that the two components react as if they were alone, and ammonium chloride in aqueous solution can be employed to convert methanol to dimethylamine[1] and *sym*-xylenol to dixylylamine. The fact that the charge and free space in the autoclave contain a large excess of gaseous ammonia does not, therefore, signify that the hot aqueous ammonia has the capacity to displace the amine from all amino hydrohalides, for there is ample evidence to the contrary. When the amino hydrohalide is insoluble, then the concentration of the $R \cdot NH_3{}^+$ ions in solution is diminished.

From the extensive literature on inhibitors, it would be expected that the amino compound being synthesized should serve as its own inhibitor, and indeed it would form a protective film if sufficient free base were available. It is well known that the addition of aniline to aniline hydrochloride will reduce the dissociation and, consequently, the corrosive action of the latter. This probably explains why it has been found efficacious to add acid inhibitors, *e.g.*, alkylamines, secondary amines, and pyridine to the autoclave charge in the preparation of nitroamines,[2] for this procedure insures the presence of free base during ammonolysis.

There are two other useful methods of controlling the pH of the autoclave charge; *viz.*, the introduction of copper-ammonio hydroxides[3] and the use of buffer salts,[4] such as chlorates which are attacked and decomposed when the concentration of the hydracid is sufficiently great. The oxidants cannot be used to advantage, however, when the amino compound, *e.g.*, aniline, is readily susceptible to oxidation.

VII. EQUILIBRIUM CONSIDERATIONS IN AMMONOLYSIS

The data in Table VII[4] are of interest not only because the controls show results that compare favorably with those obtained by the use of copper, but particularly because the experiments at 190 to 200°C. show only a maximum divergence of 0.35 per cent from the mean purity of 91.25. It appears, therefore, that despite a high NH_3 ratio a purity of

[1] Bottoms, U. S. 2,085,785 (1937).
[2] Dahlen and Foohey, U. S. 2,072,618 (1937).
[3] Britton and Williams, U. S. 1,726,170 (1929).
[4] GROGGINS and STIRTON, *Ind. Eng. Chem.*, **25**, 169 (1933).

about 91.5 represents the best results obtainable under such operating conditions. It is necessary, therefore, to conclude that, owing to the concentration of arylammonium chloride, an equilibrium is established which at lower temperatures (180 to 190°C.) prevents complete conversion and at higher temperatures (205 to 220°C.) serves only to introduce impurities in the reaction product.[1]

TABLE VII.—CONTROLS. AMMONOLYSIS OF 2-CHLOROANTHRAQUINONE
28 Per Cent NH_3 *Aq.*, 315 Gm. Capacity of Autoclave, 500 Cc. Mean Purity, Expts. 2 to 6, Incl., 91.25 Per Cent

Expt. No.	2-Chloroanthra- quinone, gm.	Temp., °C.	Time, hr.	Yield, %	Purity, %
1	36.375	180	30	98.4	80.8
2	36.375	188	30	97.4	88.7
3	36.375	190	30	98.0	91.1
4	36.375	195	24	94.5	91.4
5	36.375	200	18	95.5	91.0
6	42.5	195	24	95.6	90.9
7	42.5	200	30	94.6	91.6
8*	42.5	195	24	96.0	88.5

* Containing 0.05 gm. CuO and 0.25 gm. Cu.

By analogy with esterification it would appear logical that the reaction could be favorably completed by removing one of the products of reaction, *viz.*, ammonium chloride. It is not surprising, therefore, that compounds which introduce hydroxyl ions may be employed advantageously, especially in the preparation of easily oxidizable amines, but a compensatory penalty in the form of hydroxy impurities is to be expected.

Effect of Inorganic Oxidants on Equilibrium.—In the preparation of amines which are not readily oxidized, *e.g.*, aminoanthraquinones, oxidation has been found to be a satisfactory method of counteracting the influence of hydrochloric acid or its ammonium salts. The use of oxyhalogen compounds, particularly chlorates, leads to consistently improved results. The efficacy of potassium chlorate may probably be accounted for by the following reaction:[2]

$$6R \cdot NH_3^+ \cdot Cl^- + KClO_3 \rightarrow 6R \cdot NH_2 + KCl + 3H_2O + 3Cl_2$$

The chlorate serves, apparently, as a buffer to control the hydrogen or ammonium ion concentration.[3] The fate of the chlorine in the sug-

[1] See GROGGINS and NEWTON, *Ind. Eng. Chem.*, **21**, 369 (1929), for aminations at 215 to 220°C.

[2] GROGGINS and STIRTON, *Ind. Eng. Chem.*, **25**, 171 (1933).

[3] Mono- and dinitrobenzenoid compounds are likewise preferentially reduced but, unlike oxyhalogen compounds, introduce undesirable reaction products, either with the amino compound or with the aqueous ammonia. Lead peroxide and lead tetracetate may also be used.

gested mechanism of reaction is not definitely known. It may (1) directly or indirectly oxidize the iron surfaces of the autoclave; and (2) oxidize some of the amine, evidence of which is generally obtainable and frequently apparent.[1]

VIII. SPECULATION REGARDING MECHANISM OF THE REACTION

The mechanism of ammonolysis appears to be identical with the usual processes involving replacement in the benzene series, whose initiation is determined by the presence of key atoms[2] such as Cl, N, C=C, and O. The necessary conditions are unsaturation or pronounced free energy in one or more of the reactants and the formation of addition compounds which undergo ionization. This is followed by a rearrangement to a compound with principal valences. The final stage is stabilization, which is best interpreted as an intramolecular ionic effect. In the Friedel and Crafts reaction, this is accompanied by a splitting off of HCl; in nitration, there is a splitting off of bound nitric or other acid anion with the loosened hydrogen of the neighboring carbon atom; and in ammonolysis, there is a splitting off of the hydrogen compound of the negative atom or radical that has been replaced:

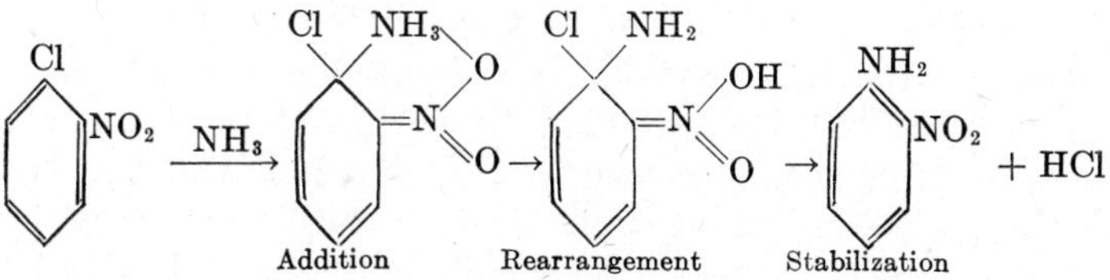

| Addition | Rearrangement | Stabilization |

In non-catalytic aminations, it is assumed that the first stage is the formation of an addition complex between ammonia and the aromatic compound. The following formulations show how such solute-solvent complexes resemble the more stable addition compounds of the amines:

$$R \cdot Cl + NH_3 \rightarrow R(NH_3)Cl \rightarrow R \cdot NH_3^+ \cdot Cl^-$$
$$R \cdot OH + NH_3 \rightarrow R(NH_3)OH \rightarrow R \cdot NH_3^+ \cdot OH^-$$
$$R \cdot SO_3H + NH_3 \rightarrow R(NH_3)SO_3H* \rightarrow R \cdot NH_3^+ OSO_2H^-$$

Since ammonia exhibits an almost vanishing capacity to form bases at increasing temperatures, it appears probable that the liberated acid or water is largely attached to the newly formed amine. The concentration of such salts or bases determines the equilibrium of the reaction for each temperature. When the ammonia system is cooled, the power of NH_3 to form the ionogen NH_4OH increases and the distribution of the

---

[1] GROGGINS and STIRTON, *Ind. Eng. Chem.*, **28**, 1051 (1936).

[2] WOHL and WERTYPOROCH, *Ber.*, **64**, 1308 (1931).

* The ammonium salt is undoubtedly first formed.

hydracid (in the ammonolysis of halogens) would depend on the basicity of the amino compound.

IX. DESIGN AND CONSTRUCTION OF EQUIPMENT

The preparation of amines through the reaction between organic compounds and ammonia generally takes place at elevated temperatures and pressures. It is, therefore, essential that the ammonolysis be carried out either in high-pressure autoclaves or in tubular systems. Autoclaves are generally adapted for discontinuous or batch operations, whereas tubular systems are particularly suitable for continuous high-pressure syntheses.

Direct-fired Autoclaves.—The use of direct-fired autoclaves for carrying out high-pressure reactions was at one time a general practice. Coke, fuel oil, and gas furnished the means of heating such vessels. To a large extent, however, the fire box has been replaced by the metal bath, or the jacket for steam or circulated fluid heat-transfer agents. Such installations provide a safer, more accurate and automatic control of the reaction.

In a limited number of operations, direct-fired operations are still used, principally on account of the fact that heating by such means sets up convection currents in the charge and thus obviates the necessity of using mechanical stirrers. In the vapor-phase ammonolysis of alcohols and aldehydes wherein the reactants pass through heated tubes containing a catalyst, direct fire or electric heat can be used to advantage.

The autoclave is provided with nozzles for charging and discharging connections and with a thermometer well. The head is a massive steel forging that seals the vessel by means of a carefully machined tongue-and-groove joint. The head is made fast with chrome-steel bolts and is removed only when the autoclave is given a thorough periodical inspection. A heavy-walled seamless steel tube is frequently threaded and welded to the head. To this tube, connections are made for the safety valve and frangible disk, pressure gage, and vent lines.

Ammonolysis in Jacketed Vessels.—When the operating temperature is sufficiently low, *i.e.*, 190°C. or lower, steam is generally employed in jacketed vessels. Above 190°C., it is customary to employ an oil circulating system or to heat with hot water under pressure. The advantages of jacket equipment over non-regulated, direct-fired apparatus may be set down as follows: (1) automatic control; (2) fuel economy; (3) saving of labor; (4) uniform temperature and product; (5) greater productivity per machine on account of the ease in cooling; and (6) better yields and purer product. Most of these advantages can be obtained in gas- or oil-fired systems which are equipped for automatic control.

The inner vessel of the jacketed autoclave is similar to that used for direct fire. A steel shell designed to withstand the jacket pressures is welded to the outside, and the autoclave is then suspended on a suitable steel structure. When steam is used for heating, it is delivered to the upper portion of the jacket, and the condensate is drained by trap connections at the base. Because heating with steam or oil creates a uniform temperature throughout the charge, it is necessary to provide mechanical agitation for charges that are not homogeneous. In the ammonolysis of aromatic halides, such as *p*-nitrochlorobenzene, the denser molten aromatic compound would, in the absence of mechanical agitation, settle out at the base with the lighter aqueous ammonia above it. Conversion to amine would then take place only at the interface of the two layers.

In the ammonolysis of compounds which are difficult to wet out and which are converted only at high temperatures, it is advisable to employ horizontal autoclaves. Such systems provide the necessary freeboard with a much smaller distance between the charge level and the top of the vessel. Horizontal vessels of this kind are provided with a number of rotating splash arms which wash any suspended material from the top of the autoclave. Such a vessel is particularly suitable for the conversion of 2-chloroanthraquinone. In vertical pressure vessels, it is therefore necessary to use a sleeve-and-turbine agitator, which drags the 2-chloro-anthraquinone down into the aqueous ammonia.

Tubular Pressure Systems.—A tubular or pipe pressure system is sometimes used to carry out the amination. The seamless steel tubing used for such construction is capable of withstanding pressures up to 1,000 atmospheres. Such a system is particularly useful where exceptionally high pressures are encountered or where continuous operations are practicable. A further advantage resides in the fact that the pressure coils comprising the reaction system contain only a relatively small quantity of material in process. Such a system may be subdivided into a number of units, each immersed in an oil or metal bath controlled at the desired temperature. Pressure gages and safety diaphragms are placed on each unit of the system to insure safe operations.

Auxiliary High-pressure Equipment.—The design and selection of proper auxiliary equipment for high-pressure reactions are as essential as choosing the pressure equipment itself. The successful operation of the whole system depends on the proper functioning of such accessories.

In well-organized plants, thermoelectric equipment is employed to regulate the temperature. Experience has shown that such devices can be relied upon to give satisfactory service.

Asbestos and lead gaskets have been found most satisfactory for sealing flanged connections in the pressure system. The metal gasket is usually employed for joints that are opened only infrequently.

Discharge lines from the autoclaves are customarily equipped with two heavy-duty steel valves, one of which is a globe or cone valve and the other a gate valve. The former is placed adjacent to the autoclave to hold the pressure and is supplied with cut asbestos gaskets, which are renewed for each run. The gate valve has many important uses in technical operations, the most obvious being the feasibility of cutting out individual autoclaves from the rest of the system.

In plant operations, it is not advisable to depend on safety or relief valves to release extraordinary pressures. It has been found best to employ a metal diaphragm supported between two steel flanges, these fittings being part of a pipe line leading directly from the autoclave. Such frangible disks should be tested accurately under precise conditions to vouchsafe rupture at definite pressures. Tin and nickel sheets have proved satisfactory for autoclaves containing ammonia. It is desirable to protect the face of the diaphragm next to the reaction vapors with a thin sheet of asbestos. Some engineers approve of placing after the diaphragm a pop valve, which will reseat after the excessive pressure has been dissipated. This valve is always set to blow about 50 lb. below the bursting point of the frangible disk. Thus, a rupture in the diaphragm is sure to be followed by the opening of the relief valve, which has been completely protected from the corrosive vapors of the autoclave. With an arrangement of this character, it is usually feasible to complete the run and then replace the metal disk and overhaul the pop valve. The possibility of effecting material savings by such an arrangement is obvious.

X. TECHNICAL MANUFACTURE OF AMINO COMPOUNDS

Ethylenediamine from Ethylene Dichloride.—The preparation of ethylenediamine from the dichloro compound is described by Curme[1] as follows:

The reaction vessel 1 (Fig. 10) is charged initially with the quantity of ammonia which is desired to maintain in excess, and this ammonia circulates through a cycle comprising the lines 6 and 9 and the tower 7. Ammonia is thereafter introduced into vessel 1 in such quantity as is only sufficient to replace that which is removed from the system either as its derivative ethylenediamine; in combination as ammonium chloride, if the latter is not decomposed in the apparatus; through leakage; or as free ammonia not recovered from the diamine solution.

The contents of the reaction vessel are kept in agitation, and a temperature sufficient to cause the reaction to proceed at a suitable rate—110 to 150°C.—is maintained.

[1] Curme, U. S. 1,832,534 (1931).

The overflow through line 6 consists of an aqueous solution of ethylenediamine hydrochloride, ammonium chloride, and ammonia. As it passes down through tower 7, this liquid is gradually heated above the temperature prevailing in the reaction vessel, and the ammonia is expelled as in standard ammonia distillation practice. This ammonia is returned through line 9 to the reaction vessel 1 so that the requisite excess of ammonia is maintained in the reaction vessel.

It will be noted that a part of the ammonia added leaves the vessel 1 as ammonium chloride. This may be decomposed for the recovery of its ammonia, either in a separate apparatus or in the same apparatus in which the free ammonia is recovered. In the drawing is shown a storage tank from which a strong base, such as sodium hydroxide, may be continuously fed into the column 7 in quantity sufficient to liberate the combined ammonia. Enough base may be used if desired to decompose the ethylenediamine hydrochloride and liberate the diamine, which, like the hydrochloride, is soluble in water.

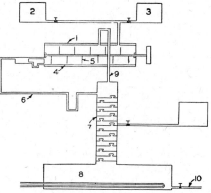

Fig. 10.—Reaction system; preparation of ethylenediamine.

1. Pressure reactor.
2, 3. Holders for ammonia liquor and ethylene dichloride.
4. Heating jacket.
5. Stirrer.
6. Overflow line.
7. Ammonia vaporizing column.
8. Kettle with heating coil.
9. Ammonia return line to reactor.
10. Discharge line for ethylenediamine.

The ethylenediamine or its hydrochloride is removed from the apparatus as an aqueous solution at 10, and the diamine compound is recovered from this solution, which also contains ammonium chloride.

The pressure prevailing in the apparatus will of course vary with the temperature. This may be 110°C., corresponding to a pressure of the order of 10 atmos. In the presence of cuprous chloride the reaction rate is accelerated.

Conversion of Alcohols to Alkylamines.[1,2,3] *Preparation of Methylamines.*—Monomethylamine is formed with only minor proportions of di- and trimethylamines by passing methanol and ammonia, in a ratio of 1:5, over alumina gel at a rate of 0.75 to 1.5 cc. per cubic centimeter of catalyst per hour. The vapors are preheated to about 350°C., and the catalyst is kept at 450°C. About 13.5 per cent of the ammonia is thus converted to primary amine. Secondary and tertiary amines are

[1] Arnold, U. S. 1,799,722 (1931).
[2] Martin and Swallen, U. S. 1,875,747 (1932).
[3] Andrews, U. S. 2,073,671 (1937).

formed in amounts representing 7.5 and 10.5 per cent, respectively, of the ammonia. The secondary and tertiary amines can be separated from the primary amine and recirculated over the catalyst with fresh methanol and a large excess of ammonia, thus increasing the proportion of primary amine and materially decreasing the proportion of secondary and tertiary amines.

It is difficult and often uneconomical and impracticable to arrange operating conditions for the production of one of the amines. It is customary, therefore, to rework the products under suitable conditions or to reintroduce them into the amination system along with fresh reactants.[1,2] Swallen and Martin[2] have shown that primary methylamine can be converted to dimethylamine and trimethylamine by repassing it through the catalytic chamber in the absence of ammonia. The results obtained when methylamine and various mixtures of it were passed over a partially dehydrated aluminum trihydrate catalyst are set forth in Table VIII.

TABLE VIII.—EQUILIBRIUM STUDIES: PREPARATION OF METHYLAMINES

Composition of feed	Temp., °C.	Space velocity, cc. gas cc. catalyst	Composition of product			
			NH_3, %	CH_3NH_2, %	$(CH_3)_2NH$, %	$(CH_3)_3N$, %
100 % CH_3NH_2	450	550	33.2	31.8	31.4	3.6
	450	550	31.8	31.3	32.6	4.3
87.0 % CH_3NH_2 13.0 % $(CH_3)_3N$	425	400	27.0	25.3	33.1	15.6
	425	400	25.4	29.8	27.7	17.1
	450	670	35.2	27.6	24.4	12.9
	450	630	39.0	33.6	16.3	11.1
	450	550	29.2	26.5	29.8	14.5
	450	550	30.4	26.4	28.6	14.6
	475	510	40.0	28.2	16.4	15.3
	475	420	38.0	26.6	17.4	18.0
65.0 % CH_3NH_2 20.2 % $(CH_3)_2NH$ 14.8 % $(CH_3)_3N$	450	680	38.6	23.6	17.4	20.4
	450	350	32.0	25.8	26.2	15.9

According to Swallen and Martin.

The reworking or recycling of unwanted amines to afford a greater yield of desired product is generally effective. Obviously, the results are more striking in the preparation of alkyl- and alkanolamines where, in addition to primary amines, the formation of secondary and tertiary

[1] Herold and Smeykal, U. S. 2,068,132 (1937).
[2] Swallen and Martin, U. S. 1,926,691 (1933).

amines occurs in substantial quantities. This is particularly true when in the interest of economy, moderate NH₃ ratios are employed. Evidence of a corresponding mechanism in the similar synthesis of arylamines is available, although here primary amines can be obtained almost exclusively.

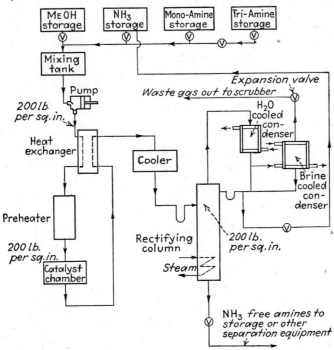

Fig. 11.—Flow diagram; preparation of dimethylamine.

When dimethylamine is the desired product, the unwanted amines are separated by fractionation and recycled along with fresh materials. The data below show that only a negligible change occurs in the per-

Constituent	Charge wgt., %	Products wgt., %
Ammonia	28.4	25.7
Monomethylamine	12.0	10.6
Dimethylamine	0	18.0
Trimethylamine	39.7	38.2
Methanol	19.9	0

centage of mono- and trimethylamines, practically all the added methanol being converted to dimethylamine.[1] The excess of ammonia is separated

[1] Greenwalt, U. S. 2,098,289 (1937).

under pressure (Fig. 11) during the course of the operations and is condensed and reused. The higher alkylamines are made in a similar manner.

The alkylamines can generally be separated from one another by careful fractionation. In the case of methylamines, this problem is difficult because of the closeness of the boiling points. Here, however, advantage can be taken of the greater basicity of the dimethylamine which combines preferentially with hydrogen chloride.[1]

Properties of Ethyl- and Methylamines.

Substance	B.p.°C.	Sol.: H_2O Gms./100 cc.	Diss. const.
$C_2H_5NH_2$......	16.5	∞	0.00056
$(C_2H_5)_2NH$........	55.9	81.5	0.00126
$(C_2H_5)_3N$..........	89.5	1.5	0.00064
CH_3NH_2...........	−6.8	Sol.	0.00047
$(CH_3)_2NH$........	7.4	Sol.	0.00102
$(CH_3)_3N$..........	3.5	V. sol.	0.00055

Manufacture of Aniline from Chlorobenzene.

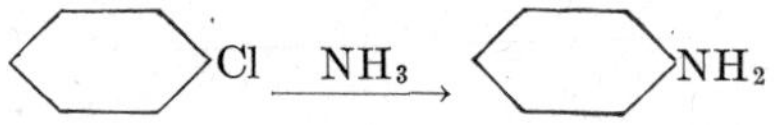

It is economically advantageous to conduct the manufacture of aniline from chlorobenzene in conjunction with the large-scale production of chlorine and chlorinated products, thus permitting the introduction of cheap chlorobenzene into the aniline plant. With such a setup, this process competes favorably with the older method involving the reduction of nitrobenzene.

The toxic character of aniline vapors and the vicissitudes of industrial operations make it desirable to provide a fireproof housing with ample headroom and also adequate ventilation. It is, further, customary to separate the high-pressure autoclave work from the subsequent separation and distillation operations. The autoclaves, which may be either vertical or horizontal, are ordinarily made of rolled steel. They are generally jacketed for use with high-pressure steam or a fluid heat-transfer agent. It is most important to provide thorough and turbulent mixing so that a uniform reaction mixture prevails.

Amination proceeds slowly under 160°C. and very rapidly at 210°C. At still higher temperatures, there is a distinct tendency to decomposition, and the increased pressure on the system makes gas-tight operation more difficult of attainment. A temperature range of 200 to 210°C.

[1] Bottoms, U. S. 2,085,787 (1937).

for the conversion of chlorobenzene to aniline gives very satisfactory results. At this temperature, with a 6:1 ammonia ratio of 28 per cent NH_3, the pressure on the system will be about 850 to 950 lb. per square inch. The influence of temperature on the course of amination is shown in Fig. 12.[1]

The data in Table IX show that an increase in the NH_3 ratio results in (1) a better yield of aniline; (2) an increase in the ratio of aniline to phenol; and (3) a slight diminution in the yield of diphenylamine.[1] These characteristics are especially marked in proceeding from three to five to six moles of NH_3 per mole of chlorobenzene. A further increase in the ratio of aqueous NH_3 has only a relatively small effect on the conversion and yield of aniline, and its use would only diminish the productivity of the autoclaves. When very small ammonia ratios are employed, there is not only a pronounced diminution in the NH_3 concentration of the liquor toward the end of the reaction, but there is also a corresponding increase in the NH_4Cl concentration which markedly retards the reaction.

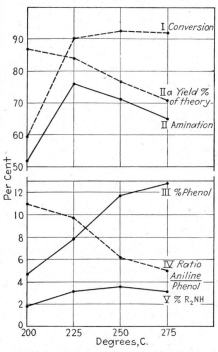

FIG. 12.—Ammonolysis of chlorobenzene: effect of temperature (freeboard 21 per cent). Time, 4 hrs.; 0.2 mole Cu_2O; NH_3 (33 %) ratio = 5.

The vapors leaving the reaction system are first expanded and then cooled below 100°C. in a suitable pipe condenser or dephlegmating column. Most of the ammonia continues to an absorption system in which the gas is recovered.

Treatment of Autoclave Charge.—The aqueous aniline, containing some ammonia, unconverted chlorobenzene, phenol, diphenylamine, as well as copper and ammonium compounds, is led to a still. Here the charge may be treated with a calculated quantity of alkali to (1) decompose the ammonium chloride; (2) convert the phenol to alkali phenolate; and (3) precipitate the copper as a sludge upon the removal of the free ammonia. By distillation with steam, the ammonia, chlorobenzene, aniline, and diphenylamine are removed. The remaining aqueous portion, which contains dissolved sodium phenolate, is filtered from the

[1] VOROZHTZOV and KOBELEV, *J. Gen. Chem.* (*U.S.S.R.*), **4**, 310 (1934).

copper sludge and transferred to another vessel. The phenol is recovered from the acidified solution by distillation.

TABLE IX.—PREPARATION OF ANILINE: EFFECT OF AMMONIA RATIO

0.2 Mole CuO per Mole Chlorobenzene. Operating Pressure 70 Atmos. = 980 lb. per Square Inch. Size of Charge Adjusted for 21 % Freeboard at Room Temp.

Mole ratio NH_3: chlorobenzene	Temp., °C.	Decomposition, %	Yield of aniline, % of theory		Yield of phenol, % of theory	Ratio of aniline to phenol	Yield of diphenylamine, % of theory
			% of C_6H_5Cl used	% of C_6H_5Cl which enters into the reaction			
3	187–244	89.1	78.3	87.8	5.2	15.1	1.7
4	188–239	98.5	89.0	90.5	5.3	16.8	1.8
3	193–242	84.2	72.2	85.7	5.5	13.1	1.5
4	193–237	95.5	83.5	87.5	5.5	14.8	1.9
5	192–230	99.1	88.2	88.9	5.6	15.8	1.5
6	196–229	99.6	89.8	90.2	5.5	16.6	1.0
8	194–222	99.5	90.0	90.4	5.2	17.3	1.0
12	192–215	98.2	90.6	92.3	5.0	17.9	0.0

According to Vorozhtzov.

An alternate and more economical procedure consists in cooling and settling the reaction mass from the autoclaves whereby the charge separates into two layers—a dark-brown lower layer, comprising principally aniline, and an almost colorless upper aqueous layer, which rapidly becomes blue on exposure to air. The volume of the water layer will, of course, be considerably greater than that of the aniline layer and will vary with the ammonia liquor ratio. When 5 moles of 32 per cent ammonia and 0.1 mole of cuprous oxide were used per mole chlorobenzene, Vorozhtzov found that the products of reaction were distributed as follows:

Aniline-layer components, % by weight	Substance	Water-layer components % by weight
81.55	Aniline	4.9
4.9	Phenol	0.33
0.85	Diphenylamine	None
Traces.........	Chloride ion (NH_4Cl)	8.84
Traces.........	Cu_2O	2.9
Traces.........	NH_3	13.8

To recover the aniline and other products, 50 per cent sodium hydroxide is added to the aniline-layer charge in an amount corresponding to 0.2 per cent of its volume. The batch is then subjected to fractional distillation using jacket heat. The first fraction is aniline-water, and this is followed by a technically pure aniline of 97 to 99 per cent purity, which contains neither phenol nor diphenylamine. The weight of aniline thus recovered corresponds to 90 per cent of the amine originally present. After the removal of the aniline, the charge still contains sodium phenolate and diphenylamine. The latter is separated by distillation with steam, while the phenol is recovered by acidifying the residue and distilling.

Alkali is also added to the water fraction in an amount sufficient to react with all ammonium compounds and with phenol. Upon fractional distillation, ammonia is first expelled and then recovered in a suitable absorption system. An aniline-water fraction is next distilled from which an aniline layer separates out on cooling. The supernatant aqueous portion containing a small quantity of amine can be used in the NH_3 absorption system. The residual solution of sodium phenolate and sodium chloride is then filtered from the precipitated copper oxides. The recovered copper oxide catalyst is washed and again used alone with fresh copper in subsequent operations.[1]

2-Aminoanthraquinone from 2-Chloroanthraquinone.—The reaction is preferably carried out in a horizontal, jacketed autoclave provided with an agitator. The latter comprises a series of splash arms, which are designed to keep the top of the pressure vessel free of any unconverted halogeno compound. By employing a horizontal pressure vessel, this very important problem is readily solved, because the necessary freeboard can be obtained with a minimum of headroom. In vertical autoclaves, it is necessary to use a sleeve-and-turbine agitator, the turbine being instrumental in dragging the supernatant 2-chloroanthraquinone down through the sleeve into the ammoniacal solution.

By employing potassium chlorate and ammonium nitrate as oxidants, it is possible to obtain directly a 2-aminoanthraquinone of 97.5 to 98.5 per cent purity. A copper catalyst is not essential, but is sometimes used to moderate the conditions of the reaction. The only treatment required is a thorough washing of the 2-aminoanthraquinone with hot, dilute, aqueous ammonia or dilute sodium hydroxide.

By employing 7.5 parts of 28 per cent ammonia liquor per part of 2-chloroanthraquinone and heating at 200°C., the reactions can be completed in 24 hr.; at 210°C. only 15 hr. is required. It is advisable to fill the autoclave up to 75 per cent of its capacity with the aqueous ammonia in order to insure against excessive freeboard.

[1] Britton and Williams, U. S. 1,726,171 (1936).

TABLE X.—EFFECT OF KClO₃-NH₄NO₃ MIXTURES IN AMMONOLYSIS OF
2-CHLOROANTHRAQUINONE

2-Chloroanthraquinone, 36.375 Gm.   28% NH₃ Aq., 315 Gm.   Capacity of Autoclave, 500 Cc.

Expt. No.	Binary mixture		Temp., °C.	Time, hr.	Yield, %	Purity, %	Net yield, %
	Materials	Gm.					
1	KClO₃	1.0	195	24	96.5	95.5	92.1
2	{ KClO₃ { NH₄NO₃	1.0 8.0	195	24	96.5	97.7	94.3
3	{ KClO₃ { NH₄NO₃	0.5 6.0	200	18	97.8	97.6	95.5
4	{ KClO₃ { NH₄NO₃	0.5 6.0	200	18	97.8	98.0	95.8
5	{ KClO₃ { NH₄NO₃	1.0 8.0	200	18	97.4	98.5	95.9

At the completion of the reaction, the ammonia vapor is vented to the absorbers until the residual pressure is about 200 lb.   The charge is then delivered to a steel vessel containing dilute alkali, to decompose the combined ammonia.   By causing the hot reaction product to come in contact with the caustic solution, a finely divided brown product is obtained.   When the product crystallizes out from its mother liquor in the autoclave, fine, long, purple-brown needles are obtained.

The ammonia is removed by distillation with steam, most of the hydroxy compounds going into solution as the sodium salt during this operation.   The aminoanthraquinone is then filtered hot and washed with hot, dilute, alkaline solutions.   Generally, no purification operation is required.   The results obtained by the foregoing procedure are set forth in Table X.

2-Aminoanthraquinone from Sodium Anthraquinone-2-Sulfonate.

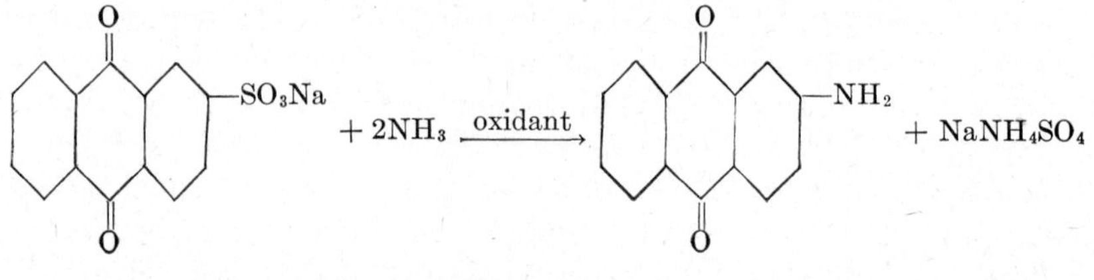

The preparation of 2-aminoanthraquinone from *silver salt* presents no particularly difficult technical problems.   Compared with the preparation of the amine from 2-chloroanthraquinone, this reaction may be carried out under distinctly milder conditions. The reactants NH$_3$ and anthraquinone-2-sulfonic acid (Na salt) are both present in aqueous solution, and the conversion to amine takes place readily.

As the reaction progresses, the amino compound separates out as a light, golden-brown product. The 2-aminoanthraquinone obtained by this process generally averages 99 per cent pure, by titration with sodium nitrite. The yields range from 90 to 94 per cent of the theoretical. Copper and its salts are not necessary, the best results being obtained by employing the technic involving the use of oxidants and the ammonium salts of oxidizing acids.

A number of important technical and economic considerations are involved in the use of sodium anthraquinone-2-sulfonate (*silver salt*) for the preparation of 2-aminoanthraquinone. The cost of chloroanthraquinone is approximately the same as anthraquinone when they are prepared according to the Friedel and Crafts reaction. The former lends itself to the direct production of an amine of 97 to 98.5 per cent purity. The product from "silver salt" is, however, of a higher purity and can, furthermore, be prepared at a lower operating temperature; *viz.*, 170 to 180°C., so that steam-jacketed equipment can be employed. Consequently, despite economic handicaps, the silver-salt process is firmly intrenched and is used to a considerable extent.

When anthraquinone-2-sulfonic acid is made by the sulfonation of anthraquinone according to traditional methods, its cost would be distinctly higher than that of 2-chloroanthraquinone because of extra operating steps and the fact that disulfonic acids are formed during the sulfonation process. The cost of production may be somewhat lowered by cyclizing the intermediate benzoylbenzoic acid with 96 per cent sulfuric acid at 130°C. and then sulfonating the anthraquinone thus formed by the addition of oleum. Another and more economical method involves the conversion of 4'-chloro-2-benzoylbenzoic acid to the sulfonic acid derivative by treatment with sodium sulfite under pressure,[1] and then cyclizing the sulfobenzoylbenzoic acid to anthraquinone-2-sulfonic acid. It is clear that this process results solely in the formation of "*silver salt*," and experience shows that the yields are good and that it can be converted to 2-aminoanthraquinone of high purity.

Preparation of p-Nitroaniline, in Jacketed Autoclaves.—A batch consisting of 500 lb. of molten *p*-nitrochlorobenzene and 2,600 lb. of 26°Bé. ammonia is introduced into a 500-gal. autoclave provided with an efficient stirrer. The ammonia liquor is run in first in order to prevent the formation of a mass of fused nitro compound at the base. The heating is at first very gradual, so that the operating temperature of 170°C.,

---

[1] Thomas and Dresher, U. S. 1,779,221 (1930).

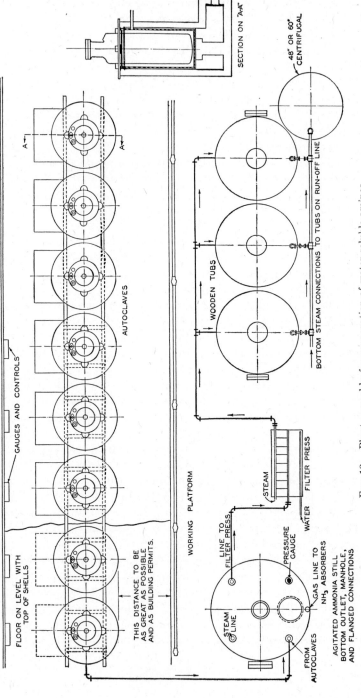

SECTION ON "A-A"

48" OR 60" CENTRIFUGAL

BOTTOM STEAM CONNECTIONS TO TUBS ON RUN-OFF LINE

WOODEN TUBS

AUTOCLAVES

GAUGES AND CONTROLS

FLOOR ON LEVEL WITH TOP OF SHELLS

THIS DISTANCE TO BE AS GREAT AS POSSIBLE AND AS BUILDING PERMITS.

WORKING PLATFORM

LINE TO FILTER PRESS.

STEAM

FILTER PRESS

WATER

STEAM LINE

PRESSURE GAUGE

GAS LINE TO NH₃ ABSORBERS

FROM AUTOCLAVES

AGITATED AMMONIA STILL BOTTOM OUTLET, MANHOLE, AND FLANGED CONNECTIONS

FIG. 13.—Plant assembly for preparation of water-soluble amines.

corresponding to a pressure of 500 to 550 lb. per square inch, is not reached until after the expiration of 3 hr.

The heating of the autoclave is continued for 16 hr. at 170°C., at which time the conversion to amine is practically complete. Some of the ammonia gas is vented to the absorption system; and when the residual pressure on the autoclave has dropped to 200 lb., the pressure-relief line is closed, as it is then safe to effect a transfer of the charge from the autoclave to the ammonia still, by means of the residual autoclave pressure (see Fig. 13).

The still is usually a large steel vessel of 1,500-gal. capacity, which can conveniently hold two autoclave charges under ordinary conditions and a third one in case of an emergency. It is provided with an agitator, gas line to the ammonia absorbers, and vent to the atmosphere, which later enables the operator to determine when the removal of ammonia is complete.

When all of the ammonia has been removed from the still, the lines to the absorbers are closed, and the steam pressure on the kettle brought up to 60 lb. The charge is then passed through a pressure filter.

The crystallizing tubs are large wooden vats provided with wooden stirrers. They are tightly covered and provided with wooden flumes which serve to remove the toxic vapors. As a result of the sudden drop of both temperature and pressure, the *p*-nitroaniline, on entering the tub, immediately crystallizes out of solution as a very finely divided canary-yellow product.

Mention has previously been made of the formation of 4, 4'-dinitro-diphenylamine, which is introduced as an impurity through a process of condensation. Being a secondary amine, it does not diazotize; consequently, when the *p*-nitroaniline made by this process is diazotized in the course of preparing lakes or dyestuffs, it will be observed that a flocculent precipitate consisting of approximately 0.3 per cent of the total product will remain in suspension as an inert solid impurity. This characteristic at one time was a powerful influence militating against a universal acceptance of this product, despite the fact that its purity averages 99 per cent. In order to remove this objectionable characteristic, recourse may be had to use of mild reducing agents. The reducto-active material is placed in the crystallizing tubs prior to the entry of the charges from the filter press. These agents, by acting on the small amount of dinitro-diphenylamine that is present, serve to effect a distinct improvement in the clarity of the diazonium solution of the *p*-nitroaniline thus treated. A similar improvement can be effected by recrystallizing the amine under pressure from weakly ammoniacal solutions, the enolized dinitro compound staying in solution.

The charge in the crystallizing tub is cooled at 30°C. and is then delivered by gravity to a centrifugal. The mother liquor leaving the centrifugal flows to an elaborate system of catch boxes, where it is cooled to room temperature. Periodically, the water in the catch boxes is syphoned out to enable the settled p-nitroaniline to be removed.

p-Nitroaniline Operating Budget

Steam-jacketed Autoclaves

SOURCES OF LOSS OF p-NITROANILINE

	Loss in Yield, %
Operations Involved	
1. Impurities in p-nitrochlorobenzene, including losses in transfer..................................	1.0
2. Charging, autoclaving, filtering.....................	1.0
3. Wash waters and centrifugal operations.............	1.0
4. Mother liquor and cleaning catch boxes.............	3.0
5. Drying and packaging.............................	1.0
Total calculated loss in yield..................	7.0
Per cent yield of theory for good operations............	93.0[1]

SOURCES OF LOSS OF AMMONIA LIQUOR

	Percentage of Total Loss
Operations Involved	
1. Delivery to operating system, including storage losses	0.5
2. Charging and discharging of autoclaves..............	0.5
3. Free and combined NH_3 left in mother liquor........	1.0
4. Losses in absorber system..........................	2.0
5. Leaky stuffing boxes and operating losses...........	2.0
Total operating loss of NH_3.....................	6.0[2]

[1] Recent small-scale operations show that yields of 96 to 97 per cent of the theoretical are possible.
[2] This figure does not, of course, include the ammonia entering into the reaction. The NH_3 consumed in the reaction is usually based on the p-nitroaniline delivered. This is obviously high, for the preceding data on p-nitroaniline losses show that some of the amine which consumed NH_3 in its preparation was lost in process.

Preparation of p-Nitroaniline in a Steel Cylinder.—In order to obviate the necessity of employing a hydraulic accumulator to regulate the internal pressure in the tubular coil system and to provide a means of examining the walls of the pressure system, Saunders[1] has suggested the use of the apparatus shown in Fig. 14 for the manufacture of p-nitroaniline. Here, the preheated aqueous ammonia is forced into the cylinder by means of pipe 11 and flows down to the bottom of the reaction vessel through the duct 14 and then passes upward inside the central annular tube. As the liquor rises upwardly through the packing 12, it meets a countercurrent flow of the heavier p-nitrochlorobenzene, which is forced into the system in a liquid condition and distributed by the

[1] Saunders, U. S. 1,911,717 (1933).

plate 13. The reaction products overflow into a central tube of comparatively small bore and are removed at the bottom of the cylinder.

It is to be noted that in this system there is provided an upper vapor phase, which takes up the fluctuations in internal pressure, as in the operation of ordinary autoclaves.

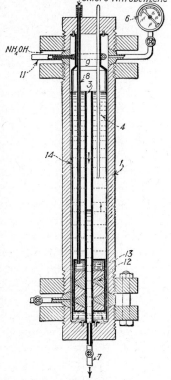

For the preparation of *p*-nitroaniline, 150 to 200 parts of liquid p-nitrochlorobenzene preheated to 225°C. is delivered to every 900 parts by weight of 26°Bé. ammonia liquor. The reaction with heated ammonia takes place in the lower part of the cylinder in the area provided with packing. The walls of the reactor in this section are made of ôr lined with stainless steel, to minimize the corrosive action of the ammonium chloride or hydrochloric acid that is split off. The operating pressure is approximately 1,200 lb. per square inch. The rate of feed of the reactants is so regulated that practically all of the *p*-nitrochlorobenzene is converted to amine. The reaction product escaping from the system is transferred to a still where the excess of ammonia is removed and the *p*-nitroaniline treated in any desired manner.

β-Naphthylamine from β-Naphthol.— When β-naphthol is treated with an excess of aqueous ammonia at 200°C., the yield of β-naphthylamine obtained is only about 75 per cent of theory. In the case of aniline, copper and its salts were introduced to catalyze the reaction and promote the conversion of chlorobenzene. In this synthesis, Bucherer[1] discovered that the amination could be carried out much more

Fig. 14.—Apparatus for continuous aminations.

1. Pressure cylinder.
3. Overflow for finished product.
4. Annular reaction zone.
6. Pressure gage.
7. Outlet for finished product.
8. Inlet tube for *p*-nitrochlorobenzene.
9. Pyrometer.
11. Ammonia liquor inlet.
12. Packing in reaction zone.
13. Distributor plate.
14. Duct for ammonia liquor.

satisfactorily and at greatly reduced pressures by introducing ammonium sulfite into the reaction mass. In the presence of ammonium sulfite, the sulfurous acid ester of β-naphthol is formed and converted to amine in the presence of an excess of strong ammonia, ammonium sulfite being

---

[1] BUCHERER, *J. prakt. Chem.*, **69**, 88 (1904). This subject matter became public five years previously in Ger. 117,471 (1899); 121,683 (1901). The reaction is generally referred to as the Bucherer reaction.

split off. The sulfite is thus instrumental in producing a compound of greater dissociating power and in this way serves as a catalyst:

$$\text{R·OH} \xrightarrow[\text{Alkali}]{\text{Bisulfite}} \text{R—O—S—OM} \xrightarrow[\text{Bisulfite}]{\text{NH}_3} \text{R·NH}_2$$
$$\underset{\text{O}}{\overset{\|}{}}$$

The ammonolysis is carried out in jacketed, agitated autoclaves. Such equipment is essential, as it is necessary to obtain a uniform temperature control in order to inhibit the formation of 2,2'-dinaphthylamine, which is appreciable above 150°C.; whereas the conversion to amine below this temperature does not progress readily, and considerable unconverted material remains in the charge. As in the preparation of p-nitroaniline, it is necessary to provide a stirrer to keep the β-naphthol in suspension in the ammoniacal liquor.

The autoclave batch consists of molecular quantities of β-naphthol and ammonium sulfite and 720 lb. of 28 per cent ammonia to provide a 12:1 NH_3 ratio to the 144 lb. of hydroxy compound taken. The charge is heated at 150°C. for 8 hr., after which it is blown to a still containing an alkali solution. Here the ammonia may be distilled off and recovered, as in the case of p-nitroaniline. In this way, the ammonia liquor entering the system is kept uniformly pure. The ammonium sulfite is converted to the alkali salt and is removed in an impure state with the mother liquor. An alternative and more economical method consists in cooling the autoclave charge under agitation. The finely granulated mass of β-naphthylamine obtained is filtered from its ammoniacal mother liquor. The filtrate, which contains the ammonia and ammonium sulfite in approximately the desired proportions, may be again used, after clarifying with a filter aid and strengthening the NH_3 content. The β-naphthylamine on the filter is washed free of unconverted β-naphthol with hot dilute caustic soda. The amine is then delivered to a vat, in which it is taken up with 300 lb. of warm 15 per cent hydrochloric acid which is free of H_2SO_4. Any remaining β-naphthol is removed by filtering this acid solution.

A pure product may be obtained by neutralizing the solution with sodium carbonate, evaporating to dryness, and then distilling the dry base at 25 mm. pressure. The purification may also be made by treating the β-naphthylamine hydrochloride with 200 lb. of sodium sulfate, whereby naphthylamine sulfate is precipitated out. The precipitate is stirred for several hours and allowed to settle. It is then filtered and washed with cold water. The free base is obtained by treating the powdered sulfate with a strong, hot sodium carbonate solution. The final product is cooled, filtered, and washed free of alkali, after which it is dried in an air dryer.

Amination of 2-Hydroxynaphthalene-3-Carboxylic Acid. *Liquid Phase: in the Presence of a Metal Catalyst.*—According to Fierz and Tobler[1] the preparation of 2-aminonaphthalene-3-carboxylic acid may be carried out as follows: 250 parts of zinc chloride is dissolved in 300 parts of water, and the solution then introduced into an autoclave provided with a stirrer and treated with 500 parts of 2-hydroxynaphthalene-3-carboxylic acid. The autoclave is then closed, and 120 to 140 parts of gaseous ammonia is introduced into it. The whole is heated for 24 hr. at 220 to 230° (temperature of the oil bath), an operation that produces a pressure of 12 to 20 atmos. The reaction mixture forms a rather thick yellow mass, which is boiled with 4,000 parts of water and 1,400 parts of concentrated hydrochloric acid, whereby almost complete solution occurs. The hot solution is filtered, and the filtrate treated with 1,200 to 1,500 parts of common salt and allowed to cool. A compound containing 2-aminonaphthalene-3-carboxylic acid—probably as an inner salt or amide—separates as colorless crystals. The latter are filtered, washed with a saturated salt solution, dissolved in 7,000 parts of a solution of sodium carbonate of 8 per cent strength, and filtered. The free 2-aminonaphthalene-3-carboxylic acid may be precipitated from the alkaline filtrate by addition of acid, or the solution may be worked up directly. Yields above 80 per cent of theory are obtainable.

Preparation of Urea.—The commercial production of urea from carbon dioxide and ammonia is carried out as a continuous process (Fig. 15).[2] Approximately 102 parts of ammonia and 44 parts of carbon dioxide are compressed and delivered separately as liquids (or compressed gases) into a steam-heated autoclave at 190°C. maintaining an internal autoclave pressure of approximately 200 atmos. About 2 hr. is required for the passage of the materials through the autoclave, during which interval the reactants are almost wholly converted to ammonium carbamate, which in turn is converted largely to urea. From the autoclave the melt, consisting of 11.7 parts of ammonium carbamate, 51 parts of urea, 68 parts of ammonia, and 15.3 parts of water, is cooled to approximately 150°C. and is then admitted to a urea still which is maintained at 60°C. Here 42.3 parts of unconverted ammonia and any unreacted carbon dioxide are removed and collected for return to the system. The urea-water solution is then delivered to a crystallizer maintained at approximately 15°C. where 18 parts of the remaining free ammonia is removed by a suitable suction pump compressor. The resultant magma is passed to a continuous centrifuge whereby 30 parts of crystalline urea are obtained. The mother liquor comprising 11.7 parts of ammonium

[1] Fierz and Tobler, U. S. 1,629,894 (1925).

[2] DeRopp and Hetherington, U. S. 2,017,588 (1935).

carbamate, 21 parts of urea, 7.7 parts of ammonia, and 15.3 parts of water, may be variously used in the manufacture of mixed fertilizer.

Materials of Construction.—Since the synthesis is carried out at elevated temperatures and at pressures from 150 to 300 atmos., it is necessary to construct the autoclave to withstand these pressures. Steel pumps of the hydraulic type are used successfully to pump liquid ammonia and liquid carbon dioxide separately into the autoclaves. The liquid

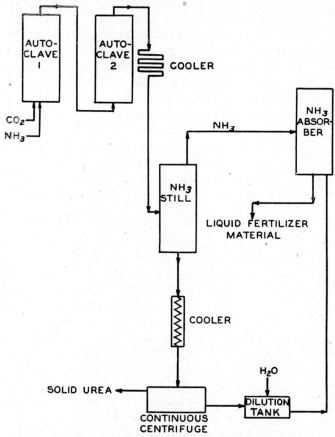

Fig. 15.—Flow diagram; urea synthesis.

in the autoclave, consisting of a mixture of urea, water, ammonium carbamate, and free ammonia, is, however, highly corrosive to ordinary materials of construction at elevated temperatures.[1] Ordinary iron and steel are rapidly dissolved in it; and chromium steel and many other alloys are rapidly attacked. Lead and silver are two of the most resistant materials, and these metals are employed as linings for the autoclave and

[1] Thompson, Krase, and Clark, *Ind. Eng. Chem.*, **22,** 735 (1930).

stills used in the process. Resistant steel alloys are used in construction of the parts where lower temperatures are encountered.

XI. CONTROL OF THE AMMONIA RECOVERY SYSTEM

The successful industrial preparation of amines by the ammonolysis of aromatic halides, phenols, and sulfonic acids depends largely upon the proper functioning of the ammonia system. This matter derives its importance from the fact that 5 to 15 moles of NH_3 is employed per mole of organic compound undergoing treatment. A large capital investment is, therefore, involved. It is essential, furthermore, that the excess of the ammonia be recovered and delivered to the reaction system at a constant and optimum strength. This is absolutely necessary to insure a maximum conversion to amine of uniform quality. In properly conducted operations, the recovery is efficiently and almost automatically carried out. This is accomplished by the choice of suitable equipment and the installation of mechanically controlled devices.

The type of apparatus that may be used for the recovery of the excess of ammonia may be varied within wide limits. The physical properties of the amine and the compound from which it is derived, along with the means utilized to effect the separation of the amine, are the principal guides in the selection of the proper apparatus.

Absorption Systems.—When anhydrous ammonia is used, the essentials of a refrigeration assembly will serve for the recovery of the excess ammonia. In liquid-phase ammonolysis the ammonia-recovery system may consist of a number of submerged coils, or double-pipe condensers, followed by a series of vertical absorbers. The submerged coils are cooled by circulating water, and the temperature of the vapors is brought down to 60 to 80°C. This practice makes it possible to condense and recover the weak liquor in a preliminary separator tank, while the free ammonia travels forward to effect the concentration of the liquor in the following vertical absorbers.

The vertical absorbers contain aqueous ammonia of varying concentrations, and a standpipe suspended from the top supplies the NH_3 gas, which is distributed at the base by means of suitable perforated fittings. Any unabsorbed gas escapes at the top and is then led to the bottom of the following absorber. The heat of solution is removed either by internal cooling coils or by an outside spray system.

The absorbers are set on a heavy foundation of masonry, at a sufficiently high level to permit bottom connections for cleaning and transfers incidental to operations. The piping can be so arranged that the ammonia vapor is led to the absorber containing the strongest solution and then made to pass into absorbers containing liquor of progressively decreasing strength. When a sufficient number of absorbers are employed, the ammonia vapors are led in a direct manner through the absorbers. In properly conducted systems, practically no ammonia gas escapes at the exhaust from the final absorber. The efficiency in recovery should be at least 90 per cent of that theoretically possible.

The absorption tanks may be arranged in a tier so that there is a constant overflow of liquid from the final absorber, which contains almost pure water, to the lowest tank, which holds the most concentrated liquor. A pump removes the strong solution, which should be ready for reuse, to a storage tank where it is cooled prior to delivery to the pressure system.

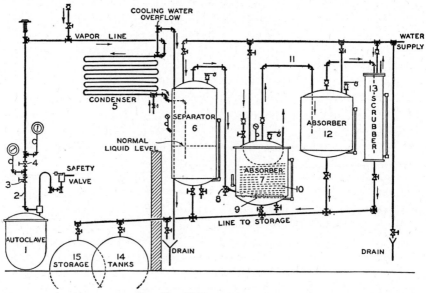

FIG. 16.—NH₃ recovery system.

Description of Recovery System.—In the preparation of 2-amino-anthraquinone, the excess of ammonia may be recovered in the following manner (Fig. 16):[1] At the end of the reaction, the gaseous constituents of the reaction mixture are gradually released through line 2 by means of the needle valves 3, 4 and allowed to expand to a pressure of about 50 lb. per square inch. The expansion causes a considerable drop in temperature, and heat is eliminated as the gaseous products flow through the cooling coil 5, resulting in a concentrated ammonia condensate. The condensate remains substantially in the separator 6. The partly dehydrated gases pass from the separator 6 to the first solution tank or absorber 7 and are further expanded to a pressure of about 5 lb. per square inch in their passage through the needle valve 8, thus being further

[1] U. S. 1,832,485 (1931).

cooled. Sufficient pressure is maintained on the gases to give a desired velocity and an injector action in the first solution tank or absorber 7, which is preferably charged with a measured quantity of water or dilute aqueous ammonia. The weak liquor or water is drawn by the injector through the pipe 9, in contact with the ammonia in the gases, and the ammonia-water mixture is diffused into the balance of the ammoniacal solution. The ammonia absorption releases heat, which is removed by the cooling coil 10, a sufficient amount of cooling medium being circulated through the coil to maintain a desired temperature commensurate with the concentration of aqueous ammonia that is desired; thus, a temperature of 35°C. or thereabouts, with a proper charge of water and a pressure of the entering ammonia of about 5 lb. per square inch, gives an aqueous ammonia of about 28% concentration. Unabsorbed gases pass through line 11 into the second solution tank or absorber 12, which is nominally at atmospheric pressure; and what gas escapes from this tank passes through the liquid in the tower 13 and out of the vent.

A number of modifications of the preceding system have given eminently satisfactory service in practical operations on a large scale. Generally, it is not advisable to release all the pressure from the autoclave. By allowing all but 150 to 200 lb. pressure to escape, it is possible then to blow the charge under its own pressure to a vessel of lighter construction in which the amino compound undergoes subsequent treatment. The receiving vessel (still) may be prepared with an alkaline solution to decompose the combined ammonia. In this vessel, the residual ammonia is effectively removed by distillation, and the ammoniacal vapors are led to the recovery system. The residual amino compound can then be treated in any desired manner most advantageously to effect its removal.

CHAPTER VII

OXIDATION

By L. F. Marek

I. TYPES OF OXIDATIVE REACTIONS

In the organic chemical industry, oxidation constitutes one of the most powerful tools used in the synthesis of chemical compounds. The oxidation processes are many and varied and are manifested in a variety of net effects. The principal types of oxidative reactions may be set forth as follows:

I. *Dehydrogenation;* as in the transformation of a primary alcohol to an aldehyde

$$C_2H_5OH + \tfrac{1}{2}O_2 \rightarrow CH_3CHO + H_2O$$

and hydroquinone to quinone

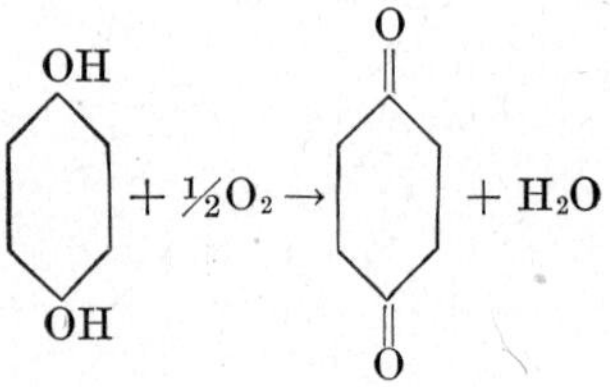

II. *An atom of oxygen may be introduced* into a molecule as is illustrated by the oxidation of an aldehyde to an acid

$$CH_3CHO + \tfrac{1}{2}O_2 \rightarrow CH_3COOH$$

or of a hydrocarbon to an alcohol

$$(C_6H_5)_3CH + \tfrac{1}{2}O_2 \rightarrow (C_6H_5)_3COH$$

III. *A combination of dehydrogenation and introduction of oxygen* may occur as in the preparation of aldehydes from hydrocarbons

$$CH_4 + O_2 \rightarrow CH_2O + H_2O$$

and the preparation of benzoic acid from benzyl alcohol

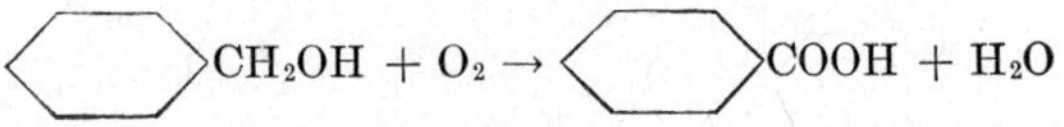

362

IV. *Dehydrogenation* may also be accompanied by molecular condensation as is the case when 2 molecules of toluene form stilbene and when methylanthraquinone is converted to Anthracene Yellow C.

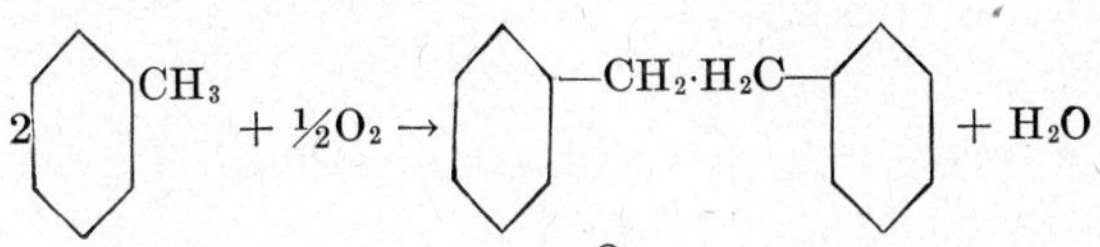

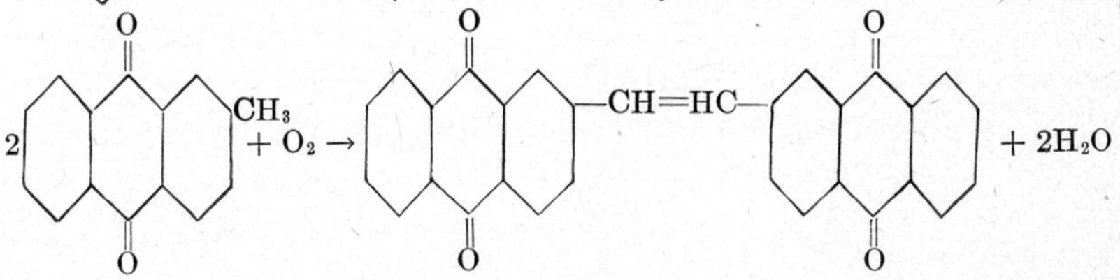

V. *Dehydrogenation, oxygen introduction, and destruction of carbon linkages* may all occur in the same process of oxidation, for example, in the oxidation of naphthalene to phthalic anhydride.

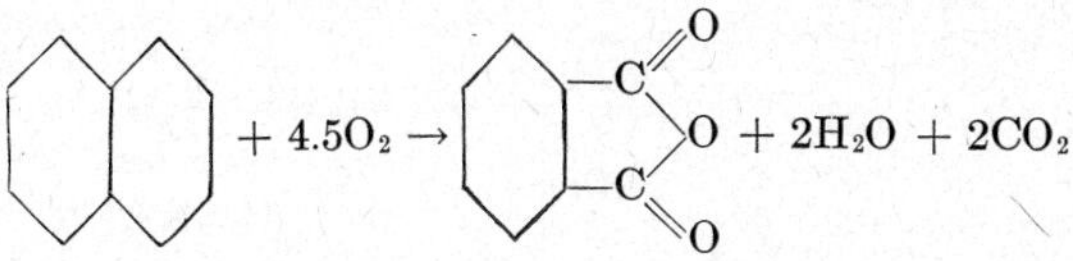

VI. *Oxidation* may be accomplished indirectly through the use of intermediate reactions

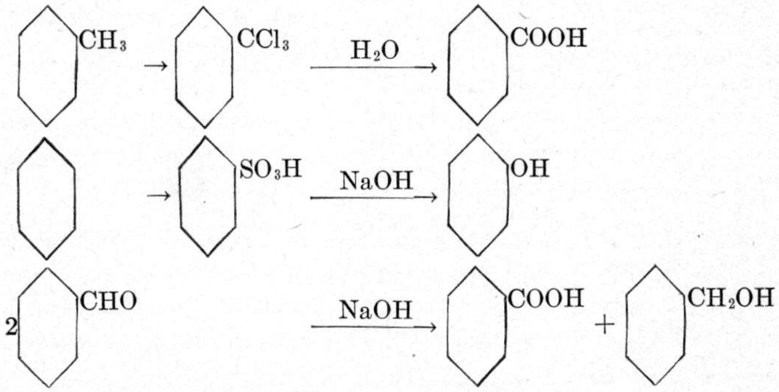

VII. *Olefins may be oxidized* under mild conditions to hydroxy derivatives and may be converted to aldehydes and carboxylic acids of lower molecular weight when stronger oxidizers are employed. Thus oleic acid can be converted to dihydroxystearic acid with alkaline potassium permanganate

$$CH_3(CH_2)_7CH{=}CH(CH_2)_7COOH \xrightarrow[\text{Alk.}]{KMnO_4}$$
$$CH_3(CH_2)_7CHOH{-}CHOH(CH_2)_7COOH$$

When sodium dichromate in acid solution is employed, fission as well as oxidation occurs and pelargonic and azelaic acids are produced.

$$CH_3(CH_2)_7CH=CH(CH_2)_7COOH \xrightarrow[\text{H}_2\text{SO}_4]{\text{Na}_2\text{Cr}_2\text{O}_7} \begin{cases} CH_3\!-\!(CH_2)_7\!-\!COOH \\ HOOC\!-\!(CH_2)_7\!-\!COOH \end{cases}$$

VIII. *Amino compounds* may be oxidized to azobenzene, *p*-aminophenol, and nitrobenzene under moderate conditions, and the N-containing radical is completely removed under drastic conditions. In this way quinone is derived from aniline.

IX. *Sulfur compounds* may be oxidized by acid permanganate, as in the preparation of sulfonals, trionals, and tetranals from $(CH_3)_2$-$C(S\!\cdot\!C_2H_5)_2$ or $(CH_3)(C_2H_5)C(S\!\cdot\!C_2H_5)_2$ or $(C_2H_5)_2C(S\!\cdot\!C_2H_5)_2$, in which the sulfide sulfur is oxidized to sulfonic groups. It should be noted that the mercaptans behave differently toward oxidizing agents than the alcohols, in that the action of strong oxidizing agents increases the valence of the sulfur atom instead of removing hydrogen, as in the case of the alcohols. Thus:

$$\underset{\text{Ethyl Alcohol}}{CH_3CH_2OH} \xrightarrow{\text{oxidation}} CH_3CHO + H_2O$$

$$\underset{\text{Ethyl Mercaptan}}{CH_3CH_2SH} \xrightarrow{\text{oxidation}} \underset{\text{Ethanesulfonic Acid}}{CH_3CH_2SO_2OH}$$

On the other hand, mild oxidation of mercaptans may result in the formation of disulfides. Thus:

$$\underset{\text{Ethyl Mercaptan}}{2CH_3CH_2SH} \xrightarrow{\text{oxidation}} \underset{\text{Diethyl Disulfide}}{C_2H_5S\!-\!SC_2H_5} + H_2O$$

Oxidation reactions, such as those enumerated above and accompanied by the formation of water, carbon oxides, or both, or by the introduction of elemental oxygen in the organic molecule or by the step down of an oxidizing compound from an unstable state of high oxidation to a more stable state of lower oxidation, are exothermic and accompanied by a free-energy decrease. Equilibrium, therefore, is favorable, and in practically all cases no means need be provided to force the completion of the reaction. Indeed, in the majority of cases, steps must be taken to limit the extent of the reaction and prevent complete loss of product through continued oxidation.

However favorable equilibrium may be, a useful process does not result until a favorable rate of reaction is obtained. The steps that have been taken to provide these favorable reaction rates and favorable methods of control in the case of organic oxidations have led to the great variety of oxidation processes now in use. The diversity of substances that may be subjected to oxidation processes in order to obtain more useful substances has made necessary a diversity of methods, and it is the purpose of this chapter to examine some of these methods and their characteristics.

The conditions imposed in these processes are such that two definite technics are used, *viz.*, vapor-phase and liquid-phase methods. Oxidations are conducted in the liquid phase in cases where high molecular weight, complex, and more or less thermally unstable substances are dealt with, and where the oxidizing agent is relatively nonvolatile. Temperatures are low or moderate, and the extent of oxidation may be readily controlled by (1) limiting the duration of operation; (2) controlling the temperature; and (3) limiting the amount of oxidizing agent. Oxidation may occur through the action of some oxidizing agent which becomes reduced during the operation or through the action of molecular oxygen in the presence of a catalyst. Vapor-phase oxidation reactions can be effectively applied only to readily volatile substances that are of sufficient thermal stability to resist dissociation at elevated temperatures. A further limitation exists in that the desired product must also be thermally stable and comparatively resistant to continued oxidation. Solid or vapor-phase catalysts may be employed with air or oxygen to produce the desired oxidation. The temperatures, as already implied, are usually high. Control is effected by limiting time of contact, temperature, proportion of oxygen, type of catalyst, or combinations of these factors.

II. OXIDIZING AGENTS

As has already been stated, the principal problem with oxidation reactions is the induction of the desired reaction rate coupled with a satisfactory control of the extent of reaction. Since this is so, a study of the processes employing oxidation would best be founded on an inspection of the materials and methods used to solve these problems.

In the case of liquid-phase oxidations it is possible to use either gaseous oxygen or compounds having oxidizing power. To illustrate the methods that are used, the processes will first be examined from the standpoint of the oxidizing agent, and the character of the action of each agent will be pointed out later by the use of exemplary reactions.

Permanganates

The solid salts of permanganic acid are powerful oxidizing agents. Calcium permanganate induces such rapid oxidation of ethanol that inflammation may result. Aqueous solutions of the permanganates also possess powerful oxidizing properties. One of the commonest and most useful of the agents employed in organic oxidations is potassium permanganate. The potassium salt is available in the form of stable crystals, whereas the sodium salt is deliquescent, and consequently the former is almost invariably used. It functions as an oxidizing agent of different strength in alkaline, neutral, and acid solutions.

The calcium and barium salts have been used for the oxidation of complex proteins. The calcium salt has the advantage in that it forms insoluble products. The calcium oxide combines with the manganese dioxide to form the insoluble $CaO:MnO_2$, thus simplifying recovery of products.

Alkaline Solution.—When potassium permanganate alone is used in aqueous solution, the solution becomes alkaline through the formation of potassium hydroxide:

$$K_2Mn_2O_8 + H_2O \rightarrow 2MnO_2 + 2KOH + 3O$$

Three atoms of oxygen are released per molecule of permanganate, and manganese dioxide in the hydrated form is precipitated.

In the case of acid products, the potassium salts usually form. After the removal of the MnO_2 by filtration, the acid may be recovered by acidification with a mineral acid. Very dilute aqueous solutions are used in the oxidation of toluene derivatives to the corresponding acids. Loss of color shows the end point. Excess of reagent is easily remedied by the addition of ethanol or other harmless reducing agent. Thus, *p*-chlorotoluene is oxidized to *p*-chlorobenzoic acid; naphthalene to phthalonic acid; maleic acid to mesotartaric acid; *o*-nitrophenol to dinitrodihydroxydiphenyl. In general, however, hydroxy and amino groups must be protected by alkylation or acylation to prevent oxidation of the substituent.

An excess of alkali may be added at the start, in which condition potassium permanganate is used for oxidizing orthosubstituted derivatives of toluene. Thus, *o*-toluic acid yields phthalic acid. Substituted cinnamic acids are oxidized to the corresponding benzoic acids. Triphenylmethane is oxidized to the corresponding alcohol; diphenyl methane to the ketone; and oleic acid to dihydroxystearic acid.

Neutral Solution.—To avoid the alkalinity produced by the use of potassium permanganate alone as an oxidizing agent, resort may be had to the introduction of carbon dioxide to neutralize the alkali or to the use of magnesium sulfate for the formation of neutral potassium sulfate and insoluble magnesium oxide. These expedients are necessary in very few cases, however.

In such a neutralized oxidizing solution, acet-*o*-toluidide gives a yield of 80 per cent of the oxidation product, acetanthranilic acid; whereas in the alkaline solution, a yield of only about 30 per cent is obtainable.

Acid Solution.—The addition of acetic or sulfuric acid to potassium permanganate solutions yields a powerful oxidizing agent useful only in the preparation of very stable compounds. The powerful action of this agent markedly restricts its applicability. In use, the oxidizing solution is added gradually to the substance undergoing oxidation, since in this way the action is limited and controllable. Each molecule of permanganate yields 5 atoms of oxygen.

$$K_2Mn_2O_8 + 3H_2SO_4 \rightarrow 2MnSO_4 + K_2SO_4 + 3H_2O + 5O$$

Acid solutions may be used for the preparation of certain naphthalene-sulfonic acids not capable of formation by other means. Both aliphatic and aromatic sulfides or hydrosulfides are oxidized to corresponding sulfonic acids. o-Iodobenzoic acid is oxidized to o-iodosobenzoic acid.

DICHROMATES

The usual form of oxidation with dichromates is in the presence of sulfuric acid and with the sodium or potassium salt. Although the dichromates exert an oxidizing tendency in the absence of acid, the oxidation reaction can be made to occur much more quickly in the presence of acid, and acid solutions are almost invariably used. The Beckmann[1] mixture consists of a solution of 60 parts of potassium dichromate in 80 parts of concentrated sulfuric acid and 270 parts of water. The Kiliani[2] mixture consists of a solution of 60 parts of sodium dichromate in a similar sulfuric acid solution. Such mixtures react to give oxygen as follows:

$$K_2Cr_2O_7 + 4H_2SO_4 \rightarrow K_2SO_4 + Cr_2(SO_4)_3 + 4H_2O + 3O$$

2 moles of chromic acid (1 mole of dichromate) giving 3 atoms of oxygen. The sodium salt is the cheaper, is much more soluble in water, and is consequently more often used.

Dichromates are used in the chrome tanning of leather and manufacture of chrome-tanning compounds; in the production of saccharin, dyes, dye intermediates, and various chemicals; as mordants and oxidizing agents in fur and wool dyeing; and to improve the fastness and brilliance of colors on cotton and wool by oxidation. The consumption of dichromates by tanners and for tanning compounds probably exceeds slightly that used by the color manufacturers.

Chromic Acid Solution.—Chromic anhydride (CrO_3), dissolved in glacial acetic acid, is sometimes used as an oxidizing agent. Two moles of the anhydride yield 3 atoms of oxygen: $2CrO_3 \rightarrow Cr_2O_3 + 3O$. In practice, only the theoretical amount of the oxidizing agent is added, and this is usually introduced gradually as the oxidation proceeds. Aromatic alcohols may be oxidized to aromatic aldehydes, provided a primary amine is present to form a Schiff's base with the aldehyde as soon as it is formed. Quinoline homologues are oxidized to quinoline carboxylic

[1] BECKMANN, Ann., **250**, 325 (1889).
[2] KILIANI and MERK, Ber., **34**, 3564 (1901).

acids.   If acetic anhydride is used, benzene homologues may be oxidized to aldehydes, since the formation of the acetyl derivatives prevents further oxidation.

Chromic acid in hot glacial acetic acid oxidizes anthracene quantitatively to anthraquinone in a very smooth reaction, but the method is too expensive for commercial application in competition with synthetic anthraquinone made from cheap phthalic anhydride and benzene by means of the Friedel and Crafts reaction.   Prior to the development of the present methods of phthalic anhydride manufacture, the process was used extensively for anthraquinone production in Europe.   The method has been recommended for anthracene analysis.

Chromic acid and the dichromates find numerous other applications as oxidizing agents in the organic chemical industry.   In the manufacture of perfumes, they may be used to oxidize anethole to anisic aldehyde; isosafrol to piperonal (heliotropin); etc.   The dichromates may be used to effect the condensation of α-naphthol with dimethyl-p-phenylenediamine to form indophenol.   They are used in the preparation of Methylene Blue, Safranine, and other dyestuffs.

Hypochlorous Acid and Salts

The sodium and calcium salts of hypochlorous acid are the only salts of the hypoacids known in the solid state.   Although they decompose easily when wet, they are stable if thoroughly dry.   Bleaching powder, formed by reacting chlorine with dry calcium hydroxide, is related to the hypochlorites and depends upon the presence of the hypochlorite radical for its characteristic action.   Chlorinated solutions of zinc and aluminum hydroxides are more active oxidizing agents than are comparably treated solutions of the alkalis or alkaline earths because of greater hydrolysis and consequent more rapid decomposition of hypochlorous acid.   But the sodium salt has the advantage of ease of preparation and handling.

Hypochlorous acid is unstable and decomposes very easily to liberate oxygen.   Decomposition rate is not violent, however, and for some purposes may even be increased by the use of a cobalt or nickel salt to act as a catalyst.   The action of the salts, especially those of the alkalis or alkaline earths, may be increased by the addition of carbon dioxide or acids because of the more rapid liberation of the hypochlorous acid caused thereby.   This property furnishes a method of control when these substances are used for oxidation.

Calcium hypochlorite is used to a large extent for bleaching linen and cotton textile materials and paper pulp.   The sodium salt is used in bleaching rayon yarn.   Both salts are used for "sweetening" uncracked gasolines by the oxidation of the mercaptans to sulfides and disulfides.

Chlorates

Chloric acid ($HClO_3$) is a powerful oxidizing agent. It may be obtained in aqueous solutions at concentrations up to about 40 per cent and is stable at temperatures up to 40°C. Such a solution will ignite paper immersed in it. By controlling the oxidizing action of this agent, it is possible to effect the oxidation of ethanol or ethyl ether to acetic acid; of ethylene to glycol; allyl alcohol to glycerine; fumaric acid to racemic acid; etc. In conjunction with mineral acids, chloric acid oxidizes aniline to aniline black. However, since its aqueous solutions must be obtained by double decomposition from its salts, its industrial usefulness is very limited, and it is more often used in the form of the soluble salts.

Potassium chlorate is a powerful oxidizing agent. However, its solubility in water is limited, being only 3.3 gm. per 100 gm. of water at 0°C. and 56.5 gm. per 100 gm. of water at 100°C. It has been widely used in the dry, finely divided state as an oxidizing agent and in the laboratory as a source of pure oxygen. Mixed with reducing agents such as carbon, sulfur, sugar, cellulose, etc., it is used in the manufacture of powder, fireworks, explosives, matches, etc. In solution, it has been used in the oxidation of aniline in the production of aniline black. When heated to above its melting point (357°C.), the dry salt tends to decompose to potassium chloride and oxygen, each molecule of chlorate giving $1\frac{1}{2}$ molecules of oxygen. Concurrently, with the above decomposition potassium chlorate decomposes to give the perchlorate and the chloride. The relative speed of the two reactions varies with the temperature and is markedly affected by catalysts. Thus, the decomposition to oxygen may completely outrun the other reaction in the presence of a manganese dioxide catalyst.

The solubility of sodium chlorate in water is far greater than that of the potassium salt, being above 80 gm. per 100 gm. of water at 0°C. and above 230 gm. per 100 gm. of water at 100°C. Also, it is less expensive, and about 15,000,000 lb. of it are used annually in the United States as a herbicide.

Peroxides

The principal peroxides used as oxidizing agents are those of lead, manganese, and hydrogen.

PbO_2.—Lead peroxide is used as an oxidizing agent in conjunction with acetic, sulfuric, or hydrochloric acids, usually the former. One mole yields one atom of oxygen, and a salt of the acid is formed during the process. It must be used in a finely divided form and for this reason is best prepared by precipitation from a solution of lead nitrate by the addition of sodium hypochlorite or bleaching powder.

MnO_2.—Manganese dioxide is widely used as an oxidizing agent in both its natural and prepared forms. It is used in conjunction with sulfuric acid and during the reaction is reduced to manganese sulfate, releasing one atom of oxygen per mole. One of its principal uses is in the oxidation of methyl groups to aldehyde groups, in which rôle it has been largely used to convert toluene to benzaldehyde.

H_2O_2.—Hydrogen peroxide is manufactured, marketed, and used as an aqueous solution, the strength of which is customarily designated in terms of the volume of free oxygen equivalent. Thus, the most widely used concentration is "100-volume peroxide" from which 100 volumes of oxygen per volume of solution may be obtained. The annual domestic production is now something above 18,000,000 lb. of 100-volume peroxide. Practically all this production is manufactured electrolytically by two processes, one using persulfuric acid and the other ammonium persulfate. A small proportion is manufactured from barium peroxide.

Although generally marketed industrially as the 100 volume product (31.3 gm. H_2O_2 per 100 cc. solution, or 28.5 per cent H_2O_2 by weight) in glass carboys, aluminum drums, and aluminum tank cars, some 130-volume material is shipped in tank cars where long hauls make the freight saving an advantage. It is possible to make stronger solutions than these, and by the persulfate process concentrations of about 60 to 70 per cent are possible. Such concentrations are not marketed, however.

The bulk of the hydrogen peroxide consumed industrially is used in textile bleaching, hydrogen peroxide having displaced chlorine and the hypochlorites in portions of this field because of use advantages and despite a relatively higher cost. Substantially all silk and wool goods, rayon fabrics, and cotton goods lighter than about 5 yd. per pound are bleached by hydrogen peroxide. Also fur skins and cotton goods partly dyed or striped are usually hydrogen peroxide bleached.

Despite the decided advantage in use of hydrogen peroxide as an oxidizing agent because of freedom from residual salts, precipitates, gases, etc., only limited use has been made of it as an oxidant in the organic chemical industry, largely because of relatively higher costs. However, with perfection of manufacturing methods, increased production, and a wider market base, lower prices may occur and the use of hydrogen peroxide as an oxidant increase.

A number of transformations are possible with hydrogen peroxide. In alkaline solutions it may be used in the preparation of organic peroxides such as benzoyl peroxide, diethyl peroxide, etc. A 3 per cent solution oxidizes piperidine to glutaric acid by rupture of the ring. Benzene yields a small amount of phenol. Phenols are converted to dihydric phenols or quinones. By the action of hydrogen peroxide in the presence of small amounts of ferrous salts, hydroxy acids are converted to aldehydo or keto acids.[1]

Very small amounts of selenium oxychloride markedly accelerate the rate of reaction of hydrogen peroxide in oxidizing aldehydes to acids.[2]

Na_2O_2.—Sodium peroxide is used in only a limited way industrially for oxidizing organic substances, partly because of the hazards associated with its storage and use.

By the action of sodium peroxide, phenanthraquinone in aqueous suspension changes smoothly to diphenic acid (bi-phenyl-2, 2'-dicarboxylic acid). By the action of a cooled solution of sodium peroxide on the acid chloride, it is possible to form benzoyl peroxide ($C_6H_5 \cdot CO \cdot O \cdot O \cdot CO \cdot C_6H_5$).

SeO_2.—Selenium dioxide presents some interesting features as an oxidizing agent. For instance, unsaturated substances containing the grouping $—CH\!\!=\!\!CHCH_2—$ can be oxidized to α, β-unsaturated ketones (α pinene to verbenone),[3] substances in which a methylene or methyl group is adjacent to a carbonyl group can be oxidized so that one or more of the hydrogen atoms become oxidized (acetone to pyruvic aldehyde, acetophenone to phenylglyoxal),[4] and substances like ethanol can be made to inflame in an SeO_2 atmosphere at 230°C. (446°F.). The SeO_2 becomes reduced to selenium metal which may be easily recovered, reoxidized by heating in the presence of oxygen, and reused.

Silver Oxides.—Silver has the capacity to act as an oxygen carrier or oxidation catalyst, presumably because it can form oxides other than the common Ag_2O. Although not extensively used as such, the oxide (Ag_2O) acts as a mild oxidation agent. Moist, freshly prepared silver oxide is frequently used in the organic chemical laboratory for the replacement of halogen atoms by the hydroxyl group.

Silver oxide (Ag_2O) acts as a mild oxidizing agent and oxidizes glycerol to glycolic acid; aldehydes to acids; o-dihydroxybenzene to o-benzoquinone, being reduced to metallic silver. The oxide is fairly readily reduced by hydrogen gas. Silver oxide made alkaline with sodium or ammonium hydroxide oxidizes $=\!CHOH$ and $=\!CO$ groups when these are attached to two $—CH_2OH$ or $—COOH$ groups or combinations. Thus, alkaline Ag_2O is reduced by tartaric acid, glycerol, mannitol, etc. Neutral or acid Ag_2O is reduced by glycolic, lactic, or malic acids.

Silver oxide is an excellent oxidation catalyst for vapor-phase reactions and is frequently used as such, particularly in experimental work.

[1] FENTON, *et al.*, *J. Chem. Soc.*, **1894**, 899; **1895**, 48; **1899**, 1.

[2] FIRTH and GETHING, *J. Chem. Soc.*, **1936**, 633.

[3] SCHWENK and BORGWARDT, *Ber.*, **65B**, 1601–1602 (1932).

[4] Riley, U. S. 1,955,890. *Cf.* also ASTIN, NEWMAN, and RILEY, *J. Chem. Soc.*, **1933**, 391–394.

Nitric Acid

Nitric acid is seldom used as an oxidizing agent in the formation of partially oxidized products. The fuming acid is used in the complete oxidation of organic compounds for the estimation of halogens or sulfur in the Carius process. The principal disadvantage of nitric acid as a partial oxidizing agent arises from its tendency to act as a nitrating agent. Even when dilute solutions are used, the products of oxidation contain nitro derivatives. The method of Krafft uses the concentrated acid (sp. gr., 1.5) and is particularly effective in the partial oxidation of substances that are already nitrated. A temperature of 0 to 5°C. is used for mixing the acid and organic compound; this is gradually raised to 50°C., and the product poured into water. Dinitroxylene is oxidized in this way to dinitrophthalic acid. Oxidation with dilute acid is slow when applied to the benzene homologues. Carboxylic acids are formed. Thus, pentamethylbenzene dissolved in benzene is converted to tetramethyl-benzoic acid by boiling for 60 hr. with dilute nitric acid. *o*-Xylene is oxidized by dilute boiling nitric acid to *o*-toluic acid. Treatment with potassium permanganate is required for the oxidation of the remaining methyl group to form phthalic acid.

Nitrobenzene

Although nitrobenzene acts as a sufficiently strong oxidizing agent to oxidize sodium methylate to sodium formate, its action is sufficiently moderate to make it a useful agent for particular reactions. Inorganic reducing reagents such as alkaline stannous chloride reduce nitrobenzene to azobenzene. When used in the quinoline synthesis, it may become reduced to aniline.

Ferric Salts

Ferric chloride is a mild oxidizing agent, 2 moles of the chloride yielding the equivalent of 1 atom of oxygen in passing to the ferrous condition.

$$2FeCl_3 + H_2O \rightarrow 2FeCl_2 + HCl + O$$

It transforms hydroquinone to quinone, naphthol to dinaphthol, and hydroxylamine derivatives to nitroso compounds. It has been used in the formation of acridine yellow by oxidizing the leuco base obtained by condensing *m*-toluylenediamine with formaldehyde.

With phenols, ferric chloride gives a variety of highly colored compounds. However, the reaction is of significance principally from its use in the identification of the substances in analysis.

COPPER SALTS

Copper is capable of existing in two states of oxidation and of passing readily from one to the other of these states by oxidation or reduction. In its higher state of oxidation, it is capable of acting as an oxidizing agent and in its lower state, as a reducing agent. This property makes the metal a useful material as an oxygen carrier or oxidation catalyst. It is more frequently used in this latter capacity than in the capacity of an oxidizing agent alone in organic chemical synthesis. When used as an oxidizing agent in solution it is generally reduced from the cupric to the cuprous state.

Fehling's Solution.—In the determination of sugars and in their study, use is made of the relative ease of oxidation. Both aldoses and ketoses are capable of oxidation, the ketoses the more readily. Hydroxy ketones resemble aldehydes in their ease of oxidation. For oxidation, Fehling's solution is commonly used. This consists of an aqueous solution of sodium potassium tartrate, sodium hydroxide, and copper sulfate, essentially an alkaline solution of cupric hydroxide. The sugar reduces the cupric ions to the cuprous form, and red cuprous oxide is precipitated. This solution has a rather weak oxidizing power and acts only on substances that are easily oxidized. Alcohols, acids, and simple ketones are not oxidized. Aldehydes, hydroxy ketones, di-, and triphenols are oxidized readily by this solution. When, for example, glucose is heated with Fehling's solution, a precipitate of cuprous oxide rapidly forms, and reaction is complete in a few minutes. Copper salts other than the sulfate may be used, and any polyhydric alcohol such as sucrose or glycerol may be used in place of the sodium potassium tartrate. Neither sucrose nor glycol is oxidized by Fehling's solution, and either one prevents the undesired precipitation of cupric hydroxide that would normally occur in the alkaline solution. An alkaline solution is used, since oxidation is more rapid.

Copper sulfate is used as a catalyst in the commercial process for the oxidation of toluene to benzaldehyde by the use of manganese dioxide and sulfuric acid. This reaction requires specific catalysts and delicate control to prevent oxidation to benzoic acid. The relatively easy oxidation or dehydrogenation of benzoin to the diketone benzil may be accomplished with complex cupric salts:

Benzoin   oxidation   Benzil

Alkali Fusion

Fusion with alkali in the presence of air (oxygen) often accomplishes oxidations impossible to obtain otherwise. For instance, the formation of oxyacids from substituted phenols by direct oxidation of side chains is difficult of accomplishment because of the much greater susceptibility of the hydroxyl group to attack and consequent tendency for the breakdown of the molecule. Alkali fusion accomplishes the desired reaction but with poor yields. Xylenols yield the corresponding mono- and dibasic acids by the reaction. Thus, *p*-xylenol is successively oxidized to *m*-homosalicylic acid and to hydroxyterephthalic acid.

The alkali fusion is of importance in the formation of certain anthraquinone vat dyes. Thus, fusion of β-aminoanthraquinone with two or three parts of potassium hydroxide at 250°C. for ½ hr. yields Bohns' Indanthrene Blue RS (N-dihydro- 1, 2:1′, 2′-anthraquinoneazine).

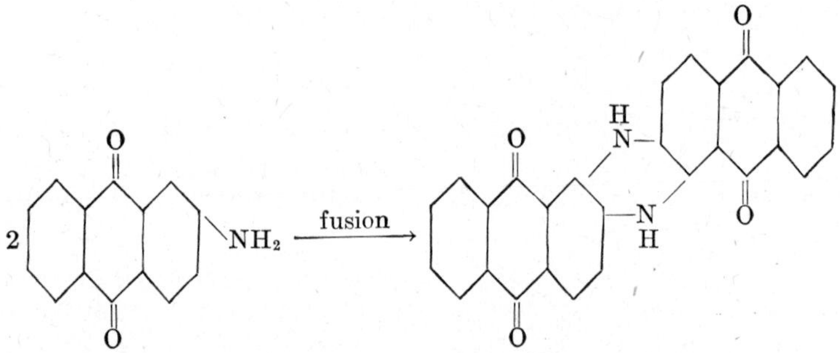

Indanthrene Blue RS

Similarly, benzanthrone yields Bally's Indanthrene Dark Blue BO.

A mixture of caustic soda and potassium nitrate or chlorate possesses oxidizing powers, whereas caustic alone acts as a condensing and dehydrating agent. A good example of the use of the oxidizing mixture is in the formation of the dye Alizarin from anthraquinone-β-sulfonic acid, sodium salt.

Arsenic Acid

Arsenic acid (H_3AsO_4) may be obtained easily by oxidizing arsenic or arsenic trioxide with nitric acid, aqua regia, or chlorine water, or slowly by oxidizing with elemental oxygen in alkaline solutions. It is easily and permanently soluble in water, the anhydride As_2O_5 being unstable in solution, in contrast to the anhydride of arsenious acid, As_2O_3. It acts as an oxidizing agent, releasing one atom of oxygen per atom of arsenic, in passing from the pentavalent form to the trivalent form. Although arsenic acid was formerly used for various organic oxidations, its toxic nature and the difficulty of suitably recovering the trioxide have gradually caused its abandonment in favor of less objectionable agents.

POTASSIUM FERRICYANIDE

A seldom used oxidizing agent is potassium ferricyanide, which becomes reduced to the ferrocyanide during the process, 658 parts (2 moles) of the salt yielding 16 parts (1 atom) of oxygen. It is difficult to remove the reduced salt from the product, and large amounts must be used to obtain a small amount of oxidation. Nitrotoluenes are oxidized to nitrobenzoic acids, *sym.*-trinitrobenzene is oxidized to picric acid, nitroso derivatives to nitro derivatives, etc.

FUMING SULFURIC ACID (OLEUM)

Fuming sulfuric acid ($H_2SO_4 + SO_3$) in the presence of mercury salts is a powerful oxidizing agent. It was formerly used extensively in this way for the oxidation of naphthalene to phthalic anhydride but has been displaced in this operation by the newer air-oxidation processes.

Fuming sulfuric acid attained some importance as an oxidizing agent for the introduction of hydroxyl groups in anthraquinone derivatives in the production of a variety of alizarin dyes. Thus, fuming sulfuric acid at low temperatures may be used to convert alizarine and other hydroxy derivatives of anthraquinone to trihydroxy or up to hexahydroxy derivatives.

An early use of sulfuric acid as an oxidizing agent was in the oxidation of ethyl mercaptan to diethyl disulfide. However, to effect this reaction,

$$2C_2H_5SH \xrightarrow{\text{oxidation}} C_2H_5S\text{—}SC_2H_5 + H_2O$$

it is necessary that the oxidation be mild and controlled, since with strong oxidizing agents the sulfonic acid is formed. Also, piperidine (hexahydropyridine) may be oxidized to pyridine. The

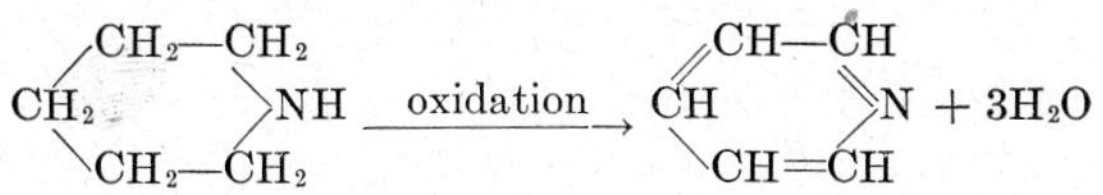

$$CH_2\begin{matrix} CH_2\text{—}CH_2 \\ \\ CH_2\text{—}CH_2 \end{matrix}NH \xrightarrow{\text{oxidation}} CH\begin{matrix} CH\text{—}CH \\ \\ CH\text{=}CH \end{matrix}N + 3H_2O$$

pyridine ring is very stable to oxidation, not being attacked by nitric or chromic acids and yielding a sulfonic acid only at high temperatures.

OZONE

For successful application of any ozone oxidation process, it is essential that cheap electric power be available for ozone generation. It is worthy of note, therefore, that the technically successful oxidation of isoeugenol to vanillin in Germany was abandoned because of economic reasons. Many other applications of ozone oxidation have been made or suggested, such as bleaching, sterilization of water, oxidation of acetylene to glyoxal, oxidation of anethole to anisic aldehyde, oxidation of manganates to permanganates, drying of printing inks, etc.

III. LIQUID-PHASE OXIDATION WITH OXIDIZING COMPOUNDS

The oxidation of aniline furnishes an example for comparison of a number of oxidizing agents. Results obtained by conducting the reaction under conditions best suited for the particular agent are shown in the following tabulation.[1]

Oxidizing Agent	Product
Manganese dioxide in sulfuric acid	Quinone
Potassium dichromate in dilute sulfuric acid at 0 to 10°C. for 24 hr	Quinone
Potassium permanganate (acid)	Aniline black
Potassium permanganate (alkaline)	Azobenzene plus ammonia
Potassium permanganate (neutral)	Azobenzene plus nitrobenzene
Alkaline hypochlorite	Nitrobenzene
Hypochlorous acid	p-Aminophenol

Another substance exhibiting a variety of actions toward oxidizing agents is furfural:

$$\begin{array}{c} HC\text{---}CH \\ \| \quad \| \\ HC \diagdown \diagup C\text{---}CHO \\ O \end{array}$$

The aldehyde group normally behaves like that of acetaldehyde toward oxidation, but in the presence of certain agents the ring structure is destroyed and polybasic acids formed.[2]

Oxidizing Agent	Product
Sodium chlorate in neutral solution with V_2O_5 catalyst	Fumaric acid
Sodium chlorate in dilute acid with OsO_4 catalyst	Mesotartaric acid
Caros' acid, $HO\cdot O\cdot SO_3H$, a strong oxidizing agent	Succinic acid
Hydrogen peroxide in presence of ferrous salts	∂-Hydroxyfurfural
Bromine water at 100°C	Mucobromic acid
Potassium permanganate (diluted solution)	Pyromucic acid

The action of oxidizing agents on organic compounds depends not only upon the nature of the agent or the compound but also upon such factors as concentration, temperature, hydrogen-ion concentration,

---

[1] BERNTHSEN, "Textbook of Organic Chemistry," rev. trans., 664, D. Van Nostrand Company, Inc. (1922).

[2] MILAS, *J. Am. Chem. Soc.*, **49**, 2005 (1927).

and method of mixing. Consequently, any comparison of the variety of effects obtainable by varying oxidizing agent or organic compound cannot be pursued too far.

Ethylenic Bonds to Dihydroxy Groups.—The oxidation of olefins and olefin derivatives with dilute aqueous *potassium permanganate* may be used for the formation of dihydroxy compounds. Thus, oxidation of 11 liters of isobutylene with 1 per cent potassium permanganate solution results in the formation of 22 gm. of isobutylene glycol, 4 gm. oxyisobutyric acid, and 1.5 gm. of acetone.[1] Ethylene reacts more slowly than either propylene or isobutylene[2] when treated in this way, and the isomeric diamylenes are quite unreactive, resisting oxidation for several days.[3] The rate of reaction is retarded by low temperatures and low concentrations of permanganate.[4]

With 2 per cent permanganate solution, cinnamic acid yields phenyl-glyceric acid through the formation of a glycol derivative. Dilute permanganate oxidizes ethylenic bonds of fatty acids to dihydroxy groups, thus oleic acid to dihydroxystearic acid.

More drastic oxidation of the ethylenic bonds of oleic, linoleic, and similar unsaturated fatty acids causes the action to go beyond the formation of oxygenated groups and to result in rupture of the bond as well as oxidation. Such agents as the dichromates, permanganates, nitric, etc., may be used to obtain the effect. Thus, oleic,[5] dihydroxy-stearic, or sterolic acids[6] yield azelaic and pelargonic acids, which products may be further oxidized if the reaction is forced.

Isoeugenol to Vanillin.—An example of an oxidation of a side chain to an aldehydic group in which it is convenient to protect one substituent against oxidation is in the formation of vanillin from eugenol. Eugenol obtained from oil of cloves is heated with an alkali such as sodium hydroxide to convert it to isoeugenol:

The hydroxyl group is protected by acetylation, and the substance oxidized and then saponified to vanillin:

[1] WAGNER, *Ber.*, **21**, 1232 (1888).

[2] DAVIS, *Ind. Eng. Chem.*, **20**, 1055 (1928).

[3] JOUBERT and NORRIS, *J. Am. Chem. Soc.*, **49**, 873 (1929).

[4] HOWES and NASH, *J. Soc. Chem. Ind.*, **49**, 113–119T (1930).

[5] GREEN and HILDITCH, *J. Chem. Soc.*, **1937**, 764.

[6] GRÜN and WITTKA, *Chemische Umschau*, **32**, 257–259, (1925).

$$\underset{\text{—CHO}}{\overset{\overset{\displaystyle\text{—OH}}{\text{—OCH}_3}}{\bigodot}}$$

The relatively slight difference in susceptibility to oxidation of the hydroxyl and propylene side chains makes it difficult to oxidize the propylene chain without affecting to some extent the hydroxyl substituent, unless it has been protected. Dichromates have been used to accomplish the oxidation step in this process of manufacture but are open to the objection that oxidation tends to go beyond the easily oxidized aldehyde stage with resultant formation of acids. The same is true of oxidation with permanganate. Less potent agents, such as nitrobenzene, have consequently been used for the direct oxidation of isoeugenol to vanillin.

Nitrobenzene has an advantage over more powerful oxidizing agents, such as the dichromates and permanganates, in the oxidation of isoeugenol to vanillin in not inducing such far-reaching oxidation of the desired aldehyde group to the undesired carboxylic group. Technically, the process may be conducted as follows: Eugenol from oil of cloves is dissolved in dilute sodium hydroxide solution, and the whole heated to 160°C. under pressure in an autoclave. This treatment converts the eugenol to isoeugenol and forms the sodium salt. For oxidation, 1 mole of nitrobenzene is added for each mole of eugenol originally transferred to the autoclave. Nitrobenzene is added slowly as the oxidation proceeds. After the reaction is complete, pressure on the autoclave is released, and the gaseous by-products are permitted to blow off. Vanillin may be recovered from the alkaline solution by precipitation with hydrochloric acid. The yield approximates 80 per cent of theory.

Isoborneol to Camphor.—*Nitric acid* has been widely used in the production of synthetic camphor from turpentine. The commonly accepted general practice for this manufacture (the one adapted by Gubelmann for use in this country) involves the following steps: (1) distillation of turpentine to obtain pinene; (2) saturation with HCl gas to obtain bornyl chloride; (3) hydrolyzing this to obtain camphene; (4) esterifying camphene to isobornyl acetate; (5) saponification to isoborneol; and (6) oxidation to camphor.

It is estimated that 12,000,000 lb. of camphor were produced in Europe during 1931 by this procedure, and the American production (1,500,000 lb. annually) started in 1931.[1] The oxidation is performed as follows: 20 parts of isoborneol are dissolved in 100 parts of 1.32 sp. gr. nitric acid to which has been added 5 parts of 50 per cent sulfuric acid,

---

[1] GUBELMANN and ELLEY, *Ind. Eng. Chem.*, **26**, 589 (1934).

and the mixture heated with stirring at 80 to 90°C. (176 to 194°F.) for
10 hr. Other oxidizing agents, such as potassium permanganate, chromic
acid, and nitric acid under other conditions, have not been found to be
satisfactory.[1]

Pinene   Bornyl Chloride   Camphene

Isoborneol Acetate   Isoborneol   Camphor

Isoborneol dissolved in benzene or chloroform is readily oxidized
to camphor with chlorine. Thus, a solution of 15.4 parts of isoborneol
dissolved in 16 parts of benzene is shaken violently with a solution of
7.1 parts of chlorine dissolved in 900 parts of water by weight. Violent
agitation is necessary to secure intimate contact of the two immiscible
solutions. Camphor is recovered from the benzene solution after
reaction is complete, in almost quantitative yield, and contains only
traces of chlorine. Use of alkaline aqueous solutions of chlorine results
in the formation of sodium chloride as a by-product.

Aniline to Quinone.—*Sodium or potassium dichromate* may be used to
oxidize aniline to quinone, but a low temperature and slow addition of
the oxidizing agent must be used to restrict the action. Although
the high stability of the quinone structure toward further oxidation
makes possible the use of so powerful an oxidizing agent as sodium
dichromate in acid solution, some care must still be exercised in order
to prevent destructive reaction. An instance of the method is as follows:
A mixture of 25 parts of aniline, 200 parts of water-white sulfuric acid,
and 600 parts of water, contained in a wooden or corrosion-resistant vat,

[1] BERI and SARIN, *J. Soc. Chem. Ind.*, **55**, (31), 605 (C & I), (1936).

is cooled by ice or refrigeration. A solution of 25 parts of sodium dichromate in 100 parts of water is then slowly added with agitation, and stirring continued for 12 hr. A solution of 50 parts of sodium dichromate in 200 parts of water is then added, and stirring continued until the reaction is complete. During the whole operation, the temperature is maintained below about 5°C. through the addition of ice or by refrigeration. Quinone is recovered by skimming from the surface of the solution and purified by steam distillation.

Quinone is readily reduced to hydroquinone, and much of the quinone that is manufactured is sold in the form of the hydrogenated product. Hydroquinone, in turn, is readily oxidized to quinone by such agents as chlorine, nitric acid, persulfuric acid, chromic acid, ferric chloride, permanganates, etc. The reduction of quinone to hydroquinone and the reoxidation of hydroquinone to quinone are very rapid processes and are strictly reversible. This reaction is one of the rare oxidation and reduction reactions of organic chemistry that are rapid and reversible, like the oxidation and reduction of inorganic ions. Quinhydrone $(C_6H_4O_2 \cdot C_6H_4(OH)_2)$ is formed as an intermediate in the process but is largely dissociated in solution. The dissociation is so rapid in speed that quinhydrone acts like a mixture of quinone and hydroquinone, and an inert electrode in a solution of quinhydrone can be made to serve as a reference electrode, or *half cell*, if connected to another half cell. This property has led to the use of quinhydrone in the potentiometric determination of hydrogen-ion concentrations in unknown solutions.

Alizarin.—*Potassium chlorate* may be used as the oxidizing agent in the preparation of alizarin from anthraquinonesulfonic acid by the caustic-fusion process. For this purpose, 50 parts of the sodium salt of anthra-

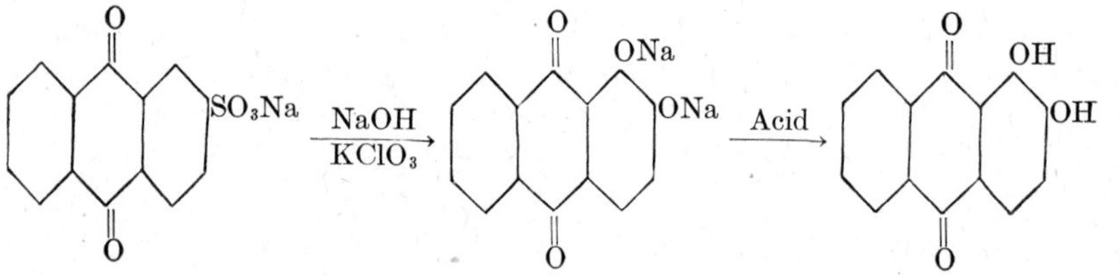

quinone-β-sulfonic acid, "*silver salt*," is stirred into 150 parts of sodium hydroxide and 150 parts of water contained in an autoclave, and 9 parts of potassium chlorate in 50 parts of water added. The substances are thoroughly mixed and heated in a closed autoclave for 30 to 36 hr. at a temperature of 170°C. The proportions of alkali may be modified so as to be but slightly in excess of theoretical, in which case modifications in temperature and time are necessary for the practical operation of the process. The alizarin is precipitated from the solution at the boiling point by the addition of sulfuric or hydrochloric acid. The fine crystals obtained in this way are filtered from the hot solution and washed with hot water until free from salts. The dye is not dried but is made up as a 16 to 20 per cent paste and marketed as such. The yield is about 70 parts of alizarin from 100 parts of the *"silver salt,"* or about 90 per cent of theoretical.

Malachite Green.—*Lead peroxide* is principally used in the oxidation of leuco compounds of the triphenylmethane group to the corresponding alcohols, the salts of which are dyestuffs. Thus, Malachite Green may be prepared as follows:[1] 16.5 gm. of tetramethyldiaminotriphenyl-methane is dissolved in 300 cc. of water and 20 gm. of concentrated hydrochloric acid. Sufficient ice is added to bring the volume to 400 cc. and the temperature to between 0 and 5°C. A lead peroxide paste made from 15.5 gm. of lead nitrate is slowly added, while the solution is rapidly stirred. The reaction is complete in 2 hr., and the lead is precipitated by the addition of sodium sulfate solution and is filtered off. The dye base is precipitated, in the form of a resinous mass, by the addition of 15 gm. of caustic soda and is recovered by filtration. For use, the base is converted to a crystalline salt of oxalic or sulfuric acid.

Leuco Base. Malachite Green   Dye Base. Malachite Green

Methyl Violet.—*Cupric sulfate* is employed in the formation of Methyl Violet from dimethylaniline. The process may be performed as follows: 600 to 800 parts by weight of finely divided sodium chloride is mixed with 50 parts of finely divided cupric sulfate, and a solution of 40 parts of phenol and 10 parts of water is added and stirred in; 100 parts of dimethylaniline is then added, and the mixture heated to 55 to 60°C. for 8 hr. or more. The hot product is poured or forced out of the reaction vessel and allowed to cool. The cooled product is broken up and added to 3,000 parts of boiling water to which 40 parts of calcium oxide has been added. The mixture is heated until free from lumps, settled, and the clear solution of salt and calcium phenate decanted off. The dye is recovered from the residue and purified by successive solution and salting out.

[1] FIERZ-DAVID, "Grundlegende Operationen der Farbenchemie," 2d ed., p. 153, Springer, Berlin (1922); "Dye Chemistry," p. 145, translated by Mason, Churchill, London (1921).

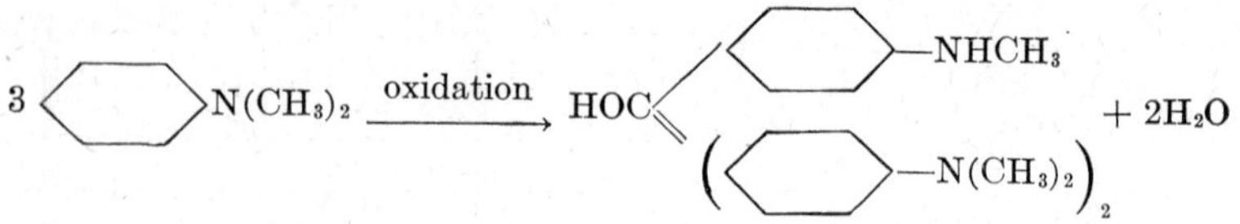

Methyl Violet Base

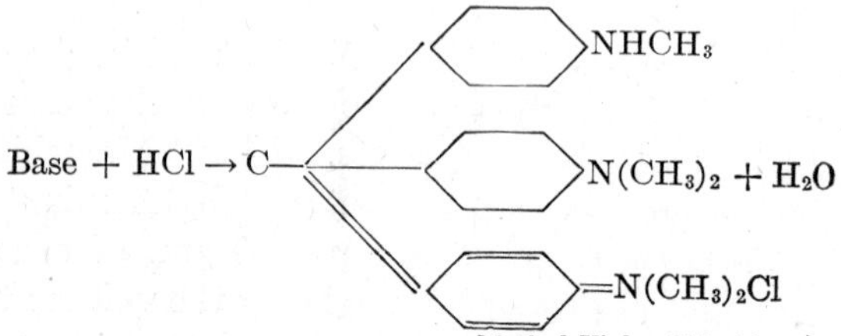

Methyl Violet Chloride

Oxidation of Toluene.—The use of *manganese dioxide* for the oxidation of toluene to benzaldehyde and benzoic acid was formerly extensive.[1] With manganese dioxide, the principal product is benzaldehyde; and for high yields of benzoic acid, a stronger oxidizing agent such as chromic acid is required. For benzaldehyde production, the reaction is usually carried to the point that about 50 parts of benzaldehyde and 250 parts of toluene are recovered from a batch operation starting with 300 parts of toluene. In order to prevent extensive oxidation to benzoic acid, oxidation is not carried further than this. The method is as follows: 300 kg. of toluene and 700 kg. of 65 per cent sulfuric acid are mixed with intense stirring, and then 90 kg. of finely powdered manganese dioxide added while the temperature is held at 40°C. Benzaldehyde is recovered by steam distillation and constitutes a chloride-free product. Benzoic acid forms as a by-product.

This method has been modified[2] so that manganese ammonium sulfate $(Mn_2(SO_4)_3 \cdot (NH_4)_2SO_4)$ is first electrolytically oxidized in dilute sulfuric acid solution and then mixed directly with toluene at 50°C. About 80 per cent of the toluene is oxidized to benzaldehyde. The manganese solution is recirculated through the oxidizing cell and reused. This process also yields a chloride-free product.

IV. LIQUID-PHASE OXIDATION WITH OXYGEN

The oxygen of the air is the cheapest available oxidizing agent but at the same time is perhaps the most difficult to control. Although atmospheric oxygen is constantly reacting with organic substances at ordinary temperature, the rates of the reactions are too slow, generally, to be of any significance from the standpoint of usefulness in chemical

[1] RASCHIG, *Chem. Ztg.*, **24**, 346 (1900); Monnet, Fr. 276,258; *Chem. Ztg.*, **22**, 929 (1898); **23**, 872 (1899).

[2] Lang, Ger. 189,178 (1907); *Chem. Zentr.*, **79**, I, 73 (1908).

synthesis. To induce molecular oxygen to react at commercially useful rates, it is usually necessary to provide a catalyst, or elevate the temperature, or to use a catalyst in conjunction with elevated temperatures. In many cases, the temperature must be elevated to the point where vapor-phase processes only are practicable. These will be dealt with later. In liquid-phase processes, catalysts may be either dissolved or suspended in finely divided form to insure contact with bubbles of gas containing oxygen which may be caused to pass through the liquid undergoing oxidation. To speed up production, means must be provided for initially raising the temperature and for later removing reaction heat. Where low temperatures and slow reaction rates are indicated, natural processes of heat flow to the atmosphere may suffice for temperature control.

Acetaldehyde to Acetic Acid.—The formation of acetic acid furnishes an excellent example of liquid-phase oxidation with molecular oxygen. Acetic acid may be obtained by the direct oxidation of ethanol, but the concentrated acid is generally obtained by oxidation methods from acetaldehyde that may have been formed by the hydration of acetylene or the oxidation of ethanol.[1] The oxidation usually occurs in acetic acid solution in the presence of a catalyst and at atmospheric or elevated pressures. Temperatures may range up to 100°C., depending upon conditions, but are usually lower.

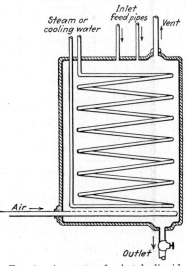

Fig 1.—Apparatus for batch, liquid-phase oxidation of acetaldehyde to acetic acid.

Figures 1 and 2 show the general type of apparatus used. The reaction vessel consists principally of an aluminum-lined steel vessel capable of holding 4,000 to 5,000 kg. (about 9,000 to 11,000 lb.) of acetaldehyde and fitted with aluminum coils for heating and cooling, inlet and outlet openings, and an air distributor.[2] In operation, about 4,500 kg. (about 10,000 lb.) of 99.0 to 99.8 per cent acetaldehyde previously cooled to 0 to 5°C. is first introduced, and then 18 to 22 kg. (about 39.6 to 48.4 lb.) of manganese acetate is introduced either in the form of a saturated acetic acid solution or as a powder ground to pass a 200-

---

[1] Cf. Hale and Haldeman, Brit. 287,064 (1927); Fr. 650,771 (1928); also, *Chem. Age*, **23**, 272–276 (1930).

[2] CADENHEAD [*Chem. Met. Eng.*, **40**, 184–188 (1933)] states that 1,000-gal. kettles are used.

mesh sieve. Air is introduced through the distributor head, and at the same time steam is passed through the aluminum coils to raise the temperature gradually to the operating point. When reaction starts, oxygen absorption from the incoming air is almost complete, and the heat of reaction must be removed by cooling water, which is substituted for the initial steam. The temperature is so controlled that after 1 hr. it approximates 27°C.; after 2 hr., 28 to 30°C.; and after 4 hr., 60°C. The most satisfactory operating temperature is about 60°C. Reaction is complete in about 12 to 14 hr. The pressure is not allowed to exceed 5 kg. per square centimeter (65.3 lb. per square inch), the nitrogen being vented

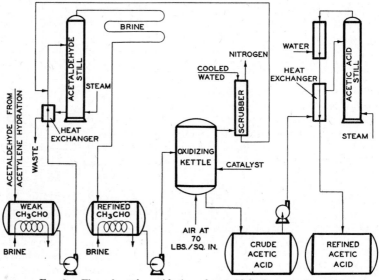

Fig. 2.—Flow sheet for oxidation of acetaldehyde to acetic acid.

through a series of condensers attached to the dome. Condensed aldehyde is returned to the kettle. Before being released, the nitrogen is passed through water scrubbers to remove the last of the aldehyde, which is later recovered. A concentrated acetic acid, exceeding 96 per cent in strength, results. Distillation is used for final concentration and purification of acid. The yield varies from 88 to 95 per cent of the theoretical. A retort of this size will yield about 60 tons of 99 per cent acid per month when operated normally or about 80 to 100 tons per month when forced.

To reduce the hazard introduced by possible formation of excessive concentrations of peracetic acid, $\left(CH_3C \underset{\diagdown O}{\overset{\diagup O\cdot OH}{}} \right)$, efforts have been made to operate in such a way that the oxidized acetic acid-peracid-aldehyde solution is made to circulate through ceramic-packed towers against the gas stream containing unreacted aldehyde.[1] In this way the acid may be built up in strength while maintaining low concentrations only of the peracid.

Ethanol to Acetic Acid.—Pure ethanol exposed to air at normal temperatures does not undergo marked oxidation, but the introduction of platinum black causes oxidation to acetic acid. Other catalysts may also be used to effect this same oxidation, but the liquid-phase oxidation of ethanol by the quick-vinegar process has been most widely practiced. In this case, the presence of *Mycoderma aceti* is used to convey oxygen to the alcohol and effect oxidation.

In the early practice of the quick-vinegar process, wooden tanks about 3 to 4 ft. in diameter and 8 to 10 ft. high filled with beechwood shavings, other cellulosic material, or even coke which carry the micro-organism *Mycoderma aceti* have been used. A dilute alcohol solution containing up to 12 to 15 per cent ethanol is allowed to trickle down over the packing material. Oxygen, as air, introduced at the bottom of the vat becomes heated from the heat of the reaction, rises, and passes out at the top. Functioning of the microorganism is best in a dilute acid solution and ceases at acid concentrations of about 12 per cent. A temperature of about 35°C. is most satisfactory. The product consists of a dilute acetic acid solution containing up to about 10 per cent acid. The small vats described are capable of producing up to about 8 gal. of this dilute acid per day. The size of vat has been dictated largely by difficulty of culture control. Improved processes at present permit the use of larger apparatus, and the trend is in this direction. One plant in this country is said to have a capacity for producing 10,000,000 lb. of acetic acid per year by this quick-vinegar process.[2] The best modern practice makes use of earthenware towers filled with beechwood shavings and fitted at the top with automatic spray devices for feeding in the dilute alcohol mixture or fermented mash solution.

Theoretically, 100 parts by weight of C_2H_5OH yield 130 parts of CH_3COOH by oxidation, equivalent to slightly over 1 kg. of acid per liter of alcohol. In practice, such 100 per cent yields are never obtained. Yields of from 80 to 90 per cent of theory have been obtained in careful laboratory work, and 70 per cent yields are normally obtained in good industrial practice. The losses may be due to incomplete oxidation or to excessive oxidation through lack of proper control. Losses are also due to volatilization of acid and alcohol in the stream of exit gases. High rates of air flow and excessive temperatures lead to increased evaporation

---

[1] Wiesler, U. S. 1,953,381 (1934).

[2] PARTRIDGE, *Ind. Eng. Chem.*, **23**, 488 (1931).

of the solution in the vats. To prevent this loss, the exit gases, after cooling, may be scrubbed with water, and the resulting solution added to the feed.

It should be noted that, although the oxidizing conditions are apparently mild, the process does not stop at the aldehyde step but continues all the way to the acid. This may in part be attributed to the mechanism of this process, but, as it is also characteristic of other oxidation reactions, the reactivity of the intermediate may be conceived to play an important part. In this case, the final product, acetic acid, is quite stable toward further oxidation. However, the intermediate aldehyde is far more reactive to oxygen than is the starting material, ethanol. In general, the simple organic acids are comparatively stable toward oxidation; aldehydes are very readily oxidized; alcohols oxidize with ease; and the corresponding hydrocarbon oxidizes only with difficulty. Exceptions are to be found to this order, however, as in the case of ethyl benzene, which has been found to oxidize more readily than the corresponding alcohol, phenylethyl alcohol. Aldehydes may be considered the most readily oxidized of the simple organic compounds.

Hydrocarbons to Acids.—Continued efforts have been made to obtain high-molecular-weight fatty acids from the oxidation of such petroleum hydrocarbons as paraffin wax, petrolatum, and petroleum white oils, and many patents have been issued for such processes. Much of this work has been directed toward the formation of fatty acids suitable for soap manufacture and the production of edible fats in nations without adequate supplies of the natural materials. Thus, in the U.S.S.R. the production of 2,000 tons of fatty acids in 1935 and a projected capacity of 20,000 tons per year in 1936 has been reported.[1] Liquid-phase oxidations of this type have been practiced in the United States for production of fatty acids suitable for use as chemical intermediates.

In general, oxidation of the paraffin hydrocarbons has been accomplished by injecting air or oxygen into the heated oil or wax and allowing the gases to bubble through a relatively thick layer of the oil. It has been necessary to use catalysts for such oxidations to keep operating temperatures low and to speed up the reaction to a point where prolonged exposure of product to oxygen and elevated temperatures would not be necessary. Many difficulties have been encountered, and progress has been slow. The acids tend to be aldehydic or hydroxylated in character; undesirable esters and other oxygenated compounds are formed; gums tend to be deposited; polymerization and condensation reactions which occur during the subsequent saponification operations give undesirable colors and odors to the product; separation of unoxidized hydrocarbons from the products is often difficult, etc. Volatile compounds, other than

[1] *Chem. Age (London),* **34,** 518 (1936).

carbon oxides and steam, also form, and may be recovered from the gases leaving the oxidation zone. Small quantities of the lower fatty acids, such as formic, acetic, propionic, etc., are produced and may be recovered with the water-soluble volatile products by scrubbing the exit gases with water, or by extracting the oxidation mass with water.

In general, soluble catalysts have been used in the form of fatty acid salts, alcoholates, etc., of the metals capable of existing in combination in more than one valence form. Manganese compounds, such as the acetate or stearate, form good examples of the catalyst types. Cobalt and mercury catalysts tend to increase gum formation, and lead catalysts are of low activity. Catalyst mixtures consisting of at least one compound of an alkali metal and of aluminum have been found effective.[1] With 1 per cent manganese stearate in a paraffin wax, it is possible to oxidize at a temperature of 125°C. by injecting air, so that after 18 hr. a product with a saponification number of 232 and an acid number of 108 is obtained. As much as 15 to 20 per cent unsaponifiable matter remains in the product, even after prolonged injection of oxygen.[2] Without catalysts, oxidation does not start at a useful rate until a temperature of 150 to 160°C. is reached and does not become rapid until somewhat higher temperatures have been attained.

Even with a catalyst, long periods of time are necessary for the oxidation of a batch of oil or wax to approach completion when air is simply bubbled through the liquid. By bringing about very intimate contact between air and the hydrocarbon oil to be oxidized through the formation of a foam of the liquid, the time of oxidation and the temperature for oxidation are both considerably reduced, losses through formation of low-molecular-weight oxidation products decreased, and the yield and quality of product increased. One method proposed for accomplishing this end is shown in Fig. 3. Admission of air through a porous diaphragm, properly placed, is used to induce a frothy condition in the material being oxidized and a portion of the reacting material is recirculated through an external heat exchanger for temperature control. By continuously admitting unoxidized material and withdrawing oxidized product in regulated streams the process may be made continuous. Either dissolved catalysts or solid catalysts fixed in place with fluid passing over them may be used.[3] Oxidation of crude paraffin wax (m. p., 50°C.) with air in the presence of a dissolved manganese catalyst for 8 hr. at 110 to 115°C. in such an apparatus yields a yellow product

[1] Dietrich and Luther, U. S. 2,000,222 (1935).

[2] ZERNER, *Chem. Zeit.*, **54**, 257–259, 279–281 (1930); also, Anon., *Chem. Age*, **23**, 254–255 (1930).

[3] Luther and Goetze, U. S. 2,015,347 (1936); U. S. 2,095,338 (1937); Keunecke, U. S. 2,095,473 (1937).

having an acid number of 95 and a saponification number of 152. Light-colored fatty acids having a saponification number of 220 may be recovered. Since the rate of reaction increases with increase in oxygen concentration, the use of enriched air, oxygen, or air under pressures of from 150 to 500 lb. per square inch has been advocated. To reduce the troublesome polymerization and condensation reactions attending the oxidation, the liquid hydrocarbon may be diluted with oxidation-resisting substances such as acetic anhydride or other low-molecular-weight organic acids or anhydrides.

The composition of the product is generally so complex as to defy chemical analysis for identification of the constituent compounds.[1] It is consequently difficult to postulate any definite series of reactions for the oxidation. Based on the experience of the I. G. Farbenindustrie A-G., Krauch has, however, proposed a tentative scheme for the oxidation mechanism by postulating that oxygen attacks the paraffin molecule toward the middle and not on the ends.[2] This proposal is supported by the facts that a portion of the acids formed contains about half the number of carbon atoms as the original paraffin molecule and that the small amounts of carbon oxides and low-molecular-weight oxidation products preclude oxidation from one end of the large molecules to form the acids in the product.

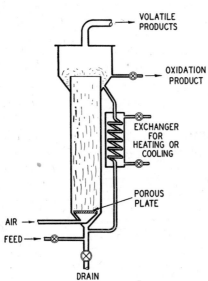

Fig. 3.—Arrangement of apparatus for liquid-phase oxidation of hydrocarbons to fatty acids.

The formation of an acid product having an average chain length of 12 to 14 carbon atoms, as calculated from the equivalent weight of the acid product, from a paraffin wax averaging 24 carbon atoms per molecule, would seem to substantiate this postulated mechanism.[3] However, the fact that such an acid product consists of a variety of acids of varying chain length makes it seem more probable that the oxygen attack is distributed and that rupture may occur at various points in the affected molecules. This action of oxygen on the high-molecular-weight paraffinic hydrocarbons at moderate temperatures and in the liquid phase is con-

[1] COLLIN, *J. Soc. Chem. Ind.*, **49**, 333T (1930).

[2] KRAUCH, *Proc. 2d Intern. Conf. Bituminous Coal*, I, 43 (1928).

[3] BURWELL, *Ind. Eng. Chem.*, **26**, 204–207 (1934).

trary to that noted in the vapor-phase oxidation of the lower-molecular-weight hydrocarbons at more elevated temperatures, where oxidation starts at the end of the longest carbon chain present in the molecule and continues from this point. The small amount of gaseous products obtained in the liquid-phase process precludes the possibility that the lower-molecular-weight products are produced by the progressive destructive oxidation of the high-molecular-weight starting material, and the low temperatures seem to eliminate the possibility that thermal decomposition can account for the low-molecular-weight material obtained.

Naturally, separation and recovery of the desired fatty acids are difficult from such mixed products, and many recovery processes have been patented. Thus, extraction of the acid portion of such oxidation product with concentrated phosphoric acid permits separation of the hydroxylated acids from the fatty acids.[1] The organic acids are usually removed from the unoxidized hydrocarbon, alcohols, aldehydes, ketones, esters, etc., by saponification with an alkali[2] and extraction as a water-soluble soap.

Indigo Synthesis.—Another example of air oxidation is to be found in the indigo synthesis. Chloroacetic acid is condensed with aniline to form phenylglycine which when fused with sodamide loses a molecule of water and forms indoxyl. The red-brown melt obtained in the fusion

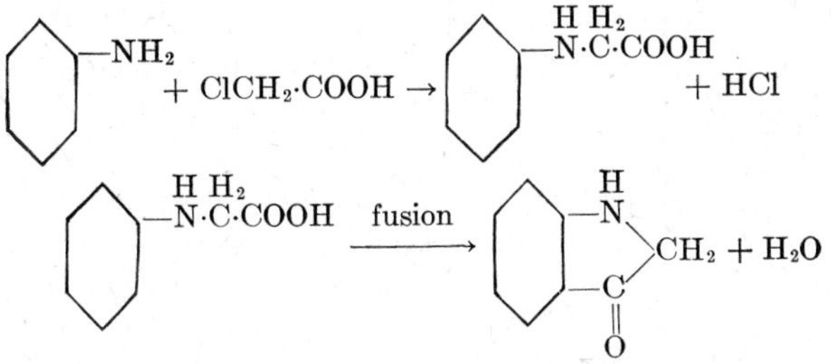

Phenylglycine   Indoxyl (Keto Form)

of phenylglycine, sodamide, and sodium hydroxide is dissolved in a large volume of water. Air is then blown through this alkaline solution for several hours, and the indoxyl becomes oxidized to indigo which separates out in small crystals. The indigo is recovered

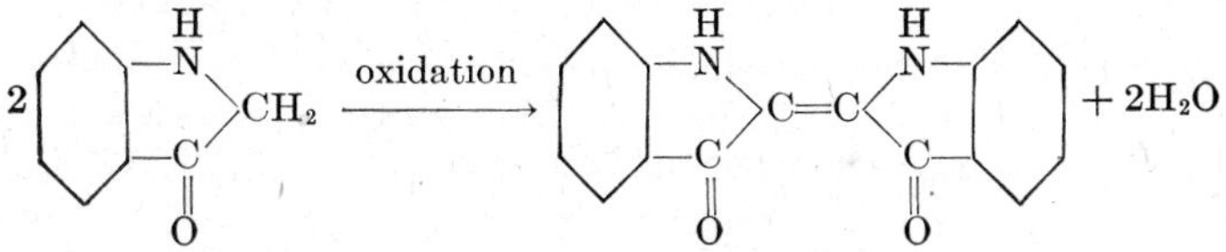

Indoxyl (Keto Form)   Indigo

[1] Vesterdal, U. S. 2,038,617 (1936).
[2] Beller and Luther, U. S. 1,931,859 (1933).

by filtration, and the crystals washed and made up to a paste with water. A yield of close to 90 per cent of theory is obtained.

This capacity to undergo ready oxidation in alkaline solution is made use of in the dyeing of fabrics with indoxyl. In practice, the indigo is reduced to the leuco base, which is water soluble; and the fabric to be dyed is soaked in an alkaline solution of this dye base. Exposure of the fabric to the air fixes the dye by the oxidation of the leuco base to the insoluble indigo blue. Such a process is known as vat dyeing, and indigo is one of the most important of the dyes applied in this manner.

V. VAPOR-PHASE OXIDATION OF ALIPHATIC COMPOUNDS[1]

Almost without exception, the vapor-phase processes employed in the partial oxidation of organic compounds use molecular oxygen as the oxidizing agent and require catalysts and elevated temperatures for operation at industrially useful rates. Only certain substances are fitted for vapor-phase processing. These must have sufficiently high vapor pressures at the temperatures required for oxidation to make it possible to mix them with air (oxygen) and pass them in the gaseous state over the catalyst material. They must be of sufficient thermal stability to resist undesired decomposition and give rise to products of comparable thermal stability. Furthermore, the products must represent configurations reasonably stable to continued oxidation and must be readily recoverable from the gaseous products.

It will be found that these various restrictions limit the materials capable of economic processing by vapor-phase oxidation to the simpler aliphatic compounds and the aromatic series of compounds. Because the methods applied to these two classes of compound are characterized by consideration for group properties, they will be treated separately.

Oxidation of Methanol.—Consideration of the reactions involved in the synthesis and decomposition of methanol shows that only low conversions to formaldehyde may be obtained by the direct catalytic decomposition of the alcohol.

$$CH_3OH \rightarrow H_2CO + H_2 \rightarrow CO + 2H_2$$

Catalysts and temperatures conducive to the dehydrogenation of methanol are also conducive to the decomposition of the formaldehyde to hydrogen and carbon monoxide. Furthermore, the reaction is endothermic, and heat must be supplied.

[1] Sections V, VI, and VII are based on parts of the *American Chemical Society Monograph*, 61, Catalytic Oxidation of Organic Compounds in the Vapor Phase, by Marek and Hahn (1922). Use has been made of text and illustrations through the kind permission of the publishers, Chemical Catalog Company.

However, if oxygen, in the form of air, is furnished to the reaction, and the process conducted in the vapor phase in the presence of suitable catalysts, industrially practicable yields of formaldehyde are obtained, and the process is made exothermic. Practically all the formaldehyde used today is produced in this way. Although the process appears simple, it requires regulation of temperature, air-to-alcohol ratio, and time of contact to insure continuous high yields at high efficiency. A simple, practical method consists in mixing air with methanol, passing the resulting air-methanol mixture over a hot copper-gauze catalyst (see Fig. 4), condensing the gaseous reaction mixture, and recovering the product.

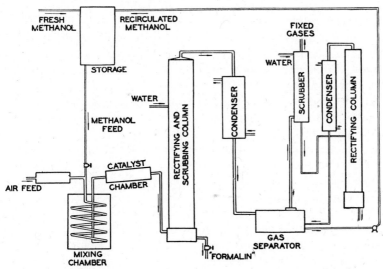

Fig. 4.—Schematic layout for oxidation of methanol to formaldehyde.

For oxidation to formaldehyde, 1 lb. of pure methanol theoretically requires 26.7 cu. ft. of dry air measured under standard conditions (2.18 lb.). By bubbling air through the liquid methanol, this proportion can be only approximately maintained, and more positive methods of control are needed. Exact control of the ratio is made possible by the use of separate, controlled streams of air and liquid methanol introduced to a vaporizing chamber, which is supplied with heat to vaporize the liquid. Cleaned, dry air is supplied through a storage tank by a compressor, and methanol enters the mixing chamber as a liquid. Only small amounts of mixed air and vapor are present at any time; the mixture passes immediately to the catalyst chamber and thence to the recovery system.

Large amounts of formaldehyde have been made with a catalyst generally consisting of copper arranged in the form of gauze rolls supported in concentrically arranged bundles of copper tubes, which, in turn, are held by headers on each end. Such a catalyst chamber may consist of six or eight copper tubes 24 in. long and 2 in. in diameter containing rolled-up copper gauze for about 4 or 5 in. of their length, fitted into suitable headers at each end, and inclosed in a cover. Means are provided for heating the catalyst mass at the start of operation. Reaction occurs at a temperature of 400 to 450°C., and operation is conducted at a temperature of about 550 to 600°C. in the catalyst mass. The rate of feed and the air-methanol ratio are maintained so as to make operation autothermal. The gaseous mixture passes from catalyst chamber to a rectifying and recovery system, where rapid countercurrent cooling is obtained by contact with the relatively cool aqueous formaldehyde solution passing down the column. Formaldehyde solution is withdrawn at the bottom of the column, and fixed gases containing the vapor of unreacted methanol are passed out of the top to a condenser where the methanol is partly recovered. The fixed gases from this condenser are scrubbed with water or dilute methanol solution for complete methanol recovery. Condensed methanol and methanol recovered from the aqueous solution by rectification are fed back to the mixing chamber for recirculation over the catalyst. Methanol containing very little formaldehyde may be obtained by the rectification of solutions containing as much as 38 per cent of formaldehyde so as to leave very little methanol in the residual aqueous solution.

The development of more active and directive catalysts for methanol oxidation has resulted in important process improvements. The use of reaction temperatures of 300°C. (572°F.), or less, by means of catalysts such as molybdenum promoted with iron, vanadium, or other elements, or vanadium promoted with an element of the fifth or sixth group of the periodic system makes it possible to use multiple-tube reaction chambers with heat removal by circulated liquids (Fig. 9) and to use air ratios such that more complete oxidation of methanol per pass is obtained without loss in yield.[1] Thus, it is possible to increase materially the capacity of a reaction unit, to reduce the by-product CO, CO_2, and acid produced, to increase the oxidation efficiency to a point where methanol need not be recovered and recirculated, and to increase the over-all process efficiency. By way of example, such an operation performed: with a catalyst formed of a mixture of molybdenum trioxide and 8 to 20 per cent by weight of ferric oxide, screened to 8-mesh particles and packed 9 in. deep in a tubular catalytic chamber immersed in a heat-removing liquid bath at 250°C. (482°F.); with a reaction mixture of

[1] Meharg and Adkins, U. S. 1,913,404–5 (1933); Punnett, U. S. 2,065,394 (1936); *Cf.* Craver, U. S. 1,914,557 (1933); 1,914,558 (1933); Punnett, U. S. 1,978,506 (1934); Bailey and Craver, U. S. 1,383,059 (1921); Downs, U. S. 1,604,739 (1926).

8 to 10 per cent by weight methanol vapor and 90 to 92 per cent air (4.2 to 5.4 times theoretical air); and with a time of contact of 0.01 to 0.03 sec., results in a 95 per cent conversion of methanol to formaldehyde and 5 per cent conversion to by-products comprised almost wholly of CO and CO_2.[1]

The water formed by reaction is not sufficient to bring the formaldehyde solution to the 37.0 to 37.5 per cent by weight concentration, at which it is generally sold, and some water must be added. Commercial formaldehyde contains some methanol, which has the effect of preventing the formation of insoluble polymers. Thus, a solution with 5 per cent methanol and 41 gm. of formaldehyde per 100 cc. of solution does not deposit a polymer on long exposure at 0°C., whereas one containing no methanol and 38.7 gm. of formaldehyde per 100 cc. deposits a solid, white polymer with only slight cooling. The presence of methanol also tends to increase the vapor pressure of formaldehyde over the aqueous solution.[2]

Formaldehyde also appears on the market as the hydrated, solid polymer *paraformaldehyde*, containing about 95 per cent formaldehyde which is prepared by the evaporation of formaldehyde solution.

According to theory, 100 gm. of pure methanol should yield 93.75 gm. of pure formaldehyde; but in practice, only about 82 to 85 per cent of theoretical yield is obtained. Conversions as high as 96 per cent are possible with laboratory methods and have been approached for short periods in commercial apparatus. At the ordinary conversion efficiency, 100 lb. of methanol yield between 190 and 200 lb. of commercial formaldehyde solution.

Oxidation of Ethanol.—On a laboratory scale, ethanol may be dehydrogenated or oxidized to acetaldehyde in the vapor phase with good yields. Various investigators have reported maximum conversions in the range of 70 to over 80 per cent. Commercially, however, this method of acetaldehyde production would have to compete with the hydration-of-acetylene process, which permits the production of acetaldehyde at a low cost. Copper- and silver-gauze catalysts are effective for oxidation[3] and chromium-activated copper catalysts[4] for the dehydrogenation.

Difficulty has been encountered, however, in effecting the direct oxidation of ethanol to acetic acid in a continuous, catalytic, vapor-phase process. Losses to formaldehyde, carbon oxides, etc., are difficult to prevent.

[1] Meharg and Adkins, *loc. cit.*
[2] BLAIR and LEDBURY, *J. Chem. Soc.*, **127**, 26–40 (1925).
[3] Fuchs, U. S. 1,956,440 (1934).
[4] Young, U. S. 1,977,750 (1934).

Oxidation of Low-molecular-weight Paraffin Hydrocarbons.—Attempts to utilize as chemical intermediates the enormous quantities of the gaseous saturated and unsaturated hydrocarbons available at low cost in the form of natural and refinery gases have stimulated numerous experimental programs on oxidation, both catalytic and non-catalytic. Many of the early investigations were conducted by simply heating mixtures of air or oxygen and the hydrocarbons. Recent efforts have been directed toward the control of oxygen concentration, temperature, and reaction rate by the use of selective catalysts and elevated pressures, with the purpose of stopping the oxidation at an intermediate stage where the products constitute useful substances. It will not be possible to enumerate all of the conditions that have been used, the catalysts that have been explored, and the results that have been obtained; examples of only a few representative cases will be given.

Although no general, large-scale developments have followed the experimental investigations in this field, considerable information has been disclosed—valuable in that it shows the limitations present in such reactions and more or less defines the probable directions that industrial development will be required to take. The laboratory work has greatly increased the store of knowledge regarding oxidation processes, in general, and combustion processes in particular. The information has been applied in many ways, both directly and indirectly.

In considering the catalysis of oxidation reactions, particularly of aliphatic hydrocarbons at atmospheric pressure, it must be recognized that the oxidation reactions are probably stepwise with each successive step occurring with greater ease. The type of reaction for the successive steps is the same; and when a carbon compound containing oxygen is oxidized further, *it is the hydrogen atoms joined to the carbon atom already in combination with oxygen that are attacked*. Thus, the point of first attack continues to be the point for successive attacks. This has been clearly shown for the case of the oxidation of the isomeric octanes, where the methyl group at the end of the longest free straight chain is first attacked and the oxidation continues along the chain to a point where a resistance to further oxidation is encountered. At such a point— represented by formation of a ketone structure at the point where the chain branch ends in the case of the iso-octanes—oxidation may be partly arrested, and the product recovered before decomposition or oxidation can destroy it. However, a considerable portion of the hydrocarbon will have been destroyed when this point is reached, a large amount of heat will consequently have been liberated, and only a low yield of any single ketone will have been obtained from a mixture of isomeric hydrocarbons.[1]

[1] Pope, Dykstra, and Edgar, *J. Am. Chem. Soc.*, **51**, 1875–1879, 2203–2213 (1929).

To obtain useful and desirable intermediate products of oxidation from the aliphatic hydrocarbons, it is necessary that only relatively small proportions of oxygen be made to react with the hydrocarbon molecule. However, this limited reaction is difficult of practical attainment; and with the normally gaseous straight-chain aliphatic hydrocarbons, almost regardless of molecular weight, appreciable yields of only formaldehyde have been reported to result from the oxidation in the presence of solid catalysts at atmospheric pressure. Alcohols have been obtained under certain special conditions to be discussed later, and ketones have been reported to result from the oxidation of branched chain hydrocarbons. The higher-molecular-weight aliphatic hydrocarbons, oxidizing more readily under less stringent conditions, may be converted to relatively long-chain acids, etc.

The principal difficulty in dealing with methane, the most abundant of these gaseous hydrocarbons, is the unreactive nature of the substance. At the temperature required for active reaction between methane and oxygen, the desired products (methanol and formaldehyde) are thermodynamically unstable at a pressure of 1 atmos. The ignition temperature of methane in air is 695 to 742°C. and represents the temperature at which the rate of reaction between methane and oxygen is sufficiently rapid to make the reaction self-sustaining and capable of propagating through the combustible mixture. Somewhat lower temperatures may be used at the longer times of contact employed in partial oxidation, and application of catalysis is of benefit in lowering the reaction temperature further. However, even at the temperatures made possible through the use of catalysts, the products are largely unstable to dissociation and are made more subject to destruction through either increased reaction rate or continued oxidation. The net result of the use of solid catalysts has been, therefore, the increased rate at which methane may be made to react with very little benefit toward increased conversions of hydrocarbon to product at per-pass yields that would warrant industrial application.

Numerous materials have been reported and patented as catalysts for the oxidation of the gaseous paraffin hydrocarbons. The majority of these, consisting mainly of metals or metal oxides, are far too active and too non-specific in action to permit the recovery of more than small amounts of intermediate oxidation product. With such relatively mild catalysts as copper oxide and glass surfaces, some high yields of formaldehyde have been obtained from methane and ethane under experimental conditions. Under conditions such that less than 10 per cent of the entering hydrocarbon is oxidized, conversions of over 50 per cent of reacting hydrocarbon to formaldehyde have been reported. The necessity of recovering formaldehyde from such dilute gaseous mixtures as may be thus obtained and of recycling the unreacted hydrocarbon militates against the industrialization of the process. Furthermore, the use of air as a source of oxygen introduces inert nitrogen, which further serves to dilute the product. Even the use of pure oxygen permits an estimated recovery of methane as formaldehyde of only about 30 per cent—too low for commercial adaptation unless the hydrocarbon is available at practically no cost.[1]

Oxidation of natural gas with very low oxygen concentrations under slight pressure and in the presence of a catalyst[2] has been shown capable of producing a useful mixture of oxygenated products, *i.e.*, formaldehyde, acetaldehyde, and methanol. Such a process, representing a by-product of the major industry of transporting natural gas, should be capable of yielding formaldehyde in competition with the usual method of forming it from methanol by oxidation.[3] The results are indicative of what may be accomplished by a modified direct oxidation process.

The aliphatic hydrocarbons become progressively more easily oxidized as the number of carbon atoms in the free straight chain is increased. This is shown by a comparison of the ignition temperatures of several normal paraffin hydrocarbons. Thus:

Hydrocarbon	Ignition Temperature,[1] °C.
Methane	695 to 742
Ethane	534 to 594
Propane	514 to 588
n-Butane	489 to 569
n-Pentane	476 to 548

[1] International Critical Tables, III, 173.

However, despite this greater ease of attack by oxygen, the gaseous paraffin hydrocarbons higher than methane have received less experimental attention, particularly as pure individuals.

As might be expected, higher yields of intermediate oxidation products, particularly formaldehyde, are obtainable from the oxidation of the higher members of the group. Indeed, the greater yield of formaldehyde obtained from ethane throws doubt on some of the high yields that have been reported from the oxidation of "methane."

By conducting the oxidation of these low-molecular-weight paraffin hydrocarbons under high pressures, it has been possible to obtain alcohols, increased yields of aldehydes, and acids as oxidation products. Conditions claimed for the pressure processes include (1) pressures of from 50 to 250 atmos.; (2) temperatures from 200 to 600°C.; (3) low oxygen to

[1] LEDBURY and BLAIR, *Dept. Sci. Ind. Research (Brit.), Rept.* 1, 1–54 (1927).

[2] Generally purported to be copper-copper oxide.

[3] BROOKS, *J. Inst. Petroleum Tech.*, **24**, 744 (1928); BURRELL, *Nat. Petroleum News*, **22**, No. 22, 80 (1930).

hydrocarbon ratios ranging from 5 to 15 mole per cent; with (4) short time of contact; and (5) the presence of a variety of catalysts. The more extreme conditions have been found necessary for the lower members of the paraffin series. Although the low proportions of oxygen may account for part of the effects that have been observed from pressure oxidation, the major results must be attributed to the effect of the elevated pressure.

One of the major effects of the elevated pressures is the lowering of the reaction temperature and the consequent lessening of the tendency for thermal decomposition of the products. Thus, whereas the non-catalytic oxidation of methane requires a temperature of 600 to 700°C. at atmospheric pressure and results in the formation of formaldehyde as the least oxidized intermediate product obtainable in appreciable quantities, a temperature of only 360°C. is required for oxidation at 100 atmos. pressure with a 9:1 methane-oxygen ratio and leads to the formation of methanol. Comparable lowering of temperature has been obtained with the higher hydrocarbons.

Since decomposition of the intermediate oxidation products results in an increase in the number of molecules, pressure is effective in further suppressing loss of the desired intermediate by decomposition. Where high oxygen ratios are used, pressure may be of additional benefit by decreasing the rate at which fresh oxygen can diffuse up to partially oxidized molecules and attack them further.

Newitt and Haffner,[1] working in Bone's laboratory, have been able to obtain considerable quantities of methanol by the slow combustion of methane at high pressures. An 8.1:1 methane-oxygen (11 mole per cent oxygen) mixture was allowed to react in a steel chamber at different temperatures and pressures. Reaction appeared to be predominantly heterogeneous, since an increase in the surface-to-volume ratio of the chamber caused a several-fold increase in reaction rate. A pronounced induction period was observed, but no peroxides were found in the product. The effects of increasing the pressure from 48.2 to 150 atmos. were to increase (1) the rate of reaction or lower the temperature required for a given rate; (2) the amount of methanol and formaldehyde in the product; and (3) the ratio of methanol to formaldehyde in the product. In all cases, carbon monoxide and carbon dioxide represented upward of 70 per cent of the methane that reacted. Results from representative runs are as shown in the table on page 398.

Pichler and Reder[2] have qualitatively confirmed the results of Newitt and Haffner on the pressure oxidation of methane but did not report such high yields on the basis of methane reacted. However, these

[1] NEWITT and HAFFNER, *Proc. Roy. Soc.* (*London*), **A134**, 591–604 (1932).
[2] PICHLER and REDER, *Z. angew. Chem.*, **46**, 161–165 (1933).

TABLE I.—PRESSURE OXIDATION OF METHANE

Pressure, atmos.	Initial temp., °C.	Time, min.	Yield based on percentage of methane reacting to form	
			Methanol	Formaldehyde
10	400	10	1.1	None
25	385	7	4.8	0.66
40	372	15	6.1	1.20
48	373	4	13.7	0.8
106.4	341	12	22.3	0.75
149	341	16	19.0	0.60

workers extended their work to include a series of flow runs at 100 atmos. total pressure. At this pressure, a series of runs was made at 500°C. and with various oxygen concentrations. These runs showed that a higher temperature was needed for reaction than in the case of the static (bomb) runs but that better yields were obtainable at comparable pressures. Conversion increased as the oxygen concentration was lowered, until at 0.6 per cent oxygen about 60 per cent of the entering oxygen appeared in the product as methanol.

Oxidation of ethane (97.3 per cent ethane + 2.7 per cent nitrogen) in batch experiments with low concentrations of oxygen at temperatures of 260 to 310°C. and pressures of 15 to 100 atmos. results in the formation of high yields of liquid, water-soluble products with considerable proportions of ethanol.[1] Representative experimental results are shown in Table II.

In general, the oxidized product from the pressure oxidation of hydrocarbons above methane in molecular weight may be expected to consist of a mixture of oxygenated organic compounds comprising alcohols, aldehydes, ketones, acids, esters, etc., together with water and carbon oxides. The recovery and purification of the small amounts of desired products from the relatively large amounts of unreacted hydrocarbons and the water present a formidable problem, especially with the higher hydrocarbons. No detailed accounts of the contemplated methods for separation of the product into useful constituents are available, but it is conceivable that the esterification of mixed alcohol fractions would furnish an outlet in the medium of a lacquer solvent. Another possible use for the alcohols would be in admixture with gasoline to furnish a non-knocking fuel, provided that they could be produced at a low cost.

Oxidation of propane at pressures up to 100 atmos. and in the temperature range of 250 to 373°C. (482 to 703°F.) with ratios of 1:20 to 1:0.5

[1] NEWITT and BLACK, *Proc. Roy. Soc.* (*London*), **A140**, 426, 439 (1933).

TABLE II.—PRESSURE OXIDATION OF ETHANE

| Conditions of experiment | | | | | | Percentage of C in reacted ethane appearing as | | | | | | |
| Composition reacting mixture, % | | Initial pressure, atmos. | Initial temp., °C. | Duration of run, min. | | C_2H_5OH | CH_3OH | CH_3CHO | $HCHO$ | CH_3COOH | $HCOOH$ | Total condensed product |
C_2H_6	O_2			Induction	Reaction							
90	10	100	272	5.5	3.25	36.5	20.0	8.0	0.30	6.5	0.4	71.7
88.2	11.8	100	262.2	25.0	15.0	22.6	10.5	6.2	0.04	27.2	0.8	67.34
84.5	15.5	100	271.8	....	....	7.4	10.0	4.8	0.90	2.4	0.15	25.65
88.4	11.6	15	315	....	3.0	16.0	19.4	1.9	4.5	0	0	41.8

Whole of free oxygen consumed at expiration of run. Remainder of C from ethane appeared as CO, CO₂, and sometimes CH₄ in the gaseous product.

propane to air results in formation of isopropyl alcohol and acetone, indicating oxygen attack at the β-carbon atom, and considerable proportions of *n*-propyl, ethyl, and methyl alcohols, indicating oxygen attack at the end of the molecule.[1]   *The higher pressures were found to favor the higher alcohols.*

Results from the oxidation of propane and *n*-butane with elemental oxygen at pressures of 130 to 170 atmos. and temperatures of 280 to 350°C. show that more than 40 per cent of the oxygen may appear in the

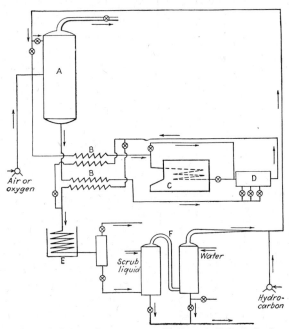

Fig. 5.—Schematic layout for pressure oxidation of aliphatic hydrocarbons.

A. Oxygen saturator.
B. Preheater (heat exchangers).
C. Furnace.

D. High-pressure reactor.
E. Cooler and gas separator.
F. Scrubbing system.

form of liquid organic products.[2]   Thus, representative yields from flow experiments are as shown in Table III.

The composition of the product, as reported, indicates that the tendency is for the formation of alcohols with one or two carbon atoms less per molecule than the parent hydrocarbon.   The lower pressures also favor the formation of greater proportions of the lower alcohols and of acids.

Pressure oxidation of the heptanes and hexanes results in the formation of still more complex mixtures, containing high proportions of alco-

---

[1] Newitt and Schmidt, *J. Chem. Soc.*, **1937**, 1665–1669.
[2] Wiezevich and Frolich, *Ind. & Eng. Chem.*, **26**, 267 (1934).

hols. Recirculation of the oxidized product results in the formation of high proportions of organic acids.

These results teach that elevated pressures are extremely useful in controlling and tempering the oxidation reaction between molecular oxygen and low-molecular-weight hydrocarbons. Even so, it is necessary to use a limited supply of oxygen and to depend upon recirculation of the hydrocarbon in order to obtain high over-all conversions to useful prod-

TABLE III.—PRESSURE OXIDATION OF HYDROCARBONS

Oxygen converted to	Oxygen converted, %		
	Propane, 170 atmos. 350°C., 7.9% inlet O_2	n-Butane, 140 atmos. 281°C., 6.4% inlet O_2	n-Butane, 33 atmos.
Formaldehyde Acetaldehyde	9.4	16.4	6.9
Acetone........................	2.3	....	1.4
Methyl alcohol..................	13.4	3.1	15.0
Ethyl alcohol...................	8	6.2	2.5
Propyl alcohol..................	5.2	9.3	3.2
Butyl alcohol...................	0.7	1.0	0.6
Acetic acid Formic acid	4.1	11.2	16.7

ucts. Oxygen concentrations of the order of only 5 to 15 mole per cent are used in the feed mixture, and, although oxygen conversions of upward of 40 per cent are obtained, the per-pass conversions of hydrocarbon to oxygenated product are not high, and recirculation of unreacted hydrocarbon is essential.

In practically all of the patented processes, low concentrations of oxygen, based on the hydrocarbon, are mentioned as desirable.[1] Methods proposed for obtaining these desired low concentrations and for preventing high oxygen ratios due to failure of equipment or control have been based on the solution of oxygen and nitrogen from high-pressure air in the liquid hydrocarbons at room temperature.[2] The meager data available for solubilities of oxygen and nitrogen in liquid hydrocarbons do not permit a determination of whether the air used for saturation will become richer or leaner in nitrogen or whether or not considerable amounts of nitrogen will have to be bled off from the reactors to prevent

---

[1] Cf. Lewis and Frolich, U. S. 1,976,790 (1934); Burke, U. S. 1,978,621 (1934); BURKE, FRYLING, and SCHUMANN, Ind. Eng. Chem., 24, 804–811 (1932).

[2] Pugh, Tauch, and Warren, U. S. 1,812,714 (1931).

accumulation in undue amounts.[1] However, the indications are that
oxygen is the more soluble and that excess nitrogen from the air may be
vented at the saturators without the necessity for passing large quantities
into the reactors with the hydrocarbon material.

The wide variety of catalysts that have been claimed for the pressure-
oxidation process throws some doubt on the real necessity for having a
specific catalyst present in order to obtain the desired reaction rates.
Indeed, the claim for such a catalyst as borax-coated copper makes it
seem that the chief function of the "catalyst" is to distribute and help
dissipate the heat generated by the reaction and prevent localized high
temperatures, which would jeopardize the continued existence of the
desired intermediate oxidation products. By employing a divided metal
of high heat conductivity, such as copper wire or turnings, and by coating
it with some substance to prevent catalysis of decomposition reactions,
which are induced by some metals, the desired end would be attained.
High gas velocities past these catalysts, of course, mean short times of
contact but also may be important from the point of view of heat transfer
from the gases to the solid heat-conducting media. High surface velocities are conducive to a high rate of heat transfer, which is desired. By
the use of low oxygen concentrations, the extent of oxidation is limited,
and the possible temperature rise restricted. Nevertheless, thorough
and rapid dissipation of the heat is required when large quantities of
gases and vapors are to be passed through a limited reaction zone.

On the basis of the foregoing, general deductions relating to the operating conditions may be made as follows: The higher the pressure at which
oxidation occurs the higher will be the conversion to alcohols and the
lower the conversion to aldehydes, acids, water, and carbon oxides. It
is not to be expected, however, that the increase in yield of intermediate
oxidation products will be a linear function of the pressure, since other
factors are of comparable importance to pressure. A high rate of flow,
i.e., high surface velocity over the catalyst, is conducive to the formation
of higher alcohols; and a low rate of flow leads to the formation of larger
proportions of water, carbon oxides, lower alcohols, aldehydes, and acids.
With other conditions fixed, an increase in temperature causes an increase
in the secondary reactions, with a consequent decrease in the conversion
to higher alcohols. Also, an increase in the concentration of oxygen

---

[1] The following data are available: Solubilities are expressed as volumes of gas at
25°C. and 1 atmos. dissolved per volume of liquid per atmosphere. Oxygen in pentane, 0.576 in the range 0 to 100 atmos.; nitrogen in butane, 0.538 in the range 0 to 180
atmos.; oxygen in gas oil, 0.151 in the range 0 to 70 atmos.; nitrogen in gas oil, 0.100
in the range 0 to 80 atmos.; [FROLICH, TAUCH, HOGAN, and PEER, *Ind. Eng. Chem.*,
23, 548 (1931)].   Air in mineral seal oil (35° A.P.I.), 0.120 in the range 0 to 32 atmos.
[Dow and CALKIN, *Bur. Mines, Repts. Investigations*, 2732 (1926)].

lowers the efficiency at which oxygen is converted to useful oxygenated products but tends to increase the yield of such products per pass through the reaction zone. Useful "times of contact" may vary from a fraction of one second to several seconds, depending upon hydrocarbon, temperature, and other conditions being employed.

Oxidation of Low-molecular-weight Olefin Hydrocarbons.—Lenher has shown that the slow non-catalytic oxidation of ethylene at temperatures of 400 to 600°C. results in the formation of ethylene oxide and formaldehyde as the major products. The formation of a peroxide or addition complex was postulated as the initial step, which is followed by a stepwise sequence of consecutive reactions, which lead in the end to the formation of water and oxides of carbon.[1] With a silver catalyst, activated with small amounts of gold, copper, or iron, and at temperatures of 150 to 400°C. (302 to 752°F.) good yields of ethylene oxide are claimed from reaction of ethylene with molecular oxygen.[2]

With elevated pressures, oxidation of ethylene occurs at much lower temperatures. Oxidation of ethylene with air in mixtures having the composition 2 parts of ethylene and 1 part of air starts at a temperature of about 150°C., when the pressure is initially 50 atmos. at room temperature.[3] Under these conditions but at a reaction temperature of 200°C., about 18.5 per cent of the inlet oxygen appears in the product as organic acids, and smaller amounts as alcohols. Practically all the alcohol fraction is reported to be methanol under these conditions. However, a small conversion to ethanol is claimed.

The direct oxidation of the olefins higher than ethylene has received relatively little attention. The non-catalytic, thermal reaction of propylene and oxygen at high propylene and low oxygen concentrations and at reactor temperatures of 500 to 600°C. results in pyrolysis as well as oxidation of the olefin. Extensive pyrolysis during the oxidation of the corresponding paraffin hydrocarbon is not encountered. In the case of propylene, the products of oxidation from experiments in which the unreacted gases have been recirculated consist of acetaldehyde, formaldehyde, formic acid, carbon oxides, and water. Concomitant pyrolysis results first in the formation of higher monoolefins, which react further to form hydrogen, paraffins, and unsaturated hydrocarbons.

Oxidation of Liquid Petroleum Hydrocarbons.—The oxidation of the higher members of the naturally occurring hydrocarbons of petroleum was one of the first reactions to be studied in regard to the utilization of such substances as organic intermediates. The use of soluble salts of metals such as manganese, copper, iron, chromium, vanadium, etc.,

---

[1] Lenher, *J. Am. Chem. Soc.*, **53**, 3737, 3752 (1931).
[2] Lefort, U. S. reissue 20,370 (1937).
[3] Pichler and Reder, *loc. cit.*

permits operating temperatures from 100 to 160°C. in liquid-phase processes in which air or gaseous oxygen is contacted with the liquid hydrocarbon. Interest in such oxidations has centered quite largely in the formation of fatty acids, usually hydroxy or aldehydic in nature, suitable for the production of soaps, fats, esters, solvents, etc., or capable of hydrogenation to high-molecular-weight alcohols, which after sulfonation are in turn suited for use as detergents.

While such liquid-phase processes have been applied to hydrocarbons having molecular weights and structures comparable to the paraffin waxes, the vapor-phase oxidation of the hydrocarbons with molecular oxygen has been applied with more success to compounds which are liquid under ordinary conditions and which have a molecular weight corresponding to the kerosene and gas-oil fractions. To make possible the use of temperatures for oxidation that are sufficiently low to prevent

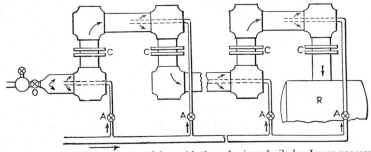

FIG. 6.—Type of apparatus used for oxidation of mineral oils by James process.

A. Air control valves.   O. Oil control valve.
C. Catalyst screens.   R. Product receiver.

complicating cracking and decomposition reactions in this latter process, it has been found expedient to use certain fixed oxidation catalysts.

The James process (Fig. 6)[1] has been directed principally to the vapor-phase, catalytic oxidation of kerosene, although heavier fractions have been processed by the method. The apparatus consists of a device for vaporizing the hydrocarbon, a reactor containing the catalysts and provided with inlets for oxygen or air, and finally a cooling and collection system. The oil vapors pass through a succession of thin catalyst screens and fresh air in controlled quantities is added to the vapor stream before the first and each succeeding catalyst screen. In this way, air is admitted at each point only sufficient to maintain the catalyst screens at the operating temperature of 350 to 400°C. for kerosene.

The oxides of certain metals of high atomic weight and low atomic volume, such as molybdenum and uranium, have been found to act as

---

[1] JAMES, *Trans. Am. Inst. Chem. Eng.*, **14**, 189–199 (1921); **14**, 201–210 (1922); *Chem. & Met. Eng.*, **26**, 209–212 (1922); BITLER and JAMES, *Trans. Am. Inst. Chem. Eng.*, **20**, 95–100 (1927).

useful catalysts in the process. Salts such as diuranyl vanadate have also been found to give good results. The catalyst is arranged in the form of multiple screens which may all be alike or contain different oxides. A combination of one uranium oxide screen with two molybdenum oxide screens has been used. Temperature control is obtained by regulation of the rate at which oil vapors pass through the apparatus, of the proportion of air or oxygen admitted between catalyst screens, and in the loss of heat from the surface of the tubular chambers.

The products from the oxidation of such mixtures of hydrocarbons as are contained in kerosene or gas oil are very complex—so much so as to defy accurate analysis. They contain aldehydes, alcohols, ketones, acids, ethers, and esters. In the oxidation of kerosene, the oxidized oil may be as high as 40 per cent of the total and consist of 30 to 40 per cent of mixed aldehydes, 40 to 45 per cent of mixed alcohols, 5 per cent of free acids, 10 per cent of esters, and some ethers. About 85 per cent recovery is claimed with kerosene. With heavy oils, recovery is said to reach 92 per cent. By oxidizing naphtha, kerosene, and wax distillate, lacquer solvents ranging through *low boilers*, *medium boilers*, *high boilers*, *plasticizers*, and *softeners* may be obtained. These solvents are largely mixtures of esters, alcohols, and ethers. The acids—generally aldehydic or aldehydic-hydroxy in type—are difficult to free of complex aldehydes, which impart objectionable odors and resinous polymerization products to soaps formed by saponification of the acid fraction with hot alkali. Methods involving the intermediate formation of calcium soaps have been proposed to avoid the inclusion of aldehydic bodies in the alkali soaps. Sulfonation of the oxidized product leads to the formation of emulsifying agents and "activators" for emulsified insecticides. Catalytic vapor-phase oxidation of petroleum hydrocarbons boiling in the range from 338 to 482°F. is used in Poland to produce an alcohol denaturant and an odorizing gas for mixture with odorless fuel gases.[1]

VI. VAPOR-PHASE OXIDATION OF AROMATIC HYDROCARBONS

The aromatic hydrocarbons are characterized by offering several points of resistance to further oxidation or decomposition during the course of the interaction with oxygen, making possible the isolation of intermediate oxidation products. For instance, in the case of naphthalene oxidation, the interaction of three atoms of oxygen results in the formation of α-naphthoquinone—a point of resistance, since appreciable quantities of this compound may be obtained under the proper conditions. The interaction of a total of nine oxygen atoms results in the formation of phthalic anhydride. Another resistance point occurs after the reaction of eighteen oxygen atoms when maleic anhydride is formed. Thus, it is pos-

[1] DE PIOTROWSKI and WINKLER, *Oil and Gas J.*, **35** (9), 58 (1936).

sible to obtain commercial yields of phthalic anhydride from naphthalene, maleic anhydride from benzene, anthraquinone from anthracene, etc. Because of the thermal stability and resistance to oxidation of the aromatic hydrocarbons and the intermediate reaction products, it is necessary to employ excess oxygen, operate at elevated temperatures, and make use of active catalysts. These factors make it possible to conduct the oxidation so as to obtain practically complete reaction of raw material with only a single pass over the catalyst.

Oxidation of hydrocarbons containing an aromatic nucleus and one or more aliphatic side chains may be effected in the side chain. The side chains, behave, in general, like aliphatic hydrocarbons and, as such, are more susceptible of attack by oxygen than the ring. Indeed, it is possible to effect oxidation of the side chains of alkylated aromatic hydrocarbons without ring rupture by the use of air or oxygen under pressure in a non-catalytic liquid-phase reaction.[1] At atmospheric pressure the principal point of resistance in such oxidized compounds is the aromatic acid formed after oxidation has reached and affected the last carbon atom attached to the nucleus. Unless low concentrations of oxygen are used or mild conditions imposed, this resistance point is the first one to be effective. Thus, ethylbenzene is oxidized to benzoic acid just as toluene is.[2] The ring structure is so stable toward oxidation or dissociation that, regardless of the length of side chains, carboxylic acids result before ring rupture occurs. Under special conditions, such as elevated pressures (50 atmos.) and mild temperatures (210°C., 410°F.), it has been shown that hydroxylated derivatives such as benzyl alcohol and products from oxidation of the aromatic nucleus such as dihydroxy toluene may be recovered.[3] The relatively greater ease of oxidation of the aliphatic side chains makes unnecessary and undesirable the high ratios of oxygen to hydrocarbon used in the oxidation of naphthalene to phthalic anhydride or of benzene to maleic anhydride. Although the reaction is highly exothermic, less heat is evolved per pound of benzaldehyde formed from toluene than per pound of phthalic anhydride from naphthalene, the proportion being of the order of 1545 to 5460 B.t.u., respectively. This ratio for the case of benzoic acid production is 2310 B.t.u. relative to 5460 B.t.u.

Non-catalytic oxidation of the aromatic hydrocarbons is slow at temperatures below 500°C. Benzene is not vigorously oxidized in glass

---

[1] Forrest and Frolich, U. S. 1,902,550; 1,936,427 (1933). This process is unique also in that temperature control is effected by control of pressure on the reactants and heat removal is effected by refluxing of the reacting hydrocarbon.

[2] MAXTED, *J. Soc. Chem. Ind.*, **47,** 101–105T (1928).

[3] NEWITT and SZEGO, *J. Soc. Chem. Ind.*, **52,** 645 (1933). BONE, *ibid.*, **53,** 963 (1934).

chambers until temperatures near 700°C. are attained. Under similar conditions, toluene is noticeably oxidized at 650°C., and xylene at 575°C.[1] Even with an active catalyst such as vanadium pentoxide, a temperature of 400 to 450°C. is required for the industrial oxidation of naphthalene to phthalic anhydride with air. Furthermore, quantities of air from one to three times that theoretically necessary for the conversion must be used. This means that 20 to 60 moles of air must be used per mole of naphthalene introduced to the oxidation chamber for oxidation to phthalic anhydride.

Benzene.—Benzene presents a very stable configuration toward both thermal dissociation and oxidation. The primary effect of exposure of benzene to elevated temperatures is the disassociation of a hydrogen atom accompanied by the joining of the residues to form diphenyl and resulting in the formation of a more stable substance, which may be recovered in good yield. Vapor-phase oxidation to phenol is possible and has been attained on a laboratory scale with low yields and conversions[2] by control of catalyst and oxidizing conditions. However, phenol does not present any great stability toward oxidation, and its formation by this method in commercial quantities is not feasible at the present stage of development. Continued oxidation results in the formation of quinol and quinone, both of which have been identified in the vapor-phase oxidation products of benzene. High yields have not been obtained, however, owing, no doubt, to the comparative instability of the ring at this stage of oxidation. Continued oxidation results in rupture of the ring and leads to the formation of maleic acid, which may be obtained in good yields. The complete combustion of benzene thus probably involves the formation of quinone and maleic acid as points of stability before complete combustion products are reached.

The commercial production of maleic acid by oxidation of benzene

$$C_6H_6 \xrightarrow{\ 4.5O_2\ } \begin{array}{c} CHCOOH \\ \| \\ CHCOOH \end{array} + H_2O + 2CO_2$$

has in a large measure been due to the early work of Weiss and Downs[3] on this particular reaction and of Gibbs and his associates at the Bureau of Chemistry in Washington on aromatic oxidations in general. Too few

[1] MARDLES, *Trans. Faraday Soc.*, **27**, 681 (1931).

[2] Yield is the measure of the amount of product obtained on the basis of the raw material actually acted upon; conversion is the measure of the raw material acted upon.

[3] WEISS and DOWNS, *Ind. Eng. Chem.*, **12**, 228 (1920); *J. Soc. Chem. Ind.*, **45T**, 193 (1926); WEISS, DOWNS, and BURNS, *Ind. Eng. Chem.*, **15**, 965 (1923); WEISS, DOWNS, and CORSON, *ibid.*, **15**, 628 (1923); WEISS and DOWNS, *J. Am. Chem. Soc.*, **45**, 1003, 2341 (1923).

details of later developments have been made public, although numerous patents have been issued to cover various improvements.

The stability of benzene and the fact that 9 atoms of oxygen are required for the oxidation of a molecule of benzene to maleic anhydride necessitate the use of high air to hydrocarbon ratios in the oxidation. Thus, the theoretical requirement would be about 106 cu. ft. of dry air at room temperature per pound of benzene oxidized to maleic anhydride. In practice, higher ratios than this are used.

The heat theoretically liberated in the oxidation of benzene to maleic acid is about 10,500 B.t.u. per pound of benzene reacting, and the heat liberated in the complete combustion of benzene is approximately 18,000 B.t.u. per pound.   In practice, where 40 per cent or more of the benzene may undergo complete combustion during reaction, the heat liberated would be 13,500 B.t.u. or more per pound of benzene reacted.   It is imperative that this reaction heat be removed from the catalyst zone and that the catalyst temperature be maintained at the proper operating level. Special means have been provided for this in commercial operation.

A variety of catalysts have been patented for this oxidation, and the oxides of metals of the fifth and sixth groups of the periodic system have been particularly stressed.   Of these, vanadium pentoxide has been shown to be one of the best when used as a single-component catalyst supported on some inert carrier as aluminum turnings or diatomaceous earth.   Mixtures of vanadium with other oxides of these groups have been patented, and a variety of multicomponent zeolitic mixtures claimed. Vanadium pentoxide becomes active in promoting the oxidation at a temperature of about 300°C. and reaches its maximum usefulness in the range of 400 to 500°C.   Data on the other catalysts are not available.

In practice, yields of 60 to 75 lb. of maleic acid per 100 lb. of benzene reacted are obtained.   This represents an efficiency of conversion of benzene to maleic acid of about 45 to 50 per cent.

Maleic acid does not have the volume demand that such oxidation products as phthalic anhydride, anthraquinone, benzaldehyde, and benzoic acid do.   However, a number of novel uses have been developed and proposed, and, with the preparation of useful derivatives, increased consumption is probable.   Maleic acid may be readily converted to malic acid by heating in aqueous solution under pressure.   Malic acid may be used in place of citric and tartaric acids as an organic acidulent. Sodium malate is recommended in foods for persons who cannot tolerate sodium chloride.   Succinic acid, derived by reduction, is being used in the formation of certain resins.   Resins formed from maleic anhydride are finding increasing use in the formation of varnishes.   Various esters and condensation products are being developed.[1]

[1] *Cf.* CAROTHERS, *Chem. Rev.*, **8**, 361 (1931); DOWNS, *Ind. Eng. Chem.*, **26**, 17–20 (1934).

It is worthy of note that the exhaust vapors from the manufacture of phthalic anhydride by the oxidation of naphthalene in the vapor phase carry considerable quantities of maleic acid. The application of proper recovery methods to these exhaust gases has made them an industrial source of maleic acid.

Toluene.—The oxidation of hydrocarbons having an aromatic nucleus and one or more side chains may be effected in the side chain without marked rupture of the ring itself, since each component behaves more or less as it would if it alone constituted the major part of the molecule. Thus, the ring component exhibits the characteristic stability of the aromatic compounds, and the aliphatic substituent shows the relatively greater ease of oxidation of the aliphatic hydrocarbons. Under specific conditions, oxidation of such substituted aromatic hydrocarbons may be controlled to give satisfactory yields of the side-chain products, *viz.*, toluene may be oxidized to benzaldehyde or benzoic acid; *o*-xylene, to phthalic anhydride; ethylbenzene, to benzoic acid; etc.

Although the direct oxidation of toluene to benzaldehyde and benzoic acid presents some difficulties, the high ratio between raw-material cost and value of the chlorine-free products makes the possibility of commercial operation of some process attractive. Practically all the benzoic acid made today is derived from the decarboxylation of phthalic acid, a process that yields a chlorine-free product. The development of this decarboxylation process has served to restrict the investigation of air-oxidation methods.

The products of toluene oxidation, chiefly benzaldehyde, benzoic acid, and anthraquinone, are obtained in proportions that depend upon catalyst, temperature, oxygen ratio, and time of contact. High temperatures, mild catalysts, and short times of contact promote the formation of benzaldehyde. High oxygen ratios and long times of contact, are, in general, conducive to acid formation. At temperatures of 280 to 300°C. reaction begins in the presence of vanadium oxide catalysts, but reaction is slow, long times of contact are required, and benzoic acid tends to be the major product. At temperatures of 400 to 450°C., reaction becomes more rapid over the vanadium oxide catalysts; and benzaldehyde, representing about 50 per cent of the toluene oxidized, becomes the principal product. Molybdenum oxide is a milder catalyst, and a temperature of 450 to 530°C. is necessary for good per-pass yields and high conversion to benzaldehyde. In the temperature range of 420 to 450°C. and in the presence of vanadium oxide catalysts, as much as 5 per cent of the reacted toluene may appear in the product as anthraquinone. At temperatures above 500°C. in the presence of molybdenum oxide catalysts, considerable proportions of the reacted toluene may appear in the product as a complex, high-boiling oil. The results of oxidations with tin vanadate as a catalyst are given in Table IV.

TABLE IV.—VAPOR-PHASE OXIDATION OF TOLUENE[1]

Catalyst of tin vanadate. Toluene carbureter temperature, 40°C.; catalyst temperature, 290°C.

Space velocity of		Vols. of air[2] per vol. of toluene vapor	Yield benzoic acid, %	Space-time[3] yields of acid
Primary air	Secondary air			
200	500	40.8	53.3	0.020
200	700	52.5	41.0	0.0112
200	1,000	70.0	36.3	0.0135
300	2,000	88.6	32.9	0.0137
300	3,000	128.6	23.8	0.0105

[1] MAXTED, *J. Soc. Chem. Ind.*, **47**, 101–105T (1928).

[2] Calculated on basis of saturation of air by toluene vapor in carbureter.

[3] Space-time yield $= \dfrac{\text{grams of product}}{\text{(hour) (cc. of catalyst space)}}$

[4] Primary air is the air admitted directly with the hydrocarbon; secondary air is subsequently admitted to this primary mixture.

Naphthalene.—In point of volume and importance to the dye and synthetic organic chemical industries, the oxidation of naphthalene to phthalic anhydride is without peer among the various processes involving aromatic hydrocarbon oxidation.   Since the development of the catalytic vapor-phase oxidation process, the price of phthalic anhydride has dropped steadily.   In 1937, the production of phthalic acid and anhydride exceeded 45,211,000 lb.[1]   Accompanying the increased production of phthalic anhydride has been a progressive decrease in selling price to a present estimated selling price of 14 cts. per pound.

Phthalic anhydride is the raw material for the manufacture of anthraquinone and a number of its derivatives by the Friedel and Crafts reaction.[2]   In this way, it finds extensive use in the manufacture of the important vat intermediates and dyes, such as alizarin and alizarin derivatives.   It is used for the fluorescein, eosine, and rhodamine dyes. Phthalate esters are widely used in the lacquer industry as plasticizers. Reacted with glycerol, phthalic anhydride forms the glyptal and rezyl types of resins which find extensive commercial use.   The manufacture of phenolphthalein and that of chloride-free benzoic acid are additional outlets for phthalic anhydride.   The availability of so cheap and reactive an organic intermediate should lead to further expansion in its use, and the increased production thus induced should lead to further lowering of the cost of manufacture.

The stability of the naphthalene structure is such that, at temperatures up to 400 or 500°C., a catalyst is necessary for commercial rates of oxidation with air as the oxidizing agent.   The first point of resistance to

[1] *U. S. Tariff Commission Report*, June, 1938.

[2] *Cf.* chapter on Friedel and Crafts reaction.

continued oxidation is marked by the formation of α-naphthoquinone, which may be obtained as a product of the oxidation by suitable regulation of conditions. For instance, the controlled oxidation of naphthalene with chromic acid in acetic acid solution may be made to yield α-naphthoquinone. Vapor-phase oxidation of naphthalene with air under conditions of limited air supply, weak catalysts, moderate temperatures, and short times of contact has been shown to lead to the formation of quantities of α-naphthoquinone. With a catalyst of 10 per cent vanadium pentoxide on pumice, a ratio of air to naphthalene about the theoretical required for oxidation to phthalic anhydride, and a temperature of about 400°C., the oxidation of naphthalene has been qualitatively shown to lead to the formation of naphthoquinones.[1]

The next stable product of the oxidation is phthalic anhydride, which is generally the intermediate desired from naphthalene oxidation. Continued reaction, however, may lead to benzoic acid formation by the splitting off of carbon dioxide from the phthalic anhydride. Continued oxidation accompanied by rupture of the benzene ring results in the formation of maleic anhydride. In the industrial production of phthalic anhydride, quantities of maleic anhydride are formed and pass out with the exhaust gases from the condenser system. Further oxygen attack leads to the complete combustion of the products or at least to the formation of small amounts of formaldehyde with the complete combustion products. Thus, the principal steps in naphthalene oxidation are the addition of oxygen to the naphthalene ring; the destruction of the naphthalene ring; and the destruction of the remaining benzene ring.

Theoretically, 9 atoms of oxygen are required per molecule of naphthalene for oxidation to phthalic anhydride. This means that 64.5 cu. ft. of dry air measured at room temperature is theoretically required for the oxidation of 1 lb. of naphthalene to phthalic anhydride. In practice, considerable excess air is used, up to three times that theoretically required. Thus, from 20 to 60 moles of air must be used per mole of naphthalene oxidized.

The heat of oxidation theoretically amounts to 5460 B.t.u. per pound of naphthalene oxidized. Owing to the fact that some complete combustion also occurs, the heat actually liberated amounts more nearly to 10,000 B.t.u. per pound of naphthalene oxidized. Specially designed catalyst chambers must be used to remove this heat without disturbing the temperature equilibrium of the catalyst mass.

Catalysts similar to those mentioned for benzene oxidation are applicable to the naphthalene reaction. The early work and published results have shown that vanadium and molybdenum oxides are effective and

[1] Unpublished results from the Research Laboratory of Applied Chemistry, Massachusetts Institute of Technology.

quite active catalysts. With supported vanadium pentoxide catalysts, commercial conversions of naphthalene to phthalic anhydride in excess of 80 per cent of theoretical are obtained. Such catalysts have a long life—six months or more of continuous use—and have yielded up to twenty thousand times their weight of phthalic anhydride.[1] Fused or supported vanadium pentoxide catalysts become active for the oxidation at temperatures of 270 to 280°C. and induce reaction at commercial rates at temperatures of near 400°C. Although pumice, crushed to size, was formerly used as a support for the vanadium catalysts, the poor heat-conducting capacity of this porous medium and the tendency for the metal oxide to react with the support have led to adaptation of other materials. Infusorial earth formed into pellets either before or after impregnation with the metal salt of the catalyst forms an inert support but has poor heat-conducting capacity. Aluminum turnings with rough surfaces form a good support, being inert and having good heat-conducting characteristics.

It has been claimed that mixtures of the metal oxides form better catalysts than the oxides alone. For instance, a mixture of 85 per cent of vanadium pentoxide with 15 per cent of molybdenum oxide is claimed to be better than the vanadium oxide alone; and a mixture of 65 per cent of vanadium pentoxide, 30 per cent of molybdenum oxide, and 5 per cent of either manganese or calcium oxide, still better.[2]

Published data show that certain salts of the catalytically active metals are effective. The vanadates of tin and bismuth are effective catalysts for the oxidation and, on a laboratory scale, permit yields of over 80 per cent in one pass of the reacting mixture over the catalyst.[3] Tin vanadate is effective in the temperature range of 250 to 320°C. when very high air ratios and space velocities[4] of 2,300 to 6,200 are used. The bismuth vanadate catalysts require considerably higher temperatures for the effective oxidation of naphthalene.

Many other catalysts have been tried and patented. Among the reputedly more useful of these are the zeolitic or base-exchanging types of siliceous and non-siliceous compounds. The majority of these zeolitic combinations that have been proposed contain such catalytically active elements as vanadium, molybdenum, tungsten, chromium, uranium, copper, nickel, etc.

The normal technique for the recovery of phthalic anhydride from the hot, dilute mixture of gases and vapors issuing from the catalytic

[1] Downs, *J. Soc. Chem. Ind.*, **45**, 188T (1926).

[2] Craver, U. S. 1,489,741 (1924); *Cf.* Wohl, U. S. 1,971,888 (1934) for other catalyst compositions.

[3] Maxted, *J. Soc. Chem. Ind.*, **47**, 191–195T (1928).

[4] Space velocity is expressed as volumes of gas measured at normal temperature and pressure passed per volume of catalyst per hour.

converter is to effect condensation of the phthalic anhydride in large, roomlike cooling chambers (indicated in Fig. 9) where the product deposits in the form of a bulky mass of long needlelike crystals. To reduce the space required for this recovery, to improve the density and control the purity, and to reduce the amount of manual labor required, it has been proposed to accomplish recovery by use of a sequence of steps: (1) cool the vaporous mixture by passage through a water-cooled tubular cooler-condenser; (2) remove the bulk of the condensed material by means of a scraper-screw conveyer in the cold end of this cooler; and (3) recover dust from the cold gases by means of a bag filter.[1]

VII. APPARATUS FOR OXIDATIONS

Liquid-phase Reactions.—Liquid-phase reactions in which oxidation is secured by the use of oxidizing compounds need no special apparatus in the sense that elaborate means must be provided for temperature control and heat removal. There is usually provided a kettle form of apparatus, closed to prevent the loss of volatile materials and fitted with a reflux condenser to return vaporized materials to the reaction zone, provided with suitable means for adding reactants rapidly or slowly as may be required and for removing the product, and provided with adequate jackets or coils through which heating or cooling means may be circulated as required. Examples of such apparatus are scattered throughout this book, and no specific examples are required here.

In the case of liquid-phase reactions in which oxidation is secured by means of atmospheric oxygen, for example the oxidation of liquid hydrocarbons to fatty acids, special means must be provided to secure adequate mixing and contact of the two immiscible phases of gaseous oxidizing agent and the liquid being oxidized. Although temperature must be controlled and heat removed, the requirements are not severe since the temperatures are generally low and the rate of heat generation controllable by regulation of the rate of air admission. All these factors are important and the apparatus must provide for them.

Figures 1, 2, and 3 show how, in general, this may be accomplished. Heat may be removed and temperature controlled by circulation of either the liquid being oxidized or a special cooling fluid through the reaction zone and then through an external heat exchanger. Mixing may be obtained by the use of special distributer inlets for the air designed to spread the air throughout the liquid and constructed of materials capable of withstanding temperatures that may be considerably higher at these inlet ports than in the main body of the liquid. With materials that are sensitive to overoxidation and under conditions where good contact must be used to partly offset the retarding effect of necessarily low tempera-

[1] Riegler, U. S. 2,067,019 (1937).

tures, thorough mixing may be provided by the use of mechanical stirring or frothing of the liquid.

The Problem of Heat Transfer in Vapor-phase Reactions

By their very nature, the vapor-phase oxidation processes result in the concentration of reaction heat in the catalyst zone from which it must be removed in large quantities at high-temperature levels. Removal of heat is essential to prevent destruction of apparatus, catalyst, or raw material; and maintenance of temperature at the proper level is necessary to insure the correct rate and degree of oxidation. With laboratory-scale apparatus, removal of this heat is relatively easy, and in some instances it is even necessary to provide an external supply of heat to maintain the operating temperature at the proper level. With plant-scale operation and with reactions involving deep-seated oxidation, removal of heat constitutes a major problem. With limited oxidation, however, it may become necessary to supply heat even to oxidations conducted on a plant scale.

In the case of vapor-phase oxidation of aliphatic substances such as methanol and the lower-molecular-weight aliphatic hydrocarbons the ratio of reacting oxygen is generally lower than in the case of the aromatic hydrocarbons for the formation of the desired products, and for this reason heat removal is simpler. Furthermore, in the case of the hydrocarbons the proportion of oxygen in the reaction mixture is generally low, resulting in low per-pass conversions and in some instances necessitating preliminary heating of the reactants to reaction temperature. Figure 4 shows a schematic layout for the oxidation of methanol to formaldehyde. Figures 5 and 6 show apparatus for the oxidation of hydrocarbons.

Rather elaborate means have been perfected for the oxidation of the aromatic hydrocarbons to useful compounds. Such apparatus must be designed to permit the maintenance of constant elevated temperatures, to permit the removal of large quantities of heat at these elevated temperatures, and to provide adequate catalyst surface to promote the reactions. One form of converter adapted to accomplish these ends consists of numerous small catalyst tubes immersed in a liquid bath.[1] The liquid bath may be used to remove heat from the reaction as latent heat of evaporation of the liquid; it may be subjected to forced circulation in contact with the catalyst tubes and cooled in an external heat exchanger; or it may be used as a means of getting reaction heat

---

[1] Downs, *J. Soc. Chem. Ind.*, **45**, 188–193T (1926); U. S. 1,374,020, 1,374,021 (1921); 1,604,739 (1926); Canon and Andrews, U. S. 1,614,185 (1927); Reissue 16,824 (1927).

to an outer retaining shell from which the heat is dissipated to the atmosphere.

Figure 7 is a diagrammatic section of a single-tube reactor and shows the principles involved in the removal of reaction heat as heat of evaporation, and the dissipation of this heat to cooling water. The entering air-hydrocarbon (naphthalene) mixture first comes in heat-transferring contact with the heated vapors of the boiling liquid and is thus preheated before coming in direct contact with the catalyst. Cooling of the first section of the catalyst is thus avoided to a certain extent, and the catalyst mass is made more effective in promoting the reaction. Reaction heat, liberated at the catalyst surface, passes from the catalyst mass through the tube wall and to the surround-

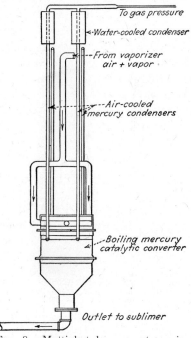

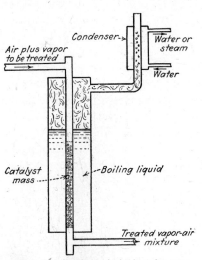

Fig. 7.—Section of single-tube reactor with boiling-liquid heat removal and temperature control.

Fig. 8.—Multiple-tube converter using two-phase mercury system.

ing liquid, where it is removed at constant temperature by the evaporization of the liquid. The evolved vapors from the bath may be condensed in a separate condenser provided with cooling water, and the condensed material returned to the bath. Continuous operation is thus obtained. In practice, it is customary to use a large number of such tubular catalyst chambers in parallel, connected at the top and bottom by common headers. Such a converter is largely automatic in operation and does not depend upon atmospheric conditions for satisfactory operation. As shown in Fig. 8, a suitable air- and water-cooled condensing system returns the mercury to the liquid reservoir and removes the heat of reaction thereby.   The mercury (liquid and vapor) is thus the means for removing the heat of a reaction at a constant temperature of about 425°C. and for dissipating it to cooling water at a temperature of about 100°C.   Heat is thus effectively removed without affecting the temperature of the catalyst adversely.

By varying the pressure on the two-phase mercury system, it is possible to control the temperature of the liquid bath and of the catalyst mass.   This may be accomplished by the use of nitrogen pressure.   It is also possible to alter the boiling point of the mercury by introducing alloying metals such as cadmium.

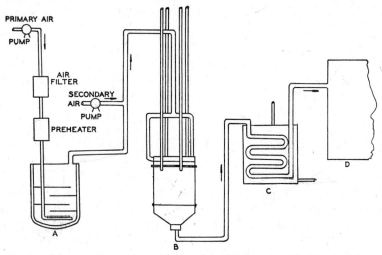

FIG. 9.—Schematic layout for oxidation of naphthalene to phthalic anhydride.
A. Vaporizer for naphthalene.   *C.* Cooler.
B. Converter for oxidation reaction.   *D.* Condenser for phthalic anhydride.

The capacity of such a converter is from 1,500 to 1,800 lb. (816.5 kg.) or even more of phthalic anhydride per 24 hr., depending upon catalyst activity, rate of feed, etc.   Production at this rate means the generation of large quantities of heat in the converter.   Although the heat of oxidation of naphthalene to phthalic anhydride is about 6000 B.t.u. per pound (3330 Cal. per kilogram) of naphthalene, the occurrence of a certain amount of complete combustion during the oxidation reaction brings the heat evolution up to approximately 10,000 B.t.u. per pound (5550 Cal. per kilogram) of naphthalene fed to the converter.   About 21,000,000 B.t.u. (5,300,000 Cal.) is generated per day and removed by the boiling mercury and as sensible heat in the hot exit products during operation on the above basis.

Figure 9 shows a diagrammatic layout for a phthalic anhydride plant.

Mercury has both advantages and disadvantages for use as the heat-removing fluid. Its boiling point of 357°C. at atmospheric pressure may be easily raised to 400 to 450°C. by the application of nitrogen pressure. It is fluid at room temperature and introduces no hazard of equipment damage due to solidification through accidental cooling due to shut-down of equipment. Latent heat of evaporation at 357°C. is 117 B.t.u. per pound (65 Cal. per kilogram). Mercury vapor is toxic, the liquid is heavy, and leaks in the pressure system are difficult to prevent. These latter factors, together with cost, operate as disadvantages. Some of these objectionable features have been overcome in practice. Proper construction and design have reduced mercury loss by leakage to about

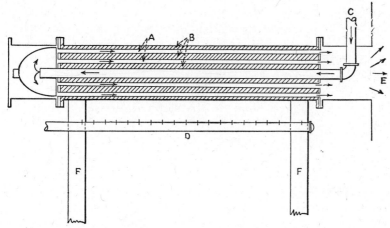

FIG. 10.—Catalytic, multiple-tube converter for oxidation reaction with heat removal from surface of shell to atmosphere.

A. Tubes containing catalyst.   *D.* Gas burners for starting.
B. Heat-conducting medium.   *E.* Condenser.
C. Inlet for air and vapors.   *F.* Supports.

1 per cent per year. Mercury has a low coefficient of thermal conductivity and does not wet the steel-tube walls. However, the violent motion given to the mercury by its own boiling tends to counteract these effects. Other materials, fluid at operating temperatures, have been proposed as superior to mercury in some respects. Among them sulfur, diphenyl, diphenyl oxide, and mercury amalgams may be mentioned here.

The method of removing heat of reaction from the reaction zone by the evaporation of a liquid from a bath, as embodied in the process described above, has been uniquely modified by Forrest and Frolich[1] in such a way that the liquid being oxidized also provides the means for heat removal and temperature control. Cyclic organic compounds are oxidized directly with molecular oxygen by contacting them with an oxygen-

[1] U. S. 1,902,550 (1933).

containing gas, such as air, in a closed system at an elevated temperature and under a pressure substantially greater than the vapor pressure of the compound at the reaction temperature. The closed system contains a condenser directly communicating with the liquid being oxidized and, by means of the circulation of a cooling medium there through the mixture of gases and vapors rising from the liquid, is cooled, and the vapors condensed and returned to the liquid batch undergoing oxidation. Air is forced in at the bottom of the liquid through a distributer head, and the non-condensable gases, *i.e.*, unreacted oxygen, nitrogen, and reaction products, are vented at a point above the condenser through a pressure-regulating valve. The temperature of operation must be below the critical of the compound being treated, but it has been found that this condition is easily satisfied.

Instead of removing reaction heat by evaporation, the liquid surrounding a batch of catalyst tubes may serve simply as a means of heat transfer. Thus, Fig. 10 shows a method of removing heat from the surface of a retaining shell by releasing it to the atmosphere. Either forced or natural circulation of the fluid may be used to convey the heat from the catalyst tubes to the point of disposal. Fluids of low vapor pressure are preferable in such methods, and fused salts such as potassium-sodium nitrate mixtures may be used.

Other methods have been patented and are used, but these will serve as illustrations of the means used to remove heat of oxidation and to control temperature.

CHAPTER VIII

HYDROGENATION

By Merrell R. Fenske

I. INTRODUCTION

Types of Reduction.—Reduction is the term usually applied to a reaction in which oxygen is withdrawn from or hydrogen added to a compound. In addition, other elements besides oxygen may be eliminated from a molecule by the action of hydrogen, the most common being nitrogen, sulfur, carbon, and halogens. In these cases, ammonia, hydrogen sulfide, methane, and the hydrogen halides are usually formed. Reduction may be performed in a variety of ways: (1) by metals in acid or basic solutions; (2) by alkali metals in alcoholic solutions; (3) by electrolysis; and (4) by molecular hydrogen and catalysts. Catalytic reduction by hydrogen is one of the most common and important methods from a commercial point of view, and the discussion here is confined to this one. Technical applications of other methods appear in Chap. II.

In order to correlate and condense the innumerable and diversified examples of catalytic hydrogenation, the following arbitrary classification has been made. This involves only the four type reactions:

1. Reduction of an ethylenic linkage:

$$R \cdot CH : CHR' + H_2 = R \cdot CH_2 \cdot CH_2R'$$

where R and R' are aliphatic or aromatic groups.

2. Reduction of a carbonyl to an alcohol group:

$$R \cdot CH_2 \cdot CO \cdot R' + H_2 = R \cdot CH_2 \cdot CHOH \cdot R'$$

where R is an aliphatic or aromatic group, and R' is the same or a hydrogen atom.

3. Reduction of a carboxyl to an alcohol group:

$$R \cdot COO \cdot R' + 2H_2 = RCH_2OH + R'OH$$

where R is preferably an aliphatic or hydroaromatic group, and R' is the same or a hydrogen atom.

4. Hydrogenolysis, or reactions involving molecular cleavage on the addition of hydrogen.

Survey of Technical Hydrogenations.—Hydrogenation processes have been steadily increasing in size, variety, and importance, and the

419

unit process of hydrogenation is becoming one of the most useful and widespread in organic synthesis. The earliest technical application of hydrogenation was practically limited to the reduction of the double bond between two carbon atoms for the purpose of converting liquid fats into solid fats, or, as it is often called, fat hardening. This industry is now well established and increasing in size, as evidenced in the United States by an increase of 10 lb. per capita in the consumption of vegetable oils. It is estimated that the annual world production of hydrogenated fats is in excess of half a million tons.

The fats resulting from the hardening of whale oil, fish oil, and the vegetable oils such as linseed, soy bean, and cottonseed oil, by the addition of hydrogen under pressure, are of two types—edible and non-edible. The edible fats are used as lard, butter substitutes, and shortening compositions in the baking industry and for the manufacture of creams and coatings for confections. The soap industry is the largest consumer of non-edible hardened oils. Other minor uses for the non-edible products are in leather dressings, electrical insulations, candle making, paint manufacture, and pharmaceutical ointments.

Another development of importance to the soap industry is the manufacture of sulfuric acid esters of long-chain aliphatic alcohols such as lauryl, cetyl, and stearyl alcohols. Instead of making the sodium salt of palmitic or stearic acid, as in ordinary soap manufacture, these acids are first reduced to the corresponding alcohols by hydrogenation at high pressure, and the alcohols then esterified with sulfuric acid. These new detergents, which are used in the form of the sodium salt, have some very interesting properties; thus, they are equally soluble in hard or soft water; *i.e.*, they are well suited for hard waters, and their emulsifying and wetting powers are better than ordinary soaps. Whereas ordinary soaps in acid media are decomposed into fatty acids that are difficultly removed, particularly from fine fabrics, the sodium palmityl and stearyl sulfates are soluble in acid, neutral, or alkaline media without decomposition into insoluble compounds. Fatty acids may either interfere with dyeing operations or later may become rancid and give off disagreeable odors. The sulfuric acid esters do not become rancid and, because of their high solubility, are easily and completely washed out of fabrics. These detergents, while more expensive than the ordinary soap, will find many applications in washing fine fabrics and fibers, in toilet preparations, and wherever else their advantages more than offset their higher price.

Commercial production of synthetic methanol and higher alcohols in this country dates from about 1925. In the year 1937 about 30,000,000 gal. of methanol was made by direct synthesis from water gas in the United States. Today, it is known that a large variety of organic chemicals can be made from water gas, or high-pressure hydrogenation of carbon monoxide.   In addition, it is also possible to make a variety of hydrocarbon mixtures suitable as motor fuels by the catalytic hydrogenation of carbon monoxide.   While the United States has extensive petroleum resources which furnish these hydrocarbons at lower cost, those countries that have coal rather than petroleum reserves are now in a position to synthesize their liquid fuels in this manner from the cheap raw materials, coal, water, and air.

The hydrogenation of petroleum, coals, and tar not only offers conservation of the petroleum supply but also makes available the enormous reserves of coal for the production of liquid fuels.   Petroleum hydrogenation is being carried out in the United States and coal hydrogenation in Germany and England, and such hydrogenations are necessarily large-scale operations.   About 65 per cent of Germany's gasoline is obtained (1937) from non-petroleum sources involving syntheses, which in turn are dependent on a variety of catalytic hydrogenations such as reduction of carbon monoxide to alcohols and liquid hydrocarbons, and the hydrogenation of coals, tars, and lignites.   About 20 per cent of this synthetic petroleum is now made by the Fischer-Tropsch synthesis in which carbon monoxide at about 2 atmos. and 180 to 200°C. is catalytically hydrogenated to yield a variety of hydrocarbons.   If the energy content of the liquid fuel is referred to that of the coal needed to prepare it, it appears, with the Fischer-Tropsch process for hydrogenating carbon monoxide, that from 20 to 30 per cent of the energy of the coal is available as the liquid fuel, while in the direct hydrogenation of coal from 30 to 40 per cent of the heat energy of the coal is available as a liquid fuel.[1] Thus these processes appear to be the answer to a possible dwindling supply of natural petroleum.

Naphthalene and phenolic oils which are obtained from coal tar are produced in excess in some countries.   Hydrogenation of naphthalene gives two liquid solvents—tetralin, which results when 4 atoms of hydrogen are added; and decalin, when 10 atoms are added. Hexalin, or cyclohexanol, and the ketone, cyclohexanone, are the products resulting from hydrogenating phenol; and methylhexalin, the product resulting from hydrogenating cresols.   These hydrogenated materials, either alone or when mixed with each other, are important solvents for camphor, fats, oils, waxes, natural and synthetic resins, and rubber. They also find application in a variety of special soaps and detergents, for they are valuable emulsifying and solubilizing agents for soaps and oils.

It is estimated[2] that some 90,000,000 gal. of technical isooctane will be produced in 1938 by nine different plants in this country.   This material, resulting from the hydrogenation of polymers of butylene and

[1] SCHLATTMANN and KOPPENGERG, *Nat. Petrol. News*, **28**, No. 37, 24E (1936).

[2] EGLOFF, *Ind. Eng. Chem., News Ed.*, **15**, No. 11, 245 (1937).

isobutylene, which in turn are segregated from petroleum refinery gases, is the highest octane number fuel now commercially available and suitable for long-range airplane flights. The increased power per pound of this fuel permits marked increases in the pay load in long-distance flying.

Thus far, only a few applications of hydrogenation to the production of foodstuffs, detergents, chemicals, and fuels have been indicated. There is a long list of applications in the field of synthetic organic chemistry relating to the reduction of all types of unsaturation such as olefinic, aldehydic, nitro, and nitrogen linkages. The applications are constantly changing and increasing in number; such is always the case in any active field of endeavor.

There are, however, certain lines of research upon which the future of hydrogenation will be dependent: (1) a better understanding of the processes and various factors in hydrogenation, together with additional knowledge concerning the chemical reactions occurring; (2) an extension of our knowledge of catalysis; and (3) the development of cheaper hydrogen. The following summary pertains to the problem of hydrogen and its production in quantity.

II. PRODUCTION OF HYDROGEN

In the development and operation of processes involving reduction by means of hydrogenation, the problem of the hydrogen supply soon becomes important. In the small-scale or research phase of the problem, hydrogen is readily available in small quantities in cylinders and is usually of sufficient purity so that, at this stage of the development work, no thought need be given to the hydrogen supply. However, just as soon as semi-plant or commercial operation of the process begins, not only the problems of hydrogen production appear but also those of purification, handling, storage, and compression. Sometimes, these seem to outweigh all the earlier problems concerned with getting the desired reaction to proceed.

The first need for hydrogen on a relatively large scale resulted from the introduction of lighter-than-air craft and from the development of the process for hydrogenation of vegetable oils—the so-called fat-hardening industry. It is estimated that several million cubic feet of hydrogen is now consumed daily in the United States for the hydrogenation of vegetable oils.

The synthetic ammonia process has steadily grown since the war. The synthesis of methanol and other alcohols, and the hydrogenation of mineral oils, tars, and coals have also progressed. Recently, the manufacture of technical isooctane, the high anti-knock aviation fuel, has undergone a remarkable development. Thus, surprisingly large quantities of hydrogen are needed by only a relatively few processes, as is evidenced by the following Table I.

TABLE I.—ESTIMATED HYDROGEN CONSUMPTION IN THE UNITED STATES IN 1937 FOR AMMONIA, METHANOL, ISOOCTANE, AND PETROLEUM HYDROGENATION

Product	Hydrogen consumed, cu. ft.
Synthetic ammonia (production, 200,000 tons)	16,800,000,000
Synthetic methanol (production, 29,500,000 gal.)	4,820,000,000
Technical isooctane[1] (production, 90,000,000 gal.)	2,160,000,000
Petroleum hydrogenation (one plant processing 5,000 bbl. per day, using perhaps 1,000 cu. ft. per barrel)[2]	1,500,000,000

[1] Figures relate to 1938.
[2] The hydrogen consumption in processing mineral oils appears to be from 1,000 to 2,000 cu. ft. per barrel of oil charged.

Upon cheap hydrogen in large quantities will depend the success of the present processes as well as the creation of new ones. Following are the most important methods available at the present time for hydrogen production.

Hydrogen from Water Gas and Steam.—The water-gas catalytic, or Bosch, process is one of the most important for producing industrial hydrogen today. Water gas is readily made in standard water-gas generators from very cheap raw materials, *viz.*, coal or coke, steam, and air. An average analysis of water gas is

	%
Hydrogen	49.2
Carbon monoxide	41.3
Carbon dioxide	4.2
Oxygen	0.2
Methane	0.8
Nitrogen	4.3

The carbon monoxide in the gas is made to react with steam in the presence of a catalyst, and additional hydrogen along with carbon dioxide is obtained.

$$CO + H_2O \rightleftarrows CO_2 + H_2$$

The result of this reaction is that the water gas is converted essentially into a gas composed of carbon dioxide and hydrogen. The carbon dioxide is easily removed by scrubbing with water under pressure or by other absorbents such as triethanolamine, leaving a gas composed essentially of hydrogen. If necessary, it is purified further to remove the small amounts of the other gases.

The water-gas catalytic process is usually carried out at about 450 to 500°C. (840 to 930°F.) and generally at substantially atmospheric pressure. The reaction is exothermic, so once it is started it is self-supporting.

While there are many catalysts that may be used, they generally consist of oxides of iron promoted by chromium oxide, cobalt oxide, and alumina. The reaction is reversible, so that if the temperature is too high the conversion is not complete. It can be forced to greater conversion, however, by using an excess of steam, which is usually the practice. The steam is easily condensed and so removed from the gases as they are cooled.

These gases, containing 60 to 80 per cent hydrogen, 20 to 40 per cent carbon dioxide, less than 1 per cent carbon monoxide, and smaller amounts of other gases, are then usually stored in gas holders. They are taken as needed from the holders to the compressors, for the hydrogen is practically always used at elevated pressure. At some intermediate stage in the compression, where the pressure may be from 250 to 1,000 lb. per square inch, the mixture of gases is led from the compressors to the scrubbing towers where the carbon dioxide is removed, after which the gas goes back to the compressors to be compressed to the final working pressure. The water gas-steam process is usually employed where high-pressure hydrogen is needed and is perhaps one of the cheapest methods for large-scale continuous production of hydrogen. The method is used in the synthesis of ammonia, methanol, and higher alcohols and in manufacturing motor fuels by the hydrogenation of coals or tars.

Hydrogen from Water Gas or Coke-oven Gas by Liquefaction.—This is a physical process of purification based on the difference in boiling points of the components of the gas when liquefied. It has developed through the work of Claude, Patart, and the Linde Company. It is not extensively used in this country, for the water-gas catalytic process appears more economical. The gas, after being freed from tar, ammonia, benzene, and sulfur in conventional ways, is scrubbed at high pressure with water and caustic. It is freed of water by cooling with ammonia to about −45°C., after which it goes to the liquefaction and fractionation apparatus, where the process is similar to the separation of nitrogen and oxygen from air.[1] Coke-oven gas, because of its nitrogen content, is usually worked up for ammonia synthesis, while water gas is more suitable for the production of hydrogen alone. Coke-oven gas may contain about 50 per cent hydrogen, some 15 to 20 per cent nitrogen, together with 20 to 30 per cent methane, unsaturated hydrocarbons, and carbon monoxide. The hydrogen produced in this process can undoubtedly be made very pure.

Hydrogen from Hydrocarbons.—Hydrogen may be prepared from hydrocarbons by two processes: (1) thermal decomposition and (2)

[1] PALLEMAERTS, *Ind. Eng. Chem.*, **21**, 22 (1929); *Intern. Conf. Bituminous Coal*, II, 212 (1929).

reaction with steam. The first of these reactions involves the complete decomposition, or cracking, of natural gas into carbon and hydrogen. At present, gases high in methane are cracked to produce carbon black by the thermatomic-carbon process. The hydrogen is a by-product and is used principally for fuel.

The second process is becoming increasingly important. It is undoubtedly the best method available for petroleum hydrogenation plants to produce hydrogen either from waste refinery gas or from the gaseous products resulting from hydrogenation. These gases are composed principally of methane, and the reaction with steam is

$$CH_4 + H_2O \rightleftarrows CO + 3H_2$$

This is a catalytic reaction and occurs at about 1000°C. (1800°F.) in special furnaces. The catalyst is an aluminum oxide base in the form of small pellets or cubes. The reaction is quite highly endothermic, and so the catalyst is contained in tubes consisting of a high-chromium, high-nickel alloy steel capable of withstanding these high temperatures. The waste heat in the flue gas from the furnaces is utilized by means of waste-heat boilers to produce about half the steam required in the process.

More steam is added to the carbon monoxide-hydrogen mixture, and the water-gas catalytic reaction is then made to take place over an iron-base catalyst at 450 to 500°C. (840 to 930°F.). The gases leaving this converter contain about 79 per cent hydrogen, 20 per cent carbon dioxide, and 1 per cent unconverted hydrocarbons and miscellaneous gases. They are cooled and scrubbed to remove the carbon dioxide, just as in the water-gas catalytic process.

The reaction of hydrocarbons and steam is thus a continuous process, capable of making available the large quantities of combined hydrogen existing in refinery gases principally as methane, ethane, and some unsaturated hydrocarbons. This reaction is used in the petroleum hydrogenation plants in this country and will probably be employed extensively in other hydrogenation plants where large quantities of similar gases are available.

Hydrogen by Electrolysis of Water.—Cheap electrical power is the principal factor determining the production of hydrogen by the electrolysis of water. The purity of this hydrogen is an asset. By-product hydrogen from electrolytic chlorine-alkali processes is available, for instance, at Niagara Falls, where it is used for ammonia synthesis. This method of hydrogen production is perhaps the best available for small plants where the operations are not large enough to warrant the large-scale water-gas catalytic method of production. Such plants usually use hydrogen in various syntheses or in the preparation of organic chemicals. Even though the cost of hydrogen by electrolysis is more than by other methods, it is practically the only convenient and workable method for plant work on a small scale.

Hydrogen from Steam and Iron.—The principal reactions for the production of hydrogen from steam and iron are

$$3Fe + 4H_2O \rightleftarrows Fe_3O_4 + 4H_2 \tag{1}$$

$$\begin{cases} Fe_3O_4 + 4H_2 \rightleftarrows 3Fe + 4H_2O \\ Fe_3O_4 + 4CO \rightleftarrows 3Fe + 4CO_2 \end{cases} \tag{2}$$

The reaction is intermittent, the iron being oxidized to produce the hydrogen and then regenerated as indicated by reactions (2) by passing water gas over it.[1] This method has been used for some time and is adapted to small- or moderate-scale operations. However, there are indications that it is gradually being supplanted by other methods of hydrogen production. The production of hydrogen from steam and iron has been extensively used in connection with hardening or hydrogenation of vegetable oils.

Properties of Hydrogen.—Apart from the more commonly known physical and chemical properties of hydrogen are a few that are of primary importance in the handling and use of hydrogen and hydrogenation equipment. Because it is the lightest gas, it will diffuse or leak where other heavier gases will not, particularly at high pressure. It is usually more difficult to have gas-tight connections and fittings when working with hydrogen than with other gases such as air or steam. Particular attention should be given to all fittings, valves, and connections that are to be used on hydrogen. A leak not only means a loss of hydrogen but is, in addition, a decided hazard owing to the inflammability and very wide explosive limits that hydrogen possesses. These limits are much wider than for most gases, as Table II shows.

These data show that a relatively small leakage of hydrogen or any carelessness in allowing air to mix with hydrogen might be dangerous.

TABLE II.—EXPLOSIVE LIMITS OF GASES[1]
Per Cent by Volume in Air

Gas or vapor	Percentage of gas	Gas or vapor	Percentage of gas
Hydrogen	4.15 to 75.0	Ethylene	3.2 to 34.0
Carbon monoxide	12.5 to 75.0	Propylene	2.2 to 9.7
Methane	4.9 to 15.4	Acetylene	1.5 to 80.5
Ethane	2.5 to 15.0	Benzene	1.4 to 8.0
Propane	2.2 to 7.3	Toluene	1.3 to 6.8

[1] YEAW, *Ind. Eng. Chem.*, **21**, 1030 (1929).

[1] ELLIS, "Hydrogenation of Organic Substances," p. 716, D. Van Nostrand Company, Inc., 3d ed. (1930).

Adding 4.15 per cent or more of hydrogen to air or 25 per cent or more air to hydrogen results in explosive mixtures. Too much care cannot be exercised in designing and operating equipment in which hydrogen is used. All apparatus and lines should be carefully purged by an inert gas such as nitrogen, carbon dioxide, or flue gases not containing oxygen, before hydrogen is admitted.

Hydrogen at elevated temperatures and pressures in contact with ordinary carbon steels is particularly corrosive. The tensile strength of these carbon steels is due to a particular iron structure and to their carbon content. With iron alone, hydrogen forms a hard, brittle hydride; and with carbon steels, in addition to the embrittling action, it causes trouble by attacking and removing carbon, reducing oxides, and producing cracks and fissures. This effect depends upon the state of the hydrogen, whether atomic or molecular, upon the composition of the metal, and on the temperature and pressure. With embrittlement and the removal of carbon, the tensile strength of the steel is greatly reduced, so that continued use of the apparatus may be dangerous. Special alloy steels are entirely resistant to this hydrogen attack. Data for the attack of hydrogen on carbon steels have been given by Cox.[1]

Alloy steels are more resistive than carbon steels. Chrome-vanadium, chrome-vanadium-aluminum, chrome-nickel-vanadium-aluminum steels, stainless steels (18 per cent chromium, 8 per cent nickel, or 24 per cent chromium and 20 per cent nickel) and BTG metal (12 per cent chromium, 60 per cent nickel, 2.5 per cent tungsten) have been found to be completely resistant. BTG metal is the special alloy developed for the Claude ammonia synthesis, where operating pressures run to 15,000 lb. per square inch and temperatures to 560°C.

Chromium has been found particularly efficient in preventing penetration and the attack of hydrogen. Chrome-vanadium steels are used extensively for high-pressure hydrogenation reactors. These steels average about 0.30 per cent carbon, 2 per cent chromium, and 0.02 per cent vanadium.

Cost of Hydrogen.—While it is realized that cost estimates are difficult to make and are sometimes unreliable and misleading, the following estimates have been prepared to indicate more particularly the relative proportions of one item to another in making up the total cost of hydrogen. For any plant, the cost of hydrogen will depend on (1) the location and proximity to cheap fuel and power; (2) the size of the plant; (3) the purity of the hydrogen required; (4) the pressure at which it is employed; and (5) the type of process by which it is made. Cost estimates have been made on producing hydrogen from water gas and by electrolysis of

---

[1] Cox, *Chem. & Met. Eng.*, **40**, 407 (1933).

water.   In either case, the final purity of the hydrogen is very high, the water-gas hydrogen having been purified so that it is substantially equivalent to electrolytic hydrogen in order that the basis for the two may be comparable.

For a small water-gas plant, the total cost, excluding the price of water gas, is about 35 cts. per 1,000 cu. ft. of hydrogen at ordinary pressure and temperature.   The preparation of hydrogen by reacting the constituent carbon monoxide with steam is about 48 per cent of this cost; the removal of the carbon dioxide by water scrubbing, about 20 per cent; and the final purification, about 32 per cent.   When water gas is available at 20 cts. per 1,000 cu. ft., the total cost per 1,000 cu. ft. of hydrogen made from it on a relatively small scale is about 60 cts.

The most important items in making hydrogen by the electrolysis of water are the cost of electric power and the amortization charges. The more expensive type of equipment needed and the charges upon it are reflected in the fact that for a plant producing about a million cubic feet of hydrogen per day by electrolysis, the costs, exclusive of power, are about 40 cts. per 1,000 cu. ft.   With power available at 0.5 ct. per kilowatt hour, the total cost of hydrogen is about $1.15 per 1,000 cu. ft., at ordinary temperature and pressure.   With power available at 0.25 ct. per kilowatt hour, the price would be about 78 cts.; and at 0.75 ct. per kilowatt hour, about $1.45.   In these calculations, no credit was given to the value of the oxygen produced along with the hydrogen; *i.e.*, it was assumed to have no value.

Compressing the hydrogen to 3,000 lb. per square inch would cost about 20 cts. per 1,000 cu. ft., if power were available at 1 ct. per kilowatt hour.   On this basis, the energy cost would be just about one-half the total cost, fixed charges, labor, maintenance and repairs accounting for the other half.

The cost of hydrogen in the large plants hydrogenating petroleum and coal may be very low—from 25 to 35 cts. per 1,000 cu. ft. compressed to 3,500 lb. per square inch.   This is due to the fact that natural gas or waste refinery gases are used; and in all these plants, the cost of power is very low—perhaps 1 mill per kilowatt hour.   In these cases, the cost of compression per 1,000 cu. ft. to 3,500 lb. is of the order of 10 cts.

Along with the cost of hydrogen, it is necessary to know the amount consumed in the various processes.   For the case of relatively pure or definite chemical compounds, the required amount of hydrogen is readily calculated.   In the fat-hardening industry, about 34 cu. ft. of hydrogen is consumed per ton of oil per unit drop in iodine value.   For hardening the common oils such as castor, cottonseed, linseed, olive, palm, rapeseed, soya bean, sunflower seed, and whale oils, the hydrogen consumption amounts to from 0.8 to 2 cu. ft. per lb.

Thus, in hydrogenating common chemicals the cost of hydrogen would probably not be more than 1 ct. per pound of material hydrogenated; while in the fat-hardening industry, it would be only a few mills per pound of hardened oil. In the petroleum, tar, and coal hydrogenation processes, the cost of hydrogen is from a fraction of a cent to 2 cts. per gallon of finished product. These figures are merely the cost of the hydrogen compressed to the pressure needed, and do not include the operating costs, fixed charges, catalyst costs, etc.

III. TYPE HYDROGENATIONS

Hydrogenation of —C = C— Linkages.

General Reaction.—

$$R \cdot CH : CH \cdot R' + H_2 \rightarrow R \cdot CH_2 \cdot CH_2 \cdot R'$$

where R and R' are aliphatic or aromatic groups. The hydrogenation of an ethylenic to a paraffinic linkage can be accomplished readily, usually in the presence of a nickel or nickel-containing catalyst and sometimes with platinum or palladium catalysts. In general, the hydrogen pressures need not be high, except when the hydrogenation is slow, and, then, increased pressure usually speeds up the reaction. Since hydrocarbons are generally more volatile than the ester or acid of the same number of carbon atoms, a considerable number of these hydrogenations take place in the vapor phase simply by passing the vaporized compound and hydrogen over the catalyst at a suitable temperature. However, it is believed that operation at somewhat lower temperatures, but with increased hydrogen pressures, may be more advantageous when hydrogenation at low pressure and high temperature causes a disruption or breaking of the carbon-to-carbon linkages. Examples of the conversion of an ethylenic to a paraffinic linkage are given in the following paragraphs.

The lower-molecular-weight olefins, such as ethylene, propylene, butenes, pentenes, hexenes, and heptenes, are readily hydrogenated to the corresponding paraffin hydrocarbon in the vapor phase by passing the olefin and hydrogen over nickel at atmospheric pressure and 100 to 200°C. Care must be taken to keep the temperature as low as possible and still permit hydrogenation; otherwise, at higher temperatures, side reactions involving cleavages in the hydrocarbon chain will occur. It is also advisable for the same reason to use a considerable excess of hydrogen. Under carefully controlled conditions, the reduction proceeds smoothly and furnishes a convenient method for preparing paraffin hydrocarbons, particularly those of lower molecular weight.

Higher-molecular-weight olefins can also be hydrogenated in the vapor phase in the presence of a nickel catalyst if they have sufficient volatility at the temperature for hydrogenation, *viz.*, 150 to 200°C. Otherwise, the reduction is accomplished in a shaking or stirred autoclave in the liquid phase; and hydrogen pressures, from a few to a hundred atmospheres, may be used. Higher hydrogen pressures generally speed up the reduction and permit lower temperatures for hydrogenation. Both these effects minimize side reactions. The catalysts, usually nickel but also platinum or palladium black or their oxides, are kept suspended in the liquid by the mechanical agitation.

Aromatic hydrocarbons, such as benzene, toluene, xylenes, as well as ethyl-, propyl, butyl-, and other substituted benzenes, can be reduced to the corresponding hexahydrobenzenes when their vapors are passed along with hydrogen over nickel catalysts maintained at temperatures of from 150 to 200°C. In the case of naphthalene or substituted naphthalenes, the product may be the tetra- or decahydronaphthalene derivative. Atmospheric pressures are usually employed in these vapor-phase hydrogenations, although higher hydrogen partial pressures are also suitable. With more substituent groups or with chains longer than butyl or amyl, secondary decomposition products resulting from cracking or the breaking of carbon-to-carbon linkages in the chain appear. In these cases, hydrogenating at lower temperatures but with higher hydrogen pressures and using platinum or nickel catalysts is more practical.

Cyclic hydrocarbons, other than five or six carbon rings, are hydrogenated with the opening of the ring or with the formation of five- or six-membered rings. Thus, cyclopropane or trimethylene is readily reduced to propane when passed with hydrogen over nickel at 80 to

TABLE III.—HYDROGENATION OF AROMATIC COMPOUNDS AT 2 TO 3 ATMOSPHERES HYDROGEN PRESSURE AND 25 TO 30°C.

50 cc. of Glacial Acetic Acid Used as Solvent

Compound	Amount of substance, gm.	Amount of catalyst, gm.	Time, hr.	Compound obtained
Benzene	15.6	0.2	2.0	Cyclohexane
Toluene	18.4	0.2	2.75	Methylcyclohexane
Ethylbenzene	21.2	0.2	7.5	Ethylcyclohexane
m-Xylene	21.2	0.2	21.5	m-Dimethylcyclohexane
Mixed xylenes	21.2	0.2	26.0	Mixed dimethylcyclohexanes
Mesitylene	12	0.2	8.5	Trimethylcyclohexane
Cymene	13.4	0.2	7.5	1-Methyl-4-isopropylcyclohexane
Diphenylmethane	16.8	0.2	7.0	Dicyclohexylmethane
Triphenylmethane[1]	8.74	0.8	48.0	Tricyclohexylmethane
α, α-Diphenylethane	18.2	0.6	26.5	α, α-Dicyclohexylethane
Dibenzyl	18.2	0.6	37.0	α, β-Dicyclohexylethane
Phenylacetic acid	13.6	0.2	5.5	Cyclohexylacetic acid
β-Phenylpropionic acid	15.0	0.2	6.0	β-Cyclohexylpropionic acid

[1] Temperature 60°C., 100 cc. of acetic acid.

180°C. Cyclobutane is hydrogenated at 180°C. to butane[1] in a similar manner, while cyclopentane and cyclohexane are not changed to pentane or hexane. These five- and six-membered rings are very stable and do not undergo any change except the usual degradative decompositions at higher temperatures. Cycloheptane and cyclooctane at 200 to 250°C., when hydrogenated with a nickel catalyst, undergo changes to methyl and dimethyl derivatives of cyclopentane and cyclohexane.[2]

Instead of using nickel and hydrogenating in the gas phase at 150 to 200°C., platinum oxide catalysts in the liquid phase and at lower temperatures (25 to 30°C.) give good results, as is shown in Table III.[3]

Examples of high-pressure hydrogenation of a few simple aromatic hydrocarbons are given in Table IV.[4]

TABLE IV.—HYDROGENATION OF AROMATIC COMPOUNDS AT HIGH PRESSURE

Compound	Temperature, °C.	Pressure, atmos.	Time, min.	Catalyst	Product
Benzene (1 mole)	220 to 235	65 to 135	510	2.4 gm. Ni 2.4 gm. copper chromite	100 % Cyclohexane
Benzene (1 mole)	200 to 300	110 to 180	540	5.0 gm. copper chromite	30 % Cyclohexane
Benzene (1 mole)	200 to 340	60 to 130	400	0.12 mole Ni	50 % Cyclohexane
Benzene (½ mole)	160 to 220	48 to 100	120	0.085 mole Ni 0.085 mole Cu	100 % Cyclohexane
Toluene (½ mole)	220 to 300	60 to 130	135	0.085 mole Ni 0.085 mole Cu	100 % Methylcyclohexane
Ethylbenzene (½ mole)	220 to 290	110 to 180	100	0.07 mole Ni 0.035 mole Cu	100 % Ethylcyclohexane
Xylene (½ mole)	200 to 280	80 to 170	200	0.1 mole Ni 0.1 mole Cu	100 % Dimethylcyclohexane
Cymene (0.8 mole)	300 to 380	130 to 165	420	0.085 mole Ni 0.085 mole Cu	40 % Menthene

The hydrogenation of *ethylenic groups in alcohols*, aldehydes, and ketones differs from those in hydrocarbons in that the conditions of hydrogenation must be milder and better controlled in order to reduce the ethylenic linkage and not the carbonyl groups. In general, the reduction of unsaturated alcohols, aldehydes, or ketones proceeds smoothly either by passing the vapor along with excess hydrogen over nickel catalysts or by hydrogenation in the liquid phase, using hydrogen pressures from 3 to 100 atmos. or more. In this latter case, the catalyst is usually suspended in the liquid.

Table V summarizes the conditions of hydrogenation of a few of the simpler compounds.

[1] WILLSTÄTTER and BRUCE, *Ber.*, **40**, 3979, 4456 (1907).
[2] WILLSTÄTTER and KAMETAKA, *Ber.*, **41**, 1480 (1908).
[3] ADAMS and MARSHALL, *J. Am. Chem. Soc.*, **50**, 1972 (1928).
[4] HERSH and GRAHAM, Undergraduate theses, Penn. State Coll. (1931).

TABLE V.—REDUCTION OF AROMATIC ALCOHOLS AND KETONES

Compound	Catalyst	Temperature, °C.	Pressure, atmos.	Phase	Products obtained	Reference
Allyl alcohol.........	Nickel	130 to 170	1	Vapor	Propyl alcohol	1
Tertiary methylheptenols	Nickel	160 to 170	0.02	Vapor	Tertiary methylheptanols with corresponding hydrocarbon	2
Phorone............	Nickel	160 to 170	1	Vapor	Diisobutyl ketone	3
Mesityl oxide........	Nickel	185	1	Vapor	2-Methylpentanone-4 methylisobutylcarbinol and 2-methylpentane	4
Mesityl oxide........	Colloidal platinum	25	1 to 2	Water solution	2-Methylpentanone-4	5
Dibenzalacetone.....	Colloidal palladium	25 to 80	2 to 3	Benzene-alcohol solution	Dibenzylacetone	6
Phenol..............	Nickel	100 to 150	15	Liquid	Cyclohexanol	7
Phenol..............	Platinum oxide	25 to 50	2 to 3	Alcohol solution	Cyclohexanol	8
Cinnamic alcohol....	Platinum black	25	1 to 3	Liquid	Cyclohexylpropanol	9
o-, m-, and p-Cresols.	Nickel	220 to 230	1	Vapor	Methylcyclohexanols	10
Xylenols............	Nickel	200	1	Vapor	Dimethylcyclohexanols and dimethylbenzenes	11
α- and β-Naphthols..	Nickel	170	1	Vapor	Corresponding decahydronaphthols	12
α- and β-Naphthols..	Nickel	250	100	Liquid	Corresponding decahydronaphthols	13
Anthraquinone	Nickel	75	50	Tetralin or decalin solution	Tetrahydroanthraquinone	14

[1] SABATIER, *Compt. rend.*, **144**, 879 (1907).

[2] GRIGNARD, *Bull. soc. chim.*, **43**, 473 (1928).

[3] GRIGNARD, *Bull. soc. chim. Belg.*, **37**, 41 (1928).

[4] SKITA, *Ber.*, **41**, 2938 (1908).

[5] *Ibid.*, **48**, 1494 (1915).

[6] PAAL, *Ber.*, **45**, 2226 (1912).

[7] SABATIER and REID, "Catalysis in Organic Chemistry," p. 216, D. Van Nostrand Company, Inc., New York, (1922).

[8] VOORHEES and ADAMS, *J. Am. Chem. Soc.*, **44**, 1404 (1922).

[9] WASER, *Helv. Chim. Acta*, **8**, 123 (1925).

[10] SABATIER and MAILHE, *Compt. rend.*, **140**, 350 (1905).

[11] *Ibid.*, **142**, 553 (1906).

[12] LEROUX, *Compt. rend.*, **141**, 953 (1905).

[13] IPATIEV, *Ber.*, **40**, 1281 (1907).

[14] SKITA, *Ber.*, **60**, 2526 (1927).

The hydrogenation of *unsaturated acids and esters* is not particularly adapted to vapor-phase reactions because of their low volatility. In general, most of these reductions are carried out in the liquid phase and at somewhat elevated hydrogen pressures. The types of catalyst employed are very similar to those used in saturating ethylenic linkages in more volatile compounds where a vapor-phase reaction is possible. Table VI summarizes a few typical examples.

Hydrogenation of Carbonyl ($> C{=}O$) Linkages. *General Reaction.*— $R \cdot CO \cdot R' + H_2 \rightarrow R \cdot CHOH \cdot R'$, where R is an aliphatic or aromatic

TABLE VI.—REDUCTION OF UNSATURATED ESTERS AND ACIDS

Compound	Catalyst	Temperature, °C.	Pressure, atmos.	Phase	Products obtained	Reference
Crotonic acid....	Nickel	190	1	Vapor	Butyric acid	1
Crotonic acid.....	Colloidal palladium	25	1	Liquid	Butyric acid	2
Sorbic acid.......	Colloidal palladium	25 to 75	1	Liquid	n-Valeric acid	3
Oleic acid........	Nickel	280 to 300	1	Vapor	Stearic acid	1
Oleic acid........	Nickel	250	1 to 10	Liquid	Stearic acid	4
Benzoic acid......	Colloidal palladium	25 to 50	2	Acetic acid solution	Hexahydrobenzoic acid	5
Ethyl benzoate...	Platinum oxide	25 to 50	2 to 3	Alcohol solution	Ethyl hexahydrobenzoate	6
Cinnamic acid....	Nickel	100	15	Amyl alcohol solution	Phenylpropionic acid	7
Cinnamic acid....	Nickel	300	100	Liquid	Cyclohexylpropionic acid	8
Cinnamic acid....	Copper chromite	175	100 to 150	Liquid	Phenylpropionic acid	9
Phenylethyl acetate	Nickel	180	1	Vapor	Cyclohexylethyl acetate	10

[1] SABATIER and MAILHE, *Ann. chim. phys.* [8] **16**, 73 (1909).
[2] BÖESEKEN, WEIDE, and MOM, *Rec. trav. chim.*, **35**, 269 (1915).
[3] FOKIN, *J. Russ. Phys. Chem. Soc.*, **40**, 276 (1908).
[4] LUSH, *J. Soc. Chem. Ind.*, **42**, 219 T (1923); **43**, 53T (1924); **44**, 129T (1925); **46**, 454T (1927).
[5] SKITA and MEYER, *Ber.*, **45**, 3589 (1912).
[6] GRAY and MARVEL, *J. Am. Chem. Soc.*, **47**, 2799 (1925).
[7] BROCHET and BAUER, *Bull. soc. chim.* (4) **17**, 50 (1915).
[8] IPATIEV, *J. Russ. Phys. Chem. Soc.*, **41**, 1414 (1909).
[9] ADKINS and CONNOR, *J. Am. Chem. Soc.*, **53**, 1903 (1931).
[10] SABATIER, *Compt. rend.*, **156**, 424 (1913).

group, and R' may be the same or a hydrogen atom. The carbonyl group in aldehydes, ketones, esters, and acids can be reduced by hydrogen with catalysts either partially, to give a hydroxyl (—OH) group; or entirely, to give a hydrocarbon group (—CH_2— or —CH_3). The partial reduction is obviously characterized as a mild hydrogenation, and catalysts in this class are, in general, applicable. Carbon monoxide may be considered the simplest compound containing this group, and its hydrogenation leads to the syntheses of alcohols, ketones, acids, and hydrocarbons, the last containing as high as some 70 carbon atoms.[1] This is because carbon monoxide, on partial reduction, can yield compounds or molecular fragments, *e.g.*, >CH_2, which are capable of undergoing extensive condensation on the same catalysts that effect the initial hydrogenation. Thus, from the simple substances carbon monoxide (and, in some cases, carbon dioxide) and hydrogen, practically unlimited syntheses are possible; the greatest problem associated with these reactions is the separation of individual compounds.

[1] FISCHER, TROPSCH, and NEDDEN, *Ber.*, **60B**, 1330–1334 (1927).

Methane results when carbon monoxide and hydrogen in the proportion of 1:3 are passed over a nickel catalyst at ordinary pressure and temperatures of 200 to 250°C.[1]   The reaction is

$$CO + 3H_2 \rightleftarrows CH_4 + H_2O$$

With less hydrogen and at higher temperatures, carbon monoxide reacts according to the following equation to form carbon dioxide, rather than with hydrogen to give methane:

$$2CO \rightleftarrows C + CO_2$$

Consequently, there is carbon deposition on the catalyst and loss in activity.   At about 250°C., and with a nickel catalyst, the following reaction[2] takes place when the ratio of hydrogen to carbon monoxide is lower.

$$2CO + 2H_2 \rightleftarrows CO_2 + CH_4$$

Methane also results from the reduction of carbon dioxide by hydrogen, according to the reaction[3]

$$CO_2 + 4H_2 \rightleftarrows CH_4 + 2H_2O$$

This equilibrium has been studied.[4]   Using a catalyst consisting of 73 per cent charcoal and 27 per cent nickel, which resulted from carbonizing a mixture of sugar and nickel acetate, the decomposition of carbon monoxide into carbon and carbon dioxide was entirely suppressed and the catalyst maintained its activity for months in producing methane. Ferric oxide, vanadium pentoxide, and cerium oxide are promoters for the nickel-charcoal catalyst.   Studies have also been made of the various reactions involved in the reduction of carbon monoxide and dioxide.[5]

Higher hydrocarbons result from the reduction of carbon monoxide by hydrogen at atmospheric pressure with cobalt-containing catalysts. Fischer and Tropsch[6] initiated this work in 1926 and have termed the product obtained *synthin*.   It may be considered a synthetic petroleum. There are formed light hydrocarbons, such as ethane, propane, butane, pentane, etc., which are present in natural gas and "casinghead" gasoline; a product also is obtained that has a distillation range equivalent to that of gasoline and consists of paraffin hydrocarbons and some olefin hydrocarbons; higher fractions equivalent to kerosene and oily products are also present; and, finally, paraffin waxes of melting points of over

[1] SABATIER and SENDERENS, *Compt. rend.*, **134**, 514, 689 (1902).

[2] ARMSTRONG and HILDITCH, *Proc. Roy. Soc.*, **103A**, 25 (1923).

[3] SABATIER and SENDERENS, *loc. cit.*

[4] RANDALL and GERARD, *Ind. Eng. Chem.*, **20**, 1335 (1928).

[5] HIGHTOWER and WHITE, *Ind. Eng. Chem.*, **20**, 10 (1928).

[6] FISCHER and TROPSCH, *Brennstoff-Chem.*, **7**, 97, 299 (1920); *Nat. Petroleum News*, Oct. 13; Oct. 20, 1926.

100°C. can be made. There may also be present some oxygenated products, such as alcohols, aldehydes, ketones, etc.[1]

The catalysts contain, iron, nickel, copper, and cobalt along with metallic oxides. Cobalt appears to be the best of the metals, and the oxides of chromium, zinc, rare earths, aluminum, magnesium, and manganese are used. Erdeley and Nash[2] use catalysts of the following combinations: cobalt-copper-aluminum oxide, cobalt-copper-manganese oxide, cobalt-copper-zinc oxide, cobalt-copper-cerium oxide, and cobalt-copper.

In general, the temperature range for the production of these hydrocarbons is between 200 and 300°C.; below 200°C., the rate of reaction is nil.; above 300°C., methane formation preponderates. If strong bases are present in the catalyst, the formation of solid paraffins is favored. The gases must be free from sulfur compounds, for these are effective catalyst poisons.[3]

Methanol results from the high-pressure hydrogenation of carbon monoxide at temperatures from 275 to 375°C. with catalysts composed principally of copper, zinc, chromium, manganese, and aluminum oxides.[4] Pressure is needed because the amount of methanol in equilibrium with carbon monoxide and hydrogen at temperatures of approximately 300°C. and at atmospheric pressure is negligible. Because of the decrease in volume attending this reaction, increase in pressure increases the yield. In this respect, the synthesis of methanol is analogous to that of ammonia from nitrogen and hydrogen. The pressures used are of the order of 3,000 lb. per square inch. Here is a striking case of the selectivity, or preferential character, of catalysts. These methanol catalysts readily reduce carbon monoxide to methanol with only a trace of methane, even though the temperature is 375°C. and pressures are as high as 4,000 lb. per square inch. On the other hand, carbon monoxide in contact with an active nickel catalyst results in a violent reduction to methane at temperatures of 200°C. and atmospheric pressure. The methanol-type catalysts, for some reason, are incapable of carrying the

[1] Elvins and Nash, *Nature*, **118**, 154 (1926); *J. Soc. Chem. Ind.*, **45**, 878 (1926).
[2] Erdeley and Nash, *J. Soc. Chem. Ind.*, **47**, 219T (1928).
[3] Fischer, *Brennstoff-Chem.*, **8**, 1 (1927).
[4] Frolich, Fenske, and Quiggle, *Ind. Eng. Chem.*, **20**, 694 (1928); Fenske and Frolich, *Ind. Eng. Chem.*, **21**, 1052 (1929); Lazier and Vaughen, *J. Am. Chem. Soc.*, **54**, 3084 (1932); Lewis and Frolich, *Ind. Eng. Chem.*, **20**, 285 (1928); Frolich, Fenske, Taylor, and Southwick, *Ind. Eng. Chem.*, **20**, 1327 (1928); Cryder and Frolich, *Ind. Eng. Chem.*, **21**, 867 (1929); Audibert and Raineau, *Ind. Eng. Chem.*, **20**, 1105 (1928); Huffman and Dodge, *Ind. Eng. Chem.*, **21**, 1056 (1929); Brown and Galloway, *Ind. Eng. Chem.*, **20**, 960 (1928); Smith and Branting, *J. Am. Chem. Soc.*, **51**, 129 (1929); Newitt, Byrne, and Strong, *Proc. Roy. Soc.*, **123A**, 236 (1929).

reduction to completion, *viz.*, to methane. Consequently, they are finding extensive application where mild hydrogenation conditions are needed.

Higher alcohols with normal boiling points up to nearly 200°C. are formed by high-pressure hydrogenation of carbon monoxide at temperatures just above those generally used in the synthesis of methanol, *viz.*, at about 350 to 450°C. The catalysts consist of iron promoted with alkalis or methanol-type catalysts containing alkalis.[1] The mechanism of formation of these higher alcohols appears to be a series of successive condensations brought about through dehydration between' smaller alcohols.[2]

$$2CH_3OH \rightarrow C_2H_5OH + H_2O$$
$$CH_3OH + C_2H_5OH \rightarrow C_3H_7OH + H_2O$$
$$2C_2H_5OH \rightarrow C_4H_9OH + H_2O, \text{ etc.}$$

Formaldehyde, acetaldehyde as well as propionic, butyric, and amylic aldehydes are reduced to the corresponding alcohols at about 100 to 150°C. in the presence of a nickel catalyst. However, there are side reactions, methane and water being formed.[3] Recently, the acetaldehyde, ethyl alcohol, and hydrogen equilibrium has been studied.[4]

The reduction of ketones by hydrogen at elevated temperatures is also a reversible reaction. Thus, in the case of acetone, at 218°C. and atmospheric pressure, the hydrogenation is about only 30 per cent complete.[5] However, this is not a serious factor, for the hydrogenation is accompanied by a decrease in volume so that increased hydrogen pressure counteracts the effect of increased temperature on the equilibrium yield. In order to give conveniently the various conditions under which aldehydes or ketones may be hydrogenated, a few typical examples are summarized in Tables VII and VIII.

Hydrogenation of Esters and Acids.

General Reaction.—

$$R \cdot COOR' + 2H_2 \rightarrow RCH_2OH + R'OH,$$

where R is usually an aliphatic group, and R' is the same or a hydro-

[1] FROLICH and LEWIS, *Ind. Eng. Chem.*, **20**, 354 (1928); FISCHER, "The Conversion of Coal into Oils," trans. by Lessing, p. 213, Ernest Benn, Ltd., London, 1st ed. (1925); GRAVES, *Ind. Eng. Chem.*, **23**, 1381 (1931).

[2] FROLICH and CRYDER, *Ind. Eng. Chem.*, **22**, 1057 (1930); PARKS and HUFFMAN, "Free Energies of Some Organic Compounds," p. 224, Chemical Catalog Company, New York, 1st ed. (1932).

[3] SABATIER and SENDERENS, *Compt. rend.*, **137**, 302 (1903).

[4] BANCROFT and GEORGE, *J. Phys. Chem.*, **35**, 2194 (1931).

[5] PARKS and HUFFMAN, "Free Energies of Some Organic Compounds," p. 23, Chemical Catalog Company, New York (1932).

TABLE VII.—REDUCTION OF ALDEHYDES TO ALCOHOLS

Compound	Catalyst	Temperature °C.	Pressure, atmos.	Phase	Products obtained	Reference
Acetaldehyde.......	Nickel	25	110	Liquid	Ethyl alcohol	1
Heptaldehyde......	Platinum oxide	25	2 to 3	Liquid	Heptyl alcohol	2
Heptaldehyde......	Colloidal platinum	25 to 50	1	Dilute acetic acid solution	Heptyl alcohol	3
Furfural..........	Platinum oxide	20 to 60	1 to 3	Liquid	Furfuryl alcohol, tetrahydrofuryl alcohol, pentanediol-1, 5, pentanediol-1, 2, and *n*-amyl alcohol	4, 5
Furfural..........	Copper chromite	150	100 to 150	Liquid	Furfuryl alcohol	6
Benzaldehyde	Platinum black or colloidal palladium	25 to 50	1 to 3	Liquid	Benzyl alcohol, toluene, and methylcyclohexane	7, 8, 9
Benzaldehyde	Nickel	25	110	Liquid	Benzyl alcohol	1
Benzaldehyde	Copper chromite	180	100 to 150	Liquid	Benzyl alcohol	6

[1] COVERT and ADKINS, *J. Am. Chem. Soc.*, **54**, 4117 (1932).
[2] CAROTHERS and ADAMS, *J. Am. Chem. Soc.*, **46**, 1682 (1924).
[3] SKITA and MEYER, *Ber.*, **45**, 3589 (1912).
[4] PIERCE and PARKS, *J. Am. Chem. Soc.*, **51**, 3385 (1929).
[5] KAUFMANN with ADAMS, *J. Am. Chem. Soc.*, **45**, 3029 (1923).
[6] ADKINS and CONNOR, *J. Am. Chem. Soc.*, **53**, 1093 (1931). U.S. 2,094,975 (1937).
[7] CAROTHERS and ADAMS, *J. Am. Chem. Soc.*, **45**, 1071 (1923).
[8] SKITA, *Ber.*, **48**, 1486 (1915).
[9] VAVON, *Compt. rend.*, **154**, 359 (1912).

gen atom. The carboxyl group in esters and acids can be reduced to the corresponding hydroxyl group by the use of mild hydrogenating catalysts and hydrogen pressures, generally of the order of 100 atmospheres or more. It is necessary that the hydrogenation conditions be controlled carefully in order to avoid dehydration of the alcohol—resulting in an olefin—or if the latter is further reduced by hydrogen, a paraffin hydrocarbon is formed. In general, the catalysts are of the type used in synthesizing methanol and higher alcohols. The reduction of the carboxyl group is most satisfactory in aliphatic or hydroaromatic compounds. In the aromatic series, the reduction to alcohols also occurs, the best results being obtained when the carboxyl group is in an aliphatic chain. If the group is directly attached or near to an aromatic ring, side reactions usually accompany the reduction. These usually involve the reduction of the alcohol group to a hydrocarbon group. Typical reductions are summarized in Table IX.

Hydrogenolyses Involving Cleavages of Carbon to Oxygen and Carbon to Carbon Bonds.—Hydrogenolysis is a more exact expression

TABLE VIII.—REDUCTION OF KETONES TO ALCOHOLS

Compound	Catalyst	Temp., °C.	Pressure, atmos.	Phase	Products obtained	Reference
Acetone..........	Nickel	115 to 125	1	Vapor	Isopropyl alcohol	1
Acetone..........	Platinum black	25	1 to 2	Acetic acid solution	Isopropyl alcohol	2
Acetone..........	Nickel	23	2 to 3	Liquid	Isopropyl alcohol	3
Acetone..........	Copper chromite	150	100 to 150	Liquid	Isopropyl alcohol	4
Methyl ethyl ketone	Platinum oxide	25 to 50	1 to 3	Liquid	Secondary butyl alcohol	5
Diethyl ketone...	Nickel	130 to 140	1	Vapor	Diethylcarbinol	1
Diethyl ketone...	Colloidal platinum	25	1 to 3	Acetic acid solution	Diethylcarbinol	6
Diethyl ketone...	Platinum black	25	1 to 2	Acetic acid solution	Diethylcarbinol	2
Methyl isopropyl ketone	Copper chromite	150	100 to 150	Liquid	Methylisopropylcarbinol	4
Methyl butyl ketone	Nickel	150	1	Vapor	Methylbutylcarbinol	1
Methyl isobutyl ketone	Nickel	150	120	Liquid	Methylisobutylcarbinol	7
Methyl isobutyl ketone	Platinum or palladium black	25	1 to 2	Liquid	Methylisobutylcarbinol	2
Pinacoline........	Copper chromite	150	100 to 150	Liquid	Methyl-*tert*- butyl-carbinol	4
Acetylacetone....	Nickel	140 to 160	1	Vapor	Pentanediol-2, 4 and pentanol-2	8
Acetylacetone....	Colloidal platinum	25 to 50	1 to 3	Acetic acid solution	Methylpropylcarbinol	6
Acetylacetone....	Platinum black	25	1 to 2	Ether or alcohol solution	Methylpropylcarbinol	2
Acetophenone....	Platinum black	25	1 to 2	Alcohol-water solution	Methylphenylcarbinol	2
Acetophenone....	Platinum black	25	1 to 2	Acetic acid solution	Ethylcyclohexane	2
Acetophenone....	Nickel	175	120	Liquid	Methylphenylcarbinol and ethylcyclohexane	7
Benzophenone....	Platinum black	25	1 to 2	Ether solution	Diphenylcarbinol	2
Quinone.........	Nickel	200	1	Vapor	Hydroquinone	9

[1] SABATIER and SENDERENS, *Compt. rend.*, **137**, 302 (1900).
[2] VAVON, *Ann. chim.*, **9**, 1, 144 (1914).
[3] COVERT and ADKINS, *J. Am. Chem. Soc.*, **54**, 4117 (1932).
[4] ADKINS and CONNOR, *J. Am. Chem. Soc.*, **53**, 1093 (1931).
[5] VOORHEES with ADAMS, *J. Am. Chem. Soc.*, **44**, 1404 (1922).
[6] SKITA, *Ber.*, **48**, 1496 (1915).
[7] COVERT, CONNOR, and ADKINS, *J. Am. Chem. Soc.*, **54**, 1658, 1932.
[8] SABATIER and MAILHE, *Compt. rend.*, **144**, 1086 (1907).
[9] SABATIER and MAILHE, *op. cit.*, **146**, 457 (1908).

than destructive hydrogenation and refers particularly to cleavages in a molecule associated with the addition of hydrogen to the molecule. The cleavages discussed here are of carbon-to-carbon and carbon-to-oxygen bonds. There may also take place the breaking of carbon to

TABLE IX.—REDUCTION OF ESTERS AND ACIDS TO ALCOHOLS, ETC.

Compound	Catalyst	Temperature, °C.	Pressure, atmos.	Phase	Products obtained	Reference
Methyl formate...	Copper	180 to 230	1	Vapor	Methanol	1
Acetic acid........	Zinc-manganese chromium oxide	400	200	Vapor	Ethyl, propyl, and butyl alcohols	2
Acetic acid........	Copper-zinc cadmium chromite	390	170 to 200	Vapor	Ethyl alcohol and ethyl acetate	3
Ethyl lactate......	Copper chromite	250	200 to 300	Vapor-liquid	Propanediol-1, 2	4
Butyric acid......	Copper-zinc cadmium chromite	390	150 to 200	Vapor	Butyl alcohol and butyl butyrate	3
Ethyl succinate....	Copper chromite	250	220	Liquid	Tetramethylene glycol	5
Ethyl trimethylacetate	Copper chromite	250	220	Liquid	Tertiary butylcarbinol	5
Ethyl valerate.....	Copper chromite	250	220	Liquid	n-Amyl alcohol	5
Di-n-butyl glutarate	Copper chromite	250	200 to 300	Liquid	Pentanediol-1, 5	5
Methyl, ethyl or butyl caproate	Copper chromite	250	200 to 300	Liquid	n-Hexyl alcohol	4
Caprylic acid......	Copper on kieselguhr	340	200	Liquid	n-Octyl alcohol	6
Methyl caprate....	Copper on kieselguhr	300 to 325	250 to 285	Liquid	n-Decyl alcohol	6
Diethyl sebacate...	Copper chromite	250	200 to 300	Liquid	Decanediol-1, 10	4
Sebacic acid......	Copper chromite	390 to 400	200	Ethyl alcohol solution	Decanediol-1, 10	3
Coconut oil acids..	Copper-zinc cadmium chromite	380	200	Liquid	n-Decyl alcohol, lauryl alcohol, and higher molecular weight alcohols	3
Lauric acid........	Copper-zinc cadmium chromite	380	200	Liquid	Lauryl alcohol, and lauryl laurate	3
Methyl laurate....	Zinc-copper chromite	300 to 325	270 to 290	Liquid	Lauryl alcohol	5–6
Oleic acid.........	Copper-zinc cadmium chromite	350 to 420	200	Liquid	Oleyl alcohol, stearyl alcohol and esters	3
Stearic acid.......	Zinc-copper chromite	325	280	Liquid	Stearyl alcohol	6
Ethyl cinnamate...	Copper chromite	250	200	Liquid	3-Phenylpropanol-1	5
Methyl salicylate..	Copper chromite	250	200 to 300	Liquid	2-Methylcyclohexanol and o-cresol	4
Ethyl hexahydrobenzoate	Copper chromite	250	200 to 300	Liquid	Cyclohexylcarbinol	4
Ethyl α-phenylbutyrate	Copper chromite	250	200 to 300	Liquid	2-Phenylbutanol-1 and hydrocarbons	4
Ethyl β-phenylpropionate	Copper chromite	250	200 to 300	Liquid	3-Phenylpropanol-1	4
Ethyl phenylacetate	Copper chromite	250	200 to 300	Liquid	2-Phenylethanol-1 and ethylbenzene	4

[1] CHRISTIANSEN, *J. Chem. Soc.*, **1926**, 413.
[2] FROLICH and CRYDER, *Ind. Eng. Chem.*, **22**, 1057 (1930); CRYDER, Doctor's thesis, Chem. Eng., Mass. Inst. Tech. (1930).
[3] Lazier, U. S. 1,839,974 (1932).
[4] FOLKERS and ADKINS, *J. Am. Chem. Soc.*, **54**, 1146 (1932).
[5] ADKINS and FOLKERS, *J. Am. Chem. Soc.*, **53**, 1096 (1931).
[6] SCHRAUTH, SCHENK, and STICKDORN, *Ber.*, **64B**, 1314 (1931).

nitrogen, sulfur, or halogen bonds, as occurs in hydrogenations in which these elements are usually eliminated as ammonia, hydrogen sulfide, or hydrogen halides. Hydrogenolysis is a term analogous to hydrolysis, alcoholysis, or ammonolysis in which a double decomposition is accomplished by means of water, alcohol, or ammonia, respectively.

Thus:

$$C_2H_5 \cdot O \cdot C_2H_5 + H_2O \rightarrow 2C_2H_5OH \text{ (hydrolysis)}$$
$$C_2H_5 \cdot O \cdot C_2H_5 + H_2 \rightarrow C_2H_6 + C_2H_5OH \text{ (hydrogenolysis)}$$

In practically all hydrogenations, undesirable side reactions occur, although in some instances only to a negligible extent. These side reactions are usually cases of hydrogenolysis. This type of hydrogenation has been emphasized and studied by Ellis,[1] and Adkins.[2] It has certain applications to problems of petroleum refining and to synthetic organic chemistry. In the hydrogenation of petroleum, coals, and tars, the application pertains to the elimination of sulfur, nitrogen, or oxygen and to the conversion of heavy, tarry, or asphaltic substances to more desirable hydrocarbon products usually of a more paraffinic or saturated type. The synthetic applications are concerned with the preparation of new compounds or with a simplified and more economical production of known compounds, either from the usual and known types of raw materials or from new or relatively undeveloped ones.

The following tables (X to XIV) illustrate the type of hydrogenolysis involving the breaking of carbon-to-carbon and carbon-to-oxygen bonds. In general, hydrogenolysis is favored by increased temperature, higher hydrogen pressures, and the more violent type of hydrogenating catalysts. However, these conditions may prove so violent that a variety of reaction products result. From a synthesis viewpoint, the cleavage of the different bonds is best controlled by a careful choice of the reaction temperature, the time of contact, the hydrogen pressure, and the type of catalyst. Frequently, in cases of carbon-to-oxygen cleavage, it may be desirable to incorporate a dehydrating catalyst along with the hydrogenating catalyst. Catalysts such as nickel-alumina and nickel-thoria are of this type. Finally, the point and the type of cleavage (whether carbon-to-carbon or carbon-to-oxygen) are profoundly influenced by the position of various substituent groups, the branching of the carbon chain, and the type of group, viz., aliphatic or aromatic, near or adjacent to the point of cleavage.

Phenols and cresols can be reduced to the corresponding hydroaromatic or aromatic hydrocarbons, depending on the temperature, the

---

[1] ELLIS, "Hydrogenation of Organic Substances," p. 564, D. Van Nostrand Company, Inc., New York, 3d ed. (1930).

[2] Adkins, "Reactions of Hydrogen," p. 69, The University of Wisconsin Press, Madison, Wis. (1937).

TABLE X.—HYDROGENOLYSIS OF OXYGENATED COMPOUNDS

Compound	Catalyst	Temperature, °C.	Pressure, atmos.	Phase	Products obtained	Reference
Ethyl ether..............	Nickel	250	1	Vapor	Ethane and ethyl alcohol	1
Acetone.................	Nickel	300	100	Vapor	Propane	2
Methylhexylcarbinol.....	Nickel	300	100	Vapor	n-Hexane and n-octane	3
Benzyl alcohol...........	Nickel	375	1	Vapor	Toluene	4
Benzyl ethyl ether.......	Nickel	175	120	Liquid	Toluene and ethyl alcohol	5
Benzaldehyde...........	Nickel	230	1	Vapor	Toluene and benzene	6
Acetophenone...........	Nickel	250	1	Vapor	Ethylbenzene, and ethylcyclohexane	7
Benzophenone...........	Nickel	300	1	Vapor	Diphenylmethane	8
Benzophenone...........	Copper chromite	175	100 to 150	Liquid	Diphenylmethane	9
Phenyl ethyl ketone......	Nickel and copper	300	1	Vapor	Propylbenzene	8
Benzoylacetone..........	Nickel	200	1	Vapor	Butylbenzene	10
Propanediol-1, 3.........	Copper chromite	250	175	Liquid	n-Propyl alcohol	11
Butanediol-1, 3..........	Copper chromite	250	175	Liquid	Butanol-2 and n-butyl alcohol	11
2-Methylpentanediol-2, 4.	Copper chromite	200	175	Liquid	Isopropyl alcohol and 2-methylpentanol-4	11

[1] ELLIS, "Hydrogenation of Organic Compounds," p. 564, D. Van Nostrand Company, Inc., New York, 3d ed. (1930).
[2] IPATIEV, *Ber.*, **40**, 1281 (1907).
[3] HERSH and GRAHAM, Undergraduate thesis, Penn. State Coll. (1931).
[4] SABATIER and SENDERENS, *Bull. soc. chim.*, **33**, 616 (1905).
[5] COVERT, CONNOR, and ADKINS, *J. Am. Chem. Soc.*, **54**, 1658 (1932).
[6] SABATIER and SENDERENS, *Compt. rend.*, **137**, 302 (1903).
[7] GRIGNARD, *Bull. soc. chim.*, **43**, 473 (1928).
[8] SABATIER and MURAT, *Ann. chim.* [9] **4**, 257 (1915).
[9] ADKINS and CONNOR, *J. Am. Chem. Soc.*, **53**, 1093 (1931).
[10] DARZENS, *Compt. rend.*, **139**, 868 (1904).
[11] CONNOR and ADKINS, *J. Am. Chem. Soc.*, **54**, 4678 (1932).

pressure of hydrogen, and the type of catalyst. These reactions are increasing in technical importance, for they are the type occurring in the hydrogenation of undesirable phenolic tars to valuable petroleum products. Phenol ($C_6H_5 \cdot OH$), at temperatures above 250°C. and with a nickel catalyst, is reduced by hydrogen to benzene; and polyphenols, *e.g.*, di- and trihydroxybenzenes, are reduced even more readily to benzene.[1] With hydrogen at pressures of 1,250 lb. per square inch and in the absence of catalysts, phenol is unchanged after heating for $2\frac{1}{2}$ hr. at 460 to 470°C. Under the same conditions but with alumina as a catalyst, a 45 per cent yield of benzene is obtained in 4 hr. Addi-

[1] MAILHE and GODON, *Bull. soc. chim.* [4] **21**, 61 (1917); SABATIER and MAILHE, *Compt. rend.*, **145**, 1126 (1907); SABATIER and SENDERENS, *Ann. chim. phys.* [8], **4**, 429 (1905).

tional data on the hydrogenolysis of phenol to benzene hydrocarbons at high pressure[1] are given in Table XI.

TABLE XI.—HYDROGENOLYSIS OF PHENOL

Catalyst	Pressure, lb. per sq. in.		Max. temp., °C.	Total time, min.	Total liquid yield	Fraction below 120°C.		Yield of benzene hydrocarbons[1]
	Initial	Max.				%	Density, 15°C.	
W₂O₅	1,400	4,600	485	240	90	44	.....	39.6
Mo₂O₅	1,400	3,100	500	240	80	43	0.868	34.4
Mo₂O₅	1,400	3,500	500	90	92	43	0.849	39.5
Mo₂O₅	1,600	4,200	490	100	80	90	0.806	72
MoO₃ (activated)	1,600	4,500	488	100	82	61	0.822	50[2]
MoO₃ (activated)	1,600	4,200	488	90	76	84	0.818	64
Al₂O₃	1,200	3,700	485	300	45	82	0.868	37
Al₂O₃ (activated)	1,200	4,700	490	240	80.5	66.5	0.863	54.5
Al₂O₃ + 20 % Mo₂O₅ (activated)	1,200	4,300	490	240	75	87.5	0.840	65.5
Al₂O₃ + Cr₂O₃ + Mo₂O₅ (activated)	1,200	3,400	488	90	75.6	85	0.845	64.3
ThO₂ + Mo₂O₅ (activated)	1,200	4,200	478	150	69.5	87	0.838	60.5
NiO + Al₂O₃ (activated)	1,200	2,700	475	120	74	62.5	0.775	46.4
MoS₂	1,200	4,100	480	100	71.6	82	0.821	59.5
NiO + Al₂O₃ (activated)	1,850	4,100	472	90	80	70	0.792	56
Cyclohexanol alone	1,400	4,600	475	90[3]	100[4]			

[1] Does not include losses and light hydrocarbons entrained by the gases.
[2] Theoretical amount of hydrogen to change phenol to cyclohexane.
[3] Thirty minutes at 75°C.
[4] The resultant liquid boiled 50 to 90°C.; density, 0.760 (15°C.).

Cresols and other hydrocarbons, when passed along with hydrogen through tubes at temperatures of about 750°C., yield aromatic hydrocarbons,[2] the best results being obtained with a tinned tube; while with porcelain tubes, the yields were negligible. Table XII, summarizes the results.

Technical *m*-cresol at 720 to 730°C., with from $3\frac{1}{2}$ to 8 times the theoretical amount of hydrogen, gives 95 to 98 per cent of the theoretical yield of benzene. With smaller amounts of hydrogen, the yields are less.[3]

The marked influence of structure on the type of cleavage occurring during hydrogenolysis of hydroxybenzenes is illustrated by the following two examples. Thus, cyclohexanediol-1, 3 $[C_6H_{10}\cdot(OH)_2]$ at about 250°C., with a copper chromite catalyst and 175 atmospheres hydrogen pressure, gives a 95 per cent yield of cyclohexanol $(C_6H_{11}\cdot OH)$. The

[1] KLING and FLORENTIN, *Intern. Conf. Bituminous Coal*, **II**, 33 (1931).
[2] MORRELL and EGLOFF, *ibid.*, 587 (1928).
[3] FISCHER and SCHRADER, *Ges. Abhandl. Kenntnis Kohle*, **6**, 128–144 (1921).

TABLE XII.—HYDROGENOLYSIS OF PHENOLS AND HYDROCARBONS AT 750°C.

Material	Yield as aromatic hydrocarbons, %	
	Tinned tube	Iron tube
Three mixed cresols...................	64	5
o-Cresol..............................	72	35
1, 3, 4-Xylenol........................	72	5
Hexane...............................	7	4
Solvent naphtha I.....................	61	63
Solvent naphtha II....................	49	48

1, 2-isomer is more difficult to reduce; under the same conditions, only about 20 per cent of cyclohexanol forms. The 1, 4-isomer undergoes hydrogenolysis to only a very slight extent, 96 per cent of the material being recovered unchanged after heating for over 8 hr. under the same conditions as for the 1, 3- or 1, 2-isomers.[1] The second example pertains to the xylenols $((CH_3)_2 \cdot C_6H_3 \cdot OH)$, which with nickel and hydrogen at about 200°C. exhibit varying degrees of hydrogenolysis, depending on the position of the methyl and the hydroxyl groups. Thus 1, 3, 4-xylenol and 1, 4, 2-xylenol give relatively high yields of the corresponding dimethylcyclohexanols, while 1, 2, 4-xylenol under substantially the same conditions gives ortho xylene as the principal product.[2]

Hydrocarbons, depending on the length of the chain or branching in the chain or the ring structure, under the combined action of hydrogen, catalysts, and heat, undergo certain cleavages that involve the splitting off of groups or molecular fragments or the opening of ring structures. The resulting products are then usually smaller molecules, are of a more stable type, and usually contain a higher percentage of hydrogen than the original material. The opening of the ring may first involve the reduction to a hydroaromatic of naphthene structure, followed by the opening of the ring with the formation of a chain or paraffin structure. These reactions are also of great technical importance, for they are probably the type of reaction occurring in the hydrogenation of heavy petroleum residues or asphaltic or aromatic base oils, whereby conversion takes place in high yields to stable, more volatile petroleum products such as gasoline and kerosene.

Acetoacetic ester derivatives, which play an important part in various syntheses, undergo different types of hydrogenolysis, depending on the number and nature of the substituent groups. The various types of

[1] CONNOR and ADKINS, *J. Am. Chem. Soc.*, **54**, 4678 (1932).
[2] SABATIER and MAILHE, *Compt. rend.*, **142**, 553 (1906).

reaction occurring when these esters are hydrogenated with a copper chromite catalyst at about 250°C. and 175 atmospheres pressure are illustrated below.

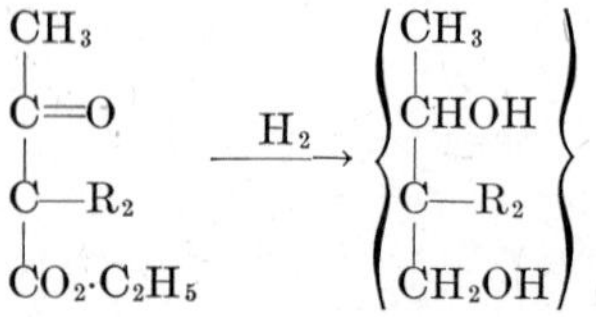

$$
\begin{array}{l}
CH_3 \\
|\\
C{=}O \\
|\\
C{-}R_2 \\
|\\
CO_2 \cdot C_2H_5
\end{array}
\xrightarrow{H_2}
\left\{
\begin{array}{l}
CH_3 \\
|\\
CHOH \\
|\\
C{-}R_2 \\
|\\
CH_2OH
\end{array}
\right\}
\begin{array}{l}
+ H_2 \rightarrow C_2H_5OH + R_2 \cdot CHCH_2OH \quad (1) \\[4pt]
+ H_2 \rightarrow CH_3OH + CH_3 \cdot CHOH \cdot CH \cdot R_2 \quad (2) \\[4pt]
+ H_2 \rightarrow CH_3 \cdot CHOH \cdot CR \cdot CH_3 + H_2O \quad (3) \\[4pt]
+ H_2 \rightarrow CH_3 \cdot CH_2CR_2 \cdot CH_2OH + H_2O \quad (4)
\end{array}
$$

With unsubstituted acetoacetic ester, the only reactions that occur are (3) and (4). With monosubstituted esters, the principal reactions are (1) and (4), with a much smaller amount of (3). With disubstituted esters, the only reaction that takes place is (1). However, the weight and chemical character of the substituent groups are important factors in determining the ease of cleavage of the carbon-to-carbon linkage, as the data in the following table (XIII) show.[1]

TABLE XIII.—THE HYDROGENOLYSIS OF MONOSUBSTITUTED ACETOACETIC ESTER DERIVATIVES

Compound	Carbon-carbon Cleavage, %
Ethyl acetoacetate	0
Ethyl α-ethylacetoacetate	50
Ethyl α-isopropylacetoacetate	60
Ethyl α-butylacetoacetate	70
Ethyl α-hexahydrobenzylacetoacetate	100
Ethyl α-benzylacetoacetate	100
Ethyl α-(β-phenylethyl)-acetoacetate	100
Ethyl α-γ-dimethylacetoacetate	100

IV. PHYSICAL FACTORS OTHER THAN CATALYSTS AFFECTING HYDROGENATION

The Reaction Must Be Possible.[2]—Since catalysts affect only the rate or speed of a reaction and have nothing to do with the inherent

---

[1] CONNOR and ADKINS, *J. Am. Chem. Soc.*, **54**, 4678 (1932).

[2] Examples of the use of free-energy data may be extended into a long list. Such is not the intention of this discussion. Applications have been made to only the four types of reduction that this chapter is concerned with, namely, ethylenic, carbonyl, and carboxyl linkages and hydrogenolysis or destructive hydrogenation. The purpose has been to show the method of applying free-energy data to such reductions and the nature of the results and conclusions that are possible therefrom. It should be pointed out that free-energy data on organic compounds are a comparatively recent development in the field of organic chemistry. Consequently, the data given here may in many cases be found to be wanting in accuracy. Nevertheless, rather than to ignore their usefulness and possibilities, it is believed to be better to show that at least semiquantitative conclusions may be drawn from them that would not otherwise be possible. On this basis alone their use is justified.

tendency of a reaction to proceed, it is obviously of real importance to know whether or not the reaction is at all possible for the conditions of temperature and pressure chosen. The concern is then with chemical affinity, and since the free-energy change of a definite, specific reaction is a quantitative measure of such chemical forces, it is desirable to have free-energy data on the substances in question if they can be had. If reliable free-energy data show the reaction to be possible, then experimental work may be started in order to find suitable catalysts that will enable the reaction to proceed at a reasonable rate.

It is difficult to get accurate free-energy data on a large number of organic compounds, but a reasonable amount of fairly reliable data are now available.[1] Figures 1*A*, 1*B*, 1*C*, 1*D*, 1*E*, 1*F*, 1*G*, and 1*H* give free-energy values for a few compounds of industrial importance. The values are for the free energy of formation from the elements of the substance in question in the gaseous state at 1 atmos. pressure. Values are given for two temperatures: 100°C. and 400°C. It is permissible to make linear interpolation between these temperatures, *i.e.*, a value at 250°C. will lie midway between the 100 and 400°C. values. To point out the relationships that exist in these straight-chain aliphatic compounds, the free-energy content per carbon atom is plotted. Therefore, to get the molal value, these values (ordinates) must be multiplied by the number of carbon atoms in the straight-chain aliphatic compound in question. Figures 1*A*, 1*B*, and 1*C* give respectively the free-energy values for carbon monoxide, water, and carbon dioxide, all in the gaseous state at 1 atmos. pressure. Figures 1*D* and 1*E* give free-energy values for the straight-chain olefins and paraffins.

When all the reactants and products are in the gaseous state at a partial pressure of 1 atmos., then the well-known relationship exists:

$$-\Delta F = 4.57T \log K \tag{1}$$

The term $-\Delta F$ is the free-energy decrease in calories for the reaction as it proceeds from left to right. It represents the difference in free-energy content of all the reactants and all the products. On the basis used here for free-energy values, all elements in their normal state of aggregation at 1 atmos. pressure, and at any particular temperature T are arbitrarily assigned the value of zero free energy. In this way the free-energy content of all compounds will have plus or minus values, since the free-energy content at any temperature T is merely the free energy of formation from the elements at T. In Eq. (1) T is the absolute temperature in degrees Kelvin, and K is the equilibrium constant for the reaction, with the products appearing in the numerator and the reactants in the

---

[1] PARKS and HUFFMAN, "Free Energies of Some Organic Compounds," Chemical Catalog Company, Inc., New York (1932).

denominator in terms of the individual partial pressures expressed in the unit of atmospheres. In making calculations this system of units must be definitely adhered to in using Eq. (1). From the equilibrium constant of a chemical reaction it is of course possible to calculate in the usual way the ultimate yields that may be expected and also to determine quantitatively the effect of pressure on the equilibrium conversion for those reactions affected by pressure, namely, those attended by a change in the number of gaseous moles. And if the equilibrium conversion at

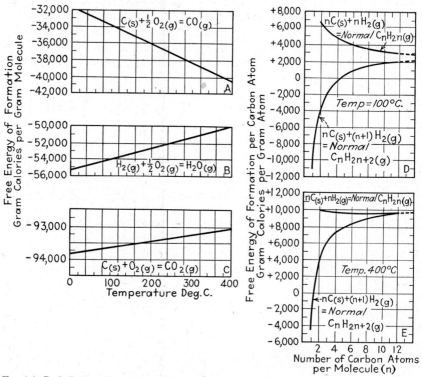

FIG. 1A, B, C, D, E.—Free energy of formation of CO, H₂O, CO₂, normal olefins, and normal paraffins in the gaseous state.

another temperature is wanted, then the free-energy change at that temperature need only be evaluated.

All spontaneous reactions, *i.e.*, those proceeding of their own accord and in the absence of any electrical influences such as magnetic or electrostatic forces, or various forms of radiation, are attended by a free-energy decrease. If a reaction involves only one compound, and an element, *e.g.*, hydrogen, yielding as the product only one other compound of the same member of carbon atoms, then the compound with the lower free energy is the more stable of the two under the experimental conditions chosen. Thus, it is seen in connection with Fig. 1D that the normal paraffins at 100°C. have lower free-energy values than the normal olefins. That is, at this temperature all normal olefins are capable of being hydrogenated to normal paraffins with good equilibrium yields. However, at 400°C. (Fig. 1E) it is seen that the free-energy difference is not so large, and for the higher olefins the free-energy decrease on hydrogenation is very small, and about zero. From Eq. (1), if $\Delta F = 0$, then the equilibrium constant is unity and so it follows that the reverse

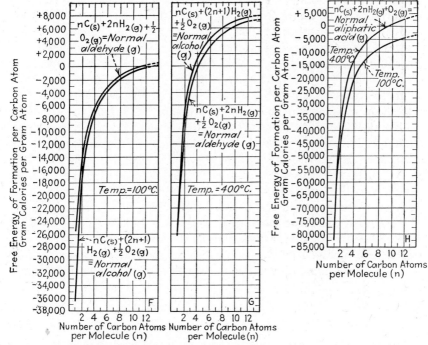

FIG. 1F, G, H.—Free energy of formation of normal aldehydes, normal alcohols, and normal aliphatic acids in the gaseous state.

reaction at this temperature is capable of proceeding to a reasonable degree. Such reactions occur in the cracking or pyrolysis of hydrocarbons, and it is well known that these pyrolytic reactions are carried out at temperatures in the vicinity of 400°C.

From Figs. 1D and 1E it can be calculated that at 400°C. in the case of a larger paraffin, e.g., hexane, there is a spontaneous tendency to decompose or crack, yielding a smaller paraffin and smaller olefin, e.g., propane and propylene. At 100°C. such a reaction does not tend to occur. Therefore, if a relatively large olefin were to be hydrogenated to a paraffin of the same molecular weight, it is seen that it would be desirable to carry out such a reduction at lower temperatures for two pertinent reasons: (a) the equilibrium yield is better; (b) decomposition or side reactions are less likely to be troublesome.   Because of this preferred lower temperature operation, catalysts must be available to operate at these lower temperatures.   Such hydrogenation catalysts are known, as was pointed out earlier in this chapter (page 429).

Inspection of Figs. 1F and 1G shows that the reduction of aldehydes to alcohols parallels in many respects that of olefins to paraffins.   At 100°C. it is seen that the normal alcohols have lower free-energy values than the corresponding aldehyde.   Hydrogenation is, therefore, feasible if catalysts can be found to effect the reduction with reasonable speed. At higher temperatures, e.g., 400°C., it is seen that the aldehyde possesses a lower free-energy value than the alcohol.   In other words the normal spontaneous tendency at this temperature is for the alcohols to dehydrogenate to yield aldehydes.   Since the reduction goes with a volume decrease, it is possible to carry it out at this temperature by the application of pressure; but without pressure, reduction would not be feasible at 400°C.   Further studies will show that, as in the case of the paraffin hydrocarbons, there is the tendency at the higher temperatures to crack or decompose into lower-molecular-weight hydrocarbons, and also at all temperatures there is the decided tendency to continue the reduction to the hydrocarbon stage (hydrogenolysis).   In other words, these few observations indicate that the reduction of aldehydes is apt to be beset with side reactions, and, in general, unless carefully chosen conditions are used, this is the actual fact.

The data of Fig. 1 may be applied to some of the various reductions of carbon monoxide.   The simplest may be indicated by the following reaction at 400°C.:

$$CO_{(g)} + 3H_{2(g)} = CH_{4(g)} + H_2O_{(g)} \qquad (2)$$
$$-40,500 + 0 + \Delta F = -4,500 - 50,000$$
$$\Delta F = -14,000 \text{ cal. at } 400°C.$$

This free-energy decrease shows that, at this temperature, reduction of carbon monoxide to methane is a very complete reaction as judged by the equilibrium yield that is possible.   However, as indicated elsewhere, most hydrogenation reactions are reversible, and if the above reaction is considered in the reverse direction, then it is seen that it is the reaction indicated on page 425 for obtaining hydrogen from hydrocarbons by causing them to react with steam at temperatures of about 1000°C. where the reverse of reaction (2) is possible.

In this connection it might be proposed to carry out a reaction as follows:

$$CH_{4(g)} + H_2O_{(g)} = CH_3OH_{(g)} + H_{2(g)} \qquad (3)$$
$$-4,500 - 50,000 + \Delta F = -26,000 + 0 \text{ at } 400°C.$$
$$\Delta F = +28,500 \text{ cal. at } 400°C.$$

While it would be highly desirable to carry out such a reaction, thereby making natural gas into a more valuable product, the magnitude of this free-energy increase indicates the impossibility of so doing at any practical temperature level. It is useless, therefore, to expend any effort in this direction. The reverse reaction is obviously predominating.

Instead of the complete hydrogenation of carbon monoxide, the partial reduction to methanol might be considered.

$$CO_{(g)} + 2H_{2(g)} = CH_3OH_{(g)} \tag{4}$$
$$-34,000 + 0 + \Delta F = -36,500 \text{ at } 100°C.$$
$$\Delta F = -2,500 \text{ cal. at } 100°C.$$

This free-energy decrease indicates the reaction is possible at 100°C. but so far no catalysts have been found sufficiently active to bring about reaction at this relatively low temperature. To get increased reaction rate it is logical to raise the temperature. If the same calculation is made by means of Figs. 1A and 1G for 400°C. the free-energy increase is found to be +14,300 cal. Thus, the above reaction is not capable of proceeding to any practical extent at this temperature even though it might be expected that now the reaction velocity might be favorable. However, the reaction as written above and the free-energy value given are for all reactants and products at 1 atmos. partial pressure. Since the reaction goes with a decrease in the number of gaseous moles, then the equilibrium yield, which is negligible at 400°C. and low pressures, can be raised to an appreciable value by working at high pressure. So it is concluded that higher reaction temperatures, *i.e.*, those up to perhaps 400°C., are allowable and so will help the reaction velocity provided pressure is applied to increase the equilibrium yield. There then remains the problem of finding a particular unusual type of catalyst that will allow the reduction to proceed to only methanol under these rather severe conditions; for, as indicated above, there is a pronounced tendency to reduce carbon monoxide completely to methane. Certain metallic oxide catalysts have been found experimentally to possess this property (pages 435, 460) and so methanol synthesis from water gas is a practical reality.

In the same way, and from similar reasoning from the data of Figs. 1C and 1G, it is apparent that methanol may be synthesized from a carbon dioxide-hydrogen mixture, rather than from carbon monoxide and hydrogen, should this be desired.

The Fischer-Tropsch atmospheric-pressure synthesis, from water gas, of hydrocarbons larger than methane may be analyzed by the data given in Fig. 1. It is found that such reactions are entirely possible even at atmospheric pressure and temperatures up to 400°C. However, it should again be realized that the higher-molecular-weight hydrocarbons that result from this synthesis are likely to be further reduced to methane, since methane is the most stable hydrocarbon at temperatures below 400°C. This destructive hydrogenation or hydrogenolysis would be more apt to occur at higher temperatures, for all reaction velocities are increased, and the specificity of a catalyst is in general markedly reduced. Temperature control has been found to be a highly important factor in the successful operation of this process. Also, in addition to hydrogenating tendencies, it follows that the catalyst must have condensation properties to build up hydrocarbons having higher molecular weights than methane.

It is possible to analyze the mechanism indicated on page 436 for the higher alcohol synthesis. This may be typified by:

$$2CH_3OH_{(g)} = C_2H_5OH_{(g)} + H_2O_{(g)} \tag{5}$$
$$2(-26,200) + \Delta F = 2(-8,400) - 50,000 \text{ at } 400°C.$$
$$\Delta F = -14,400 \text{ cal. at } 400°C.$$

This condensation is then entirely possible, for the reaction proceeds with a relatively large free-energy decrease. To carry out such a reaction, catalysts possessing dehydration as well as condensation properties would be desirable. Thus, free-energy data are useful not only in determining whether or not a particular over-all reaction is possible, but also in interpreting reaction mechanisms and in aiding in a choice of catalysts for those mechanisms that seem most feasible.

The data of Figs. 1B, 1F, 1G, and 1H may be used to study the direct hydrogenation of acids to alcohols. For example:

$$CH_3CO_2H_{(g)} + 2H_2 = C_2H_5OH_{(g)} + H_2O \tag{6}$$
$$2(-37,000) + 0 + \Delta F = 2(-8,400) - 50,000 \text{ at } 400°C.$$
$$\Delta F = +7,200 \text{ cal. at } 400°C.$$

While there is an actual free-energy increase indicated which is not very large, the reaction also proceeds with a decrease in volume so that equilibrium yields can be definitely helped by carrying out the reaction at relatively high pressures (Table XI). The equilibrium yield is more favorable at lower temperatures, but here again the slower reaction velocity must be considered. Care must be exercised in the choice of catalysts so that they will have little, if any, dehydrating tendencies, and their hydrogenating ability must not be too violent (page 460); otherwise, the hydrocarbon rather than the alcohol will result as the product. These problems have been worked out, and the high-pressure hydrogenation of acids or, more particularly, their simple esters, which are more volatile, is a successful commercial process.

Temperature.—For the most part, the temperature for hydrogenation reactions is usually below 400°C., except in reactions where pyrolytic decomposition occurs concurrently with the hydrogenation reactions. In these cases, the temperature may extend to 500°C. Temperature is one of the most important variables affecting a reaction. Practically every hydrogenation reaction can be reversed by increasing temperature. It becomes necessary, then, to work at as low a temperature as possible where the rate of reaction will still be satisfactory. Whereas catalysts affect only the speed and course of a reaction, temperature affects the equilibrium position, the speed, and the path, or course, of a reaction. In general, then, increasing temperature adversely affects the equilibrium position, so that the maximum ultimate yield is decreased; but it affects favorably the speed of a reaction, so that in a given time a greater quantity of product can be obtained. It becomes necessary to balance the less favorable equilibrium position with the faster rate of reaction. Fortunately, in recent years the knowledge of catalysis has been so extended that satisfactory reaction rates are possible at lower temperatures where a more favorable equilibrium position prevails.

In some cases, an increase in temperature may adversely affect a catalyst, so that the reaction rate is decreased or reduced to practically nothing. These are the cases known as *sintering* of the catalyst; *i.e.*, the highly extended and porous surfaces of the catalysts are in some way collapsed or fused together so that the efficiency of the catalyst is seriously reduced. Here, again, a study of promoters, or substances that catalyze or accelerate the activity of a catalyst, may surmount the difficulties due, at least in part, to sintering.

Finally, a statement is necessary concerning the temperature coefficient of hydrogenation reactions. Barring decrease in activity of the catalyst (such as sintering), few if any hydrogenation reactions fit the generalized statement that the speed of a reaction may be doubled for every 10 to 15°C. increase in temperature. It usually takes 50°C. or more to double the speed of a hydrogenation reaction.

In general, the noble metal catalysts, such as platinum or palladium, are used from room temperatures to 150°C.; catalysts of the nickel and copper type, from 150 to 250°C.; and various combinations of metals and metal oxides, from 250 to 400°C.

Pressure.—Pressure, like temperature, can affect the rate of reaction as well as the equilibrium position. The rate of reaction is generally increased by increasing pressure, because a gas phase is usually present, and increased pressure gives increased concentration. In general, increased concentration speeds up a reaction. Pressure affects the equilibrium yield in a hydrogenation reaction when there is a decrease in the volume of the reaction as it proceeds. This is the simple application of the mass-action law, or LeChatelier's principle. In hydrogenation reactions, there is usually a decrease in volume.

Thus, pressure would have a greater effect on equilibrium yield in the reaction

$$CO + 2H_2 \leftrightharpoons CH_3OH$$

than in the reduction of formaldehyde

$$CH_2O + H_2 \leftrightharpoons CH_3OH$$

for the change in volume is greater in the first case. In simple cases, the effect of pressure on the equilibrium yield can be quantitatively estimated from application of mass-action principles.

The effect of pressure on the reaction rate is not subject to any definite quantitative laws. The results of one reaction may not occur in another. The point is best settled by experimental data. In general, however, increased pressure will result in an increased reaction rate. Thus, Brochet[1] observed that phenol is hydrogenated very slowly at 150°C. at atmospheric pressure using a nickel catalyst but that at 15 atmospheres at the same temperature the reaction was complete and rapid. Maxted[2] and Armstrong and Hilditch[3] observed the velocity of hydrogenation to be proportional to the pressure. Armstrong[4] reported that the speed of hydrogenation of pyridine to piperidine varied as the square of the hydrogen pressure. In the hydrogenation of acetone to isopropyl alcohol with identical batches of a copper chromite catalyst, Adkins and Connor[5] observed the following conversions in reactions of $\frac{1}{2}$ hr. duration.

TABLE XIV.—EFFECT OF PRESSURE IN THE HYDROGENATION OF ACETONE

Pressure, Atmos.	Conversion, %
35	17
148	70
212	95

Again, Folkers and Adkins[6] found that an increase in pressure from 100 to 200 atmospheres increases the rate of hydrogenation of ethyl laurate to lauryl alcohol sevenfold, and an increase in pressure from 100 to 300 atmospheres increases it twenty-eightfold. Results of hydrogenating acetoacetic ester, benzene, phenol, and aniline at various pressures have also been reported,[7] and there are many other references in the literature pointing to the general conclusion that an increase in

---

[1] BROCHET, *Bull. soc. chim.* (4), **15**, 588 (1914); *Compt. rend.*, **158**, 1352 (1914).

[2] MAXTED, *J. Soc. Chem. Ind.*, **40**, 169T (1921).

[3] ARMSTRONG and HILDITCH, *Proc. Roy. Soc.*, **100A**, 240 (1921).

[4] ARMSTRONG, Lecture before the British Institute of Chemical Engineers, Oct. 30, 1931.

[5] ADKINS and CONNOR, *J. Am. Chem. Soc.*, **53**, 1093–1095 (1931).

[6] FOLKERS and ADKINS, *J. Am. Chem. Soc.*, **54**, 1153 (1932).

[7] ADKINS, CRAMER, and CONNOR, *J. Am. Chem. Soc.*, **53**, 1403 (1931).

pressure usually gives an increased rate of reaction. In general, then, the conclusion that increased pressure results in increased rate of reaction appears well substantiated.

There may be cases, however, where pressures below atmospheric are desirable, particularly when the reaction may need to be stopped at some intermediate stage of hydrogenation. Thus, Grignard[1] observed, in hydrogenating at pressures less than atmospheric with nickel, copper, and platinum catalysts, that hydrogenations could be stopped at the first stage. Phenol was reduced to cyclohexenol; benzaldehyde, to benzyl alcohol; benzonitrile, to benzaldimine; and phenylacetonitrile, at about 220 mm. pressure and 200°C., to phenylacetaldimine.

Time.—The time necessary for a hydrogenation reaction may vary from a few seconds to several hours, depending on the materials being hydrogenated, the catalyst, the temperature, and the pressure. In general, the more reactive the compound the faster the hydrogenation reaction. Thus, simple aldehydes are hydrogenated very readily, while the reduction of aromatic rings to saturated cyclic compounds or of esters to alcohols is a slower reaction. The type of apparatus or equipment used will depend on the speed of hydrogenation. The usual type of bomb reactor is admirably suited to slow reactions, while an apparatus where the materials can be continually passed over the catalyst is best for fast reactions.

The Ratio of Hydrogen to the Substance Being Hydrogenated.— The ratio of hydrogen to the substance being hydrogenated is conveniently expressed in terms of partial pressures. It frequently happens that the speed or path of a certain hydrogenation can be affected by the proportion of hydrogen to the substance. While no extensive data on this phase of hydrogenation are available in the literature, it has been found that ethyl lactate and malonate are reduced to the corresponding alcohols in good yields in a flow system at pressures of about 1,300 lb. per square inch, where practically the entire pressure is hydrogen, and the partial pressure of the esters only a few centimeters. Similar results are obtained in the course of other hydrogenations.[2] Usually, such hydrogenations are carried out at considerably higher total pressures, *viz.*, about 3,000 lb. per square inch. In the examples previously cited, the higher total pressure was lessened, and a higher ratio of hydrogen pressure to the partial pressure of the substance being hydrogenated was employed. This method of operation is, however, somewhat different from that usually employed.

Liquid- or Gas-phase Reactions.—The hydrogen, the substance being hydrogenated, and the product of hydrogenation may exist entirely

---

[1] GRIGNARD, *Bull. soc. chim. Belg.*, **37**, 41 (1928).

[2] TRENT, Unpublished results, Penn. State Coll. (1933).

in the gas phase, or the substance and the product may exist as a liquid phase. In this latter case, the hydrogen is in contact with the substance, either as a gas phase above or dissolved in it. Hydrogenation reactions obviously cannot occur without intimate contact of the hydrogen with the reacting substance. The type of reaction may differ, depending on whether the hydrogenation is in the gas phase or the liquid phase. Thus, Lush[1] found, in hydrogenating naphthalene, using a nickel catalyst, that tetralin was the principal product formed in the vapor-phase reaction, whereas decalin was produced by the liquid-phase hydrogenation.

In liquid-phase reactions, there must be opportunity for intimate contact of hydrogen with the substance being hydrogenated. This is usually accomplished by some means of shaking, by stirring, or by circulating hydrogen through the liquid. Another factor that greatly facilitates intimate contact is the solubility of hydrogen in the substance undergoing hydrogenation. Increased pressure favors greater solubility of hydrogen, and an intimate contact comparable to gas-phase reaction is thus possible. The principal difference is the ratio of hydrogen to the substance being hydrogenated. In the gas phase, this ratio may be varied over a very wide range; but in the liquid phase, it is governed by the solubility of hydrogen.

Solubility of Hydrogen.—The effect of the solubility of hydrogen in the reacting substance obviously relates only to liquid-phase reactions. As indicated above, an increase in the pressure of hydrogen increases the solubility in a given liquid, and it had been found[2] that this increase in solubility with pressure follows Henry's law with reasonable accuracy at ordinary temperatures in various liquids, such as methanol, isopropanol, paraffin hydrocarbons, and heavy oils. However, it does not follow that the solubility of hydrogen in liquids will decrease with increasing temperatures, as might be expected. Thus, Grimm[3] in discussing the catalytic hydrogenation of coal and oil states that the solubility of hydrogen in oils increases with the temperature, it being three times as great at 300 as at 20°C. The solubility of hydrogen in liquids undoubtedly plays an important, if not the principal, rôle in liquid-phase hydrogenations.

The Exothermic Character of the Hydrogenation Reaction.—The values for the heat of reaction are generally obtained from thermochemical data, when data relating specifically to the problem are not available. Depending on the type of hydrogenation reaction, varying amounts of heat may be liberated. Hydrogenations are usually exothermic; and since the reaction occurs only because of the catalyst, local temperatures

[1] Lush, *J. Soc. Chem. Ind.*, **46**, 454T (1927).

[2] Frolich, Tauch, Hogan, and Peer, *Ind. Eng. Chem.*, **23**, 548 (1931).

[3] Grimm, *Intern. Conf. Bituminous Coal*, **II**, 49 (1931).

in the surfaces of the catalyst may reach surprisingly high values. These not only tend to divert the reaction to side reactions such as cracking, but they are likely to impair the efficiency of the catalyst because of sintering, which is the collapse of the active catalytic surface due to excessive heat. In problems of commercial design, the exothermic character of the reaction must consequently be given careful attention. Uncontrolled temperatures not only influence the course of the reaction and diminish the efficiency of the catalyst but also necessitate materials of construction to withstand the maximum conditions of temperature and pressure that are likely to occur. In large units, temperature control is usually best obtained through proper heat interchange with the incoming materials.

V. GENERAL PRINCIPLES CONCERNING HYDROGENATION CATALYSTS

Catalysts are essential to most hydrogenation reactions. Very few hydrogenations occur in the absence of some sort of catalyst. These cases of non-catalytic reactions may happen when another reaction is occurring along with the hydrogenation reaction, so that extremely active or liberated hydrogen is available from this other reaction in limited amounts. In other cases, the reaction temperature may be high where, in addition to hydrogenation reactions, pyrolytic or cracking reactions are also occurring so that hydrogen gas in the absence of catalysts can add to the molecular fragments produced by the cracking. Thus, the earlier work of Bergius on coal hydrogenation was non-catalytic, but more recently the process has become practically entirely catalytic through the developments of the I. G. Farbenindustrie in Germany.

Excepting these few instances, the large bulk of hydrogenation reactions use hydrogen gas as the source of hydrogen, and the function of the catalyst is to effect the over-all result of chemically combining the gaseous hydrogen with the substance capable of adding hydrogen to its molecular structure. It is the purpose of the catalyst to effect this combination along the desired path as quickly as possible. The following brief discussion is intended to clarify some of the essential features of a catalyst.

Surface.—For the most part, hydrogenation catalysts are solids consisting of metals and metal oxides. The hydrogenation is effected at the surface of the catalyst, so a highly extended surface is essential. However, a catalyst surface differs considerably from that produced by simply an extensive mechanical subdivision of matter. Taking a piece of bar nickel or copper and subdividing it mechanically to pass, say, a 50-mesh sieve would not produce an active nickel or copper catalyst. Usually, the preparation of a catalyst is associated with some chemical reaction whereby a highly extended, porous, and honeycombed surface is produced so that the density of the surface metal is far less than that of the bulk metal.   Certain surface atoms may become so removed from other adjoining ones that they may approach a gasified state, at conditions far removed from the normal vaporization of the metal.   Certain valence bonds of these atoms which normally would be shared with other atoms in the usual dense metallic state are freed, and here is believed to lie the reason for the catalyst's activity.   These surface atoms, having varying degrees of unsaturation compared with the bulk metal or metal oxide, will strongly adsorb other substances with which they may come in contact, and active catalysts usually have high adsorptive powers.   While adsorption is closely related to the successful performance of a catalyst, it may ruin an active catalyst, because other substances called catalyst poisons may be so strongly retained by these active atoms that the substance being hydrogenated can no longer reach the active or catalytic areas.

The speed of a hydrogenation will depend on the type and amount of active surface available.   Increasing the ratio of catalyst to the substance undergoing hydrogenation usually increases the speed of the hydrogenation, although not necessarily in direct proportion to the increase in amount of catalyst.   In batch operations, the catalyst usually is from about 1 to 10 per cent by weight of the substance being hydrogenated. Following are some data of Carothers and Adams[1] on the hydrogenation of benzaldehyde with varying amounts of the same batch of a platinum oxide-platinum black catalyst.   In each experiment, 21.2 gm. of benzaldehyde was used and dissolved in 50 cc. of alcohol.

Grams of Catalyst Used	Time for Complete Hydrogenation
0.0288	5.5 hr.
0.0575	60 min.
0.115	34 min.
0.23	23 min.

Mixed-metal Catalysts.—Because an apparently small and inappreciable amount of substance might impair or poison the activity of a catalyst, strenuous efforts must be made to prepare the catalyst as nearly chemically pure as possible.   But it will usually be found that in this state, activity is either nil or very low.   The solution to this dilemma is to recognize more clearly the class of substances to which poisons and promoters belong.   Catalyst poisons are usually substances which can react chemically with the catalyst or else, because of their volatility, can condense on to and blot out the active areas of the catalyst. The common poisons are halogens, sulfur, arsenic, and sometimes metals of low melting point such as mercury, lead, tin, etc.

---

[1] CAROTHERS and ADAMS, *J. Am. Chem. Soc.*, **45**, 1071 (1923).

Promoters, or substances that increase a catalyst's activity, are usually quite stable and frequently exist in physical combination with the catalyst. It frequently happens that they themselves are catalysts for the same or a similar type of reaction. Thus, a small amount of chlorine or sulfur will render a copper catalyst used for the dehydrogenation of methanol entirely inactive,[1] while the addition of about 3 per cent of zinc oxide to a pure copper catalyst, when used under exactly the same conditions, will increase the activity threefold.[2]

The use of mixed-metal catalysts or promoted catalysts has been rapidly extended in recent years. More common mixtures with the well-known types of catalysts are nickel-copper, nickel-alumina, copper-zinc oxide, copper-chromium oxide, and zinc oxide-chromium oxide. However, the recent chemical and patent literature describes the use of combinations of practically every metal and metal oxide in the periodic system.

Stability.—The period of activity of a catalyst is a rather indefinite thing. This is because such activity depends not only on the nature of the materials brought in contact with it but also on the stability and permanence of the active areas, which most likely are responsible for the functioning of the catalyst. Loss in activity from contamination with foreign materials is best characterized as poisoning. Loss in activity from a collapse and aggregation of the highly distended surface is best termed sintering. It should be remembered that a catalyst, like any other system, is striving to reduce its surface energy to a minimum for just the same reasons that a droplet of water forms a sphere. Thus, there is always a force tending to bring about the collapse of the extended surface, with the result called sintering. A function of promoters is to maintain and prolong the existence of the active areas of a catalyst.

It is sometimes possible to reactivate a catalyst that has lost its activity, especially when the loss in activity is due to some adsorbed materials. Passing hydrogen alone over the catalyst for a period of time may help, or in some cases it is possible to reactivate the catalyst by passing a small amount of oxygen over it. In these cases, the adsorbed materials are probably burned off. Oxygen was found to reactivate catalysts used in the synthesis of methanol from carbon monoxide and hydrogen[3] but quite effectively to poison an iron catalyst used in the synthesis of ammonia.[4]

---

[1] FROLICH, FENSKE, PERRY, and HURD, *J. Am. Chem. Soc.*, **51**, 187 (1929).

[2] FROLICH, FENSKE, and QUIGGLE, *Ind. Eng. Chem.*, **20**, 694 (1928).

[3] FENSKE and FROLICH, *Ind. Eng. Chem.*, **21**, 1052 (1929); NUSSBAUM and FROLICH, *Ind. Eng. Chem.*, **23**, 1386 (1931).

[4] ALMQUIST and BLACK, *J. Am. Chem. Soc.*, **48**, 2815 (1926).

Usually, catalysts of a very high initial activity are short-lived, and it becomes necessary to choose between a high initial rate of hydrogenation and a somewhat lower but better average rate, such as is obtained in a stable catalyst. These stable catalysts are often obtained through the use of mixed metal or promoted catalysts where the active areas are large. In addition, the mixtures of metals and metal oxides usually afford the best protection against sintering. Then by careful elimination of any foreign materials in the reactor, in the hydrogen, or in the substance being hydrogenated, a reasonable period of catalyst activity can be assured.

Preparation.—Hydrogenation catalysts can be prepared in practically an unlimited number of ways. However, there are again certain generalized or fundamental steps that are quite common to the preparation of any active catalyst. These principles are intended to serve as a guide to catalyst preparation when other more definite information is not available. It may be found later that certain of these steps are not necessary or are relatively unimportant. However, it is believed that if they are recognized, a higher average success in catalyst preparations will result. The five most important principles are as follows.

a. To insure the production and duplication of a reasonably active catalyst, relatively pure materials should be used in its preparation. Because of the small amounts of a substance that may act as either a poison or a promoter, the purity of the starting chemicals should be known; this will be the difference between the building up of successful catalysts by hit-or-miss methods and by a rationalized procedure.

b. Generally the better practice is to prepare the catalyst through a chemical reaction rather than by a mere physical or mechanical method. Thus, in the preparation of a nickel catalyst, it is far better to prepare it by precipitation of nickel hydroxide from nickel nitrate and alkali and reduce the hydroxide to oxide and to metallic nickel by hydrogen than to prepare it by subdividing a nickel bar. A finer and more active state of subdivision together with a greater possibility of reproduction of the catalyst generally results by applying rather simple and definitely known chemical reactions.

In mixtures of metal and metal oxide catalysts, generally anything that can be done to promote or bring about more intimate contact between the materials will result in an improved catalyst. While this may be obvious, sometimes it may not be fully appreciated. This point may be illustrated in the preparation of copper-zinc oxide catalysts.[1] By rating the efficiency of the coprecipitated hydroxides of copper and zinc as 100, other methods of preparation compared as follows when studying the decomposition of methanol:

---

[1] FROLICH, FENSKE, and QUIGGLE, *Ind. Eng. Chem.*, **20**, 694 (1928).

TABLE XV.—EFFECT OF METHOD OF PREPARATION ON CATALYST EFFICIENCY

Method of Preparation	Decomposition Efficiency, %
1. Hydroxides precipitated together	100
2. Hydroxide gels mixed	83
3. Zinc hydroxide precipitated on suspended copper hydroxide	75
4. Calcined nitrates	70
5. Copper hydroxide precipitated on suspended zinc hydroxide	67

The activity of nickel catalysts supported on kieselguhr is dependent on the method of preparation,[1] and likewise the method of preparing copper oxide-chromium oxide catalysts affects their activity.[2]

c. Precautions should be taken in the course of the preparation of a catalyst to keep it free from any contaminating substances other than those definitely desired in the catalyst. The catalyst should be prepared just as any pure substance is; experience indicates that effort in this direction is well expended. When precipitation of the hydroxide or oxide may occur in the course of preparing a metal catalyst, it is desirable to use the nitrate of the metal and ammonium hydroxide as a precipitant when there are no other conflicting chemical reactions. In this way, any ammonium salts or excess hydroxide are easily volatilized by careful heating.[3]

d. When it is necessary to reduce a catalyst prior to use, precautions must be taken in its reduction. It may be said that catalysts are either made or destroyed in this reduction operation. The reduction of metal oxides by hydrogen is generally exothermic; consequently, the catalyst's activity may be seriously impaired by sintering if reduction temperatures are uncontrolled. Careful measurement and regulation of the temperatures of reduction are important. Sometimes, it is advisable to use hydrogen diluted with nitrogen. In general, the temperatures of reduction should be no higher than necessary to effect a gradual and controlled reduction of the oxide. It is relatively easy to raise the catalyst temperature to incandescence and even to destruction of its activity, through carelessness in controlling the temperature during reduction.

e. If the catalysts must be stored, it is generally better to store them in the more stable state. Thus, if the catalyst needs to be reduced prior to use, it is generally better practice to store the oxide and reduce batches of catalyst as needed. These are simple precautions which enable the catalyst to have its maximum activity when used. In addition, storage in containers free from materials that are liable to be poisons is obviously

[1] COVERT, CONNOR, and ADKINS, *J. Am. Chem. Soc.*, **54**, 1652 (1932).

[2] FOLKERS and ADKINS, *J. Am. Chem. Soc.*, **54**, 1153 (1932).

[3] FROLICH, FENSKE, and QUIGGLE, *J. Am. Chem. Soc.*, **51**, 61 (1929).

necessary. Cork- or glass-stoppered bottles are preferable to rubber-stoppered ones, as there is danger of sulfur contamination from the latter.

General Classification of Hydrogenation Catalysts.—The number of catalysts capable of effecting hydrogenations is large, and in addition many types of hydrogenation are possible. Practically any type of unsaturation can be hydrogenated catalytically. It has been pointed out that hydrogenation may involve the saturation of a carbon-to-carbon linkage or the reduction of carbonyl or carboxyl or hydroxyl groups and may even involve the breaking of carbon-to-carbon linkages, as in the hydrogenation of coals and mineral oils. In general, however, hydrogenation catalysts may be classified as follows:

Violent Hydrogenation Catalysts.—These catalysts are usually characterized by the fact that they carry the hydrogenation to the greatest extent possible, so that the maximum addition of hydrogen to compound occurs under the particular operating conditions. Thus, in the case of simple aldehydes, the reduction will pass beyond the alcohol stage and end at the saturated hydrocarbon. Even here, the tendency to saturate the carbon atoms may be sufficiently great to cause cracking or to break the carbon-to-carbon bonds so that still more hydrogen can be added, the final result being the formation of the hydrocarbon with the greatest hydrogen-to-carbon ratio, *viz.*, methane. Cracking tendencies are usually associated with these violent hydrogenation catalysts, although through control of the variables of temperature and pressure the cracking reactions can usually be suppressed. Common catalysts belonging to this class usually consist of the nickel, cobalt, or iron type and sometimes of molybdenum and tungsten oxides or sulfides.

Mild Hydrogenation Catalysts.—The term mild should not be confused with activity. These catalysts will effect hydrogenations just as rapidly as the violent hydrogenation types, but they are able to carry out only one step at a time in a hydrogenation, or at least they do not permit the reaction to proceed to the hydrocarbon stage. A great many catalysts belong to this class, and they are being developed rapidly. These catalysts will easily reduce an aldehyde or ketone to the alcohol or an acid or ester to an alcohol. The large number of catalysts developed for the direct synthesis of methanol from water gas belong to this class, and they usually contain copper, zinc oxide, chromium oxide, and manganese oxide and may include some of the rarer elements as promoters. In addition, the noble metal catalysts such as platinum or palladium or their oxides belong to this class.

Catalysts with Properties Other than Hydrogenation.—The synthesis of higher alcohols from water gas involves a condensation as well as a hydrogenation reaction. These so-called higher-alcohol catalysts are usually of the mild hydrogenating type but contain some more alkaline materials, such as sodium, calcium or barium carbonates, or aluminum or magnesium oxides. Other types of catalyst are capable of splitting out water from a molecule along with the hydrogenation but do not possess any appreciable cracking tendencies. These usually are of the violent hydrogenating type but contain considerable and even sometimes preponderating quantities of dehydrating catalysts, such as alumina, thoria, tungstic oxide, or chromium oxide. They can effect such reductions as phenol to benzene and as cresols to aromatic hydrocarbons and convert various hydroxy compounds to hydrocarbons, with little or no other changes in the molecular structure.

VI. APPARATUS AND MATERIALS OF CONSTRUCTION

The trend in hydrogenation practice appears to be toward the use of higher pressures, where the apparatus is smaller. Under such conditions, the reaction velocity is increased; the equilibrium positions made more favorable; the reaction path better defined, with fewer side reactions; and heating and cooling and heat interchange are facilitated. The design and construction of equipment for high-pressure work are, however, somewhat more complicated than for low-pressure operations. Alloy steels are by far the most common materials of construction.

Reaction chambers or autoclaves are usually of two types, one in which the contents are agitated or stirred in some way, and the other in which the reactor and contents are stationary. The first is used with materials such as solids or liquids to bring intimate contact among the catalyst, the material, and the hydrogen. The second type is used where the substance may have sufficient vapor pressure at the temperature of operation so that a gas- as well as a liquid-phase reaction is possible. It is also most frequently used in continuous operation where larger quantities of material need to be processed than can be done conveniently with batch or autoclave methods. In this case, the reacting material, if liquid, is passed along with hydrogen over the catalyst. A drawing of a small, experimental-scale, stirred autoclave is shown in Fig. 2. Here the packing around the stirrer is water cooled to facilitate a tight joint. Figure 3 shows a small-scale type of agitated reaction vessel in which the entire reactor is rocked through a sufficient angle to give intimate mixing of the contents.

A convenient small-scale unit is shown in Fig. 4, page 463. The material to be hydrogenated, if a liquid, is fed into the small, high-pressure pump—or, if a solid, it is dissolved in a suitable solvent. All that the pump needs to do is to put sufficient pressure on the liquid to raise it to the pressure on the reactor. Since liquids are relatively incompressible, the work expended in this operation is small. The material is heated near the inlet end of the reactor to the reaction temperature, and then it flows along with the hydrogen over the catalyst contained in the middle or latter half of the reactor. It simply flows or vaporizes through the reactor, the time of contact with the catalyst being dependent on the rate of pumping. Small, high-pressure proportioning pumps are readily available, which enable the rate of flow to be accurately maintained as

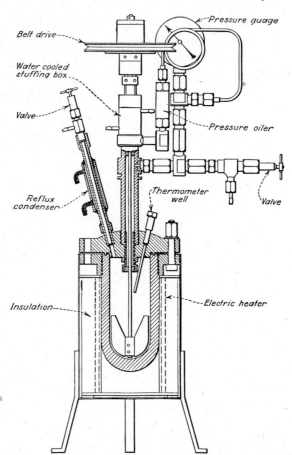

Pressure guage

Belt drive

Water cooled stuffing box

Valve

Pressure oiler

Thermometer well

Valve

Reflux condenser

Electric heater

Insulation

Fig. 2.—Diagrammatic sketch of high-pressure autoclave.

well as readily varied. At the exit end of the reactor, the liquid is condensed, and a trap allows it to be withdrawn from the system without undue loss of hydrogen. Instead of dropping the hydrogen pressure down to substantially atmospheric pressure to measure the amount passing over the catalyst per unit volume or per mole of material being hydrogenated, it is measured at full operating pressure by determining the amount of water displaced from the hydrogen-control tank on the right. This gives an accurate control and measure of the hydrogen passed over the catalyst and avoids reducing the hydrogen pressure with a corresponding loss of hydrogen. By having a two-unit proportioning pump, water can be pumped into the hydrogen-control tank to bring it back to pressure and thus make up for the hydrogen consumed in the reaction. In this way, by careful working, the hydrogen lost is practically only that which is consumed in the reaction. It is also important to note that in this operation the ratio of hydrogen to the substance being hydrogenated is very large. This facilitates the hydrogenation reaction. The substance may flow through the reactor at only a fraction of an atmosphere partial pressure, while the partial pressure of hydrogen may be 100 or 200 atmos. It has been found that

Fig. 3.—Shaking autoclave for pressures to 15,000 lb. per square inch.

hydrogenations in this type of set-up proceed very satisfactorily at considerably lower pressures than when operating in a batch or autoclave type of apparatus. This is undoubtedly because the higher total pressure has been in part replaced by a higher ratio of the partial pressure of hydrogen to the partial pressure of the substance undergoing reduction.

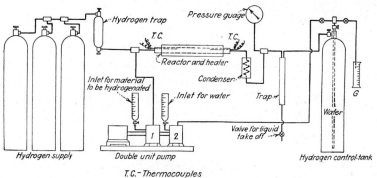

Fig. 4.—Flow-system apparatus for hydrogenations.

In the operation of large units, heating of the ingoing materials is best accomplished by heat exchange with the outgoing materials and adding additional heat by means of high-pressure pipe coils. A pipe coil is the only convenient and efficient method of heating, for the reactor is usually so large that the heating of it is very difficult. It is usually better practice to add all the heat needed to the materials before they enter the reactor and then simply have the reactor properly insulated thermally. Hydrogenation reactions are usually exothermic, so that once started the problem may be one of heat removal. This is accomplished by allowing the heat of reaction to flow into the ingoing materials, by heat exchange in the reactor, or, if it is still in excess, by recycling and cooling in heat exchangers the proper portion of the material to maintain the desired temperature.

VII. INDUSTRIAL PROCESSES

Of the many industrial applications of hydrogenation, only four will be described here: (1) The hydrogenation or hardening of vegetable or marine oils; (2) the synthesis of methanol and higher alcohols from water gas; (3) the reduction of long-chain fatty acids to alcohols, and (4) the hydrogenation of coal and mineral oils. These four processes cover a wide variety of catalysts used in hydrogenation reactions; they deal with the processing of raw materials in the form of solids, liquids, and gases; and they employ practically the entire range of pressures and the temperatures used in any sort of hydrogenation. Finally, each of these four processes is an application of one of the four types of hydrogenation discussed at the beginning of this chapter.

Hydrogenation or Hardening of Fats.—The purposes of the hydrogenation of vegetable and animal oils are (1) to produce a hard fat or one of greater consistency than the original liquid oil and (2) to remove certain impurities that are not removable by any other means, thus rendering the oil useful for purposes for which it could not otherwise be adapted. The process is essentially one of converting the glycerides of the unsaturated fatty acids into glycerides of saturated acids; thus, in the case of olein, the addition of six atoms, or only 0.68 per cent by weight of hydrogen, converts it into stearin:

$$(C_{17}H_{33} \cdot CO \cdot O)_3 C_3 H_5 + 3H_2 \rightarrow (C_{17}H_{35} \cdot CO \cdot O)_3 C_3 H_5$$

The reaction is carried out at temperatures from 100 to 250°C. (212 to 480°F.), at pressures usually less than 200 lb. per square inch, with nickel as a catalyst. The processing of edible oils is usually carried out with considerable care and at lower temperatures, to minimize undesirable side reactions.

A variety of oils may be used in the process. There are glycerides not only of oleic acid but also of linoleic acid, the latter containing two double bonds instead of one, as in oleic acid. Furthermore, there are a number of isomeric *oleins*, where the unsaturation is at different points in the long chain of carbon atoms. Each of these compounds or isomers behaves a little differently from the others on hydrogenation. In the case of marine oils, fatty acids of from 14 to 24 carbon atoms are known to be present. Table XVI gives an approximate analysis of several of the more commonly used oils,[1] and Table XVII pertains to the composition of whale oil.[2]

TABLE XVI.—PERCENTAGE COMPOSITION OF OILS USED IN HARDENING PROCESSES

Material	Saturated glycerides	Olein	Linolein
Cottonseed oil	22.6	26.9	50.5
Peanut oil	40.0	20.5	39.5
Corn oil	13.0	46.0	41.0
Olive oil	12.4	80.1	7.5
Leaf lard	37.0	52.4	10.6

When these oils are completely hydrogenated, solids result; and when partially hydrogenated, fats of various consistencies or melting points are obtained. The degree of hydrogenation is readily determined for any given oil by the melting point, iodine-absorption number, or refractive

TABLE XVII.—PERCENTAGE COMPOSITION OF FATTY ACIDS OF WHALE OIL

Material	%
C_{14} acids, myristic	4.5
C_{16} acids, palmitic	11.5
palmitoleic	17.0
C_{18} acids, stearic	2.5
unsaturated (nearly all oleic)	36.5
C_{20} acids; unsaturated	16.
C_{22} acids; unsaturated	10.
C_{24} acids; unsaturated	1.5
Unsaponifiable material	0.7

index. The following table (XVIII) gives the melting points of some hydrogenated products.[3]

TABLE XVIII.—MELTING POINTS OF COMPLETELY HYDROGENATED OILS

Oil	M.p., °C.
Coconut	43 to 45
Whale oil	52 to 56
Cottonseed	62 to 63
Olive	68 to 69
Soy bean	69 to 71
Castor	86 to 90

[1] MOORE, RICHTER, and VAN ARSDEL, *Ind. Eng. Chem.*, **9**, 455 (1917).

[2] RICHARDSON, KNUTH, and MILLIGAN, *Ind. Eng. Chem.*, **17**, 80 (1925).

[3] HILDITCH, "Catalytic Processes in Applied Chemistry," p. 226, D. Van Nostrand Company, Inc., New York (1929).

The process of hydrogenating a mixture of olein with more unsaturated glycerides such as linolein is selective; *i.e.*, the linolein, or fatty acids containing two double bonds, is practically entirely converted into olein, before this, in turn, is hydrogenated to stearin.   In other words, during the hydrogenation of the more highly unsaturated oils, it passes through a stage where it is practically equivalent to olive oil (see Table XVI), before it proceeds to complete saturation.   This selectivity is not so apparent in the hydrogenation of whale and menhaden oils. In the hardening of these oils, a more abrupt change occurs at an iodine value of about 84, at which time nearly all the acids of more than two double bonds have disappeared.   Below this point, hydrogenation results both in the formation of saturated acids and in the conversion of the C_{20} and C_{22} acids containing two double bonds to corresponding acids of one double bond.   Thus, the hydrogenation of these marine oils is different from that of typical vegetable oils, in which substantial increases in the quantity of saturated acids present is coincident with the almost complete disappearance of acids containing more than one double bond.[1]

The oils to be hydrogenated should be reasonably free from materials likely to poison the catalyst.   Impurities that may be present and that are poisonous to nickel, in decreasing order of toxicity, are organic sulfur compounds, oxidized unsaturated fatty compounds, colloidal suspensions of protein, of mucilage, etc., moisture, and free higher fatty acids.   Free fatty acids, up to about 3 per cent, do not seriously interfere.   Moisture should preferably be kept low, because certain nickel catalysts tend to adsorb water in preference to oils; and in the preparation of palatable oils, moisture is apt to produce undesirable materials through saponification.   Organic sulfur compounds, while difficult to remove, are fortunately very seldom present in amounts likely seriously to impair the activity of the nickel.   Oxidized materials and other colloidal and high-molecular-weight compounds can be removed either with an aqueous alkali wash or by adsorption, using certain earths or charcoals.

Nickel is by far the most commonly used catalyst in oil hardening. The catalyst problem consists of three phases: (1) preparation of a suitable catalyst; (2) the maintenance of its activity as long as possible; and (3) the recovery and reactivation of the spent catalyst.   Nickel catalysts are of different types, depending upon the operation in which they are used.   They may be in a relatively fine state, particularly in those processes where stirring or other agitation of the oil is used, or they may be supported on inert materials such as clays, kieselguhr, charcoal, or pumice, which extend the surface of the catalyst and facilitate the filtration of the catalytic mass from the oil.   Finally, in continuous processes, the nickel may be in a massive form, *i.e.*, as turnings, wool, or

[1] RICHARDSON, KNUTH, and MILLIGAN, *Ind. Eng. Chem.*, **17**, 80 (1925).

screen, which has previously been activated by special processes involving alternate oxidation and reduction to produce an active nickel surface.

There are numerous patents pertaining to apparatus and processes for hydrogenating oils. For the most part, these may be divided into three types: (1) a vessel nearly full of oil containing the catalyst in suspension through which hydrogen is circulated by mechanical means, possibly also with circulation of the oil to maintain the suspension of the catalyst; (2) a vessel full of hydrogen and oil in which an intimate mixture is attained without moving parts, or stirrers; and (3) continuous processes in which the catalyst is maintained stationary and through which oil and hydrogen are continuously circulated.

Apparatus belonging to the first type consists of a cylindrical tank, containing a helicoid or spiral propeller, driven by a pulley. Hydrogen is admitted through a perforated pipe, and internal coils provide ample means for heating or cooling the charge of oil contained in the vessel.

Another apparatus pertaining to the second type is in Fig. 5. Here there are no moving agitators, and consequently no stuffing boxes to leak.[1] This apparatus is built in various sizes, sometimes 20 to 30 ft. tall. The essential features are intimate contact of the liquid and gas phases and the maintenance of this intimate contact over as large a portion of the whole bulk of oil as is practicable. The catalyst is suspended in the oil in a finely divided state. The oil and gas

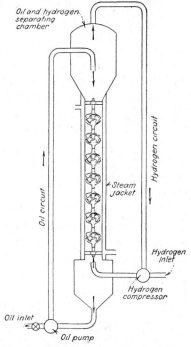

FIG. 5.—Recycling apparatus for hydrogenating oils.

flow countercurrently through the tall mixing column, intimate contact being caused by the action of fixed propeller-like baffle plates, causing the oil and gas mixture to rotate alternately in opposite directions. In addition, the inclination of the baffles is such that they exert, along with the rotating motion, such an action on the hydrogen-oil mixture that this is alternately thrown toward the center of the column and its periphery.

In operation, the column (Fig. 5) is filled with oil. It enters at the top and is recirculated by the pump. The enlarged section at the top serves to effect a separation of the intimate hydrogen-oil mixture so that hydro-

[1] MAXTED, U. S. 1,313,407 (1919).

gen may be withdrawn at the top of the apparatus, repressured by the gas compressor, and then returned at the bottom of the column.   The degree of mixing of hydrogen and oil may be varied by the rate at which the gas compressor and oil pump operate.   A steam jacket serves to heat the charge and maintain suitable temperatures.   This process is said to effect very rapid hydrogenation, for instance, of peanut or cottonseed oil, in from 15 to 25 min., with an initial temperature of 130°C.   Because of the rapid reaction at low temperature, this process is particularly applicable to hardening of oils for edible purposes, where the product must possess a good flavor.   The usual working pressure is about 60 lb. per square inch.[1]

The third type, or continuous process, involves the use of a massive or rigid catalyst over which the hydrogen-oil mixture passes.   This procedure obviates the use of filtration for removing the catalyst from the oil and with respect to its capacity usually makes the plant more compact.   The nickel catalyst is in the form of a wire screen or turnings contained in tubes or reactors.   The hydrogen-oil mixture may flow in the same or in countercurrent directions.   Generally, more than one reactor is used, and these are provided with suitable connections so that they may be operated in series or in parallel with each other.   This permits either the capacity or extent of hydrogenation to be varied readily. The process developed by Bolton and Lush[2] uses a nickel catalyst in the form of turnings or wire, prepared in a special way.   In order to get active nickel, the nickel metal is oxidized by means of anodic oxidation; *i.e.*, the nickel wires or turnings are made the anode, an electrolyte such as sodium carbonate being used.   This does not allow the nickel to pass into solution but converts the surface into nickel oxides, which are then subsequently reduced by hydrogen under carefully controlled conditions. The conditions of operation during hydrogenation are about 180°C. and 60 to 100 lb. per square inch hydrogen pressure.   The catalyst maintains its activity for relatively long periods of time; but when it needs reactivation, the anodic oxidation is again used, the activity of the catalyst being restored on reduction.

In all the various processes for oil hardening, the quantity of nickel used is generally less than 1 per cent by weight of the oil hardened.   In those operations where the nickel catalyst needs to be removed from the oil, it is usually done by filtration of the hot liquid fat.   The catalyst is then washed, redissolved, and reused in preparing fresh catalyst.   Thus,

[1] ELLIS, "Hydrogenation of Organic Substances," p. 421, D. Van Nostrand Company, Inc., New York, 3d ed. (1930).

[2] ELLIS, *ibid.;* BOLTON, *J. Soc. Chem. Ind.*, **41**, 384R (1922); **46**, 444T (1927); LUSH, *J. Soc. Chem. Ind.*, **42**, 219T (1923); **43**, 53T (1924); **44**, 129T (1925); **46**, 454T (1927).

except for small mechanical losses, the catalyst is continually reused. Figure 6 is a flow diagram for the hydrogenation of cottonseed oil.

The Synthesis of Methanol and Higher Alcohols.—The synthesis of methanol from carbon monoxide and hydrogen is a reversible reaction. The physical aspects of this problem are many and varied, but the combined application of physical and chemical principles has rapidly developed a variety of syntheses from water gas. The methanol, carbon monoxide, and hydrogen equilibrium has been the subject of several

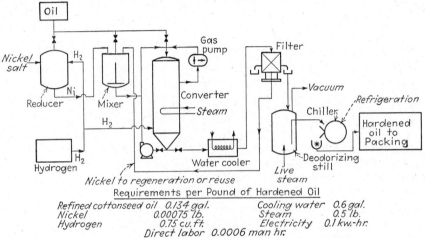

Requirements per Pound of Hardened Oil

Refined cottonseed oil 0.134 gal.   Cooling water 0.6 gal.
Nickel   0.00075 lb.   Steam   0.5 lb.
Hydrogen   0.75 cu.ft.   Electricity   0.1 kw.-hr.
Direct labor 0.0006 man hr.

Fig. 6.—Flow sheet for the hydrogenation of cottonseed oil.

investigations. The following values of the equilibrium constant are available:[1]

$$K_p = \frac{P_{\text{CH}_3\text{OH}}}{P_{\text{CO}} \times P^2_{\text{H}_2}}$$

Table XIX.—The Equilibrium Constant K_p, for the Methanol Synthesis

Temperature, °C.	K_p
260	1.2×10^{-3}
300	1.6×10^{-4}
340	2.9×10^{-5}
380	6.3×10^{-6}

These data show that the equilibrium constant is small and that it decreases rapidly with temperature. Consequently, the temperature interval over which the synthesis is operative from a practical viewpoint is not very large. At temperatures much below 300°C. (572°F.), the rate of reaction is slow, so that the capacity of the apparatus is small. Above 400°C. (752°F.), the equilibrium becomes too unfavorable. Despite the small values of the equilibrium constant, very satisfactory

[1] Newitt, Byrne, and Strong, *Proc. Roy. Soc.*, **A123**, 236 (1929).

conversions are obtained. This is because of the decrease in volume attending the reaction

$$CO + 2H_2 \rightleftarrows CH_3OH$$

so that by the application of pressure the reaction is driven to the right, or to higher conversions. Thus, at 300°C. and 3,500 lb. per square inch, using the theoretical mixture, *i.e.*, one volume of carbon monoxide to two of hydrogen, the equilibrium yield is above 60 per cent; while under exactly the same conditions but working at 150 lb. pressure, the yield is less than 2 per cent. The pressures used in this synthesis are usually from 3,000 to 4,000 lb. per square inch.

Along with the synthesis of methanol, other side reactions, or parasitic reactions, are possible. Some of these are

$$CO + 3H_2 \rightarrow CH_4 + H_2O + 50{,}000 \text{ cal.}$$
$$2CO + 2H_2 \rightarrow CH_4 + CO_2 + 60{,}280 \text{ cal.}$$
$$2CO \rightarrow C + CO_2 + 41{,}950 \text{ cal.}$$
$$xCO + yH_2 \rightarrow \text{high-molecular-weight alcohols, hydrocarbons, etc.}$$

Not only do these reactions consume carbon monoxide and hydrogen, but also make control more difficult, for they are more exothermic than the methanol reaction. Such reactions as the last type tend to build up heavy nonvolatile materials, which impair the catalyst's activity. In this synthesis, a catalyst is selected that causes reduction principally to methanol, and a variety of materials are now known to do this surprisingly well, with practically complete exclusion of the side reactions.

The carbon monoxide-hydrogen mixture is usually prepared from water gas, the water-gas catalytic reaction being used to furnish the desired ratio of hydrogen to carbon monoxide. There are, however, instances where carbon dioxide-hydrogen mixtures are available, and methanol is also made readily from these under practically the same conditions as would be used for carbon monoxide-hydrogen mixtures. The reaction

$$CO_2 + 3H_2 \rightleftarrows CH_3OH + H_2O$$

produces a methanol-water solution instead of pure methanol. Despite the apparent simplicity of the raw materials, a large variety of complex organic products can be readily obtained by only minor changes in the catalyst and operating conditions. This is because condensation as well as hydrogenation reactions occur.

The catalyst is contained in special reactors designed to withstand the pressures and temperatures used. By heat interchange either in the reactor or in special heat exchangers, the heat of the reactor—some 24,620 cal. per gram mole of methanol formed—is absorbed. Some of this is used to heat the entering gas to reaction temperature. By proper choice of the space-time yield, or, in other words, the amount of methanol produced per volume of catalyst per hour, and the amount of heat removed in the heat exchangers, the temperature of the catalyst can be kept reasonably constant. Once started, the reaction is self-supporting; *i.e.*, the problem is one of heat removal and not addition.

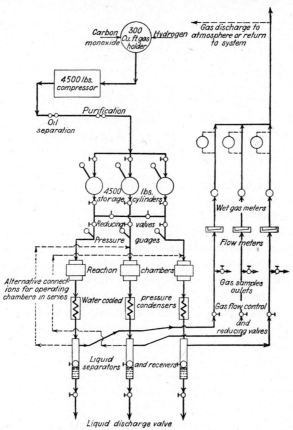

Fig. 7.—Flow sheet for the synthesis of methanol from carbon monoxide and hydrogen.

The methanol-containing gases leave the reactor and, after passing through heat exchangers, are finally led through condensers where the methanol is condensed, usually under full operating pressures (3,000 to 4,000 lb. per square inch). This procedure frees the gas more completely of methanol than if the condensation took place at lower pressure. Any drop in pressure in the reactor and cooling system is repressured by *booster compressors*. If a gas mixture other than the 1:2 ratio of carbon monoxide to hydrogen is used, the composition of the gases must be continually adjusted as it is recycled, and provision must also be made for venting inert or other gaseous side-reaction products. It has been found that the partial pressure of carbon monoxide is the dominant factor upon which the rate of fouling of the catalyst depends owing to adsorption of high-molecular-weight nonvolatile compounds. For this reason, a higher hydrogen-to-carbon monoxide ratio than the theoretical one of 2:1 is sometimes used. Figure 7 (page 471) is a diagram of the apparatus used in the synthesis of methanol on a small scale.[1]

The catalysts usually consist of metal and metallic oxide mixtures, the most common constituents being copper with oxides of zinc, chromium, manganese, and aluminum. For the synthesis of methanol alone, contact of the hot gases with iron should be avoided. In this case, the reactors are lined, usually with copper or some other material not affecting the catalyst. The catalysts for pure methanol are usually susceptible to iron carbonyl, formed when carbon monoxide is in contact with iron. This impairs the catalyst's activity or else induces undesirable side reactions. Practical operations usually involve the production of other alcohols along with methanol. In this case, a somewhat different type of catalyst is used; and the presence of iron is not particularly objectionable, since it also catalyzes the formation of higher alcohols from carbon monoxide-hydrogen mixtures.

With the proper catalyst and the exclusion of sulfur and iron, methanol of a purity of 99 per cent or better can be produced. As an alternative, methanol may result as part of the synthesis of other valuable higher alcohols, where the exclusion of iron is no longer necessary. The largest single use of methanol is for the preparation of formaldehyde, this product consuming some 40 per cent of the production. Denaturing operations use about 30 per cent of the production; miscellaneous solvents, some 20 per cent; and the manufacture of dimethylaniline, about 5 per cent.

Higher alcohols are produced when operating temperatures are slightly higher (350 to 475°C.) than those used in methanol synthesis and with methanol catalysts containing alkalis or else iron-base catalysts containing alkalis. The reaction product may be so complex that complete separation and identification of the constituents are very difficult. Of course, the lower-molecular-weight alcohols are more readily separated and identified, and for this reason this synthesis has been one of the principal sources of solvents for nitrocellulose and resinous products.

While the mechanism of the formation of these higher alcohols is not entirely understood and several theories have been suggested, the following method of formation appears the most probable. Certain steps in it have been demonstrated experimentally.[2] This scheme

---

[1] LEWIS and FROLICH, *Ind. Eng. Chem.*, **20**, 285 (1928).

[2] GRAVES, *Ind. Eng. Chem.*, **23**, 1381 (1931); FROLICH and CRYDER, *Ind. Eng. Chem.*, **22**, 1057 (1930).

involves three simple assumptions, which are: (1) Higher alcohols result from intermolecular dehydration of two lower-alcohol molecules; (2) dehydration involves removal of hydrogen either from the hydroxylated carbon atom, thus producing secondary alcohols (except in the case of methanol), or from the carbon atom adjacent, producing primary alcohols; (3) hydrogen separates most readily from a $>CH_2$ group, with more difficulty from a $-CH_3$ group, and not at all from a $\equiv CH$ group. For example:

$$R \cdot CH_2OH + R' \cdot CH_2OH \rightarrow R \cdot CH_2 \cdot CHOH + H_2O$$
$$\underset{\displaystyle R'}{|}$$

$$R \cdot CH_2OH + R' \cdot CH_2 \cdot CH_2OH \rightarrow R \cdot CH_2 \cdot CH \cdot CH_2OH + H_2O$$
$$\underset{\displaystyle R'}{|}$$

The higher-alcohol mixture has been found to contain the following primary alcohols: n-propanol, isobutanol, 2-methyl-1-butanol, 2-methyl-1-pentanol, 2, 4-dimethyl-1-pentanol, 4-methyl-1-hexanol; and the following secondary alcohols: isopropanol, 3-methyl-2-butanol, and 2, 4-dimethyl-3-pentanol. In addition, there are definite indications of 2, 4-dimethyl-1-hexanol, 4 or 5-methyl-1-heptanol, 3-pentanol, 2-pentanol, and 2-methyl-3-pentanol.[1]

With catalysts containing iron, nickel, copper, and cobalt along with other metallic oxides, at 1 to 2 atmos. pressure and 180 to 200°C., carbon monoxide is reduced according to the following type reactions:

$$nCO + (2n + 1)H_2 = C_nH_{2n+2} + nH_2O$$
$$2nCO + (n + 1)H_2 = C_nH_{2n+2} + nCO_2$$

These reactions, known as the Fischer-Tropsch synthesis of hydrocarbons, are used in Germany to produce liquid fuels or synthetic gasoline from water gas. It is estimated that some 70,000,000 gal. of fuel was produced in Germany in 1937 by this method.

Hydrogenation of Acids or Esters to Alcohols.—The direct reduction of the carboxyl group to an alcohol by means of molecular hydrogen and catalysts occurs at temperatures usually from 300 to 400°C. (570 to 750°F.) and with hydrogen pressures of about 3,000 lb. per square inch. The acids or esters may be of the long, straight-chain type such as occur in vegetable oils and fats; or they may be of the shorter-chain type, with more complicated groupings or branchings. The oil-hardening processes use long-chain acids and esters and saturate only the olefinic linkages in the carbon chain; in the reductions to be described here, the carboxyl group ($-COOH$) is changed to an alcohol group ($-CH_2OH$), and the olefinic bonds in the chain may or may not be reduced at the same time. This is again an illustration of the remarkable specificity of catalysts; normally, the olefinic bonds would be considered far more

[1] GRAVES, *Ind. Eng. Chem.*, **23**, 1381 (1931).

reactive in hydrogenations than a carboxyl group.   Yet they may not be reduced while the carboxyl group is being converted to an alcohol.

The earlier methods of reducing acids or esters to alcohols involved the use of metallic sodium with anhydrous alcohols; also, an acid derivative, such as the acid chloride, could be reduced by direct hydrogenation to an aldehyde by palladium catalysts.   The direct reduction, using molecular hydrogen at high pressure, involves two moles of hydrogen per mole of acid reduced, as shown in the following reaction:

$$R-\overset{\overset{\displaystyle O}{\|}}{C}-OH + 2H_2 \rightarrow R-\overset{\overset{\displaystyle H}{\diagup}\overset{\displaystyle H}{\diagdown}}{C}-OH + H_2O$$

where R represents a group preferably of the aliphatic or the hydro-aromatic series.   A secondary reaction consists of esterification of a portion of the alcohol formed with a portion of the unchanged acid.   The proportion of ester present in the product depends chiefly on the completeness of the hydrogenation.   When conducting the reaction under conditions that yield only partial reduction of the acid, the process may be altered to give esters as the main products, according to the equation

$$2R-\overset{\overset{\displaystyle O}{\|}}{C}-OH + 2H_2 \rightarrow R-\overset{\overset{\displaystyle O}{\|}}{C}-O-CH_2-R + 2H_2O$$

If R in these formulas contains an unsaturated or olefinic bond, partial reduction of the carbon-carbon unsaturation may occur.   It is sometimes more suitable to conduct the reaction to favor alcohol or ester formation and then further reduce the olefinic bonds at lower pressures and temperatures with nickel catalysts in the same manner as that used in hardening oils. . This brings all the reaction products to the same completeness of hydrogenation, yielding new compositions—usually solids—from which alcohols and esters may be separated if desired.   The stability of high-molecular-weight acids and alcohols under high-pressure hydrogen at high temperatures is very different from that which would be expected when heating these compounds in air.   Decarboxylation of the acid to form carbon dioxide and a hydrocarbon of fewer carbon atoms does not occur in hydrogenation.   The dehydration of the alcohol to an olefin, or the more complete reduction of the —CH$_2$OH to a —CH$_3$ group, occurs only slightly.   However, this is dependent on the other groups near the alcohol group; with straight hydrocarbon chains, these decompositions occur to a very minor extent.

The reductions may be carried out in a batch system or in a flow system, the latter being preferable.   The catalyst in granular form is held in place in a heated tube capable of withstanding the pressure and temperature.   The acid or ester if solid may be melted or may be dissolved in a solvent such as normal butyl alcohol or ethyl alcohol, and it is then pumped into the reactor and over the catalyst. The use of acids, or esters of the acids and simple alcohols, is preferable to the use of the glycerides, because the presence of glycerol and its decomposition products makes the separation of the reaction products difficult. The acid or ester is pumped through the reactor at the rate of 2 to 8 volumes of material per volume of catalyst per hour, a considerable excess of hydrogen being passed along with the material over the catalyst. From 2 to 10 moles of hydrogen is used per mole of acid hydrogenated.[1] The proportion of esters to alcohols produced in the hydrogenation will depend on this ratio of hydrogen to the acid being reduced.

The catalysts are of the mild hydrogenating type such as supported copper, copper chromite, zinc-copper chromate, nickel-copper zincate, and sometimes certain salts of molybdic acid. These catalysts usually require a reduction with hydrogen prior to use. A specific catalyst preparation is as follows: A solution is prepared by dissolving 245 parts by weight of crystallized zinc nitrate, 23 parts of hydrated cadmium nitrate, and 24 parts of copper nitrate in about 750 parts of water. A second solution is prepared by dissolving 100 parts by weight of chromic anhydride (CrO_3) in 500 parts of water and then adding 135 parts of 28 per cent aqueous ammonia. Precipitation of the hydrogenating metals of the first solution as chromates is effected by stirring and adding the second solution at room temperature. The mixture is exactly neutralized with additional ammonium hydroxide and allowed to settle. The clear supernatant liquid is poured off, and the precipitate is washed several times by decantation with an adequate volume of wash water, after which it is filtered and dried at about 100°C. The next step consists of igniting the dried filter cake at 400°C. for 4 hr. This process converts the double ammonium chromates of the copper, zinc, and cadmium to metallic chromites, in which form they are employed as catalyst. Suitable physical form is obtained by granulating the friable chromite powder and briquetting it into the form of tablets, which may or may not be broken up into grains of various sizes. In some cases, it is advisable to prereduce the hydrogenation catalyst with hydrogen or other reducing gas before loading it into the converter. In others, the catalyst reduction is carried out *in situ* by heating up slowly in a stream of hydrogen, prior to the introduction of the acid to be hydrogenated.[2]

The hydrogenation of oleic acid provides a very suitable starting point for the synthesis of oleyl and stearyl alcohols and their esters. Owing to its low melting point oleic acid is more convenient to pump than stearic acid. In Table XX are some results of hydrogenating oleic acid.[2] Pure oleic acid was pumped over 100 cc. of catalyst at the rate of

[1] Lazier, U. S. 1,839,974 (1932).

[2] Lazier, *loc. cit.*

400 cc. per hour.   The hydrogen flow was about 15 cu. ft. per hour, and
the pressure 2,800 lb. per square inch.   The temperature was varied
between 350 and 420°C., and the reaction product at each temperature
was analyzed for acid, ester, and alcohol.

TABLE XX.—HYDROGENATION OF OLEIC ACID

Temp., °C.	Composition of product, %			
	Acid	Ester	Alcohol	Total
350	19	36	39	94
360	8	36	50	94
370	6	34	58	98
390	2	30	68	100
400	2	29	67	98
410	2	26	65	93
420	1	21	60	82

The lower temperatures favor the formation of waxes, which are hydrogenated at the higher temperatures to free alcohols.   The optimum
temperature is about 390°C.

Although the efficiency of reduction of the carboxyl group may be
high, the saturation of the carbon-carbon linkages in the unsaturated
acids, alcohols, and esters may be only partial.   In a typical experiment
with oleic acid, the acid was 65 per cent hydrogenated, as judged by
the decrease in the acid and saponification numbers, while the iodine
number decreased from an initial value of 88 to a value of only 50.   In
order to obtain the pure stearyl alcohol, these mixed alcohols are hydrogenated in the liquid phase with a reduced nickel catalyst.   Using about
5 per cent by weight of a nickel on kieselguhr catalyst at 125 to 150°C.
(257 to 300°F.) and hydrogen at 150 lb. per square inch pressure, the
reduction is rapid and complete in 1.5 hr.

These alcohols are finding a variety of interesting uses.   Not only are
these hydrogenations useful in preparing many new alcohols for synthetic
purposes, but the higher alcohols and esters are valuable as waxes and in
the preparation of new detergents.

Hydrogenation of Petroleum, Tar, and Coal.—The purposes of
hydrogenating petroleums, tars, and coals are (1) to improve existing
petroleum products or develop new uses and products; (2) to convert
inferior or low-grade materials such as heavy oils and tars into valuable
petroleum products; and (3) to transform solid fuels such as lignites and
coals into liquid fuels.   The distinguishing feature of these operations
is that both the raw materials and finished products are very complex
mixtures of relatively unknown composition.   All types and sizes of

molecules are present along with a variety of contaminating impurities. Thus, in the hydrogenation process, a variety of reactions may be occurring simultaneously and to varying extents, and yet the final product may be very satisfactory, meeting all the required specifications.

These complicated mixtures are identified and recognized by certain properties, sometimes more physical than chemical in character. Thus, gasoline specifications are concerned with sulfur content, gum-forming materials, general stability and resistance to chemical change or oxidation, and detonation and volatility characteristics. Kerosenes are identified by their sulfur content, specific gravity, burning qualities, and volatility. Lubricating oils are judged by their stability toward heat and oxidation, their carbon-forming tendencies, lubricating qualities, viscosity characteristics, color, and volatility. Tars are recognized by their aromatic and phenolic hydrocarbon content, their specific gravity, volatility, and viscosity. Coals are classified according to their age, ash content, the carbon, hydrogen, nitrogen, oxygen and sulfur analysis, and the volatile matter. Hydrogenation may result in an upgrading of one or all of the properties of the material. In processing petroleums, tars, and coals, the operation is far more complex than in working with pure or relatively pure materials.

Catalysts must not only speed up these hydrogenations, but they must also guide and direct the desired reactions and effect a balancing and harmonizing of many factors so that just the correct over-all result is attained. They must also be able to operate on liquid, solid, or gaseous materials and, in addition, cause impurities that are common catalytic poisons, such as sulfur, oxygen, and nitrogen, to be detached from their molecular linkages and removed as hydrogen sulfide, water, or ammonia. All these things the hydrogenation catalysts must do rapidly and at relatively low temperatures. While at first it may seem incredible, catalysts are now known that perform all these functions satisfactorily. The elements of group 6 of the Periodic System are very suitable, particularly molybdenum, tungsten, and chromium, as oxides or sulfides or more complicated mixtures with one another.

The extent to which these new catalysts increase the velocity of hydrogenation is indicated in the case of effecting improvements in lubricating oils.[1] At 200 atmospheres pressure, there was no improvement without catalysts; and even at 1,000 atmospheres without catalysts, the improvement, if any, was very slight. The hydrogenation velocity in the presence of catalysts and about 200 atmospheres pressure is, however, about a hundred times greater than without catalysts. In the conversion of heavy, nonvolatile materials into lighter products such as gasoline, the catalyst must favor cracking reactions as well as hydrogena-

[1] GRIMM, *Intern. Conf. Bituminous Coal*, **II**, 49 (1931).

tion reactions.   Yet these two must be in the proper balance.   Cracking must not proceed faster than the hydrogenation of the cracked products; condensation and polymerization of unsaturated or reactive molecular fragments must not proceed faster than their hydrogenation.   Otherwise, high-molecular-weight products would accumulate on the surface of the catalyst, decreasing or completely destroying its activity.   With the conditions of temperature, pressure, and catalyst delicately coordinated, complex hydrogenations proceed with surprising smoothness.

Hydrogenations involving petroleum, tar, or coal are usually exothermic.   Table XXI sets forth some of the approximate quantities of heat liberated by different hydrogenations.[1]

TABLE XXI.—EXOTHERMIC HEAT OF REACTION OF DIFFERENT HYDROGENATION REACTIONS

Reaction	Raw material	
	Cal. per gm.	B.t.u. per lb.
Hexane + H_2 → methane	730	1315
Bituminous coal + H_2 → light oil	450	810
Middle oil from bituminous coal + H_2 → gasoline	400	720
High boiling crude oil fraction + H_2 → lubricating oil	50	90
N_2 + H_2 → ammonia	750	1350
CO + H_2 → methanol	700	1260

The hydrogen consumed in the process obviously depends on the difference in hydrogen content of the raw material and finished product and on the extent to which gases containing methane and other low-boiling hydrocarbons are formed.   In the hydrogenation of bituminous coals, and tars derived from such coals, from 8 to 16 cu. ft. of hydrogen are required per pound of coal.   In crude oils, poor in hydrogen, the consumption is about 3 to 6 cu. ft. of hydrogen per pound of oil, while in oils rich in hydrogen, from 0.5 to 2 cu. ft. per pound are consumed. These data are for reductions in which no gaseous products form.

The additional hydrogen consumption for gasification depends on the extent of the hydrogenation, whether paraffinic or aromatic products are formed, and on the hydrogen content of the raw materials.   In processing coal or coal tars, the hydrogen consumed in making gaseous products such as methane and its homologues is about 0.3 to 0.4 cu. ft. per pound of charging stock for each 1 per cent of gaseous products; in processing petroleum, brown coal tars, and the light oils, the gaseous products use about 0.15 to 0.25 cu. ft. of hydrogen per pound of material charged.

[1] *Ibid.*, p. 477.

The yield of liquid reaction products will depend on the amount of gasification during hydrogenation. A yield of 55 per cent by weight or more of marketable gasoline appears possible by hydrogenating brown coals or lignites. With suitable bituminous coals, it may be 65 per cent by weight or more. These figures are for the ash-free dry coal. In the case of tars, the yield may be 80 to 85 per cent by weight, which is over 100 per cent yield by volume.

In operating hydrogenation processes, it has been found advantageous to divide them into two parts: (1) liquid-phase reactions, where pulverized coal and *pasting* oil or heavy oils are contacted with hydrogen; and (2) gas-phase reactions, where the light oil exists practically entirely in the gas phase during hydrogenation. It has been found, in processing heavy oils or in processing coals in one step, that the extent of hydrogenation was insufficient and the yield low because heavy materials tended to be preferentially adsorbed, thus excluding the light oils from hydrogenation. Under these conditions, the latter accumulate, and, instead of being hydrogenated to gasoline, uncontrolled cracking and polymerization reactions take place. The polymerization of unstable materials produced by cracking builds up high-molecular-weight compounds, resulting in low yields of gasoline. These difficulties are avoided in the two-step operation for producing gasoline. Materials with normal boiling points below about 300 to 350°C. (570 to 660°F.) are used in the gas-phase operation, while those boiling higher than this are hydrogenated in the liquid phase.

Petroleum Hydrogenation.—The principal applications of petroleum hydrogenation in this country[1] are as follows:

Gasoline production.

Lubricating oil improvement.

Burning oil or kerosene improvement.

Up-grading of heavy oils and residues.

Specialty products, such as petroleum cuts of very high solvency and safety fuels of high anti-knock quality.

Cracking or pyrolysis occurs along with the hydrogenation of the petroleum. If pyrolysis alone takes place, progressive cracking and polymerization generally lead to the final products: (1) gaseous and low-boiling liquid compounds of high hydrogen content; (2) liquid material of intermediate molecular weight and a hydrogen-to-carbon ratio differing more or less from that of the original feed stock, depending on the method of operation; and (3) liquid material of high molecular weight, such as tar and petroleum coke, possessing a lower ratio of hydrogen to carbon than the starting material.

---

[1] HASLAM and RUSSELL, *Ind. Eng. Chem.*, **22**, 1030 (1930); SWEENEY and VOORHIES, *Ind. Eng. Chem.*, **26**, 195 (1934).

An essential difference between pyrolysis and hydrogenolysis of petroleum is that in pyrolysis, a certain amount of polymerized heavier

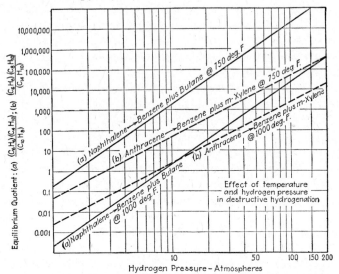

Fig. 8*A*.—Effect of temperature and pressure on the hydrogenation-dehydrogenation equilibria.

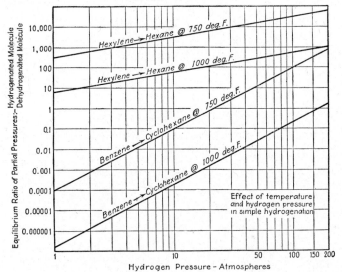

Fig. 8*B*.—Effect of temperature and pressure on the hydrogenation-dehydrogenation equilibria.

products, such as tar and coke, is always formed along with the light products, such as gas and gasoline; whereas in hydrogenolysis or destructive hydrogenation, polymerization may be partly or even entirely prevented, so that only light products are made. The prevention of tar and coke formation usually results in an increased gasoline yield. The condensed type of molecule, such as naphthalene or anthracene, is one that is closely associated with the building up of tar and coke; but in an atmosphere of hydrogen and in contact with catalysts, these condensed molecules are changed over into lower-molecular-weight compounds which are more saturated and boil within the gasoline range. Figure 8 shows the pronounced effect of temperature and hydrogen partial pressure on the hydrogenation-dehydrogenation equilibria of a few condensed types of hydrocarbons.[1] These data show that it is possible to get varying degrees of hydrogenation. At low temperatures and high hydrogen pressures (200 atmospheres), the product can be made very saturated; or if the temperature is raised and the partial pressure of hydrogen lowered, a

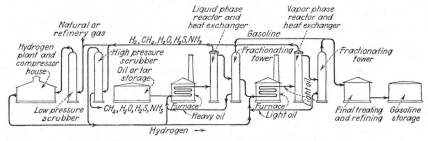

Fig. 9.—Flow sheet of the hydrogenation of heavy oil and tar.

more aromatic product can be made. These factors are important in producing motor fuels of varying anti-knock qualities. The aromatic content, which is related to the anti-knock properties of a fuel, can be retained under conditions wherein sulfur compounds and resinous and asphaltic materials are hydrogenated and thus removed or converted into more valuable products.

Table XXII gives some experimental results on hydrogenating gas oil with various catalysts. The gas oil used had a density at 20°C. of 0.894, 73.4 per cent by weight distilling over between 234 to 280°C., and 22.2 per cent between 280 to 310°C.[2] Figure 9 is a flow sheet for hydrogenating oils and tars. The relationships between the liquid- and gas-phase operations are shown. In general, the temperatures used range from about 400°C. (750°F.) to 540°C. (1000°F.), depending on whether a paraffinic or aromatic material is being made; and the pressures extend up to about 3,600 lb. per square inch.

Tar Hydrogenation.—The manufactured-gas and coke-oven industries produce large quantities of tars, and these can be hydrogenated to produce

[1] SWEENEY and VOORHIES, *loc. cit.*
[2] TROPSCH, *Intern. Conf. Bituminous Coal*, **II**, 35 (1931).

TABLE XXII.—HYDROGENATION OF GAS OIL

Temperature, 440°C. (825°F.); time, 1 hr.

Catalyst	H₂ pressure, lb. per sq. in.			Yields of reaction products, weight % of gas oil used				Fraction up to 230°C., weight %				Fraction 230 to 270°C., weight %				Liquid reaction products, weight %	
	Initial at 20°C.	Maximum	Final at 20°C.	Gaseous hydrocarbons, %	Liquid hydrocarbons %	D_4^{20}	Loss	Gas oil used	Liquid reaction products	D_4^{20}	Iodine No.	Gas oil used	Liquid reaction products	D_4^{20}	Iodine No.	Residue above 270°C.	Gas + loss
No catalyst	1,160	2,800	1,100	3.2	92.4	0.8691	4.4	21.1	22.9	0.800	86.8	40.2	43.5	0.893	39.7	32.1	1.5
MoO₃	1,160	2,800	990	3.3	91.3	0.8675	5.4	20.6	22.6	0.796	42.7	41.7	45.7	0.895		30.2	1.5
MoO₃ (reduced by H₂ at 600°C.)	1,160	2,900	1,070	3.6	88.4	0.8650	8.0	22.8	25.8	0.795		39.4	44.6	0.897		27.8	1.8
MoS₃	1,150	2,600	870	5.5	89.2	0.8324	5.3	43.9	49.3	0.791	20.9	30.0	33.7	0.890	25.3	14.5	2.5
(NH₄)₂MoS₄	1,160	2,800	880	4.5	86.8	0.8128	8.7	55.3	64.0			22.5	26.0			6.4	3.6
(NH₄)₂MoS₄ (reduced by H₂ at 500°C.)	1,150	2,600	960	2.9	91.2	0.8523	5.9	32.9	36.2	0.801		35.5	39.0	0.886		22.9	1.9
Molybdenite (MoS₂)	1,150	2,800	1,050	4.9	88.4	0.8641	6.7	27.0	30.7	0.793		38.2	43.4	0.899		24.9	1.0
MoSe₃	1,160	2,800	1,020	4.6	92.5	0.8520	2.9	32.4	35.0	0.798		41.3	44.7	0.892		23.3	
WS₃	1,160	2,700	820	5.3	82.7	0.8098	12.0	44.4	54.1	0.765	21.9	24.4	29.7	0.883		15.8	0.4
NiS₃	1,160	3,200	1,020	4.9	93.4	0.8482	1.7	38.0	40.8	0.800	57.1	34.1	36.6	0.893		20.5	2.1
ZnS	1,160	2,900	1,050	1.8	90.6	0.8611	7.6	26.4	29.4	0.795		37.5	41.8	0.834		27.0	1.8

satisfactory motor or Diesel fuels. In Europe coals are subjected to low-temperature carbonization where the tar yield is considerable, and these tars are then hydrogenated to produce fuels instead of directly hydrogenating the coal. The processing of tar is much easier than that of coal, and the operation is more closely related to petroleum hydrogenation than coal hydrogenation. Practically twice as much motor fuel can be produced by hydrogenating the tars than by cracking them to produce similar products. Molybdenum oxide has been found to be a suitable catalyst, and an even greater activity is shown by molybdenum sulfide. Temperatures of from 450 to 500°C. (840 to 930°F.) are used, and the pressures are approximately 3,000 to 4,000 lb. per square inch. In addition to the catalysts' effecting cleavages of hydrocarbons of high molecular weight and hydrogenating these into stable more volatile products, they must also be able to effect the reduction of phenolic and organic nitrogen compounds to hydrocarbons.

Coal Hydrogenation.—The hydrogenation of coal is a special application of the liquid-phase process. Coal is a complex mixture of very high-molecular-weight compounds, and the successful hydrogenation of it to give high yields of liquid motor fuels depends not only on high-pressure hydrogen but also to a very great extent upon catalysts that facilitate and accelerate the entry of hydrogen into coal or its decomposition products.

In general, the coal is first mixed with a high boiling oil, called a *pasting oil*, and this mixture is forced into the high-pressure reaction chamber. The coal paste, which is made up of about equal parts of finely ground bituminous or brown coal and a high-boiling oil, is mixed also with a finely divided catalyst, and this highly viscous liquid is pumped through pipes and heat exchangers into the reaction chamber. The catalyst may also be added at successive stages in the operation, or the coal may be soaked with a solution of the catalyst.

The reaction is highly sensitive to changes in temperature because of the high-molecular-weight compounds present in the coal. Great care must be taken to avoid overheating, particularly during the preheating operations; otherwise, the components of the coal that still have their original molecular structure will tend to form coke and inert products not suitable for further hydrogenation. Another difficulty lies in completing the hydrogenation reaction, for although the coal is finely ground, the particles are solid, and contact with hydrogen is possible, therefore, only on the surface. After partial hydrogenation and reduction of oxygen compounds in the coal have occurred, the particles aided by the action of the heavy oil, swell and partly dissolve, resulting in an almost completely liquid mass. The oil also serves to maintain the temperature uniform throughout the reaction chamber. The primary hydrogenation products are heavy, high-boiling oils, which crack, if maintained at temperatures of

450°C. (840°F.) or above, into lighter oils, gasoline, and gas. By controlling the time of hydrogenation, the liquefied product from the coal may be obtained as light oils, gasoline, or gas, with the heavy pasting oil recovered unchanged.

Figure 10 shows a flow sheet for the hydrogenation of coal. The finely ground coal is first mixed with the heavy oil and catalyst. This viscous coal paste is sent through the preheaters to the reaction chamber. The reaction products then go to a hot separator, where the vapor fractions and a part of the pasting oil are removed together with the hydrogen.

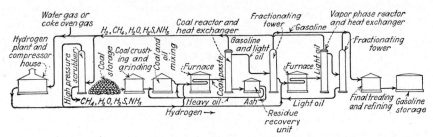

Fig. 10.—Flow sheet for the hydrogenation of coal.

The residue, containing the high-boiling oils, the ash, and a small amount of unchanged coal, along with the catalyst, then passes on to the residue-recovery unit. Here the oil is freed from solid particles and again used for mixing with fresh coal. The gasoline that may be formed in the coal or liquid-phase reactor goes to distillation units, and the light oils pass on into the gas-phase process, where they are converted into gasoline. All types of lignite and most bituminous coals, except those that have progressed too far in the coalification process, such as anthracite, are suitable raw materials for liquefaction. Young coals, which at present have the least value, are most suitable for high-pressure hydrogenation.

CHAPTER IX

ALKYLATION

By R. Norris Shreve

I. INTRODUCTION

Types of Alkylated Compounds.—Alkylation may be defined as the introduction of an alkyl radical by substitution or addition into an organic compound. We also include under this procedure the introduction of an aralkyl radical, such as benzyl. Alkylation is of five general types, depending on the linkage effected:

1. Substitution for hydrogen in the hydroxyl group of an alcohol or a

$$C_2H_5O\text{--}C_2H_5$$

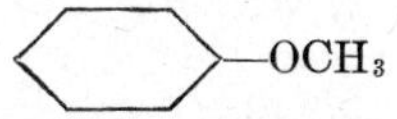

phenol. Here the alkyl is bound to oxygen.

2. Substitution for hydrogen attached to nitrogen. Here the alkyl

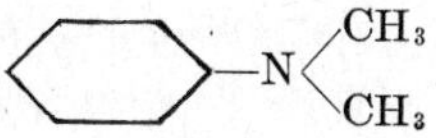

is bound to trivalent nitrogen.

3. Addition of an alkyl halide or an alkyl ester to a tertiary nitrogen

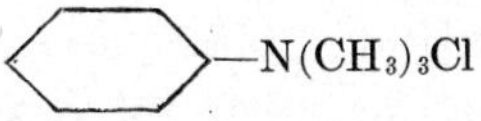

compound. Here the trivalent nitrogen becomes pentavalent, and the binding of the alkyl is to the nitrogen.

4. Substitution for hydrogen in carbon compounds. This is nuclear

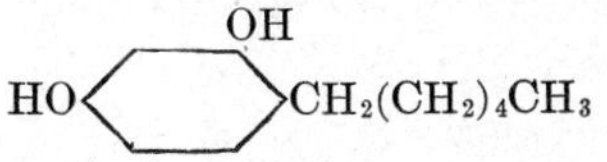

alkylation when an aromatic hydrogen is substituted. The carbon of the alkyl is bound to carbon of either aliphatic or aromatic compounds. This is carbon-to-carbon alkylation.

5. Alkyl-metallic compounds. Here the alkyl is bound to the metal.

$$Pb(C_2H_5)_4$$

While the number of possible different alkyl radicals is very large, the following are the principal ones of technical importance: methyl, ethyl,

485

propyl, butyl, amyl, and hexyl. The introduction of the aralkyl or benzyl radical, as well as the unsaturated allyl group, may also be included here for they are technically important.

Products Derived by Alkylation.—An examination of the products obtained as a result of alkylation shows that this *unit process* is used in the making of anesthetics, antipyretics, alkaloids, antiseptics, dyes, explosives, flavors, hypnotics, intermediates, perfumes, photographic chemicals, plastics, rubber accelerators, solvents, soporifics, synthetic gasoline, etc.

Among our anesthetics, mention need be made only of ether and procaine; and, among antipyretics, acetophenetidine, antipyrine, and pyramidone. In the field of alkaloids, opium contains some codeine; but to augment this supply, the phenolic hydroxyl of morphine is methylated. The caffeine market is partly supplied by methylation of theobromine. Antiseptics include many alkylated products which exemplify several different types of alkyl linkage; hexylresorcinol and thymol being examples of nuclear alkylation, while in guaiacol we find oxygen alkylation.

The alkylation process enters into dye manufacture in two ways, because dyes may be formed from alkylated intermediates, or, in a lesser number of instances, an intermediate may be subjected to alkylation as a final step. For instance, dimethylaniline is condensed with phosgene to give tetramethyldiaminobenzophenone (Michler's ketone). From this ketone are formed many dyes, such as Crystal Violet and Victoria Blue. On the other hand, the alkylation process may be almost the last step in the manufacture of a dye, for example, when the disazostilbene dye Paper Yellow 3G is ethylated to give Chrysophenine G.

Among the booster explosives, we find tetranitromethylaniline, commonly called tetryl or tetralite. An outstanding example of an alkylated compound in the field of flavors is vanillin. Alkylation plays a striking part in the preparation of hypnotics, *e.g.*, barbital (veronal), phenobarbital (luminal), and amytal, rendering them lipoid soluble.

Alkylation is of paramount importance in the preparation of intermediates, for the manufacture of dyes, perfumes, flavors, rubber accelerators, medicinals, and the like. Among alkylated intermediates, dimethylaniline has probably the most extensive and varied application. Other important members of this class are benzylethylaniline, benzylmethylaniline, diethylaniline, dianisidine, *m*-diethylaminophenol, and trimethylphenylammonium chloride. Perfumes include numerous instances of alkylated compounds, such as nerolin (β-naphthyl methyl ether) and artificial musk. As a photographic developer, metol (N-methyl-*p*-aminophenol sulfate) has long held an important place. Rubber accelerators include such compounds as thionex (tetramethyl thiuram sulfide).

In the field of solvents, many new alkylated compounds have been synthesized, these being principally complex ethers of ethylene glycol, e.g., ethylene glycol ethyl ether and diethylene dioxide, or p-dioxane.

The petroleum industry first obtained gasoline by straight-run distillation. Next the longer molecules were cracked. Now gasoline is being synthesized. For this purpose the most important reaction in all probability is an alkylation wherein olefins, by the aid of metal halides or dehydrating mineral acids as catalysts, are made to combine with other molecules. Ipatieff[1] refers to the present as the "catalytic period" of the petroleum industry, because of the large number of new syntheses that have been made possible from the olefins obtained from cracking operations through the intervention of catalysts. These syntheses are discussed in several chapters of this volume and are given consideration here particularly to exemplify reactions involving alkyl bound to carbon.

II. ALKYLATING AGENTS

Alcohols.—Methanol and ethanol are among the oldest and most widely employed reagents for technical alkylation. This is largely a result of their availability, relatively low cost, and the excellent yields that frequently result from their use. In practically every case, a catalyst is necessary to cause the alkylation to proceed smoothly; and in many instances, this is a mineral acid. Alcohols are used in the manufacture of ethers, such as ordinary ethyl ether, isopropyl ether, Carbitol, Cellosolve and naphthyl methyl ether. It should be noted that while naphthols react on alcohol in the presence of a mineral acid, the aryl alkyl ethers cannot be formed by this reaction in the case of phenols.

Dimethylaniline is made from aniline and methanol in the presence of a small amount of sulfuric acid, while diethylaniline is prepared from aniline and ethyl alcohol using hydrochloric acid. The ethylation does not proceed so completely as the methylation.

The alcohols are employed to effect the replacement of aromatically bound halogen atoms by heating in the presence of an alkali. In this way p-nitrophenetole and o-nitroanisole are made by treating p-nitrochlorobenzene with ethanol and o-nitrochlorobenzene with methanol.

The lower alcohols have also been employed extensively for the catalytic vapor-phase synthesis of alkylamines and for the alkylation of phenols.

The preceding describes the use of alcohols as alkylating agents involving oxygen and nitrogen linkages. They also serve for carbon-to-carbon alkylations,[2] wherein the alcohol is first esterified with sulfuric

---

[1] IPATIEFF, Problem of the Rational Utilization of Petroleum and Petroleum Distillation, *Am. Petroleum Inst.*, Nov. 11, 1936.

[2] Günther, U. S. 1,670,505 (1928); Verley, U. S. 1,756,575 (1930).

acid and this ester reacted with an aromatic compound. An example of such an alkylation is the preparation of isopropylbenzene from iso-propyl alcohol, sulfuric acid, and benzene. The reaction is quite similar to alkylation with olefins, using sulfuric acid or phosphoric acid as the catalyst.

Alkyl Halides.—The alkyl halides are probably the most commonly used laboratory alkylating agents. Most of the lower alkyl halides are now abundant and cheap because of recent developments relating to (*a*) addition of HCl to olefins; and (*b*) dehydrochlorination of poly-chlorinated paraffins. These reactions, which are discussed at length under Halogenation, may be represented as follows:

$$CH_3CH=CH_2 + HCl \rightarrow CH_3CHClCH_3$$

$$CH_2Cl \cdot CH_2Cl \xrightarrow{\text{KOH}} CH_2=CHCl$$

The tertiary alkyl halides react vigorously and in the case of *tert*-amyl chloride can alkylate phenols without the intervention of a catalyst. Methyl iodide is used in the preparation of such methylated products as Pinaverdol and other sensitizing dyes, which possess a pentavalent nitrogen.

Phenols, such as *o*-nitrophenol (*cf*. Acetophenetidine), are alkylated by heating with alkyl chlorides in the presence of aqueous alkali. Ethyl chloride serves as the alkylating agent in making diethylamine (*q.v.*) by heating with ammonia in an absolute alcohol medium in an autoclave. It is also employed for the carbon alkylation leading to barbital and for the alkylated metals, *e.g.*, lead tetraethyl (*q.v.*). Methyl and ethyl bro-mides or iodides react very smoothly and, in spite of their cost, find application in the field of dyes and medicinal products, *e.g.*, pyramidone and antipyrine, for the preparation of simple and mixed ethers and for the alkylation of phenols and amines. Allyl bromide is employed for making diallylbarbituric acid (dial).

Alkyl Sulfates.—In recent years, the alkyl sulfates have been growing in technical importance. Dimethyl sulfate has long been available at reasonable cost, and diethyl sulfate is now similarly obtainable. The dialkyl sulfates are usually caused to react in the presence of an alkali, thus producing the alkali alkyl sulfate.

In certain cases such as are detailed under Anisole (*q.v.*), the second methyl of the dimethyl sulfate enters into reaction. Dimethyl sulfate is employed in the methylation leading to alkyl oxygen compounds, *e.g.*, β-naphthyl methyl ether, etc.; to alkyl nitrogen compounds *e.g.*, caffeine and acriflavine; and to many others.

Diethyl sulfate, while reacting not quite so smoothly as dimethyl sulfate, is highly recommended[1] for various ethylations, *e.g.*, those yield-

---

[1] CADE, *Chem. & Met. Eng.*, **29**, 319–323 (1923).

ing β-naphthyl ethyl ether, phenetole, diethylaniline, and Cellosolve (*q.v.*). Both ethyl groups of diethyl sulfate can be made to react when the reaction system is practically anhydrous. Only one ethyl group reacts, however, in the presence of substantial amounts of water. In alkylations with dimethyl sulfate or diethyl sulfate, the use of autoclaves can generally be avoided.

In certain instances, monoalkyl acid sulfate may be regarded as the active alkylating reagent, as, for example, in the formation of ether from ethyl alcohol and sulfuric acid.

Aralkyl Halides.—Benzyl chloride is almost universally used for the introduction of the benzyl group, for instance, in the preparation of benzylethylaniline from ethylaniline. In actual practice, the benzyl-ethylaniline is usually obtained by alkylating a mixture of ethylaniline and diethylaniline and fractionating. Benzyl chloride is also used in the preparation of benzyl cellulose.

Arylsulfonic Alkyl Esters.—Among the arylsulfonic alkyl esters, we find of importance the methyl or ethyl ester of *p*-toluenesulfonic acid and also the higher alkyl esters. These compounds are found suitable for the alkylation of certain amines for which the alcohols are not satisfactory. Under Codeine (*q.v.*) is described the use of methyl benzenesulfonate and of methyl toluenesulfonate in the preparation of tetraalkylammonium compounds. Sekera and Marvel[1] report favorably on the preparation and use of the higher alkyl (C_{10} and above) esters of *p*-toluenesulfonic acid and *p*-bromobenzenesulfonic acid as alkylating agents for making alkylamines, such as *n*-butyllaurylamine, *n*-butyl-cetylamine, and *n*-butyldicetylamine. These higher alkyl esters of *p*-toluenesulfonic acid are more satisfactory than the sluggish higher alkyl halides and are more easily obtained than the higher alkyl sulfates.

Alkyl Quaternary Ammonium Compounds.—These have long been applied in certain special fields, and their further use may well be warranted in many instances. A detailed specific example of this application is given under Codeine, where the preparation and use of phenyltri-methylammonium chloride $[C_6H_5N(CH_3)_3Cl]$ is described. These quaternary alkyl substances have also been recommended for alkylations leading to phenetole, antipyrine, pyramidone, acriflavine, and caffeine.

Olefins.—In the presence of a metal halide or sulfuric or phosphoric acid the olefins are able to enter into syntheses involving alkylation. During the course of the reaction there is a transfer of hydrogen from the carbon of an aliphatic, aromatic, or hydroaromatic compound to the carbon of the olefin, thereby forming an alkyl radical. These reactions may be represented thus:

[1] Sekera and Marvel, *J. Am. Chem. Soc.*, **55**, 345 (1933); *cf.* Slotta and Franke, *Ber.*, **63B**, 678–691 (1930).

$$CH_3CH_2CH_3 + CH_2{=}CH_2 \rightarrow \begin{array}{c} CH_3 \\ CH_3 \end{array}\!\!\!\!{>}CHCH_2CH_3$$

$$C_6H_6 + CH_3CH{=}CH_2 \rightarrow C_6H_5CH\!\!\!\!{<}\begin{array}{c} CH_3 \\ CH_3 \end{array}$$

$$C_6H_{12} + CH_2{=}CH_2 \xrightarrow{\ HCl\ } C_6H_{11}C_2H_5$$

Ipatieff has employed ethylene, propylene, and the higher olefins in similar reactions and has obtained mono- and polyalkylated derivatives. In general, the olefins of higher molecular weight, *e.g.*, amylene, and most branched chains, *e.g., tert*-butyl chloride, react more readily than do propylene and ethylene.

Miscellaneous Alkylating Agents.—Noller and Dutton[1] have recommended the trialkyl phosphates for alkylation and have discussed their preparation. Ethers are formed by using one equivalent of the trialkyl phosphate per mole of phenol. The yields of ether in the accompanying table are based on the amount of the alkyl radical available and hence are a measure of the relative alkylating ability of the various esters.

TABLE I.—YIELDS OF PHOSPHATES AND PHENOL ETHERS

Ester	Phosphates		Phenol ethers	
	Yield, %	B.p., °C.	Yield, %	B.p., °C.
Ethyl sulfate............	....	....	73.0	168–170
Ethyl phosphate........	51.7	104–107 (16 mm.)	21.6	167–170
n-Propyl phosphate.....	63.5	128–134 (15 mm.)	Not run	
n-Butyl phosphate......	74.0	160–162 (15 mm.)	39.0	204–211
sec-Butyl phosphate.....	44.0	119–129 (8–12 mm.)	18.7	188–198
n-Amyl phosphate......	63.7	158–163 (6 mm.)	15.0	125–128 (25 mm.)

Riedel[2] describes the methylation of *p*-aminophenol to metol, using formaldehyde followed by reduction with activated aluminum.

Carbon-bound alkyl groups are frequently introduced by special procedures such as in the preparation of hexylresorcinol (*q.v.*) by reduction of a ketone derivative and in the making of thymol[3] by the rearrangement of isopropyl *m*-tolyl ether.

III. TYPES OF ALKYLATION

The five different types of alkylation treated in this chapter are sharply defined from a structural viewpoint. However, the linkage of

---

[1] NOLLER and DUTTON, *J. Am. Chem. Soc.*, **55**, 424 (1933); *cf.* Consortium für Electrochem. Ind., Brit. 433,927 (1935).

[2] Riedel, Ger. 406,533 (1922).

[3] NIEDERL and NATELSON, *J. Am. Chem. Soc.*, **54**, 1063–1070 (1932); SOWA, HINTON, and NIEUWLAND, *ibid.*, 2019; NIEDERL and STORCH, *ibid.*, **55**, 284–294 (1933).

alkyl to oxygen, nitrogen, carbon, or a metal can in many instances be effected by the same alkylating agent, *e.g.*, ethyl chloride. Naturally, there is some variation in the conditions under which such a reagent is employed to produce these various compounds.

Alkyl Bound to Oxygen.—The compounds of this class are generally prepared by substituting an alkyl group for a hydrogen in the hydroxyl group of an alcohol or a phenol. Typical compounds containing this alkylation linkage are the following:

Aliphatic Ethers:
  Cellulose ethers
  Ethylene glycol ethers:
    Carbitol
    Cellosolve
  Ethyl ether
  Isopropyl ether

Phenol Ethers and Derivatives:
  Acetophenetidine
  o-Anisidine
  Anisole
  Chrysophenine G
  Codeine (methyl ether of morphine)
  o-Dianisidine
  Ethylmorphine
  Guaiacol
  β-Naphthyl methyl ether
  o-Nitroanisole
  Phenetole
  Vanillin

Aliphatic Ethers.—The aliphatic ethers used in industry are made usually by the action of sulfuric acid upon an alcohol. Here the active alkylating agent is the monoalkyl sulfate produced by the dehydrating[1] action of the sulfuric acid. Ethyl ether and isopropyl ether[2] are thus prepared. Wuyts and Lacourt,[3] studying the action of sulfuric acid upon propyl alcohol, assert that ethylenic compounds are intermediate products in this method of ether formation.

For mixed ethers, the Williamson synthesis is particularly applicable:

$$C_2H_5ONa + CH_3I \rightarrow C_2H_5OCH_3 + NaI$$

Often, a cheaper and sufficiently satisfactory procedure is to react an alcohol and an alkyl halide in the presence of alkali. Mixed ethers can also be made by certain aspects of the Grignard synthesis, as, for example,

$$C_2H_5MgBr + BrCH_2OCH_3 \rightarrow C_2H_5CH_2OCH_3 + MgBr_2$$

The cellulose ethers are generally made by the action of alkyl or aralkyl halides on alkali cellulose. The reactions are carried out under pressure at about 100°C. In connection with ethers, reference should be made to the examples in this chapter describing the preparation of Carbitol (diethylene glycol ethyl ether) and Cellosolve (ethylene glycol ethyl ether).

[1] SENDERENS, *Compt. rend.*, **176**, 813–816 (1923); **179**, 1015–1019 (1924); **181**, 698–700 (1925).

[2] Mann, U. S. 1,482,804 (1924).

[3] WUYTS and LACOURT, *Bull. soc. chim. Belg.*, **39**, 157–173 (1930).

Phenol Ethers.—The phenol ethers are manufactured frequently by the reaction of the sodium phenolate with an alkyl halide, alkyl sodium sulfate, or dialkyl sulfate or the alkyl ester of toluenesulfonic acid (*cf.* Anisole and Vanillin). Under Acetophenetidine is detailed a method whereby good yields are obtained by ethylating *p*-nitrochlorobenzene with alcoholic potash in the presence of potassium sulfite. The naphthol ethers[1] are a little easier to form and result, for example, by heating together naphthol, methanol, and sulfuric acid.

Alkaloids.—Some of the most difficult oxygen alkylations are those involving the alkaloids, where the alkylation is often carried out to replace the hydrogen of the hydroxyl group in the presence of the tertiary nitrogen of the alkaloid. The best commercial example of the work that has been done with this particular group of compounds is the formation of codeine by the alkylation of the phenolic hydroxyl in morphine. Details of this alkylation with quaternary ammonium compounds are given under Codeine. Such procedure is also used for theobromine, antipyrine, etc.

Alkyl Bound to Trivalent Nitrogen.—In this division, the compounds may be considered as being derived by the substitution of an alkyl group for a hydrogen attached to a trivalent nitrogen. Examples of such substitution are as follows:

Aliphatic Alkylamines:
  Diethylamine
  Dimethylamine
  Adrenaline (side chain)
  Methylamine
  Procaine (side chain)
  Tetramethyl thiuram sulfide
  Trimethylamine
Heterocyclic Alkylamines:
  Pyramidone
  Antipyrine

Aromatic Alkylamines:
  Benzylethylaniline
  m-Diethylaminophenol
  Diethylaniline
  m-Dimethylaminophenol
  Dimethylaniline
  Metol
  Tetryl
Alkaloids:
  Caffeine
  Codeine
  Ethylmorphine

Aliphatic Alkylamines.—In the aliphatic series, dimethyl sulfate is a particularly valuable alkylating agent, which reacts easily with amines in nitrobenzene, alcohol, chloroform, or other solutions—often without any external heating. Methyl iodide also reacts readily, but the methyl bromide requires some heating. In this series, the tendency commercially is to alkylate with the alcohol, often employing special procedures such as are exemplified by the making of methylamines from ammonia and excess methanol in the vapor phase and in contact with alumina at 400°C. Reference should be made to the discussion of diethylamine for details of the alkylation, where ammonia is heated with ethyl chloride in presence of absolute ethyl alcohol.

---

[1] Gattermann, *Ann.*, **244**, 73 (1882); Witt and Schneider, *Ber.*, **34**, 3173 (1901).

In a number of substances, such as adrenaline and procaine, where alkyl groups occur in a side chain, the actual alkylation is usually effected in simpler compounds such as methylamine and diethylamine, which are then condensed onto the main product. Similarly the alkyl groups of tetramethyl thiuram sulfide, $(CH_3)_2N(S)CSC(S)N(CH_3)_2$, are introduced by dimethylamine.

Aromatic Alkylamines.—In the aromatic series, the use of methanol and sulfuric acid is exemplified in the commercial process for making dimethylaniline. The sulfuric acid forms methyl sulfate, and this is to be compared with the alkylation procedure resulting in the formation of ethyl ether from alcohol and sulfuric acid (*cf.* Dimethylaniline). Diethylaniline is also made similarly, employing ethyl alcohol, but here sulfuric acid cannot be used because ethyl ether would be formed; consequently, hydrochloric acid is the catalyst chosen.

Carleton and Woodward[1] claim an improvement in making ethyl- and diethylaniline from aniline and ethyl alcohol, by using with the alcohol less than a molecular equivalent (per mole of amine) of either ethyl chloride or hydrogen chloride. In both cases the reactants are heated under pressure and at a temperature of 180 to 185°C.[2]

Benzylethylaniline is an important dye intermediate which is made by the action of benzyl chloride on ethylaniline. Martin and McQueen[3] find that the addition of benzyl chloride at about the rate it is used up in the reaction is advantageous. Livingston[4] carries on the benzylation in toluene or other hydrocarbon solvent and in the presence of an acid binding agent (Na_2CO_3).

To avoid some of the ordinary by-products arising when dimethylaniline is made from methanol with sulfuric acid as a catalyst, Britton and Williams[5] use from 1 to 2 per cent of methyl bromide by weight, and 3 to 4 moles of methanol per mole of aniline. The reactants are heated in a stirred iron autoclave for approximately 16 hr. at from 230 to 240°C. and under a corresponding pressure of about 700 lb. Most of the methyl bromide can be recovered as the quaternary compound: phenyltrimethylammonium bromide. Indeed this quaternary compound can be introduced as the catalyst, as it decomposes under the conditions of the alkylation. The reaction may be formulated:

$$C_6H_5NH_2 + 2CH_3OH + CH_3Br \rightarrow C_6H_5N(CH_3)_3Br + 2H_2O$$
$$C_6H_5N(CH_3)_3Br \rightarrow C_6H_5N(CH_3)_2 + CH_3Br$$

[1] Carleton and Woodward, U. S. 1,994,851; 1,994,852 (1935).

[2] This use of hydrochloric acid as a catalyst in the making of ethyl- and diethylaniline has been known for some time.

[3] Martin and McQueen, U. S. 1,887,772 (1932).

[4] Livingston, U. S. 1,854,553 (1932).

[5] Britton and Williams, U. S. 1,794,092 (1931).

The use of aromatic sulfonic acids[1] as catalysts in the methylation of primary aromatic amines by aliphatic alcohols has been reported.

When alkylating primary, secondary, or tertiary aromatic alkyl-amines, much heat usually is evolved; this can be controlled by initial cooling or dilution. Such heat development is more pronounced when using dimethyl sulfate and alkyl toluenesulfonic esters than with alkyl halides, but even the latter must be handled carefully. To secure the best yields, no water must be present; if water is present, it will react with the dimethyl sulfate, yielding methyl sulfate, which will, in turn, form a salt with the amine and withdraw it from alkylation.

Dimethyl sulfate has been employed[2] successfully in the methylation of *p*-aminophenol to metol, but special precautions must be taken to secure good yields. The almost quantitative monalkylation of *p*-amino-phenol is claimed by Zimmerli[3] by first forming an aldehyde amine before treating with the methylating agent. Using furfural and dimethyl sulfate the reaction in dry chlorobenzene as a solvent can be represented by the following equations:

$$HOC_6H_4NH_2 + C_4H_3OCHO \rightarrow HOC_6H_4N{=}CHC_4H_3O + H_2O \qquad (1)$$

$$HOC_6H_4N{=}CHC_4H_3O + (CH_3)_2SO_4 \rightarrow HOC_6H_4\underset{\overset{|}{OSO_3CH_3}}{N(CH_3)}CHC_4H_3O \qquad (2)$$

$$2HOC_6H_4\underset{\overset{|}{OSO_3CH_3}}{N(CH_3)}CHC_4H_3O + 2H_2O + Na_2CO_3 \rightarrow$$

$$2HOC_6H_4NHCH_3 + 2C_4H_3OCHO + 2NaCH_3SO_4 + CO_2 + H_2O \quad (3)$$

Compounds containing alkyl attached to trivalent nitrogen are unusually important in the dye field. Almost invariably, the presence of this alkyl group attached to nitrogen is dependent upon the use of alkylated aromatic amines, such as dimethylaniline, as intermediates. Among the dyes[4] so formed are Auramine, Malachite Green, Methyl Violet, Crystal Violet, and Methylene Blue. In the early stages of the development of the dye industry, some nitrogen alkylation was practiced, wherein after the formation of the central dye-ring alkylation was effected by the use of the alkyl halide in the presence of caustic soda (*cf.* Hoffman's Violet, No. 679, and related dyes in Colour Index; Society of Dyers and Colourists, Bradford).

Alkaloidal Amines.—The presence of a methylated tertiary nitrogen is fairly common among alkaloids, such as morphine, codeine, caffeine, and theobromine. As caffeine differs from theobromine by having one

---

[1] Laptev and Khaikin, Russ. 42,553; *C. A.* **31**, 7067.

[2] Schwyzer, "Die Fabrikation pharmazeutischer und chemischtechnischer Produkte," pp. 223–226, Julius Springer, Berlin (1931).

[3] Zimmerli, U. S. 1,987,317 (1935).

[4] *Cf.* Shreve, "Dyes Classified by Intermediates," Chemical Catalog Company (1922), for further details.

more nitrogen methylated, it is made by treating theobromine with dimethyl sulfate in the presence of sodium ethylate or by boiling in an alkaline alcoholic solution with methyl *p*-toluenesulfonate.

Heterocyclic Amines.—The pyrazolones—pyramidone[1] and antipyrine—are prepared by using methyl bromide in an acid medium as the alkylating agent whereby the formation of by-products is lessened. Adkins and Cramer[2] effect the N-alkylation of heterocyclic amines, such as piperidine, by alcohols, *e.g.*, 1-butanol in the presence of a nickel catalyst and hydrogen or nitrogen under high pressure.

Alkyl Bound to Pentavalent Nitrogen.—In this division, alkylation is effected by addition, the trivalent nitrogen becoming pentavalent. There are not included here those tertiary alkyl compounds wherein the nitrogen becomes pentavalent by simple salt formation.

The preparation of this type of compound is relatively simple, in that an alkyl halide, an alkyl sulfate, or an alkyl ester is added to a tertiary amine. Details for the making of the quaternary ammonium compounds—phenyltrimethylammonium chloride and phenyltrimethylammonium tolysulfonate—are later described under Codeine. These substances are excellent methylating agents, particularly when it is desired to methylate a phenolic hydroxyl in the presence of a tertiary nitrogen.

Acriflavine, containing a methylated pentavalent nitrogen and one of the widely used medicinal dyes, is prepared by methylating the tertiary ring nitrogen in diaminoacridine by either dimethyl sulfate or methyl *p*-toluenesulfonate in nitrobenzene or a benzene solution. While generally the two amino groups have been protected by acetylation prior to the methylation of the ring nitrogen, this step is not necessary. The methylated product is converted by hydrochloric acid to the chloride monohydrochloride which is known as Acriflavine.[3]

Acriflavine

Alkyl Bound to Carbon.—These compounds may be considered as being derived by the substitution of an alkyl group for hydrogen in carbon compounds. Examples are hexylresorcinol, thymol, barbital, and other

[1] SCHWYZER, "Die Fabrikation pharmazeutischer und chemischtechnischer Produkte," pp. 164–172, Julius Springer, Berlin (1931).

[2] Adkins and Cramer, U. S. 2,058,547 (1936).

[3] SHREVE, "Dyes Classified by Intermediates," pp. 82–83, Chemical Catalog Company (1922).

barbituric acid alkyl derivatives.   This type of alkylation is frequently referred to as alkylation of hydrocarbons, and many of the instances are nuclear alkylations.   In the main, the same reagents are employed as for the other classifications.   In some instances, an alkyl bound to nitrogen or to oxygen may wander to the nucleus.   For example, aniline is converted to dimethylaniline by heating to around 205° with methanol and a small amount of sulfuric acid; if the temperature is raised to around 250 to 300°, considerable nuclear alkylation takes place, the reaction probably being as follows:

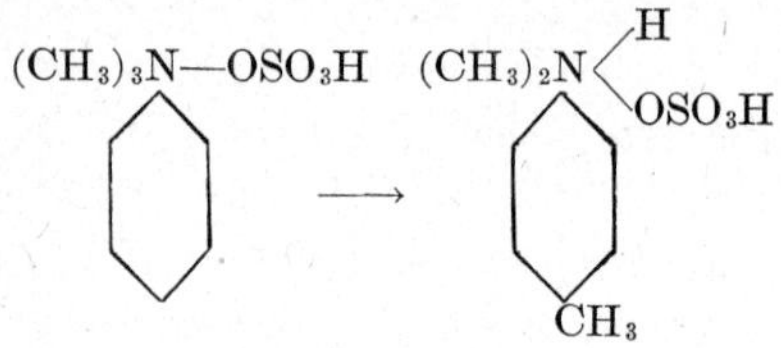

In the presence of excess methanol and at higher temperature (300 to 350°), mesidine as well as the mono- and dimethyl derivatives are formed.

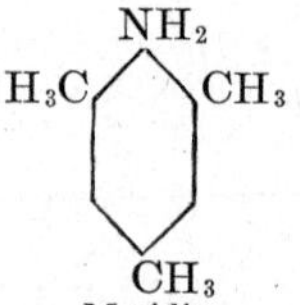

Mesidine

A similar wandering of the ethyl group in the case of diethylaniline has been studied by Johnson, Hill, and Donleavy.[1]

The nuclear alkylations that would lead to the commercially important thymol have been reported.[2]   Wagner[3] has pointed out how nuclear methylations can be carried out by the aid of formaldehyde followed by reduction and has studied the intermediate products formed.   This procedure leads to N-methylation of alkylanilines if the initial condensation products are promptly reduced, while the alkyl-p-toluidines (nuclear alkylation) are obtained in every case where the intermediate bases were allowed to precipitate and then separated and reduced.

Alkylation logically overlaps with other reactions.   Thus, the condensation of alkyl or aralkyl halides according to the Friedel and Crafts synthesis is a form of nuclear alkylation for the preparation of aromatic compounds.

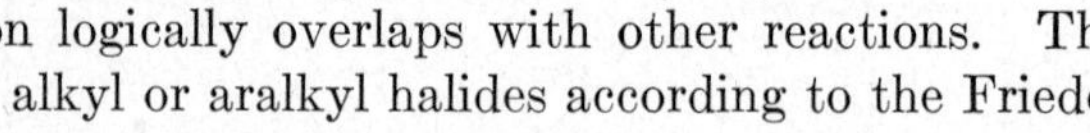

[1] JOHNSON, HILL, and DONLEAVY, Ind. Eng. Chem., **12**, 636–642 (1920).

[2] NIEDERL and STORCH, J. Am. Chem. Soc., **55**, 284 (1933); SMITH, ibid., 849.

[3] WAGNER, J. Am. Chem. Soc., **55**, 724 (1933).

To avoid duplication, such alkylations are discussed under the Friedel and Crafts reaction when a metal halide is used as the condensing agent. When, however, the alkylations are catalyzed by other agents, *e.g.*, mineral acids, they are discussed here. Similarly, carbon linkage alkylation includes the Wurtz reaction for the preparation of aliphatic compounds.

$$CH_3Br + 2Na + BrC_2H_5 \rightarrow CH_3 \cdot C_2H_5 + 2NaBr$$

Alkylations with Olefins.[1]—Reactions involving olefins may be represented as follows:

$$R'H + RCH{=}CHR \rightarrow RR'CHCH_2R$$

where R is either a hydrogen atom or a monovalent radical, *e.g.*, methyl. The reactions of propylene with propane and benzene may be written thus:

$$CH_3CH{=}CH_2 + CH_3CH_2CH_3 \rightarrow CH_3CHCH_3 \tag{1}$$
$$\underset{\displaystyle C_3H_7}{|}$$

$$CH_3CH{=}CH_2 + \quad \rightarrow \tag{2}$$

Alkylation of RH with olefins appears, therefore, to involve addition of R at one of the doubly bound carbon atoms and hydrogen at the other. From the preceding it can be contended that, when R' is alkyl, a paraffin is used as the alkylating agent, and, when R' is aryl, RH is an arylating agent. In such alkylations the olefins can be made to attach to a considerable variety of other compounds, thus forming (1) longer chain compounds of the paraffin series; (2) mono- or polyalkylated aromatics; or (3) mono- or polyalkylated naphthenes (alicyclics).

Olefin Alkylations of Benzene Catalyzed by Acids.—Benzene can be alkylated by olefins in the presence of strong sulfuric acid as shown by Ipatieff, Corson, and Pines.[2] Thus, dodecene, nonene, octene, pentene and butene (isobutene and butene-1) and propene as well as ethene (ethylene) have been employed for the alkylation of benzene. Ethylene does not give satisfactory yields of ethylbenzene at either atmospheric or superatmospheric pressure, only a trace being obtained. Octene, however, does give good yields of the mono-, di-, and trioctylbenzenes, and propene and butenes also give high yields of alkyl derivatives. Accompanying the alkylation, some esterification occurs with the formation of the dialkyl esters of sulfuric acid, particularly with weaker sulfuric acids. In their presence the reaction product cannot be distilled satis-

---

[1] IPATIEFF, "Catalytic Reactions at High Pressures and Temperatures," The Macmillan Company, New York (1936); EGLOFF, "Reactions of Pure Hydrocarbons," Reinhold Publishing Co., New York (1937).

[2] IPATIEFF, CORSON, and PINES, *J. Am. Chem. Soc.*, **58**, 919 (1936).

factorily, since these esters decompose and form tarry products at about 120 to 130°C.

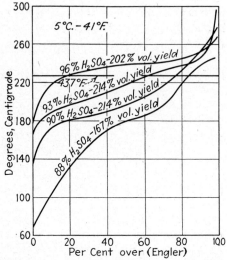

FIG. 1.—Alkylating action of butene-1 upon benzene at 5°C. using sulfuric acid as a catalyst. "Engler" refers to distillation procedure. (*After Ipatieff.*)

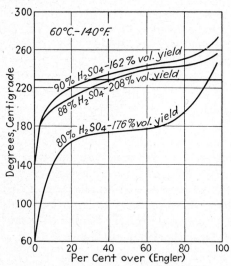

FIG. 2.—Alkylating action of butene-1 upon benzene at 60°C. using sulfuric acid as a catalyst. (*After Ipatieff.*)

While these esters can be removed from the reaction product by treatment with strong sulfuric acid (95 to 96 per cent), the better procedure is to carry out the alkylation by olefins with sulfuric acid containing phosphoric acid[1] or with phosphoric acid alone. Phosphoric acid catalytically effects the decomposition of the dialkyl sulfates so that the final product contains no dialkyl sulfate and can be distilled without decomposition. Phosphoric acid also brings about the alkylation of certain hydrocarbons, as well as of phenols, at ordinary and at super-atmospheric pressures and at relatively low temperatures. Ipatieff and Corson[2] have catalyzed the alkylation of benzene by isobutylene at 60°C. with phosphoric acid, and have obtained a mixture of half *tert*-butylbenzene, and half triisobutylene. Ipatieff and Pines[3] found that alkylation under pressure with phosphoric acid gave exclusive alkylation of benzene without formation of olefin polymers.

Although ethylene does not alkylate benzene using sulfuric acid as a catalyst, 85 to 89 per cent phosphoric acid under similar conditions yields mono-, *m*-di-, *sym*-tri- and tetraethylbenzene.[4]

The nature of the alkylating action of normal butene (butene-1) upon benzene[5] in the presence of sulfuric acid at 5 and 60°C; is indicated in Figs. 1 and 2; and Fig. 3 gives the solubility data for buty-lene in H_2SO_4. It is apparent from the curves that the stronger the sulfuric acid, the farther the alkylation proceeds and the higher is the boiling point of the product. The primary reactions may be represented thus:

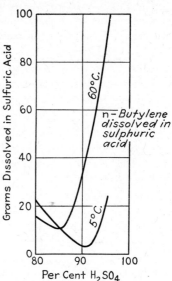

Fig. 3.—Solubility of butene-1 in sulfuric acid. (*After Ipatieff.*)

$$C_6H_6 + CH_3CH_2CH{=}CH_2 \rightarrow C_6H_5{-}CH \Big\langle {\begin{array}{l} CH_3 \\ CH_2CH_3 \end{array}} \quad \text{and Polyalkylated Products}$$

Secondary butylbenzene boils at 171 to 173°C., and secondary dibutyl-benzene boils at 231 to 235°C. An example of such an alkylation using benzene, cracked gases, and sulfuric acid is detailed on page 527 under Alkylations, wherein alkyl is bound to carbon.

[1] Ipatieff, U. S. 2,006,695; 2,039,798 (1937).

[2] IPATIEFF, "Catalytic Reactions at High Pressures and Temperatures," p. 659, The Macmillan Company, New York (1936).

[3] *Ibid.*, p. 660.

[4] IPATIEFF, PINES, and KOMAREWSKY, *Ind. Eng. Chem.* **28**, 222 (1936).

[5] IPATIEFF, "Catalytic Reactions at High Pressures and Temperatures," p. 658, The Macmillan Company, New York (1936).

The action of aluminum chloride, while falling under the classification of the Friedel and Crafts reaction (*q.v.*) should be mentioned for the sake of completeness. Paraffins, benzene,[1] toluene, and xylenes are alkylated by olefins and cyclopropane, in the presence of aluminum chloride. Usually hydrogen chloride is also needed.

It cannot be overemphasized that the action of aluminum chloride is quite varied in the products it may cause to be formed because polymerization, isomerization, dealkylation, etc., can occur concurrently. It is not so effective an initial alkylating agent as sulfuric acid. Aluminum chloride is, however, a more effective agent to dealkylate the polyalkyl aromatics, with formation of lower alkyl aromatics. This is discussed later under Synthetic Gasoline.

Alkyl Bound to a Metal.—The alkyl group may be caused to unite with metals, such as lead, mercury, zinc, magnesium, and arsenic. The examples of this type of alkylation, which are later described, are lead tetraethyl and merthiolate. The intermediate in the formation of merthiolate—ethylmercuric chloride—is also being used as a fungicide. Among the lethal poison gases is ethyldichloroarsine ($C_2H_5AsCl_2$), which is prepared by the following reactions:

$$C_2H_5Cl + Na_3AsO_3 \rightarrow C_2H_5AsO_3Na_2 + NaCl \tag{1}$$
$$C_2H_5AsO_3Na_2 + H_2SO_4 \rightarrow C_2H_5AsO_3H_2 + Na_2SO_4 \tag{2}$$
$$C_2H_5AsO_3H_2 + SO_2 + H_2O \rightarrow C_2H_5AsO_2H_2 + H_2SO_4 \tag{3}$$
$$C_2H_5AsO_2H_2 \rightarrow C_2H_5AsO + H_2O \tag{4}$$
$$C_2H_5AsO + 2HCl \rightarrow C_2H_5AsCl_2 + H_2O \tag{5}$$

IV. FACTORS CONTROLLING ALKYLATION

Concentration.—The concentration of the reagents in alkylation is often high, particularly when alcohols are the alkylating agents, as, for example, when methanol and aniline are treated under pressure in the presence of a small amount of sulfuric acid. On the other hand, it is advantageous frequently to dilute certain energetic alkylating agents in order better to control the reaction; this is done when alkylating with alkyl halides or with dialkyl sulfates. In vapor-phase alkylations, usually no diluent is needed.

Temperature.—When such alkylating agents as methanol or ethyl alcohol or the alkyl halides are employed, a much higher temperature is necessary than that required with dimethyl sulfate or diethyl sulfate or even methyl *p*-toluenesulfonate. As is described later, the methylation of aniline to dimethylaniline will take place around 200°. Alkylations that are carried on in the vapor phase call for much higher temperatures —around 400°—as when phenol is methylated with methanol by passing the vapors over an alumina catalyst or when methylamines are formed

---

[1] BERRY and REID, *J. Am. Chem. Soc.*, **49**, 3142–3149 (1927).

by conducting methanol and ammonia in the vapor phase over an alumina catalyst.

A number of alkylating reactions are exothermic, as for example, when aminoantipyrine is methylated with methyl bromide to give pyramidone, and here cooling is advisable in the early stages of the methylation.

Increased temperature frequently causes migration of alkyl groups to an aromatic nucleus. Dimethylaniline sulfate gives N-methyl-*p*-toluidine in this manner.

Pressure.—In numerous instances pressure is necessary to keep reactions in the liquid phase. This is true in the N-methylation of aniline by methanol giving dimethylaniline, and in some of the C—C alkylations leading to alkylated aromatics or to higher paraffins, pressure is needed to maintain the liquid state at the temperature required.

Solvents.—Alcohols, chloroform, benzene, or nitrobenzene are used as solvents in alkylating procedures. As a rule, though not invariably, they should be anhydrous. The use of a solvent is for two purposes, not only to lessen the vigor of some reactions but also to cause products or by-products to crystallize out. For instance, when dimethyl sulfate is employed for certain alkylations, it is dissolved in benzene and added to an alcoholic solution of the sodium phenolate derivative to be alkylated. In the presence of these solvents, sodium methyl sulfate is very little soluble and is precipitated out. This procedure tends to give good yields. Similar conditions are applied to other alkylating agents.

Alkylations in Liquid or Vapor Phase.—While most alkylations are carried on in the liquid phase, some of the newer procedures are conducted in the vapor phase, as are described under Catalysis.

Catalysis.—In alkylation catalysis becomes more and more important each year as further research brings an increasing number of catalysts into use. In reviewing this subject Ipatieff makes the following classification:

1. We may view the catalyst as a reaction multiplier. Here the catalyst actually enters into the reaction, forming an unstable intermediate compound with the reacting substance. As the intermediate compound decomposes in the course of the reaction, the catalyst is continually regenerated.

2. Many catalysts act in an unknown manner. Here the formation of the intermediate compound is doubtful and the chemical mechanism is not understood. Ipatieff calls this eka-catalysis, or unknown catalytic action.

3. Physical catalysis includes a number of those reactions, such as photo-catalysis, wherein light or energy, other than chemical, influences the course of reaction.

Most of the alkylation catalytic reactions come under the classification of reaction multiplier, and in a considerable number of these catalytic alkylations the unstable intermediate compound with the catalyst is known. In the carbon-to-carbon alkylation of both aromatic and paraffinic hydrocarbons by olefins through the catalytic intervention of sulfuric acid, there is much evidence that the olefin is converted to an alkyl sulfate which then alkylates the other hydrocarbon, the sulfuric acid being regenerated during the process. This is also true of phosphoric acid, and we may postulate these reactions as follows:

$$C_5H_{10} + H_2SO_4 \rightarrow SO_2\!\!\begin{array}{c} O-C_5H_{11} \\ OH \end{array}$$

$$SO_2\!\!\begin{array}{c} O-C_5H_{11} \\ OH \end{array} + C_6H_5H \rightarrow C_6H_5C_5H_{11} + H_2SO_4$$

$$\begin{array}{c} CH_3 \\ CH_3 \end{array}\!\!C{=}CH_2 + H_3PO_4 \rightarrow O{=}P\!\!\begin{array}{c} O-C\!\!\begin{array}{c} CH_3 \\ CH_3 \\ CH_3 \end{array} \\ OH \\ OH \end{array}$$

$$O{=}P\!\!\begin{array}{c} O-C\!\!\begin{array}{c} CH_3 \\ CH_3 \\ CH_3 \end{array} \\ OH \\ OH \end{array} + C_6H_6 \rightarrow C_6H_5{-}C\!\!\begin{array}{c} CH_3 \\ CH_3 \\ CH_3 \end{array} + H_3PO_4$$

The use of sulfuric acid as a catalyst is discussed under Dimethylaniline (*q.v.*) and in the preparation of ethyl ether. Some technical operations in the vapor phase have been carried on in the presence of a catalyst, and anisole[1] is stated to be formed with very good yield when the vapors of phenol (1 vol.) and methanol (1.5 vols.) are conducted over alumina at 390 to 420°C.

A technical procedure for the preparation of methylamines is to pass the vapors of ammonia and methanol over aluminum oxide at around 400°C. The pressure is practically atmospheric, and the methanol is used in excess. Mono-, di-, and trimethylamines are obtained. This synthesis is discussed fully in Chap. VI, Ammonolysis.

Effect of Ratio of Reactants.—An excess of the methylating agent acts frequently to better the yield. This is particularly true when the less vigorous alkylating agents, such as the alcohols, are employed in the preparation of dimethyl- or diethylaniline. Use of excess of the alcohol tends to lessen the formation of the monoalkyl derivatives. Diethylation of aniline is more difficult than dimethylation, consequently, the procedure is to separate the monoethylaniline from the diethylaniline by benzylating the monoethylaniline to benzylethylaniline and distilling. In dimethyl sulfate, the first methyl group acts more vigorously than the second, and consequently in difficult alkylations it is better to so proportion the reactants as to use only one of the methyl groups.

[1] SABATIER and MAILHE, *Compt. rend.*, **151**, 339 (1910).

Alkylations are carried on in alkaline, acid, or neutral media. With dialkyl sulfates, alkali speeds up the reaction (*cf*. Anisole). The vigorous reaction of methyl bromide in alkaline medium is disadvantageous in the methylation of 5-methyl-2-phenylpyrazolone to antipyrine[1] as it leads to trimethylpyrazolones. So here the alkylation is conducted in an acid medium.

In many instances, there is more than one place in the molecule where alkylation can take place. This is true in the methylation of morphine to codeine, where an alcoholic hydroxyl, a phenolic hydroxyl, and a tertiary nitrogen are present. In such cases, it is necessary that only the proper amount of the alkylating agent be used or that special conditions be employed (*cf*. Codeine).

Physical Condition of Alkylating Agent.—The choice of the alkylating agent depends often upon the conditions necessary to handle it, and this sometimes may lead to the use of the less volatile and more expensive alkyl bromide rather than the alkyl chloride. On the other hand, now that dimethyl sulfate and diethyl sulfate are more reasonably priced, they are supplanting the use of the volatile alkyl halides, because with the sulfates autoclaves are not so necessary.

Recovery of Alkylated Product.—Wherever possible, rectification furnishes the most convenient and cheapest procedure. Even in those instances in which the boiling points are rather close together, as is true of the alkyl- and dialkylanilines, a separation can be effected by first benzylating the monoalkyl derivative and then distilling.

The choice of a proper solvent will in many instances lead to the crystallization of the alkylated product and to its convenient recovery.

The products from the alkylation of ammonia with methanol are water; mono-, di-, and trimethylamine; and excess methanol. The separation is not easy, but it is carried out by partial condensation to remove excess methanol and water. The vapors are then compressed to several hundred pounds and fractionally distilled under this pressure, yielding some ammonia and the separated amines.

V. EQUIPMENT FOR ALKYLATIONS

Materials of Construction.—Fortunately steel can be quite generally used even in the presence of the strong acid catalysts, as their corrosive effect is much lessened by the formation of esters as catalytic intermediate products. Enameled liners, or completely enameled vessels, are available and are increasingly employed; these are quite resistant to acids. In a few cases copper or tinned copper is still used.

Corrosion of Apparatus.—As described later on in the manufacture of dimethylaniline, a steel autoclave is employed even though a small

---

[1] FOURNEAU, "Organic Medicaments and Their Preparation," p. 38, J. & A. Churchill, London (1925); *cf*. SCHWYZER, *loc. cit.*, pp. 164–169.

amount of sulfuric acid is used as the catalyst; the large amount of the aniline and dimethylaniline present serves to protect the steel from the action of the acid. The corrosion that takes place is principally localized at the liquid level in the autoclave.

However, there are many cases in which the agents used in alkylation are corrosive. In the alkylation of aniline to diethylaniline by heating aniline and ethyl alcohol, sulfuric acid cannot be used, because it will form ether; consequently, hydrochloric acid is employed, but these

Before bursting   After bursting
Fig. 4.—Safety diaphragm (frangible disk) for the relief of excessive autoclave pressures.

conditions are so corrosive that the steel autoclaves used to resist the pressure must be fitted with replaceable enameled liners.

Certain other alkylations employing alkyl halides are carried out in an acid condition. For example, hydrobromic acid is formed when methyl bromide is used in the alkylations involved in the synthesis of both antipyrine and pyramidone. For such reactions, an autoclave with a replaceable enameled liner and a lead-coated cover is suitable.

In the manufacture of pharmaceutical and photographic products, great care is necessary to prevent contamination with heavy metals. Here either tinned iron or tinned copper or an enameled coating is frequently employed. A lead lining is suitable in the kettle for the alkylation leading to metol, N-methyl-p-aminophenol sulfate; and in some instances, the new chromium steel alloys have found favor, as in the reaction of ethyl chloride on ammonia to produce diethylamine.

Type of Equipment.—In many cases of alkylation, autoclaves are necessary. These are generally constructed of steel, with or without an anti-corrosion liner. In most instances, it is necessary to heat the autoclave; and this is done, as a rule, through the use of a jacket, although steel autoclaves have been directly heated in a suitably designed furnace using gas flame. When jackets are provided, the most convenient source of heat is direct steam. For higher temperatures, as in the manufacture of dimethylaniline (*q.v.*), superheated steam is used in the jackets of the autoclaves. The circulation of hot oil through the jackets has also been used for supplying the necessary heat. Figure 7, page 523, depicts the type of jacketed autoclave that has been used for the manufacture of dimethylaniline (*q.v.*).

Naturally, these autoclaves must be provided with inlet and outlet tubes, pressure gage, thermometer well, and either a safety valve or, better, a safety disk (Fig. 4) that will yield before a dangerous pressure is reached. The safety disk is more certain to function than the safety valve, which may become corroded or clogged. As a rule, it is not necessary to provide a stirring mechanism in the autoclave, in that the heating generally causes sufficient homogeneity, but the contents should always be well stirred before the autoclave is closed and the heating started. Figure 5, however,

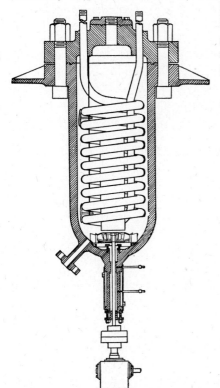

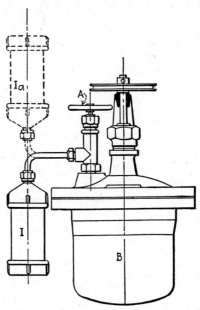

FIG. 5.—Agitated internally heated auto-clave. (*Courtesy Blaw-Knox.*)

FIG. 6.—Autoclave, showing means for introducing volatile alkyl halide. (*After Fierz-David.*)

does show an excellent stirring mechanism for those alkylations where agitation is desired. This figure likewise depicts a cheaper and better method of applying heat or cold by means of an internal coil rather than by a jacket.

Special means are required for introducing certain alkylating agents into autoclaves, *e.g.*, ethyl chloride. Here the best laboratory procedure is that of Fierz-David as depicted in Fig. 6, wherein the necessary amount of cooled alkyl halide is first led into the small bomb,[1] which, after being

[1] FIERZ-DAVID, "Dye Chemistry," p. 75, J. & A. Churchill, London (1921).

attached to the autoclave, is inverted and warmed by a very hot, moist cloth, after which the autoclave valve is opened. Such a procedure is utilized for the introduction of the alkyl chloride in the alkylation step leading to barbital, Chrysophenine G, nitroanisole, *p*-nitrophenetole, etc.

By substituting for alkyl halides dimethyl or diethyl sulfate, and in some instances by the use of methyl *p*-toluenesulfonate or even alcohol, it is possible to proceed without the use of an autoclave. A jacketed stirred kettle is generally used, and in these cases the operation is carried on at lower temperatures. Such an apparatus is employed in the making of *p*-nitrophenetole from *p*-nitrochlorobenzene by heating with alcoholic potash in the presence of potassium sulfite at 50 to 80°C. (*cf.* Acetophenetidine). Similarly, a lead-lined agitated jacketed kettle is suitable for the methylation of *p*-aminophenol with dimethyl sulfate to furnish metol.

Control of Operation.—To insure safety, in the control of autoclave procedures, the apparatus should be removed from use for periodic tests or inspection. In most cases, it is sufficient to apply a hydrostatic pressure 50 per cent higher than is used in practice. It is necessary to remove the safety disk, or safety valve, as they are usually set to blow at lower than test pressure. Naturally, these instruments and all others must be frequently checked. It is wise to provide not only a mercury thermometer in a well tube but also a recording thermometer.

VI. EFFECT OF ALKYLATION

While the effect of alkylation on the properties of organic compounds is sometimes contradictory, there are some general observations that are of value, particularly in the field of medicinals, dyes, and solvents.

Medicinally, this effect has been studied and compiled for numerous compounds and series of compounds. Hartung[1] gives an excellent review of these studies for various aliphatic alkylamines and compounds related to adrenaline, from which the following is quoted:

The physiological effect of aliphatic amines may be exhibited in various ways. Ammonia in small doses is a respiratory stimulant, but larger doses cause convulsions; it produces a rapid but very transitory depression of the blood pressure. As alkyl groups replace the hydrogen atoms of ammonia, the stimulating action is diminished, becoming less as the size of the alkyl group increases; as the alkyl chain becomes longer, a depressant action on the heart and convulsions of spinal origin appear, the depressant action being perceptible even in isoamylamine.

Schmiedeberg formulated a series of rules regarding the effect of alkyl groups on physiological activity which May[2] summarizes as follows: In the first place, a close connection exists between "medical" action and the ordinary physical properties of volatility and solubility. In the aliphatic paraffin series, the lower members which are more volatile

[1] HARTUNG, *Chem. Rev.*, **9**, 389–465 (1931).

[2] MAY, "The Chemistry of Synthetic Drugs," 3d ed., Longmans, Green & Company, London (1921).

exhibit a narcotic effect that is absent in the insoluble nonvolatile higher members.

Alkylation often causes very poisonous compounds to lose this effect; for example, the nitriles (RCN) and isonitriles (R—N≡C) are poisonous only when HCN is split off. The action of alkyl radicals can be masked or inhibited by the presence of other radicals; this is illustrated by the behavior of methyl-, dimethyl-, and trimethylamine, which react like ammonia but have no narcotic effect. In this conduct, these amines follow Schmiedeberg's preceding rule and are less toxic than ammonia.

In the alcohols and the ethers, the physiological action is ascribed to the nature of the alkyl groups. For the ethers, single or mixed, the effect is due to the presence of the alkyls, each of which acts independently of the other.

One of the most interesting studies of the effect of various alkyl groups on physiological activity is illustrated by the alkyl derivatives of resorcinol, which are discussed under Hexylresorcinol. The bactericidal action at first increases with the length of the side chain and then diminishes because of decreased solubility of the alkylresorcinol. Coincident with this increase is found a decrease in toxicity.

Phenol was the first antiseptic used, and a thorough study of its derivatives has been made. The substitution of a methyl group for the hydrogen in the ring of phenol, forming the cresols, increases the antiseptic action. In the case of the dihydroxybenzenes, the alkyl derivatives of resorcinol have been carefully investigated, and it is found that the entrance of the methyl group into the ring, forming orcinol, depresses the bactericidal power. The influence of higher alkyl groups of the nucleus of the resorcinol molecule is considered under Hexylresorcinol (*q.v.*).

In the field of dyes, many observations have been made on the relation of alkylation to the physical properties of these compounds and, in particular, to the color, either visible or as determined by the spectrophotometer. Reference need be made here only to Watson's excellent monograph[1] for the details.

Nietzki early formulated the rule that by increasing the molecular weight of a dye by adding groups to it, a deepening of the color would result. While the rule is not of universal application, yet it holds closer for the alkyl radicals and in particular when this substitution is effected in the triphenylmethanes.

The table at the top of page 508 (adapted from Watson, *loc. cit.*) is an illustration.

The specific linkage of the alkyl has much influence on any effect the alkyl group may have on color. When the alkyl is united to carbon

---

[1] WATSON, "Colour in Relation to Chemical Constitution," Longmans, Green & Company, London (1918).

COLOR AND CHEMICAL CONSTITUTION

Name	Mol. formula	Mol. wt.	Shade of dyeing
Paramagenta............	$C_6H_4 \cdot NH_2$ $C-C_6H_4 \cdot NH_2$ $C_6H_4 = NH_2Cl$	281.5	Magenta
Methyl Violet R..........	$C_6H_4 \cdot NHCH_3$ $C-C_6H_4 \cdot NHCH_3$ $C_6H_4 = NHCH_3Cl$	323.5	Reddish violet
Crystal Violet............	$C_6H_4 \cdot N(CH_3)_2$ $C-C_6H_4 \cdot N(CH_3)_2$ $C_6H_4 = N(CH_3)_2Cl$	365.5	Violet
Rosaniline Blue...........	$C_6H_4 \cdot NHC_6H_5$ $C-C_6H_4 \cdot NHC_6H_5$ $C_6H_4 = NHC_6H_5 \cdot Cl$	509.5	Blue
Iodine Green.............	$C_6H_4 \cdot N(CH_3)_2$ $C-C_6H_4 \cdot N(CH_3)_3I$ $C_6H_4 = N(CH_3)_2I$	599	Green

in a ring, it does not exert any special influence. However, when the alkyl is combined with oxygen or tertiary nitrogen, the effect on color is marked, the alteration being toward the blue. In the dyes Azo Blue (Colour Index, No. 463) and Benzoazurine (Colour Index, No. 502), there is a change in the former from —CH₃ to —OCH₃, with a color alteration on cotton from reddish violet to a reddish indigo blue.

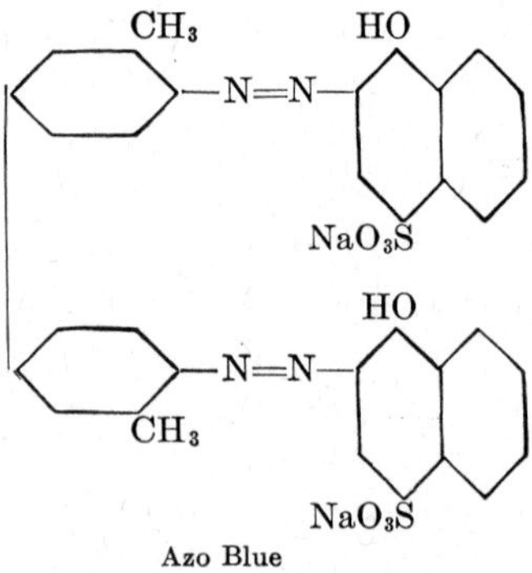

Azo Blue 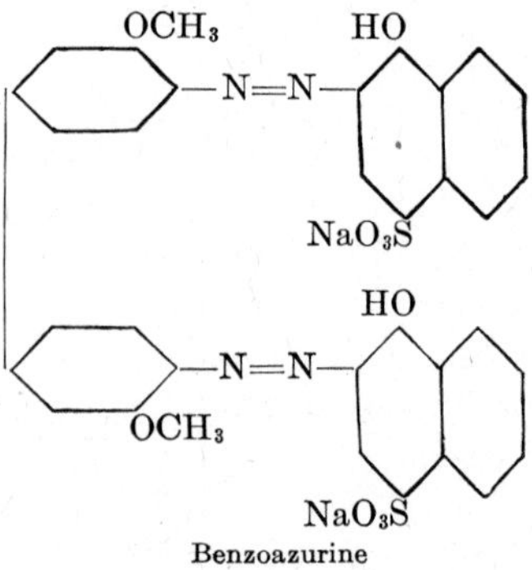   Benzoazurine

Among the solvents, a particularly detailed study has been made of the different alkyl derivatives of the glycols, and the tabulation under Cellosolve (*q.v.*) depicts the relationship between the various alkyl ethers of ethylene glycol and certain physical properties of this series.

VII. TECHNICAL ALKYLATIONS

A few selected examples of technical alkylation are here given to illustrate various and typical procedures. These are chosen to illustrate the different linkages and are classified by the type of alkylation linkage.

Alkyl Bound to Oxygen.

ACETOPHENETIDINE
PHENACETIN

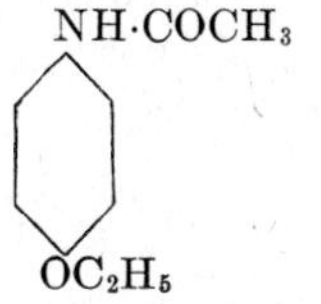

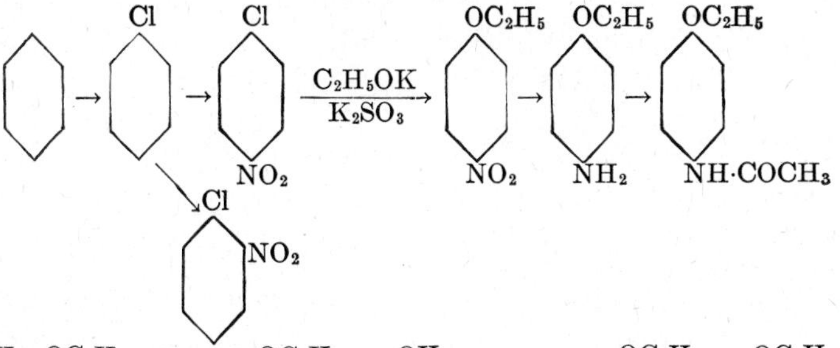

(1)

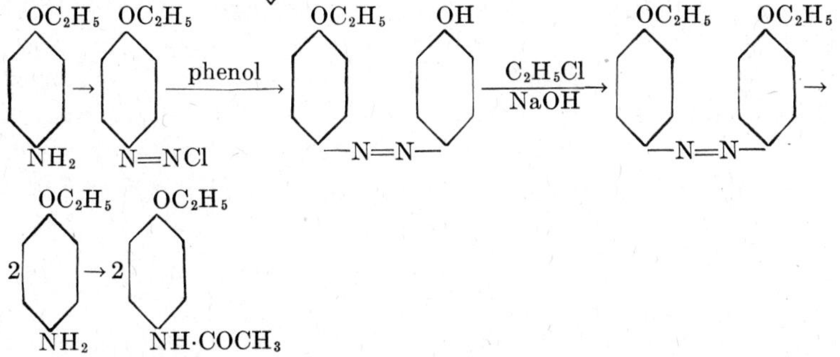

(2)

Acetophenetidine is an important analgesic and antipyretic that has attained widespread use in medicine. The principal series of reactions for its preparation are given above; the one involving the nitration of chlorobenzene is of most value technically. These reactions are intertwined with the preparation of other products; for example, the ortho-nitration product of either chlorobenzene or of phenol is methylated to give *o*-nitroanisole, which is made into guaiacol or dianisidine. In general, the alkylation of nitrochlorobenzenes or of the nitrophenols is effected by use of either the alkyl halide or the alcohol—in both cases, in the presence of an alkali. Diethyl sulfate (or dimethyl sulfate) is also used and can be handled more easily than the alkyl halide.

p-Nitrophenetole from p-Nitrochlorobenzene (Reaction 1).—As Schwyzer[1] points out, *p*-nitrochlorobenzene when heated with alcoholic potash yields but little of the *p*-nitrophenetole. In the presence of sulfites, however, the reaction proceeds smoothly and without the formation of by-products. Potassium sulfite is best, and it should be introduced in powdered form. The temperature also has much effect on the amount of product obtained.

A stirred iron kettle of 1,700 liters capacity, provided with a jacket for hot water, is recommended. One thousand liters of 95 per cent alcohol is introduced into the kettle, and 63 kg. of 94 per cent KOH is dissolved in it at 45°. Five kilograms of powdered potassium sulfite and 157 kg. of *p*-nitrochlorobenzene are then added. The temperature is raised to 50°C., at which point the reaction starts. The charge is maintained at 50°C. for 6 hr., then for 6 hr. at 55°C., and the temperature raised 5°C. at 6-hr. intervals until 80°C. is reached, where the reaction mass should be kept for 12 hr. At each temperature increase, 1 kg. of finely powdered potassium sulfite is added.

During these operations, the stirrer should be kept operating; and at the end, the alkalinity of the filtered solution should have become constant, and about 95 per cent of the *p*-nitrochlorobenzene transformed into *p*-nitrophenetole. The precipitated potassium chloride is put on a pressure filter while still hot, and 7 kg. of potassium sulfite is added to the filtrate which is returned to the reactor. After three hours at 80°, the filtration is repeated. After this, the transformation is practically complete with almost a theoretical yield. The alcohol is distilled off and can be used again so long as its ethanol content has not dropped below 85 per cent. *p*-Nitrophenetole is isolated from the residuum from the alcohol distillation.

Phenetidine is obtained from *p*-nitrophenetole by reduction with iron and hydrochloric acid. It is then acetylated to *p*-acetophenetidine by heating with glacial acetic acid in a silver-lined still.

p-Phenetidine from 4-Ethoxy-4'-Hydroxyazobenzene (Reaction 2).— The series of reactions depicted under (2) above, leading to acetophenetidine, involve the coupling of diazotized phenetidine with phenol and its subsequent ethylation and reduction to give two molecules of phenetidine. These are fully described by Barrowcliff and Carr,[2] the ethylation steps being as follows:

[1] Schwyzer, *loc. cit.*, pp. 211–212.

[2] Barrowcliff and Carr, "Organic Medicinal Chemicals," pp. 116–117, Baillière-Tindall and Cox, London (1921).

The ethylation is carried out by dissolving 24.2 kg. (100 moles) of the 4-ethoxy-4'-hydroxyazobenzene in 100 liters of alcohol containing 4 kg. of caustic soda placed in a lead-lined autoclave. Seven kilograms (108 moles) of ethyl chloride is introduced into the autoclave (see Fig. 6). The autoclave is kept at 90 to 100°C. for five to six hours and then cooled and emptied. The 4, 4'-diethoxyazobenzene (m.p., 156°C.) is filtered off, the filtrate being available for a subsequent operation.

The 4, 4'-diethoxyazobenzene is reduced with hydrochloric acid and tin, the reaction liquor made alkaline with caustic solution, and the p-phenetidine steam distilled. The p-phenetidine is acetylated to the p-acetophenetidine by heating with glacial acetic acid in a silver-lined still.

ANISOLE

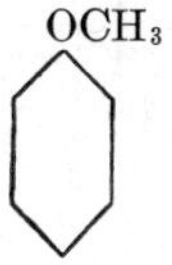

OCH_3

Outline of Reactions.

$$C_6H_5ONa + \overset{H_3CO}{\underset{H_3CO}{\diagdown}}\!\!\!\!>\!\!SO_2 \rightarrow C_6H_5OCH_3 + \overset{NaO}{\underset{H_3CO}{\diagdown}}\!\!\!\!>\!\!SO_2 \qquad (1)$$

$$C_6H_5ONa + \overset{NaO}{\underset{H_3CO}{\diagdown}}\!\!\!\!>\!\!SO_2 \rightarrow C_6H_5OCH_3 + Na_2SO_4$$

$$C_6H_5ONa + CH_3Cl \rightarrow C_6H_5OCH_3 + NaCl \qquad (2)$$

Anisole is used directly in perfumery and as an intermediate for further synthesis. It is prepared by the action of methyl chloride or of dimethyl sulfate on phenol. When dimethyl sulfate is employed, both of its methyl groups can be made to react, yielding about 72 to 75 per cent of theory of the anisole. Causing only one of the methyl groups to react, the yield is higher, being from 85 to 95 per cent of theory, but it is usually more economical to use both of the available methyl groups.

Ullmann[1] directs that the reaction be carried out at not higher than 50 or 60°C., treating 9.4 parts of phenol with 50 parts of 10 per cent caustic soda and 12 vol. parts of dimethyl sulfate, thus obtaining 10.5 parts of anisole, or 96 per cent of theory. The concentration of the caustic soda does not have much effect upon the yield, but solutions stronger than 10 per cent cause the reaction to go more rapidly. The proportions just given are calculated to leave sodium methyl sulfate in solution.

[1] ULLMANN, "Enzyklopädie der technischen Chemie," 2te. Auflage, I, 239, Urban und Schwarzenberg, Berlin (1928–1932).

This, however, can be used for alkylation by adding still more phenol and alkali and boiling for rather a long time under a reflux condenser.[1]

The influence of water and time of reaction in the methylation of phenol to anisole is shown in the accompanying table.[2]

TABLE II.—FORMATION OF ANISOLE AT 100°C.
(Influence of Water and Time of Reaction)

Time, hr.	Dimethyl sulfate, moles	Phenol, Moles	Sodium hydroxide, moles	Water, moles	Anisole, %
1	0.1	0.2	0.3	0.0	54.5
1	0.1	0.2	0.3	0.2	70.0
1	0.1	0.2	0.3	0.4	64.5
1	0.1	0.2	0.3	0.8	61.8
1	0.1	0.2	0.3	1.6	54.6
1	0.1	0.2	0.3	3.2	39.3
5	0.1	0.2	0.3	0.2	90.1
5	0.1	0.2	0.3	0.4	81.2

From the data in Table II the authors conclude that the first methyl group in dimethyl sulfate reacts rapidly to form anisole, and that the second methyl group reacts slowly, particularly in the presence of a relatively large amount of water. If the water concentration is reduced and sufficient time is allowed, the second methyl group may be largely used.

Anisole is stated to be formed with very good yield when the vapors of phenol (1 vol.) and methanol (1.5 vols.) are passed over alumina at 390 to 420°C.[3]

CARBITOL
DIETHYLENE GLYCOL ETHYL ETHER
2-(β-ETHOXYETHOXY)ETHANOL

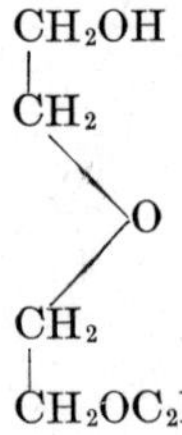

$$CH_2OH$$
$$CH_2$$
$$\diagdown O$$
$$CH_2$$
$$CH_2OC_2H_5$$

[1] ULLMANN and WENNER, *Ber.*, **33**, 2476 (1901); ULLMANN, *Ann.*, **327**, 114 (1930); GRAEBE, *Ann.*, **340**, 208 (1905); GILMAN, *Organic Syntheses*, Collective Vol. I, p. 50, John Wiley & Sons, Inc., (1932).

[2] LEWIS, SHAFFER, TRIESCHMANN, and COGAN, *Ind. Eng. Chem.*, **22**, 34 (1930).

[3] SABATIER and MAILHE, *Compt. rend.*, **151**, 339 (1910).

Polyethylene glycols as high as the octaethylene glycol have been prepared.[1] The ethers of these polyethylene glycols have attained commercial significance, and this is particularly true of the diethylene glycol ethyl ether, which is sold commercially under the name of Carbitol. This product is especially useful in the manufacture of laminated glass, wherein the celluloid interleaf is misted over with a spray of Carbitol, which increases the adhesion to the glass. In the printing and dyeing of textile fabrics, it makes possible more economical use of dyes.

Carbitol is a solvent with a mild odor and a low rate of evaporation, with a boiling point of 201.9°C. It enters into the manufacture of wood stains, and automobile polishes, and is used as a lacquer solvent. However, it is particularly valuable in the cosmetic field, where it is employed for creams and hair tonics.

Preparation.—The diethylene glycol ethyl ether is prepared by ethylation with alcohol and is also obtained as a by-product in the manufacture of ethylene glycol ethyl ether (*cf.* Cellosolve), where it is found in the residue after the distillation of the latter.

$$
\begin{array}{ccccc}
CH_2OH & CH_2OH & & & CH_2OC_2H_5 \\
| & | & & & | \\
CH_2OH & CH_2 & & C_2H_5OH & CH_2 \\
+ & \rightarrow & >O & \xrightarrow{\quad\quad} & >O \\
CH_2 & CH_2 & & & CH_2 \\
| \;>O & | & & & | \\
CH_2 & CH_2OH & & & CH_2OH
\end{array}
$$

CELLOSOLVE
ETHYLENE GLYCOL ETHYL ETHER
2-ETHOXYETHANOL

$$
\begin{array}{l}
CH_2\text{—}OH \\
| \\
CH_2\text{—}OC_2H_5
\end{array}
$$

Ethylene glycol ethyl ether belongs to three major chemical families, containing an alcoholic group, —OH; a hydrocarbon group, $CH_2 \cdot CH_2$; and an ether group, —CH_2—OC_2H_5; and it is not surprising that this compound and its homologues have proven to be useful solvents.

Since the ethylene glycol ethers contain an ether as well as an alcohol group, they are very good solvents for cellulose esters. The ethylene glycol methyl ether is an excellent solvent for both nitro- and acetylcellulose, while the ethyl and the higher homologous ethers dissolve only the nitrocellulose.

Because of the strong solvent action of the methyl ether of ethylene glycol, the so-called Methyl Cellosolve, it is used to seal the cellophane-

[1] LAWRIE, "Glycerol and Glycols," pp. 381 *et seq.*, Chemical Catalog Company (1928).

covered cigarette packages. Here only six drops are needed per package, and yet Methyl Cellosolve is sold in carload quantities.

Preparation.

$$
\begin{array}{c}
CH_2 \\
| \quad \rangle O + C_2H_5OH \rightarrow \\
CH_2
\end{array}
\quad
\begin{array}{c}
CH_2\text{—}OH \\
| \\
CH_2\text{—}OC_2H_5
\end{array}
$$

Absolute ethyl alcohol is introduced into an autoclave, and ethylene oxide[1] as a liquid under pressure is introduced in such a quantity as to leave the alcohol in 15 per cent excess. The autoclave is closed and the temperature raised to 150°C. for 12 hr., or 200°C. for 4 hr. At 150°, the pressure mounts to 250 lb. at the start of the reaction, falling toward the end to 125 lb. The autoclave is discharged, and the product fractionally distilled. After the removal of the excess alcohol, the ethylene glycol ethyl ether passes over at around 134°C. A yield of about 70 per cent, based upon the alcohol consumed, is obtained. In the still are the higher-boiling reaction products, such as the ethyl ethers of di- and triethylene glycol. The excess alcohol presumably diminishes the amount of these by-products.

Other reactions are available whereby these glycol ethers can be formed. According to one patent,[2] ethylene glycol, diethyl sulfate, and caustic soda, in the quantities required by the equation below, are boiled for 3 hr. in a kettle under a reflux.

$$2HO \cdot CH_2 \cdot CH_2 \cdot OH + 2NaOH + (C_2H_5)_2SO_4 \rightarrow$$
$$2HO \cdot CH_2 \cdot CH_2OC_2H_5 + Na_2SO_4 + 2H_2O$$

The products are rectified by distillation, leaving the inorganic matter in the still. The yield is 60 per cent or over. Ethylene oxide[3] has been reacted with ethyl alcohol under the influence of heat and pressure and a small quantity of diethyl sulfate, to form ethylene glycol ethyl ether. The ethylene oxide and alcohol reaction has also been catalyzed by boiling with special hydrosilicates.[4] In another process[5] these ethers are formed from ethylene chlorohydrin, a slight excess of diethyl sulfate and solid caustic soda by boiling under a reflux condenser for 3 hr. The yield is 60 per cent or greater.

$$2HOCH_2 \cdot CH_2Cl + 4NaOH + (C_2H_5)_2SO_4 \rightarrow$$
$$2CH_2OH \cdot CH_2O \cdot C_2H_5 + Na_2SO_4 + 2NaCl + 2H_2O$$

In the foregoing reactions, various alcohols can be used as alkylating agents, even those containing an aromatic group; but the principal

[1] U. S. 1,696,874 (1928).
[2] U. S. 1,614,883 (1927).
[3] Birch and Scott, U. S. 1,882,564; Ger. 580,075.
[4] Ger. 558,646.
[5] U. S. 1,732,356 (1929).

ones that have found favor are methyl, ethyl, and butyl alcohols. As a rule, the diethers have little or no advantage over the monoethers, the

TABLE III.—BOILING POINTS, SPECIFIC GRAVITY, AND REFRACTIVE INDICES OF ETHYLENE GLYCOL ETHERS[1]

Monoalkyl ether	B.p.,[2] °C.	Sp. gr., 15°C./15°C.	Refractive index (η_D) at 26°C.
Methyl.....................	124.3	0.9748	1.4004
Ethyl.....................	135.1	0.9360	1.4042[3]
Isopropyl.................	144.0	0.9139	1.4080
n-Propyl.................	150.0	0.9110	1.4125
Isobutyl.................	158.8	0.9130	1.4135
n-Butyl..................	170.7	0.9188	1.4177
Isoamyl.................	181.0	0.9000	1.4198

[1] Lawrie, *op. cit.*
[2] 743 mm. pressure.
[3] 24°C.

alcohol-ether compound giving the most desirable properties. The data in Table III permit a comparison of some of the physical properties of these ethers and show the influence of different alkyl groups upon the boiling point, specific gravity, and refractive index of this series.

ETHYLCELLULOSE

The cellulose ethers obtained by the alkylation of cellulose are important plastic materials. They are more stable than the cellulose esters, and are incapable of undergoing hydrolysis, which makes them more resistant to acid and alkalis. The alkyl ethers are, however, soluble to a considerable extent in water and alkalis, more so than benzyl cellulose but less than cellulose acetate.

The data below show how the solubility of the alkyl ethers varies with the percentage of etherification.[1]

Ether	Soluble in alkali	Soluble in water	Soluble in organic solvents
Methyl cellulose	3–4 % —OCH_3	22–26 % —OCH_3	40 % —OCH_3
Ethyl cellulose	5 % —OC_2H_5	27 % —OC_2H_5	47 % —OC_2H_5

The alkali-soluble compounds are of interest to the textile industry but are not suitable for the preparation of lacquers.

[1] TRAILL, *Oil and Colour Trades J.*, (1936), pp. 1109.

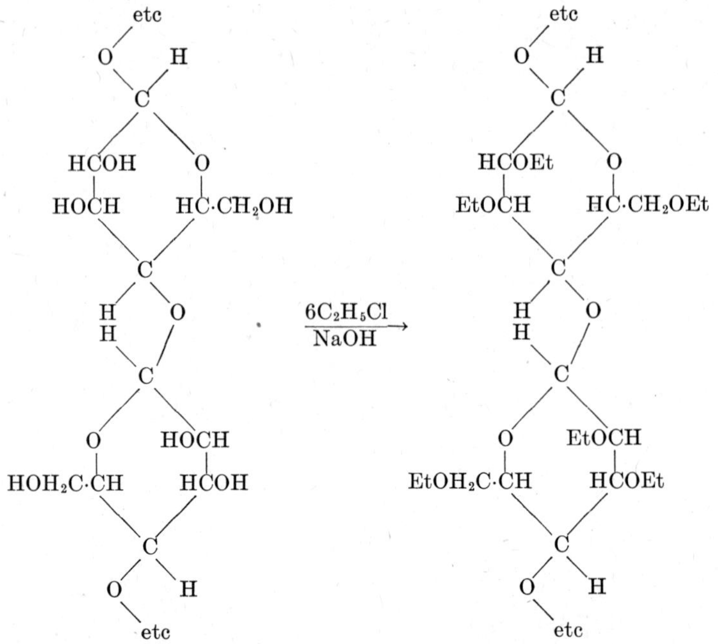

$$\xrightarrow[\text{NaOH}]{6C_2H_5Cl}$$

Preparation.—The preparation of ethyl cellulose may be carried out as follows:[1]

One hundred parts of cellulose is impregnated within 1,000 parts of a 20 per cent sodium hydroxide solution and after standing from 24 to 72 hr. are pressed until the weight has decreased to 600 parts. The pressed residue is then disintegrated and after standing for 1 to 3 days is placed in a vacuum shelf dryer or vacuum kneading machine and is dried at a temperature below 10°C. until a test shows that the soda cellulose contains from 10 to 25 per cent of water. The dried alkali cellulose is then placed in an autoclave which is rotated and which is provided with a stirring device, two hundred parts of ethyl chloride is then added and the mixture is heated to 90 to 100°C. for 20 hr. During the reaction the mass is stirred, and the autoclave is kept turning.

After the autoclave has cooled, the contents are mixed with water and are poured into a filter or a decanting apparatus, washed with water, treated with dilute sulfuric or hydrochloric acid, again washed, and then dried.

The resulting ethyl cellulose is a powdery flocculent substance which is soluble in a number of organic solvents (*e.g.*, chloroform, alcohol, chloroform-alcohol mixture, chloroform-methyl alcohol mixture, glacial acetic acid, amyl acetate, nitromethane, etc.) and these solutions give clear, transparent, flexible and water-resistant films when evaporated.

[1] U. S. 1,683,682; 1,683,831 (1928).

The aralkyl celluloses, *e.g.*, benzyl cellulose and phenylethyl cellulose, are made in a similar manner. Their purification may be accomplished by treating the crude alkylation mass with a selective solvent, *e.g.*, propanol, diamyl ether, etc., which remove organic impurities.[1] The granular precipitate is then washed with methanol and finally with water.

CODEINE

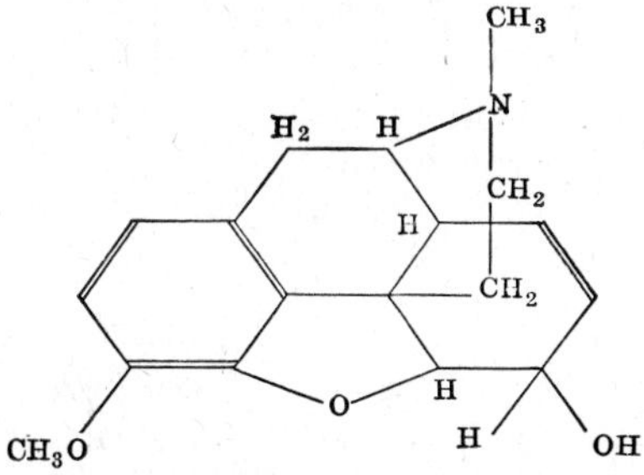

Codeine [$CH_3O(C_{17}H_{17}ON)OH$] occurs naturally in opium and is extracted industrially along with morphine. It is derived from morphine ($HO(C_{17}H_{17}ON)OH$) by methylation of the phenolic hydroxyl. Because the demand for codeine for many years has exceeded the quantities that were available by natural extraction from opium, a great deal of work has been done on the synthesis of codeine from morphine.[2]

In this and similar methylations, it is particularly difficult to secure the excellent yields that are necessary for the economic handling of such high-priced materials. In the morphine and codeine molecules, a tertiary nitrogen is present that can be alkylated to a pentavalent condition by the simple addition of methyl iodide or similar alkylating agents, whereupon the ring system is very liable to be destroyed, probably following the reaction known as Hofmann's exhaustive methylation. Consequently, the treatment of morphine with the ordinary simple methylating compounds results in low yields of codeine and considerable destruction of the molecule. This applies to the treatment of the anhydrous solution of sodium morphinate with the ordinary alkylating agents, such as a methyl halide or dimethyl sulfate.[3]

On the other hand, as has been described by Boehringer,[4] Rodionov,[5] Schwyzer,[6] and Small,[7] high yields are obtained if a quaternary methylat-

[1] U. S. 2,101,032 (1937).

[2] SMALL, Chemistry of the Opium Alkaloids, Supplement 103 to Public Health Reports, pp. 147, 175–176, 188, U. S. Government Printing Office, Washington, D. C. (1932).

[3] BARROWCLIFF and CARR, *loc. cit.*, pp. 55–57.

[4] Boehringer and Söhne, Ger. 247,180 (1909).

[5] RODIONOV, *Bull. soc. chim.*, **39**, 305–325 (1926); **45**, 109–121 (1928).

[6] SCHWYZER, *loc. cit.*, pp. 374, 388–392.

[7] *Loc. cit.*

ing agent is employed. With a quaternary ammonium base having nitrogen in the pentavalent condition, there is little or no tendency to form a pentavalent nitrogen derivative on the morphine nitrogen with consequent destruction of the morphine-ring system. Hence, the methylation proceeds almost exclusively on the phenolic hydroxyl, resulting in excellent yields of the methyl ether, codeine.

Methylation Reactions with Quaternary Nitrogen Methyl Derivatives.[1]

$$C_6H_5N(CH_3)_2 + CH_3Cl \rightarrow C_6H_5N(CH_3)_3Cl \qquad (1)$$
$$2C_2H_5OH + 2Na \rightarrow 2C_2H_5ONa + H_2$$
$$HO(C_{17}H_{17}ON)OH + C_6H_5N(CH_3)_3Cl + C_2H_5ONa \rightarrow$$

Morphine   Phenyl-   Sodium Ethylate
trimethyl-
ammonium
Chloride

$$CH_3O(C_{17}H_{17}ON)OH + C_6H_5N(CH_3)_2 + C_2H_5OH + NaCl$$

Codeine   Dimethylaniline   Ethanol

$$C_6H_5SO_3H + ClSO_2OH \rightarrow C_6H_5SO_2Cl + H_2SO_4 \qquad (2)$$
$$C_6H_5SO_2Cl + CH_3OH + NaOH \rightarrow C_6H_5SO_2OCH_3 + NaCl + H_2O$$
$$C_6H_5SO_2OCH_3 + C_6H_5N(CH_3)_2 \rightarrow C_6H_5N(CH_3)_3OSO_2C_6H_5$$
$$C_6H_5N(CH_3)_3OSO_2C_6H_5 + NaOH \rightarrow C_6H_5N(CH_3)_3OH + NaOSO_2C_6H_5$$
$$C_6H_5N(CH_3)_3OH + HO(C_{17}H_{17}ON)OH \rightarrow$$
$$CH_3O(C_{17}H_{17}ON)OH + C_6H_5N(CH_3)_2 + H_2O$$
$$p\text{-}CH_3C_6H_4SO_2OCH_3 + C_6H_5N(CH_3)_2 \rightarrow C_6H_5N(CH_3)_3OSO_2C_6H_4CH_3 \qquad (3)$$
$$HO(C_{17}H_{17}ON)OH + C_6H_5N(CH_3)_3OSO_2C_6H_4CH_3 + C_2H_5ONa \rightarrow$$
$$CH_3O(C_{17}H_{17}ON)OH + C_6H_5N(CH_3)_2 + NaOSO_2C_6H_4CH_3 + C_2H_5OH$$

Methylation According to Reaction (1).—Phenyltrimethylammonium chloride is an excellent methylating compound not only for morphine but for a number of other compounds such as antipyrine and theobromine. It is prepared and used according to the method of Schwyzer[2] by warming dimethylaniline with methyl chloride in a 100-liter stirred autoclave provided with an enameled liner. Into this autoclave are charged 10 kg. of dimethylaniline, 4 kg. of absolute alcohol, and 4.5 kg. of methyl chloride. The autoclave is closed and heated gradually to 100 to 120°C., whereupon the pressure rises to about 400 lb., chiefly because of the presence of the excess of methyl chloride. The stirrer is run one-half day; and as the reaction progresses, the pressure drops. The autoclave is allowed to cool and is opened the following morning. The crystals are filtered off, dried immediately at 50 to 60°C., and then transferred while still warm into closed containers. These crystals are very hygroscopic. The yield amounts to 12.5 to 13 kg. The sodium ethylate is prepared by dissolving metallic sodium in absolute alcohol. Schwyzer directs that 96 per cent alcohol be used, but other workers prefer absolute alcohol.

Using this methylating compound, it is necessary to conduct the operation in an autoclave which should be charged with 10 kg. of anhy-

---

[1] It is clear that the formation of phenyltrimethylammonium chloride exemplifies alkyl bound to pentavalent nitrogen.

[2] SCHWYZER, *loc. cit.*, pp. 388–390.

drous morphine alkaloid, 7 kg. of absolute alcohol, and 14.1 liters of sodium ethylate solution of such strength that 25 cc. will neutralize 60 cc. normal hydrochloric acid. The autoclave contents are carefully mixed, and 6.5 kg. of phenyltrimethylammonium chloride are then introduced, the autoclave closed and slowly warmed to a pressure of 60 lb. The vapors are blown off, and the autoclave allowed to cool overnight.

The contents of the autoclave are dissolved in 20 liters of water, and the alcohol distilled off, after which the product is made acid to litmus with dilute sulfuric acid, 60 liters of water added, and the dimethylaniline distilled off. Codeine is separated from the small amount of unaltered morphine by extraction with 40 liters of benzene after making alkaline with caustic soda. The benzene-codeine extraction is repeated twice. About 500 to 700 gm. of unaltered morphine can be recovered by acidifying the alkaline aqueous liquor and adding ammonia. Codeine is obtained usually by treating the benzene extracts with 40 liters of 1:10 sulfuric acid. The yield is 91 to 93 per cent.

Methylation According to Reaction (2).—By the use of dimethylaniline and the methyl esters of benzene- and toluenesulfonic acids, the quaternary methylating compound can be prepared according to the method of Rodionov. These compounds can be used as phenyltrimethylammonium derivatives of either phenyl- or toluenesulfonates in the presence of an alkali, according to reaction (3), or the bases can be prepared according to reaction (2). Following reaction (2), a suspension of the phenyltrimethylammonium benzenesulfonate [$C_6H_5N(CH_3)_3 \cdot O\text{-}SO_2C_6H_5$], in absolute alcohol, is treated with a calculated amount of caustic soda, whereupon the sodium salt is thrown out and the phenyltrimethylammonium hydroxide dissolved in the alcohol. The precipitated sodium salt is washed with alcohol, and these washings added to the main solution. The alcoholic solution of the phenyltrimethylammonium hydroxide is added to a toluene suspension of anhydrous morphine. In this case, good yields can be obtained without using an autoclave by boiling the toluene mixture under a reflux.

Methylation According to Reaction (3). *By the Method of Rodionov.*—The methylation of morphine to codeine using phenyltrimethylammonium benzenesulfonate, is described by Small[1] as follows: Phenyltrimethylammonium benzenesulfonate is prepared by heating 25 gm. of methyl benzenesulfonate with 18 gm. of dimethylaniline on a water bath. The mixture solidifies, then melts again with considerable evolution of heat, and hardens to a crystalline mass. The yield is nearly quantitative. After recrystallization from alcohol the melting point is 180 to 181°C. (Phenyltrimethylammonium toluenesulfonate, m.p., 160 to 161°C., is prepared and used for methylation in a similar manner.)

[1] SMALL, *loc. cit.*, pp. 188–189.

4.5 gm. of sodium is dissolved in 45 cc. of absolute alcohol, and to it is added a solution of 55 gm. of phenyltrimethylammonium benzene-sulfonate in 130 cc. of absolute alcohol. The crystalline sodium ben-zenesulfonate which separates is filtered off and washed with a little absolute alcohol. The alcoholic filtrate containing phenyltrimethylam-monium hydroxide is treated with 42 gm. of anhydrous morphine. The alcohol is distilled from the solution on an oil bath, and the temperature is allowed to rise to 110° and held there for three-fourths to one hour. The mixture is acidified with 15 per cent acetic acid and steam-distilled until all dimethylaniline is removed. After filtering, the contents of the flask are made alkaline with a large excess of 20 per cent sodium hydrox-ide, whereupon the codeine separates as an oil, which soon crystallizes. The alkaline mother liquors still contain some codeine, which is extracted by benzene, bringing the yield to about 29 gm. of codeine. The alkaline solution contains about 9 gm. of morphine, which may be regained, mak-ing the yield of codeine, based upon the morphine which reacted, 84 to 85 per cent.

VANILLIN
3-METHOXY-4-HYDROXYBENZALDEHYDE

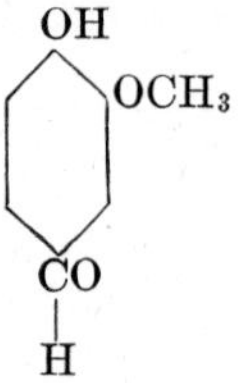

The chemical transformation of a closely related, naturally occurring product into vanillin has long been the important source of supply. Among such available materials, oil of cloves is used most extensively, the eugenol being converted into isoeugenol and then into vanillin. In this case, the methoxy group found in vanillin is present in the original eugenol.

A great amount of work has been done on the synthesis of vanillin from cheap organic compounds. Several processes have been able to compete, probably the most important being that which introduces the formaldehyde group into guaiacol by the reaction of guaiacol[1] with

$$C_6H_4\begin{smallmatrix}SO_3H\\\\NHOH\end{smallmatrix} + C_6H_4\begin{smallmatrix}OCH_3\\\\OH\end{smallmatrix} + HCHO \rightarrow C_6H_4\begin{smallmatrix}SO_3H\\\\NH_2\end{smallmatrix} + C_6H_3\begin{smallmatrix}OCH_3\\-OH\\\\CHO\end{smallmatrix} + H_2O$$

formaldehyde, and phenylhydroxylaminesulfonic acid.

[1] Fr. 283,920 (1899); Ger. 105,798 (1900).

Another synthetic process involving alkylation depends on the conversion of pyrocatechol to pyrocatechuic aldehyde, which is then methylated to vanillin according to the following equation:

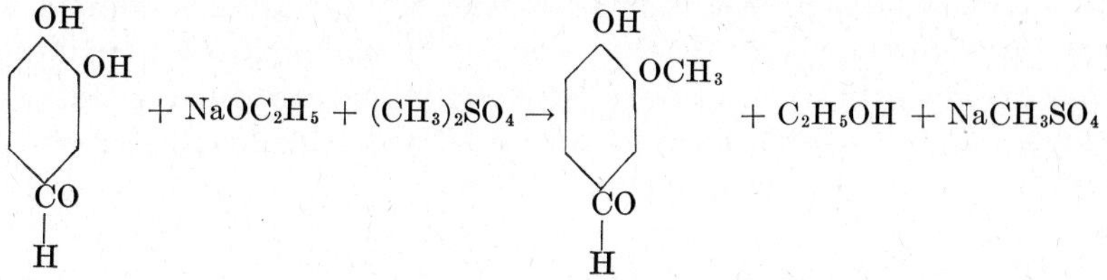

$$\text{(OH, OH, CHO benzene)} + NaOC_2H_5 + (CH_3)_2SO_4 \rightarrow \text{(OH, OCH_3, CHO benzene)} + C_2H_5OH + NaCH_3SO_4$$

To carry out this reaction according to the details given by Schwyzer a solution of 4 kg. of sodium and 75 kg. of absolute alcohol is introduced into an agitated kettle; 15 kg. of pyrocatechuic aldehyde is then run in, keeping the temperature under 10°C. During agitation, 15 kg. of dimethyl sulfate previously dissolved in 20 kg. of absolute alcohol is run in slowly, the temperature is then raised over 4 to 5 hr. to 50°C., after which the contents of the kettle are cooled, acidified (to Congo Red) with hydrochloric acid, and the alcohol distilled off. The residue is dissolved in 50 liters of water, extracted twice with 50 kg. of chloroform, the chloroform distilled off, and the crude vanillin purified. The yield of crude vanillin is about 8 kg.

Alkyl Bound to Trivalent Nitrogen.

DIETHYLAMINE

$$(C_2H_5)_2NH$$

Diethylamine finds extensive use in the preparation of wetting and dispersing agents and enters into many syntheses. Through its employment the alkyl groups are introduced into procaine. Its preparation from ethanol and ammonia by ammonolysis is described in Chap. VI. Here the synthesis from ethyl chloride and ammonia as given by Schwyzer[1] is presented.

$$2C_2H_5Cl + 3NH_3 \rightarrow 2NH_4Cl + NH(C_2H_5)_2$$

A 500-liter autoclave made of corrosion-resisting steel tested to 900 lb. and provided with a jacket for heating and cooling may be employed to advantage. A filter press and a fractionating still are also needed. Fifty kilograms of absolute alcohol is introduced into the autoclave, cooled by brine to −15°C., and 10 kg. of ammonia is added. Twenty-six kilograms of pure ethyl chloride and, as a catalyst, 100 gm. of powdered pyrolusite are then introduced.

The autoclave is warmed, using steam and proceeding very carefully and slowly. A pressure of 150 to 225 lb. will be obtained if the reaction

[1] SCHWYZER, *op. cit.*, pp. 230–233.

is kept under control; otherwise, this will mount much higher. Toward the end of the reaction, the pressure will drop and the temperature should then be raised to 95 to 100°C. When the pressure remains constant at the same temperature, the reaction is completed. The reaction mixture is cooled to 0°C., and the product passed through a closed filter into the rectification apparatus. This reaction mixture contains the following, besides ammonium chloride and a trace of ethyl chloride:

Products	B.p., °C.
$C_2H_5NH_2$	18
$(C_2H_5)_2NH$	56
C_2H_5OH	80
$(C_2H_5)_3N$	89

These products can be separated by fractionation, the yield being between 7 and 10 kg. of diethylamine. The ethylamine should be added to the next run. The triethylamine can be sold as such or used to make ethyl chloride and diethylamine by heating the triethylamine hydrochloride.

DIMETHYLANILINE

$$N(CH_3)_2$$

Dimethylaniline is very widely used as an intermediate in the manufacture of dyes, rubber accelerators, explosives, and some medical products. Such important dyes as Auramine, Malachite Green, Methyl Violet, Crystal Violet, and Methylene Blue are derived from dimethylaniline. This compound also finds application in the preparation of quaternary alkylating compounds, such as are described under Codeine. The explosive tetryl, which is tetranitromethylaniline, is manufactured by the nitration of dimethylaniline.

The present technical preparation of dimethylaniline depends upon heating aniline, methanol, and an acid in an autoclave.

$$C_6H_5NH_2 + 2CH_3OH \xrightarrow{H_2SO_4} C_6H_5N(CH_3)_2 + 2H_2O$$

While the literature states that either hydrochloric or sulfuric acid can be used, technically only the sulfuric is employed, as the hydrochloric acid is too corrosive.

The technical preparation of dimethylaniline proceeds along these lines: 200 lb. of aniline is mixed with 220 lb. of methanol, and 20 lb. of 66°Bé. sulfuric acid is added. The mixture becomes warm, and considerable aniline sulfate separates out; this is well stirred and then pumped into a steel autocalve of sufficient capacity to allow for expansion of the charge when hot. The autoclave is heated during the course of 2 hr. to around 205°C. and then maintained at 205°C., or slightly higher, for five or six hours, the pressure rising to around 525 lb. or sometimes 550 lb. The autoclave can either be allowed to cool or can be discharged while still hot, through a cooling condenser into a neutralizing vessel. Here the acid is neutralized with caustic soda, after which the products of the reaction are subjected to vacuum distillation for the recovery of the excess methanol and the purification of the dimethylaniline produced. A yield of around 95 per cent, based on aniline used, is obtained; the net yield, based on the methanol, is somewhat smaller. When the reaction is carried to completion, the dimethylaniline should not contain more than 0.4 per cent of monomethylaniline.

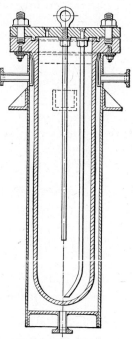

An unlined steel autoclave can be used very satisfactorily for this purpose (see Fig. 7), although periodic hydraulic tests should be made on the apparatus at 500 lb. in excess of working pressure, to insure its continued good condition. An occasional inspection should be made, at least of the upper section at the vapor line where corrosion is most likely to occur. Various heating mediums have been employed, such as direct fire, circulated hot oil, or superheated steam. For the last, which is certainly the cleanest and most convenient heating medium, 200 to 250°F. superheat should be given to the ordinary steam at 100 lb. pressure.

It is necessary that dimethylaniline be free from all except a few tenths of 1 per cent of

Fig. 7.—Autoclave.

monomethylaniline; consequently, great care must be taken in conducting the initial reaction, as monomethylaniline is difficult to separate by distillation because of the small boiling-point difference between the two. Benzylation of the monomethylaniline yields benzylmethylaniline and this derivative can be separated easily from the dimethylaniline by fractionation. The formation of similar derivatives of monomethylaniline with toluenesulfonyl chloride or with phthalic acid[1] removes this by-product more completely.

In this methylation, a number of side reactions occur to a small extent. The quaternary ammonium salt $[C_6H_5N(CH_3)_3 \cdot HSO_4]$ is formed and is quite stable, being decomposed by heating with concentrated caustic soda only when the temperature is elevated considerably (170 to

[1] Britton and Holmes, U. S. 1,890,246 (1932).

180°C.). There are some nuclear methylated products which are very probably formed from the quaternary compound. Nuclear methylation is more pronounced at temperatures of around 250°C. and is one of the reasons for avoiding such high temperatures or local overheating. In case the reaction does not go to completion, the heating period rather than the temperature should be increased. Excessive sulfuric acid also appears to lead to formation of nuclear products. Nuclear methylation can be carried far enough, for example, by heating under pressure at a temperature of 300 to 350°C., to form mesidine (2, 4, 6-trimethylaniline) as well as *p*- and *o*-toluidine, *m*-xylidine, etc. However, it is unlikely that the conditions in the manufacture of dimethylaniline ever go beyond the following reaction:

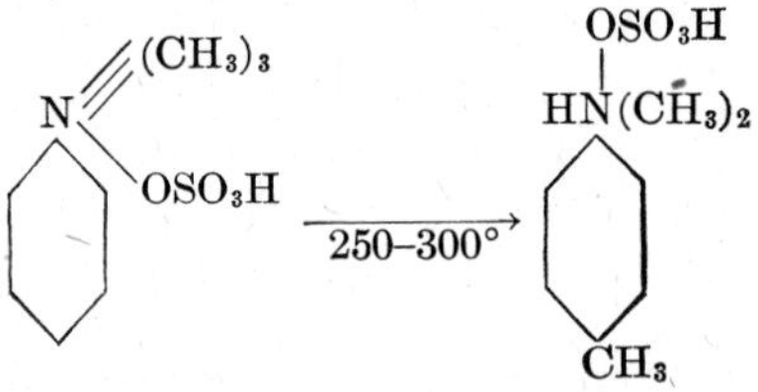

In the technical manufacture of dimethylaniline, the formation of some substituted diphenylmethanes is observed. Here, undoubtedly part of the methyl alcohol is oxidized to formaldehyde, causing this condensation. Much of the loss of methanol is due to the formation of methyl ether, which is usually lost in the blow-off at the end of the run.

Alkyl Bound to Pentavalent Nitrogen.

PHENYLTRIMETHYLAMMONIUM CHLORIDE

Note. This product is described under Codeine.

Alkyl Bound to Carbon.

HEXYLRESORCINOL
CAPROKOL

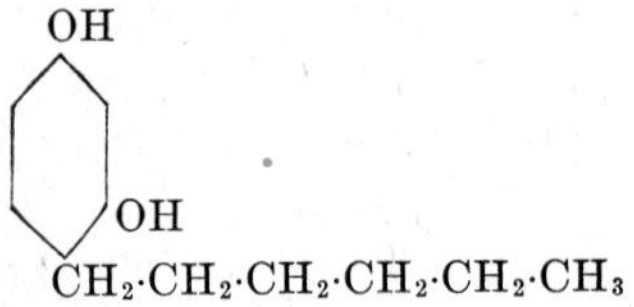

The normal hexylresorcinol has been found to possess marked germicidal properties with a phenol coefficient of over 50. It is relatively nontoxic when administered by mouth and is partly excreted by the kidneys. A great number of acyl- and alkylresorcinols have been studied as regards their germicidal action.[1] The normal alkylresorcinols par-

---

[1] DOHME, Cox, and MILLER, *J. Am. Chem. Soc.*, **48**, 1688 (1926); SCHAFFER and TILLEY, *J. Bact.*, **14**, 259 (1927).

ticularly have been found to be of value, a very pronounced increase being observed in the bactericidal power shown by these compounds

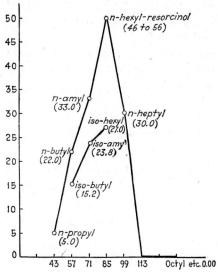

Fig. 8.—Bacterial activity of the alkylresorcinols. The curve is obtained by plotting the phenol coefficients (U. S. Hygienic Laboratory technic) as ordinates against the sum of the atomic weights of the atoms in the alkyl chain as abscissas. (*According to Dohme, Cox, and Miller.*)

up to normal nonylresorcinol. This action then decreases as the length of the chain increases because of the diminishing solubility of the alkyl-

TABLE IV.—COEFFICIENTS OF THE NORMAL RESORCINOLS WITH DIFFERENT STRAINS OF *Staphylococcus aureus*

Name	Phenol coefficients*		
	Strain No. 1	Strain No. 2	Strain No. 3
Ethyl................................	1.55	1.5	1.5
Propyl................................	3.9	3.7	3.7
Butyl................................	10.7	10	10.2
Amyl................................	30.2	30.2	30.6
Hexyl................................	97	98	98
Heptyl................................	295	280	280
Octyl................................	690	680	725
Nonyl................................	1,000	980	1,000

* At 25°C.

resorcinol. In Fig. 8 is shown the relationship between the atomic weight of the alkyl chain and the phenol coefficient (ratio of antibacterial power measured against *B. typhosus* relative to that of phenol under the same conditions). Similar experiments with different strains of *Staphylococcus aureus* gave the results which are shown in Table IV, page 525.[1]

Preparation.—According to various patents[2] pertaining to the manufacture of hexylresorcinol, resorcinol and caproic acid are heated with a condensing agent, such as zinc chloride, whereby the intermediate ketone derivative is formed. This is purified by vacuum distillation. By reduc-

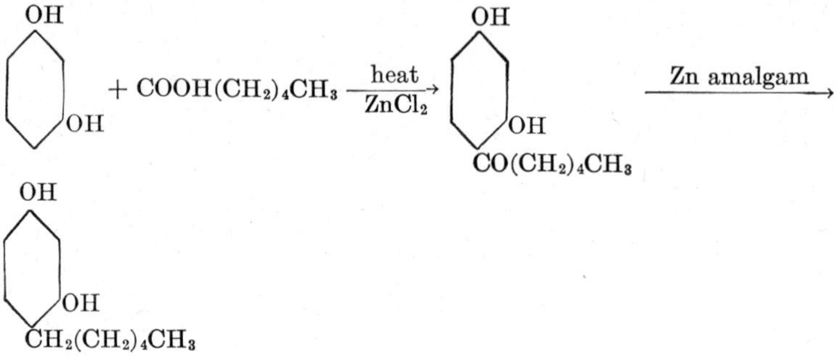

tion with zinc amalgam and hydrochloric acid, impure hexylresorcinol results which can be purified by vacuum distillation.

TERTIARY AMYLPHENOL

Preparation.—The alkylation of phenols by alkyl halides is sometimes brought about through the intervention of a metal halide, *e.g.*, AlCl$_3$. When *tert*-amyl chloride is condensed with phenol and its homologues no catalyst is necessary, although the presence of 3 to 5 per cent metal halide hastens the reaction. The following procedure may be employed for the preparation of *tert*-amylphenol in the absence of a catalyst.[3]

Eight moles of *tert*-amyl chloride are placed in a 5-liter flask with 8 moles of phenol and gently boiled under efficient reflux at a temperature of 80 to 100°C. for a period of 18 hr. During this period a slow steady stream of hydrogen chloride gas is evolved. At the conclusion of 18 hr. the evolution of hydrogen chloride has ceased, and the contents of the flask are then vigorously refluxed for a period of ½ hr. at a temperature of 180°C. The material is then distilled at normal pressure through an efficient column. The distillation gives approximately the following cuts:

---

[1] SCHAFFER and TILLEY, *ibid.*

[2] U. S. 1,649,670 (1927); Can. 264,841 (1926); Can. 264,842 (1926); Can. 265,025 (1926); Brit. 220,668 (1923).

[3] U. S. 2,091,483 (1937).

Cut	B.p., °C.	Material	Weight, gm.	Softening point, °C.
1	60–100	*tert.*-Amyl chloride	168	
2	100–200	Phenol	279	
3	200–248	Intermediate	30	About 45
4	248–255	*tert.*-Amyl phenol	734	85
5	Residue	. . . .	18	

SYNTHETIC MOTOR FUEL
(Synthetic Gasoline)

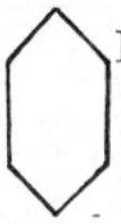

Synthetic motor fuels[1] are derived by polymerization or alkylation and dealkylation accompanied by conjoint realkylation. As a result of these various reactions involving olefins and lower paraffins there are obtained hydrocarbon fractions, falling within the gasoline boiling range, from products which until now have been very largely burned as fuel gas. These changes not only give a more valuable product, but also remove from the market fuel gases of which there is a surplus.

Preparation.—The preparation of a synthetic motor fuel, involving carbon-to-carbon alkylation of aromatics with olefins under the influence of sulfuric acid, is given consideration in the following paragraphs. As is true of all these alkylations, not only mono- but polyalklated aromatics are obtained, and some of the polyalkylated benzenes, for example, boil too high for motor spirits. A so-called destructive alkylation is then made, during which process alkyl groups are split out from the higher alkylbenzenes under the influence of a catalyst such as aluminum chloride or sulfuric acid, and a simultaneous further alkylation of additional benzene occurs. We may express these reactions as follows:

Alkylation.

$$\underset{\text{Propylene}}{C_3H_6} + \underset{\text{Benzene}}{C_6H_6} \xrightarrow{\text{H}_2\text{SO}_4} \underset{\text{Isopropylbenzene}}{C_3H_7 \cdot C_6H_5}$$

$$\underset{\text{Propylene}}{3C_3H_6} + \underset{\text{Benzene}}{C_6H_6} \xrightarrow{\text{H}_2\text{SO}_4} \underset{\text{Triisopropylbenzene}}{(C_3H_7)_3 \cdot C_6H_3}$$

Destructive Alkylation or Reforming Treatment.

$$\underset{\substack{\text{Triisopropyl-}\\\text{benzene}}}{(C_3H_7)_3C_6H_3} + \underset{\text{Benzene}}{2C_6H_6} \underset{\text{AlCl}_3}{\rightleftharpoons} \underset{\text{Isopropylbenzene}}{3C_3H_7C_6H_5}$$

[1] IPATIEFF, The Problem of the Rational Utilization of Petroleum and Petroleum Distillates, *Am. Petroleum Inst.*, Chicago, Nov. 11, 1936.

The gas used for alkylation may contain approximately 30 to 40 per cent of olefins such as propylene, butylenes, and amylenes, with propylene predominating.   Although propylene is given as the typical reacting olefin, butylenes and amylenes also react, while ethylene does

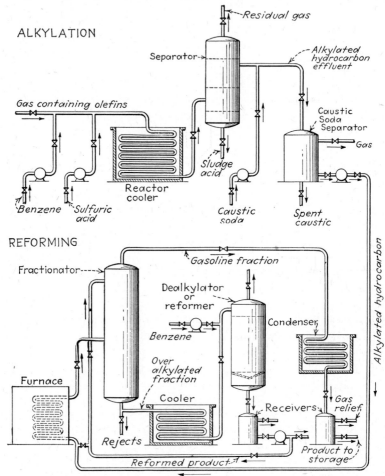

Fig. 9.—Schematic layout for "alkylation" or synthetic motor fuel.

so only to a smaller extent.   The products of such reactions can be brought within the boiling range of ordinary gasoline.   The motor fuel has the great advantage of having a high anti-knock value.   The yield of gasoline is also increased.

In making such synthetic motor fuel the operation[1] is divided into two parts, namely, alkylation and dealkylation.   The accompanying

[1] Egloff, U. S. 2,010,948; 2,010,949 (1935); Ipatieff, U. S. 2,006,695 (1935); 2,039,798 (1936).

diagram (Fig. 9) shows the arrangement of apparatus. Olefins from the cracking of petroleum are mixed with benzene and sulfuric acid. These constituents flow through the continuous-pipe reactor, which is essentially a cooler, in that the temperature is maintained at some fairly low point, which may be as low as 30 to 40°F. (0 to 5°C.). The reaction products then flow into the separator, out of the top of which passes the residual gas which can be either recycled or used as fuel. The sludge acid separates from the bottom and can also be used over or regenerated. The hydrocarbon effluent leaves the upper part of the separator and is then washed with sodium hydroxide to decompose any of the soluble alkyl sulfates. In the caustic separator, any gas and the spent caustic are removed while the alkylated hydrocarbons pass on to the next stage.

The mono- and polyalkylated hydrocarbons are heated in a furnace and then fractionated in a column. The overhead gasoline fraction is conducted through a condenser and receiver. The higher alkylated products are withdrawn from the bottom of the fractionator and passed through a cooler and then into the dealkylator-alkylator or reformer. Additional benzene is also introduced here. The reformer contains a catalyst, such as aluminum chloride, properly supported on some inert material. In this apparatus a migration of alkyl groups from the polyalkyl compounds occurs, and these serve to alkylate the fresh benzene, thus producing a further quantity of the low-boiling gasoline fractions. The product passes out at the bottom of the reformer and is pumped back to the upper section of the fractionator.

A 24 A. P. I. gravity Mid-Continent residuum may be cracked in a commercial cracking plant at a temperature of 930°F. (500°C.) and a pressure of 250 lb. The cracking yields are given in the accompanying table. The resulting gas will contain from 20 to 25 per cent of olefins with the propylene predominating.

TABLE V.—CRACKING YIELDS: MID-CONTINENT RESIDUUM

Product	Yield	Per cent by weight of charge
Gas, 1.20 sp. gr.	700 cu. ft. per bbl. of oil. .	20
Gasoline, 56° A. P. I. gravity.	65 % by volume.	56
Intermediate recycle stock, 28° A. P. I. gravity.	5 % by volume.	5
Coke.	60 lb. per bbl. of oil.	19

The total fixed gases are passed through the apparatus into which is pumped 5 gal. of technical benzene per barrel of cracked stock and about 5 per cent by weight of 66° Bé. sulfuric acid (based on the benzene).

After the reforming operation, the yield of the synthetic products per barrel of oil originally cracked is approximately 7.5 gal. with an anti-knock value twice that of the original benzene. By blending this synthetic motor spirit with the cracked gasoline, the volume yield of

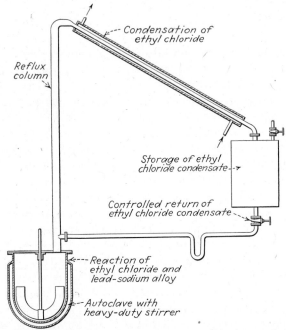

Fig. 10.—Flow diagram for the preparation of lead tetraethyl.

gasoline is raised from 65 to 82 per cent by volume, and the anti-knock value from 65 to 80.

Alkyl Bound to Metal.

LEAD TETRAETHYL

$Pb(C_2H_5)_4$

Lead tetraethyl is widely used for the prevention of knocking in high-compression gasoline engines—0.04 per cent tetraethyl lead being as efficient in this respect as 25 per cent of benzene. In order to prevent the deposition of lead in the exhaust sections of the engine, three parts by volume of tetraethyl lead are mixed with two parts of ethylene bromide ($CH_2Br \cdot CH_2Br$). The ethylene bromide converts the lead oxide formed during the combustion into the volatile lead bromide.

Preparation.—Lead tetraethyl is prepared industrially by the action of ethyl chloride on a lead sodium alloy.[1]   Ethyl chloride reacts very rapidly

[1] Kraus and Callis, U. S. 1,697,245 (1929); Fr. 796,791; Daudt, U. S. 2,091,114 (1937); Amick and Parmelee, U. S. 2,091,112 (1937).

with the alloy PbNa but not with the higher alloys. The final product of the reaction is very pure $Pb(C_2H_5)_4$. Very little is known regarding the mechanism of the reaction, and there are no indications of other alkylation products being formed as either intermediates or by-products. We may formulate the reaction as follows:

$$4PbNa + 4C_2H_5Cl \rightarrow Pb(C_2H_5)_4 + 3Pb + 4NaCl$$

The process is simply the interaction of the alloy PbNa with ethyl chloride in an autoclave and in the absence of water, catalysts, or any other material.

The alloy must be well subdivided, preferably so as to pass a 10-mesh screen, and the temperature should not be higher than 70°C., except at the end, when 100°C. is permitted. The autoclave (Fig. 10) wherein the main reaction takes place must be equipped with a heating and cooling jacket and a strong stirring device so that the lead alloy can be brought into contact with the ethyl chloride and at a carefully controlled temperature. To start the reaction it is necessary to warm up to about 35°C. with subsequent cooling to keep the temperature at from 40 to 60°C. The time for completion of this reaction is from 2 to 6 hr. At the end the excess ethyl chloride is distilled off and condensed. The lead tetraethyl is steam distilled from the reaction mass.

Contrary to the action of the ethyl chloride, it is found that ethyl bromide and iodide do not react at all with PbNa, but do react with $PbNa_2$ or, to less extent with $PbNa_4$ if a small amount of water or alcohol is added from time to time. The yields are not so high as when the ethyl chloride is used. Depending upon the temperature, the product may contain a fair amount of $Pb_2(C_2H_5)_6$, which is not very stable and decomposes. These reactions may be written:

$$2PbNa_2 + 4C_2H_5Br \rightarrow Pb(C_2H_5)_4 + Pb + 4NaBr$$
$$3PbNa_2 + 6C_2H_5Br \rightarrow Pb_2(C_2H_5)_6 + Pb + 6NaBr$$
$$2Pb_2(C_2H_5)_6 \rightarrow 3Pb(C_2H_5)_4 + Pb$$

There is no evidence that $Pb(C_2H_5)_2$ is formed in these reactions, even as an intermediate.

MERTHIOLATE
SODIUM ETHYLMERCURITHIOSALICYLATE

COONa

S·Hg·C₂H₅

The antiseptic merthiolate, which contains 49 per cent of mercury in organic combination, is an example of an alkyl group bound to mercury. This product is much less toxic than mercuric chloride. It is an effective germicide for spore bearing and non-spore bearing bacteria, and it remains active in the presence of serum and tissue exudates. It is employed for sterilizing skin surfaces and mucous membranes and for disinfecting instruments.

This compound is prepared according to the patents by Kharasch,[1] and the following are the reactions involved:

$$C_2H_5MgBr + HgCl_2 \rightarrow C_2H_5HgCl + MgBrCl$$
$$C_2H_5HgCl + NaOH \rightarrow C_2H_5HgOH + NaCl$$

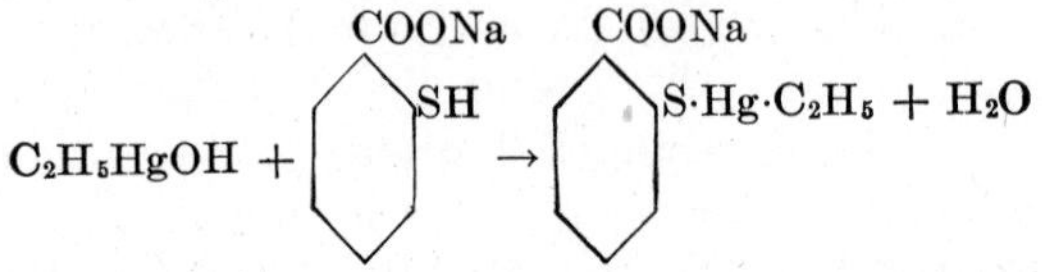

The proportions and the conditions used for making this compound are covered by Waldo's description,[2] wherein ethylmercuric chloride, moistened with alcohol, is treated with 2 moles of caustic soda solution and with a 95 per cent alcoholic solution containing 1 mole of thiosalicylic acid. After filtering the solution, the ethylmercurithiosalicylic acid is precipitated by acidifying with 10 per cent sulfuric acid. Crystallization from 95 per cent alcohol results in a yield of 80 to 85 per cent. Exact neutralization of the pure acid with caustic soda gives merthiolate.

Kharasch and Marker[3] and Waldo[4] studied the stability of ethylmercurithiosalicylic acid and related compounds and found that the higher homologues in the alkyl series are more stable than the lower members and that aryl groups are less stable than alkyl or aralkyl groups. The germicidal value in relation to toxicity was decreased when the ethyl group was changed to methyl or isoamyl.

[1] U. S. 1,589,599 (1926); reissue 16,921 (1927); 1,672,615 (1928).
[2] WALDO, J. Am. Chem. Soc., **53**, 992 (1931).
[3] KHARASCH and MARKER, J. Am. Chem. Soc., **48**, 3130 (1926).
[4] WALDO, loc. cit.

CHAPTER X

ESTERIFICATION

By E. Emmet Reid

An ester is usually defined as a compound formed by substituting a group such as ethyl ($-C_2H_5$) for the ionizable H of an acid. In many instances it is probably more accurate to regard it as an alcohol of which the hydroxyl H has been replaced by the acyl group—$C\overset{\diagup O}{\underset{\diagdown R}{}}$.

In this chapter, esterification will be considered in the broadest sense of the word as including all processes by which esters are produced. The great commercial importance of esters is a matter of recent development. For that reason, and because some limit must be set, the references given are mostly for the last thirty years, except a few of historical interest. The references are by no means complete, but it is hoped that enough have been given so that the student may obtain a picture of developments. Attention is called to articles by Keyes[1] and Schotz[2] on special phases of this subject and to a review of recent developments.[3] It has been thought best to give the processes in broad outline, emphasizing the principles that underlie them. The principles are matters of general knowledge and do not change; the details of their application vary from time to time and from plant to plant and are usually kept secret as long as they are of private advantage. In fact, there is no absolutely best way to make any one ester such as ethyl acetate; an experienced and skillful operator can determine the most economical method for a certain scale of operation to produce a specified grade of ester with acetic acid, alcohol, and steam at certain prices; but for another scale or with materials at other prices, an entirely different process may have the advantage. Anyone with a thorough understanding of the principles can apply them to special cases as they arise. Manufacturing processes are given for several esters, but these are presented as examples of how the principles may be applied, rather than as recipes.

I. ESTERIFICATION REACTIONS

A number of reactions by which esters are produced is listed. These may be divided into groups—those in which two compounds react to

---

[1] Keyes, *Ind. Eng. Chem.*, **24**, 1096 (1932).

[2] Schotz, *Chem. Age*, **9**, 446 (1923).

[3] Reid, *Ind. Eng. Chem.*, **29**, 1344 (1937).

give an ester and a second compound, as is the case when an acid reacts with an alcohol; and those in which an ester is formed by the addition of one compound to another, as when ethylene is taken up by sulfuric acid.

In direct esterification, an alcohol reacts with an acid, either organic or inorganic:

$$CH_3COOH + HOC_2H_5 \rightleftarrows CH_3COOC_2H_5 + H_2O \tag{1}$$
$$\text{Acetic Acid} \quad \text{Ethyl Alcohol} \quad \text{Ethyl Acetate}$$

$$C_2H_5OH + HNO_3 \rightarrow C_2H_5ONO_2 + H_2O \tag{2}$$
$$\text{Ethyl Nitrate}$$

$$C_2H_5OH + HO \cdot SO_2 \cdot OH \rightleftarrows C_2H_5O \cdot SO_2 \cdot OH + H_2O \tag{3}$$
$$\text{Monoethyl Sulfate}$$

Closely allied with direct esterification are alcoholysis, in which an alcohol displaces another alcohol, and acidolysis, in which an acid drives out another acid:

$$CH_3COOC_2H_5 + HOCH_3 \rightleftarrows CH_3COOCH_3 + HOC_2H_5 \tag{4}$$
$$CH_3COOC_2H_5 + C_5H_{11}COOH \rightleftarrows C_5H_{11}COOC_2H_5 + CH_3COOH \tag{5}$$

An exchange of alkyls may take place between two esters:

$$C_6H_5COOC_2H_5 + CH_3COOCH_2C_6H_5 \rightleftarrows C_6H_5COOCH_2C_6H_5 + CH_3COOC_2H_5 \tag{6}$$
$$\text{Ethyl Benzoate} \quad \text{Benzyl Acetate} \quad \text{Benzyl Benzoate} \quad \text{Ethyl Acetate}$$

These reactions appear to be much like those that take place with inorganic acids, bases, and salts, but the resemblance is in form only, as the mechanisms are probably far different.

An amide, which is the nitrogen analogue of an acid, may react with an alcohol:

$$CH_3CONH_2 + C_2H_5OH \rightleftarrows CH_3COOC_2H_5 + NH_3 \tag{7}$$

An acid anhydride or chloride may react with an alcohol or phenol or their sodium derivatives:

$$C_2H_5OH + (CH_3CO)_2O \rightarrow CH_3COOC_2H_5 + CH_3COOH \tag{8}$$
$$(CH_3)_3COH + (CH_3CO)_2O \rightarrow CH_3COOC(CH_3)_3 + CH_3COOH \tag{9}$$
$$C_6H_5ONa + (CH_3CO)_2O \rightarrow CH_3COOC_6H_5 + CH_3COONa \tag{10}$$
$$C_2H_5OH + ClCOCl \rightarrow C_2H_5OCOCl + HCl \tag{11}$$
$$C_2H_5OH + C_2H_5OCOCl \rightarrow (C_2H_5O)_2CO + HCl \tag{12}$$
$$3C_2H_5ONa + Cl_3PO \rightarrow (C_2H_5O)_3PO + 3NaCl \tag{13}$$
$$C_6H_5ONa + CH_3COCl \rightarrow C_6H_5OCOCH_3 + NaCl \tag{14}$$

The salt of an acid may react with an alkyl or aralkyl halide:

$$CH_3COONa + C_2H_5Br \rightarrow CH_3COOC_2H_5 + NaBr \tag{15}$$
$$\text{Sodium Acetate} \quad \text{Ethyl Acetate}$$

$$CH_3COONa + C_6H_5CH_2Cl \rightarrow CH_3COOCH_2C_6H_5 + NaCl \tag{16}$$
$$\text{Benzyl Chloride} \quad \text{Benzyl Acetate}$$

In all of the above, the formation of the by-product water, hydrogen chloride, or sodium chloride is very important from the energy standpoint. Thermodynamically, reactions (13), (14), and (16), for example, may be regarded as syntheses of sodium chloride, since the intense affinity of sodium and chlorine for each other is the driving force that causes these reactions to go. The yield of sodium chloride is quantitative; the other parts of the original molecules may get together to form the ester, or they may not.

In the second group are placed reactions in which esters are formed by the addition of two compounds. In these reactions, the driving force may be some sort of strained condition in a double bond or the possibility of rearranging the atoms so as better to satisfy their affinities.

As a sort of transition between the two groups, we may put the reaction of the anhydride of a dibasic acid with an alcohol or a sodium alcoholate:

$$C_6H_4{<}^{CO}_{CO}{>}O + C_2H_5OH \rightarrow C_6H_4{<}^{COOC_2H_5}_{COOH} \tag{17}$$

$$CS_2 + C_2H_5ONa \rightarrow SC{<}^{OC_2H_5}_{SNa} \tag{18}$$

In reaction (17), an ester and an acid are formed as in (9), but, being parts of the same molecule, they remain together.

In esterification according to reaction (1), a molecule of water is eliminated, part coming from the alcohol and part from the acid. If a whole molecule of water is eliminated from either the alcohol or the acid previously, an ester can be formed by simple addition. Thus, ketene ($CH_2:CO$) is acetic acid minus a molecule of water; and phenyl isocyanate bears the same relation to phenylcarbamic acid:

$$CH_3COOH - H_2O = CH_2:CO \tag{19}$$
$$C_6H_5NH{\cdot}CO{\cdot}OH - H_2O = C_6H_5N:C:O \tag{20}$$

Ketene and phenyl isocyanate both add to an alcohol to form an ester:

$$CH_2:CO + C_2H_5OH \rightarrow CH_3COOC_2H_5 \tag{21}$$
$$C_6H_5N:CO + C_2H_5OH \rightarrow C_6H_5NHCOOC_2H_5 \tag{22}$$

These reactions take place spontaneously, the driving force being the unsaturation.

Ethylene is alcohol minus a molecule of water and adds directly to acids:

$$CH_2:CH_2 + H_2SO_4 \rightarrow CH_3CH_2OSO_3H \tag{23}$$
$$CH_2:CH_2 + CH_3COOH \rightarrow CH_3COOC_2H_5 \tag{24}$$

The addition of an acid such as acetic takes place only in the presence of sulfuric acid or other catalyst, and it is probably more correct to say that the ethyl acetate is formed by the action of the acetic acid on the ethylsulfuric acid in the equation above.

Subtracting a molecule of water from the unstable ethylidene glycol, we have the hypothetical vinyl alcohol; and taking away another, acetylene is left:

$$CH_3 \cdot CH(OH)_2 - H_2O = CH_2 : CHOH \tag{25}$$
$$CH_2 : CHOH - H_2O = CH : CH \tag{26}$$

Acetylene takes up one molecule of acetic acid to give vinyl acetate or two to form ethylidene acetate:

$$CH : CH + CH_3COOH \rightarrow CH_3COOCH : CH_2 \tag{27}$$
$$CH : CH + 2HOCOCH_3 \rightarrow CH_3CH(OCOCH_3)_2 \tag{28}$$

The passage of a nitrile into an ester may be represented as the addition of a molecule of water and one of alcohol:

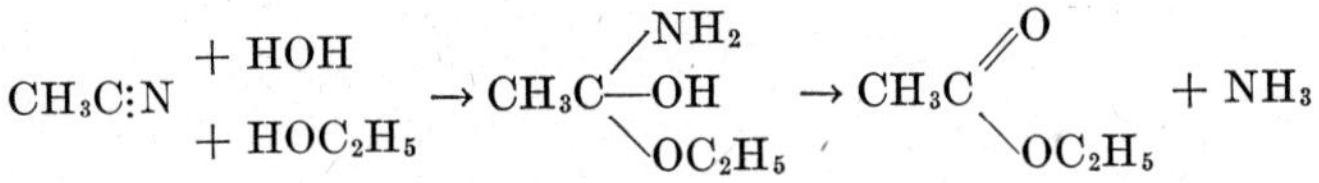

$$CH_3C:N \begin{array}{l} + HOH \\ + HOC_2H_5 \end{array} \rightarrow CH_3C\begin{array}{l} \diagup NH_2 \\ -OH \\ \diagdown OC_2H_5 \end{array} \rightarrow CH_3C\begin{array}{l} \diagup\!\!\!\diagup O \\ \diagdown OC_2H_5 \end{array} + NH_3 \tag{29}$$

To avoid assuming a third-order reaction, we may assume that the molecule of water is taken up to form the amide, which is then esterified [reaction (7)]; or that the alcohol is added to give an iminoester, which is hydrolyzed:

$$CH_3C:N + H_2O \rightarrow CH_3CONH_2$$
$$CH_3C:N + HOC_2H_5 \rightarrow CH_3C(:NH)OC_2H_5$$
$$CH_3C(:NH)OC_2H_5 + H_2O \rightarrow CH_3COOC_2H_5 + NH_3$$

Subtracting a molecule of water from ethylene glycol, we have ethylene oxide, which adds to an acid to give a mono-ester of glycol:

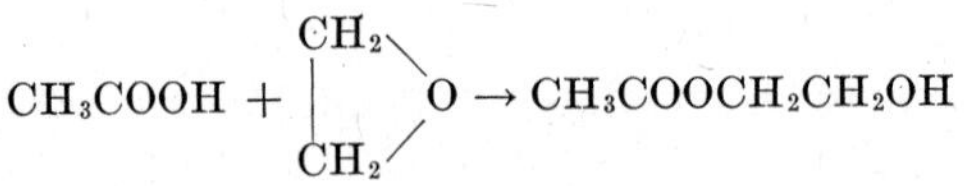

$$CH_3COOH + \begin{array}{l} CH_2 \\ | \quad\diagdown \\ \quad\quad O \rightarrow CH_3COOCH_2CH_2OH \\ | \quad\diagup \\ CH_2 \end{array} \tag{30}$$

There is another reaction that does not come under any one of these classes, and that is the combination of two molecules of an aldehyde to give one of an ester:

$$2CH_3CHO \rightarrow CH_3COOCH_2CH_3 \tag{31}$$

Carbon monoxide, the anhydride of formic acid, may combine with an alcohol:

$$CO + ROH \rightarrow HCOOR \tag{32}$$

Carbon monoxide may unite with an alcohol to give an acid, which may then react with another molecule of the alcohol to form an ester:

$$CO + CH_3OH \rightarrow CH_3COOH \tag{33}$$
$$CO + 2CH_3OH \rightarrow CH_3COOCH_3 + H_2O \tag{34}$$

Esterification with Inorganic Acids.—In esterification by inorganic acids, theory has received little attention, but practice has gone far, particularly in nitration [reaction (2)]:

$$C_2H_5OH + HNO_3 \rightarrow C_2H_5ONO_2 + H_2O$$

$$\underset{\text{Glycol}}{C_2H_4(OH)_2} + 2HNO_3 \rightarrow \underset{\text{Glycol Dinitrate}}{C_2H_4(ONO_2)_2} + 2H_2O$$

$$\underset{\text{Glycerol}}{C_3H_5(OH)_3} + 3HNO_3 \rightarrow \underset{\text{Glyceryl Trinitrate}}{C_3H_5(ONO_2)_3} + 3H_2O$$

$$\underset{\text{Cellulose Unit}}{[C_6H_7O_2(OH)_3]} + 3HNO_3 - \underset{\text{Nitrocellulose Unit}}{[C_6H_7O_2(ONO_2)_3]} + 3H_2O$$

There are two cases: The alcoholic compound, such as glycerol, may dissolve in the acid or may be insoluble, as is the case with cellulose. In both cases, the operations are simple, though the working out of the exact details for obtaining the desired products in high purity and good yields has required much painstaking experimentation. So-called *mixed acid,* which is employed in nitrations, is a mixture of nitric and sulfuric acids and may contain water or sulfur trioxide, the concentrations of these being accurately adjusted to give the desired intensity of reaction.

In the nitration of cellulose, the reaction is carried out under accurately controlled conditions, so that a product is obtained with the desired properties. These properties are different according to the use for which the material is destined. The product, nitrocotton, is always classified by the percentage of nitrogen that it contains. In carrying out the reaction, the most important thing is uniformity of action, since the value of the product is largely dependent on its approach to homogeneity.

A monosulfate is formed when sulfuric acid reacts with an alcohol [reaction (3)]:

$$C_2H_5OH + HO\cdot SO_2\cdot OH \leftrightharpoons C_2H_5O\cdot SO_2OH + H_2O \qquad (3)$$

This reaction is used for converting the higher alcohols into their monosulfates, which have recently come into use as detergents and wetting agents.

$$C_{12}H_{25}OH + H_2SO_4 \rightarrow C_{12}H_{25}OSO_2OH + H_2O$$

The reactions of alcohols with nitric and sulfuric acids slow down and come to a standstill when the water formed accumulates. They are aided by an excess of sulfuric acid or sulfur trioxide.

An alkyl monosulfate may be made in quite a different manner by the addition of an unsaturated hydrocarbon to sulfuric acid, as represented in reaction (23):

$$CH_2:CH_2 + H_2SO_4 \rightarrow CH_3CH_2OSO_2OH \qquad (23)$$

The addition takes place on simple contact of the hydrocarbon with the acid, but the speed of the reaction depends on the strength of the acid and the nature of the hydrocarbon. To keep down polymerization and isomerization of the hydrocarbons, the temperature is kept relatively low, usually below about 40°C. and commonly lower than that—even down to 0°C. The sulfuric acid may be from 10 to 100 per cent or may even contain some sulfur trioxide, the strength used depending on the hydrocarbon. Some of the terpenes react with the 10 per cent acid, while ethylene reacts extremely slowly with acid of less than 90 per cent. When a reactive hydrocarbon is shaken with the 10 per cent acid, the alkylsulfuric acid may be formed and hydrolyzed immediately, so that apparently the hydrocarbon simply takes up a molecule of water. By choosing the right strength of sulfuric acid, the absorption may be made selective, so that certain unsaturated hydrocarbons are taken out of a mixture. Thus, if a mixture of ethylene and propylene is brought into contact with 85 per cent sulfuric acid, the propylene is completely absorbed and the ethylene practically untouched. The normal butylenes are absorbed by somewhat weaker sulfuric acid than is propylene, but the difference in reactivity is not sufficient for a sharp separation.[1] Isobutylene reacts particularly readily and may be selectively absorbed by 65 per cent sulfuric acid with cooling.

The best known case of the use of this reaction is the manufacture of "Petrohol," or isopropyl alcohol, from cracking still gases. The more easily condensable constituents of the still gas, the butylenes and higher, are removed by condensation or absorption; and the residue, consisting of ethylene and propylene (with some hydrogen, methane, and ethane), is cooled and passed up through towers over the packing of which 85 per cent sulfuric acid flows. The acid, which is largely isopropylsulfuric acid, is drawn off at the bottom of the tower, diluted with water, and boiled. The isopropylsulfuric acid is hydrolyzed, and the isopropyl alcohol distills over. Under 100 lb. pressure a second molecule of propylene is taken up to form isopropyl sulfate, which separates on the addition of water.[2]

Ethyl sulfate may be obtained by distilling the ethylsulfuric acid at 10 mm.[3] Methyl sulfate may be made by combining sulfur trioxide directly with methyl ether.[4]

---

[1] Apgar, U. S. 1,846,666; N.-V. de Bataafsche Petroleum-Maatschappij, Ger. 541,628; Fr. 718,943; 730,829; Dutch 25,123; 27,237; Brooks, U. S. 1,879,599; 1,894,-661; 1,904,200; Davis, U. S. 1,844,208; Engs and Moravec, U. S. 1,854,581; Can. 323,969; Markovich and Pigulerskii, *J. Russ. Phys. Chem. Soc.*, 24, 880 (1892); 25, 599 (1893); Taveau, U. S. 1,845,007.

[2] Brooks, U. S. 1,919,617.

[3] Kuh, U. S. 1,411,215; Lillienfeld, U. S. 1,074,633; Ger. 272,339.

[4] Haworth and Irvine, U. S. 1,401,693.

By adding an organic acid, or a salt from which one may be set free, to the alkylsulfuric acid, an ester of the organic acid is obtained.[1]

Esterification with Organic Acids.—This is esterification in its narrow sense and is what comes to mind when the term is used. It has long excited the curiosity of chemists and has been extensively studied by both organic and physical chemists. It has been one of the most useful reactions in preparative organic chemistry, one of the best examples of the application of the mass-action law, and one of the most baffling problems in homogeneous catalysis.

That an alcohol heated with an acid gives an ester and that the ester heated with water reverts to the alcohol and acid has long been a well-known fact; *i.e.*, the reaction

$$C_2H_5OH + HOCOCH_3 \rightleftarrows C_2H_5OCOCH_3 + H_2O$$

is reversible, but it remained for Berthelot and Péan de St. Gilles,[2] in 1862, to make exact measurements on it and determine the equilibrium point. The numerous experiments that they performed were simple but were carried out with painstaking accuracy. They heated ethyl alcohol with one equivalent of acetic acid at 100, 170, and 200°C. for definite intervals of time, which were increased until the ester content of the mixture became constant. The reactants were weighed into small glass tubes, which were sealed off, heated the requisite time, cooled, broken open, and the remaining acid titrated. At 100°C. in 200 hr., 65.6 per cent of ester was formed; at 170° in 24 hr., 66.5 per cent; and at 200° in the same time, 67.3 per cent. Starting from the other end, they heated ethyl acetate with an equivalent of water and found that equilibrium was reached at the same point. They tried several equivalents of acid to one of the alcohol and found that higher percentages of it esterified. Similarly, they showed that two or more equivalents of alcohol to one of acid give correspondingly higher amounts of ester. They performed similar experiments with other alcohols and acids and obtained similar results. They left some samples of the alcohol-acetic acid mixture sealed up at room temperature for fifteen years and found 65.2 per cent of ester. Their results were discussed by Van't Hoff, Thomsen, and others[3] and found to be in accordance with the mass-action law.

[1] Archibald and Lebo, U. S. 1,844,536; Ellis and Cohen, U. S. 1,365,049; 1,365; Frolich and Young, U. S. 1,877,291; Hunt, Brit. 173,538; 173,786; Lommel and Engelhardt, U. S. 1,903,868; Merley and Spring, U. S. 1,924,615; Shukoff, Brit. 20,526; SIMON, *Compt. rend.*, **176**, 583 (1923); Spring, U. S. 1,924,575; Wilson, U. S. 1,979,575.

[2] BERTHELOT, *Ann. chim.* [3], **66**, 110 (1862); **68**, 274 (1863); [5], **14**, 437 (1878); **15**, 220, 238 (1878); *Bull. soc. chim.* [2], **31**, 341 (1879); BERTHELOT and PÉAN DE ST. GILLES, *Ann. chim.* [3], **65**, 385 (1862); **66**, 5 (1862); **68**, 225 (1863).

[3] VAN'T HOFF, *Ber.*, **10**, 669 (1877); THOMSEN, *Ber.*, **10**, 1023 (1877); URECH, *Ber.*, **19**, 1700 (1886).

Writing the reaction after the manner of physical chemists as an equilibrium, we have:

$$\frac{[\text{Ester}] \times [\text{water}]}{[\text{Acid}] \times [\text{alcohol}]} = K$$

This means that the product of the concentrations of ester and water divided by the product of the concentrations of acid and alcohol is equal to a constant. The constancy of this K has been questioned.[1] Recent data are:[2] for ethyl alcohol and acetic acid, 1:1, $K = 3.82$ and 3.74;

TABLE I.—RATES AND LIMITS OF ESTERIFICATION
Acetic acid at 155°C. with Various Alcohols

No.	Alcohol	Per cent conversion		K
		1 hr.	Limit	
1	Methyl	55.59	69.59	5.24
2	Ethyl	46.95	66.57	3.96
3	Propyl	46.92	66.85	4.07
4	Butyl	46.85	67.30	4.24
5	Allyl	35.72	59.41	2.18
6	Benzyl	38.64	60.75	2.39
7	Dimethylcarbinol	26.53	60.52	2.35
8	Methylethylcarbinol	22.59	59.28	2.12
9	Methylisopropylcarbinol	18.95	59.31	2.12
10	Diethylcarbinol	16.93	58.66	2.01
11	Methylhexylcarbinol	21.19	62.03	2.67
12	Diallylcarbinol	10.31	50.12	1.01
13	Menthol	15.29	61.49	2.55
14	Trimethylcarbinol	1.43	6.59	0.0049
15	Dimethylethylcarbinol	0.81	2.53	0.00067
16	Methyldiethylcarbinol	1.04	3.78	0.0015
17	Dimethylpropylcarbinol	2.15	0.83	0.000070
18	Dimethylisopropylcarbinol	0.86	0.85	0.000073
19	Phenol	1.45	8.64	0.0089
20	Thymol	0.55	9.46	0.0192

for 3:1, 2.47 and 2.52; and for 1:3, 4.74 and 4.95. Its value is altered by the presence of salts.[3] For the acetic acid-water mixture, this would be:

$$\frac{66.5 \times 66.5}{33.5 \times 33.5} = K = 3.94$$

[1] CORSO and DURRUTY, *Anales asoc. quím. Argentina*, **20**, 140 (1932); KNOBLAUCH, *Z. physik. Chem.*, **22**, 268 (1897); POZNANSKI, *Roczniki Chem.*, **8**, 377 (393 Eng.) (1928).

[2] SWIETOSLAWSKI, *J. Phys. Chem.*, **37**, 701 (1933); CORIA, *Rev. facultad cienc. quím. (Univ. La Plata)*, **10**, 67 (1935).

[3] CANTELO and BILLINGER, *J. Am. Chem. Soc.*, **50**, 3212 (1928); SCHLESINGER, *Ber.*, **59**, 1965 (1926); SCHLESINGER and MALKINA-OKUN, *Ber.*, **60**, 1479 (1927).

Menschutkin[1] made a comparative study of a large number of acids and alcohols. He found striking differences among primary, secondary, and tertiary alcohols, as to both the rates and the limits of esterification. Table I gives some of his results for acetic acid heated to 155°C. with equivalent amounts of various alcohols. The mixtures were heated for 1 hour to find the relative rates and for a much longer time—usually 100 or 200 hr.—to get the limits.

It will be observed that of all the alcohols studied, methyl shows the greatest initial velocity and the highest limit. The primary alcohols, ethyl, propyl, and butyl, have approximately the same initial velocities and limits but are inferior to methyl alcohol in both of these respects. Allyl alcohol is much slower than propyl, the saturated alcohol with the same number of carbon atoms. The presence of the phenyl group in benzyl has a retarding influence.

The secondary alcohols (Nos. 7 to 13, Table I) are markedly lower than the primary in both initial velocity and limit but vary considerably among themselves. The tertiary alcohols (Nos. 14 to 18) show little esterification in 1 hr. and hardly any more in 100. In the case of the tertiary alcohols, the "limit" is seldom if ever reliable, since there is such a great tendency for these alcohols to split off water, leaving unsaturated hydrocarbons. It is not unusual with tertiary alcohols to find less ester after long than after short heating. Phenol and thymol, which may be regarded as tertiary alcohols but which cannot split off water, show low initial velocities but comparatively high limits.

As was pointed out by Michael,[2] the three classes of alcohols are not always sharply separated as in the above examples; *i.e.*, some tertiary alcohols may go as fast and as far as certain secondaries, and primary alcohols have been found that do not esterify so readily or so completely as some secondary. The general statement is that the more branched the carbon chain and the nearer the branches are to the hydroxyl group the slower will be its esterification and the lower the limit. Many other more or less similar studies have been made.[3]

[1] MENSCHUTKIN, *Ann.*, **195**, 334 (1879); **197**, 193 (1879); *Ber.*, **13**, 162 (1880); *Ann. chim.* (5), **23**, 14 (1881); **30**, 81 (1883); *Z. physik. Chem.*, **1**, 611 (1887); **9**, 237 (1892); *Ber.*, **42**, 4020 (1909).

[2] MICHAEL, *Ber.*, **42**, 310 (1909); **43**, 464 (1910); MICHAEL and OECHSLIN, *Ber.*, **42**, 317 (1909); MICHAEL and WOLGAST, *Ber.*, **42**, 3157 (1909).

[3] CAUQUIL, *J. chim. phys.*, **23**, 586 (1926); CHARABOT and HÉBERT, *Bull. soc. chim.* [3], **25**, 884, 955 (1901); DOBROCHOTOW, *J. Russ. Phys. Chem. Soc.* [6], **27**, 341 (1895); *Z. physik. Chem.* **23**, 555 (1897); DOLEMAN, Thesis, Mass. Inst. Technol., 1931; MARCKWALD and McKENZIE, *Ber.*, **32**, 2130 (1899); MEISENHEIMER and SCHMIDT, *Ann.*, **475**, 157 (1929); PANOFF, *J. Russ. Phys. Chem. Soc.*, **35**, 93 (1903); PETRENKO-KRITSCHENKO, BOGATSKY and LUBMAN, *Z. physik. Chem.*, **115**, 289 (1925); PRAGER, *Z. physik. Chem.*, **66**, 292 (1909); REICHER, *Ann.*, **228**, 257 (1885); SKRABAL and

Mercaptans, or thioalcohols, are esterified under the same conditions as alcohols, the products being thiol esters for the most part:[1]

$$CH_3COOH + HSC_2H_5 \rightleftarrows CH_3COSC_2H_5 + H_2O$$

The reaction is reversible, the same equilibrium point being reached from either end; but the limit is far lower than with the corresponding alcohols, as can be seen in Table II.

TABLE II.—ESTERIFICATION LIMITS OF MERCAPTANS

Acid	Methyl	Ethyl	Propyl	n-Butyl	sec-Butyl
Acetic.....................	16.21	13.02	12.75		
Propionic..................	15.26	11.64	11.29		
Benzoic...................	19.2	15.0	14.60	14.38	8.93

The mercaptans show the same relative positions as do the corresponding alcohols.[2]

Similar experiments were made by Menschutkin, using isobutyl alcohol with a variety of acids. Some of the results are given in Table III.

TABLE III.—RATES AND LIMITS OF ESTERIFICATION, ISOBUTYL ALCOHOL WITH VARIOUS ACIDS AT 155°C.

No.	Acid	1 hr.	Limit	K
1	Formic	61.69	64.23	3.22
2	Acetic	44.36	67.38	4.27
3	Propionic	41.18	68.70	4.82
4	Butyric	33.25	69.52	5.20
5	Isobutyric	29.03	69.51	5.20
6	Methylethylacetic	21.50	73.73	7.88
7	Trimethylacetic	8.28	72.65	7.06
8	Dimethylethylacetic	3.45	74.15	8.23
9	Phenylacetic	48.82	73.87	7.99
10	Phenylpropionic	40.26	72.02	7.60
11	Cinnamic	11.55	74.61	8.63
12	Hydrosorbic	43.00	70.83	5.90
13	Sorbic	7.96	74.72	8.74
14	Benzoic	8.62	72.57	7.00
15	p-Toluic	6.64	76.52	10.62

MATIEVIC, Monatsh., **45**, 39 (1924); VAVON and GUEDON, Bull. soc. chim. [4], **47**, 901 (1930); WILCOX and BRUNEL, J. Am. Chem. Soc., **38**, 1821 (1916).

[1] REID, Am. Chem. J., **43**, 489 (1910); STEWART and McKINNEY, J. Am. Chem. Soc., **53**, 1482 (1931).

[2] FABER and REID, J. Am. Chem. Soc., **39**, 1930 (1917); KIMBALL and REID, J. Am. Chem. Soc., **38**, 2757 (1916); PRATT and REID, J. Am. Chem. Soc., **37**, 1934 (1915); SACHS and REID, J. Am. Chem. Soc., **38**, 2746 (1916).

By examining the data for the per cent conversion for the first hour, we are struck with the similarity of their relationships to those observed in Table I. Formic acid reacts much more rapidly than the other straight-chain acids; and the branched-chain acids trimethylacetic and dimethylethylacetic are particularly slow. The introduction of a phenyl group, as in Nos. 9 and 10, does not retard esterification, but the purely aromatic acids benzoic and p-toluic are very slow. Contrasting cinnamic with phenylpropionic and sorbic with hydrosorbic, we see that the double bond has a marked retarding effect. Maleic acid is esterified fourteen times as rapidly as fumaric.[1] An alcohol dissolved in excess of formic acid is esterified several thousand times as rapidly as in acetic.[2]

While, with the alcohols, slow esterification and a low limit go together, it is quite otherwise with the acids. Thus, dimethylethylacetic acid gives only 3.4 per cent of ester in 1 hr. but finally, after 500 or 600 hr., reaches a limit that is even higher than the limit for acetic acid. The unsaturated acids, cinnamic and sorbic, start off much more slowly than the corresponding saturated acids but go somewhat further. Formic acid, which has an extremely high initial rate, has a relatively low limit.

A special case which has received much attention is that of 2,6-disubstituted benzoic acids, which, as shown by Victor Meyer and others,[3] are esterified with extreme slowness. Even one ortho group has a marked effect; methyl reduces the esterification velocity of benzoic acid by 68%, ethyl by 80 and propyl by 83.[4]

The experiments cited above were with equivalent amounts of alcohols and acids; but by assuming that the mass-action law holds, we can calculate the percentage of an alcohol that will be esterified when more than one equivalent of acid is used. If x is the percentage of ester formed, it will also be the percentage of water, and we have, when n equivalents of alcohols are used to 1 of acid:

$$\frac{[\text{Ester}] \times [\text{water}]}{[\text{Acid}] \times [\text{alcohol}]} = K = \frac{x^2}{(100 - x)(100n - x)}$$

In the case of acetic acid and ethyl alcohol, K was found to be 3.94. If we take $K = 4$ and use 5 moles of alcohol to 1 of acetic acid this becomes

$$\frac{x^2}{(100 - x)(500 - x)} = 4$$

Solving this, we get 94.5 per cent. In an actual experiment, Berthelot

[1] Schwab, Rec. trav. chim., **2**, 46 (1883).

[2] Kailan and coworkers, Monatsh., **62**, 284 (1933); **63**, 155 (1933); **68**, 109 (1936).

[3] Meyer, Ber., **27**, 510 (1894); **28**, 182, 2773 and 3197 (1895); Hufferd and Noyes, J. Am. Chem. Soc., **43**, 925 (1921); Prager, J. Am. Chem. Soc., **30**, 1908 (1908); Rosanoff and Prager, J. Am. Chem. Soc., **30**, 1895 (1908).

[4] Zwecker, Ber., **68**, 1289 (1935).

and Péan de St. Gilles heated 1 mole of acetic acid with 5 of ethyl alcohol for 83 hr. at 100°C. and found 96.6 per cent of it esterified. In another experiment in which the proportions were reversed, they found 97.2 per cent of the alcohol esterified in 330 days at room temperature. Considering the difficulty of handling volatile liquids without loss and the limited accuracy of titration methods, these results are in close agreement with the calculated.

It is evident, however, that no matter what excess of one reactant, the other is never completely used up. Practically, an excess of one of the reactants is nearly always employed so as to use up the other as completely as possible. Which of the reactants is to be used in excess is determined by their relative costs and the ease of recovery. Thus, ethyl alcohol is relatively cheap and is readily recovered with small loss by distillation; so in making ethyl esters, a large excess of the alcohol is commonly put in, while the reverse is the case when expensive alcohols are to be esterified with acetic acid. However, a large excess of one of the reactants may make the separation and purification of the ester more difficult or may be undesirable for other reasons.

II. SPEEDING UP ESTERIFICATION

If from a mixture of acetic acid and ethyl alcohol, standing at room temperature, samples are taken out and titrated every now and then, a slow decrease in acidity can be observed; but days and even months will elapse before the minimum value, or limit, is reached. Like most other reactions, the speed of esterification approximately doubles with a 10°C. rise in temperature. According to this rule, it should go sixty-four times as rapidly at the boiling point of alcohol as at 18°C., going as far in a single minute at the higher temperature as in an hour at the lower. Hence, it has been customary to use heat to speed up esterification reactions. From the figures given above, it appears that the limit is not reached in an hour even at 155°C., a temperature inconveniently high when low-boiling acids and alcohols are concerned. Except in the case of a high-boiling alcohol such as glycerol with a high-boiling acid such as stearic, esterification cannot be effected at atmospheric pressure in a reasonable time without some other means of speeding up the reaction. Fortunately, there is such a means.

Catalytic Esterification.—It has long been known that the process of esterification may be enormously hastened by the addition of a strong acid, such as sulfuric or hydrochloric. The limit of the reaction is not greatly altered, as was shown by Berthelot,[1] who added 0.67, 4.77, and 11.84 gm., respectively, of hydrogen chloride to three 106-gm. portions

---

[1] BERTHELOT and PÉAN DE ST. GILLES, *Ann. chim. phys.* [3], **65**, 385 (1862); **66**, 5 (1862); **68**, 225 (1863).

of acetic acid and ethyl alcohol in equivalent amounts. After 10 hr. at 100°C., he found the limits in the three mixtures to be 67.6, 68.8, and 62.0 per cent of ester. In the one containing 11.84 gm. of the catalyst, some of the alcohol was used up in the formation of ethyl chloride. In 1883, Ostwald[1] found a close relation between the activity of an acid in the hydrolysis of methyl acetate and in the inversion of sugar with its conductivity and concluded that the acceleration is due to the hydrogen ion. Some of his figures are given in Table IV.

The same figures may be taken as representing the relative efficiency of these acids as catalysts in the reverse reaction of esterification. It will be noted that the very strong acids have nearly the same effect while the organic acids with the exception of oxalic are poor catalysts. The introduction of chlorine into acetic acid greatly increases its strength. Sulfuric acid appears to be only slightly more than half as effective as hydrochloric, i.e., if it is counted as dibasic, while ethylsulfuric and ethylsulfonic rank with the strongest.

TABLE IV.—RELATIVE RATES OF HYDROLYSIS OF METHYL ACETATE WITH VARIOUS ACIDS AS CATALYSTS

Acid	Rate of hydrolysis, %	Acid	Rate of hydrolysis, %
Hydrochloric............	100	Benzenesulfonic.........	99.0
Hydrobromic............	89.3	Oxalic................	17.46
Nitric.................	91.5	Malonic...............	2.87
Sulfuric................	54.7	Succinic...............	0.496
Ethylsulfuric............	98.7	Malic.................	1.18
Ethylsulfonic............	97.9	Tartaric...............	2.30
Chloroacetic............	4.3	Formic................	1.31
Dichloroacetic...........	23.0	Acetic................	0.345
Trichloroacetic..........	68.2	Lactic................	0.901

In general practice, hydrochloric and sulfuric acids are the ones most commonly used,[2] the former being in favor in the laboratory on account of its efficiency, and the latter in the plant on account of its cheapness and because it is less corrosive on metals. Sulfuric acid may cause the dehydration of an alcohol if used in too great an amount or at too high a temperature. Thus, cyclohexanol boiled 30 min. with 2 moles of acetic acid and 3 per cent by volume of sulfuric acid gave

[1] OSTWALD, J. prakt. Chem. [2], **28**, 449 (1883); **30**, 93 (1884); **35**, 122 (1887).

[2] MAILHE, Chem. Ztg., **37**, 777 (1913); SENDERENS and ABOULENC, Compt. rend., **152**, 1671, 1855 (1911); **153**, 881 (1911); **155**, 168, 1254 (1912); **158**, 581 (1914); Ann. chim., **18**, 145 (1922).

30 per cent cyclohexene.   The use of any strong acid as a catalyst may cause isomerization or destruction of a tertiary alcohol such as linalool.

Perchloric and phosphoric acids have been recommended.[1]   Phosphoric acid, while less efficient, is sometimes used on account of its less destructive action.[2]

The sulfonic acids, particularly those containing a considerable number of carbon atoms,[3] are desirable catalysts on account of their high efficiency, solubility in the higher alcohols and acids, and less destructive action.   They do not cause such serious darkening as sulfuric.   The relative cheapness of *p*-toluenesulfonic acid makes it the most commonly used of this class, but it is too expensive for large-scale operations.   Boron and silicon fluorides are efficient catalysts.[4]

Acid salts, such as mono-sodium and mono-potassium sulfates, and salts of strong acids with weak bases, such as aluminum sulfate, have been tried as esterification catalysts.[5]   Senderens and Aboulenc attributed the effectiveness of aluminum sulfate to its great affinity for water, but Phelps and coworkers[6] concluded from comparative measurements that a mole of such a salt as mono-potassium sulfate is less effective than half a mole of sulfuric acid.   The activity of these salts may be attributed to the hydrogen ions that are present in the solutions containing them.

Zinc chloride has been found to be superior to other chlorides when used along with hydrochloric or sulfuric acid.[7]   The use of a large amount of calcium chloride in conjunction with hydrochloric acid has been patented.   The calcium chloride dissolves in the water that is formed in the esterification and causes its separation as a layer.   Ferric chloride[8] and a large number of salts have been recommended.[9]

Many salts, such as the sulfates of zinc, nickel, manganese, and copper, crystallize with water of hydration.   This fact suggested the use of these salts to take up the water that is formed in the esterification reaction.   Some have attributed the accelerating of esterification by

---

[1] Smith and Orton, *J. Chem. Soc.*, **95**, 1060 (1906).

[2] Holzverkohlungs-Industrie, Brit. 295,275; Fr. 657,812; Brit. 320,113.

[3] Twitchell, Brit. 371,689; Ciocca and Semproni, *Ann. chim. applicata*, **25**, 319 (1935); Zaganiaris and Varvoglis, *Ber.*, **69**, 2277 (1936).

[4] Nieuwland and coworkers, *J. Am. Chem. Soc.*, **57**, 1549 (1935); **58**, 271, 786 (1936).

[5] Kotake and Fujita, *Bull. Inst. Phys. Chem. Research (Tokyo)*, **7**, 734; (Eng. ed.) **1**, 65 (1928); Lichtenthaeler, U. S. 1,805,775; Senderens and Aboulenc, *Compt. rend.*, **152**, 1671, 1855; **153**, 881 (1911); **155**, 168, 1254 (1912); **158**, 581 (1914); *Ann. chim.*, **18**, 145 (1922).

[6] Phelps and coworkers, *Am. J. Sci.*, **23**, 368 (1907); **25**, 39 (1908); **26**, 243, 257, 264, 290, 296 (1908).

[7] *Ibid.*

[8] Vassallo, *Olii minerali, dii grassi colori vernici*, **14**, 9 (1934).

[9] Strange and Kane, Fr. 752,008.

sulfuric acid to its known affinity for water.[1] Anhydrous nickel and copper sulfates have given the best results,[2] but as the alcohol-acetic acid mixture was refluxed 264 hr., the action of the copper sulfate cannot be said to be efficient so far as speed is concerned, but it must certainly take care of much of the water formed.

In several patents, the use of metallic soaps is claimed.[3] Aluminum stearate, cobalt linoleate, and lead oleate appear in one; magnesium oleate, in another;[4] and aluminum, magnesium, tin, and zinc soaps, in a third.[5] Metals in the finely divided state are recommended in several other patents,[6] zinc being particularly favored; but tin, manganese, bismuth, lead, silver, and copper also are claimed. An impartial comparison of these catalysts with hydrochloric and sulfuric acids would be interesting.

Alumina prepared in a special way[7] is claimed as an esterification catalyst; so is a *base-exchange material.*[8] In one article[9] and one patent,[10] silica gel is said to be a good catalyst; while in another article[11] it is said to be ineffective.

Ultra-violet light,[12] sound waves,[13] electrical vibrations,[14] and an alternating current[15] have been found to aid in esterifications. An indifferent solvent may influence the reaction. A trace of pyridine was found by one investigator[16] to retard; while others[17] report large amounts of it as being a more effective catalyst than sulfuric acid.[18] A pressure of 1,500 atmospheres accelerated the saponification of ethyl acetate 37 per cent.[19]

The most interesting and mysterious catalysts are enzymes, though they are not employed in commercial esterifications. Enzymes are

[1] Bogojawlensky and Narbutt, *Ber.,* **38,** 3344 (1905); *J. prakt. Chem.* [2], **81,** 420 (1910); Habermann and Brezina, *J. prakt. Chem.* [2], **80,** 349 (1909); Whitacre and Briscoe, *Proc. Indiana Acad. Sci.,* **38,** 187 (1929).

[2] Whitacre and Briscoe, *ibid.*

[3] Adams, Brit. 310,854.

[4] I. G. Farbenindustrie A-G., Fr. 654,535; Brit. 302,411; Ger. 556,658.

[5] *Ibid.*

[6] Gruber, Fr. 677,711; Haddan, Brit. 183,897; I. G. Farbenindustrie A-G., Fr. 654,535; Brit. 302,411; Ger. 556,658.

[7] Mackert, Ger. 486,597.

[8] Jaeger, Brit. 308,582.

[9] Korolev, *J. Chem. Ind. (Moscow),* **4,** 547 (1927).

[10] Rosenstein and Hund, U. S. 1,851,405.

[11] Chelberg and Heisig, *J. Am. Chem. Soc.,* **52,** 3023 (1930).

[12] Störmer and Ladewig, *Ber.,* **47,** 1803 (1914).

[13] Flosdorf and Chambers, *J. Amer. Chem. Soc.,* **55,** 3051 (1933).

[14] Forjaz, *Compt. rend.,* **197,** 1124 (1933).

[15] Spellmeyer, U. S. 2,047,839.

[16] Bailey, *J. Chem. Soc.,* **1928,** 1204, 3256.

[17] Schelsinger and Malkina-Okun, *Ber.,* **60,** 1479 (1927).

[18] Smith and Orton, *J. Chem. Soc.,* **95,** 1060 (1906).

[19] Cohen and Kaiser, *Z. physik. Chem.,* **89,** 338 (1918).

probably responsible for the synthesis and hydrolysis of esters in living organisms. Certain of them, called esterases, cause ester formation *in vitro*. They are sometimes selective in their action on optical isomers.[1]

III. COMPLETING ESTERIFICATION

The practical problem that confronts the chemist in carrying out any reaction is obtaining the largest possible amount of the desired product— as nearly 100 per cent as is possible. The esterification reaction, as has been stated above,

$$CH_3COOH + HOC_2H_5 \rightleftarrows CH_3COOC_2H_5 + H_2O$$

is reversible; *i.e.*, it comes to a standstill when a certain percentage of ester has been produced. We come back to the dictum learned in quantitative analysis: If a gaseous or insoluble product can be formed in a reaction, it will be formed, and the reaction will go to completion in that direction. The equilibrium

$$\frac{[\text{Ester}] \times [\text{water}]}{[\text{Acid}] \times [\text{alcohol}]} = K$$

fixes the relative amounts of the four substances that can coexist. If by some magic a considerable part of either the ester or the water be removed, the equilibrium will be disturbed, and a readjustment must take place. An additional amount of the acid will react with an equivalent amount of alcohol, producing more water and ester until the equilibrium is again established. A numerical example will make this clear. If a mixture of equivalent amounts of acetic acid and alcohol be allowed to come to equilibrium, the percentages of the four substances present will be represented by the fraction below, taking $K = 4$:

$$\frac{66.7 \times 66.7}{33.3 \times 33.3} = 4$$

Now, suppose that all of the water is withdrawn. An amount x of acid must react with an equivalent amount of alcohol to form ester and water. When equilibrium is restored, we shall have

$$\frac{(66.7) + x)(0 + x)}{(33.3 - x)(33.3 - x)} = 4$$

Solving this gives $x = 15.4$, so that the quantities become

$$\frac{82.1 \times 15.4}{17.9 \times 17.9} = 3.95$$

---

[1] Dietz, *Z. physiol. Chem.*, **52**, 279 (1907); Fabisch, *Biochem. Z.*, **234**, 84 (1931); Gottschalk and Neuberg, *Biochem. Z.*, **154**, 292 (1924); Rona and Ammon, *Biochem. Z.*, **217**, 34 (1930); Rona, Ammon and Werner, *Biochem. Z.*, **221**, 381 (1930); Rona and Mühlbock, *Biochem. Z.*, **223**, 130 (1930); Walle, *Nederland. Tijdschr. Hy. Microbiol. Serol.*, **1**, 71 (1926); Weber, *Biochem. Z.*, **129**, 208 (1922).

This gives $K = 3.95$ instead of 4, as decimals were rounded off in the calculations. The amount of ester is raised from 66.7 to 82.1 per cent. If by the same magic process this 15.4 per cent of water is withdrawn, the equilibrium will again be adjusted by forming more ester:

$$\frac{(82.1 + x)(0 + x)}{(17.9 - x)(17.9 - x)} = 4$$

We find $x = 6.2$, and the amounts present will be

$$\frac{88.3 \times 6.2}{11.7 \times 11.7} = 4$$

If the magic abstraction of water were to continue, more and more ester would be formed while the alcohol and acid would diminish. It would be even better if the magic would work continuously and eliminate the water as formed. Then the reaction would go to completion, 100 per cent of ester being formed and the alcohol and acid disappearing.

Berthelot and Péan de St. Gilles[1] saw this clearly in 1863 and did by a clever experiment what we have supposed to be done by magic and cumbersome mathematics. They said:

It can be demonstrated that the presence of water is the only cause which comes in to limit the combination of an acid with an alcohol. In order to obtain complete saturation, it is sufficient to eliminate the water as it is formed in the progressive action of the acid on the alcohol. This can be realized by operating with a fixed alcohol or a fixed acid, *e.g.*, stearic.

They weighed 0.690 gm. of stearic acid and 0.606 gm. (a 2 per cent excess) of cetyl alcohol into a small tube, closed at one end. This was placed upright in a larger tube containing barium oxide, which was then sealed. The whole was heated 26 hr. at 215°C. The barium oxide took up the water that escaped from the reaction mixture. The product dissolved in alcohol was neutral to litmus, showing that the esterification was complete. Bellucci[2] passed a slow current of carbon dioxide through a mixture of stearic acid and cetyl alcohol heated to 220°C. and obtained a 95 per cent yield of the ester. The preparation of nitric acid esters, wherein the water of reaction is evaporated in a vacuum, has been claimed.[3]

Phelps and Hubbard[4] pointed out that to obtain a high yield of ester, the most important factor is the removal of the water as it is formed in the reaction. They obtained complete esterification of succinic acid by

[1] BERTHELOT and PÉAN DE ST. GILLES, *Ann. chim. phys.* [3], **65**, 385 (1862); **66**, 5 (1862); **68**, 225 (1863).

[2] BELLUCCI, *Chem. Ztg.*, **35**, 669 (1911).

[3] Hofwimmer, Brit. 360,394.

[4] PHELPS and coworkers, *Am. J. Sci.*, **23**, 368 (1907); **25**, 39 (1908); **26**, 243, 257, 264, 290, 296 (1908).

distilling off the water with the alcohol, which was continuously renewed. Thompson[1] made benzyl esters by refluxing benzyl alcohol with various nonvolatile acids, using an air condenser of such length that the water escaped. Esters of various alcohols and nonvolatile acids have been made by distilling the water off with a part of the alcohol, which was dried and returned.[2] Dutt[3] obtained esters of oxalic acid by passing the vapors of alcohols through the acid, relying on the excess of the alcohol to carry off the water. Esters of nonvolatile acids are readily made, as shown by Coutzen-Crowet,[4] by using an excess of the alcohol to form with the water a binary mixture which distills out. As *n*-butyl alcohol forms with water a binary boiling at 92.5°C., esterification of nonvolatile acids with this alcohol is particularly convenient.[5] Fortunately, this binary separates into two layers the lower of which contains the most of the water. The upper layer can be run back into the reaction vessel to bring over more water.

Bellucci and Manzetti[6] showed that a nearly theoretical yield of a glyceride can be obtained by heating together equivalent quantities of glycerol and a fatty acid, either under reduced pressure or with a current of carbon dioxide. Garner studied the effects of passing different gases through the mixture and the effects of reduced pressure (15 mm.). At 200°C., the esterification of oleic acid was 80 per cent complete in 2 hr. Numerous patents[7] have been granted for making esters such as glycerides by heating nonvolatile acids and alcohols and providing for the elimination of the water.[8] The mixture containing a catalyst may be kept at a moderate temperature until the water separates as a layer which is drawn off.[9] In making glycerides, to insure the complete esterification of all the molecules of the polyvalent glycerol, it is necessary to use an excess of the acid, which is subsequently removed by washing with water or alkali.[10]

[1] THOMPSON and LEUCK, *J. Am. Chem. Soc.*, **44**, 2894 (1922).

[2] LANG, MACKEY, and GORTNER, *Proc. Chem. Soc.*, **24**, 150 (1908); Carswell, Stehlby, and Alozerij, U. S. 1,905,144; Zimmerli, U. S. 1,708,404.

[3] DUTT, *J. Chem. Soc.*, **123**, 2714 (1923).

[4] COUTZEN-CROWET, *Bull. soc. chim. Belg.*, **35**, 165 (1926).

[5] Crowell and Ebe, U. S. 1,864,893.

[6] BELLUCCI and MANZETTI, *Atti accad. Lincei* (v), **20**, i, 125, 235 (1911).

[7] Bolton and Lush, Brit. 163,352; Grolea and Weyler, Brit. 131,678; Held and Luther, Ger. 548,370; U. S. 1,881,563; I. G. Farbenindustrie A-G., Fr. 671,123; 685,433; Brit. 307,471; 332,267; Luther and Knilling, Ger. 514,503; Twitchell, Brit. 25,747; Van Schaack, U. S. 1,697,295; 1,700,103; 1,802,623; Zimmerli, U. S. 1,708,404.

[8] Adams, U. S. 1,917,681; Backhaus, U. S. 1,400,849; 1,400,850; 1,400,851; 1,400,852; 1,403,224; 1,403,225; 1,425,624; 1,425,625; 1,454,462; 1,454,463; Can. 211,675; 211,676; 217,703; 261,187; Hilditch, U. S. 2,073,797; Johnston, U. S. 1,924,934; I. G. Farbenindustrie A-G. Ger. 563,203; 564,783; 565,477; Kaiser, U. S. 2,074,963.

[9] H. Th. Böhme A-G., Ger. 592,053.

[10] Wecker, Fr. 635,452; Brit. 273,276; Wecker and Held, Ger. 553,821.

Ester gum, which is widely used as a resin, is manufactured by heating rosin with glycerol; and the glyptal resins are similarly obtained from glycerol with phthalic anhydride and other acids.[1]

To assist the removal of the water, certain liquids which are insoluble in water and distill with it at temperatures below its regular boiling point are frequently added to the esterification mixture. Favorite liquids for this purpose are benzene, toluene, chloroform, ethylene chloride, and carbon tetrachloride.[2] When one of these is present, it goes over with the water or with the water and the ester as a constant-boiling mixture which separates into two layers in the receiver. The non-aqueous layer is returned to the reaction vessel from which it distills again bringing out more of the water. This can be kept up until there is no more water to bring. The separation and return of this auxiliary liquid can be made automatic. Benzene, ethyl alcohol, and water go over at 64.85°C. in the proportions 74.1 : 18.5 : 7.4.[3]

It is just as effective to distill out the ester.[4] Thus, ethyl nitrite, which boils at 16.4°C., is evolved as a gas when alcohol and nitrous acid are brought together in a strongly acid solution.[5] The reaction is so complete that it may be used for the quantitative determination of nitrous acid.[6] Ethyl borate may be distilled out of a reaction mixture.[7] Bodroux[8] and, later, Purgotti showed that ethyl acetate can be obtained from a mixture containing much water.

[1] BABCOCK, *Proc. Am. Soc. Testing Materials*, **30**, Part II, 795; BEEGLE, *Ind. Eng. Chem.*, **16**, 953, 1075 (1924); BRENDEL, *Farben-Ztg.*, **31**, 576 (1925); *Farbe u. Lack*, **31**, 297 (1926); Dmitrov, Russ. 23,393; 24,897 (1932); MATSUMOTO and YAMADA, *Repts. Imp. Ind. Research Inst.*, *Osaka, Japan*, **10**, No. 20; NAKAYA, *Bull. Kyoto Ind. Research Inst.*, **3**, 1 (1928); Norman, U. S. 1,779,710; 1,839,161; Symmes, U. S. 1,696,337; Williamson and Beisler, U. S. 1,734,987.

[2] Bannister, U. S. 1,695,449; 2,076,111; Borglin, U. S. 2,011,707; Buckley, U. S. 1,869,660; FRITZWEILER and DIETRICH, *Z. angew. Chem.*, **45**, 605 (1932); Gabriel, U. S. 2,063,240; Holt, U. S. 2,031,603; I. G. Farbenindustrie A-G., Brit. 259,204; Fr. 680,671; 689,275; Brit. 341,158; *Kao* and *Chen*, *J. Chinese Chem. Soc.*, **2**, 173 (1934); LOCQUIN and ELGHOZY, *Bull. soc. chim.*, **41**, 445 (1927); LONGINOV and SVETLOV, *Khim. Farm. Prom.*, **1932**, 411; MUND and HEIM, *Bull. soc. chim. Belg.*, **41**, 349 (1932); Norman, Ger. 582,266; Schwabe, Ger. 516,135; Steffins, U. S. 1,421,604; 1,433,308; SWIENTOSLAWSKI and POZNANSKI, *Compt. rend.*, **184**, 92 (1927); *Roczniki Chem.*, **8**, 527 (1928); THIELPAPE and FULDE, *Ber.*, **66**, 1454 (1933); Vanillin-Fabrik, Ger. 593,723; Alexander Wacker Ges., Ger. 564,405; 594,681; WAHL, *Bull. soc. chim.* [4], **37**, 713 (1925); Wickert, U. S. 2,032,679; Wietzel, U. S. 1,732,392; Ger. 490,250; 491,491.

[3] FRITZWEILER and DIETRICH, *Z. angew Chem.*, **45**, 605 (1932).

[4] WUYTS and BAILLEUX, *Bull. soc. chim. Belg.*, **29**, 55 (1920).

[5] FISCHER, *Z. physik. Chem.*, **65**, 61 (1909).

[6] FISCHER and SCHMIDT, *Z. anorg. allgem. Chem.*, **179**, 332 (1929).

[7] KHOTINSKII and PUPKO, *Ukrain. Khem. Zhur.*, **4**, Sci. Part 13 (1929).

[8] BODROUX, *Compt. rend.*, **156**, 1079 (1913); **160**, 204 (1915).

In 1873, Markownikoff[1] prepared ethyl acetate continuously by adding alcohol and acetic acid to sulfuric acid in a flask kept at 130°C. In 1905, Wade[2] made a careful study of this method and laid the foundation for modern esterification methods.   He found it possible to make this ester continuously, starting with a mixture of alcohol and acetic acid, with some sulfuric acid, heating this until the ester begins to distill out, and then adding the mixture of alcohol and acetic acid at such a rate that the volume remains constant.   What was particularly important was his discovery that the distillate is a ternary mixture of ethyl acetate, 83.2 per cent; alcohol, 9.0 per cent; and water, 7.8 per cent.   He found the boiling point of this ternary to be 70.3°C., while pure ethyl acetate boils at 77°C.   He found a binary, 69.4 per cent of the ester and 30.6 per cent alcohol, boiling at 71.8°C. and a binary of 8.6 per cent water and 91.4 per cent ester boiling at 70.45°C.   The important thing is that the ternary boils lower than any of the constituents or either of the binaries and is what comes out at the top of an efficient column as long as all three of its constituents are present in the still.   As this ternary behaves on distillation like a pure substance, some other means of separating its components is required.   Wade extracted the most of the alcohol from this mixture by washing with water.   Roberts,[3] who compared several processes, recommended two volumes of water—less than is used in large operations.   When this washed ethyl acetate is distilled, the first thing that goes over is again the ternary—ester, water, and alcohol, boiling at 70.3°C., though owing to the washing out of most of the alcohol there can be only a limited amount of it.   This is followed by a binary of the ester with either the water or the alcohol, according to which remained from the ternary; then the boiling point goes up to 77.15°C., and pure dry ethyl acetate is obtained.

It is evident that this investigation gives a satisfactory method of converting a given amount of acetic acid completely into ethyl acetate. It can also be seen that if the ester is removed as rapidly as it is formed, esterification must go on even in the presence of a considerable proportion of water.   To form the ternary, a small excess of alcohol must be put in.

As an illustration, the case of making ethyl acetate from a dilute solution of acetic acid, such as is obtained by the quick-vinegar process, will be considered.   Let us take 100 gm. of 5 per cent acetic acid, which would be 0.083 mole of the acid and 5.28 moles of water.   If 5 gm. of alcohol (0.108 mole) be added to this along with a catalyst, when equilibrium is reached there will be an amount x of ester formed.

$$\frac{5.28x}{(0.083 - x)(0.108 - x)} = 4$$

[1] MARKOWNIKOFF, *Ber.*, **6**, 1177 (1873).

[2] WADE, *J. Chem. Soc.*, **87**, 1656 (1905); *J. Soc. Chem. Ind.*, **24**, 1322 (1905).

[3] ROBERTS, *J. Soc. Chem. Ind.*, **43**, 295 (1924).

which gives $x = 0.0060$ mole or 0.528 gm. This is all that can be formed if all four substances remain in the mixture. Distillation will remove this along with 0.057 gm. of alcohol and 0.0495 gm. of water as the ternary. As soon as this ester is out of the way, more will be formed. If the ester be distilled out continually, esterification will proceed until the last trace of acetic acid is gone. This will leave a slight amount of alcohol, which may be taken off separately as the binary with water and used in another esterification.

As can be readily seen from the above, the manufacture of ethyl acetate becomes a matter of distillation. Obviously, an efficient column is required with ample capacity to take care of the production without being pushed beyond its proper rate. By making proper adjustments of rates of esterification and distillation, the two can be made to go on simultaneously, giving a continuous process. Actually, the liquor containing acetic acid, with the proper amount of sulfuric acid as a catalyst, is fed into the column at the proper plate where it meets the alcohol. Esterification takes place right on the plates in the column, and the ternary of ester, alcohol, and water comes out at the top continuously. This ternary is washed with water, as Wade suggested, and the ester passed to another column. The dilute alcohol obtained by washing the ternary goes to a still for the recovery of the alcohol, which is returned to make more ester. The preparation and purification of ethyl acetate have been considered recently by Rozhdestvenskii, Pukirev, and Longinov.[1]

For other volatile esters, there are corresponding ternaries and binaries. In general, the ternary of an alcohol, its ester, and water boils slightly lower than the binary of the ester and water. The percentage of water in the ternary increases, and that of the ester decreases with increase in molecular weight of the alcohol, as can be seen from the following data (Table V), the most of which are from Hannotte.[2] Methyl acetate boils 10°C. lower than methyl alcohol, but the boiling points of the alcohols rise less rapidly with increasing molecular weight than do those of the acetates. Furnas[3] and coworkers have studied several systems and Lecart has included esters in his general investigation of azeotropes. Others have contributed to our knowledge of this important subject.

[1] Rozhdestvenskii, Pukirev, and Longinov, *Trans. Inst. Pure Chem. Reagents, Sci. Tech. Dept.*, U. S. S. R., **300**, 123 (1929).

[2] Hannotte, *Bull. soc. chim. Belg.*, **35**, 86 (1926).

[3] Brunjes and Furnas, *Ind. Eng. Chem.*, **27**, 396 (1935); Furnas and Leighton, *ibid.*, **29**, 709 (1937); Lecart, *Ann. soc. sci. Bruxelles*, **55B**, 43, 253 (1935); **56B**, 41 (1935); Kireev, Klinov, and Grigorovich, *J. Chem. Ind.* (*Moscow*), **12**, 936 (1935); Mund and Heim, *Bull. Belg.*, **41**, 349 (1932); Sklyarenko and Baranaev, *Z. physik. Chem.*, **A175**, 203 (1935).

Graphical methods have been developed by Gay, Mion, and Auméras[1] for determining the conditions for complete esterification for various

TABLE V.—BOILING POINTS OF ESTERS, ALCOHOLS, THEIR BINARIES, AND TERNARIES
WITH WATER, °C.

E = ester, A = alcohol, W = water

	A B.p.	E B.p.	Binary E-W		Binary E-A		Ternary			
			B.p.	H_2O, %	B.p.	A %	B.p.	E %	A %	W %
Propyl formate............	97.2	81	71.6	2.3	80.6	9.8	70.8	82	5	13
Butyl formate............	117.7	106.9	83.8	16.5	105.8	23.7	83.6	68.7	10	21.3
Isobutyl formate.........	107.9	98.5	80.4	7.8	97.8	20.6	80.2	76	6.7	17.3
Isoamyl formate..........	131.6	123.3	90.2	21	123.6	26	89.8	48	19.6	32.4
Methyl acetate...........	64.6	54.0	.....	....	54	18.5				
Ethyl acetate............	78.3	77.1	70.45	8.6	71.8	30.6	70.3	83.2	9	7.8
Propyl acetate...........	97.2	101.6	82.4	14	94.2	40	82.2	59.5	19.5	21
Butyl acetate............	117.7	125.1	90.2	28.7	117.2	47	89.4	35.3	27.4	37.3
Isobutyl acetate..........	107.9	116.3	87.4	16.6	87.4	16.6	86.8	46.5	23.1	30.4
Amyl acetate.............	137.8	148	95.2	41	.....	....	94.8	10.5	33.3	56.2
Isoamyl acetate..........	131.6	139	93.8	36.2	.....	....	93.6	24	31.2	44.8

mixtures. Later, these authors[2] give experimental verification of their theories. A study of the above table will show that operating conditions should be adapted to the particular acid and alcohol. Not only the boiling points of the ternaries and binaries come in for consideration but also the solubilities of the esters and alcohols in water. The percentages of ester, alcohol, and water in the ternaries look quite differently when they are put on a molar basis.

TABLE VI.—MOLAL COMPOSITION OF TERNARIES

	Weight percentages			Molar ratios		
	Ester	Alc.	Water	Ester	Alc.	Water
Ethyl acetate..................	83.2	9	7.8	2.18	0.45	1
Butyl acetate..................	35.3	27.4	37.3	0.147	0.178	1

In the case of ethyl acetate, 2.18 moles of ester come over to 1 of water. Hence, esterification is completed by distilling out the ester. In the butyl acetate ternary, only relatively small amounts of ester and alcohol are required to bring over all the water. If a mixture of 1 mole of acetic acid and 1.031 of dry butyl alcohol is slowly distilled, 1 mole of water

[1] GAY, MION, and AUMÉRAS, *Bull. soc. chim.* [4], **39**, 1329 (1926).
[2] *Ibid.*, **41**, 1027 (1927).

should come over, bringing with it 0.147 mole of ester and 0.178 mole of alcohol. Since all the water that can be formed has been withdrawn from the mixture, the reaction must be complete, and 0.853 mole of pure butyl acetate remains in the still pot. Thus, 85 per cent of the calculated amount of ester is obtained pure and the rest of it as a mixture with the alcohol and water. Water is only slightly soluble in this mixture of butyl acetate and butyl alcohol, so that most of the water in the distillate separates out, bringing with it only a little of the alcohol and ester. For simplicity of calculation, we may suppose that the separation is complete, leaving 0.147 mole of ester and 0.178 mole of alcohol. Since the proportion of these two in their binary is different from what it is in the ternary, they can be separated by alternate distillations with and without water, but the practical thing to do is to add the mixture to another mole of acid and another of butyl alcohol and repeat the esterification and distillation. The ternary from this will contain 0.147 mole of ester and 0.178 mole of the alcohol to the 1 of water, which will leave 1 mole of ester in the still.

In practice,[1] the distillate is caught in a vessel from the bottom of which the water runs off and from the top of which the ester-alcohol mixture is continuously returned to the still. Obviously, an indefinite amount of water may be brought over in this way, which means that it is not necessary to use 100 per cent acetic acid and dry butyl alcohol. When all the water is off, the boiling point rises first to that of the binary and finally to that of the pure butyl acetate. In order that the amount of ester coming over with the alcohol in the binary may be small, only a slight excess of alcohol is used in the original mixture.

Although, as pointed out by Wade, the principles involved in taking advantage of ternaries and binaries in the manufacture of esters are few and simple, many patents[2] have been taken out on particular applications of these principles and on arrangements of apparatus for carrying out the various processes.

As has been shown above, advantage can be taken of ternaries to remove the ester or the water, as the case may be, and allow the esterification to go to completion. In the case of ethyl acetate, the ternary

---

[1] HULTMAN, DAVIS, and CLARKE, *J. Am. Chem. Soc.*, **43**, 366 (1921).

[2] Arentz, Brit. 246,526; Ayres, U. S. 1,869,837; Backhaus, U. S. 1,400,849; 1,400,850; 1,400,851; 1,400,852; 1,403,224; 1,403,225; 1,425,624; 1,425,625; 1,454,462; 1,454,463; Can. 211,675; 211,676; 217,703; 261,187; Bannister, U. S. 2,029,694; Buc and Clough, U. S. 1,726,945; Edlund, Can. 326,768; Holzverkohlungs-Industrie, Brit. 352,647; Horsley and I. C. I., Brit. 301,523; Fr. 671,238; U. S. 1,700,779; Haner, U. S. 1,827,653; Graves, U. S. 1,869,193; I. G. Farbenindustrie A-G., Fr. 671,123; 685,433; Brit. 307,471; 332,267; Invention Gesellschaft, Brit. 387,573; Marks, Brit. 147,337; Soc. anon. des distilleries des Deux-Sèvres, Brit. 234,458; Standard Oil Devel. Co., Brit. 300,418; 305,308; U. S. Ind. Alc. Co., Brit. 130,968; 130,969; 130,970; 195,117; 195,118; 195,177; 287,607.

boils at 70.3°C., which is a rather low reaction temperature for rapid esterification unless a large amount of catalyst is used, which may be undesirable. In making methyl acetate, this difficulty would be even greater. Benzene, toluene, and other hydrocarbons are employed to assist in the removal of the water from low-boiling binaries and ternaries with the alcohols and water.   In order to speed up the esterification without increasing the amount of catalyst, the reaction may be carried on at a higher temperature, which is effected by putting pressure on the whole system. This elevates the boiling points of the water, ester, alcohol, and binaries and ternaries without greatly changing their relations. The binaries and ternaries are somewhat different in composition but can be used in the same way for separations.[1]   Raising the temperature 20°C. practically quadruples the esterification rate and does not require excessive pressure.   A number of patents have been taken out along this line.[2]

It has been proposed[3] to cause the separation of the ester by mixing with a high-boiling mineral oil, from which it may be removed subsequently.

In some cases, a salt of an acid may be more available than the free acid, particularly where the acid is separated from a mixture by precipitation as a slightly soluble salt.   An ester may be made directly from a salt by adding the desired alcohol together with sufficient sulfuric acid to liberate the organic acid and to serve as a catalyst for the esterification.[4]

IV. VAPOR-PHASE ESTERIFICATION

In 1863, Berthelot and Péan de St. Gilles,[5] as a part of their study of esterification, tried the effect of changing the volume of the container.

TABLE VII.—ESTERIFICATION AT 200°C. IN 22 HR.

Vol., cc. per gm.	Limit	Vol., cc. per gm.	Limit	System
5.3	66.4	37	72.3	Alcohol + acid
8.3	66.8	38	72.7	Ester + H_2O
21.2	71.7	53	76.0	Alcohol + acid
24.4	72.9	62	78.4	Ester + H_2O

[1] MERRIMAN, *J. Chem. Soc.*, **103**, 1790, 1801 (1913).

[2] Fuchs, Brit. 320,113; U. S. 1,791,238; Holzverkohlungs-Industrie, Brit. 295,275; Fr. 657,812; Brit. 320,113; Roka and Fuchs, Ger. 507,205; U. S. 1,800,319; Wietzel, U. S. 1,732,392; Ger. 490,250; 491,491.

[3] Buc, U. S. 1,651,666; 1,808,155; Mann, U. S. 1,541,430; Standard Oil Development Co., Brit. 300,418; 305,308.

[4] Burghart, U. S. 1,426,457; Hartwich, Ger. 518,388; Mills, Australian 25,884; Schering-Kahlbaum, Brit. 319,043; Wagner, Ger. 529,135; 546,806.

[5] BERTHELOT and PÉAN DE ST. GILLES, *Ann. chim. phys.* [3], **65**, 385 (1862); **66**, 5 (1862); **68**, 225 (1863).

The usual mixture of alcohol and acetic acid was sealed up in tubes of different sizes. Their results are given in the Table VII. The limit goes up as the volume of the tube increases. With very large volumes, the reaction was too slow; at 1,562 cc. to 1 gm., there was only 49.0 per cent of ester after 458 hr. at 200°C.

In 1911, Sabatier and his coworkers Mailhe and de Godon[1] began experiments with oxide catalysts, thoria, titania, and zirconia, over which they passed the vapors of mixtures of alcohols and acids at from 300 to 400°C. For equivalent amounts of ethanol and acetic acid they got 69 per cent of ester and concluded that the limits are nearly the same in both liquid and gas phase. They had no evidence that equilibrium had been reached and had overlooked the results given in Table VII.

Beryllium oxide at 310°C. has been claimed[2] as giving high yields even with tertiary alcohols. Silica gel,[3] zirconia,[4] alum,[5] and special contact masses[6] have been used as catalysts, also porous supports moistened with sulfuric or phosphoric acids or zinc chloride, etc.[7]

There is general agreement,[8] except in one case,[5] that considerably higher percentages of esters are obtained in the vapor phase than in the liquid, but disagreement as to whether the equilibrium is shifted up or down or not at all as the temperature is raised. More thorough investigation[9] has shown that there is less ester, the higher the temperature, 84.5 per cent at 150°C. and only 79.8 at 200°C.

While the higher percentages of esters obtained in the vapor phase make this method attractive, the large size of equipment required for handling tons of acids and alcohols in the vapor form has been against the commercial use of this method. Unfortunately, the vapors must be passed over the catalyst slowly to get high conversion. No commercial developments have been described.

[1] MAILHE, *J. usines gaz*, **48**, 17 (1924); MAILHE and DE GODON, *Bull. soc. chim.*, **29**, 101 (1921); SABATIER and MAILHE, *Compt. rend.*, **152**, 358, 494, 669, 1094 (1911).

[2] HAUSER and KLOTZ, *Chem. Ztg.*, **37**, 146 (1913); Ger. 261,878.

[3] MILLIGAN, CHAPPELL, and REID, *J. Phys. Chem.*, **28**, 872 (1924); TIDWELL and REID, *J. Am. Chem. Soc.*, **53**, 4353 (1931).

[4] FROLICH, CARPENTER, and KNOX, *J. Am. Chem. Soc.*, **52**, 1565 (1930).

[5] GAJENDRAGAD, *Proc. 15th Indian Sci. Congr.*, **1928**, 148.

[6] Jaeger, U. S. 1,819,613; 1,819,818.

[7] Boake, Roberts and Co., and Durrans, Brit. 131,088; Durrans and Ellis, Can. 211,664.

[8] EDGAR and SCHUYLER, *J. Am. Chem. Soc.*, **46**, 64 (1924); FROLICH, CARPENTER and KNOX, *J. Am. Chem. Soc.*, **52**, 1565 (1930); HAUSER and KLOTZ, *Chem. Ztg.*, **37**, 146 (1913); Ger. 261,878; MILLIGAN, CHAPPELL, and REID, *J. Phys. Chem.*, **28**, 872 (1924); SWIETOSLAWSKI and POZNANSKI, *Compt. rend.*, **184**, 92 (1927); *Roczniki Chem.*, **8**, 527 (1928).

[9] ESSEX and CLARK, *J. Am. Chem. Soc.*, **54**, 1290 (1932); JATKAR and GAJENDRAGAD, *ibid.*, **59**, 798 (1937).

V. ALCOHOLYSIS

The Esterification of an Ester

$$CH_3COOC_2H_5 + HOCH_3 \rightarrow CH_3COOCH_3 + HOC_2H_5 \qquad (4)$$

The reaction [(4), above] is spoken of as *alcoholysis* and also as ester interchange. Both names are objectionable. Alcoholysis means the breaking of a molecule by alcohol, —H being added to one part and —OR to the other, just as in hydrolysis —H and —OH are added to the fragments. This definition is too broad and includes the esterification of acetic acid, since in this the acetic acid is broken up and —OR added to one part of it to give the ester and —H added to the —OH to form water. "Ester interchange" does not describe the process, since only a part of the ester is interchanged. It is simply making an ester from another ester. An example of this reaction was observed by Guthrie[1] in 1859, but it was long before its generality was recognized. It has been discovered more times than probably any other reaction, since many of those observing a case of it have investigated it as new.

Guthrie added amyl nitrite to a mixture containing ethyl alcohol and sulfuric acid and obtained ethyl nitrite as a distillate. Friedel and Crafts[2] heated ethyl acetate with amyl alcohol and amyl acetate with ethyl alcohol and observed alcoholysis in both cases. They even heated ethyl benzoate and amyl acetate together and got ethyl acetate and amyl benzoate, through they found this reaction to be slow below 300°C. They say, "The ethers [esters], which are easily decomposed by water, are best suited for this decomposition by alcohols. Both sorts of action are of similar nature." Bertoni[3] made nitrites by alcoholysis. Purdie,[4] in 1885, used sodium alcoholates to accelerate the reaction, studying a number of alcohols and esters, and recognized its general application and its complete reversibility.[5]

If methyl alcohol is added to ethyl benzoate,[6] a part of the ethyl alcohol is replaced, and some methyl benzoate is formed. As the reaction is reversible,[7] the mixture comes to an equilibrium:

$$\frac{[\text{Me benzoate}] \times [\text{EtOH}]}{[\text{Et benzoate}] \times [\text{MeOH}]} = K$$

[1] Guthrie, *J. Chem. Soc.*, **11**, 245 (1859).

[2] Friedel and Crafts, *Ann.*, **130**, 198 (1864); **133**, 207 (1865).

[3] Bertoni, *Gazz. chim. ital.*, **12**, 435 (1882); **16**, 522 (1886); Bertoni and Truffi, *Gazz. chim. ital.*, **14**, 23 (1884).

[4] Purdie, *J. Chem. Soc.*, **47**, 855 (1885); **51**, 627 (1887); *Ber.*, **20**, 1555 (1887); Purdie and Marshall, *J. Chem. Soc.*, **53**, 391 (1888).

[5] Pfannl, *Monatsh.*, **31**, 301 (1910).

[6] Reid, *Am. Chem. J.*, **45**, 479 (1911).

[7] Bruni, *Chem. Ztg.*, **35**, 614 (1911); Pfannl, *Monatsh.*, **31**, 301 (1910).

This K can be calculated from the esterification constants of the two alcohols severally with benzoic acid.

$$K = \frac{K^1}{K^{1\prime}} = \frac{5.237}{3.968} = 1.32$$

This means that if 1 mole of methanol is added to 1 mole of ethyl benzoate, 53.5 per cent of the methyl ester will be formed, and a like amount of ethyl alcohol set free. At room temperature, in the absence of a catalyst, a long time would be required for the establishment of the equilibrium. As this reaction is a variety of esterification, it should be accelerated by esterification catalysts—and so it is. The strong acids that are used in ordinary esterification serve equally well for alcoholysis;[1] but another sort of catalyst, sodium alcoholate, is far more active.[2] This catalyst can be used only in an anhydrous system, since it is readily hydrolyzed by water and disappears in the saponification of the ester. The usual practice is to dissolve a small amount of sodium in the anhydrous alcohol and to add the ester. A small concentration of this catalyst causes the transformation to take place rapidly even at room temperature. Ammonia or pyridine can also catalyze alcoholysis.[3]

The remarkable thing about alcoholysis is its rapidity, at least with sodium alcoholate as a catalyst, as compared with esterification and saponification. The saponification of phenylbenzoate in aqueous alcohol would ordinarily be represented by (b):

$$C_6H_5COOC_6H_5 + NaOC_2H_5 \rightarrow C_6H_5COOC_2H_5 + C_6H_5ONa \qquad (a)$$
$$C_6H_5COOC_6H_5 + NaOH \rightarrow C_6H_5COONa + C_6H_5OH \qquad (b)$$

What actually takes place is the alcoholysis as represented in (a), which was estimated by Gibby and Waters[4] as one thousand times as rapid as the saponification according to (b). Then the ethyl benzoate is slowly saponified. This may be shown qualitatively by a simple experiment. Some triacetin $[C_3H_4(OCOCH_3)_3]$, which is odorless, is added to a solution of caustic soda in 50 per cent alcohol; the odor of ethyl acetate is apparent at once, showing that the immediate reaction is the formation of ethyl acetate. On this account, it is necessary to use an efficient reflux condenser when determining saponification numbers of even high-boiling acetates.[5]

Since, as mentioned above, the alcoholysis equilibrium depends on the esterification constants of the two alcohols, a tertiary alcohol even in large excess would not be expected to replace a primary, and only

[1] Röse, *Ann.*, **205**, 240 (1880).

[2] Sudborough and Karvé, *J. Indian Inst. Sci.*, **3**, 1 (1919); **5**, 1 (1922).

[3] Weddige, *J. prakt. Chem.* [2], **12**, 434 (1895).

[4] Gibby and Waters, *J. Chem. Soc.*, **1932**, 2643.

[5] Béhal, *Bull. soc. chim.* [4], **15**, 565 (1914); Hasche, Pardee, and Reid, *Ind. Eng. Chem.*, **12**, 129, 481 (1920); Pinnow, *Z. Elektrochem.*, **24**, 270 (1918).

a small yield is obtained with a secondary.[1] The relative activity of the alcohols has been measured by Kolhatkar and by Fehlandt and Adkins.[2]

An interesting case is the preparation of the monomeric cyclic polymethylene carbonates which can be obtained in no other way. A higher polymethylene glycol and sodium are heated with butyl carbonate to obtain the polymeric polymethylene carbonate. This, still containing the catalyst, is heated in a high vacuum; the trace of monomeric cyclic ester x that is present distills out and more is formed by rearrangement until nearly all the material is obtained in the desired form.[3]

Completing Alcoholysis.—The situation here is just the same as was discussed above in esterification; the removal of one of the reaction products permits the reaction to go to completion. Such removal is usually effected by distillation. Thus, a higher alcohol such as butyl, amyl, or benzyl is added to methyl or ethyl acetate with a catalyst, and the mixture heated under a fractionating column. The most volatile thing present is the methyl or ethyl alcohol, which distills out, leaving the ester of the other alcohol.[4] Or the new ester may distill off,[5] as when ethyl alcohol reacts with glycol acetate. The esters and alcohols are so chosen that there will be a convenient spread between the boiling points of the compounds to be separated. It is particularly easy to eliminate such low-boiling compounds as methyl alcohol and methyl acetate. Thus, the fractionation can be much simplified.

Equipment and Operation for Alcoholysis.—As only anhydrous esters and alcohols and an alkaline catalyst, none of which causes corrosion, are used, the equipment may be of the simplest sort; a kettle and a column with suitable attachments suffice. Usually, the alcohol is put in the kettle first, and the sodium metal (0.1 to 1 per cent of the weight of the ester) introduced. The ester is run in, the heat turned on, and distillation begun.

Glycerides have been the starting materials for many ester transpositions.[6] As they have relatively high molecular weights (tristearin, 891),

---

[1] REIMER and DOWNES, *J. Am. Chem. Soc.*, **43**, 945 (1921).

[2] KOLHATKAR, *J. Chem. Soc.*, **107**, 921 (1915); FEHLANDT and ADKINS, *J. Am. Chem. Soc.*, **57**, 193 (1935).

[3] CAROTHERS and associates, *J. Am. Chem. Soc.*, **55**, 5031 (1933); **57**, 929 (1935); U. S. 2,020,298, Brit. 433,632; Fr. 768,807; 796,410.

[4] Burghart, U. S. 1,491,076; Graves, U. S. 1,869,092; 1,882,808; Hurtley and Wheeler, Brit. 346,486; Martin and Krchma, Can. 299,555; U. S. 1,770,414; Steimmig and Ulrich, Can. 278,557; U. S. 1,817,425; Ger. 515,306.

[5] Graves, U. S. 1,860,092; 1,882,808; Rodebush, U. S. 1,454,604.

[6] GRÜN, *Chem. Umschau Fette, Öle, Wachse, u. Harze*, **32**, 225 (1925); I. G. Farbenindustrie A-G., Ger. 575,911; KREMANN, *Monatsh.*, **29**, 23 (1908); LIPP and MILLER, *J. prakt. Chem.* [2], **88**, 261, (1913); MADINAVEITIA, *Anales soc. españ. fis. quím.*, **12**, 426 (1914); ODA, *J. Soc. Ch. Ind. Japan*, **35**, Suppl. binding 515 (1932); **36**, 113, 292, 331, 334, 496, 571 (1933); Alexander Wacker Ges., Ger. 642,454; Fr. 752,150.

heating 1 part of the glyceride with 3 to 10 parts of methanol (mol. wt., 32) and a catalyst should transform the most of it into methyl esters. This has been used as a preparation method for the methyl and ethyl esters of acids, which occur in natural products as glycerides.[1] The liberated glycerol cannot be distilled out so as to complete the reaction, but it may be washed out. Thus, a glyceride may be treated with methyl alcohol (and sodium), the product washed with water, dried and retreated with more alcohol and sodium, until the glycerol is substantially eliminated. The ester remaining is fractionated *in vacuo*.

As noted above, Friedel and Crafts[2] found that interchange takes place between two esters. This has been applied to the making of useful mixed esters by heating glycerides with other slightly volatile esters either in the presence of catalysts or at a very high temperature.[3]

Two esters may be interchanged, as ethyl benzoate and butyl acetate into ethyl acetate and butyl benzoate.[4]

VI. ACIDOLYSIS

$$CH_3COOC_2H_5 + C_{15}H_{31}COOH \leftrightharpoons C_{15}H_{31}COOC_2H_5 + CH_3COOH$$

The counterpart of alcoholysis—acidolysis—in which one acid displaces another from its ester [reaction (5)] is so similar to alcoholysis that it is taken for granted and is seldom considered separately. No studies seem to have been made of the equilibriums, but it may be assumed that one acid displaces another to an extent that can be calculated from their esterification constants. Butyric acid can be introduced into a glyceride by simply heating this acid with the fat.[5] A neutral ester of a dibasic acid may be heated with a mole of the acid to give a mono-ester.[6] The reaction goes to completion when one of the products is eliminated by distillation, as when an ester is heated with abietic acid.[7] In a similar manner, ethyl formate is fractionated out from ethyl acetate and formic acid.[8] Alcohols may be acetylated by heating with ethylidene acetate and a catalyst.[9] As an acid catalyst, such as sulfuric acid, is used, the

[1] HALLER, *Compt. rend.*, **143**, 657 (1906); PERKINS, *Philippine J. Sci.*, **24**, 621 (1924); STEWART and McKINNEY, *J. Am. Chem. Soc.*, **53**, 1482 (1931); TAMAYO, *Anales soc. españ. fis. quím.*, **28**, 177 (1930).

[2] FRIEDEL and CRAFTS, *Ann.*, **130**, 198 (1864); **133**, 207 (1865).

[3] Chemische Fabrik Kurt Albert G.m.b.H., Fr. 697,470; Brit. 356,616; Ger. 555,812. Knoll and Co.,Ger.,187,254; 201,369. Loon, Brit. 249,916; U. S. 1,744,596.

[4] Graves, U. S. 1,860,092; 1,882,808; PISTOR, *Farben Z.*, **30**, 3056 (1925); *Farbe u. Lack*, **1925**, 456.

[5] NORMAN, *Chem. Umschau*, **30**, 250 (1924).

[6] FOURNEAU and SABETAY, *Bull. soc. chim.*, **43**, 859 (1928); **45**, 834 (1929).

[7] PISTOR, *Farben Z.*, **30**, 3056 (1925); *Farbe u. Lack*, **1925**, 456.

[8] Graves, U. S. 1,860,092; 1,882,808.

[9] Boiteau, Brit. 15,919 (1914); Fr. 478,435.

kettle must be acid resistant. The displaced acid may be removed by washing with aqueous alkali.

VII. ESTERIFICATION OF AMIDES

An excellent way to make an acid amide is to treat an ester with ammonia:

$$CH_3COOC_2H_5 + NH_3 \leftrightarrows CH_3CONH_2 + HOC_2H_5$$

Though the reaction is reversible [reaction (7)], the yield of the amide is almost quantitative, since the equilibrium is far over to that side. However, it is easy to convert an amide completely into the ester by the addition of an excess of an acid such as sulfuric or hydrochloric which combines with the ammonia. When a high-boiling alcohol is used, the ammonia can be driven off by heating. This reaction has been studied by several investigators[1] and there are a few patents on its applications.[2] It has been found useful for making dithio-esters.[3]

VIII. USE OF ACID ANHYDRIDE

Reactions (8), (9), and (10) go to completion, since the acid that is formed cannot decompose the ester.

$$(CH_3CO)_2O + C_2H_5OH \rightarrow CH_3COOC_2H_5 + CH_3COOH \qquad (8)$$
$$(CH_3CO)_2O + (CH_3)_3COH \rightarrow CH_3COOC(CH_3)_3 + CH_3COOH \qquad (9)$$
$$(CH_3CO)_2O + C_6H_5ONa \rightarrow CH_3COOC_6H_5 + CH_3COONa \qquad (10)$$

Furthermore, acetic anhydride reacts more rapidly with a given alcohol than does acetic acid under the same conditions, though the relative velocities with different alcohols as measured by Menschutkin[4] are much the same. This discussion will be limited to acetic anhydride, the cheapest anhydride of a monobasic acid and the one commonly used.

The simpler primary and secondary alcohols can be satisfactorily esterified by the methods already described, but certain tertiary alcohols, mercaptans, and phenols require the use of acetic anhydride. It is frequently used for small lots of expensive alcohols in cases where speed and completeness of esterification are of more importance than the added cost of the anhydride.

The usual method is to boil the alcohol and an excess of acetic anhydride with 10 per cent of anhydrous sodium acetate for several hours.

---

[1] MAGILL, *Ind. Eng. Chem.*, **26**, 611 (1934); REID, *Am. Chem. J.*, **41**, 483 (1909); TAYLOR and DAVIS, *J. Phys. Chem.*, **32**, 1467 (1928).

[2] Gibson and Payman, Brit. 307,137; Ger. 523,189; U. S. 1,877,847; Nieuwland and Sowa, U. S. 2,036,353; Smith, Fr. 665,162; Brit. 313,316; Trusler, U. S. 1,584,907; Brit. 255,887.

[3] REID, *Orig. Com. 8th Intern. Congr. Appl. Chem.* (Appendix), **25**, 423.

[4] MENSCHUTKIN, *Ann.*, **195**, 334 (1879); **197**, 193 (1879); *Ber.*, **13**, 162 (1880); *Ann. chim.* (5), **23**, 14 (1881); **30**, 81 (1883); *Z. physik. Chem.*, **1**, 611 (1887); **9**, 237 (1892).

The sodium acetate speeds up the reaction somewhat. The product is cooled and agitated with warm water, which hydrolyzes the remaining acetic anhydride and dissolves out the acetic acid. The acetate is separated and washed several times with water and finally with weak soda until it is neutral.

The great bulk of the 125,000,000 lb. of acetic anhydride annually produced in the United States goes into the manufacture of cellulose acetate.

Reactions with acetic anhydride are greatly accelerated by sulfuric acid, zinc chloride, phosphorus pentoxide, ferric chloride, etc.,[1] but such catalysts cannot be used with sensitive alcohols, like linalool, which are isomerized or otherwise affected by them. An aromatic anhydride may be made to react by the addition of caustic soda.[2] A tertiary base may be used to assist esterifications by acid anhydrides.[3]

IX. USE OF ACID CHLORIDES

Reactions (11), (12), (13), and (14) involve the use of an acid chloride and result in the formation of hydrogen chloride or sodium chloride.[4] The remarks that were made about acid anhydrides might be repeated with little change about acid chlorides. The latter are more generally used, since the chlorides of many acids are available. They are even more reactive than the anhydrides. The hydrogen chloride formed from an acid chloride and an alcohol may isomerize or otherwise affect the alcohol. For this reason, this method of esterification is not recommended for sensitive alcohols.

There is one special case where the acid chloride method is the only one that can be used—the making of alkyl or aryl carbonates [reactions (11) and (12)]. Phosgene, the chloride of carbonic acid, is readily available and very reactive, while esters cannot be obtained from free carbonic acid or its anhydride. When a dialkyl carbonate, such as ethyl carbonate, in which both alkyls are the same, is desired, the case is very simple. The phosgene is led into an excess of the cold alcohol. The first stage [reaction (11)] goes rapidly at room temperature or below. The second [reaction (12)] is much slower and may be aided by heating. In case it is desired to produce a mixed carbonate having two different alkyls, the two reactions (11) and (12) are separated, and care is taken

[1] ALOE, *Rend. accad. sci.* (*Napoli*), **27**, 75 (1921); BAKUNIN and GIORDANI, *Rend. accad. sci. fis. nat.* (*Napoli*), III, **12**, 125 (1916); BOULEZ, *Bull. soc. chim.* [4], **1**, 117 (1907); **35**, 419 (1924); KNOEVENAGEL, *Ann.*, **402**, 111 (1914).

[2] AUTENREITH and THOMAE, *Ber.*, **57**, 1002 (1924).

[3] Malm and Fordyce, U. S. 2,023,485.

[4] Blieberger, U. S. 1,254,970; I. G. Farbenindustrie A-G., Brit. 291,773; Ger. 478,127; Fr. 664,770; 668,686; Ger. 523,802; 534,213; Knoll and Co., Ger. 187,254; 201,369.

that a minimum of dialkyl carbonate is formed in the first stage. This is accomplished by adding the alcohol to an excess of phosgene, keeping the temperature down to about 0°C., preferably with good agitation. After the reaction is complete, the excess of phosgene may be removed by blowing with dry air or by gentle heating. The monoalkyl chloro-carbonate thus obtained is caused to react with the second alcohol, which is used in slight excess. This reaction may be aided by heating or by the addition of a tertiary amine such as pyridine or dimethyl-aniline[1] or a weak base[2] or even caustic soda.[3]

There is a great deal of difference in the reactivity of different acid chlorides; those derived from aromatic acids react much more slowly than aliphatic, and arylsulfonyl chlorides are still slower. Thus, benzoyl chloride dissolved in an excess of ethyl alcohol and kept at 0°C. requires 4 hr. for complete reaction, while acetyl chloride reacts practically instantly. To speed up the reaction of a sluggish acid chloride, the mixture is sometimes heated,[4] or the Schotten-Baumann[5] method is used [reaction (14)]; *i.e.*, the alcohol or phenol is mixed with 10 or even 25 per cent caustic soda solution, and the acid chloride is added slowly with vigorous agitation, while keeping the temperature of the mixture down to 0°C. or below.[6] Phosgene and aromatic sulfonyl chlorides may be caused to react by this means.[3] Instead of the aqueous alkali, anhydrous tertiary bases may be used and the mixture heated.[7] As the esters formed by the Schotten-Baumann method are insoluble in the aqueous alkali, they are readily separated. They are washed with water, dried, and distilled or recrystallized according to their physical prop-erties. When a tertiary base is used, the reaction product is poured into cold dilute acid, and the ester separated, washed, dried, and fractionated or recrystallized.

One case demands special attention on account of the desirability of some of the products, and that is the synthesis of trialkyl or triaryl phosphates as represented by reaction (13). Phosphorus oxychloride

   [1] Schwing, Fr. 650,100; 34,412 (1927).

   [2] KREMANN, *Monatsh.*, **29**, 23 (1908).

   [3] DRAKE and CARTER, *J. Am. Chem. Soc.*, **52**, 3720 (1930); Grether, U. S. 1,877,304; 1,877,305.

   [4] Blieberger, U. S. 1,254,970.

   [5] BAUMANN, *Ber.*, **19**, 3218 (1886); SCHOTTEN, *Ber.*, **17**, 2545 (1884); **23**, 3430 (1890).

   [6] IZMAILSKII and RAZORENOV, *J. Russ. Phys. Chem. Soc.*, **52**, 359 (1920); MENALDA, *Rec. trav. chim.*, **49**, 967 (1930); Suzuki and Kaisha, Jap. 38,647.

   [7] Harris, U. S. 2,025,958; I. G. Farbenindustrie A-G., Brit. 291,773; Ger. 478,127; Fr. 664,770; 668,686; Ger. 523,802; 534,213; Neumann and Zeltner, U. S. 1,123,572; Neumann and Co., Fr. 466,804; PALOMAA, SALMI, JANSSON, and SALO, *Ber.*, **68**, 303 (1935); SABETAY, *Bull. soc. chim.* [4], **47**, 436 (1930); STIMMEL and KING, *J. Am. Chem. Soc.*, **56**, 1724 (1934); Suzuki and Kaisha, Jap. 38,647.

is made to react with an alcohol or with mixtures of alcohols or, more commonly, phenol, cresols, or mixtures of these. The reactants are brought together at room temperature or below but may be heated later. The hydrogen chloride may be removed by a current of air or taken care of by the addition of alkali.[1]

X. ESTERS FROM METAL SALT AND ALKYL HALIDE

Heating a metal salt of an acid with an alkyl halide [reactions (15) and (16)] substitutes the alkyl for the metal, thus forming an ester.

$$CH_3COONa + BrC_2H_5 \rightarrow CH_3COOC_2H_5 + NaBr \tag{15}$$
$$CH_3COONa + ClCH_2C_6H_5 \rightarrow CH_3COOCH_2C_6H_5 + NaCl \tag{16}$$

This reaction is frequently used for preparing esters,[2] especially those that may identify the acids.[3] For this purpose, we choose the halide of a radical which is likely to give a crystalline ester. Silver salts, which are readily prepared from acids, are frequently employed for this purpose, since no solvent is required and the resulting esters require little purification. Thallium salts are said to give particularly good yields of esters. For manufacturing purposes, this reaction is useful in a few cases only—those in which the alkyl halide is cheaper than the corresponding alcohol or in which the ester is difficult to obtain by direct esterification. The best known case is that of the manufacture of benzyl acetate from sodium acetate and benzyl chloride.[4] As the benzyl chloride is made by chlorinating toluene, it is the most available benzyl compound. The two reactants are brought together in a mutual solvent, which may be acetic acid or aqueous alcohol, and the mixture is heated until the benzyl chloride disappears, which is apparent by the disappearance of the sharp odor. Dilution with water throws out the benzyl acetate, which is washed, dried, and fractionated. Amyl chloride, from the chlorination of pentane, is used for the large-scale manufacture of amyl acetate.[5]

[1] Bass, U. S. 2,071,323; Bryner, U. S. 1,856,862; Chem. Fab. Griesheim Elektron, Brit. 181,835; EVANS, DAVIES, and JONES, *J. Chem. Soc.*, **1930**, 1310; Hand and Magoun, U. S. 1,866,852; I. G. Farbenindustrie A-G., Brit. 291,773; Ger. 478,127; 523,802; 534,213; Fr. 664,770; 668,686; Laska and Prillwitz, U. S. 1,425,392; 1,425,393; Nicolai, U. S. 1,844,408; Nicolai, Schönburg, and Bruck, U. S. 1,869,768.

[2] Consortium für Elektrochem. Ind., Fr. 465,965; Ger. 277,187; 277,188; Brit. 26,825; 26,826 (1913); Ger. 277,111; 285,990; 286,812; Brit. 4,887 (1915); Swiss 74,445; Norw. 30,419; 30,906; Dykstra, U. S. 2,072,739; Nicholl, U. S. 1,984,982; Schering-Kahlbaum A-G., Ger. 592,131.

[3] JUDEFIND and REID, *J. Am. Chem. Soc.*, **42**, 1043 (1920); LYONS and REID, *ibid.*, **39**, 1727 (1917); MOSES and REID, *ibid.*, **54**, 2101 (1932); RATHER and REID, *ibid.*, **41**, 75 (1919); REID, *ibid.*, **39**, 124 (1917).

[4] ARSEN'EV, *Masloboino Zhirovoe Delo*, **1935**, 33; BÉHAL, *Compt. rend.*, **147**, 1478 (1908); Hefti and Schilt, Brit. 229,958.

[5] Ayres, U. S. 1,869,837; Ayres and Haabestad, U. S. 1,691,425.

Esters can be made from rosin by heating its sodium salt with alkyl halides.[1] Caustic soda is dissolved in alcohol, and an equivalent amount of rosin added, followed by ethyl chloride in slight excess. This solution is heated to 160°C. in an autoclave for an hour; the pressure developed is around 200 lb. The ethyl abietate may be purified by distillation (b.p., 200°C. at 10 mm.). Diethyl sulfate may be used instead of the ethyl chloride.[2]

Patents have been granted on the preparation of glycol acetate from ethylene chloride[3] and methyl acetate from methyl chloride.[4] Various compounds particularly amines, are claimed as catalysts.[5]

Instead of the sodium salt, the free acid may be used with an alkyl halide and an organic base.[6]

Since reactions of this type are slow, except at temperatures above 100°C., they are usually carried out in autoclaves to avoid loss of volatile materials. When the reaction is complete, the autoclave is cooled and the charge drowned in water. The ester is separated, washed free of salts, dried, and rectified.

XI. ESTERS FROM ANHYDRIDES OF DIBASIC ACIDS

Monoalkyl phthalates are obtained with great ease by heating phthalic anhydride with an alcohol [reaction (17)]

$$C_6H_4 \underset{CO}{\overset{CO}{\diagup\diagdown}} O + C_2H_5OH \rightarrow C_6H_4 \underset{COOH}{\overset{COOC_2H_5}{\diagup\diagdown}} \tag{17}$$

The speed of this reaction is dependent on the nature of the alcohol. Advantage is taken of this fact to separate alcohols of the various classes; primary alcohols diluted with benzene are supposed to react completely with phthalic anhydride at 80° in an hour, while secondary have to be heated to 130 to 140°C. for several hours. Tertiary alcohols are dehydrated before they combine. The phthalic anhydride and one equivalent of the alcohol are heated until combination takes place, usually at 130°, the melting point of the anhydride. The monoalkyl phthalate so obtained may be freed from any uncombined alcohol by a quick steam distillation; from unreacted phthalic anhydride or acid, by solution in ether or benzene; from dialkyl ester, by solution in sodium carbonate or caustic soda. To form the sodium salt, the exact amount of alkali must

[1] Langmeier, U. S. 1,697,530.

[2] Hercules Powder Co., Fr. 656,821; Johnston, U. S. 1,682,280; 1,749,482; 1,771,044; 1,824,020; 1,840,395.

[3] Rodebush, U. S. 1,430,324.

[4] Carter and Coxe, U. S. 1,459,971; Can. 244,388; Wade, Brit. 220,721.

[5] Coleman and Moore, U. S. 2,021,852; Givaudan and Cie, Swiss 169,040; Lawson, U. S. 2,049,207.

[6] Badische, Ger. 268,621.

be added to the monoalkyl phthalate, since the sodium alkyl phthalate is readily salted out by an excess of alkali. The monoalkyl phthalate may be precipitated from the purified solution of its sodium salt.

Heating the monoalkyl ester with an excess of the alcohol gives the dialkyl ester, but this reaction is slow and requires either a high temperature or a catalyst.

$$C_6H_4{\nwarrow{COOC_2H_5} \atop \searrow{COOH}} + C_2H_5OH \rightarrow C_6H_4{\nwarrow{COOC_2H_5} \atop \searrow{COOC_2H_5}} + H_2O$$

Esters from Dibasic Acids and Polyhydric Alcohols.—Esters of this type are usually polymeric mixtures, nonvolatile on account of their high molecular weights and plastic or resinous because they are very complex mixtures. The glyptals, which are made by heating glycerol with phthalic anhydride, mixed with other acids, are esters of this type and have become very important. They are made by heating the constituents in a kettle and driving off the water that is formed in the reaction.

XII. PREPARATION OF XANTHATE

Carbon disulfide may be regarded as the anhydride of a dibasic acid:

$$SCS + H_2O \rightarrow SC{\nearrow{SH} \atop \searrow{OH}}$$
Dithiocarbonic Acid

This reaction does not take place, but carbon disulfide does combine readily with a sodium alcoholate, as in reaction (18).

$$SCS + NaOC_2H_5 \rightarrow SC{\nearrow{SNa} \atop \searrow{OC_2H_5}}$$
Sodium Xanthate

The product is the sodium salt of the monoalkyl ester of the above acid. The reaction is readily carried out: Metallic sodium is dissolved in the anhydrous alcohol, or caustic soda is mixed with the alcohol, which may contain some water, and carbon disulfide is added.[1] The union takes place at room temperature, and the sodium or potassium xanthate may be purified by recrystallization.

Cellulose xanthate which is made in enormous quantities—tens of thousands of tons annually—as an intermediate in the manufacture of rayon and Cellophane will be taken up in a later section.

XIII. ESTERIFICATION BY KETENE

At the present time, there is much interest in ketene as a means of producing esters, since it unites directly with alcohols.

$$CH_2:CO + C_2H_5OH \rightarrow CH_3COOC_2H_5 \tag{21}$$

[1] Christmann and Jayne, U. S. 1,810,552; 1,852,110; Hirschkind, U. S. 1,704,249; 1,872,452; Rosenstein, U. S. 1,854,525; 1,872,821.

The reaction is an attractive one, as the ester is formed by direct addition, since the ketene is highly reactive. The drawback so far has been the high cost of the ketene, but with improved methods for making it, this method of esterification is becoming important.[1] Ketene is made by passing acetone through a hot tube:

$$CH_3COCH_3 \rightarrow CH_2:CO + CH_4$$

XIV. ADDITION OF AN ACID TO AN UNSATURATED HYDROCARBON

The addition of an organic acid to an unsaturated hydrocarbon is not so simple a matter as is represented by reaction (24).

$$CH_2:CH_2 + CH_3COOH \rightarrow CH_3COOC_2H_5 \qquad (24)$$

The olefin and organic acid may be brought together in the presence of sulfuric acid, which is then spoken of as a catalyst though it is assumed that an intermediate compound such as a monoalkyl sulfate is formed which then reacts with the organic acid. Temperatures up to 125°C. are mentioned, and pressures of several atmospheres are beneficial.[2] Phosphoric esters can be obtained in the same way.[3] This reaction does not go with ethylene but does with some of the higher alkenes, particularly with some of the terpenes.[4]

$$C_{10}H_{16} + CH_3COOH \rightarrow CH_3COOC_{10}H_{17}$$

Instead of sulfuric acid, which has a strong polymerizing influence, boron fluoride may be used at moderate temperatures, and milder catalysts, such as zinc chloride, at higher temperatures, up to 300°C.[5]

XV. ESTERS FROM ACETYLENE

When acetylene and acetic acid are brought together with a suitable catalyst, union takes place to form a vinyl ester or an ester of ethylidene glycol according to reactions (27) and (28).

$$CH:CH + CH_3COOH \rightarrow CH_3COOCH:CH_2 \qquad (27)$$
$$CH:CH + 2CH_3COOH \rightarrow CH_3CH(OCOCH_3)_2 \qquad (28)$$

[1] Frolich and Wiezevich, U. S. 1,018,759; Graves, U. S. 2,007,968; Middleton, U. S. 1,685,220.

[2] Bataafsche, Fr. 778,418; Brooks, U. S. 1,894,662; Coleman, U. S. 2,021,851. Davis, U. S. 2,079,652; Dreyfus, Brit. 394,376, Fr. 746,463; Edlund and Evans, U. S. 2,006,734; Frolich and Young, U. S. 1,877,291; Graves, U. S. 1,915,308.

[3] Ipatieff, U. S. 1,915, 308.

[4] Austerweil, Ger. 468,229; Isajev, Brit. 251,147; Ruder, Can. 247,784; Schmidt, Brit. 306,385; 306,387; Fr. 633,431; 663,431; U. S. 1,836,287; 1,836,288; Ger. 532,395; 543,429; Stephan and Ulffers, Ger. 508,893; U. S. 1,838,465; Suida, U. S. 1,836,135.

[5] Brezinski and Frolich, U. S. 1,951,747; DORRIS, SOWA and NIEUWLAND, J. Amer. Chem. Soc., 56, 2689 (1934); Hilcken, U. S. 1,902,364; I. G. Farbenindustrie A-G., Fr. 774,342; Isham, U. S. 1,929,870; Schering-Kahlbaum, Ger. 573,797; Schneider, U. S. 2,065,540; Strange, Brit. 398,527.

The one reaction or the other may be favored by changing conditions.[1] The catalyst may be mercuric sulfate or phosphate or a more or less complex mixture. There are many patents.[2] Ethylidene diacetate seldom gets out of the plant where it is manufactured but is of great importance as the intermediate from which enormous amounts of acetic anhydride are produced. Other aliphatic and even aromatic acids may be used instead of acetic.

XVI. ESTERS FROM NITRILES

$$CH_3CN + H_2O + C_2H_5OH \rightarrow CH_3COOC_2H_5 + NH_3 \qquad (29)$$

This reaction (29) is of importance for the reason that the nitriles are intermediate steps in the synthesis of certain acids, and if the ester is wanted it saves one operation to make it directly from the nitrile instead of saponifying the nitrile and then esterifying the acid in the usual way. The nitriles of hydroxy acids, in particular, are readily obtained by the addition of hydrocyanic acid to an aldehyde:

$$CH_3CHO + HCN \rightarrow CH_3CH(OH)CN$$

The esterification of the nitrile presents no great difficulty. Enough acid must be used to combine with the ammonia that is formed and more to act as catalyst. A higher temperature and longer time are required than for simple esterification. Sulfuric acid is the usual catalyst, but hydrochloric acid may be employed, and zinc chloride may be added. The equipment is the same as for esterification, and the purification of the esters is the same. The amount of water may be kept low, but a considerable excess of alcohol is used, so that the ester has to be separated from the alcohol. As the esters prepared in this way are usually high boiling (ethyl lactate boils at 154°C.), the alcohol and water are distilled off from the ester. An inert solvent in which the ammonium salt is insoluble is frequently added to take up the ester. After filtering

[1] MORRISON and SHAW, *Trans. Electrochem. Soc.*, **63**, 23 (1933).

[2] Baum, Deutsch, and Hermann, Ger. 483,780; 485,271; Boehringer and Soehne, Brit. 427,448; Fr. 770,154; Brown and Courtaulds, Ltd., Brit. 353,318; Canadian Electro Products Co., Ger. 559,436; Consortium für Elektrochem. Ind., Brit. 182,112; 285,095; Fr. 649,455; Dykstra, U. S. 1,849,616; Hermann, Deutsch, and Baum, U. S. 1,790,920; Imperial Chemical Ind., Ltd., Brit. 351,318; I. G. Farbenindustrie A-G., Ger. 582,544; 588,352; 589,970; 604,640; 636,212; 637,257; 638,003; Fr. 773,476; Klatte, U. S. 1,084,581; Matheson and Skirrow, Can. 237,664; Morrison, Can. 287,495; U. S. 1,710,181; Mugdan and Rost, Ger. 553,071; Plauson, U. S. 1,425,130; Rabald, U. S. 2,011,011; Skirrow, Can. 287,496; Skirrow and Dick, Can. 228,127; U. S. 1,449,918; Skirrow and Herzberg, Can. 237,841; U. S. 1,638,713; Skirrow and Morrison, Can. 287,494; 318,838; U. S. 1,855,366; 1,855,367; 1,710,197; Brit. 308,169; Strain, U. S. 1,849,647; Weibezahn, U. S. 1,912,608.

off the ammonium salt, the solution of the ester may be washed with water, separated, and fractionated.[1]

XVII. ESTERIFICATION WITH ETHYLENE OXIDE

Ethylene oxide reacts with water to form glycol, with an alcohol to form a glycol ether, and with acetic acid to form a glycol monacetate:

$$\begin{matrix} CH_2 \\ | \\ CH_2 \end{matrix} \Big\rangle O + HOH \rightarrow \underset{\text{Glycol}}{HOCH_2CH_2OH}$$

$$\begin{matrix} CH_2 \\ | \\ CH_2 \end{matrix} \Big\rangle O + C_2H_5OH \rightarrow \underset{\text{Glycol Ether}}{C_2H_5OCH_2CH_2OH}$$

$$\begin{matrix} CH_2 \\ | \\ CH_2 \end{matrix} \Big\rangle O + CH_3COOH \rightarrow \underset{\text{Glycol Acetate}}{CH_3COOCH_2CH_2OH} \tag{30}$$

The esterification reaction is carried out by passing the ethylene oxide into the heated acid containing sulfuric acid or a similar catalyst. Under these conditions, a second molecule of the acid if available will esterify the free alcohol group of the mono-ester to produce the diester of glycol.[2]

XVIII. ESTERS FROM ALDEHYDES

Tischenko[3] found that in the presence of aluminum alcoholate one molecule of an aldehyde reacts with another [reaction (31)] to give a molecule of ester.

$$2RCHO \rightarrow RCOOCH_2R \tag{31}$$

This reaction is thoroughly discussed by Child and Adkins.[4] The aldehyde requires 7 per cent of solid aluminum ethylate, or 2.85 per cent if it is used in concentrated xylene solution, and yields 90 to 95 per cent of the ester.

XIX. ESTERS FROM ALCOHOLS

An ester may be prepared directly from an alcohol by passing it over a catalyst containing chromium at 375 to 425°C., usually under high pressure.

$$2C_2H_5OH \rightarrow CH_3COOC_2H_5 + 2H_2$$

[1] Barsky, U. S. 1,678,719; Bauer, Brit. 313,877; U. S. 1,829,208; Hurtley, Brit. 341,961; I. G. Farbenindustrie A-G., Brit. 259,204; Fr. 680,671; 689,275; Brit. 341,158; Fr. 39,892; Matheson and Blaikie, Brit. 257,907; 264,143; Michael and Haag, U. S. 1,831,025; Pfeiffer, *Ber.*, **51**, 805 (1918); Pfeiffer, Engelhardt, and Alfuss, *Ann.*, **467**, 158 (1928); Schmidt and Niemann, Ger. 544,499; Spiegel and Szydlowsky, *Ber.*, **51**, 296 (1918).

[2] I. G. Farbenindustrie A-G., Brit. 265,233; 292,059; 302,041; Fr. 671,123; 685,433; Brit. 307,471; 332,267; Loehr, Can. 285,356; U. S. 1,701,424; 1,810,318; Monnet and Carter, Brit. 128,911; Steimmig and Ulrich, Can. 278,557; U. S. 1,817,425; Ger. 515,306.

[3] Tischenko, *J. Russ. Phys. Chem. Soc.*, **38**, 355 (1906).

[4] Child and Adkins, *J. Am. Chem. Soc.*, **45**, 3013 (1923); **47**, 798 (1925).

It has been supposed that the alcohol is dehydrogenated to the aldehyde, 2 molecules of which give the ester, but no ester was obtained by passing ready-made acetaldehyde over the same catalyst.[1]

This reaction looks enticingly simple and has attracted considerable attention as evidenced by a number of articles and patents.[2] The difficulties have been low conversion and unwanted by-products. Recently these seem to have been overcome by Russian investigators.[3]

XX. ESTERS FROM CARBON MONOXIDE

Carbon monoxide may be considered the anhydride of formic acid. Actually, it unites, under high pressure and at a fairly high temperature, with caustic soda to give sodium formate.

$$CO + NaOH \rightarrow HCOONa$$

Similarly, it reacts with an alcohol at 90°C. in the presence of an alcoholate under 200 atmospheres pressure to give an alkyl formate.[4]

Carbon monoxide unites with an alcohol to form an acid:

$$CH_3OH + CO \rightarrow CH_3 \cdot CO \cdot OH \tag{33}$$

This synthesis takes place at high pressures (200 to 300 atmospheres) and at 300 to 400°C. in the presence of suitable catalysts. The acid so produced may react at once with a second molecule of the alcohol to give the ester. Thus, methyl acetate is obtained directly from methyl alcohol and carbon monoxide.[5]

$$2CH_3OH + CO \rightarrow CH_3COOCH_3 + H_2O \tag{34}$$

Or a single molecule of ether may react.[6]

$$CH_3OCH_3 + CO \rightarrow CH_3COOCH_3$$

An olefin, an alcohol, and carbon monoxide may unite.[7]

Processes along these lines may be expected to become important.

[1] ABRAMORA and DOLGOV, *J. Gen. Chem.* (*U.S.S.R.*), **7**, 1009 (1937).

[2] Chem. Forschungsges., Ger. 615,073; du Pont, Fr. 652,845; Ger. 515,678; 597,718; Brit. 424,284; Greenewalt, U. S. 1,858,823; Lazier, Brit. 313,575; U. S. 1,857,921; 1,949,425; 1,964,001; 1,975,853; Fr. 683,623; Martin and Krchma, U. S. 1,817,898; 1,869,761; SUMIYA, YAMADA, and TAJIMA, *Chem. News*, **114**, 328 (1932); Usines de Melle, Fr. 798,842; Woodruff, Martin, and Krchma, Can. 302,533; U. S. 1,875,540; Zeisberg, U. S. 1,708,460; Brit. 287,846.

[3] BEĬZEL, HEL'MS, and LEL'CHUK, *Org. Chem. Ind.* (*U.S.S.R.*), **1**, 102 (1936); BUKREEVA-PROZOROVSKAYA and YANNISHEVA, *Sintet Kauchuk*, **1936**, No. 3, 13; DOLGOV, KOTON, and LEL'CHUK, *J. Gen. Chem.* (*U.S.S.R.*), **5**, 1611 (1935); *J. Chem. Ind.* (*Moscow*), **12**, 1066 (1935); *Org. Chem. Ind.* (*U.S.S.R.*), **1**, 70 (1936).

[4] Ges. f. Kohlentechnik, Ger. 588,763; Wietzel and Kremp, U. S. 1,698,573.

[5] Bader, Brit. 337,053; British Celanese and Geoffrey, Brit. 361,378; Brit. 340,939; U. S. 1,879,605; 1,879,606; du Pont, Brit. 397,852; I. G. Farbenindustrie A-G, Brit. 320,457; 40,400; Oxley, U. S. 1,927,414; Plant, U. S. 1,909,630; Woodhouse, U. S. 1,979,518–9; 2,019,754.

[6] Dreyfus, U. S. 1,884,628.

[7] Vail, U. S. 1,979,717; Can. 342,957.

XXI. DESIGN AND OPERATION OF ESTERIFICATION PLANT

By Theodore Baker[1]

A plant for making esters from organic acids and alcohols on the large scale may be of three general types, depending on whether (1) the product is low boiling and is to be fractionated from an accumulated excess of water, as in the manufacture of methyl and ethyl acetates; (2) the ester is somewhat higher boiling and carries over with it considerable water that readily separates after condensation as a lower layer that can be decanted, as is the case with butyl and amyl acetates; or (3) the ester is of such low volatility that it is more practical to accumulate it in the still, and merely volatilize the water and/or the excess of acid or alcohol if these cannot be made to react completely. Examples of this type are the ethyl and butyl phthalates.

The first of these types of process may be run either as a batch or continuously. Both methods require efficient distilling columns, which may be of perforated plate or bell-cap design or even of the packed type. In every case, it is now customary to employ a catalyst, which is usually sulfuric acid, in admixture with the alcohol and acid that are to react. The function of this acid is not that of dehydration but merely to accelerate the reaction in the direction of equilibrium, and even less than 1 per cent is sufficient for the purpose. Esterification takes place to some extent even in the presence of large amounts of water and will continue as long as the acid and alcohol remain, if the ester is removed (by boiling) as fast as it is produced. In making ethyl acetate industrially, ethyl alcohol of 95 per cent by volume and acetic acid of 80 per cent or less concentration are generally used. There being no definite lower limit of acid concentration, it is merely a matter of economic balance as to how far the exhaustion of the acetic acid may be carried. About 1 per cent acetic acid to 99 per cent of water is not uncommonly attained when using a continuous process such as that of Backhaus,[2] especially when using dilute acid to start with.

Copper apparatus is generally used for large-scale esterification, as this metal is fairly resistant both to organic acids and to sulfuric acid when temperature and concentration are not excessive and free oxygen or compounds readily yielding oxygen are excluded. Steam coils, also of copper, are the usual means of heating. In the copper work, autogenous welding is to be preferred to brazing, although silver solder gives fair results. Gunmetal and phosphor bronze are to be preferred to

---

[1] E. I. du Pont de Nemours & Co.

[2] Backhaus, U. S. 1,400,849; 1,400,850; 1,400,851; 1,400,852; 1,403,224; 1,403,225; 1,425,624; 1,425,625; 1,454,462; 1,454,463; Can. 211,675; 211,676; 217,703; 261,187.

brass, while chrome nickel steel (18–8) can be used on condensers but not in parts where sulfuric acid is used.

Class I. Low-boiling Esters: Fractionated from Accumulation of Water.—Figure I illustrates a batch still layout for making crude ethyl acetate and the like. The organic acid and alcohol are employed in about molecular proportions, and at the start the still may be filled to about four-fifths of its capacity. The catalyst H_2SO_4 may be added

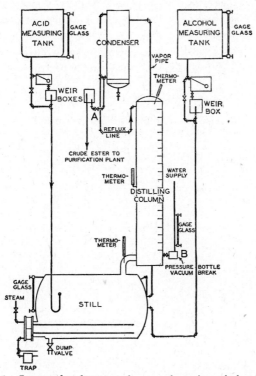

Fig. 1.—Layout: batch process for manufacturing ethyl acetate.

directly to the still charge or previously blended with the organic acid. The charge is brought up to the boil, and the whole distillate is refluxed for a time by closing the take-off valve A. The steam supply must be limited so that the condenser does not run hot or the pressure bottle show more than the normal back pressure of the column, this being about 1 to $1\frac{1}{4}$ in. per plate according to the design. After about an hour, the thermometer at the top of the column should read about 70°C. for ethyl acetate and remain steady, while the mid-column thermometer will gradually show a drop in temperature. When the latter indicates that several plates are charged with liquor boiling about 70°C., the take-off valve may be opened to bleed off the ethyl acetate as fast as it is formed and so hold the temperature in the mid-column practically constant. As the still charge diminishes owing to the formation and removal of ester, more acid and alcohol can be added gradually through the feed weir boxes to keep the still contents nearly constant in volume. The distillate is approximately the constant-boiling ternary mixture whose composition is 82.6 per cent ethyl acetate, 8.4 per cent ethyl alcohol, and 9 per cent water. Commonly, a slight excess of alcohol is present that prevents any separation into two layers, and a trace of free acid is also present. This distillate is stored, to be purified in a separate apparatus later on. The exact boiling point of the ternary is reported as being 70.23; but under manufacturing conditions, a variation of even 1° up or down is often noted due to the presence of small amounts of other materials.

As less water is carried over than is formed in the reaction

$$\text{Acetic acid} + \text{alcohol} = \text{ester} + \text{water}$$
$$60 \quad + \quad 46 \quad = \quad 88 \quad + \quad 18$$

and as the acid used will generally contain at least 20 parts of additional water and the alcohol about 4 parts, a fairly rapid accumulation of water is taking place in the still. This causes a slowing up of the reaction and requires a higher rate of reflux. After a while, the accumulation of water is so great that a clean up is necessary. At this stage, an excess of alcohol is fed to the still, and the acid feed discontinued. The distillate is then diverted to another tank and reused in a following charge. When the acid and alcohol are sufficiently exhausted, the residual water is dumped, and the still recharged. The refining of the charge comprises neutralizing with sodium carbonate or lime under agitation, followed by water washing, which removes the excess of alcohol. The washing is often done countercurrent in a packed tube, the water flowing downward and the ester upward, the same apparatus acting as a decanter. The ester layer, holding about 4 per cent water in solution, has to be redistilled through a column. The distillate, which contains most of the water, is reseparated or rewashed, and the washings are separately redistilled to recover their contents of ester and alcohol, these being returned to the process. Formerly calcium chloride was used to dry the ternary mixture, but this leaves a part of the alcohol unseparated, and a part of the calcium chloride stays in solution in the dried mixture. When such a mixture is redistilled, crusts are formed from which water is liberated at the end of the distillation.

A continuous process (Fig. 2) for making ethyl acetate, which is especially adapted to the utilization of dilute acetic acid, has been patented by Backhaus.[1] In this process, the residual acid water, exhausted of its acid and alcohol to as low a point as is economical, is

[1] Backhaus, *loc. cit.*

promptly and continuously discharged from the apparatus. The regulation of the still is thus practically fixed. Another advantage is that the final purification and working up of the wash waters can be tied in with the production of the crude ester. Figure 2 illustrates the essentials of this process. The raw materials are first blended in the correct proportions and fed from the feed tank in a steady stream through a preheater into the esterifying column. From the top of this is taken off a mixture of about 20 per cent ester, 10 per cent water, and 70 per cent alcohol, while a suitable amount of the same distillate is refluxed back

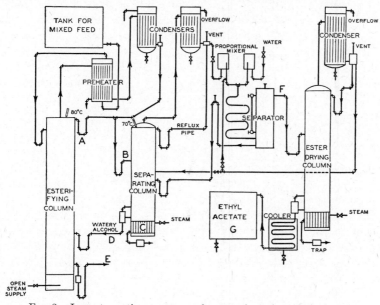

Fig. 2.—Layout: continuous process for manufacturing ethyl acetate.

to the column at *A*. The ternary mixture taken off passes to the separating column at point *B*. Here it is rectified by closed steam in the calandria *C*. Part of the condensate is returned as reflux to the top of the column, and the take off goes to a proportional mixing device, where it is blended with about an equal volume of water, which causes a separation into two layers. These are settled out in the separator tank, the watery portion overflowing back to the lower part of the separating column, whence blended with the alcohol and water accumulating in the base of this it is passed by pipe *D* to a point in the esterifying column. On the lower plates of the column, the alcohol is exhausted and distills upward as vapor, while the slop water goes to waste at *E*. The washed ester, containing a little dissolved water and alcohol, overflows from the separator at *F* and enters the drying column in which a sufficient amount is distilled off to carry with it the water and alcohol, which may go either to the separating column or back to the mixer, washer, and separator. The dry ethyl acetate that accumulates in the calandria of the drying column is taken off through a cooler to the receiving tank G. In general, this ester, though dry and holding very little alcohol and free acid, needs to be redistilled before it can be placed on the market, because it may contain salts of copper and higher-boiling esters formed from other acids present as impurities in the crude acetic acid employed.

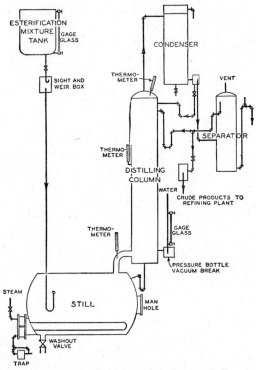

Fig. 3.—Layout: for manufacturing butyl or amyl acetates.

The working up of crude ester made by the batch process is very similar to that employed in the continuous process; but in the former, a special still must be provided for working up the weak wash waters unless this is done in the main batch still between esterification charges.

Class II. Esters Such as Butyl and Amyl Acetates.—This process differs from the first in that much more water is carried over with the ester when it distills from the esterification column or still. As this, in general, can exceed the total water formed during the reaction plus the free water in the raw materials, there is a general tendency for the still charge to go "dry." In any case, there is no building up of a watery still charge that has to be discharged as with ethyl and methyl acetates.

Consequently, an apparatus (shown in Fig. 3) that is nearly as simple as that shown in Fig. 1 can be operated continuously over long periods. A separator is used from which part of the oil layer can be refluxed if necessary, while part of the reflux can be taken directly from the condenser without separation, depending on the amount of water to be eliminated. The distillate is always a ternary one, containing ester and alcohol as well as water. This is not in general objectionable, as a product is often required that contains a certain proportion (10 to 15 per cent) of uncombined alcohol. The richness of the distillate in ester may be improved, if desired, by keeping the still charge stronger on the acid side. If an ester of 100 per cent is required, this may be obtained by rectification of the ester-alcohol mixture after drying. The foreshots in such a distillation contain a mixture richer in alcohol, while the tailings can be practically pure ester. The alcohol-rich fraction can be reworked in the esterifying process.

By employing an adequate reflux and avoiding too dry a column and still charge, the acetic acid can be substantially kept out of the distillate as it is carried down the column by the reflux, while the lower-boiling ternary mixture accumulates in the heads. The lower temperature and the wetness of the charge also tend to check the formation of sulfur dioxide resulting from reduction of the sulfuric acid.

Class III. Esters of Very Low Volatility.—In this case, the ester does not appreciably volatilize with the water that forms or was originally present but stays behind in the still while the free acid and alcohol gradually diminish. In general, the arrangement shown in Fig. 3 may be used, merely changing the method of operation. In the case of ethyl alcohol derivatives, by adding benzene to the charge, the water can be eliminated by taking it off from the separator as a lower layer containing some alcohol, which can be rectified elsewhere and its alcohol recovered. In the case of butyl and amyl compounds, the use of benzene is unnecessary, as the employment of an excess of the alcohol serves the same purpose, the water going over as a binary with the alcohol and separating out in the same way. In the case of an easily volatilized acid, as acetic, the water may be eliminated as formed, by adding to the charge a compound such as dichloroethylene or ethyl acetate. Such substances form with water binaries of low boiling points; these concentrate at the top of the column and separate after condensation, the water layer being taken off, in one case at the top and in the other at the bottom.

When the reaction is practically complete, the sulfuric and excess of organic acid are neutralized, and the charge distilled to dryness, being finally heated in a high vacuum to eliminate low-boiling residues.

Other purification treatment, such as filtration, may be required finally to yield a first-class product.

XXII. TECHNICAL ESTERIFICATIONS[1]

PREPARATION OF BUTYL ACETATE. BATCH PROCESS[2]

It is important that the acetic acid used should be free from other acids; its water content is not so important. The butyl alcohol must be free from other alcohols and is used in about 10 per cent excess. The catalyst is about 0.1 per cent sulfuric acid.

The still (Fig. 3) is heated under total reflux until the temperature at the top of the distilling column becomes constant at approximately 89°C. Then the distillate is withdrawn from the condenser as rapidly as can be done without permitting the temperature to rise above 90°C. (89.4°C. being the boiling point of the ternary of ester, alcohol, and water). The percentage composition of the distillate after separation into two layers is given in Table VIII.

These are separated in an automatic separator, the upper being sent back to the kettle. When the temperature starts to rise and the amount of water coming over becomes small, the reflux ratio is greatly increased so

TABLE VIII

Layer	%	Ester, %	Butyl alcohol, %	Water, %
Upper.............	75	80.5	13.4	6.1
Lower.............	25	1.92	1.69	97.39

as to increase the sharpness of the fractionation. The completion of the esterification is indicated by the absence of water in the distillate, a sample of which is mixed with benzene from time to time. This mixture is cloudy as long as any water is present. A sample is taken from the kettle, and the acetic acid determined. The residual acidity may be neutralized by soda or lime.[3]

On continuing the distillation, the binary of ester and butyl alcohol is next obtained. When the alcohol is exhausted, the temperature rises, and the pure butyl acetate that comes over is collected as finished product. The binary of alcohol and ester may be added to the next batch. The water layer, drawn off from the ternary, as shown above, contains some ester and alcohol which are recovered by distillation and utilized.

A kettle of 2,000 gal. capacity with a 30-plate, 30-in. column can produce 1,000 gal. of finished ester in 48 hr., provided that anhydrous acetic acid and butanol are used. The presence of any considerable

[1] Some of the esterifications to be described contain patented features which are not especially pointed out in order to avoid possible repetition.

[2] From information furnished by C. Barbre and O. B. Helferich.

[3] Hancock and Carnarius, U. S. 1,875,447.

amount of water decreases the capacity of the apparatus and lengthens the distillation time.

ACETYLATION OF CELLULOSE

In the space available here, it is possible to do no more than present a brief outline of the general technical features of the production of cellulose acetate. A list of books,[1] and references[2] to several recent reviews are given below for the convenience of the student.

The product of the acetylation of cellulose is the triacetate (containing 44.8 per cent of acetyl), which may be represented by the empirical formula $C_6H_7O_5(CH_3CO)_3$. The reaction by which this product is formed is not so simple as, for example, the esterification of ethyl alcohol. Attempts to acetylate cellulose with glacial acetic acid alone, even in the presence of dehydrating agents or catalyst, have not been successful; a more effective acetylating agent is required, such as acetyl chloride or acetic anhydride. With the latter reagents, the reaction for the formation of a single triacetate molecule may be represented as follows:

$$C_6H_{10}O_5 + 3CH_3CO \cdot Cl \rightarrow C_6H_7O_5(CH_3CO)_3 + 3HCl \qquad (a)$$
$$C_6H_{10}O_5 + 3(CH_3CO)_2O \rightarrow C_6H_7O_5(CH_3CO)_3 + 3CH_3CO \cdot OH \qquad (b)$$

best results being obtained when a catalyst is present. The cellulose (usually bleached cotton linters) may be caused to react with the vapors of foregoing reagents or in the presence of a liquid medium that does not dissolve the cellulose acetate formed, such as benzene or carbon tetrachloride, or the reaction may be caused to take place in the presence of acetic acid, liquid SO_2 or other solvents for the cellulose acetate.

Cellulose triacetate itself has been of little industrial importance, chiefly because of its limited solubility in the common non-toxic solvents; it is receiving increased attention as new solvents are developed. Since, however, cellulose as usually acetylated yields a triacetate only, it is necessary to prepare it as an intermediate product in the production of commercially useful solvent-soluble acetates. These more soluble secondary acetates are formed by partial hydrolysis of the primary acetate.

In spite of the numerous alternative methods cited for the preparation of cellulose acetate, one procedure is most commonly used; in this method, the cellulose reacts with acetic anhydride in the presence of glacial acetic acid and a catalyst, usually sulfuric acid. A large number of other

---

[1] WORDEN, "Technology of Cellulose Esters," vol. VIII (1916); "Technology of Cellulose Ethers," vol. II (1933); LIPSCOMB, "Cellulose Acetate" (1933); MULLIN, "Acetate Silk and Its Dyes" (1927); KRÜGER, "Zelluloseazetate und die andern organischen Ester der Zellulose," Steinkopff, Dresden (1933).

[2] YARSLEY, "British Plastics Yearbook," 49–55 (1932) (a short review); CHAUMETON and YARSLEY, "British Plastics" (1929–1931) (an extended series of articles).

catalysts have been proposed, among them being zinc chloride, perchlorates, mixtures of sulfuric and phosphoric acid, acid sulfates, phosphorus and sulfur chloride, and sulfonic acids.

While chemically the acetylation of cellulose by acetic anhydride may be represented by the simple equation (*b*) shown above, the reaction is greatly complicated by the physical and colloidal characteristics of the cellulose and of the cellulose acetate formed. The esterification reaction proper is accompanied by (*a*) degradation of the cellulose and (*b*) dispersion of the resulting cellulose acetate in the glacial acetic acid present. The heterogeneous nature of the reaction mass and the high viscosity of the resulting product require special means of agitation in order to secure uniformity of results. The equipment for this purpose, which

CELLULOSE ACETATE

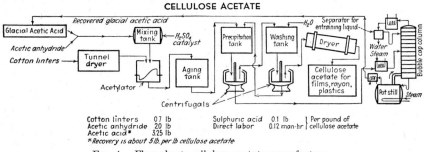

Fig. 4.—Flow sheet: cellulose acetate manufacture.

must of course be resistant to corrosion by the reagents, sometimes takes the form of a rotating vessel of the ball-mill type, with or without baffles and of varied shapes, and in other cases is a heavily constructed agitated vessel of the dough-mixer type.

Close attention must be given to the time and the temperature of the reaction and the amount of catalyst used. As a further insurance of uniformity of reaction, the cellulose is usually subjected to a pretreatment prior to the acetylation; a rather large number of pretreatments have been suggested, their principal purpose being to get the cellulose into such a physical form that it will be uniformly reacted upon. Among the materials suggested are formic acid, acetic acid, alkalis, oxidizing agents, sulfuric acid, lactic acid, etc.

The primary stage of acetylation is complete when the cellulose has finally dissolved owing to the formation of the soluble cellulose triacetate. When this point is reached, as determined by the complete disappearance of the cellulose fibers, the resulting clear viscous solution may either be diluted with sufficient water or other diluent to precipitate the triacetate, or the latter may first be converted into the secondary acetone-soluble acetates, which contain between 41 and 37 per cent of acetyl.

This conversion is caused to take place by introducing into the mass sufficient water to effect the desired hydrolysis within a convenient time. The amount of water added, the amount of hydrolysis catalyst (usually sulfuric, phosphoric, or hydrochloric acid), and the time and temperature of the hydrolysis differ widely in practice. In some cases, this *ripening* is allowed to take place at room temperature over a period of several days; whereas in others, at an elevated temperature (40 to 60°C.), it may take place in a few hours. The progress of the reaction may be followed by periodically removing samples of the solution, precipitating the cellulose acetate, and determining its composition (percentage acetyl) or observing its solubility in different solvents.

When the reaction has proceeded to a point where a product of the desired composition is obtained, the cellulose acetate is precipitated from the solution. Numerous methods of precipitation have been described.[1] The more common one consists in flowing the viscous acetic acid solution into an excess of water, with suitable agitation, in such proportions that the resulting supernatant liquor is below the concentration in acetic acid which will soften the cellulose acetate. This supernatant acetic acid may be drawn off and recovered; the precipitated acetate is then washed with water until it is acid free, after which it may be dried under controlled conditions in any one of the usual technical dryers.

The product of primary acetylation, upon analysis, usually shows about 44.0 per cent of acetyl instead of the theoretical 44.8 per cent; the remaining hydroxyl groups appear to have been esterified by sulfuric acid. A product of this composition is distinctly unstable toward heat and toward hydrolysis, and the combined sulfuric acid must be removed in order to obtain a stable material. This removal is effected during the ordinary hydrolysis to the secondary acetate, although in some cases additional means of stabilizing the precipitated acetate are considered necessary.

The cellulose acetate thus prepared is a white, fibrous or flaky material, of specific gravity 1.3, having ready solubility in acetone, from which it can be deposited as a tough, transparent, flexible film upon evaporation of the solvent. The cellulose acetates of commerce are characterized by two important properties:

a. Viscosity, usually measured in acetone solution.

b. Composition, as percentage of acetyl.

The range of possible viscosities is rather wide, thus permitting the adaptation of the product to various uses. The usual range of acetyl values is between 37 and 41 per cent, solubility in different solvents being greatly dependent upon the precise composition.

In addition to the above variable properties representing the type of the cellulose acetate are certain others that indicate its stability, uni-

[1] U. S. 1,899,061; 1,844,017.

formity, and general quality.   An acetate is usually examined with
respect to its moisture content (which may be as high as 6 per cent,
depending upon relative humidity conditions), the free acid present, the
stability toward heat or toward hydrolysis, and the completeness of its
solubility in the solvent (usually acetone) in which it is to be used.

The Xanthation of Cellulose

By W. D. Nicoll[1]

The xanthation of cellulose and the spinning of the viscose are represented in the flow sheet (Fig. 5).   The cellulose, which may be bleached

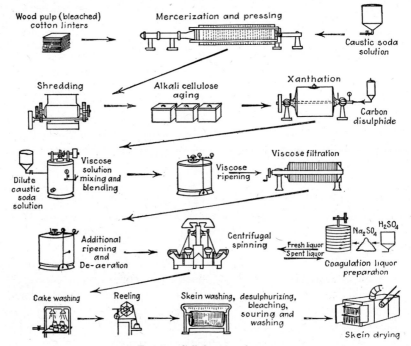

Fig. 5.—Cellulose xanthate.

wood pulp or cotton linters or a mixture of the two, in sheets, is placed in
a steeping tank, which is also a press.   It is impregnated with a caustic
soda solution of definite strength—usually 17.5 to 18 per cent—and then
pressed out until the wet weight bears the desired relation to the dry.
This material, called *alkali cellulose*, is shredded in Werner and Pfleiderer
shredders having serrated edges and saddle.   The shredded alkali
cellulose, which in physical appearance resembles moist bread crumbs, is
loaded into boxes which are stored in a constant-temperature room for a

[1] E. I. du Pont de Nemours & Co.

definite time to effect the *ageing*. During this period, the oxygen of the air acts on the cellulose and brings about a reduction of the viscosity of solutions made from it. In the next step, which is carried out at constant temperature in a rotating drum called a baratte, the alkali cellulose is treated with a definite amount of carbon disulfide in vapor form. At the completion of the reaction, the orange-yellow cellulose xanthate is agitated with a definite amount of caustic soda solution. The resultant solution, or dispersion, is the viscose. This, in turn, must be aged, or ripened, to a state that has been shown by experience to give the best results in spinning. If the viscose is ripened too long, it sets to a gel, which cannot be spun or sheeted. The ripened viscose is deaerated and filtered before being forced through small holes into a salt-acid bath in the spinning of rayon or through a slot for making cellophane.

When sodium cellulose-xanthate is brought into contact with acid, cellulose-xanthic acid is set free:

$$SC\begin{matrix} \diagup SNa \\ \diagdown OCel \end{matrix} + HCl \rightarrow SC\begin{matrix} \diagup SH \\ \diagdown OCel \end{matrix} + NaCl$$

Cellulose-xanthic Acid

The free cellulose-xanthic acid is unstable and decomposes into carbon disulfide and cellulose:

$$SC\begin{matrix} \diagup SH \\ \diagdown OCel \end{matrix} \rightarrow CS_2 + Cel \cdot OH$$

Cellulose

The regenerated cellulose is in the form of fine threads or sheets.

MANUFACTURE OF GLYCERYL TRINITRATE (NITROGLYCERIN)

BY J. L. BENNETT[1]

Glycerol [$C_3H_5(OH)_3$], a by-product of soap manufacture, is a sweet, syrupy liquid at ordinary temperatures but freezes when exposed for a long time at temperatures below 10°C. (50°F.), especially if crystals of frozen glycerol are introduced into the material. Glycerol produced for the manufacture of glyceryl trinitrate [nitroglycerin, $C_3H_5(O \cdot NO_2)_3$] generally contains not less than 98.72 per cent glycerol (sp. gr., 1.2620 at 15.6°C./15.6°C.).

Since the freezing point of glyceryl trinitrate is about 13.3°C. (56°F.) and many commercial explosives are required for use in cold weather, the freezing point of nitroglycerin is lowered by adding varying percentages of ethylene glycol [$C_2H_4(OH)_2$] to the glycerol before nitration or by polymerizing part of the glycerol to diglycerol [$C_6H_{10}O(OH)_4$].

[1] Hercules Powder Company.

Commercial ethylene glycol for nitration should contain not less than 99 per cent ethylene glycol. The specific gravity should be 1.116 to 1.119 at 15.6°C./15.6°C. Ordinary cane sugar (sucrose, $C_{12}H_{22}O_{11}$) also may be dissolved in dynamite glycerol, either with or without ethylene glycol or diglycerol, and satisfactorily nitrated.

Therefore, the nitrated product prepared for use in commercial explosives may be glyceryl trinitrate or a mixture of this ester with varying percentages of either one or more of the following products:

Ethylene dinitrate.............................. $C_2H_4(O\cdot NO_2)_2$
Diglyceryl tetranitrate......................... $C_6H_{10}O(O\cdot NO_2)_4$
Sucrose octanitrate............................ $C_{12}H_{14}O_3(O\cdot NO_2)_8$

The process of making nitroglycerin, either with or without the other esters, comprises four principal steps, *viz.*, nitration proper, separation, prewashing, and neutralization. The process consists of adding glycerol slowly to a suitable charge of mixed nitric and sulfuric acids to form nitroglycerin and spent acid; separating nitroglycerin from spent acid; washing the nitroglycerin with water to remove most of the dissolved or entrained acids; and neutralization of the remaining acids with an alkali to give a neutral and stable nitroglycerin.

Equipment.—The *nitrator* is a covered cylindrical steel vessel provided with mechanical agitators. Steel coils are located around the inside wall of the nitrator so that heat liberated by the reaction may be removed by circulating brine through them. The bottom of the nitrator slopes to an iron- or chemical-ware cock, which allows the mixture of spent acid and nitroglycerin to be discharged to the separator. The nitrator is equipped with indicating thermometers for control of the temperature of nitration. Situated at one side and above the nitrator is a small scale-tank holding the glycerol for one charge.

The *separator* is a shallow lead vessel with open top, located close to the nitrator but on a lower level. The bottom slopes to an outlet cock of chemical ware, and thermometers are provided at two levels to indicate the temperature of the spent acid and nitroglycerin. A rectangular plate-glass window is cemented in the side of the separator to permit inspection of the mixture. A large tank containing water is installed below the nitrator and separator so that their contents can be discharged into it if the operation does not proceed normally.

The outlet from the separator discharges spent acid into a pipe line leading to the spent acid storage and discharges the nitroglycerin to the *prewash tank*. This is a partially covered wooden or lead tank provided with a vent pipe in the cover and an outlet at the bottom. Through the bottom outlet, the nitroglycerin is delivered to the *neutralizing tank*, which is a vertical, cylindrical, lead tank provided with a cover and vent pipe and bottom outlet. The prewash and neutralizing tanks are equipped with air agitators for mixing the nitroglycerin and wash waters. The agitators are usually made of hard rubber in the form of a hub and hollow spokes, the spokes being drilled with small holes to distribute the air uniformly up through the contents of the tank.

Small, open-top labyrinths (baffled boxes) are provided at suitable points, so that all wash waters can pass through them in order to settle out any suspended nitroglycerin. The effluent may then be discharged safely into the drainage system.

Operation.—The acid mixture usually consists of approximately equal parts of nitric and sulfuric acid and has a total acidity of close to 100 per cent. The composition of the mixture varies with the total acidity, and the relative percentages of nitric and sulfuric acid are adjusted so that with the water liberated during nitration, the composition of the spent acid is approximately the same in all cases. The mixed acid should be well settled before use so as to contain a minimum of suspended impurities, such as iron sulfate, which will interfere later with the separation of nitroglycerin from the spent acid.

A definite weight of mixed acid is placed in the nitrator, and a definite amount of glycerol, calculated from the nitric content of the mixed acid being used, is delivered into the glycerol scale tank. The mechanical agitator is started, and brine circulated through the coils until the acid mixture is reduced to the desired nitrating temperature. While a pre-determined temperature is maintained during nitration, this temperature may vary from 2.2°C. (36°F.) to 7.7°C. (46°F.) or higher, at different plants.

When the thermometer registers the desired temperature, the glycerol is allowed to run continuously into a nitrator at a rate that maintains the temperature at the desired point. The reaction is very rapid, so that within 3 to 5 min. after the last of the glycerol is in the nitrator, the mixture is discharged to the separator. In order to facilitate separation of the nitroglycerin from the spent acid, a small amount of material such as sodium fluoride is added to the nitrator charge prior to delivery to the separator.

The charge of mixed acid used in the United States is approximately 7,000 lb. The glycerol used with it is approximately 1,500 lb. and produces about 3,500 lb. of nitroglycerin. The time required for nitration depends on the capacity of the brine system to remove the heat of reaction and in general practice varies from 60 to 90 min. per charge.

The spent acid-nitroglycerin mixture discharged from the nitrator is allowed to remain quietly in the separator from 45 to 60 min., during which time the nitroglycerin, having a specific gravity of 1.6, gradually separates from and rises to the surface of the acid. The progress of the separation is observed through the plate-glass window in the side of the separator. A distinct line of demarcation between the nitroglycerin and spent acid indicates when the separation is satisfactorily completed.

The spent acid is delivered through the bottom outlet cock and pipe line to the spent acid storage tanks; and the nitroglycerin, carrying dissolved and entrained nitric and sulfuric acids, is delivered to the pre-wash tank, which is partly filled with warm water. By means of air agitation, the nitroglycerin is intimately mixed with the wash water, which dissolves the greater portion of the acid. The nitroglycerin is allowed to settle from the acid water and is then delivered to the neutralizing tank, which is generally located in another building. Delivery is made through a covered wood gutter, lined with sheet rubber.

The nitroglycerin enters the neutralizing tank, which contains a warm, dilute water solution of sodium carbonate, and the gutter is flushed down with an additional quantity of sodium carbonate solution to wash all the nitroglycerin into the neutralizing tank.

The nitroglycerin and alkaline water are intimately mixed by air agitation until a sample of the nitroglycerin is neutral. Litmus paper is sometimes used to test for neutrality, but the pH method is more reliable. The neutral nitroglycerin is very stable and, after being settled from the wash water, is ready for use in commercial explosives.

All waste waters from the preliminary washing and sodium carbonate neutralizing operation, as well as the water used for washing out equipment used in the process, are passed through settling tanks in which small amounts of suspended nitroglycerin are settled out and returned to the washing tanks.

The spent acid delivered from the separator to storage tanks is passed through a recovery operation. The nitric acid and nitrogen oxides are separated from the sulfuric acid by denitration with the aid of steam in a suitable tower (see chapter on Nitration). Typical spent acids from the nitration of glycerol will analyze 74 to 75 per cent H_2SO_4 and 8 to 9 per cent HNO_3 when the total nitrogen present is calculated to HNO_3. The spent acid contains nitroglycerin in solution, which is safely decomposed by the heat evolved by the interaction of steam and the acid mixture.

Simple calculations will show that 100 lb. of pure glycerol should produce 246.61 lb. of glyceryl trinitrate and would require 205.31 lb. of nitric acid. Likewise, 100 lb. of pure ethylene glycol should produce 245.03 lb. of ethylene dinitrate with a consumption of 203.09 lb. of nitric acid. In practice, an excess of 10 to 15 per cent of nitric acid is provided in the mixed acid and is recovered from the spent acid.

In average practice in the United States, the yield of nitroglycerin is 96 to 97 per cent of the theoretical amount, while approximately 3 per cent is lost by solution in the spent acid. Small amounts are also lost by solution in the wash waters, see chapter I.

The manufacture of glyceryl trinitrate and similar esters may be classed as an extremely hazardous operation unless conducted under suitable conditions and in properly designed equipment. It should never be undertaken, even on a small scale, by anyone who is not fully informed and not protected by approved safety devices.

THE MANUFACTURE OF CELLULOSE NITRATE

BY E. E. THOENGES[1]

When cellulose $(C_6H_{10}O_5)x$ is treated with mixed acid, it undergoes nitration readily, and the reaction for the highest nitrate may be presented as follows:

$$C_6H_7O_2(OH)_3 + 3HONO_2 \rightarrow C_6H_7O_2(O \cdot NO_2)_3 + 3H_2O \ (N=14.16\%)$$

The nitrogen content of any particular nitrate largely defines its solubility and other properties, and consequently its technical application. The relationship between the nitrogen content and industrial application is as follows:

Nitrogen, %

10.7–11.2 Soluble in ethyl alcohol. Used with camphor and triphenyl phosphate to produce cellulose plastics.

11.2–11.7 Soluble in methyl alcohol, ether alcohol, ethyl acetate, etc. Used for photographic films and artificial silk.

11.8–12.3 Soluble in ester solvents, *e.g.*, amyl acetate, acetone, etc. Used as a basis for cellulose lacquers, artificial leather, and gelatinous explosives.

12.4–13.0 Insoluble in the usual solvents but soluble in acetone. Used for smokeless powders and explosives.

Two forms of cellulose are generally employed for nitration, *viz.*, purified cotton linters and the better grades of bleached sulfite pulp. Cotton linters have previously been the chief raw material, but within recent years methods have been developed for the preparation of wood pulp for industrial nitrations and this source of cellulose is used very extensively at present.

The three major steps of the process are, nitration, purification, and dehydration.

Nitration.—Forty pounds of dried and loosely formed cellulose is forked into the nitrating dipping pots and thoroughly agitated in a large excess of mixed acid for 20 to 30 min. at a temperature of 15 to 20°C. The mixed acid varies widely for the different types of nitrocellulose, but may have an approximate composition of 25 per cent nitric acid, 55 per cent sulfuric acid, and 20 per cent water, which gives a product containing approximately 11.5 per cent nitrogen.

[1] Hercules Powder Company.

After nitration, the charge is dropped into centrifugals to remove the spent acid. The acid-wet nitrocellulose is quickly forked from the sides of the basket of the centrifugal and dropped into water in immersion bowls. The nitrocellulose is then floated in a stream of water to the purification area. The spent acid is analyzed and fortified with strong nitric and sulfuric acids to the proper composition for reuse.

Purification.—The first step in the purification process is the removal of the retained acid from the nitrocellulose by washing. The nitrocellulose suspended in water is then pumped by a centrifugal pump to

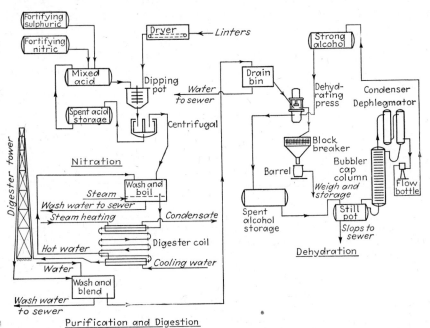

Fig. 6.—Flow sheet: cellulose nitrate manufacture.

the boiling tubs where it is heated by injecting live steam. This operation breaks down unstable cellulose compounds, formed during nitration, into a condition whereby they may be washed out. "Straight" nitration types are then pumped to treating tubs, given additional washes or treatment, depending upon their ultimate use, and blended for viscosity. Low-viscosity types are spoken of as *digester types* and are pumped from the boiling tubs to the digester building.

Reduction in viscosity may be effected by chemical treatment with ammonia, but pressure digestion is generally used and is a more satisfactory process. Pressure digestion was formerly carried out in large pressure vessels, and this process is still used to some extent in Europe. In the United States, however, pressure digestion is accomplished in a

Milliken continuous digester. This equipment consists of a 4-in. jacketed coil approximately 4,000 ft. long made entirely of chrome steel. At the discharge end of the digester, the pipe line rises over a 200-ft. tower and thereby provides a hydrostatic back pressure. Pumping against the hydrostatic leg and friction in the system result in a pressure of 100 lb. per square inch inside the coil. It is possible, therefore, to heat a nitrocellulose-water mixture to a temperature of about 160°C. During a 20-min. passage through the digester, the viscosity of the nitrocellulose is substantially and uniformly reduced. The mixture is cooled by water jackets before it flows over the digester tower. Like the straight nitration types, the digester types are then pumped to treating tubs.

Dehydration.—Following purification, the product is pumped to chrome-steel drain bins. After the excess water has drained off, the wet nitrocellulose is dehydrated. About 60 lb. of the water-wet product are placed in a hydraulic press and 250 lb. pressure applied for a short time. The dehydrating agent, usually denatured ethyl alcohol, is then pumped through the block in the press to displace the remaining water. The pressure in the press is then increased to 3,000 lb., reducing the excess alcohol to something less than 30 per cent of the weight of nitrocellulose. The blocks so formed are then put through a breaker and dropped into barrels for shipment. The weak alcohol produced in dehydration is rectified in standard alcohol stills for reuse.

CHAPTER XI

HYDROLYSIS

By Stewart J. Lloyd and G. D. Palmer, Jr.

I. DEFINITION AND SCOPE

The term hydrolysis is applied to reactions of both organic and inorganic chemistry wherein water effects a double decomposition with another compound, hydrogen going to one component, hydroxyl to the other:

$$XY + H_2O \rightarrow HY + XOH$$
$$KCN + H_2O \rightarrow HCN + KOH$$
$$C_5H_{11}Cl + H_2O \rightarrow HCl + C_5H_{11}OH$$

For inorganic chemistry, hydrolysis is usually the reverse of neutralization; but in organic chemistry its scope is broader. Here it includes, among other things, the inversion of sugars, the breaking down of proteins, the saponification of fats and other esters, the final step in the Grignard reaction, all of which can be carried on with water alone, albeit slowly and incompletely. For convenience, the meaning of the term has been extended also to cover the numerous cases in which an alkali is added to the water and in which the alkali salt of an acid is usually one of the final products:

$$CH_3COOC_2H_5 + NaOH \rightarrow CH_3COONa + C_2H_5OH$$

Even more common is the application of the term to reactions in which an acid is added to the water in large or small amounts. This addition, like that of alkali, invariably hastens the hydrolysis even if it does not initiate it. The saccharification of cellulose, wherein glucose is produced as an intermediate product in the making of alcohol from wood, and the enormous production of glucose from starch fall in this category. Accelerating agents other than acid and alkali are known but, with the single exception of enzymes, are not important. The enzymes (organic catalysts) are of surpassing importance in vital processes, both animal and plant, especially in preparing food for use in the body, and many of the reactions catalyzed by them are hydrolytic.

The use of alkali in aqueous solution leads naturally to another type of hydrolytic reaction, the *alkali fusion*, wherein the proportion of alkali is greatly increased and that of water correspondingly reduced.

$$C_6H_5SO_3Na + 2NaOH \rightarrow C_6H_5ONa + Na_2SO_3 + H_2O$$

followed by

$$C_6H_5ONa + HCl \rightarrow C_6H_5OH + NaCl$$

Quite a number of important preparations, such as that of β-naphthol, fall under this heading and may conveniently be classed as cases of hydrolysis, even though oxidation and reduction may be involved[1] and water plays but a minor part.

The line between hydrolysis and hydration is not very sharply drawn. The reaction

$$BaCl_2 + 2H_2O \rightarrow BaCl_2 \cdot 2H_2O$$

is surely hydration, while the saponification of a nitrile

$$C_2H_5CN + H_2O \rightarrow C_2H_5CONH_2$$

or the conversion of starch into glucose, whether wisely or not, has always been regarded as hydrolysis. For this reason, some interesting and important cases of hydration involving olefines and acetylene are included, regardless of consistency.

We may recognize, then, five types of hydrolysis:

1. Pure hydrolysis where water alone is used.
2. Hydrolysis with aqueous acid, dilute or concentrated.
3. Hydrolysis with aqueous alkali, dilute or concentrated.
4. Alkali fusion, with little or no water but at high temperatures.
5. Hydrolysis with enzymes as catalysts.

Still another classification would be to divide all cases of hydrolysis into

1. Those taking place in the liquid phase or phases.
2. Those taking place in the vapor phase.

Class 1 contains practically all cases of commercial importance, but interest in the vapor-phase reactions is growing. The passage of chlorobenzene vapor and steam at an elevated temperature over a solid catalyst to produce phenol and hydrochloric acid is an example of the latter type.

In this chapter, the subject matter will be presented as follows:

a. A brief review of the chief hydrolyzing agents.
b. A list of the materials susceptible to hydrolysis.
c. A discussion of the theory and mechanism of hydrolysis.
d. Equipment, materials of construction, etc., for hydrolysis.
e. Technical operations involving hydrolysis.

II. HYDROLYZING AGENTS

Although the word hydrolysis means decomposition by water, cases in which water unaided brings about *effective* hydrolysis are rare, and

[1] FRY and BUTZ, *Rec. trav. chim.*, **52**, 129–138 (1933).

high temperatures and pressures are usually necessary even then. For complete and speedy reaction, an accelerating agent of some kind is nearly always indispensable, whatever the mechanism of its reaction may be. The most important of these are alkalis, acids, and hydrolyzing enzymes. A succinct survey of the use and peculiarities of these three agents, preceded by a list of cases in which water alone may be used, is given next.

Water.—The Grignard reagent, so useful in synthesis, is hydrolyzed quickly and completely by water, as are the less manageable zinc alkyls and other organo-metallic compounds. The conversion of acetaldehyde into isopropyl alcohol by the Grignard reaction is a good illustration.

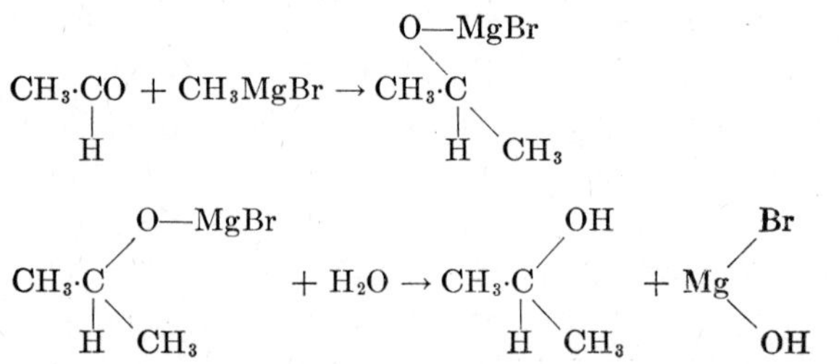

$$CH_3 \cdot CO + CH_3MgBr \rightarrow CH_3 \cdot C \overset{O—MgBr}{\underset{H \quad CH_3}{}}$$

$$CH_3 \cdot C \overset{O—MgBr}{\underset{H \quad CH_3}{}} + H_2O \rightarrow CH_3 \cdot C \overset{OH}{\underset{H \quad CH_3}{}} + Mg \overset{Br}{\underset{OH}{}}$$

The acid anhydrides, lactones, lactides, and other internal anhydrides such as ethylene oxide are readily hydrolyzed by water alone, acetic anhydride reacting much more rapidly than either benzoic or phthalic. Digallic acid, an anhydride despite its name, changes rather slowly into gallic acid. Mixed anhydrides, among which, for convenience, are included the acid halides, react with vigor, especially acetyl chloride, which is more reactive than acetic anhydride itself. In general, the stronger the two acids in these mixed anhydrides the more vigorous the hydrolysis; *e.g.*, acetyl chloride is more readily hydrolyzed than butyryl bromide. Benzoyl chloride, however, reacts with less readiness than acetyl chloride, despite the greater strength (dissociation) of benzoic acid. This is probably due to the lower solubility of benzoyl chloride in water.

Alkyl halides of complex composition react with water alone, though the simple halides like ethyl chloride are but slightly affected. Mustard gas, for example, probably owes some of its effect to the reaction:

$$ClH_4C_2—S—C_2H_4Cl + 2H_2O \rightarrow HOH_4C_2—S—C_2H_4OH + 2HCl$$

which takes place fairly rapidly. Diazonium salts when heated with water hydrolyze completely.

$$C_6H_5N{\equiv}N + H_2O \rightarrow C_6H_5OH + N_2 + HCl$$
$$\overset{|}{Cl}$$

Phenol can thus be made, though not economically, from aniline. The alkyl sulfates, *e.g.*, ethyl hydrogen sulfate, hydrolyze when heated with water. Aronovsky and Gortner[1] found that cooking poplar wood with water for two hours at 100 lb. pressure (170°C.) dissolved out 20 per cent of the weight of the wood, part of the dissolved material no doubt resulting from hydrolysis. The sodium salt of acetoacetic ester is completely hydrolyzed by water, as are the metallic alcoholates and a few other unimportant substances. A slight degree of hydrolysis seems to occur with numerous materials—esters, proteins, carbohydrates, etc.—especially upon boiling, but it should be emphasized again that water by itself is able to bring about complete and rapid hydrolysis of only very few substances. For all others, the intervention of a third reactant of some kind is required.

The use of steam instead of liquid water has brought results in a few cases. Benzenesulfonic acid with steam yields benzene and sulfuric acid

$$C_6H_5SO_3H + H_2O \text{ (steam)} \rightarrow C_6H_6 + H_2SO_4$$

and similarly α-naphthalenesulfonic acid hydrolyzes to naphthalene. Steam and chlorobenzene passed through porous silica at 575°C. give a 95 per cent yield of phenol, while similar results but with smaller yields have been obtained with other aryl and alkyl halides. The Twitchell (see page 610) and autoclave processes of making fatty acids from fats might almost be included, though both use a small amount of catalyst.

Acid Hydrolysis.—In 1811, Kirchhoff observed that starch was transformed by aqueous mineral acids into glucose and showed that no acid was used up in the process. Braconnot, in 1819, hydrolyzed linen (cellulose) with strong sulfuric acid, obtaining a fermentable sugar. This use of acid in hydrolysis was rapidly extended to other classes of organic materials—the esters, sugars, amides, etc.—and it was found that wherever water brought about hydrolysis, acid accelerated the reaction, and in addition the latter seemed in many cases to initiate reaction where water alone failed. The acid hydrolysis of acetate esters has come to be a sort of proving ground for theories of catalysis. It is customary to attribute the effect of acid to the hydrogen ion content, and with dilute acid in many reactions there is at least a rough proportionality between the velocity of reaction and the hydrogen ion concentration. Like many other generalizations in chemistry, this relation is more honored in the breach than the observance, and with concentrated acids it does not hold at all. The undissociated acid and the negative radical have both been called upon from time to time to account for certain anomalous results.

Hydrochloric and sulfuric acids are naturally the most commonly used, though many others have been experimented with. Formic and

[1] ARONOVSKY and GORTNER, *Ind. Eng. Chem.*, **22**, 264–274 (1930).

trichloroacetic appear to be lower in activity than would be expected, while oxalic and benzenesulfonic are more active than sulfuric. Concentrations from very high to very low are used in both laboratory and commercial practice. The Bergius process for saccharifying wood employs 41 per cent hydrochloric, while the Scholler-Tornesch system, which is described later, uses 0.5 per cent sulfuric acid for the same purpose.

Sulfuric acid is particularly useful because it forms with many types of organic substances intermediate compounds which themselves readily undergo hydrolysis. This is exhibited in the acid process of fat splitting to make fatty acids, as well as in the similar Twitchell system, in making alcohol from ethylene, and probably also in the hydration of acetylene to make aldehyde. In all these, sulfuric acid exhibits a specific action, distinct from its hydrogen ion concentration, and cannot be replaced by other acids.

Although acid and alkali may frequently be used interchangeably on the same materials to give essentially the same products, this is not invariably true. The action of acid on acetoacetic ester and its derivatives leads to acetone, carbonic acid, and alcohol and its related products, while alkali on the same ester produces acetic acid and alcohol. Stieglitz[1] has pointed out that the imido esters can be hydrolyzed by water in two distinct ways, depending upon whether the solution is acid or basic.

Alkali Hydrolysis.—We may distinguish three different cases of hydrolysis with alkali:

1. The use of low concentrations of alkali in the hydrolysis of esters and similar materials: Here the hydroxyl ion is supposed to catalyze the reaction as the hydrogen ion does in catalysis by dilute acid. Since one of the products of reaction is usually an acid which reacts immediately with the hydroxyl ion, this case is of significance only in theoretical studies, where an instantaneous value of a reaction velocity is desired.

2. The use of sufficient caustic under pressure, and in high concentrations to unite with all the acid produced:

$$C_6H_5Cl + aq.\ NaOH \rightarrow C_6H_5OH + aq.\ NaCl$$

sometimes followed by

$$C_6H_5OH + NaOH \rightarrow C_6H_5ONa + H_2O$$

A variant of this is presented by McKee[2] and by MacMullin and Gegenheimer,[3] in which the vapors of chlorinated hydrocarbons mixed with

[1] STIEGLITZ, *Am. Chem. J.*, **39**, 166 (1908).
[2] McKee, U. S. 1,688,726 (1928).
[3] MacMullin and Gegenheimer, U. S. 1,549,779 (1925).

steam are passed over solid alkaline materials, such as lime, yielding alcohols.

$$2CH_3Cl + Ca(OH)_2 \xrightarrow{\text{Steam}} 2CH_3OH + CaCl_2$$

3. The fusion of organic materials with caustic soda or potash: This develops naturally from case 2 by decreasing the ratio of water. The formation of carvacrol from sodium p-cymenesulfonate is an example:

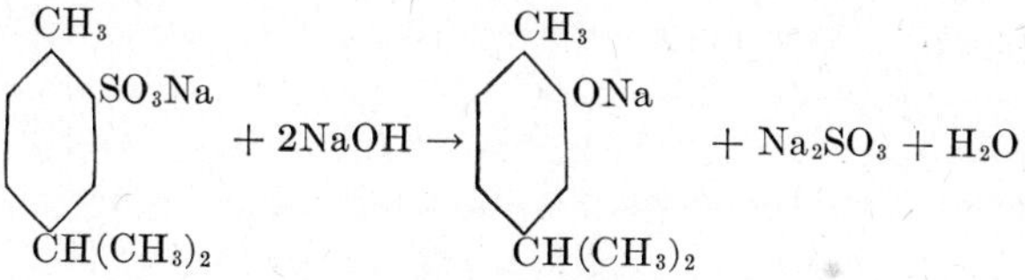

with of course the subsequent acidulation of the sodium salt.

This alkali fusion process is limited essentially to sulfonic acids, though the elimination of carbon dioxide is sometimes accomplished in this way.[1] Chlorinated and nitrated compounds do not seem to have been successfully subjected to this mode of treatment.

Rogers[2] and Kokatnur[3] have suggested the addition of an inert diluent, especially kerosene, to the mixture, thereby facilitating mixing, and claim that the necessary quantity of caustic is thereby reduced.

Alkali is practically excluded from one field in which acids are very useful—the hydrolysis of carbohydrates. Cellulose is rather resistant to alkali and when attacked is broken down but not distinctly hydrolyzed, while sugars are subject to deep-seated changes in alkaline solution. Glucosides, for the same reason as sugars, are not suitable materials for alkaline hydrolysis; and although proteins yield hydrolytic products rapidly and completely, there are certain disadvantages attached to the use of alkalis with them.

Caustic soda is the base most commonly used, but the alkali carbonates and bicarbonates as well as the alkaline-earth hydroxides all find occasional application. Potassium compounds show no advantage over the cheaper sodium materials, except that potassium hydroxide in some alkaline fusions permits the use of a lower temperature. Ammonium hydroxide and ammonium salts are rarely used.

Enzymatic Hydrolysis.—Comparatively few large-scale operations depend upon enzymes for hydrolysis. One or two enzymes (urease) are used for analytical purposes. Molasses is converted by invertase in the manufacture of industrial alcohol, and of course the whole brewing industry depends upon the complex hydrolysis of starch into maltose and glucose by the amylases. Despite its occasional industrial applica-

[1] PHILLIPS, *Ind. Eng. Chem.*, **13**, 759–769 (1921).

[2] Rogers, U. S. 1,644,493 (1927).

[3] Kokatnur, U. S. 1,667,480 (1928).

tion, enzymatic hydrolysis is, however, primarily the concern of the biochemist.[1,2]

III. MATERIALS SUSCEPTIBLE TO HYDROLYSIS

There do not appear to be any general rules or far-reaching generalizations that will enable us to predict the behavior of organic materials toward hydrolyzing agents. For this reason, it is necessary to review one by one the chief types of compounds and to describe explicitly their behavior.

Hydrocarbons.—Saturated aliphatic hydrocarbons apparently do not suffer hydrolysis directly. There is no record of the reaction

$$C_nH_{2n+2} + H_2O \rightarrow C_nH_{2n+1}OH + H_2$$

taking place to the slightest degree, even with caustic or acid or enzymes or at high temperatures and pressures or any combination of these, nor has the reverse reaction been recorded. It is true that methane and steam have been converted into carbon monoxide and hydrogen and ultimately into carbon dioxide and hydrogen, by passage over a solid catalyst at an elevated temperature:

$$CH_4 + H_2O \rightarrow CO + 3H_2$$
$$CO + H_2O \rightarrow CO_2 + H_2$$

but this would hardly be classed as hydrolysis. Hydrolytic rupture of the C—C bond occurs in many reactions of hydrocarbon derivatives such as chloral or acetoacetic ester with alkali.

With unsaturated hydrocarbons, the case is different. The reaction

$$C_nH_{2n} + H_2O \rightarrow C_nH_{2n+1}OH$$

has been effected on a large scale with ethylene, through the formation of an intermediate compound with strong sulfuric acid; and even less difficulty is experienced with the homologues (propylene, butylene, etc.). The *direct* addition of water, without the aid of acid, has not yet been made practical. The reverse reaction whereby ethylene is made from alcohol vapor passed over a solid catalyst, such as alumina, is well known.

The addition of water to acetylene

$$C_2H_2 + H_2O \rightarrow CH_3CHO$$

whereby acetaldehyde and ultimately acetic acid are produced, has long been recognized and is today practiced on a large scale. Sulfuric acid containing either dissolved mercury sulfate or suspended mercuric oxide serves as the hydration catalyst.

---

[1] Waldschmidt-Leitz, "Enzyme Actions and Properties," trans. and extended by R. P. Walton, John Wiley & Sons, Inc. (1929).

[2] Gortner, "Outlines of Biochemistry," pp. 714–716, John Wiley & Sons, Inc. (1929).

This addition of water to the olefins and acetylene just mentioned takes place in the liquid phase. Benzene vapor when passed with steam through a hot quartz tube (650°C.) gives rise to detectable amounts of phenol:[1]

$$\underset{\text{Steam}}{C_6H_6 + H_2O} \rightarrow C_6H_5OH + H_2$$

This result has been confirmed by Lloyd,[2] who obtained a conversion into phenol of 0.3 per cent of the benzene passed through the tube. Various solid catalysts such as chromium oxide and zinc ferrite had little effect on the yield. The reverse reaction is complete. No attempt to make the naphthols in a similar way is on record.

Carbohydrates.—Cellulose is hydrolyzed to glucose by acids and to cellobiose by its own specific enzyme cellulase. Alkali is not effective. Later on page 613 a detailed description of the large-scale saccharification of wood cellulose to glucose is presented. The 12-carbon sugars— sucrose, maltose, etc.—yield the corresponding monosaccharides on hydrolysis with enzyme or dilute acid, but alkali brings about other changes in them. Enzymes and dilute acids hydrolyze starch into maltose and glucose, while inulin yields only fructose by this treatment. Other carbohydrates, like pectins, xylan, and araban, suffer corresponding changes with acids or enzymes. It should be emphasized that alkalis are not as a rule useful with this class of substances.

Esters.—Organic esters of all kinds, including the esters of carbohydrates, are quite subject to hydrolysis with acids, bases, and in many cases enzymes. In this connection, the term saponification is commonly used instead of hydrolysis. The most important example is that of the saponification of fats and oils to make glycerol and either soap or fatty acids. All three common hydrolyzing agents find commercial application here, in the acid, the autoclave, and the enzymatic process of producing fatty acids. The decomposition of ethyl and methyl acetates by water plus a catalyst has probably received more attention than any other case of hydrolysis by reason of its bearing on the general subject of catalysis. Hydrolysis of esters is reversible, unlike that of the carbohydrates, so that the equilibrium point may be approached from both sides. The following equations represent typical cases of ester hydrolysis:

$$CH_3COOC_2H_5 + H_2O \xrightarrow{\text{HCl}} CH_3COOH + C_2H_5OH$$

$$
\begin{array}{l}
C_{17}H_{35}COO-CH_2 \\
C_{17}H_{35}COO-CH \\
C_{17}H_{35}COO-CH_2
\end{array}
+
\left\{
\begin{array}{l}
H_2O \\
H_2O \\
H_2O
\end{array}
\right.
\xrightarrow{H_2SO_4}
\begin{array}{l}
C_{17}H_{35}COOH \\
C_{17}H_{35}COOH \\
C_{17}H_{35}COOH
\end{array}
+
\begin{array}{l}
CH_2OH \\
CHOH \\
CH_2OH
\end{array}
$$

Glyceryl Tristearate (Fat)   Stearic Acid   Glycerol

[1] FISCHER, *Ges. Abhandl. Kenntnis Kohle,* **5,** 417–419 (1920).

[2] LLOYD, Unpublished research.

The esters of inorganic acids, ethyl and methyl sulfates, ethyl hydrogen sulfate, the alkyl phosphates, glyceryl nitrate, etc., may all be hydrolyzed, generally speaking, by acids and bases. The most interesting case is that in which sulfuric acid furnishes the acid radical, as the formation and subsequent hydrolysis of its ester are the essential features in production of alcohols from olefins, of fatty acids from fats, and probably of acetaldehyde from acetylene.

Ethers (Organic Oxides).—Ether may be hydrolyzed to ethyl alcohol in the presence of a dilute aqueous acidic catalyst, such as 10 per cent sulfuric acid, at a temperature of 272°C., and under pressure of over 225 lb. per square inch.[1] A 46 per cent conversion of ether to alcohol has been obtained at 275 to 300°C. and 120 atmos. pressure with aluminum oxide containing 5 per cent nickel oxide.[2] Secondary alcohols are more readily formed from ethers than primary. Ethylene oxide and trimethylene oxide hydrolyze fairly readily with water to form the corresponding glycols. The higher polymethylene ethers are less reactive with water, the penta- and hexamethylene ethers have exceedingly stable ring systems as is to be expected from the Baeyer strain theory. The addition of water to diphenyl oxide has been studied in connection with the production of phenol by the hydrolysis of chlorobenzene and is favored by a large excess of caustic alkali:

$$(C_6H_5)_2O + H_2O \xrightarrow{\text{NaOH}} 2C_6H_5OH$$

Hydrolysis of phenol and naphthol ethers with concentrated hydrochloric acid shows that meta derivatives decompose the least and para derivatives the most; and that acidic groups increase the stability.[3]

Organic Halides.—These useful compounds differ markedly in their behavior toward hydrolyzing agents, the acid halides, like acetyl chloride, reacting readily with water alone, while varying degrees of resistance are shown by the alkyl and aryl compounds. The alkyl chlorides are not appreciably hydrolyzed by acids, but alcoholic solutions of caustic potash convert them into the corresponding alcohols.[4]

$$C_2H_5Cl + KOH \text{ (alcohol)} \rightarrow C_2H_5OH + KCl$$

The hydrolysis of the amyl chlorides with sodium oleate and caustic soda solution to form the corresponding alcohols is the basis of a flourishing industry and is discussed on another page. Laboratory production of methyl and ethyl alcohols has resulted from the passage of the vapors of the corresponding chlorides along with steam over a solid catalyst,[5]

[1] U. S. 2,045,785 (1936).

[2] BALANDIN, SHUIKIN, NESVIZHSKII, and KOZMINSKAYA, *Ber.*, **65B**, 1557–1561 (1932).

[3] KOLHATKAR and GHASWALLA, *J. Indian Chem. Soc.*, **8**, 511–516 (1931).

[4] GRANT and HINSHELWOOD, *J. Chem. Soc.*, **1933**, 258.

[5] U. S. 1,849,844 (1932).

hydrochloric acid gas being a by-product. The substitution of the inert solid catalyst by lime or other alkaline oxide, whereby the acid is neutralized, has been mentioned before (page 595). The ease of removal of halogen increases markedly from chlorine to iodine and with increasing complexity of the compound. Ethylene chlorohydrin, for example, is easily and smoothly hydrolyzed to ethylene glycol by aqueous sodium bicarbonate:

$$CH_2OHCH_2Cl + NaHCO_3 \ aq. \rightarrow CH_2OHCH_2OH + CO_2 + NaCl$$

A differentiation should be made between the hydrolysis of simple halogen compounds and chlorohydrins, since a difference in reaction mechanism, and in many cases a difference in order of magnitude of yield, is involved. Ethylene oxide is considered to be an intermediate between ethylene chlorohydrin and ethylene glycol.[1] The aromatic halides are much more difficult to hydrolyze. Acids are without effect upon them, save in the case of meta-chlorinated pyridine,[2] while in the Dow process for making phenol from chlorobenzene a pressure of 4,200 lb. and a temperature of 350°C. are required to make alkali effective. The presence of small amounts of copper facilitates this last reaction immensely:

$$C_6H_5Cl + Na_2CO_3 \ aq. \xrightarrow{\ Cu\ } C_6H_5OH + NaCl + NaHCO_3$$

Similar results have been reported for naphthol.[3] As stated in the introduction, phenol can be made economically by passing steam and chlorobenzene through a silica catalyst,[4] and a small yield of hydroquinone has been secured in a similar way from steam and *p*-dichlorobenzene. *p*-Chloronitrobenzene has likewise been commercially converted into *p*-nitrophenol by heating to 160°C. with aqueous caustic soda.

It has been found by Brittain[5] that when an aryl or alkyl substituted aromatic halohydrocarbon is hydrolyzed at a relatively high temperature, *i.e.*, 300 to 400°C., in the absence of copper, there is formed a substituted phenol in which the hydroxyl group is in a position which is ortho or para to the original position of the halogen, together with a certain amount of the expected phenol. For example, both *o*-phenylphenol and *m*-phenylphenol are prepared from *o*-chlorobiphenyl. The hydroxy compounds are not convertible into isomers by treatment with alkalis in like manner. Similar results were obtained in the production of naphthols from bromo- and chloronaphthalenes.[6]

[1] SCHRADER, The Glycol Industry, *Z. angew. Chem.*, **42**, 541–546 (1929).
[2] U. S. 1,778,784 (1930).
[3] U. S. 1,882,825, 1932; 1,992,154 (1935).
[4] U. S. 1,735,327 (1929).
[5] U. S. 1,996,744 (1935).
[6] U. S. 1,996,745 (1935).

Nitrogen Compounds.—Aliphatic and aromatic amines—ethylamine and aniline—resist hydrolysis even under extreme conditions, though the production of α-naphthol from α-naphthylamine under pressure is recorded.[1] 1-Naphthol-4-sulfonic acid is produced by a "reverse Bucherer reaction" by the hydrolysis of naphthionic acid with bisulfite.[2] Amides are hydrolyzed to the ammonium salt of the corresponding acid when heated with water, but in the presence of acids and bases there is a marked increase in the rate of hydrolysis.

$$CH_3CONH_2 + H_2O \rightarrow (CH_3COOH + NH_3) \rightarrow CH_3COONH_4$$

The hydrolysis of two interesting and fairly important nitrogenous sweetening substances—dulcin and saccharin—has been minutely studied by Täufel[3] and associates. Dulcin (*p*-phenetylcarbamide) in strongly acid or alkaline solution is converted to ammonia and *p*-phenetylcarbamic acid:

$$\underset{\begin{array}{c}\\ NH_2\end{array}}{\overset{\begin{array}{c}NH-C_6H_4-OC_2H_5\\\end{array}}{CO}} + H_2O \rightarrow \underset{\begin{array}{c}\\ OH\end{array}}{\overset{\begin{array}{c}NH-C_6H_4-O-C_2H_5\\\end{array}}{CO}} + NH_3$$

but in boiling water more complicated changes occur. The conclusion is drawn that this material when used for sweetening purposes should be added *after* cooking. Saccharin boiled in neutral water does not hydrolyze appreciably but in alkaline media changes to *o*-sulfoamidobenzoic acid, while acid catalysts carry the hydrolysis farther to the ammonium salt:

$$C_6H_4\underset{CO}{\overset{SO_2}{<}}NH + 2H_2O \rightarrow C_6H_4\underset{COOH}{\overset{SO_2NH_2}{<}} \rightarrow C_6H_4\underset{COOH}{\overset{SO_3NH_4}{<}}$$

A temperature of 100°C. in the foodstuffs to which it is added does not cause appreciable hydrolysis.

Nitriles undergo a fairly complete but peculiar form of hydration when heated with water, especially if alkali or acid be present. Thus, the hydrolysis of ethyl cyanide does *not* proceed as follows:

$$C_2H_5CN + H_2O \rightarrow C_2H_5OH + HCN$$

instead, the bond between the carbon and nitrogen is broken, and we have

$$C_2H_5CN + 2H_2O \rightarrow C_2H_5COONH_4$$

Benzonitrile acts in a similar way to form benzoic acid but requires sulfuric acid in the reacting mixture.

[1] Ger. 74,879 (1892); VOROZHTZOV and GUTORKO, *J. Gen. Chem. (U.S.S.R.)* **5**, 1581 (1935).

[2] U. S. 1,880,701 (1933).

[3] TÄUFEL, *Z. Elektrochem.*, **34**, 115–127; 281–291 (1928).

Isocyanides are stable toward alkalis but hydrolyze in the presence of acids to form an acid and an amine:

$$CH_3NC + 2H_2O \rightarrow CH_3NH_2 + HCOOH \rightarrow H \cdot COONH_3CH_3$$

Nitro compounds, like nitrobenzene and nitromethane, are not readily hydrolyzed. Indeed, nitroethane may be distinguished in this way from ethyl nitrite, which hydrolyzes readily with caustic alkali:

$$C_2H_5ONO + NaOH \rightarrow C_2H_5OH + NaNO_2$$
Ethyl Nitrite

Sulfonic Acids.—The sulfonic acids require rather drastic methods of hydrolysis. The aliphatic members of the group do not hydrolyze; for example, ethylsulfonic acid $(C_2H_5SO_3H)$ may be boiled with caustic soda solution or with concentrated acids without decomposition, whereas the ester ethyl hydrogen sulfate hydrolyzes readily:

$$C_2H_5OSO_3H + H_2O \rightarrow C_2H_5OH + H_2SO_4$$

Benzenesulfonic acid, when treated with steam under pressure, yields benzene and sulfuric acid:

$$C_6H_5SO_3H + H_2O \rightarrow C_6H_6 + H_2SO_4$$
Steam

but, when fused with caustic soda, sodium phenolate is the product:

$$C_6H_5SO_3H + 3NaOH \xrightarrow{\text{fusion}} C_6H_5ONa + Na_2SO_3 + 2H_2O$$

The action of steam on α-naphthalenesulfonic acid similarly yields naphthalene. Practically all aromatic sulfonic acids may be hydrolyzed with mineral acids to the parent hydrocarbons, but each sulfonic acid requires a specific minimum temperature. α-Naphthalenesulfonic acid hydrolyzes at a much lower temperature than the beta compound. However, the β-compound with fused caustic acts quite like the corresponding benzenesulfonic acid to give β-naphthol, sodium sulfite, and water. Under certain conditions steam may replace the more expensive fused caustic alkalis in the hydrolysis of aromatic sulfonates which are volatile with steam.[1] The principle here involved is also employed in the preparation of the aliphatic alcohols and may be represented by the following reaction:

$$RSO_3M + ROM + H_2O \rightleftharpoons M_2SO_3 + 2ROH$$

The reaction involves hydrolysis of the alkali sulfonates in the presence of the phenolate at temperatures corresponding to those employed in alkali fusions, *viz.,* 350 to 400°C. To avoid difficulties in agitation, an excess of the phenolate is employed. The accumulated sulfite is removed by diluting the reaction mass and filtering while hot. The condensed vapors yield a 20 to 30 per cent phenol suspension.

[1] U. S. 1,992,167 (1935).

IV. THEORY AND MECHANISM OF HYDROLYSIS

The preceding part of this chapter has dealt with the reagents of hydrolysis and the behavior of the organic materials undergoing the reaction. The mechanism of the hydrolytic process is now to be studied as well as the various factors which influence its course. In liquid-phase hydrolysis, the reaction mechanism has usually been viewed as a special case of the general question of homogeneous catalysis, and the two classic examples of organic hydrolysis—saponification of esters and inversion of sucrose—have been favorite proving grounds for the numberless theories advanced in this field. A brief discussion of these reactions should serve to set forth the past and present status of hydrolytic mechanism in the liquid phase, especially from the "ion" point of view. In view of the diverse materials which undergo hydrolysis, it is too much to expect any single far-reaching generalization, unless it should refer to some peculiar property of water.

Hydrolysis of Esters.—The early investigators recognized that esters of the organic acids were partially hydrolyzed by water alone but that the reaction was very slow and did not go to completion. The addition of almost any acid speeded up the reaction immensely but scarcely shifted the equilibrium point, while the addition of a base likewise quickened the rate; and if enough were added to neutralize wholly the acid formed, the reaction was carried to completion.[1] The accelerating effect of the acid, since it could not be attributed to the neutralization of a product, obviously required another explanation. Since hydrogen alone is common to all acids and to water, it was natural to attribute the catalyzing effect to it. However, the acceleration due to different acids did not prove to be proportional to the hydrogen added by them to the solution, so that when the appearance of the Arrhenius dissociation theory afforded an opportunity to distinguish between *active* (dissociated) and *inactive* (combined) hydrogen, it did not take long to discover that, for dilute acids at least, the acceleration was roughly proportional to the active hydrogen, or *hydrogen ion concentration*. No very definite ideas were advanced at this time as to the exact way in which the hydrogen ions acted, whether by impact or by intermediate compound formation, or otherwise.

Deviations from even this rough proportionality were soon found with dilute as well as concentrated acids, and the next step was to assume the existence of two kinds of hydrogen ion—unhydrated (active) and hydrated (inactive)—only the former having catalytic properties.[2] Finally, Karlsson, in an illuminating paper,[3] finds it even necessary to

---

[1] See chapter on Esterification.

[2] LAPWORTH, *J. Chem. Soc.*, **107**, 857 (1915); RICE, *J. Am. Chem. Soc.*, **45**, 2808 (1923).

[3] KARLSSON, *Z. anorg. allgem. Chem.*, **145**, 1–57 (1925).

assume that hydrogen ions, hydroxyl ions, undissociated acid, and neutral salt all catalyze materially the hydrolysis of esters.

These results, disconcerting as they are in the light of the original pronouncement of Ostwald and Arrhenius that hydrogen ions alone were effective in ester catalysis, are brought somewhat into line again by Brönsted's broadening of the definition[1] of the terms acid and base and his assumption that uncombined (unhydrated) hydrogen ion cannot exist in aqueous solution, that ordinary hydrogen ion is H_3O^+. If we accept his definition of an acid as a *proton donor* and of a base as a *proton acceptor*, we can include under the terms acid and base all the substances so far found to catalyze ester hydrolysis and can state that only acids and bases, as newly defined, catalyze this reaction.

The growing complexity of the subject and the appalling amount of data already assembled make it necessary to reduce the treatment here to a few categorical statements, to most of which exception can probably be taken. Even if these statements are correct for ester hydrolysis, it is questionable how far they apply to hydrolysis of other types of substances:

1. Hydrogen ions are chiefly responsible for accelerating acid hydrolysis of esters of weak (organic) acids, such as methyl acetate.

2. Hydrogen ions do *not* catalyze the hydrolysis of esters of strong (mostly inorganic) acids—phosphoric, sulfuric, nitric, benzenesulfonic, trichloroacetic.[2]

3. Proportionality between the rate of reaction and the hydrogen ion concentration is usually approximate only. Since hydrogen ions cannot be supplied without corresponding negative ions, the deviations find an easy but futile explanation in the assumed effect of the latter or even of the undissociated molecule.[3]

4. No real evidence of the existence of intermediate compounds between water, the ester, and the hydroxyl ions has been presented, though such compounds have repeatedly been postulated, and elaborate calculations based upon their presence made.

The above points have to do chiefly with acid hydrolysis. There is unimpeachable evidence that hydroxyl ions, and indeed all bases defined according to Brönsted, catalyze the hydrolysis of esters. Wijs[4] showed that the rate of hydrolysis of methyl acetate in pure water was proportional to the sum of the concentrations of the hydrogen and the hydroxyl ion. The exact relationship between hydroxyl ion and reaction velocity is, of course, clouded by the shift in the equilibrium point due to the

---

[1] Brönsted, *Trans. Faraday Soc.*, **24**, 635–640 (1928).

[2] Olivier and Berger, *Rec. trav. chim.*, **41**, 637 (1922)

[3] Bates and Taylor, *J. Am. Chem. Soc.*, **49**, 2444 (1927); **51**, 771 (1929).

[4] Wijs, *Z. physik. Chem.*, **12**, 514 (1893).

removal by alkali of the acid produced in the reaction. This difficulty is not encountered with acids.

The preceding discussion of acid and base hydrolysis, which applies specifically to esters, may be extended to most cases where dilute acids or alkalis appear as catalysts at moderate temperatures. It has no application to hydrolysis with concentrated acids and alkalis at high pressures and temperatures and of course none to alkali fusion. Since most commercial applications of hydrolysis fall in these latter classes, we cannot expect much application of theory to practice.

Effect of Temperature on Hydrolysis.—Temperature changes influence hydrolytic reactions, as they do most others, in two ways, by shifting the equilibrium point and by changing the rate of reaction. Very little has been published on the former point, but no doubt the general relationship connecting the heat of the reaction, the equilibrium constant, and the temperature is valid here, as elsewhere:

$$\frac{d \ln K}{dT} = \frac{\Delta H}{RT^2}$$

where K is the equilibrium constant, ΔH the heat absorbed, and T the absolute temperature. Expressed qualitatively, if the hydrolytic reaction is accompanied by an evolution of heat, it will proceed farther at low temperatures, and *vice versa*. In commercial processes, the necessity of completing the operation in a minimum of time has led to the use of the highest temperatures practicable in order to take advantage of the greater speed of reaction, regardless of the possibly unfavorable shift of the equilibrium point. A mixture of equivalent amounts of ethyl acetate and steam kept in contact with silica gel gave the following figures:

°C.	Percentage Hydrolyzed
At 150	15.3
200	16.7
250	21.7
300	25.1

Evidently, the hydrolysis in this case is endothermic.

More important than the effect upon the equilibrium point is the influence of temperature upon the speed of reaction. Hydrolytic reactions, like most others, follow the rule that the rate doubles approximately for every 10° rise in temperature. For the temperature interval 25 to 35°C., the hydrolysis of ethyl acetate, formylacetic acid, and ethylcyanoacetate shows a rate increase of 2.4; the acid hydrolysis of amides, 3.4, and cane sugar inversion 4. For this same temperature interval, the rate of hydrolysis of organic acid anhydrides increases 1.84 times. Enzymatic hydrolysis does not differ in this respect materially from that produced by other catalysts, but only a small temperature range has been covered. Values as high as 5.3 for trypsin and as low as 1.2 for lipase are recorded. The rapid destruction of enzymes at temperatures over 60°C. complicates this case. The fact, however, that their temperature coefficients are of the same order of magnitude as those for acids and bases is of importance in arriving at a correct idea of enzyme action.

The general effect of the operating temperature in a case of industrial hydrolysis is brought out in the following table, which gives the results obtained by heating *p*-chloronitrobenzene for 12 hr. with four times its weight of caustic soda in aqueous solution, to form *p*-nitrophenol:

TABLE I.—EFFECT OF TEMPERATURE HYDROLYSIS OF *p*-CHLORONITROBENZENE

$$Cl\langle\bigcirc\rangle NO_2 + NaOH \rightarrow HO\langle\bigcirc\rangle NO_2 + NaCl$$

Temp., °C.	Conc. NaOH, %	Chloronitrobenzene recovered, %	Nitrophenol yield, %
120	15	91.2	8.8
140	15	2.3	90.6
160	15	trace	74.6

Evidently, the rate of reaction at 120°C. is far too slow, though no waste of material occurs; while at 140°C. the rate is much faster, and only 7 per cent of the starting material is destroyed. The temperature 160° is either too high or the heating is continued too long, since one-fourth of the raw material is lost. Actually, the proper time of heating is about 4 hr., and 160°C. is a suitable temperature.

Figure 1 illustrates the relation between temperature and time of heating necessary to secure a 92 per cent yield of phenol from chlorobenzene and aqueous caustic.[1] At 370°C., 12 min. is sufficient; at 295°C., 3 hr.

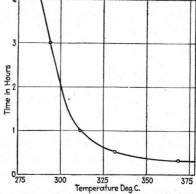

FIG. 1.—Curve showing relation between temperature and time necessary to secure a 92 per cent yield of phenol from chlorobenzene and aqueous caustic.

Few data have been published dealing with the effect of temperature on vapor-phase reactions, other than the ethyl acetate hydrolysis already discussed. Unpublished experi-

[1] HALE and BRITTON, *Ind. Eng. Chem.*, **20**, 117 (1928).

ments by Lloyd show that the rate of formation of phenol from chlorobenzene and steam in the presence of silica gel is negligible at 350°C. but exceedingly rapid at 575°C.

Effect of Concentration of Reactants.—Increase in the concentration of the hydrolyzing reagent would naturally be expected to speed up the reaction, other things being equal, but a high concentration sometimes leads to undesirable by-products. In the reaction just mentioned, hydrolysis of chlorobenzene, a quick and fairly complete conversion of chlorobenzene to phenol is effected by a very high caustic concentration, but the production of tar is greatly increased, also. The following table, which relates to the production of *p*-nitrophenol from *p*-chloronitrobenzene shows the relation between reaction times, yields, and reagent ratios for this particular case:

TABLE II.—EFFECT OF NaOH CONCENTRATION: HYDROLYSIS *p*-CHLORONITROBENZENE
Temperature, 160°C.

Ratio NaOH to halide	Conc. NaOH %	Time, hours	Halide recovered	Phenol yield, %
2:1	15	4	41.8	53.7
3:1	15	4	17.17	80.1
4:1	15	4	Trace	99.8
3:1	20	4	0.4	99.5
4:1	20	4	Trace	98.4
2:1	15	6	36.0	55.1
3:1	15	6	14.9	73.0
4:1	15	6	Trace	99.5

Catalysts.—It will be convenient to divide the large number of catalysts included under a broad definition of the term into two classes: (1) materials that are present in large amounts and that in some cases react with one of the products, like caustic soda or sodium carbonate in the Dow phenol process, or hydrochloric acid in the Bergius wood saccharification method; and (2) substances present in small amounts, like sulfuric acid in the Scholler-Tornesch saccharification process or hydrochloric acid in the making of glucose from starch. Acids and bases may fall into both classes, while enzymes are confined to the latter. The necessity of cataloguing hydrogen and hydroxyl ions is avoided by adopting Brönsted's definitions of the terms acid and base. In addition to these more or less general catalysts, there are a few specific ones such as quinine, sodium oleate, manganese sulfate, and small amounts of copper salts, the last being especially useful in the hydrolysis of aromatic halides. Mercuric oxide along with sulfuric acid promotes the hydration of acetylene, while ultra-violet light[1] hydrolyzes aqueous acetone to methane and acetic acid. Finely divided charcoal and platinum as well as stannous chloride have also found application.

[1] QURESHI and TAHIR, *J. Phys. Chem.*, **36**, 2670–2673 (1932).

These are mostly cases of homogeneous catalysis, in the liquid phase. The passage of steam along with the vapor of the substance to be hydrolyzed, both in the vapor phase, over and through an activating solid, has introduced another set of catalysts. To hydrolyze esters in this way, the oxides of titanium, thorium, and silicon (silica gel) have been largely used. In the vapor-phase hydrolysis of aromatic halides, silica gel, titania, thoria, and iron-free alumina in as porous a form as possible have been used, while patent claims also cover the use of metal phosphates and silica gel impregnated with phosphoric acid. Here, again, the presence of a little copper in some form, in the silica gel, is an improvement.

Reversibility.—Many hydrolytic reactions, including the decomposition of esters, are reversible; while others, such as sucrose inversion and protein hydrolysis, though not necessarily complete, have not been reversed. In this respect, they differ not at all from reactions in general. It has been definitely shown that hydrolyzing enzymes catalyze in both directions and are capable of synthesizing natural products, notably the glucosides.

Vapor-phase Hydrolysis.—The preceding treatment of the theory and mechanism of hydrolysis has dealt almost altogether with reactions in the liquid phase or phases. Enzymatic hydrolysis, however, probably constitutes a two-phase system predominantly liquid; and in certain commercial processes, we have hydrolysis taking place at the intersurface of emulsions. A few vapor-phase hydrolytic reactions have come to light of late years in addition to the well-known hydrolysis of esters, and considerable interest is apparent in this field. Such reactions afford good examples of heterogeneous catalysis, as they take place at the surface of a solid catalyst. The hydration of acetylene may be regarded as a connecting link between the liquid- and vapor-phase group.

V. CONSTRUCTION AND CONTROL OF EQUIPMENT FOR HYDROLYSIS

Materials of Construction. General.—If the examples of commercial hydrolysis later described be examined carefully, it will be seen that they take place, without exception, either in acid or in alkaline media. The acids used are confined to sulfuric or hydrochloric; the bases include caustic soda or potash and the alkaline salts of weak acids. The acids may be dilute or concentrated; the bases, aqueous or fused. It is obvious that different materials of construction are required for these different cases. Alkaline processes have, in general, the great advantage that with rare exceptions they may be carried out in iron or steel vessels. Only in exceptional cases do we find caustic soda attacking iron to produce hydrogen. In the original Dow process, where a 10 per cent aqueous solution of caustic passed through an iron pipe at 350°C. and at a pressure of 4,000 lb., sufficient hydrogen was produced to burn steadily at the end of the line. This led to the substitution of copper for the iron. In general, no great difficulties are encountered with materials of construction in alkaline hydrolysis. Even the severe treatment experienced by the cast-iron pots used for caustic fusion does not shorten their life so much as might be expected.

Only two acids—sulfuric and hydrochloric—require consideration under acid hydrolysis. Until the advent of Duriron (high-silicon iron), lead-lined equipment was essential for all processes in which sulfuric acid was used, except for very concentrated acid. Saccharification of wood with very dilute sulfuric acid takes place in lead-lined or refractory brick apparatus, while the absorption of olefins requires acid of specific gravity 1.84, and lead-lined containers are not needed. The hydrolysis of the resulting sulfate, whereby dilute acid is produced, must be conducted in lead equipment, which may further be protected by close-fitting Pyrex glass bricks. Duriron is successfully used in acetylene hydration, where dilute sulfuric acid is encountered, but it is not so adaptable or easily fabricated as lead.

Hydrochloric acid as a hydrolyzer and as a product of hydrolysis in the absence of alkali has been the source of much trouble. In the laboratory, glass and silica are of course satisfactory, but their use is limited in commercial work. The starch-glucose transformation takes place in an acid concentration of less than 1 per cent, and at low temperature, so that bronze and copper metal containers suffice. The Bergius wood saccharification method uses superconcentrated hydrochloric acid (40 per cent) and makes extended use of stoneware, and of iron lined with acid-resisting tiles joined by a special cement. Rubber-lined iron is also used in the evaporator required for this process. The difficulty of handling wet hydrochloric acid gas has been one of the retarding factors in the development of vapor-phase hydrolysis of organic halides but the use of tantalum is finding favor in continuous processes involving large production. The interesting discovery[1] that Toncan metal (an alloy of iron, molybdenum, and copper) is preferentially wetted by an organic material rather than by aqueous acid and is therefore much less subject to corrosion may be of significance. An iron-nickel-molybdenum alloy (Hastelloy A) shows similar properties.

VI. TECHNICAL OPERATIONS INVOLVING HYDROLYSIS

Soap, Glycerol, and Fatty Acids.—Oils and fats are glycerol esters of fatty acids, saturated and unsaturated. By hydrolyzing these fats with steam or acid or enzymes, we obtain the glycerol and organic acid directly; if we add caustic soda to the water in hydrolyzing, common soap results instead of the fatty acid.

---

[1] AYRES, *Trans. Am. Inst. Chem. Eng.*, **22**, 23 (1929).

$$C_{17}H_{35}COO-CH_2 \quad \left.\begin{array}{l} NaOH \\ NaOH \\ NaOH \end{array}\right\} \quad CH_2OH$$

$$C_{17}H_{35}COO-CH \quad + \quad NaOH \rightarrow 3C_{17}H_{35}COONa \quad + \quad CHOH$$

$$C_{17}H_{35}COO-CH_2 \qquad \qquad \qquad \qquad CH_2OH$$

$$\text{Glyceryl Tristearate} \qquad \qquad \text{Sodium Stearate} \qquad \text{Glycerol}$$

Eighty per cent of our soap is made through the process described by the above equation. In ordinary soap making, the fats are placed in a large steel pan (kettle) provided with a perforated steam coil; steam is blown in until the resulting liquid is heated to 80°C., and some water from the condensed steam appears at the bottom of the kettle. Caustic soda is then gradually added, while live steam keeps the mass stirred and emulsifies it. At this stage, one of the three acid radicals combined with the glycerol is removed. More alkali is added, and the boiling with steam continued until the solution of soap is pasty, a condition indicating that the second acid radical has been properly hydrolyzed off from the glycerol. Salt is added to the mass at the proper time to salt out the soap which rises to the top, while the salty aqueous solution containing glycerol settles to the bottom, and may be drawn off. More alkali is now added, and boiling renewed, and the soap again salted out. This operation may be repeated to insure complete hydrolysis of the fat, or as often as desired, depending upon the nature and quality of soap desired. Finally the pan is covered, to retain the heat, and the contents separated into three layers, of which the top is good soap. This layer is skimmed off and put in frames to solidify.

Not only in its manufacture but in its use does soap involve hydrolysis. Like other salts of strong bases and weak acids, sodium stearate and the other sodium soaps spontaneously hydrolyze somewhat in water, and upon this hydrolysis to some extent depends the detergent (cleansing) effect of soap.

Fatty Acids.—The above process is the natural and direct one by which to make soap, but if the fatty acids are wanted, for candle-making and other purposes, the use of alkali must be avoided unless subsequent treatment with acid at additional expense is to be incurred. For these fatty acids, four distinct processes are available. In one—the autoclave method—1 to 3 per cent of lime or magnesia or zinc oxide is added to the fat or oil in an iron autoclave and the mixture agitated with steam at 8 to 10 atmos., for 6 to 8 hr. The fatty acids rise to the top of the mass, and the aqueous glycerol extract remains below. The oxide added acts as a catalyst but ultimately combines with some of the fatty acid and must be removed by the subsequent addition of sulfuric acid. The higher the pressure employed the lower need be the amount of oxide used.

In the *acid* process for fatty acids, the dehydrated fat is violently churned up for 30 min. with 4 to 6 per cent of 66°Bé. sulfuric acid, producing a black mixture of *sulfonated* fat. No hydrolysis has taken place up to this point. This black mixture is now boiled with water, which accomplishes the hydrolysis, the fatty acids as usual rising to the surface and leaving the acidic glycerol solution underneath. This acid method has the advantage of converting any oleic acid (liquid) in the fats into isooleic (solid), thereby increasing the total yield of desirable solid acid.

Since oil or liquefied fat is insoluble in water, two liquid phases exist during hydrolysis, and the reaction rate, of course, depends upon their

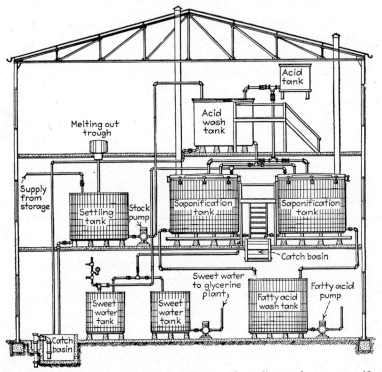

Fig. 2.—Twitchell process fat-splitting plant, with settling tank, two saponification tanks, sweet-water tanks, and fatty-acid wash tank. (*Courtesy of Wurster and Sanger, Inc., Chicago.*)

surface of contact—the greater the surface the faster the saponification. The best way to secure a large surface of contact between two liquids is to emulsify them thoroughly. Twitchell[1] discovered that a small amount (2 per cent) of a sulfo-aromatic compound added to the system produced such an excellent emulsion that a current of steam without any mineral acid or base effected complete saponification. In this Twitchell process (Fig. 2), the fat is first freed from foreign matter by boiling in a lead-lined tank with dilute sulfuric acid and is then transferred to a second lead-lined tank with a close-fitting cover. After the addition of one-third

[1] Twitchell, U. S. 1,601,603 (1926).

its weight of water, the mixture is treated with 1.0 per cent of the Twitchell reagent and heated with live steam for 24 hr. Ninety per cent of the fatty acids is set free in this time. The glycerol-water lower layer is drawn off, and the fatty acids that have risen to the surface are boiled again with fresh water for 12 hr., and the separation repeated. Low-grade fats and greases can be effectively treated in this way. Twitchell's reagent may be made by adding concentrated sulfuric acid to benzene and oleic acid, while the temperature is kept below 30°C.

$$C_6H_6 + C_{17}H_{33}COOH + H_2SO_4 \rightarrow C_6H_4(SO_3H)(C_{17}H_{35}COO) + H_2O$$

Glycerol.—From all these different processes for hydrolyzing fats into soap or fatty acids, glycerol is recovered and refined for the various purposes to which it is now applied. Practically all glycerol refining is now accomplished by distillation with steam under diminished pressure.

Hydrolysis of Carbohydrates.—The chief carbohydrates are the sugars, cellulose, and starch with its related polysaccharides. Of these, the only one actually hydrolyzed on a large scale in an established and prosperous industry is starch, from which corn syrup, glucose, and, finally, alcohol are secured in large quantities in the United States and abroad. The commercial production of furfural depends on the conversion of the pentoses of oat hulls, and this procedure is intimately related to hydrolysis.[1]

Xylose has been produced on a pilot-plant scale by the hydrolysis of xylan in cottonseed hulls, but the failure to find any important uses for this sugar has discouraged exploitation of the process.[2]

The saccharification of the cellulose in waste wood to make sugar, mostly glucose, and subsequently alcohol has had a chequered career, but it is again showing promise, particularly abroad. A description of commercial starch hydrolysis is given on account of its present importance, and the recent installations for wood saccharification are discussed in view of their future significance.

Hydrolysis of Starch.—In Germany, starch is derived principally from potatoes (Irish); but in the United States, it is obtained almost exclusively from Indian corn (Zea Mays).[3] The latter process includes the following steps:

1. The clean corn grain is soaked or steeped for one or two days in warm water containing 0.25 per cent sulfur dioxide, the latter to keep the mixture sweet. This process is carried on in large hopper-bottomed steeping vats, capable of holding 2,500 bu. each. By means of steam

---

[1] HURD and ISENHOUR, *J. Am. Chem. Soc.*, **54**, 317 (1932).

[2] EMLEY, *Chem. & Met. Eng.*, **37**, 283–285 (1930).

[3] The production of starch from sweet potatoes is now being successfully conducted on a plant scale, the process being based on the research of the Bureau of Chemistry and Soils, U. S. D. A.

syphons, the water is kept in circulation and at the same time maintained at a temperature between 46 to 52°C. (115 to 125°F.). In some plants, a battery steeping system in which fresh water passes successively from the most thoroughly steeped to the fresh grain has supplanted the above.

2. The softened grain is torn apart in attrition mills and transferred to the separators—huge cast-iron vats, in which the germ rises to the surface and is separated continuously from the ground corn and starch milk.

3. The bran is retained on the surface of silk sieves through which the mass is filtered.

4. The starch settles down on inclined tables, while the gluten passes on.

From this point, the hydrolysis proper begins.

The accumulated starch is transferred to closed copper or bronze converters, 6 ft. in diameter and 20 ft. high, in which a mixture is made of 100 parts of starch, 250 of water, and 0.5 per cent hydrochloric acid. The starch is introduced carefully and gradually and treated with steam at 30 lb. pressure. Hydrolysis takes place, to dextrins and glucose. For corn syrup, treatment for 30 min. is sufficient to accomplish the 40 to 50 per cent hydrolysis necessary; but for corn sugar, fairly complete reaction is necessary, requiring 1 hr. 30 min. The mixture is then blown to neutralizing vats and exactly neutralized by sodium carbonate. This releases the remaining gluten, which is removed in filter presses, and the liquid is then passed through three filters, each 24 ft. high and 10 ft. in diameter and containing 35 tons of bone char. These remove the coloring matter, and the clear solution after evaporation *in vacuo* is crystallized, for sugar production. The crystallization problem was not easy to solve, as glucose forms several varieties of both hydrated and anhydrous crystals. The bone char used in filtration is revivified and reused.

Typical analyses of the two products are

Components	Corn syrup, %	Crystalline corn sugar, %
Water	19	4.0
Dextrose	38.5	94.6
Dextrin	42.0	0.7
Ash	0.5	0.7

The simple equation usually written to describe the hydrolysis of starch

$$C_6H_{10}O_5 + H_2O \xrightarrow{\text{HCl}} \underset{\text{Glucose}}{C_6H_{12}O_6}$$

gives a very inadequate conception of the process, which undoubtedly takes place in a number of stages.[1]

Saccharification of Wood. Hydrolysis with Dilute Sulfuric Acid.
Scholler-Tornesch Process :

When cellulose is hydrolyzed according to the empirical equation

$$C_6H_{10}O_5 + H_2O \xrightarrow{H_2SO_4} C_6H_{12}O_6$$

the resulting glucose if left in contact with the acid at high temperature and pressure is partly decomposed. The earlier plants built to hydrolyze

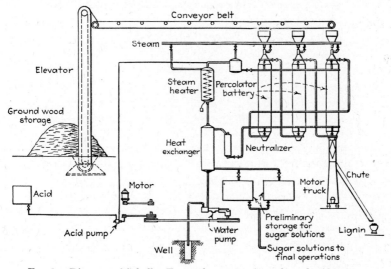

Fig. 3.—Diagram of Scholler-Tornesch system of wood saccharification.

wood used a batch cook in digesters under considerable steam pressure, much as the modern chemical pulp mills do, so that the glucose first formed was left in contact with the acid solution for some time. Hence, their final yield of glucose was the difference between the total produced by hydrolysis and the amount decomposed during the later stages of the cooking. Scholler has materially improved the yield by substituting pressure percolation for batch cooking, so that the resulting sugar is promptly removed and cooled before decomposition can set in. The commercial plant put in operation in 1930 at Tornesch (Holstein) is illustrated in Fig. 3.

The percolators are cylinders 31 ft. high with diameters from 5 to 6 ft. One is lead lined throughout, the others are protected by acid-proof brick. The brick-lined percolators contain 5,000; the lead one, 6,150 gal. The

[1] An excellent bibliography of starch hydrolysis is given by R. P. Walton, "A Complete Survey of Starch Chemistry," vol. I, Chemical Catalog Company (1928).

lower ends of the cylinders are fitted with an acid-proof filter, to separate the sugar-containing wort from the residues.

The small acid-proof pump and the large water pump are used for the percolating liquid and both are motor driven. The acid pump delivers sulfuric acid of 40 per cent strength from the reservoir. The water pump delivers water through the counterflow heater at a pressure of 10 atmos., the water being preheated by the inflowing hot wort. The water already warmed to about 150°C. is now heated up to the reaction temperatures of 160 to 190°C. by means of fresh steam. The heated water reaches the mixing apparatus where 40 per cent sulfuric acid is added in such quantity that the material going to the percolator contains 0.2 to 0.6 per cent of acid. This mixture passes through the distributing pipe into the ring-shaped distributor and then flows through the percolators. After the hydrolyzing mixture has passed, either in series or in parallel as desired, through the contents of the percolators (always reaching the freshest wood last) and has absorbed the sugar formed, it enters the filter in the form of sugarwort and reaches the neutralizer. This neutralizer is filled with ordinary granulated phosphate and raw lime, thus neutralizing the sugarwort during its passage. The neutralized wort now enters the counterflow heater, heating the incoming cold fresh water. The cooled wort then passes the throttle valve and reaches the wort reservoir. The pressure used throughout is from 8 to 10 atmospheres.

The raw material at Tornesch consists of wood chips, sawdust shavings, machine shavings, and raspings. It need not be dry for this process, nor must it all be finely divided or of uniform size. It is charged into the percolators through manholes, and the lignin residue is removed in the same way.

Soft wood material treated in this way yields about 40 gal. of 100 per cent alcohol per ton of dry wood by fermenting the crude sugar solutions. Even the bark of pine trees yields 25 gal. per ton. Based on a daily consumption of 60 tons of waste (dry) wood, the cost of a gallon of alcohol works out at 18 cts. per gallon, of which the wood itself based at $4.75 per ton accounts for 7.2 cts. So far, the only use to which the resulting lignin has been put is to supply the necessary heat for fermentation and distilling. It is very pure, has little ash, and briquettes easily. A process for producing crystallized glucose and xylose from the raw sugar has been developed.[1]

It will be observed that the essential feature of this scheme is the quick passage of acidulated water under pressure through the wood. To assure success, the temperature, concentration of acid, time of reaction, and rate of flow must all be well balanced.

[1] BERGIUS, *Ind. Eng. Chem.*, **29**, 253 (1937).

Hydrolysis of Butyl Chlorides. *a. Conversion of Isobutyl Chloride.*

$$\underset{CH_3}{\overset{CH_3}{\diagdown}}CHCH_2Cl \xrightarrow{\ NaOH\ } \begin{cases} \underset{CH_3}{\overset{CH_3}{\diagdown}}CH \cdot CH_2OH \\[6pt] \underset{CH_3}{\overset{CH_3}{\diagdown}}COH \cdot CH_3 \\[6pt] \underset{CH_3}{\overset{CH_3}{\diagdown}}C{=}CH_2 \end{cases}$$

A mixture of 8 moles of isobutyl chloride, 8.4 moles of sodium hydroxide, and 205.5 moles of water is heated in a pressure vessel at 220°C. for a period of 10 min. On distillation, the reaction mass shows the presence of isobutyl alcohol 39.9 per cent; *tert*-butyl alcohol, 7.5 per cent; and isobutylene, 45.2 per cent. Data for similar experiments with various hydrolyzing agents are given in Table III, page 616.[1]

A comparison of run 6 with runs 2, 10, and 11 shows that by employing a water-soluble metal hydroxide, *e.g.*, sodium hydroxide, as the hydrolyzing agent rather than a metal hydroxide which is relatively insoluble in water, *e.g.*, a hydroxide of calcium, lead, or magnesium, the yield of isobutyl alcohol becomes increased while the yields of *tert*-butyl alcohol and isobutylene are each lowered.

From a comparison of runs 8 and 9 with runs 2, 6, 10, and 11, it will be noted that by using an alkali metal carbonate or *bicarbonate* as the hydrolyzing agent, rather than a metal hydroxide under otherwise similar operating conditions, each of the alcohol products is formed in high yield, and the yield of isobutylene is lowered.

The yield of *tert*-butyl alcohol can be increased at the expense of the isobutylene by acidifying the hydrolyzed mixture with a strong acid, *e.g.*, sulfuric acid. If the operating procedure described above is repeated and the reaction mass acidified with H_2SO_4, so as to provide a 0.16 N aqueous sulfuric acid solution, and then heated under pressure, it is found that the isobutylene content is markedly reduced on fractionation, and the products obtained are: isobutyl alcohol, 41.6 per cent; *tert*-butyl alcohol, 30.6 per cent; and isobutylene, 10.7 per cent. It is clear that two types of hydrolysis are here involved: (1) alkali hydrolysis; and (2) catalytic acid hydration, *viz.*,

$$\underset{\ \ \ CH_3}{CH_3 \cdot C{=}CH_2} + H_2O \rightarrow \underset{\ \ \ \ \ CH_3}{CH_3 \cdot COH \cdot CH_3}$$

It is to be observed that addition of H·OH takes place according to Markownikoff's rule[2] (see chapter on Halogenation). As is to be expected

[1] U. S. 2,067,473 (1937).

[2] MARKOWNIKOFF, *Annalen*, **153**, 256 (1876).

TABLE III.—HYDROLYSIS OF ISOBUTYL CHLORIDE

Run No.	Reaction mixture									Yield per cent		
	Iso-butyl chlo-ride, moles	Base		H$_2$O, moles	Mole ratio of H$_2$O to iso-butyl chlo-ride	Chemical equiva-lents of base per mole of isobutyl chloride	Time of heat-ing, hr.	Tem-pera-ture, °C.	Conver-sion, %	Isobutyl alcohol	Tert-Butyl alcohol	Isobuty-lene
		Kind	Moles									
1	6	Ca(OH)$_2$	3.24	66.7	11.1	1.08	4	185	96.5	19.0	8.6	66.4
2	4	Ca(OH)$_2$	2.16	88.8	22.2	1.08	4	170	95.2	21.8	21.7	53.3
3	2	Ca(OH)$_2$	1.08	88.8	44.2	1.08	4	165	98.1	21.7	27.0	45.5
4	4	Ca(OH)$_2$	2.10	205.5	51.4	1.05	0.25	220	97.5	23.6	26.6	43.7
5	6	NaOH	7.2	66.7	11.1	1.20	4	180	98.7	42.1	6.2	46.1
6	4	NaOH	4.32	88.8	22.2	1.08	4	155	91.5	43.2	9.1	41.4
7	4	NaOH	4.32	88.8	22.2	1.08	0.08	300	97.9	37.7	10.4	43.2
8	8	K$_2$CO$_3$	4.32	177.7	22.2	1.08	4	165	97.2	43.1	27.0	30.0
9	8	NaHCO$_3$	8.64	177.7	22.2	1.08	4	165	88.3	45.1	29.2	19.3
10	4	Pb(OH)$_2$	2.16	88.8	22.2	1.08	4	175	98.0	23.9	21.5	52.3
11	4	Mg(OH)$_2$	2.16	88.8	22.2	1.08	4	175	99.5	20.4	18.5	53.6

the sulfuric acid causes some polymerization of isobutylene to diisobuty-lene (2, 4, 4-trimethylpentene-1) to occur.

b. Hydrolysis of 1, 2, 3-Trichloroisobutane.—1, 2, 3-Trichloro-2-methylpropane may be converted to 3-chloro-2-methallyl alcohol by two methods. The first procedure occurs in two steps: (1) pyrolysis to effect dehydrochlorination to 1, 3-dichloroisobutene-1; and (2) hydrolysis of the chloroölefin.

$$\underset{\underset{CH_3}{|}}{\overset{\overset{Cl}{|}}{ClCH_2-C-CH_2Cl}} \xrightarrow{\Delta} \underset{\underset{CH_3}{|}}{ClCH=C-CH_2Cl} \xrightarrow{Ca(OH)_2} \underset{\underset{CH_3}{|}}{CHCl=C-CH_2OH}$$

In the second method, the trichloroisobutane is treated directly with

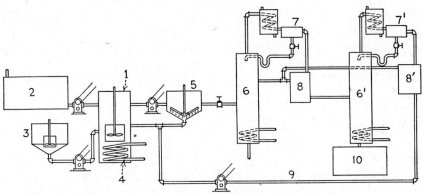

Fig. 4.—Flow diagram: hydrolysis of trichloroisobutane.

1. Digester or hydrolyzer	6-6'. Rectifying columns
2. Trichlorobutane holder	7-7'. Weir boxes
3. Milk of lime slaking tank	8-8'. Decanters
4. Heat-transfer coils for hydrolyzer	9. Return line to digester
5. Separator—thickener	10. Alcohol storage

alkali or alkaline-earth hydroxides to effect simultaneously the loss of hydrogen and tertiary chlorine as well as the replacement of one of the terminal chlorine atoms by a hydroxyl group. Here only the second procedure will be described.[1]

Triisochlorobutane is delivered from its storage tank 2 (Fig. 4) to the digester 1 which contains approximately five volumes of milk of lime to one of the halogeno compound. By maintaining the hydrolyzer at a temperature of 180 to 220°C., a fairly complete conversion to 3-chloro-2-methallyl alcohol is obtained in about 1 hr. The reaction mass is delivered to the thickener 5, where the mixture separates into two layers, *viz.*, an upper layer containing water, calcium chloride, and alcohol with small quantities of trichlorobutane, and a lower layer containing the bulk of the unconverted halogeno compound, which is returned to the

[1] U. S. 2,061,519 (1936).

hydrolyzer along with calcium hydroxide, which collects for the most part at the bottom of the upper layer.

The alcoholic layer is run off from the separator and delivered to an intermediate point in a continuous rectifying column 6, from the bottom of which a solution of calcium chloride, relatively free of chlorobutane, is withdrawn. The aqueous alcoholic vapors leaving the column are condensed and separated in a weir box 7 into reflux and take-off portions. The latter goes to the decanter 8 in which it separates into two layers: an upper layer consisting of water saturated with alcohol and trichloro-butane which is returned to the rectifier on a plate containing a liquid composition corresponding to the returned solution, and a lower layer consisting principally of alcohol saturated with water which is delivered to an intermediate point in the second rectifying column 6' from the bottom of which a commercial grade of 3-chloro-2-methallyl alcohol (b.p., 163 to 164°C.) is withdrawn into the storage tank 10.

The overhead product from the rectifier 6' is condensed and separated for reflux and take-off as before. In the decanter 8' the lower portion which contains some unreacted trichloro isobutane is returned to the digester.

Preparation of Amyl Alcohols from Chloropentanes.—New and enlarged uses for the amyl alcohols and their derivatives, particularly in pyroxylin lacquers, have called for enlarged production, which could not remain dependent upon incidental fusel oil from molasses and potato fermentation. This new production has come from the pentanes of natural gasoline through the chlorination-hydrolysis process developed by Ayres.[1]

This process consists in the isolation from natural gasoline of two of the three pentanes; their chlorination (see chapter on Halogenation) to form monochlorides as far as possible; the hydrolysis under moderate pressure of these monochlorides by water containing sodium oleate and caustic soda; and, finally, the distillation of the alcohols from the reacting mixture. From the chlorination to the distillation inclusive, the process is continuous.

Hydrolysis is accomplished in a system of reservoirs, heaters, and pumps through which a hot emulsion of amyl alcohol, water, and sodium oleate is circulating at the rate of 500 gal. per minute. Amyl chlorides and an aqueous solution of caustic soda are continuously pumped into this circulation material, and two things are continuously withdrawn: (1) a saturated salt solution, which is returned to electrolytic cells for manufacture of chlorine and caustic soda; and (2) a vapor containing

[1] Ayres, U. S. 1,691,424–5–6 (1928); *Ind. Eng. Chem.*, **21**, 899 (1929).

principally amyl alcohols. Three hundred gallons of amyl chloride is present at all times in the hydrolysis system, and 300 gal. is hydrolyzed each hour.

The vapors from hydrolysis are separated by a train of fractionating columns into five components: (1) unchanged amyl chlorides, which are returned to hydrolysis; (2) amylene, which is later hydrated to amyl alcohol; (3) diamyl ether; (4) amyl alcohol fractions that are cut out for special uses; and (5) the mixture of amyl alcohols marketed under the

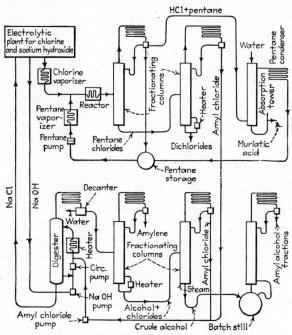

Fig. 5.—Diagram of plant for production of amyl alcohols from pentane, according to E. E. Ayres.

trade name Pentasol for use in pyroxylin lacquers. The general layout is given in Fig. 5.

A condensed but inadequate description of the chlorination and hydrolysis is given by the equations

$$C_5H_{12} + Cl_2 \rightarrow C_5H_{11}Cl + HCl$$
$$C_5H_{11}Cl + NaOH \rightarrow C_5H_{11}OH + NaCl$$

The operation of the hydrolysis can be followed from the accompanying diagram (Fig. 5). The mixture of water, caustic, sodium oleate, and amyl chloride is circulated through two digesters (only one is shown in the figure), one of which is larger than the other and serves also as a still.

About 2 per cent of the amyl chloride present is hydrolyzed during each cycle. Like all other heterogeneous reactions, this proceeds more rapidly the more thoroughly the mixture is emulsified; and it has been found that by introducing the caustic soda *before* the circulating pump, the agitation due to the latter much improves the emulsification. A temperature of 170°C. is maintained by a steam heater placed outside the digesters and through which the mixture is continually circulated.

Two pentanes (normal and iso) serve as starting products for chlorination, and these give rise to primary, secondary, and tertiary chlorides. The tertiary and secondary chlorides will hydrolyze with water; the primary and secondary, with sodium oleate. This catalyst really acts therefore in two ways: (1) It puts water in colloidal contact with amyl chloride, thereby promoting *rapid* hydrolysis of the secondary and tertiary chlorides; (2) it is itself in colloidal contact with the chlorides so that the primary and secondary compounds can form with it the amyl oleates, which are readily decomposed by caustic. Amyl chloride must not be present in excess over sodium oleate, or amylene will form in quantity.

The reaction is a surface one, and a coating of sodium oleate forms over the caustic, which must be mechanically dispersed; hence, the necessity for efficient agitation.[1]

Preparation of Alcohols from Olefins.—An abundant and hence cheap raw material is almost sure to find in time a use to which it can be economically put. The cracking of petroleum, especially vapor-phase cracking, produces tremendous volumes of olefin gases, which are now extensively used as raw materials for alcohol production. In addition, ethylene—the simplest of these—is present in small quantity in coke-oven gas. The alcohols made by this procedure are ethyl from ethylene, isopropyl from propylene, butyl indirectly from ethylene, secondary butyl from butylene, and secondary amyl from amylene. Attesting the economic importance of this process is the great number of recent patents granted in this field.

All these alcohols are produced through reactions common apparently to all olefins—the union of the gas with concentrated sulfuric acid (or phosphoric acid) to form the corresponding monosulfate and the subsequent hydrolysis of this ester.

$$C_nH_{2n} + H_2SO_4 \rightarrow C_nH_{2n+1}OSO_3H \qquad (1)$$
$$C_nH_{2n+1}OSO_3H + H_2O \rightarrow C_nH_{2n+1}OH + H_2SO_4 \qquad (2)$$

It is interesting to note that the water molecule which enters the olefin distributes itself in such a way that the hydroxyl ion becomes

---

[1] U. S. 1,691,424–5–6 (1928); 1,953,745 (1934); AYRES, *Ind. Eng. Chem.*, **21**, 899 (1929); CLARK, *Chem. & Met. Eng.*, **38**, 206 (1931).

attached to the carbon having the least hydrogen, so that secondary and tertiary alcohols—not primary—result.

The diluted acid must of course be reconcentrated for further use, which is a considerable item of cost. Apparently, the more complex the olefin the lower the temperature at which reaction (1) will take place. Ethylene requires a much higher temperature for efficient absorption than its homologues. Both mono- and dialkyl sulfates are formed simultaneously when ethylene, or propylene, is absorbed in sulfuric acid. An appreciable amount of diethyl sulfate is formed when the acid has reacted with about $\frac{1}{3}$ mole of ethylene.[1] In addition, appreciable amounts of the corresponding ethers are produced. Ethyl ether, for example, is largely formed by the reaction of alcohol with diethyl sulfate.[2]

$$(C_2H_5)_2SO_4 + C_2H_5OH \rightarrow (C_2H_5)_2O + C_2H_5HSO_4$$

Some recent processes use *dilute* acid under high pressures,[3] an increased yield of alcohol being obtained with a corresponding decreased yield of ether. The yield of ether may be also decreased by removal of alcohol from contact with unreacted sulfate liquor, as rapidly as it is formed, by immediate distillation in hot water.[4] Brooks and others have shown the advantages of absorption of ethylene under pressure.[5] Various catalysts are used in these processes,[6] and ethyl alcohol has been prepared by the direct combination of ethylene with water in the presence of catalysts and under pressure.[7]

Preparation of Isopropyl Alcohol (Petrohol).—The particular olefin which will be absorbed by sulfuric acid free from catalysts is largely determined by the temperature and the concentration of the acid. Ethylene absorption takes place best between 93 and 120°C. (200 and 250°F.), while propylene is best absorbed between 21 and 27°C. (70 and 80°F.). At this last temperature, 97 per cent sulfuric acid will absorb approximately 50 per cent by weight of propylene. The following equations illustrate the chemical changes accompanying absorption and subsequent hydrolysis:

[1] PLANT and SIDGWICK, *J. Soc. Chem. Ind.*, **40**, 14T (1921).

[2] BROOKS, *Ind. Eng. Chem.*, **27**, 283 (1935).

[3] U. S. 1,951,740; 1,955,417 (1934); 2,045,842; 2,050,442; 2,050,443; 2,050,444; 2,050,445 (1936).

[4] U. S. 2,038,512 (1936).

[5] Brooks, U. S. 1,885,585; 1,919,618 (1933); 1,960,633 (1934); STRAHLER and HACHTEL, *Brennstoff-Chem.*, **15**, 166 (1934).

[6] U. S. 1,977,632 (1934); 1,999,620; 2,014,740 (1935); 2,051,046; 2,064,116 (1936); 2,087,290 (1937).

[7] U. S. 1,977,632; 1,978,266; 1,978,270 (1934); 2,084,390 (1937); BLISS, *Ind. Eng. Chem.* **29**, 19 (1937).

$$H_3C-\overset{\displaystyle H}{\underset{\displaystyle H}{C}}=\overset{\displaystyle H}{\underset{\displaystyle H}{C}} + \overset{\displaystyle HO}{\underset{\displaystyle HO}{\overset{\displaystyle O}{\underset{\displaystyle O}{S}}}} \rightarrow H_3C-\overset{\displaystyle O}{\underset{\displaystyle H}{\overset{\displaystyle S-OH}{\underset{\displaystyle O}{C}}}}-\overset{\displaystyle H}{\underset{\displaystyle H}{C}}-H$$

$$H_3C-\overset{\displaystyle O}{\underset{\displaystyle H}{\overset{\displaystyle S-OH}{\underset{\displaystyle O}{C}}}}-\overset{\displaystyle H}{\underset{\displaystyle H}{C}}-H + H_2O \rightarrow H_3C-\overset{\displaystyle HO}{\underset{\displaystyle H}{C}}-\overset{\displaystyle H}{\underset{\displaystyle H}{C}}-H + \overset{\displaystyle HO}{\underset{\displaystyle HO}{\overset{\displaystyle O}{\underset{\displaystyle O}{S}}}}$$

The cracking still gases, after losing their gasoline constituents by compression or absorption, are passed through Fuller's earth impregnated

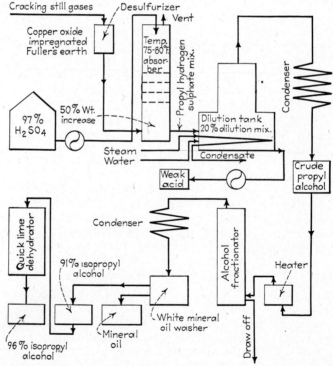

Fig. 6.—Diagram of plant for the production of isopropyl alcohol from propylene in cracking still gases.

with calcined copper oxide, which takes out completely the sulfur compounds. (See Fig. 6.[1]) The absorption of the propylene is accomplished

[1] From *Refiner and Natural Gasoline Mfr.*, 225 (February, 1932).

by passing the gases through an absorption tower cooled by brine to hold the temperature between 24 and 27°C. (75 and 80°F.). The reaction is strongly exothermic.

Practically no ethylene is absorbed at this temperature, but the higher olefins, such as butylene, amylene, hexylene, etc., are absorbed along with propylene. In some plants, batch absorbers equipped with cooling coils and high-speed agitators are used. The reaction mixture is drawn from the absorber to lead-lined equipment and diluted with two or three volumes of water or steam. The heat of dilution warms up the mixture, and additional steam is used to drive off the dilute crude alcohol. This is

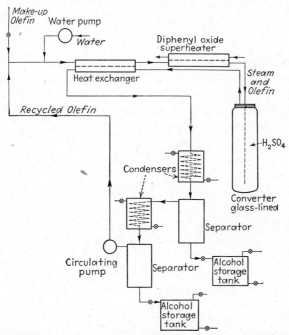

Fig. 7.—Flow diagram: continuous vapor phase production of alcohols from olefins.

then sent to the rectifier for concentration, and a 91 per cent technical isopropyl alcohol is obtained. Chlorine, sodium hypochlorite, or potassium permanganate is used for purification.

The higher alcohols are much more soluble in white mineral oil than is isopropyl and are removed by selective absorption. Absolute isopropyl alcohol may be made by passing the 91 per cent material over quicklime. The diluted sulfuric acid sp. gr., about 1.4 is concentrated to sp. gr. 1.8 and returned to the absorption step, but the gradual accumulation of polymerized and tarry material in the acid makes it necessary to discard it ultimately.

A yield of 70 per cent of propylene in the gases is obtained in the form of isopropyl alcohol.

Continuous Vapor-phase Production of Alcohols from Olefins.— The continuous preparation of alcohols from olefins can be carried out in the apparatus shown diagrammatically in Fig. 7.[1] For the preparation of ethanol, fresh and recycled ethylene are mixed with water and passed under pressure through a heat exchanger and then through a superheater kept at approximately 300°C. The heated reactants as vapors are delivered under a pressure of about 900 lb. per square inch into a converter containing dilute (*i.e.*, <50 per cent) sulfuric or phosphoric acids. Because the temperature of the acid is above its normal boiling point, it acts as a catalyst to convert part of the ethylene and steam to ethanol. The alcohol admixed with unreacted vapors is passed through a series of condensers and separators. The condensed aqueous ethanol is collected for rectification, and the uncondensed ethylene is recycled under pressure.

The proportions of steam and olefin will vary depending on the temperature, pressure, and acid concentration, these factors being interdependent. The pressure converter is made of steel, lined with lead. To protect the lead lining against the dilute acid at high temperatures, an inner insulating lining of glass bricks is used. Proper dispersion of the reacting vapors through the superheated mineral acid is obtained by providing the pressure converter with a distributer and using Raschig rings as packing.

Preparation of Ethylene Glycol

$$CH_2OHCH_2Cl + NaHCO_3 \rightarrow CH_2OHCH_2OH + NaCl + CO_2$$

The chlorohydrin for this process may be made as follows: Ethylene gas in fine bubbles is passed through a cooled hypochlorous acid solution in a reaction tower, the ethylene being in excess at all times, and the temperature remaining below 10°C. The solution passes through a second cell, where more chlorine is added to transform the residual sodium hypochlorite to hypochlorous acid, and ethylene again passed through in a reaction tower. Chlorites and hypochlorites are removed by sodium bisulfite, and the solution made neutral by calcium carbonate. Solutions containing 20 per cent ethylene chlorohydrin can be made in this way, and may be concentrated to 35–40 per cent by distillation. The chlorohydrin solution is now ready for hydrolysis and is treated with the exact amount of sodium bicarbonate solution required at a temperature of 70 to 80°C. with constant stirring. The reaction is carried out in a closed steam-jacketed kettle provided with a stirrer, and the carbon dioxide evolved is used to carbonate fresh caustic solution. Hydrolysis

[1] U. S. 2,087,290 (1937).

proceeds smoothly with a continuous evolution of carbon dioxide and under normal conditions is completed in 4 to 6 hr. The glycol solution may be concentrated in a steam-jacketed vessel and under reduced pressure if desired.

Ethylene glycol may be prepared also by reacting ethylene dichloride with alkalis or alkaline-earth carbonates or bicarbonates and boiling in an autoclave under pressure at approximately 150 to 170°C.[1] It may also be prepared from ethylene, oxygen, and water in the presence of catalysts.[2] The primary action is presumably the formation of ethylene oxide,[3] which readily adds water to form the glycol

$$CH_2{=}CH_2 \xrightarrow{\;O_2\;} H_2C\overset{\displaystyle\diagdown\;\diagup}{\underset{O}{}}CH_2 \xrightarrow{\;H_2O\;} CH_2OH{\cdot}CH_2OH$$

Mixed glycols which are suitable as anti-freeze agents can be made from ethylene and propylene. The cracking-still mixture is treated in an absorption tower with chlorine in the presence of water to produce a 15 per cent chlorohydrin solution. In a separate still, the chlorohydrins are separated from alkalene chloride and hydrochloric acid as a constant-boiling mixture (b.p., 96°C.) by distillation with steam. These are converted to alkalene oxides by treatment with hydrated lime. The oxides are further hydrolyzed by 0.5 per cent sulfuric acid to glycols. The sulfuric acid is precipitated by the addition of lime and removed as calcium sulfate. The mixture of crude glycols is then purified by distillation.[4]

Production of β-Naphthol

Fusion with sodium or potassium hydroxide has been found useful in introducing the hydroxyl radical into aromatic nuclei which have previously been sulfonated or halogenated, the alkali metal combining with the sulfonic group or halogen atom and substituting its own hydroxyl. The older commercial method for synthesizing phenol involves sulfonation of benzene and subsequent caustic fusion. Similarly, carvacrol and Alizarin are made by sulfonating cymene and anthraquinone, respectively, and fusing the resulting sodium sulfonates with caustic. The production of β-naphthol, an important intermediate, will be described as an example of this type of hydrolysis.

β-Naphthol is made from naphthalene by sulfonating it, then desulfonating with steam the small proportion (15 per cent) of the alpha acid formed, converting the free β-sulfonic acid to the sodium salt with

[1] U. S. 1,695,250 (1928); U. S. 1,928,240 (1933); Fr. 774,186 (1934); U. S. 2,041,272 (1936).

[2] Fr. 722,000 (1931); Ger. 561,049 (1930); 619,195 (1935); U. S. 1,982,545 (1934); 2,071,395 (1937).

[3] U. S. 1,998,878 (1935) also Reissue 20,370 (1937).

[4] U. S. 2,103,849 (1937).

sodium chloride, fusing the sodium naphthalenesulfonate with caustic to form sodium β-naphtholate, and releasing the free naphthol by acid.

The sulfonation process is discussed in a separate chapter, and only those steps following the production of the sodium naphthalenesulfonate will be dealt with here. The complete chain of reactions is as follows:[1]

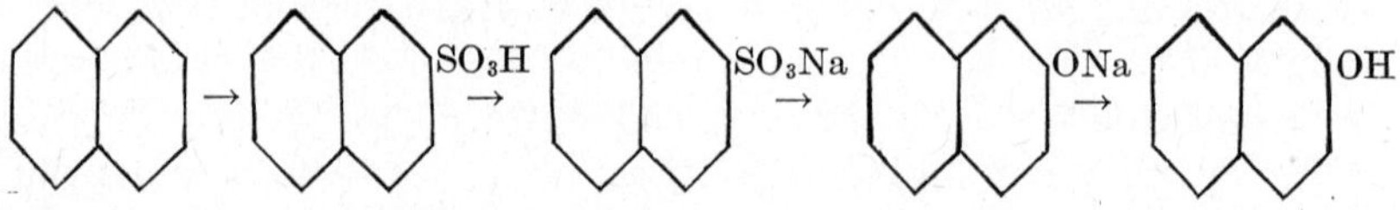

To convert the sodium naphthalenesulfonate into the sodium naphtholate, the following procedure may be adopted. Caustic soda is introduced into the fusion pot—a deep vessel 7 ft. 3 in. in diameter—water is added, and the mixture is stirred and heated until the temperature reaches 305°C. At this point, the sodium naphthalenesulfonate, containing 30 per cent water, is added until the temperature drops to 295°C., the temperature is then allowed to rise, and more sulfonate added until all has been introduced. The temperature is kept always between 295 and 305°C. during the introduction of the sulfonate. The fusion is now maintained for 6 hr. at 300°C., after which it is discharged into the weak washings from the previous β-naphthol crude washings. For this step, the relative weights of materials are

Sodium naphthalenesulfonate............................... 21.8
95 % caustic soda... 6.6
Water... 1.0

The weak washings just mentioned are contained in quenching tanks, each having a capacity of 3,500 gal., in which the fused mass from the previous step dissolves more or less completely. The resulting hot solution is filtered through iron filter presses, the filtrate going into the acidification tanks, while the washed cake is discarded. To convert the sodium salt of the β-naphthol into the naphthol itself, the following procedure may be used:

Into the hot filtered solution dilute sulfuric acid is run until the mixture is acid to phenolphthalein. If necessary, live steam is turned in to raise the temperature to 200°F. (93°C.), thereby liquefying the β-naphthol. After 20 min. standing, a separation will have taken place, the sulfite liquor lying at the bottom with the crude β-naphthol floating on top. The sulfite liquor is then run into a separate tank, where it is cooled to recover the 10 per cent of naphthol contained in it. The liquid naphthol is then transferred to the wash tank and washed repeatedly and thoroughly until the wash water shows a specific gravity of 1. The crude naphthol is then dried with steam at 115°C. and transferred to the

[1] SHREVE, *Color Trade J., & Textile Chem.*, **14**, 42 (1924).

still. Here a temperature of 200°C. is maintained at first, without vacuum, but the main distillation is carried out with 28 in. of vacuum and at 248°C. The naphthol distills over into cooled zinc-lined boxes, where it solidifies. The necessary fine powdering is effected by a Raymond mill.

A 74 per cent yield is obtained from the caustic fusion point to final salable product, and a 64 per cent yield based on the naphthalene used.

For a plant capable of producing 8,000 lb. of β-naphthol by the above complete process, the raw-material list is

	Pounds
Naphthalene	11,200
Sulfuric acid (93 %)	13,370
Sulfuric acid (50 %)	10,200
Salt	20,000
Caustic soda (95 %)	7,900
Abundance of water	
Total	62,670

It will be seen that the weight of the raw materials is nearly eight times that of the final product. By a proper integration of operating steps, this ratio can be substantially reduced, and in the manufacture of phenol about 4.3 lb raw material per pound of product is required.

Manufacture of Synthetic Phenol.—Synthetic phenol from benzene affords examples of three commercial methods of manufacture by hydrolysis. The process which dominated the field at first, involves the caustic fusion of sodium benzenesulfonate. In this process a seemingly large number of separate operations are required to effect the simple transformation

$$C_6H_6 \rightarrow C_6H_5OH$$

Although the by-products in each step of this process are advantageously employed in some phase of the synthesis, it is obvious, from the description below, that relatively large quantities of materials (4.3 lb. per lb. phenol) have to be handled. The process of the Dow Company, which now accounts for a substantial percentage of domestic production, starts from chlorobenzene, hydrolyzing it under high pressure in an aqueous alkaline solution with copper as catalyst.

Recent patents[1] by Raschig and his associates describe processes whereby chlorobenzene is prepared from benzene by use of hydrochloric acid and oxygen at temperatures above 150°C.; the chlorobenzene then

---

[1] Raschig, Fr. 730,462 (1932); 756,814 (1933); Ger. 588,649 (1933); U. S. 2,009,023 (1935); 2,035,917 (1936).

being hydrolyzed by steam at temperatures above 350°C. The phenol and hydrochloric acid formed are separated from the reaction products while they are still in the gaseous state.

$$C_6H_6 + HCl + O \rightarrow C_6H_5Cl + H_2O$$
$$C_6H_5Cl + H_2O \rightarrow C_6H_5OH + HCl$$

By combining the above two processes (see page 631), the reaction represented by the following equation is obtained:

$$C_6H_6 + O \rightarrow C_6H_5OH$$

Sulfonation and halogenation of benzene are described in other chapters of this book. The initial discussion of phenol production will start with sodium benzenesulfonate and chlorobenzene as raw materials.

Phenol from Benzenesulfonic Acid.—The reaction involved in the caustic fusion of sodium benzenesulfonate to form sodium phenolate is

$$C_6H_5SO_3Na + 2NaOH \rightarrow C_6H_5ONa + Na_2SO_3 + H_2O$$

A typical mode of operation is as follows:

About 2,000 lb. of fused caustic soda are put into the fusion kettle immediately after a previous run has been discharged. The lumps are permitted to melt for about one hour, and 40 to 50 gal. of water is added. The heating (with gas or oil) is started, and the temperature brought up to 280°C. in a period of one hour. The temperature will continue to rise to 300 to 320°C., at which time the solution of sodium benzenesulfonate is pumped, in a regulated manner, *under* the surface of the caustic melt. About three molecular equivalents of alkali are employed. Since exposure to air appreciably diminishes the yield of phenol, it is necessary to have a submerged feed for the sulfonate.

The temperature is maintained at 305 to 310°C. for 6 hr. and brought up to 330°C. for an hour before the run is completed. The temperatures are about the same as those used in the fusion for β-naphthol production. Since the sodium sulfite formed is practically insoluble in a concentrated solution of caustic soda containing sodium phenolate, the fusion mass is run into a vessel containing a measured quantity of sodium phenolate wash waters from previous charges. The sodium sulfite separates out and is filtered off by pumping the aqueous suspension on to a nickel gauze.

The water from previous washes is taken for the first wash, and this added to the solution of sodium phenolate. The next two washes are saved for use in the quenchers and for washes, respectively.

Neutralization of the sodium phenolate to release the phenol may be done by carbon dioxide, mineral acids, benzenesulfonic acid, or preferably with the SO_2 liberated when the benzenesulfonic acid is treated with the by-product Na_2SO_3 to form the required sodium benzenesulfonate.

Usually, some sulfuric acid must be finally added to ensure complete neutralization. The phenol containing some water separates out as an upper layer over an aqueous solution containing the appropriate sodium salt. The phenolic layer is decanted and distilled *in vacuo*, while the aqueous layer, which still contains some phenol, goes back to the operating cycle.

Phenol from Chlorobenzene.—The advantages of chlorobenzene as a starting point for phenol manufacture are apparent, but no serious effort was made to use it until 1917, when Aylesworth[1] brought together chlorobenzene and aqueous caustic soda under high pressure and temperature to make the alkali phenolate

$$C_6H_5Cl + 2NaOH \rightarrow C_6H_5ONa + NaCl + H_2O$$

Later, the process was taken up by the Dow Company, and the imperfections of the earlier procedure were eliminated. One of these was the production of diphenyl oxide as a side reaction:

$$C_6H_5ONa + C_6H_5Cl \rightarrow C_6H_5OC_6H_5 + NaCl$$

This was checked by the addition to the reacting mixture of diphenyl oxide itself in about the same quantity as would normally be formed, which proved effective in inhibiting the further formation of the side product. In addition, the use of the sodium salt of a weak acid, *e.g.*, sodium carbonate, instead of sodium hydroxide, in the presence of copper metal as a catalyst, led to the production of phenol itself, not the sodium phenolate, so that the acidification step became unnecessary.

No authoritative description of the specific operating details of the Dow process has been published, except as they have been set forth in patents, and several alternative forms of the process are there described. Essentially, the method consists in the bringing together of 1 mole of chlorobenzene, 10 per cent by weight of diphenyl oxide, and a 10 per cent aqueous sodium carbonate solution ($1\frac{1}{4}$ moles) at a pressure of 3,000 lb. and a temperature of 320°C. The resulting emulsion is pumped through a tubular pressure system, made of copper, with recirculation and continuous discharge of a small portion, which is made up by the entering charge. The tubes of the autoclave have thick copper walls, $1\frac{1}{4}$ in. outside diameter, and the passage of the emulsion through them is sufficiently turbulent to maintain dispersion of the organic liquid. Diphenyl oxide vapor under moderate pressure serves as a heating medium. Phenol is formed as such, not as sodium phenolate, and the conversion is nearly quantitative. The reaction is·

$$C_6H_5Cl + Na_2CO_3 + H_2O \rightarrow C_6H_5OH + NaCl + NaHCO_3$$

On leaving the reaction vessel, the liquid passes through an exchanger to heat the incoming liquid, then through coolers, after which the pressure

[1] U. S. 1,213,142 (1917).

is released. The free phenol formed separates as an upper layer over the cold solution of bicarbonate. The upper layer is run off and distilled from a chromium-plated still, the water, unchanged chlorobenzene (b.p., 132°C.), and finally the phenol (b.p., 181°C.) passing over, while the diphenyl oxide (b.p., 259°C.) remains in the still. The sodium bicarbonate liquor is blown free of phenol by means of steam, brought back to carbonate by addition of caustic, and used again.

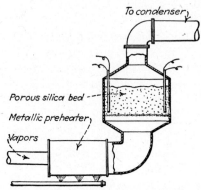

To condenser

Porous silica bed

Metallic preheater

Vapors

Fig. 8.—Apparatus for vapor-phase hydrolysis of chlorobenzene with steam.

The copper tubes may be replaced by iron, and under such circumstances about 0.1 per cent soap is added to the reaction mass to inhibit the deposition of magnetite scale in the reaction and cooling zones.[1] Caustic soda may be used instead of sodium bicarbonate and under such conditions the resultant sodium phenolate can be decomposed by any available by-product hydrochloric acid. When hydrated lime is employed as the hydrolyzing agent, at approximately 350°C., the following results are obtained:

TABLE IV.—HYDROLYSIS OF CHLOROBENZENE

Water, lb.	Chlorobenzene, lb.	Calcium hydroxide, moles per mole of chlorobenzene	Amount of diphenylether formed, % of the amount of phenol
1,000	200	1	32
1,000	200	0.55–0.60	21
1,000	150	0.60	18

A yield of about 95 per cent of theory is claimed for the process.[2]

Vapor-phase Hydrolysis of Chlorobenzene.—The direct production of phenol by the interaction of steam and chlorobenzene, with hydrochloric acid as a by-product, has naturally attracted attention and has resulted in a few patents.[3] In pilot-plant operation a yield of over 90

[1] U. S. 1,986,194 (1935).

[2] U. S. 2,085,429 (1937).

[3] U. S. 1,735,327 (1929); 1,849,844; 1,884,710 (1932); 1,936,567 (1933); 1,950,359; 1,961,834; 1,966,281 (1934); Brit. 288,308 (1929); 354,948; 358,903 (1931); Jap. 91,160 (1931); Fr. 709,184 (1931); CHALKLEY, *J. Am. Chem. Soc.*, **51**, 2489–2495 (1929).

per cent has been obtained, using porous silica as a catalyst. Figure 8 shows a type of apparatus that may be used for this purpose.

By proper treatment, the catalyst has an indefinite life. The process, of course, is continuous, and the phenol is recovered by fractional condensation.

Manufacture of Phenol by Regenerative Process.[1]—The regenerative or Raschig process for the production of phenol is based on a combination of two well-known processes:

I. The production of chlorobenzene from benzene and hydrogen chloride and air (see Chap. IV).

II. The hydrolysis of chlorobenzene with water vapor in the presence of a catalyst.

An examination of the reactions which are involved show that the by-products obtained in one step are used in the other, thus:

$$C_6H_6 + HCl + O \xrightarrow[\text{Catalyst}]{\text{Cu-Fe}} C_6H_5Cl + H_2O \tag{1}$$

$$C_6H_5Cl + H_2O \xrightarrow[\text{Catalyst}]{\text{SiO}_2} C_6H_5OH + HCl \tag{2}$$

In the first step, hydrogen chloride is consumed and water is produced, while, in the second, water is consumed and hydrochloric acid is produced. It is clear, therefore, that by a suitable combination of the two steps phenol can be produced in a most economical manner by the consumption of only benzene and atmospheric oxygen,

$$C_6H_6 + O \rightarrow C_6H_5OH \tag{3}$$

In addition to the pronounced economy in materials there is a further advantage in that the process permits a most economical utilization of fuel, steam, and cooling water.

In recovering the hydrogen chloride from the hydrolytic step, it is essential to use only a limited quantity of water in the washing operations so that the hydrochloric acid is obtained as a 17 per cent solution, which is suitable for the subsequent step involving the halogenation of benzene.

For the production of 10,000 lb. of phenol per day, the operations can be carried out in the following manner: By means of a blower 1 (Fig. 9), 5,500 lb. of chlorobenzene and 5,000 lb. of water at 100°C. are sent per hour through a heat recuperator. Here, their temperature is raised to 400°C. by exchange with vapors at 500°C. which have already passed through the furnace for the catalytic hydrolysis of chlorobenzene. The vapors are heated to 500°C. in a preheater common to the first and second stages of the process and are then passed through the contact furnace, where catalytic hydrolysis is effected. The catalysts which

---

[1] This process is covered by a number of patents, in particular U. S. 1,963,761 and 2,035,917, which are assigned to F. Raschig. G.m.b.h. In the United States, the process is controlled and operated by General Plastics, Inc.

are adapted for this purpose are materials containing catalytically active silicic acid or phosphates of metals of the second group, *e.g.*, magnesium,

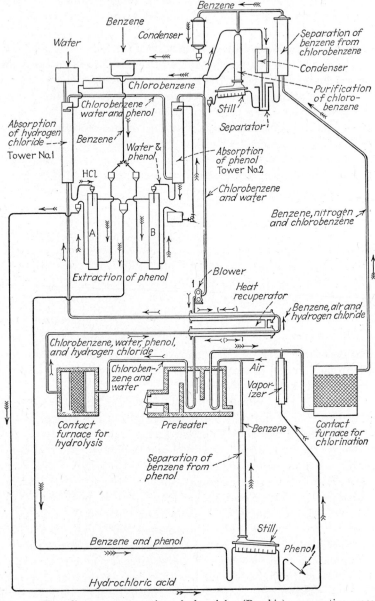

Fig. 9.—Flow diagram: preparation of phenol by (Raschig) regenerative process.

calcium, and zinc. The mixture of vapors leaving the catalytic chamber is cooled to about 200°C. in the heat recuperator and then passes to a washing tower constructed of acid-proof material. Here, by the addition of 1,400 lb. of water and 1,000 lb. of chlorobenzene per hour, the hydrogen chloride is washed out, and the chlorobenzene and water consumed in the reaction are replaced in the circulating mixture of vapors.

The vapors are then led to a second tower in which the phenol is absorbed by washing with water delivered at the rate of 8,000 lb. per hour from the phenol extraction tower *B*. The excess of water and chlorobenzene introduced into the first wash tower for the absorption of hydrogen chloride pass as vapors to a condenser while the bulk of the vapors is again returned to the operating cycle by the blower.

The hydrochloric acid which runs off at the base of tower 1 passes to the extractor *A* filled with benzene containing some phenol and then to the hydrochloric acid vaporizer. The solution of phenol which runs off at the base of tower 2 at the rate of 400 lb. of phenol and 8,000 lb. of water per hour passes through the phenol extractor *B* and is then pumped back. From a storage tank, benzene is run at a rate of 600 lb. and 4,000 lb. per hour into phenol extractors *A* and *B*, respectively. In extractor *A* the benzene extracts the phenol contained in the hydrochloric acid, while in *B* it extracts the phenol contained in the aqueous solution. The solutions of phenol in benzene which leave the extractors pass to a still having a column where the benzene is distilled and led through the preheater used in conjunction with the hydrolysis of chlorobenzene. From the base of the still, phenol is run off at the rate of 420 lb. per hour or 10,000 lb. per day. This corresponds to a conversion of approximately 10 per cent per pass on the 5,500 lb. of chlorobenzene recycled per hour.

The preheated benzene vapors (approximately 4,600 lb.) are mixed with 1,400 lb. of hydrochloric acid of 17 per cent strength and 1,000 lb. of air per hour and are introduced by means of a blower into a contact furnace. Here the benzene is chlorinated at approximately 200°C. in the presence of a copper-iron or copper-cobalt catalyst supported on Florida earth or aluminum hydroxide.

The chlorobenzene, which is formed at the rate of 550 lb. per hour, *i.e.*, 12 per cent conversion per pass, is advantageously recovered by fractional condensation in a column. After separation from water by decantation and from benzene and dichlorobenzene in a still, it is returned to the operating cycle in the first washing tower, where it serves as a coscrubber for the hydrogen chloride. Unchanged benzene passes from the still column to a condenser and is then pumped to the benzene storage.

Small quantities of hydrochloric acid are lost to the regenerative system, owing to the formation of by-product dichlorobenzene and polychlorinated products. Some diphenyl oxide is also formed during the hydrolytic process. These losses constitute the replenishment charges on the system.

CHAPTER XII

THE FRIEDEL AND CRAFTS REACTION

By P. H. Groggins

I. INTRODUCTION

In 1877, Charles Friedel and James Mason Crafts showed that anhydrous aluminum chloride could be used as a condensing agent in a "general synthetical method for furnishing an infinite number of hydrocarbons and even oxygenated compounds." They subsequently found that ferric and zinc chlorides as well as the double salt sodium-aluminum chloride could also be employed but that these were less reactive than aluminum halides.[1]

Ordinarily, $AlCl_3$* is used to carry out the various syntheses, because it is efficient and cheap. Stimulated by the intensity of competition, investigators have found many new and related uses for aluminum chloride which are beyond the purview of the original Friedel and Crafts reaction. Some of these new and important syntheses bear names that testify to the inventive genius of the investigator.

Although Friedel and Crafts made their original observations on a reaction involving the replacement of hydrogen in an aliphatic compound, *i.e.*, amyl chloride,

$$C_5H_{11}Cl + C_5H_{11}Cl \xrightarrow{\text{Al}} C_{10}H_{21}Cl + HCl$$

and numerous similar syntheses have subsequently been reported, it is, nevertheless, true that from the standpoint of yield of desired specific product, ease of operating control, and technical utility, the usual Friedel and Crafts reactions ordinarily involve at least one ring nucleus such as benzene, phenol, naphthalene, furan, cyclohexane, etc. As is shown later, the notable exceptions to this generalization are the prep-

---

[1] Brit. 4,769 (1877).

* From vapor-density and vapor-pressure studies (Fischer, Rahlfs, and Benze, *Z. anorg. Chem.*, **205**, 1 (1932)) the structural formulation of aluminum chloride in the gaseous state is probably the dimer

$$\begin{array}{c}Cl \\ Cl\end{array}\!\!\!\!>\!\!Al\!\!<\!\!\begin{array}{c}Cl \\ Cl\end{array}\!\!\!\!>\!\!Al\!\!<\!\!\begin{array}{c}Cl \\ Cl\end{array}$$

This is in accord with the determinations of the molecular weight in organic solvents [Ulich, *Z. physik. Chem.*, **152**, 423 (1931); *Z. Elektrochem.*, **37**, 559 (1931)].

TYPES OF FRIEDEL AND CRAFTS SYNTHESES

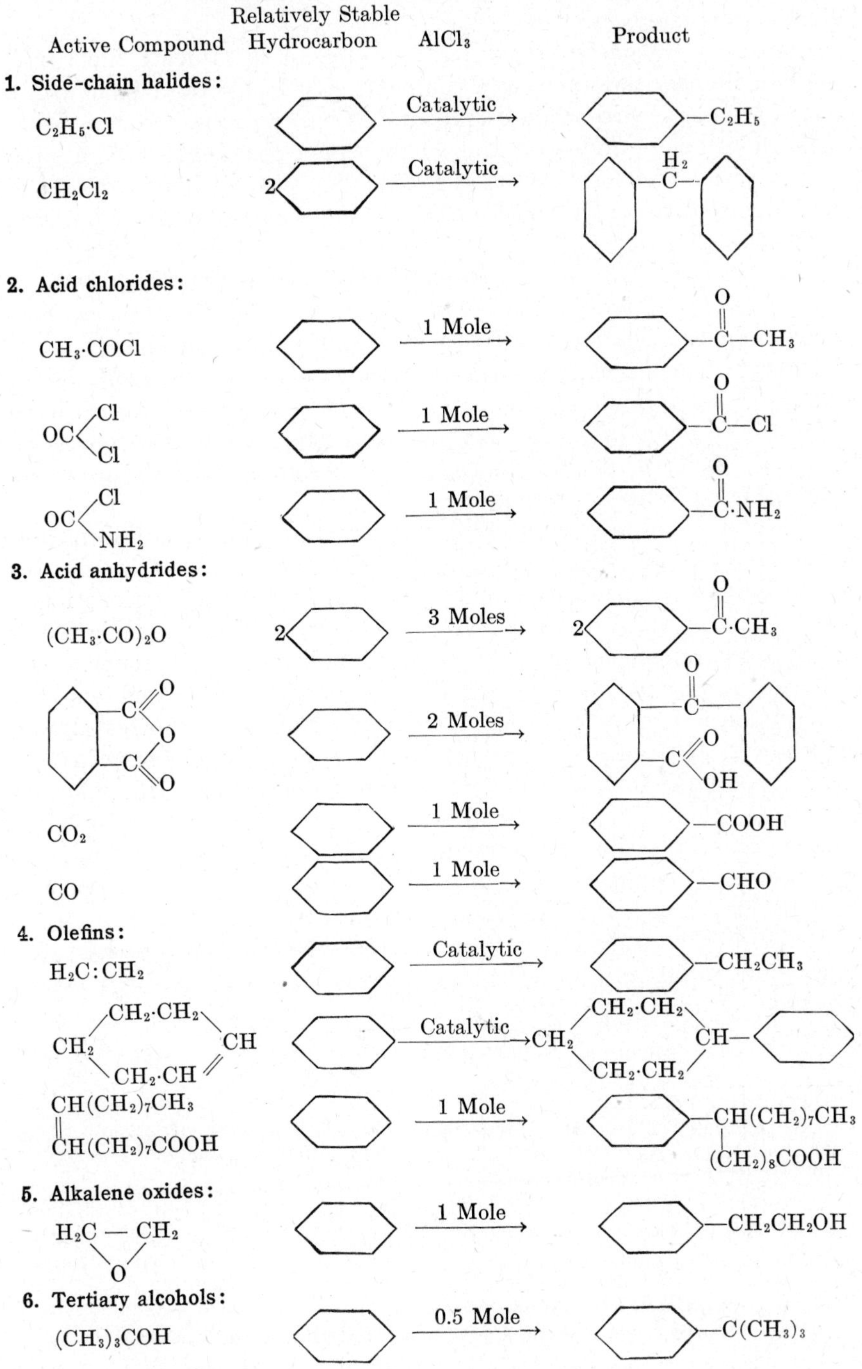

Relatively Stable

Active Compound   Hydrocarbon $AlCl_3$ Product

1. Side-chain halides:

$C_2H_5 \cdot Cl$ Catalytic $\longrightarrow$ —C_2H_5

CH_2Cl_2 2   Catalytic $\longrightarrow$ $\overset{H_2}{\underset{}{C}}$

2. Acid chlorides:

$CH_3 \cdot COCl$ 1 Mole $\longrightarrow$ $-\overset{O}{\overset{\|}{C}}-CH_3$

$OC\overset{Cl}{\underset{Cl}{\big\langle}}$ 1 Mole $\longrightarrow$ $-\overset{O}{\overset{\|}{C}}-Cl$

$OC\overset{Cl}{\underset{NH_2}{\big\langle}}$ 1 Mole $\longrightarrow$ $-\overset{O}{\overset{\|}{C}}\cdot NH_2$

3. Acid anhydrides:

$(CH_3 \cdot CO)_2O$ 2   3 Moles $\longrightarrow$ 2 $-\overset{O}{\overset{\|}{C}}\cdot CH_3$

$\overset{-C\overset{O}{\diagup}}{\underset{-C\diagdown_O}{}} O$ 2 Moles $\longrightarrow$ $\overset{C\diagdown_O}{\underset{-C\overset{O}{\diagdown}OH}{}}$

CO_2 1 Mole $\longrightarrow$ —COOH

CO 1 Mole $\longrightarrow$ —CHO

4. Olefins:

$H_2C:CH_2$ Catalytic $\longrightarrow$ —CH_2CH_3

$CH_2\overset{CH_2 \cdot CH_2}{\underset{CH_2 \cdot CH}{\diagup\diagdown}}CH$ Catalytic $\longrightarrow$ $CH_2\overset{CH_2 \cdot CH_2}{\underset{CH_2 \cdot CH_2}{\diagup\diagdown}}CH-$

$\overset{CH(CH_2)_7CH_3}{\underset{CH(CH_2)_7COOH}{\|}}$ 1 Mole $\longrightarrow$ $-\overset{CH(CH_2)_7CH_3}{\underset{(CH_2)_8COOH}{}}$

5. Alkalene oxides:

$H_2C\overset{}{\underset{O}{—}}CH_2$ 1 Mole $\longrightarrow$ —CH_2CH_2OH

6. Tertiary alcohols:

$(CH_3)_3COH$ 0.5 Mole $\longrightarrow$ —$C(CH_3)_3$

aration of alkyl and acyl halides through the catalytic intervention of aluminum chloride.

Narrowly considered, *syntheses* according to the Friedel and Crafts reaction involve the union of a comparatively active compound with a relative stable hydrocarbon or substituted hydrocarbon in the presence of a halide of aluminum, iron, zinc, boron, tin, or titanium. For purposes of elucidation, benzene is used as the relatively stable hydrocarbon and aluminum chloride as the metal halide in the general reactions shown on page 635.

Clearly, other alkyl or aralkyl halides, *e.g.*, isopropyl chloride or *p*-chlorobenzyl chloride can be substituted for the illustrative side-chain halides. Similarly, other acid chlorides, carboxylic acid anhydrides, etc. can be employed in comparable syntheses. Finally, other cyclic or heterocyclic compounds can replace benzene. It is to be emphasized, therefore, that the preceding are merely type reactions, and the development of similar syntheses is limited only by the vision and ingenuity of the investigator.

By and large, the orientation of substituents introduced by means of the Friedel and Crafts reaction is the same as other aromatic substitution reactions, *e.g.*, nitration and halogenation. The exceptions relate largely to alkylation reactions wherein the alkyl halides may migrate or undergo rearrangement to the most highly branched alkyl groups. The tendency to give unexpected results is accentuated by increased temperature, abnormal proportions of reactants or the presence of catalyzing substances. Because reactions catalyzed by metal halides may involve double decomposition, addition, fission and migration, etc., it is not at all surprising that abnormalities do occur when aluminum chloride is employed as activating or condensing agent. These exceptions, however, only serve to emphasize the large body of normal, dependable, and technically useful Friedel and Crafts syntheses.

According to Calloway[1] the relative ease with which unsubstituted rings undergo substitution by means of the Friedel and Crafts reaction in the order of decreasing activity is as follows:[2]

For the substituted nuclei, the influence of groups on the order of activity is usually as follows, the activity decreasing from left to right:

[1] CALLOWAY, *Chem. Rev.*, **17**, 327 (1935).

[2] Unsubstituted furan undergoes acylation readily but has not been alkylated.

$$-\text{OH and} -\text{OCH}_3, \ (\text{CH}_3)_2\text{N}-, \ \text{CH}_3-, \ \text{H}-, \ \begin{cases} \text{Cl}- \\ \text{Br}-, \\ \text{I}- \end{cases} \begin{cases} -\text{CHO} \\ -\text{COCH}_3 \end{cases},$$

In general an increasing electronegativity or "acidity" of the group increases the difficulty of substitution.

II. CLASSIFICATION OF SYNTHESES

The classification of syntheses grouped under the Friedel and Crafts reaction may be set forth as follows:

A. Alkylation reactions.
   1. HYDROCARBON SYNTHESES.
   2. ALKYLPHENOLS.
   3. FURAN DERIVATIVES.
B. Aldehyde syntheses.
C. Carboxylic acid derivatives.
   1. BY ACTION OF CO₂.
   2. FROM CYAPHENINES.
   3. BY ACTION OF PHOSGENE.
D. Ketone synthesis.
   1. SIMPLE KETONES.
   2. RING KETONES.
   3. OPEN DIKETONES.
   4. RING DIKETONES AND DERIVATIVES.
   5. KETO ACIDS.
   6. KETIMIDES.
   7. UREAS.
E. Reaction of nitro compounds.
F. Preparation of primary and secondary amines.
G. Synthesis of arylalkanols.
H. Halogeno compounds.
   1. ALKYL CHLORIDES.
   2. ACID CHLORIDES.
   3. AROMATIC HALOGENO COMPOUNDS.
I. Dehydration reactions.
J. The synthesis of hydrocarbon derivatives containing phosphorus, sulfur, selenium, and arsenic.

Other important reactions, such as the cracking of petroleum, the Fries migration, and Scholl reaction, all of which are catalyzed by aluminum chloride, are also given consideration.[1]

ALKYLATION REACTIONS

A-1. Hydrocarbon Syntheses.—The following reactions illustrate the formation of aromatic hydrocarbons. The process involves the elimination of hydrogen chloride in the presence of aluminum chloride, the hydrogen atom being linked to a carbon in a ring, while the halogen atom must be linked to a carbon not in a ring.

[1] See also KRANZLEIN, "Aluminiumchlorid in der organischen Chemie," for a general survey of Friedel and Crafts reactions. Verlag Chemie, Berlin (1932).

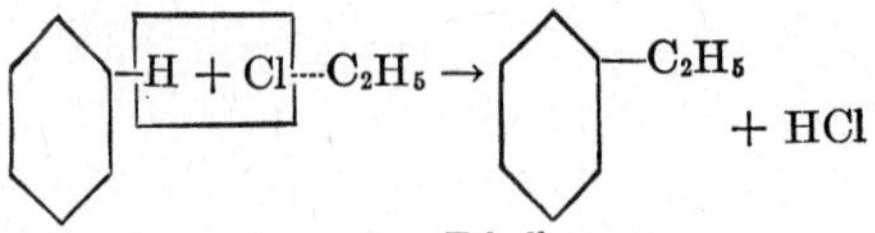

Ethylbenzene

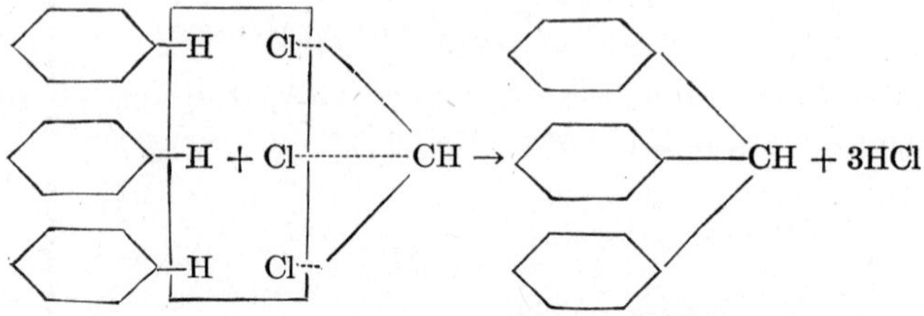

Triphenylmethane

In place of the saturated aliphatic halides, Norris and Couch[1] have shown that the unsaturated olefins may be used. Ethylene may thus replace ethyl chloride in the synthesis of ethylbenzene, since the former passes into ethyl chloride during the course of reaction. Similarly, cyclohexene reacts with benzene to yield cyclohexylbenzene,[2] and isobutylene condenses with *m*-xylene[3] to form 3, 5-dimethyltertiarybutyl-benzene:

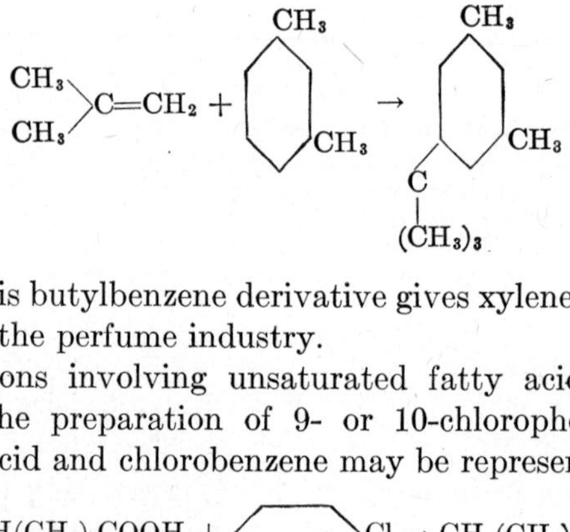

On trinitration this butylbenzene derivative gives xylene musk, a product of importance to the perfume industry.

Similar reactions involving unsaturated fatty acids lead to aryl-stearic acids. The preparation of 9- or 10-chlorophenyloctadecanoic acids from oleic acid and chlorobenzene may be represented thus:

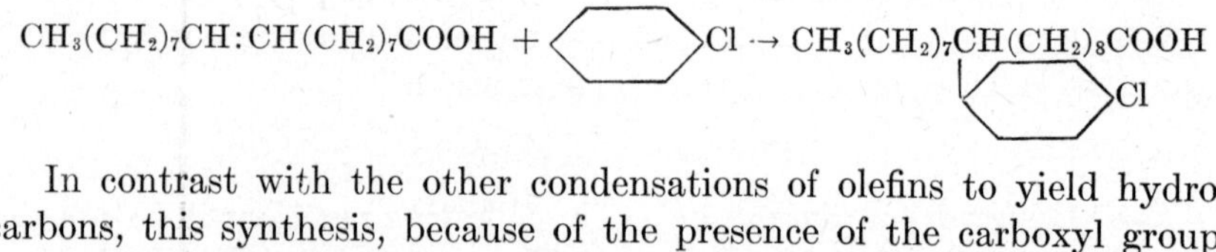

In contrast with the other condensations of olefins to yield hydro-carbons, this synthesis, because of the presence of the carboxyl group, requires a slight excess over 1 mole $AlCl_3$ instead of the usual catalytic quantities. Aluminum chloride as a condensing agent usually behaves in such a way that there is a definite relationship between the type of sub-

[1] NORRIS and COUCH, *J. Am. Chem. Soc.*, **42**, 2329 (1920).

[2] U. S. 1,969,984 (1934).

[3] Ger. 184,230 (1906).

stance formed and the amount of chloride used. In some instances (as in the preparation of ketones or keto acids), a molar or dimolar quantity of aluminum chloride is required to effect a condensation; and, in others, the quantity is so small (as in the synthesis of hydrocarbons and alkylphenols) that the reaction partakes of the nature of catalysis. This subject is further elaborated on page 657.

Aralkyl chlorides react in the same manner as do alkyl halides. Diphenylmethane is thus obtained by the condensation of benzyl-chloride with benzene:

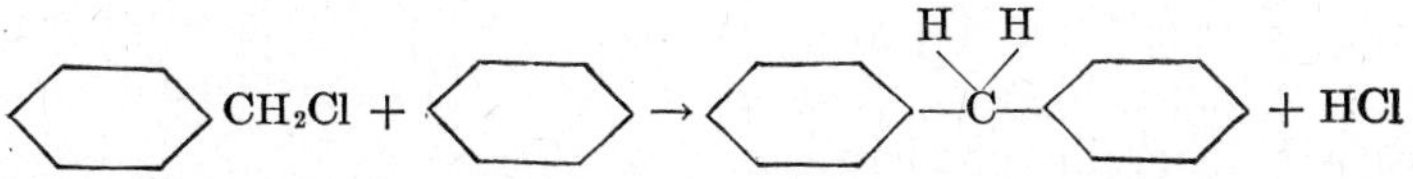

Braun and Deutsch[1] have shown that when the aliphatic chain of an aralkyl halide is sufficiently long, an inner ring closure is effected by anhydrous aluminum chloride. In this way, 1-phenyl-4-chlorobutane yields tetralin:

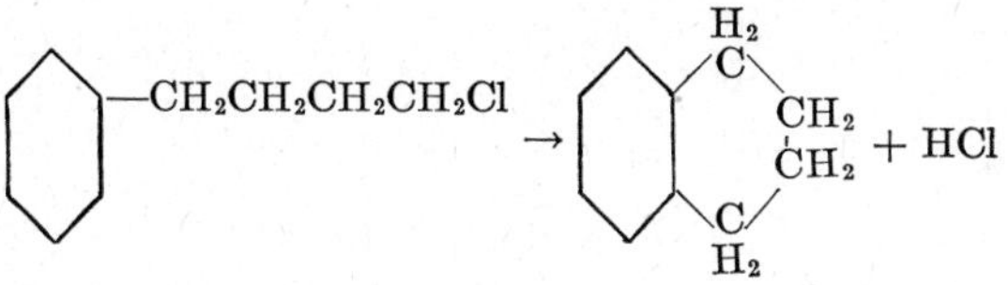

Although halogenobenzenes do not condense with the loss of halogen from the ring, an anthrone containing halogen in the meso position is capable of reacting with benzene with the loss of halogen, 9-phenyl-anthrone being obtained in this manner:[2]

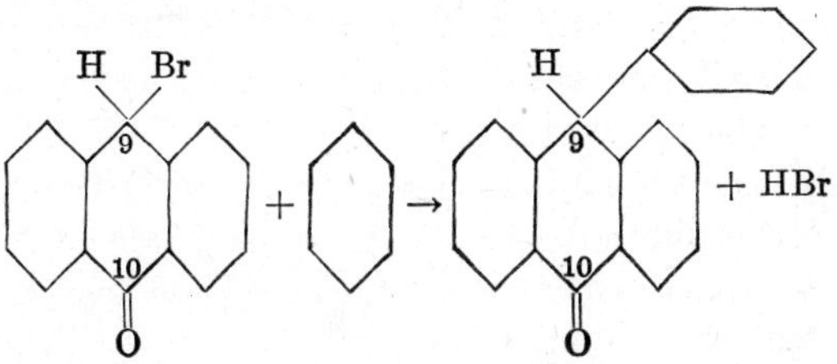

In the preparation of hydrocarbons according to the Friedel and Crafts reaction, alkyl halides and unsaturated hydrocarbons may be replaced by alkyl borates or aralkyl borates. The following is a typical reaction:[3]

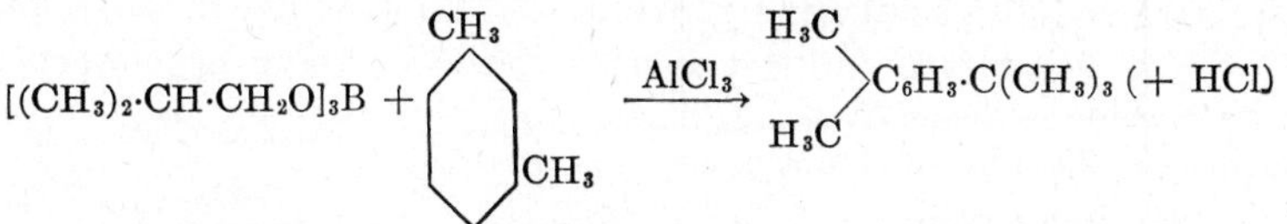

| Triisobutylborate | *m*-Xylene | Tertiarybutylxylene |

[1] Braun and Deutsch, *Ber.*, **45**, 1267 (1912).
[2] Barnett and Cook, *J. Chem. Soc.*, **123**, 2636 (1923).
[3] Fr. 720,034 (1932).

The borates are formed practically quantitatively by simply heating the alcohol with boric acid, water being eliminated during the process. The trialkyl borates possess a higher boiling point than the corresponding alkyl chlorides, *e.g.*, C_2H_5Cl (b.p., 12°C.); $(C_2H_5O)_3B$ (b.p., 112°C.). This characteristic permits of a simple control of their purity by distillation. Unusually high yields of hydrocarbon, *i.e.*, 80 to 90 per cent of the theoretical, are claimed for the process. The quantity of higher-boiling fractions is small, while the formation of resinous products is negligible.

Alkyl sulfates and carbonates have been employed for the alkylation of hydrocarbons.[1] Such processes give only mediocre yields of alkyl derivative and, in addition, require a ratio of 1.5 moles $AlCl_3$ per mole of alkyl ester undergoing condensation.

A-2. Preparation of Alkylphenols.—The methods that are usually employed for the preparation of hydrocarbons are also suitable for the alkylation of phenols. In addition to alkyl and aralkyl esters and olefins, secondary and particularly tertiary alcohols can be condensed with mono- and dihydric phenols by the use of aluminum chloride.[2]

The reaction mechanism for the preparation of *tert*-butylphenol from *tert*-butyl alcohol and phenol is not known but may be as follows:

$$(CH_3)_3COH + AlCl_3 \rightarrow \left[\begin{array}{c} (CH_3)_3C \quad\quad H \\ \diagdown \diagup \\ O \\ \diagup \diagdown \\ Cl \quad\quad AlCl_2 \end{array} \right] \rightarrow (CH_3)_3CCl + HOAlCl_2 \quad\quad (1)$$

$$(CH_3)_3CCl + C_6H_5OH \xrightarrow{AlCl_3} (CH_3)_3C\cdot C_6H_4OH + HCl \quad\quad (2)$$

The mechanism of reaction is undoubtedly more complex. In all probability the hydrogen chloride which is liberated [Eq. (2)] serves to convert some of the residual alcohol to the chloride which accounts for the need of only about 0.5 mole $AlCl_3$ per mole of *tert*-butyl alcohol. The intermediate formation of the reactive alkyl chloride can easily be demonstrated.[3] When *tert*-butyl alcohol (b.p., 82.8°C.) is gradually added to a suspension of aluminum chloride in nitrobenzene at 70°C., *tert*-butyl chloride (b.p., 51°C.) distills over. These observations point to the desirability of working under a slight pressure and of fitting the reactor with an efficient reflux condenser.

When a *tert*-alkyl halide, *e.g.*, *tert*-butyl chloride is condensed with a phenol in which the 2 and 4 positions are free, there is formed 4-*tert*-

[1] KANE and LOWY, *J. Am. Chem. Soc.*, **58**, 2605 (1936).

[2] Huston, U. S. 2,051,300 (1936); HUSTON and HSIEH, *J. Am. Chem. Soc.*, **58**, 439 (1936). TSUKERVANIK and NAZAROVA, *J. Gen. Chem. (U.S.S.R.)*, **5**, 767 (1936).

[3] GROGGINS and SWERN, Unpublished investigations. The initial formation of an olefin which adds HCl to form the same alkyl chloride is of course not excluded:

$$(CH_3)_3COH \xrightarrow{AlCl_3} (CH_3)_2C{=}CH_2 \xrightarrow{HCl} (CH_3)_3CCl$$

butylphenol as the principal product along with appreciable quantities of 2-*tert*- and 2, 4-di-*tert*-butylphenols.[1]

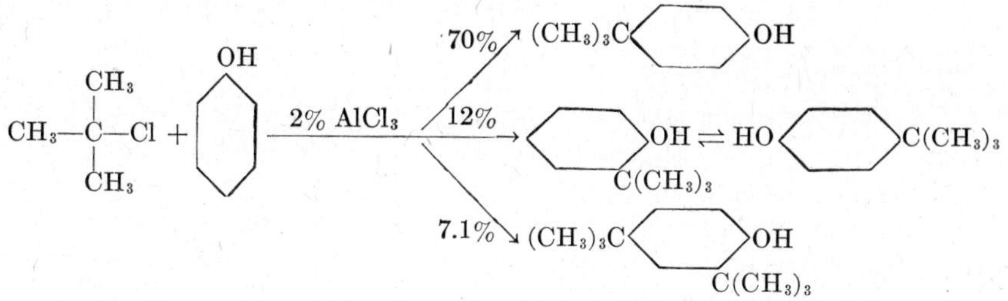

Thymol and carvacrol, which are important antiseptics, can be synthesized by reacting equivalent quantities of isopropyl chloride with *m*- and *o*-cresols respectively at −10°C. in the presence of a solvent.[2] In contrast with the synthesis of butylphenol which requires only catalytic quantities of aluminum chloride, this reaction needs at least molar equivalents of the condensing agent.

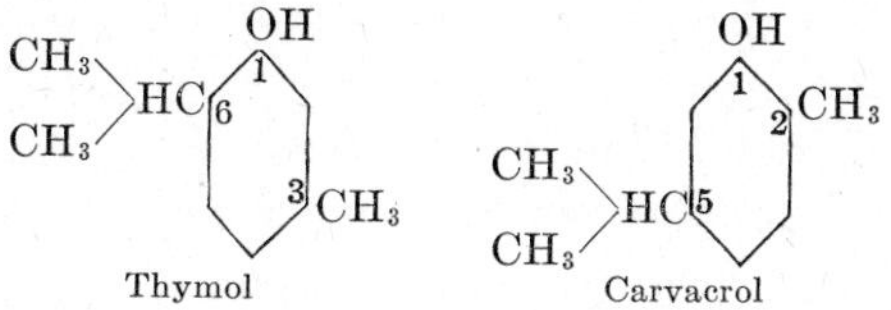

Thymol   Carvacrol

When initial and final temperatures of 20 and 60°C. respectively are used in the condensation of *m*-cresol, the product is not thymol, but the isomeric 3-methyl-5-isopropylphenol. Likewise, in the carvacrol synthesis, there is obtained about 15 per cent of the isomeric 2-methyl-3-isopropylphenol when the reaction temperature is as low as −15°C.

A-3. Alkylation of Furans.—Although no direct alkylation of furan occurs, methyl 2-furoate undergoes alkylation to yield methyl 5-alkyl-2-furoates.[3]

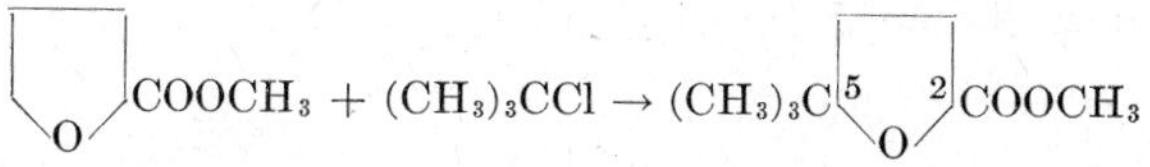

Normal, iso- and *sec*-butyl halides can be used in the above reaction, but the product, however, is always the most highly branched methyl 5-*tert*-butyl-2-furoate. Furfural similarly undergoes alkylation, but, surprisingly, the new substituent goes into the 4- instead of the expected 5- position.[4]

[1] Perkins *et al.*, U. S. 1,972,599 (1934).
[2] Carpenter, U. S. 2,064,885 (1936).
[3] GILMAN and CALLOWAY, *J. Am. Chem. Soc.*, **51**, 4197 (1933).
[4] GILMAN, McCORKLE, and CALLOWAY, *J. Am. Chem. Soc.*, **56**, 745 (1934).

B. Aldehyde Synthesis.

Aldehydes may be made by reacting carbon monoxide with aromatic hydrocarbons or their substitution products under 1,200 lb. pressure in the presence of aluminum chloride.[1,2,3] The reaction proceeds very slowly at first, but once under way the velocity increases progressively. Hydrogen chloride or a limited amount of water, which causes the liberation of HCl, has been found a useful agent in initiating the reaction, thus shortening the long and costly induction period.   More recently, it has been found satisfactory to leave a residue of aldehyde-aluminum chloride complex in the autoclave into which fresh reactants are then added.   This stratagem is instrumental in cutting down the induction period from 10 to 3.5 hr.[4] Another technic achieving this end is to prepare an addition compound of formyl chloride by causing carbon monoxide to react with hydrogen chloride in the presence of aluminum chloride and copper under 130 atmos. pressure at 50°C.   The addition complex, which is unstable in the presence of moisture, may of course be employed for the preparation of aromatic aldehydes.[5]

When aromatic nitro compounds are used as solvents, the preceding aldehyde synthesis can be made to take place at 60°C. without the use of pressure.[6]

C. Carboxylic Acid Derivatives.   *By Direct Action of* CO_2.—Carboxylic acids can be prepared by the direct reaction of carbon dioxide with benzene in the presence of aluminum chloride.[7]

[1] Ger. 281,212 (1914).
[2] Brit. 3,152 (1915).
[3] HOLLOWAY and KRASE, *Ind. Eng. Chem.*, **25**, 497 (1933).
[4] Larson, U. S. 1,989,700 (1935).
[5] U. S. 1,976,682 (1934).
[6] Ger. 403,489 (1924).
[7] Brit. 307,223 (1929).

In a similar manner, acid chlorides and benzophenone are obtained when $COCl_2$ is used instead of CO_2.

When phenols are treated with CO_2 under a pressure of 50 atmospheres, several products may be obtained, depending on the proportions of reactants used and the temperature employed. The formation of salicylic acid and of *m*-cresotic acid may be represented as follows:

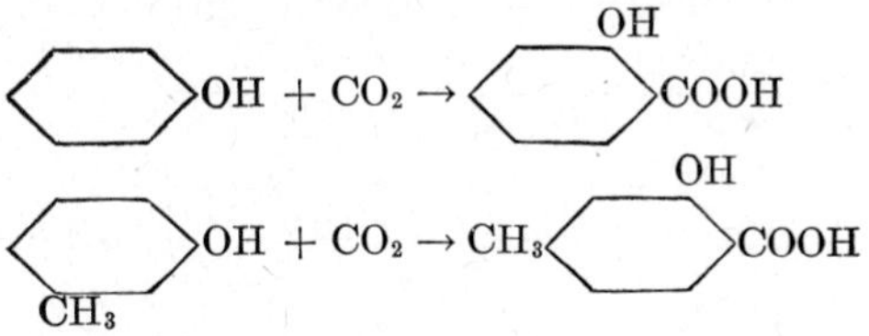

When the ratio of $AlCl_3$ to phenol is increased, 4,4'-dihydroxybenzophenone is the principal product.[1] An increased yield of carboxylic acid is favored by lower temperatures and the substitution of a milder condensing agent such as zinc chloride. *p*-Ethylaminobenzoic acid and *p*-dimethylaminobenzoic acid can be obtained by condensing the requisite alkylaniline with CO_2 in the presence of zinc chloride:

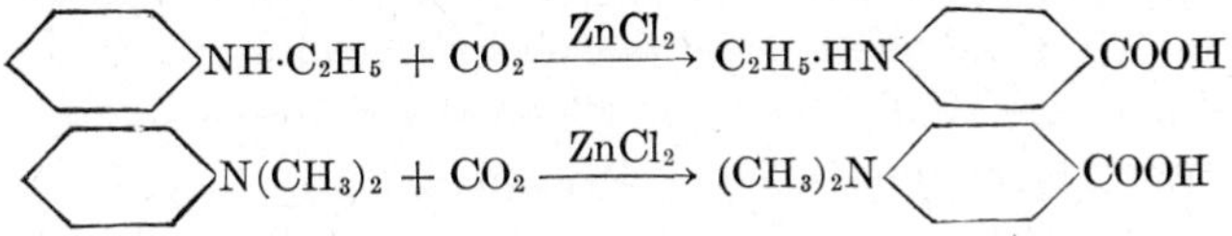

Amides are obtained by condensing carbamyl chloride with hydrocarbons according to the following reaction:-

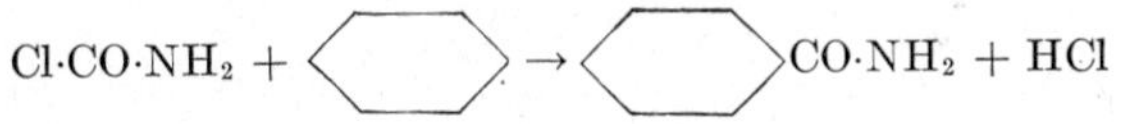

From Cyaphenines.—When benzene or its homologues are treated with cyanuric chloride in the presence of aluminum chloride,[2] cyaphenine or its homologues are obtained. When cyaphenine is hydrolyzed with sulfuric acid, benzoic acid is produced. The reactions involved are as follows:

$$3CNCl \rightarrow (CNCl)_3 \qquad (1)$$

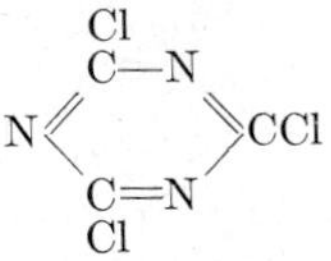

$$(CNCl)_3 + 3AlCl_3 + 3C_6H_6 \rightarrow (C_6H_5CN)_3 \cdot 3AlCl_3 + 3HCl \qquad (2)$$
$$(C_6H_5CN)_3 \cdot 3AlCl_3 + 6H_2O \rightarrow 3C_6H_5COOH + 3AlCl_3 + 3NH_3 \qquad (3)$$

The ammonia formed in reaction (3) will, of course, combine with the excess of sulfuric acid present in the hydrolysis. Cyanuric chloride[3]

---

[1] Brit. 353,464 (1931).
[2] U. S. 1,734,029 (1929).
[3] Ger. 433,100 (1928).

condenses with α-naphthol to form a compound of the following constitution:

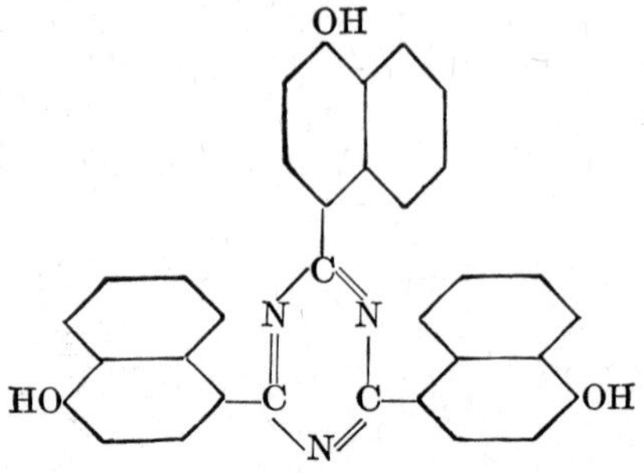

On hydrolysis, this complex yields three molecules of 1-hydroxynaphthalene-4-carboxylic acid.

D. Ketone Synthesis.   *Simple Ketones.*—Friedel and Crafts[1] showed that it was a simple matter to prepare ketones from aliphatic acid chlorides and aromatic compounds. They also demonstrated[2] that aromatic acid chlorides would behave like the corresponding aliphatic compounds. Noller and Adams[3] showed that aliphatic acid anhydrides could be substituted for acid chlorides, and recently Groggins and his coworkers[4] have demonstrated that the alkyl aryl and diaryl ketones could be derived directly from carboxylic acids. Typical ketone syntheses are represented by the following reactions:

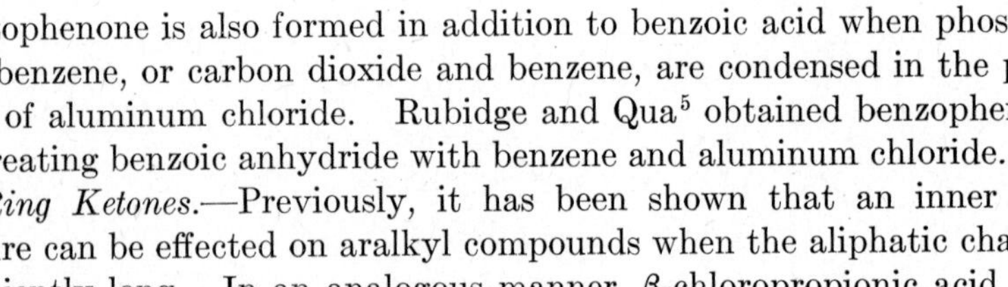

Benzophenone is also formed in addition to benzoic acid when phosgene and benzene, or carbon dioxide and benzene, are condensed in the presence of aluminum chloride. Rubidge and Qua[5] obtained benzophenone by treating benzoic anhydride with benzene and aluminum chloride.

Ring Ketones.—Previously, it has been shown that an inner ring closure can be effected on aralkyl compounds when the aliphatic chain is sufficiently long. In an analogous manner, β-chloropropionic acid condenses with hydrocarbons to form ring ketones.

---

[1] FRIEDEL and CRAFTS, *Ber.*, **17**, 376 (1884).

[2] FRIEDEL and CRAFTS, *Ann. chim.* (6), **1**, 510 (1884).

[3] NOLLER and ADAMS, *J. Am. Chem. Soc.*, **36**, 736 (1914).

[4] GROGGINS, NAGEL, and STIRTON, *Ind. Eng. Chem.*, **26**, 1313 (1934); U. S. 1,966,797 (1934).

[5] RUBIDGE and QUA, *J. Am. Chem. Soc.*, **36**, 732 (1914).

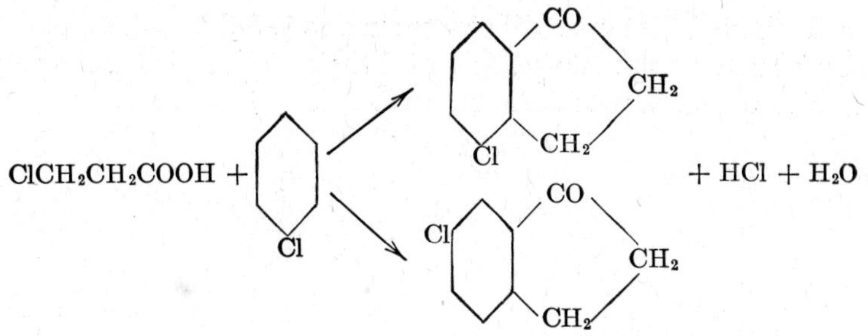

$$ClCH_2CH_2COOH +$$

A similar ring synthesis is the preparation of 1,6-dihydroxypyrene from 2, 2'-(diacetylchloride)-biphenyl: *i.e.*, xenene-2, 2'-diacetyl chloride

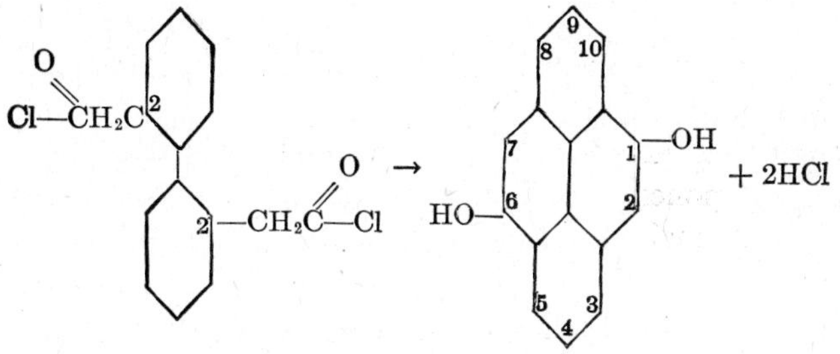

Open Diketones.—When ethers of aromatic hydrocarbons are condensed with oxalyl chloride in the presence of anhydrous aluminum chloride, open diketones are formed. In many reactions, oxalyl chloride reacts similarly to phosgene. The formation of 4, 4'-dimethoxybinaphthoyl by this method is shown below.

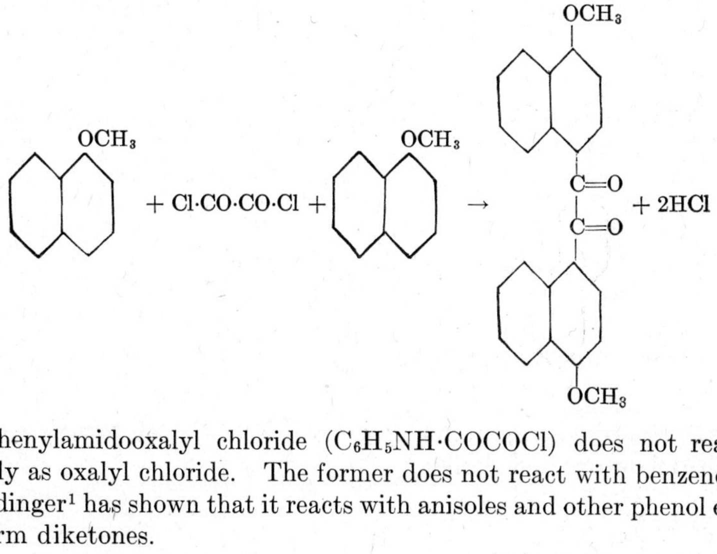

Phenylamidooxalyl chloride ($C_6H_5NH \cdot COCOCl$) does not react so readily as oxalyl chloride. The former does not react with benzene, but Staudinger[1] has shown that it reacts with anisoles and other phenol ethers to form diketones.

[1] STAUDINGER, SCHLENKER and GOLDSTEIN, *Helv. Chim. Acta.*, **4**, 334 (1921).

Scholl[1] showed that open diketones such as 1, 5-dibenzoylnaphthalene could be formed by condensing 1, 5-naphthalenedicarbonyl chloride with benzene in the presence of aluminum chloride.

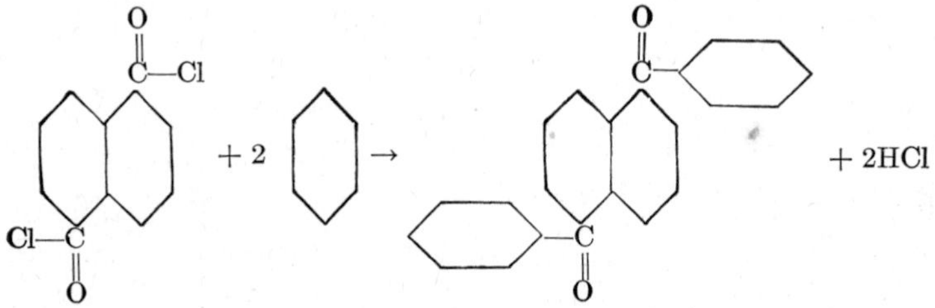

Two benzoyl groups can be introduced directly into naphthalene to obtain the same product.[2]

Ring Diketones.—In this class are included the isatins, thioisatins, and acenaphthenequinones.   Isatins in which the N is substituted may be prepared by condensing secondary amines and oxalyl chloride:[3]

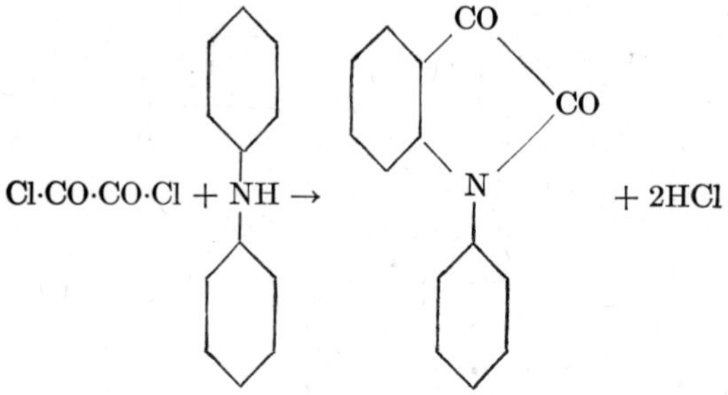

When aryloxamic acid chlorides are treated with aluminum chloride, isatins in which the N is not substituted are obtained:

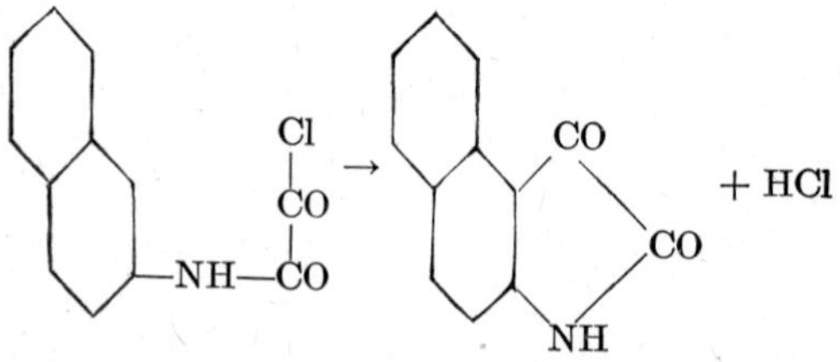

Thioisatins are obtained from thioaryloxalic acid chloride, according to a method developed by Stollé:

[1] Scholl, *Ber.*, **55,** 126 (1922).
[2] Brit. 291,347 (1929).
[3] Stollé, Ger. 281,046 (1913).

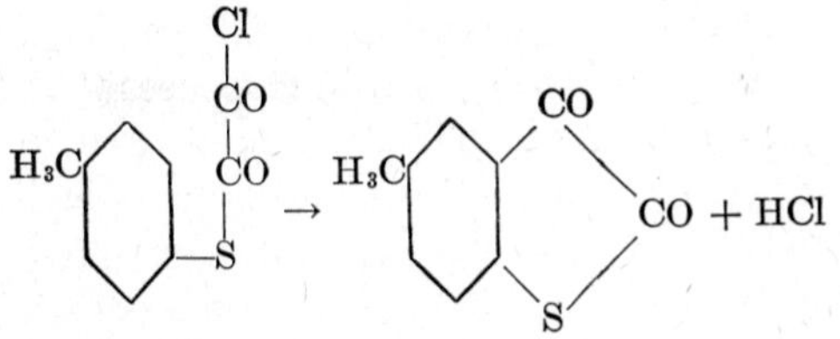

In a manner entirely analogous to the preceding synthesis of diketones, dimethylacenaphthenequinone can be prepared from oxalyl chloride and 1, 6-dimethylnaphthalene:[1]

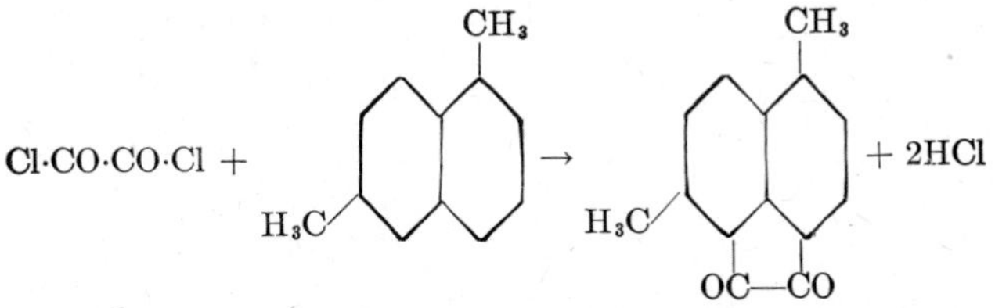

Keto Acids.—The preparation of keto acids is probably the most important industrially of the numerous syntheses made possible by the Friedel and Crafts reaction. The benzoylbenzoic acids, which are obtained by condensing phthalic anhydride with aromatic compounds, can readily be converted to anthraquinone derivatives by simple dehydration with sulfuric acid. The steps involved in the synthesis of anthraquinone may be represented as follows:

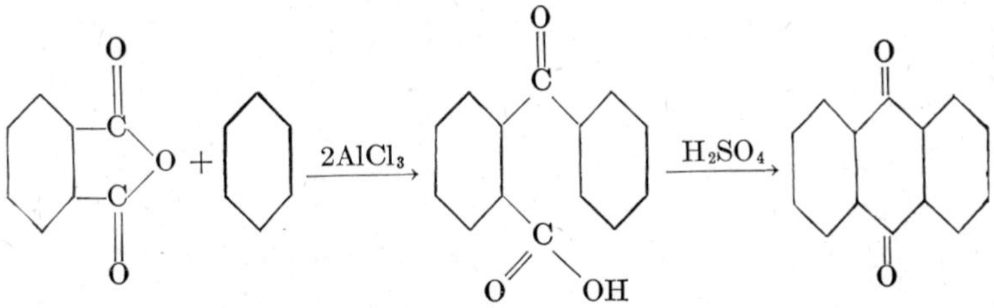

Because of the unusual industrial importance of keto acids to the vat-dye industry, the theoretical and technical aspects of this synthesis will be discussed in some detail later in this chapter. When substituted benzenoid compounds (except nitro derivatives) are used, it is feasible to obtain analogous anthraquinone derivatives as end products. Similar syntheses may be made employing substituted phthalic anhydride (including nitro derivatives) as one of the reactants.

When hydroxy compounds are condensed with phthalic anhydride, it is possible, when employing elevated temperatures, to proceed directly

[1] LESSER, *Ber.*, **60**, 242 (1927).

to the hydroxyanthraquinone derivatives.   Hystazarin[1] is thus prepared
by treating pyrocatechol in the presence of an excess of phthalic anhydride.
For the production of quinizarin, hydroquinone is used, and the double salt
sodium-aluminum chloride is advantageously employed.   Gubelmann[2]
has shown that it is feasible to use concentrated sulfuric acid instead of
aluminum chloride in condensing 3, 4-dichlorophenol with phthalic anhydride to prepare 2- (or 3-) chloro-1, 4-dihydroxyanthraquinone.

When phenols are condensed in inert solvents with phthalic anhydride
under comparatively mild conditions, it is possible to obtain the hydroxy
keto acid in substantially good yields.   Ullmann[3] describes the preparation of a number of such compounds.   The condensation of phthalic
anhydride and phenol at 120°C. in the presence of zinc chloride leads
almost exclusively to phenolphthalein.   The reaction is accelerated

by the addition of relatively small quantities of concentrated sulfuric
acid.[4]

Ketimides.—Houben and Fischer[5] have shown that acid nitriles react
with phenols and phenol ethers in the presence of aluminum chloride.
Hydrocarbons can also be condensed when the very active trichloro-
acetonitrile is used, and the formation of ω-trichloromethyl *p*-tolyl ketone
may be represented as follows:

Ureas.—When carbon dioxide is condensed with amines in the presence
of aluminum chloride, ureas and alkylaminobenzophenones are obtained.

[1] Ger. 298,345 (1914).

[2] Gubelmann, U. S. 1,655,863 (1928).

[3] Ullmann, Ger. 282,493 (1913).

[4] Hubacher, U. S. 1,940,494 (1933).

[5] HOUBEN and FISCHER, *J. prakt. Chem.* [2], **123,** 89, 262, 313 (1929).

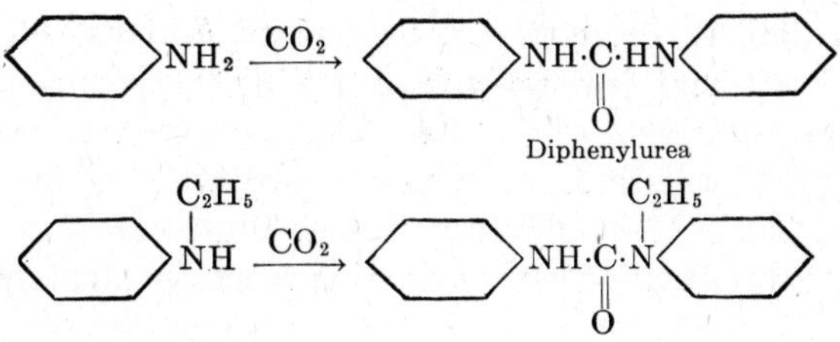

Diphenylurea

In addition to the ureas, the reaction may be modified to lead to the formation of aromatic ketones and amino aromatic carboxylic acids,[1] thus:

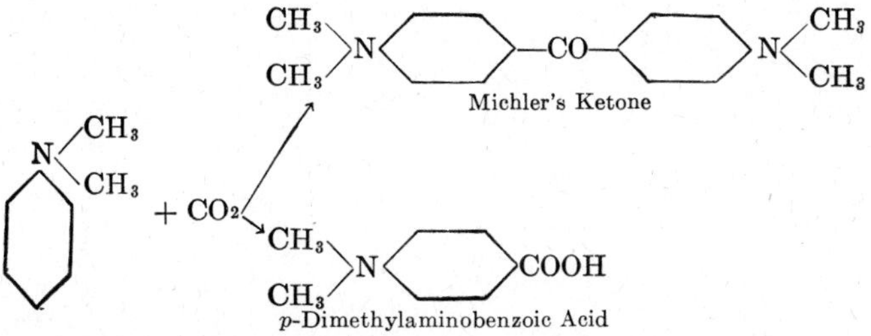

Michler's Ketone

p-Dimethylaminobenzoic Acid

E. Reactions of Nitro Compounds.—Nitrobenzene does not enter into normal Friedel and Crafts syntheses. When reacted with an alkylating agent such as isopropyl bromide, reduction of the nitro group and halogenation of the benzene nucleus occur, and a slight conversion of nitrobenzene to o- and p-chloroanilines occurs. If, however, the aromatic nucleus contains a highly activating substituent in addition to the nitro group, then normal reactions become possible.

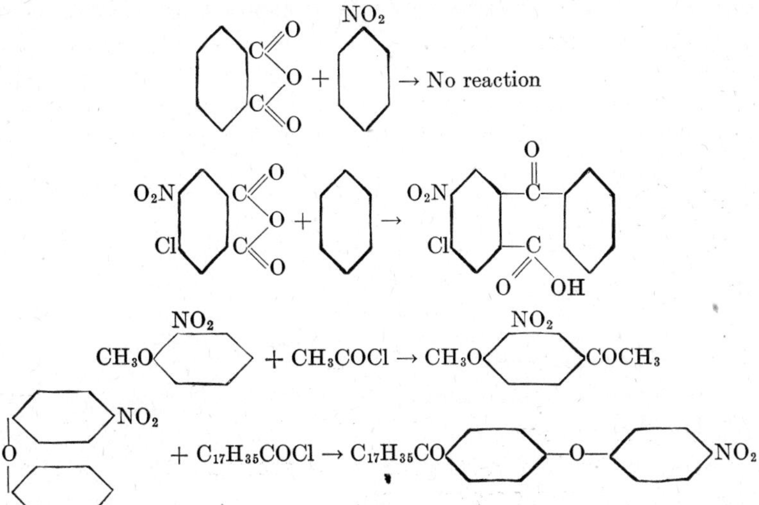

$\rightarrow$ No reaction

CH_3O⟨⟩NO_2 $+ CH_3COCl \rightarrow CH_3O$⟨$NO_2$⟩$COCH_3$

$+ C_{17}H_{35}COCl \rightarrow C_{17}H_{35}CO$⟨⟩$-O-$⟨⟩$NO_2$

[1] Brit. 353,464 (1931).

F. Preparation of Primary and Secondary Amines.—Kränzlein and coworkers[1] have found that aminobiphenyl derivatives can be prepared by causing hydrocarbons of the benzene series to act upon benzenoid N-halogen acyl derivatives of amino compounds in the presence of aluminum chloride. The following scheme illustrates the course of the reaction in the preparation of xenylamine from N-chloroacetanilide and benzene.

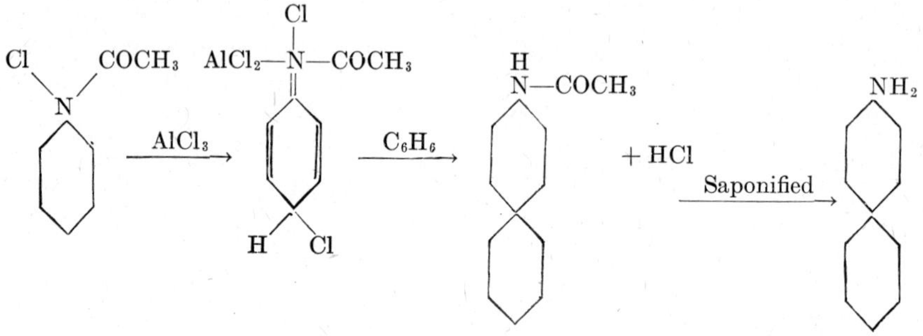

In all probability the reaction takes place in such a manner that the AlCl$_3$ forms an unstable intermediate addition complex with the N-chloroacetanilide. In this complex the added labile chlorine atom adjacent to the activated hydrogen atom in the 4 position enters into reaction in the presence of benzene, thus resulting in the formation of a biphenyl derivative and the splitting out of hydrogen chloride. Upon saponification, the acetaminobiphenyl is converted to xenylamine, *i.e.*, 4-aminobiphenyl.

Secondary aromatic amines enter into reaction with highly reactive substances of the *tert*-butyl chloride type to yield biphenyl derivatives which are useful in rubber compounding. The reaction products of diphenylamine with triphenylmethyl chloride are *p*-phenylaminotetraphenylmethane and 4-diphenylmethyl-4′-phenylaminobiphenyl:[2]

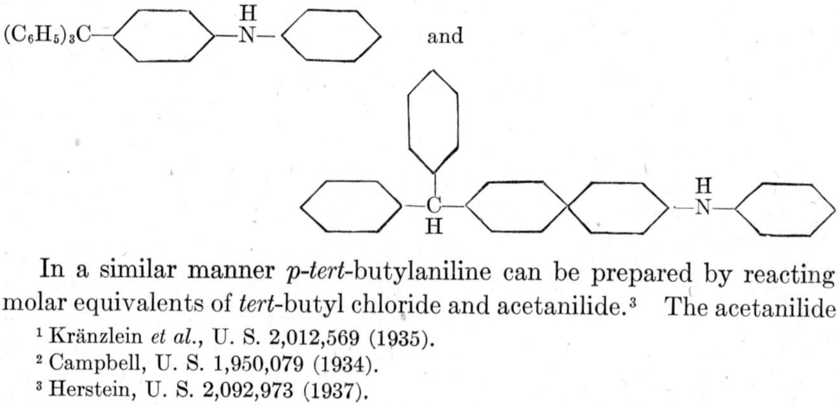

In a similar manner *p-tert*-butylaniline can be prepared by reacting molar equivalents of *tert*-butyl chloride and acetanilide.[3] The acetanilide

---

[1] Kränzlein *et al.*, U. S. 2,012,569 (1935).

[2] Campbell, U. S. 1,950,079 (1934).

[3] Herstein, U. S. 2,092,973 (1937).

is suspended in ethylene dichloride containing molar proportions of aluminum chloride, and the mixture is cooled to $-10°C$. *tert*-Butyl chloride is then added slowly, maintaining the temperature at $-5°C$. By decomposing the reaction complex with water and removing the solvent with steam, *p-tert* butylacetanilide is obtained as a crystalline mass. The primary amine is obtained by hydrolysis of the anilide with alkali or acid.

G. Synthesis of Arylalkanols.—The synthesis of β-phenylethyl alcohol, which is an important constituent of rose oil and many blended perfumes, has attracted many investigators.[1,2,3,4] When ethylene oxide and benzene are condensed in the presence of aluminum chloride, β-phenylethyl alcohol is obtained. Tolyl and xylyl derivatives, as well as propanol derivatives, can, of course, be prepared in a similar manner.

$$H_2C\text{---}CH_2 + AlCl_3 \rightarrow [ClCH_2CH_2OAlCl_2] + \bigcirc \xrightarrow{AlCl_3} \bigcirc\text{CH}_2\cdot\text{CH}_2\text{OH} + HCl$$

The preceding suggested mechanism of reaction indicates that 1 mole $AlCl_3$ is required for the formation of an addition complex after the oxide ring is broken. An excess over this amount is presumably required to effect the normal condensation of the alkyl halide with benzene. In practice it has been found desirable to use about 1.5 moles $AlCl_3$ per mole of ethylene oxide so that the reaction can be carried out at the lowest practical temperature. The removal of the liberated hydrogen chloride by passing a current of air through the reactor has been found instrumental in inhibiting the formation of undesirable by-products. It has also been suggested that the alkylene oxide be separately dissolved in benzene and then run into a suspension of cooled aluminum chloride in benzene at 0 to 10°C.[5] for temperature control is an important factor in obtaining good results.

H. Formation of Halogeno Compounds. 1. *Alkyl Halides*.—When ethylene, propylene, and similar olefins are reacted with hydrogen chloride in the presence of aluminum chloride, the corresponding alkyl halide is formed, thus:

$$CH_2\text{=}CH_2 + HCl \rightarrow CH_3\cdot CH_2Cl$$

If these olefins are used in alkylation reactions, they combine with the liberated hydrogen chloride and are transformed into the reactive alkyl halides. The presence of some hydrogen chloride initially tends to increase the yield of alkylated compound.

[1] Valik and Valik, U. S. 1,944,959 (1934).
[2] Carpenter, U. S. 2,013,710 (1935).
[3] Hopff, U. S. 2,029,618 (1936).
[4] Klipstein, Can. 340,555 (1934).
[5] Theimer, U. S. 2,047,396 (1936).

2. *Acid Chlorides.*—Carboxylic acid anhydrides behave similarly to olefins and form acid chlorides. Thus, ketene yields acetyl chloride

$$CH_2=C=O + HCl \rightarrow CH_3C\underset{\displaystyle Cl}{\overset{\displaystyle O}{<}}$$

Carbon monoxide and hydrogen chloride form a formyl chloride complex with aluminum chloride, whereas, carbon monoxide and chlorine yield oxalyl chloride at 200°C.[1]

$$CO + HCl \xrightarrow{\text{AlCl}_3} HC\underset{\displaystyle Cl}{\overset{\displaystyle O \cdots \text{AlCl}_3}{<}} \qquad \text{50°C. and 1,200 lb. Pressure}$$

$$2CO + Cl_2 \xrightarrow{\text{AlCl}_3} \underset{\displaystyle \overset{|}{COCl}}{COCl} \qquad \text{200°C. and 200 lb. Pressure}$$

Reid[2] has shown that β-chloroisobutyryl chloride, an intermediate in the synthesis of methyl methacrylate can be produced by passing equimolar proportions of phosgene and propylene into an autoclave containing aluminum chloride and maintained at 60 to 70°C. and 20 to 30 atmos. pressure.

$$OC\underset{\displaystyle Cl}{\overset{\displaystyle Cl}{<}} + CH_2{:}CH{\cdot}CH_3 \rightarrow CH_2Cl{\cdot}\underset{\displaystyle \overset{|}{COCl}}{CH}{\cdot}CH_3$$

3. *Aromatic Halogeno Compounds.*—The customary chlorination of benzene, naphthalene, etc., in the presence of ferric or aluminum chloride is generally classified as a halogenation process. Mention only is made of it here for the purpose of showing the relationship of these two unit processes.

I. Dehydration Reactions.—A number of syntheses are made possible through the dehydrating action of aluminum chloride. Although such syntheses involve the removal of the elements of water from 1 or 2 molecules of organic compound, hydrogen chloride is always liberated as the volatile product of reaction. The preparation of anthraquinone, dypnone, and chalcone by this procedure may be represented as follows:

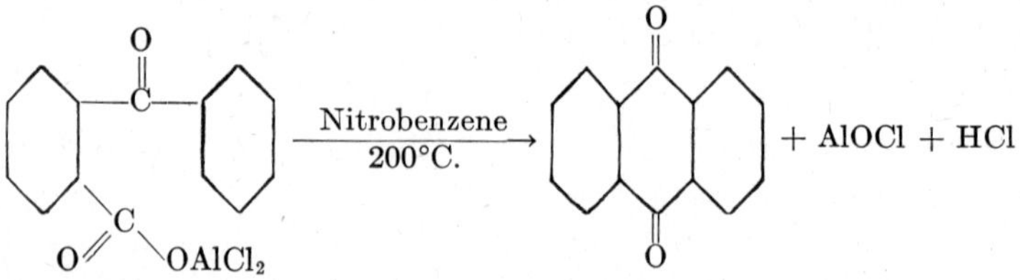

AlCl₂ Salt of Keto Acid   Anthraquinone

$$\xrightarrow[\text{200°C.}]{\text{Nitrobenzene}} \quad + \text{AlOCl} + \text{HCl}$$

[1] Wiezevich, U. S. 2,055,617 (1936).
[2] Reid, U. S. 2,028,012 (1936).

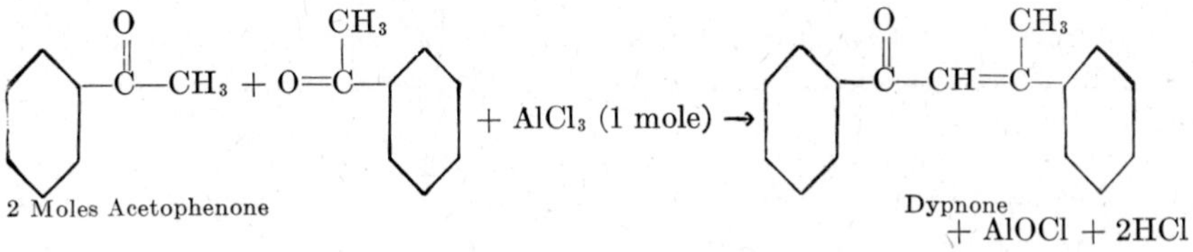

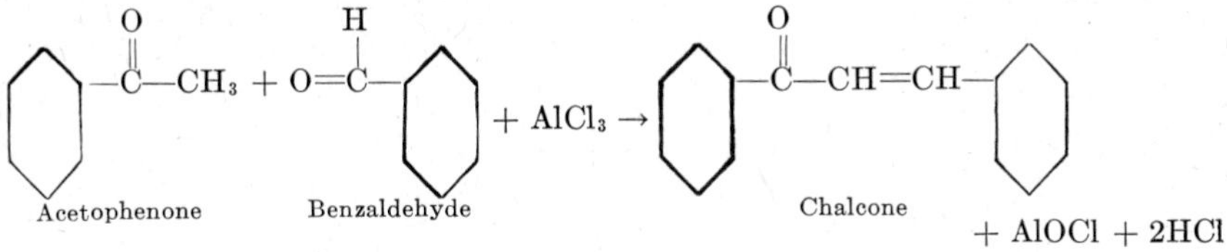

Ordinarily sulfuric acid is employed for the cyclization of keto acids to anthraquinone derivatives, but when the use of this dehydrating acid leads to a sulfonation product, aluminum chloride may sometimes be used. Thus, when 4'-phenyl-2-benzoylbenzoic acid, which with sulfuric acid undergoes sulfonation before cyclization, is treated in nitrobenzene solution with aluminum chloride, phenylanthraquinone is obtained.[1] In a similar manner, the aluminum chloride salts of many keto acids can be converted to the corresponding anthraquinones. This procedure is not employed industrially, however, because of the low cost of cyclization with sulfuric acid and the purer product thus obtained.

Calloway[2] has shown that dypnone can be obtained with yields of 73 per cent when 2 moles of acetophenone are condensed with the loss of water through the action of 1 mole of aluminum chloride. The reaction is carried out at room temperature using carbon bisulfide as a solvent. Similarly, a yield of 91 per cent chalcone, *i.e.*, benzylidene acetophenone, is obtained when molar proportions of acetophenone and benzaldehyde are reacted with 1 mole of aluminum chloride at room temperature for a period of 4 days.

J. The Synthesis of Hydrocarbon Derivatives Containing Phosphorus, Sulfur, and Arsenic.—When aromatic compounds such as chlorobenzene and toluene are treated with phosphorus trichloride in the presence of aluminum chloride, phosphines are obtained. The preparation of 4-chlorophenyldichlorophosphine is shown below:

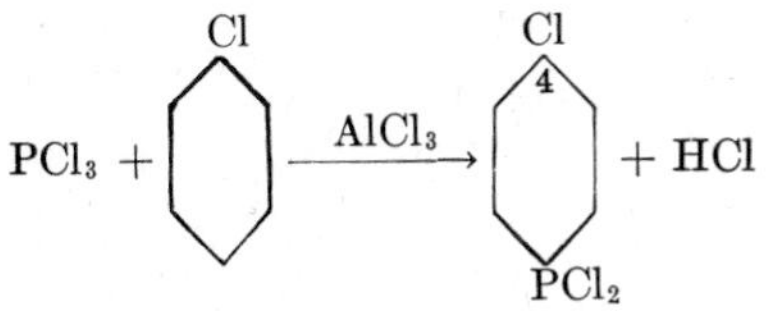

[1] GROGGINS, *Ind. Eng. Chem.*, **22**, 629 (1930).
[2] CALLOWAY, *J. Am. Chem. Soc.*, **59**, 809 (1937).

The preparation of diphenylsulfone from benzenesulfonylchloride and benzene is similar to that of diaryl ketones referred to previously.

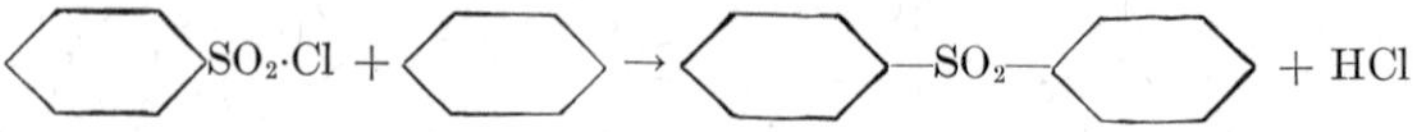

OTHER REACTIONS CATALYZED BY ALUMINUM CHLORIDE

In addition to activating the preceding synthetical processes, aluminum chloride exerts a disruptive influence on hydrocarbons. Large molecules are broken down, the groups migrate and then unite to form stable saturated compounds. The chemical cracking of petroleum and the refining of lubricating oils are based on these reactions. Although chemical cracking results in the formation of new compounds, the process is not a true synthesis according to the generally accepted use of the term. Other important syntheses are based on the activating properties of aluminum chloride, and these are discussed under the title of the Fries migration and the Scholl reaction.

The Disruptive Influence of Aluminum Chloride.—The disruptive action of aluminum chloride on both aromatic and aliphatic compounds has been shown by numerous investigators. The loosening of atomic bonds with the migration of atoms or groups may be represented by the following reactions:

$$(CH_3)_3C \cdot COCl \rightarrow CO + HCl + C_4H_8$$ [BOESEKEN, *Rec. trav. chim.*, **29**, 85 (1910)]

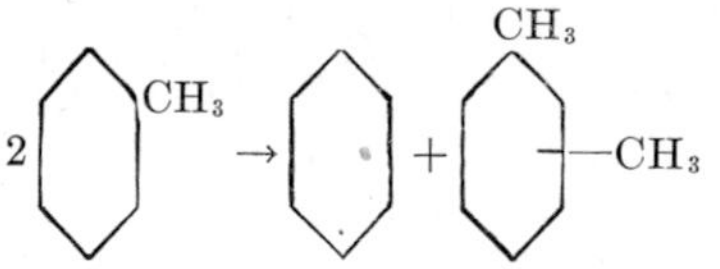

[COPISAROW and LONG, *J. Chem. Soc.*, **119**, 1806 (1921)]

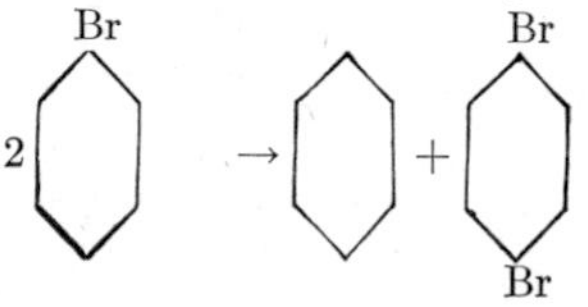

[DUMREICHER, *Ber.*, **15**, 1867 (1882)]

When used in the treatment of lubricating oils and in petroleum cracking processes, aluminum chloride not only probably functions as a disruptive or fission agent but also exercises a catalytic condensing and polymerizing action. From our knowledge of the composition of crude oils and the nature of the distillates after cracking, it appears that all of the above reactions proceed concurrently. Large molecules are labilized and broken down, the fission of the larger nuclei being favored by extreme conditions of temperature and aluminum chloride concentration. Side chains become chlorinated and either form condensation compounds or migrate. The smaller migratory groups then condense or polymerize, forming more stable compounds. Finally, as Bastet[1] has shown, unsaturated compounds of the series C_2H_4 to C_2Cl_4 react to form addition compounds, the net result being the production of new compounds which become saturated under the conditions provided.

Fries Migration.—When aluminum chloride causes the migration of groups in the aromatic series, the reaction is often referred to as the Fries migration.[2] This property of aluminum chloride makes possible the preparation of many important intermediates that would not be susceptible to practical syntheses by other methods.

The acyl groups of acylphenols thus migrate, forming o or p-hydroxyaryl ketones:

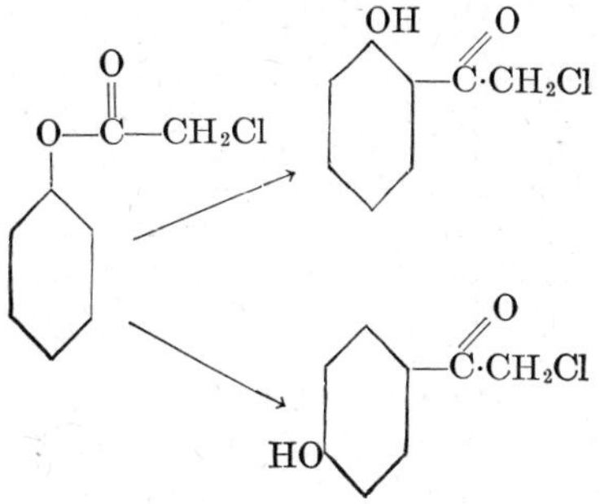

Phenyl ω-Chloroacetate

When the para position is occupied, the acyl group goes exclusively to the position ortho to the hydroxyl:

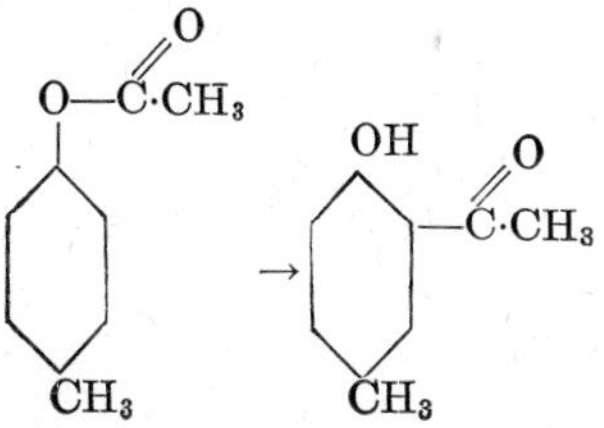

Tolyl Acetate o-Acetyl-p-Cresol

The chemistry of the Fries migration has been studied by Rosenmund and Schnurr,[3] who have shown that it is not an intramolecular wandering of the acidic group but rather a fission and a reunion of the cleavage products in the fashion of the numerous examples previously cited for the Friedel and Crafts reaction. In the reaction between aluminum chloride and a mixture of 2-chloro-4-methylacetylphenol and 4-methylbenzoyl-phenol, the acyl group not only wanders within the molecule but also crosses over to condense with the other phenol to form a ketone. This

[1] Bastet, *Chem. Ztg.*, **37**, 564 (1913).
[2] Fries, *Ber.*, **43**, 214 (1910).
[3] Rosenmund and Schnurr, *Ann.*, **460**, 56 (1928).

migratory action is in all probability caused by the preliminary formation of an acid chloride due to the action of aluminum chloride on a carboxylic acid component. Acetic anhydride (acetyl acetate) as is shown later behaves in this manner and yields of 60 to 70 per cent of acetyl chloride can thus be obtained. The aromatic acetates or benzoates which are generally employed in the Fries migration presumably react in an analogous manner. Cox[1] also showed that when esters of phenols are treated with aluminum chloride in the presence of diphenyl oxide, the end products contained not only acyl phenols but also acyldiphenyl ether:

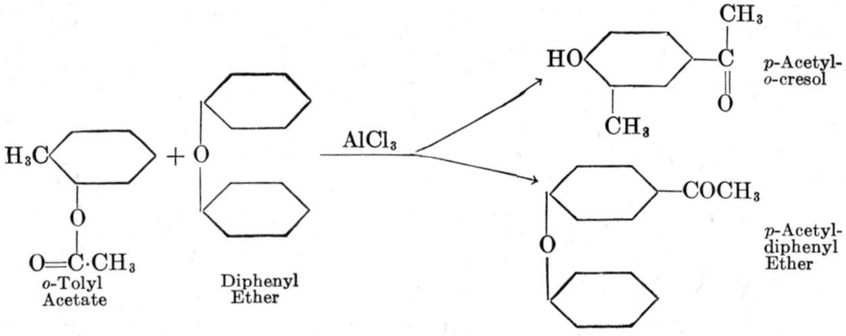

H_3C ... $O=C \cdot CH_3$
o-Tolyl Acetate

+ O Diphenyl Ether

$AlCl_3$

HO ... CH_3 ... CH_3 ... O
p-Acetyl-*o*-cresol

$COCH_3$ ... O
p-Acetyl-diphenyl Ether

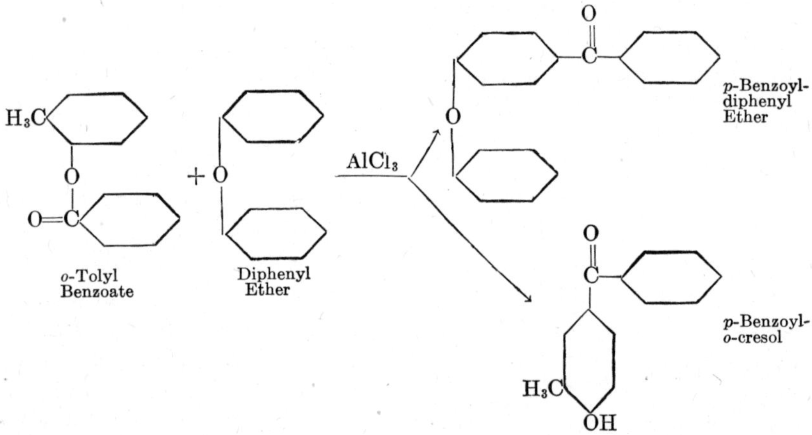

H_3C ... O ... $O=C$
o-Tolyl Benzoate

+ O Diphenyl Ether

$AlCl_3$

O ... C ... O
p-Benzoyl-diphenyl Ether

O ... C ... H_3C ... OH
p-Benzoyl-*o*-cresol

The Scholl Reaction.—Scholl[2] showed that condensations in the aromatic series could be effected whereby intramolecular union of nuclei took place with the splitting off of nuclear hydrogen. The simplest example of this reaction[3] is the transformation of α-benzoylnaphthalene into benzanthrone.

[1] Cox, *J. Am. Chem. Soc.*, **52**, 352 (1930).
[2] SCHOLL, *Ann.*, **394**, 111 (1912); *Ber.*, **43**, 1737 (1910).
[3] Brit. 16,271 (1910).

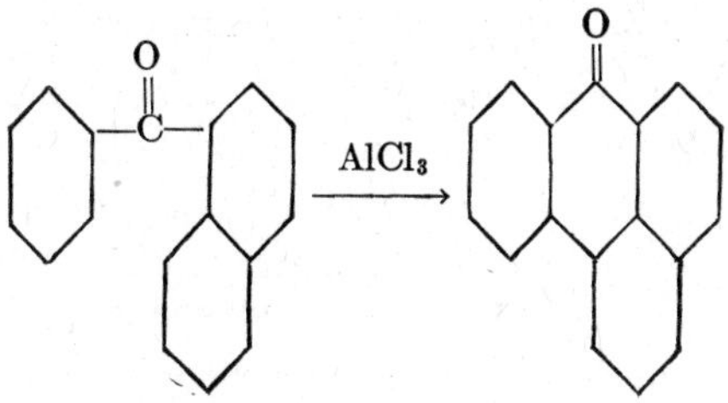

It is apparent that the synthesis comprises the preliminary formation of the benzoyl compound according to the Friedel and Crafts reaction, this step being followed by a more drastic treatment with aluminum chloride to effect cyclization. As will be shown later in this chapter, this procedure is of considerable technical importance and finds many applications in the preparation of intermediates for dyes.

III. CHEMICAL AND PHYSICAL FACTORS

A number of chemical and physical factors have an important bearing on the successful control of the Friedel and Crafts reaction. The most important of these are

1. Quantity of aluminum chloride required.
2. Substitution of acid chlorides and anhydrides by carboxylic acids.
3. Effects of other metal halides in aluminum chloride.
4. Effect of size of aluminum chloride particles.
5. Removal of liberated hydrogen chloride.
6. Effect of temperature.
7. Influence of solvents.
8. Hydrolysis of aluminum chloride addition compounds.

Quantity of Aluminum Chloride Required.—The synthesis of hydrocarbons, such as ethylbenzene and its homologues, leads to the primary formation of unstable aluminum chloride addition compounds which possess no marked unsaturation and which decompose with the formation of the hydrocarbon and the liberation of the aluminum halide. In such reactions, only a relatively small quantity of catalyst is required to carry on the reaction.

In the preparation of ketones by condensing acid chlorides, it is necessary to employ 1 mole of $AlCl_3$. The data (Table I) relating to the preparation of benzophenone show the relation between the quantity of catalyst used and the yield of ketone obtained.

When phthalic anhydride is condensed with aromatic compounds to form keto acids, it is necessary to employ 2 moles of aluminum chloride. This was first pointed out by Heller,[1] and later Rubidge and Qua[2] found

[1] HELLER, *Ber.*, **41**, 3627 (1908).
[2] RUBIDGE and QUA, *J. Am. Chem. Soc.*, **36**, 736 (1919).

TABLE I.—PREPARATION OF BENZOPHENONE. VARIATION OF YIELD WITH AMOUNT OF CATALYST

$$C_6H_5 \cdot COCl + C_6H_6 \xrightarrow{AlCl_3} C_6H_5COC_6H_5$$

Moles AlCl₃	Yield	
	Gm.	%
1.5	29.0	93.3
1.3	28.6	92.0
1.1	29.3	94.2
1.0	28.0	90.1
0.9	25.1	80.7
0.8	22.5	72.4
0.6	18.0	57.8
0.4	12.0	38.6
0.2	5.8	18.6
0.0	0.7	2.2

that when a smaller quantity of halide was used there was a corresponding decrease in yields.

When aliphatic carboxylic acid anhydrides are condensed with aromatic compounds to form alkyl aryl ketones, the use of 2 moles of aluminum chloride results in a yield of approximately 100 per cent based on only one acyl group being reactive. When 3 or more moles of aluminum chloride per mole of anhydride are used, then yields of 75 to 85 per cent based on both acyl groups are obtainable.[1]

TABLE II.—PREPARATION OF ACETOPHENONE FROM ACETIC ANHYDRIDE AND BENZENE

Run No.	Moles AlCl₃	Substance added	Yield, %*	M. p.,‡ °C.	Conditions
1	1.1	Control	12	18.2	Time, 5.5 hr.
2	2.3	Control	52 to 53	18.7	Temp., 90°C.
3	2.8	Control	65 to 68	18.8	Benzene, 5 moles
4	3.3	Control	76†	18.8	Acetic anhydride, 1 mole
5	4.4	Control	81 to 82	18.4	
6	3.3	10 gm. Fe	73†	18.8	
7	3.3	5 gm. Al	75 to 77	18.4	
8	3.3	10 gm. SOCl₂	57†	19.0	

* Yield per cent, based on both acetyl groups.
† Represents two experiments which check exactly.
‡ The m.p. of acetophenone is 19.6°C.

The relation between the active component, *e.g.*, acid chloride, acid anhydride, or carboxylic acid, and the aluminum chloride may be explained as follows. When an acid chloride, *e.g.*, acetyl chloride, is

[1] GROGGINS, NAGEL, and STIRTON, *Ind. Eng. Chem.*, **26**, 1313 (1934).

condensed, the function of the AlCl$_3$ is presumably to labilize the chlorine by adding on to the carbonyl group and forming with it a nonvolatile conducting complex, which may then react with benzene to form the AlCl$_3$ addition compound of acetophenone.

$$\underset{\substack{\text{Nonvolatile}\\\text{Active Complex}}}{\text{CH}_3\text{COCl} + \text{AlCl}_3 \rightarrow \underset{\underset{\text{AlCl}_3}{|}}{\overset{\overset{\text{O}}{\|}}{\text{CH}_3\text{C·Cl}}} \xrightarrow{\text{C}_6\text{H}_6}} \underset{\underset{\text{AlCl}_3}{\dots}}{\overset{\overset{\text{O}}{\|}}{\text{CH}_3\text{C}}}\!\!-\!\!\bigcirc$$

When aliphatic or aromatic carboxylic acid anhydrides are similarly condensed, a series of reactions may occur depending on the molar ratio of AlCl$_3$ used. The first mole accomplishes the fission of the acid anhydride with the production of an acid halide and the formation of the aluminum chloride salt of the carboxylic acid. For acetic anhydride the reactions are probably the following:

$$\begin{matrix} \overset{\text{O}}{\overset{\|}{\text{CH}_3\text{·C}}} \\ \diagdown \\ \diagup \\ \underset{\underset{\text{O}}{\|}}{\text{CH}_3\text{·C}} \end{matrix} \text{O} + \text{AlCl}_3 \rightarrow \overset{\text{Volatile}}{\text{CH}_3\text{COCl}} + \text{CH}_3\text{COOAlCl}_2$$

When two molecular proportions of AlCl$_3$ are employed, the acid chloride that is first formed combines with the aluminum chloride to produce the nonvolatile active complex, which in the presence of aromatic compounds reacts to produce alkyl aryl ketones.

$$\begin{matrix} \overset{\text{O}}{\overset{\|}{\text{CH}_3\text{·C}}} \\ \diagdown \\ \diagup \\ \underset{\underset{\text{O}}{\|}}{\text{CH}_3\text{·C}} \end{matrix} \text{O} + 2\text{AlCl}_3 \rightarrow \underset{\substack{\text{Nonvolatile}\\\text{Active Complex}}}{\underset{\underset{\text{AlCl}_3}{|}}{\overset{\overset{\text{O}}{\|}}{\text{CH}_3\text{C·Cl}}} + \text{CH}_3\text{COOAlCl}_2}$$

It is apparent from the preceding equations that aluminum chloride acts as a chlorinating agent and it is also clear that the maximum yields of ketone obtainable with approximately two molecular proportions of AlCl$_3$ would be about 100 per cent based on one acetyl group and only half as much in terms of both acyl groups. This is confirmed by the data in Table II (page 658). The second acetyl group, which is fixed as the aluminum chloride salt, can also be made to react by adding a third molecular proportion of AlCl$_3$. The reaction is probably as follows:

$$\text{CH}_3\text{COOAlCl}_2 + \text{AlCl}_3 \rightarrow \underset{\substack{\text{Active Complex}}}{\underset{\underset{\text{AlCl}_3}{|}}{\overset{\overset{\text{O}}{\|}}{\text{CH}_3\text{C·Cl}}} + \text{AlOCl}}$$

Further confirmation of this mechanism is presented in Table III, where it is shown that aliphatic (and aromatic) carboxylic acids react according to the Friedel and Crafts reaction in the presence of at least two molecular proportions of aluminum chloride.[1]

From the preceding discussion of the reaction of aluminum chloride on aliphatic acid anhydrides, it is reasonable to presume that the action of $AlCl_3$ on phthalic anhydride is as follows:

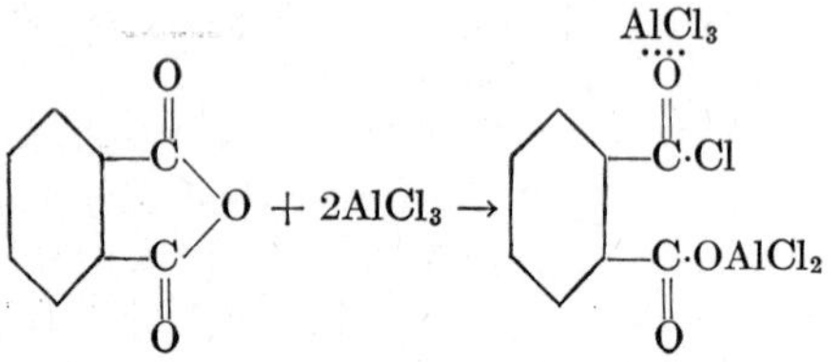

Reactive
Acid Chloride
Complex

In the various syntheses made possible by the Friedel and Crafts reaction, it has always been found advisable to incorporate a slight excess of aluminum chloride to insure a complete reaction. When the aluminum halide is known to contain inactive or less active constituents, a proportionate allowance is made therefor. Generally, an excess of 5 to 10 per cent over that theoretically required has been found to be productive of the best yields. The limiting conditions will be the purity of the halide and the absence of moisture in the reactants, operating atmosphere, and reaction vessel.

Substitution of Carboxylic Acids for Acid Anhydrides and Acid Chlorides. The discovery that both acyl groups of aliphatic carboxylic acid anhydrides could be made reactive by employing at least three molecular proportions of $AlCl_3$ indicated that unsubstituted carboxylic acids could be employed for the preparation of alkyl aryl and diaryl ketones. It was subsequently found that acetic, propionic, benzoic, and terephthalic acids, etc.,[2] could be employed for making a wide variety of ketones and that the procedure was of wide application and of distinct technical value. The use of carboxylic acid depends on its conversion to an acid chloride complex, as shown above and this requires two moles of aluminum chloride. The data in Table III relating to the preparation of *p*-methylacetophenone show that favorable results are obtainable. The yields in similar preparation of 4, 4'-dichlorobenzophenone are somewhat higher.

The $>C=O$—$AlCl_3$ Bond and Consecutive Reactions.—In the preparation of aryl alkyl ketones; *e.g.*, acetophenone, the $AlCl_3$ is closely bound to the carbonyl of the ketone (before hydrolysis) and is not available for other normal syntheses involving acylation or alkylation. Thus, the addition of acetyl chloride to a benzene solution of CH_3CO⟨ ⟩

$AlCl_3$

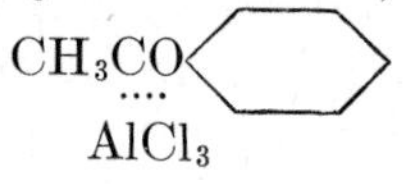

[1] Groggins and Nagel, U. S. 1,966,797 (1934).
[2] NEWTON and GROGGINS, *Ind. Eng. Chem.*, **27**, 1397 (1935).

does not result in an increased yield of the ketone. Likewise, the addition of *n*-butyl chloride does not result in the formation of butylbenzene or butylacetophenone. When, however, an excess of aluminum chloride

TABLE III.—PREPARATION OF *p*-METHYLACETOPHENONE FROM ACETIC ACID AND TOLUENE

Expt. No.	Substance added	Moles, AlCl$_3$	Yield, %	Conditions
1	Control	2.0	61.2	Time, 7 hr.
2	2 gm. Al	2 0	67.2	Temp., 100°C.
3	2 gm. Al	2.5	78.7	Moles toluene, 5
4	2 gm. Al	3.0	67.9	Moles acetic acid, 1
5	5 gm. Fe	2.0	66.7	
6	5 gm. Fe	3.0	73.1	

is also provided, then iso- and *sec*-butylbenzenes are formed and not the alkylated acetophenone.[1]

It is important to note that, when an attempt is made to carry out the concurrent alkylation and acetylation of benzene in the presence of slightly less than the calculated quantity of AlCl$_3$ required for acylation, in some instances, *e.g.*, *n*-butyl chloride, only acylation occurs despite the fact that this reaction requires molar proportions of the condensing agent; whereas only catalytic amounts are necessary for alkylations. This phenomenon is to be attributed to the preferential attachment of the aluminum chloride to the carbonyl group of the acylating agent as shown on page 659. The course of such competitive reactions depends, however, on the reactivity of the alkyl halide. When the highly reactive *tert*-butyl chloride is used instead of the normal halide under similar conditions, then alkylation as well as acylation occurs. Thus, acetyl chloride and *tert*-butyl chloride in benzene solution react exothermally, 30 to 80°C., to give *tert*-butyl- and *p*-di-*tert*-butylbenzenes in addition to acetophenone.[1] It is significant also, that when alkyl and acyl groups are both present in the same molecule, *e.g.*, ω-chloracetyl chloride (ClCH$_2$COCl) the acyl halide reacts preferentially with benzene to form the lachrymatory agent ω-chloroacetophenone. An excess of AlCl$_3$ does not activate the alkyl chlorine, again indicating the comparative inactivity of the carbonyl-AlCl$_3$ addition complex.

Effect of Other Halides in Aluminum Chloride.—Thomas[2] showed that ferric chloride could be used not only as a condensing but also as a chlorinating agent for the preparation of halogenobenzenes. He was able to prepare the entire series of chlorobenzenes (C_6H_5Cl to C_6Cl_6), by successive treatments with ferric chloride. The reaction was character-

---

[1] GROGGINS and SWERN, Unpublished investigations.

[2] THOMAS, *Compt. rend.*, **125**, 1211 (1898).

ized by the liberation of hydrogen chloride and the reduction of the iron halide.

Boswell and McLaughlin[1] found that the amount of hydrogen chloride evolved in the reaction of benzene with chloroform was a maximum when an equimolecular mixture of aluminum chloride and ferric chloride was used. The liberation of the hydrogen chloride cannot, however, be used as an index of the catalytic activity of mixed halides, for it has been shown that the ferric halide may act as a chlorinating agent, this action being accompanied by the splitting off of the acid. Ferric chloride as a minor constituent of aluminum chloride in the preparation of ω-chloro-acetophenone exercises a catalytic activity which is not so great as that of aluminum chloride.[2]

TABLE IV.—EFFECT OF QUALITY AlCl₃ IN PREPARATION OF 4'-BROMO-2-BENZOYL-
BENZOIC ACID
Experiments in Iron Mill

Expt. No.	Phthalic anhydride, gm.	Bromo-benzene used, gm.	Temp., °C.	Time, hr.	Yield keto acid, %	M.p., °C.
1 tech.....	150	157	70 to 75	12	68.9	170.3 to 170.8
1 ref.......	150	157	70 to 75	12	67.5	170.3 to 170.8
2 tech.....	150	157	75 to 80	12	78.4	170.3 to 170.8
2 ref.......	150	157	75 to 80	12	76.4	170.2 to 170.6
3 tech.....	148	173	75 to 80	12	73.8	169.8 to 170.6
3 ref.......	148	173	75 to 80	12	73.8	170.0 to 170.5
4 tech.....	148	173	70 to 75	14	79.4	170.0 to 170.5
4 ref.......	148	173	70 to 75	14	84.0	169.8 to 171.0
5 tech.....	148	196	70 to 75	14	80.5	170.0 to 170.5
5 ref.......	148	196	70 to 75	14	82.0	169.8 to 170.6

Aluminum chloride used, 1 mole + 10%. Mol. wt. phthalic anhydride, 148.
Tech. = technical AlCl₃; ref. = refined AlCl₃. M. p. pure 4'-bromo-2-benzoylbenzoic acid,
Mol. wt. bromobenzene, 157. 172.0°C.

A number of investigations have been made in which the operating efficiency of technical aluminum chloride, containing about 1.5 per cent of $FeCl_3$, was compared with that of a colorless, screened product. The reactions were carried out in an iron mill, using approximately the combining proportions of the reactants. Under such conditions, the results shown in Table IV indicate that both products give substantially the same yields in the preparation of 4'-bromo-2-benzoyl-benzoic acid.[3] In the preparation of alkyl aryl ketones, however, wherein

[1] BOSWELL, and McLAUGHLIN, *Can. J. Research*, **1**, 400 (1929).
[2] MILLER, Edgewood Arsenal, U. S. War Department Report.
[3] GROGGINS, STIRTON, and NEWTON, *Ind. Eng. Chem.*, **23**, 893 (1931).

the oily ketonic layer has to be separated from the hydrolyzed reaction mass, it has been found that the use of a purer aluminum chloride not only gives better yields but also affords a quicker and cleaner separation.

Riddell and Noller[1] have made a comprehensive study of mixed catalysts in the Friedel and Crafts reaction. They found that in the preparation of alkyl phenyl ketones from acid chlorides and benzene the yields diminished as $AlCl_3$ is replaced by $FeCl_3$. When acid anhydrides were used for the similar preparation of the phenones, the yield decreases rapidly to a minimum, then rises to a maximum and finally falls off to the value obtained with pure $FeCl_3$.

Effect of Size of Aluminum Chloride Particles.—In carrying out the Friedel and Crafts reaction, practical considerations would recommend the use of aluminum chloride in the form of granules or small lumps. As compared with powdered material, these would be less hygroscopic in storage and handling and less troublesome in delivering to the reactor;[2] and, finally, the larger particles would not react so readily, thus contributing to a better regulated initial reaction.

TABLE V.—PREPARATION OF 4'-CHLORO-2-BENZOYLBENZOIC ACID IN AN ENAMEL-LINED VESSEL. EFFECT OF SIZE OF $AlCl_3$ PARTICLES
Atmospheric pressure

Expt. No.	Kind $AlCl_3$	Yield, %	M. p., °C.
1	Lump, 15 to 20 mm. dia.	88.5	148.6
2	Pea size, 4 mm. dia.	92.5	148.4
3	Sand size, 0.5 to 1.0 mm. dia.	94.0	147.8
4	Powder	94.3	148.0

Reduced pressure to remove HCl

Expt. No.	Kind $AlCl_3$	Yield, %	M. p., °C.
1	Lump	88.9	147.6
2	Pea size	96.8	147.6
3	Sand size	96.0	147.0
4	Powder	97.0	148.0
5	Powder, containing 1.5 % $FeCl_3$	96.2	148.0

Phthalic anhydride (tech.), 296 gm. = 2 moles   Monochlorobenzene (b.p., 132°), 1,350 gm. = 12 moles
Aluminum chloride, 612 gm. = 4.6 moles, $AlCl_3$ Temperature, 50°C.; time, 5 hr.

In the preparation of alkyl aryl ketones and some keto acids,[3] it is found that the effect of the size of aluminum chloride particles is closely related to the efficiency of the agitation. With moderately good agita-

[1] RIDDELL and NOLLER, *J. Am. Chem. Soc.*, **54**, 290 (1931).

[2] GROGGINS, *Ind. Eng. Chem.*, **23**, 152 (1931).

[3] GROGGINS and NAGEL, *Ind. Eng. Chem.*, **25**, 1083 (1933).

tion, particles up to the size of a pea can be used with success in the preparation of keto acids. The data relating to the preparation of 4'-chloro-2-benzoylbenzoic acid are given in Table V.

Since the Friedel and Crafts synthesis can be employed for the preparation of hydrocarbons, aldehydes, ketones, etc., and may involve the use of gases or very volatile liquids as reactants, it is clear that different types of reaction require individual consideration. Possibly, the only general permissible conclusion is that practical and theoretical considerations favor the use of the coarsest material that gives the highest yields.

Removal of the Liberated Hydrogen Chloride.—In most Friedel and Crafts syntheses, hydrogen halide is liberated as a volatile product of reaction. The quantity of the gas produced is closely proportional to the extent of the reaction,[1] and, with certain exceptions which are noted below, its removal is instrumental in accelerating the completion of the strictly synthetical reactions. The preparation of acetophenone may be used to typify such syntheses:

$$CH_3 \cdot CO \cdot Cl + C_6H_6 \rightarrow C_6H_5 \cdot CO \cdot CH_3 + HCl$$

In the preparation of some ketones and keto acids, it is found that by maintaining a slightly reduced pressure in the reaction vessel, thereby drawing a slow stream of warm, dried air over the charge, practically theoretical yields are obtained. By referring to the previous Table V, it will be seen that the removal of the liberated hydrogen chloride exercises a beneficial effect in the preparation of 4'-chloro-2-benzoylbenzoic acid.

The preceding data and observations lead to the conclusions that in the liquid-phase Friedel and Crafts synthesis of keto acids and ketones, it is necessary to provide a practically homogeneous reaction mass and to remove the volatile product of the reaction, hydrogen chloride. The apparatus best suited for this purpose should, therefore, (1) provide thorough mixing; (2) scrape the walls of the reactor; and (3) break the surface of the reaction mass to facilitate the escape of the liberated hydrogen chloride.

In reactions catalyzed by aluminum chloride, wherein fission, migration, addition, and polymerization may occur, the presence of hydrogen chloride may be desirable. The following reactions should serve to indicate the differences in the character of the processes:

a. Synthesis, by double decomposition:

$$CH_3 \cdot Cl + C_6H_6 \xrightarrow{\text{AlCl}_3} C_6H_5 \cdot CH_3 + HCl$$

b. Fission and migration:

$$CH_3 \cdot C_6H_4 \cdot CH(CH_3)_2 \xrightarrow{\text{AlCl}_3} C_6H_5 \cdot CH_3, \text{ etc.}$$

c. Chlorination, by addition:

$$H_2C:CH_2 + HCl \xrightarrow{\text{AlCl}_3} CH_3CH_2Cl$$

[1] Numerous investigations have shown that the quantity of HCl liberated is in excess of amount combined in organic halides. This appears to be due to the degradation of AlCl_3, since the ratio of Cl to Al in the residue is low.

d. Combination:

$$CO + C_6H_6 \xrightarrow[\text{HCl}]{\text{AlCl}_3} C_6H_5 \cdot CHO$$

Although aluminum chloride catalyzes the formation of ethyl chloride from ethylene, it is not satisfactory in causing the conversion of amylene to amyl chloride, because of loss through polymerization. On the other hand, amylene can be used in a typical Friedel and Crafts synthesis, because the amyl chloride formed through the catalytic intervention of aluminum chloride promptly combines with aromatic hydrocarbons that may be present.

Effect of Temperature.—In organic synthesis, the general effect of operating at higher temperatures is to increase the rate of reaction. In some unit processes, *e.g.*, sulfonation of naphthalene, variations in temperature also affect the orientation of the new substituent. In Friedel and Crafts syntheses, these and other deep-seated changes occur when the reaction temperature is not rigidly controlled at the optimum for a particular synthesis. A moderate elevation in temperature may bring about secondary condensations which are accompanied by the splitting out of hydrogen chloride or water from 1 or 2 molecules. With excessive heating, almost all Friedel and Crafts reaction masses can be largely converted to oily or resinous masses of complex or uncertain constitution.

Phthalyl chloride reacts in its two isomeric forms with benzene in excess, to give benzoylbenzoic acid, diphenyl phthalide, *o*-triphenyl-methylbenzoic acid and 9-diphenylanthrone, depending on the temperature employed.

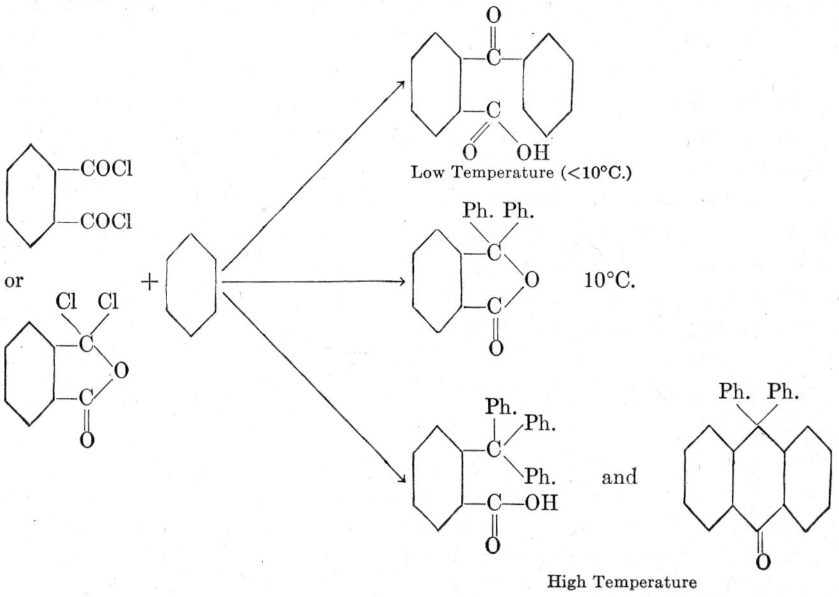

Low Temperature (<10°C.)

10°C.

and

High Temperature

Benzophenone, which forms a comparatively stable complex with aluminum chloride at low temperatures, will condense at higher temperatures with other active molecules, *e.g.*, dimethylaniline to give carbinols and hydrocarbons.

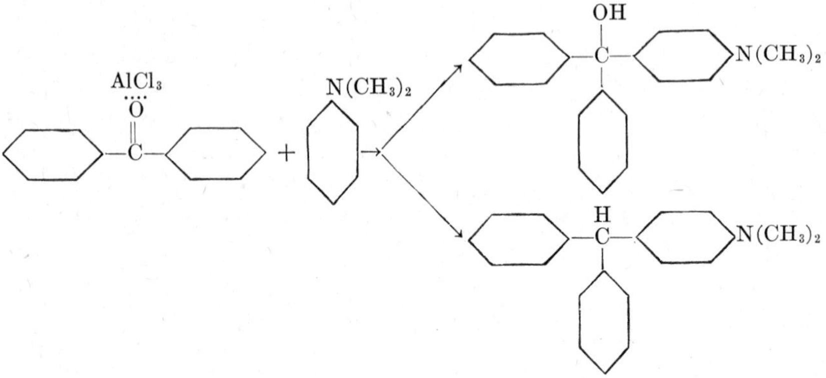

Effect of Solvents.—Friedel and Crafts syntheses are usually carried out in a fluid medium. Most frequently, as in the preparation of keto acids, alkyl aryl ketones, and arylalkanols, the solvent is an excess of the reacting aromatic hydrocarbon or substituted hydrocarbon. When a comparatively inert extraneous solvent is preferred or required, carbon disulfide finds favor, but ethylene tetrachloride, nitrobenzene, and saturated, petroleum fractions are also used, particularly for reactions at higher temperatures.

Although various solvents exert a significant influence on the course of some reactions, the principal functions are (1) to provide a practically homogeneous reaction mass; and (2) to act as a good heat-transfer agent. There is difficulty in obtaining such a condition when highly reactive substances are condensed at low temperatures. Under such circumstances, substances of high solvent power for the organo-aluminum chloride complex are chosen, even when such solvents are known to be reactive in similar syntheses at higher temperatures. Thus, when benzene or *o*-dichlorobenzene is used as a vehicle for the preparation of α-naphthoylbenzoic acid, the liquid component serves merely as a solvent, for in this instance naphthalene reacts more readily and captures the phthalic anhydride-aluminum chloride complex. The data in Table VI show that a lower yield and inferior product are obtained when a less efficient or smaller quantity of solvent is employed.

In the chlorination of biphenyl and naphthalene with gaseous chlorine, it was shown that benzene could be used to advantage as a solvent. This similarity in operating technic is to be expected, since chlorination in the presence of a halogen carrier may reasonably be considered as a Friedel and Crafts reaction. The employment of normally reactive fluid substances as solvents for more highly reactive materials is not confined to aromatic compounds, for ethylene dichloride, tetrachloroethane, carbon tetrachloride, etc., have also been used for this purpose.

Nitrobenzene finds use as a solvent because of (1) its excellent solvent properties; (2) its high boiling point; and (3) its ability to moderate, sometimes to a remarkable degree, the course of certain reactions. The moderating influence may be attributed to the fact that nitrobenzene forms a loose $AlCl_3$ complex and gives up the catalyst in a regulated fashion. Consequently, it is particularly useful in highly reactive condensations involving phenols, amines, and volatile acid chlorides. In the preparation of benzaldehyde from carbon monoxide and benzene, the use of nitrobenzene as a solvent makes possible carrying out the reaction at normal instead of 1,000 lb. pressure.

TABLE VI.—COMPARISON OF SOLVENTS IN PREPARATION OF α-NAPHTHOYLBENZOIC ACID

No. Expt.	Reaction time, hr.	Reaction temp., °C.	Solvent	Solvent ratio	Solvent recovery, %	Yield N.B.A., %	M.p., °C.
1	2	15	C_6H_6	12:1	97	97.6	165 to 168
2	4	5	C_6H_6	6:1	97	95.0	150 to 160
3	5	0	C_6H_6	3:1	97	92.0	140 to 155
4	2	15	CS_2	12:1	90	95.0	145 to 155
5	4	5	CS_2	6:1	90	93.0	140 to 150
6	5	0	CS_2	3:1	90	92.0	135 to 145
7	2	15	$C_6H_4Cl_2(1, 2)$	12:1	99	97.5	167 to 170
8	4	5	$C_6H_4Cl_2(1, 2)$	6:1	99	97.0	168 to 171
9	5	0	$C_6H_4Cl_2(1, 2)$	3:1	99	97.5	170 to 172

Hydrolysis of Reaction Mass.—In hydrolyzing the anhydrous aluminum chloride complex of ketones, keto acids, etc., it is best to keep the temperature of the suspension below the maximum used during the Friedel and Crafts condensation. This dictum applies whether the reaction has been carried out in the liquid phase in the presence of solvents or only combining proportions of the reactants are employed. When molecular proportions of the reactants are treated in a horizontal mill reactor, this step involves little difficulty. The powdered aluminum chloride complex is merely added slowly to the cold dilute acid in the hydrolyzer, which may be a wooden vessel, since there is no solvent to be recovered.

When a liquid reaction mass is hydrolyzed by the addition of mineral acid to the charge, there is danger that the temperature will mount to prohibitive levels before the charge is completely hydrolyzed. Such excessive heating is conducive to the formation of an impure product. The charge from liquid-phase reactions is generally run while warm into another vessel containing either mineral acid or dilute alkali. When keto acid complexes are thus treated with sodium carbonate solutions, the aluminum is precipitated as the hydroxide, while the sodium salt of the keto acid remains in solution. It has been found difficult quantitatively to remove all of the keto acid salt from the aluminum hydroxide unless large quantities of hot water are employed. This practice will, of course, increase the solubility losses.

IV. CHEMICAL ENGINEERING PROBLEMS

A number of general chemical engineering problems are involved in the practical application of the Friedel and Crafts synthesis. To some extent, the nature of these problems can be forecast by a study of the theoretical and chemical aspects of the reaction. Efficient operation depends, largely, on (1) proper preparation and handling of reacting materials; (2) scientific design and construction of apparatus; and (3) control of the reaction so as to lead practically exclusively to the formation of the specific products desired.

Assuming, merely as a basis of discussion, that the synthesis relates to the preparation of *o*-benzoylbenzoic acids, which are the intermediate compounds in the manufacture of anthraquinone derivatives,

we may then expect to be confronted by the following considerations:

   I. Handling of materials:
      1. Anhydrous aluminum chloride.
      2. Anhydrides and acid chlorides.
      3. Aromatic hydrocarbon.
         a. Storage and transportation.
         b. Effects of moisture.
         c. Preparation for use in the reaction.
  II. Design and construction of apparatus:
      1. For reactions using molecular proportions of the reactants.
      2. For reactions using an inert solvent or an excess of liquid aromatic hydrocarbon.
         a. Materials of construction.
         b. Mechanical devices for feeding the charge.
         c. Type of agitation.
            (1) Relation of size of charge to size of vessel.
            (2) Relation of size of charge to type of agitation.

    d. Discharging and hydrolyzing the reaction mass.
III. Control of Friedel and Crafts reaction:
    1. Obtaining homogeneity.
    2. Insuring formation of intermediate addition compounds without deleterious by-products.
    3. Maintaining anhydrous operating conditions.

Experience has shown that the preceding considerations are to a large extent common to all Friedel and Crafts syntheses, and detailed discussion of the idiosyncrasies of individual reactions does not appear necessary.

Handling of Materials.—When anhydrous aluminum chloride is packed in iron drums under conditions that insure the absence of appreciable moisture, it may be stored for long periods or conveyed over long distances with safety. When, however, water is permitted to come in contact with it hydrogen chloride is certain to be formed. The quantity of hydrogen chloride will depend on the amount of water and the degree of agitation of the halide. If sufficient moisture is present, particularly in the free space in the container or reaction vessel or at the point of contact with the outside atmosphere, then hydrochloric acid is formed. The presence of this acid leads to problems of corrosion.

The highly active acid anhydrides, acid chlorides, and alkyl halides are readily susceptible to hydrolysis. The absorption of moisture by these reagents results in compounds which are less active, which require more aluminum chloride for condensation, and which generally lead to lower yields of desired product. Furthermore, the ingress of moisture into storage containers for these active components usually results in corrosion problems.

The aromatic hydrocarbons—benzene, toluene, naphthalene, etc.—offer no special corrosion problems and may, therefore, be stored in any suitable sealed containers.

Design of Apparatus. *Fluid Reactions.*—Most of the early investigators of the Friedel and Crafts synthesis carried out the reactions in a liquid medium. This procedure insured a practically homogeneous reaction mass. By providing sufficient solvent or sufficient liquid vehicle for the viscous intermediate reaction product, little difficulty was experienced in stirring the charge.

When aluminum chloride functions as a true catalyst, as in the synthesis of hydrocarbons, the reactants and final products are generally liquids, and no problem in merely rotating the agitator is encountered. In the preparation of ketones and keto acids, the formation of viscous intermediate addition compounds necessitates utilizing either an excess of the liquid aromatic reactant (benzene, toluene, chlorobenzene) or an extraneous inert solvent such as carbon disulfide, nitrobenzene or tetrachloroethane. In some instances, where there is considerable variation in the reactivities of aromatic compounds at fixed temperatures,

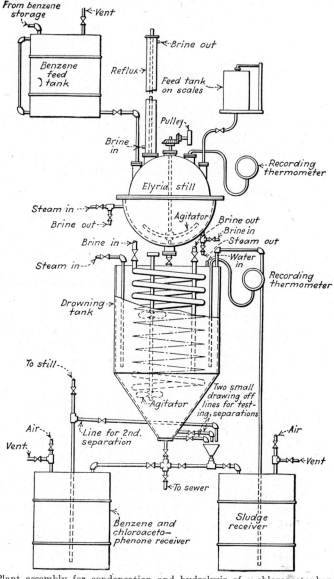

Fig. 1.—Plant assembly for condensation and hydrolysis of ω-chloroacetophenone and other alkyl aryl ketones.

one can be used as a vehicle while the other enters into the reaction. Thus, Groggins and Newton[1] successfully employed *o*-dichlorobenzene

[1] GROGGINS and NEWTON, *Ind. Eng. Chem.*, **22**, 157 (1930).

as the inert solvent in the Friedel and Crafts preparation of α-naphthoyl-benzoic acid by condensing naphthalene with phthalic anhydride.

Heller and Schulke[1] have pointed out that in the preparation of keto acids the reaction proceeds from the liquid stage to the viscous addition compound. During this transition, it is difficult to stir the charge with the usual vertical-type agitators unless a solvent is employed to provide the necessary fluidity.

These considerations have led to the adoption of several types of apparatus for carrying out such syntheses. The older procedure involves the use of lead- or enamel-lined, jacketed, agitated vessels. In these (Fig. 1), the charge is kept fluid by the most desirable expedient, as previously indicated. The preparation of ω-chloroacetophenone or other alkyl aryl ketones usually follows this procedure. In Fig. 1 is shown diagrammatically the arrangement of the apparatus that is used.

It is obvious that the introduction of inert solvents or an excess of aromatic hydrocarbon entails an economic loss of considerable magnitude. It involves (1) cost of solvent recovery; (2) loss of solvent or equivalent; (3) increase in operating time; (4) more complex and more costly operating system; and (5) additional problems regarding corrosion.

When the solvent ratio is low, difficulty is experienced in drawing off the charge for hydrolysis. Consequently, this step must be carried out in the principal reaction vessel. Experience has shown that sooner or later flaws will develop in enamel linings, thus necessitating replacement.

Molecular Reactions in Iron Reactor.—Appreciating the inherent deficiencies of the prior methods of operation, Stone and Jacobson[2] utilized the apparatus which is shown in Fig. 2, for the preparation of keto acids. This is essentially a horizontal rotary ball mill which is provided with inlet and outlet connections for solids, liquids, and gases, so that it constitutes a closed reactor. The reacting materials may be introduced in any desired sequence and then mixed at a temperature so low that practically no reaction takes place.

When a reaction vessel of this type is used, it is possible to employ approximately the molecular combining proportions of the reactant materials. This economical procedure now becomes feasible because practical homogeneity of the reaction mass is obtained by the grinding action of the balls or bars, in the reactor. The rotary effect and grinding action of the iron weights thoroughly mix the reactants, and with proper control of temperature a smooth and substantially complete reaction is obtained. The charge in the mill becomes viscous and porous during the intermediate stages of the reaction, even when all of the reactants are solid.[3]

[1] HELLER and SCHULKE, *Ber.*, **41**, 3627 (1908).

[2] Stone and Jacobson, U. S. 1,656,575 (1928).

[3] GROGGINS, *Ind. Eng. Chem.*, **22**, 620 (1930).

During this period, the din of the crushing mechanism becomes deadened. If insufficient balls are present, they will be enmeshed in the viscous charge, and no grinding action takes place. As the reaction progresses, the anhydrous aluminum chloride compound of the keto acid is formed and separates out as a fine colored powder.

That the aluminum chloride complex of the keto acid may be obtained as a freely flowing dry powder is a matter of great importance. This fact makes possible a division of operations, such as condensation in the reactor followed immediately or subsequently by hydrolysis in any

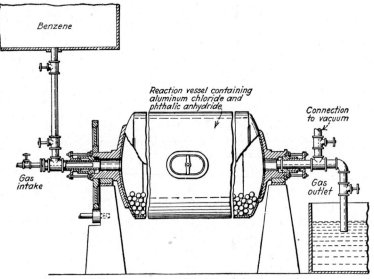

Fig. 2.—Mill-type reactor for Friedel and Crafts reactions.

suitable covered, agitated vessel. Since hydrolysis generally takes place in solutions that are slightly acid with mineral acid, it is advisable to use vessels of wood, silicon iron, lead, or other suitable acid-resistant material for this operation. The dry, powdery, hygroscopic aluminum salt may be delivered to a dry, inclosed hopper, where it is cooled. It is then delivered in a regulated stream into the hydrolyzer, which contains cold, dilute mineral acid. The hydrolysis can therefore be easily controlled, so that the maximum temperature does not rise above the optimum for condensation. This precaution leads to the formation of purer products.

Probably the most important advantage in the use of the horizontal mill reactor is the practicability of using iron in its construction. When the necessary precautions have been observed, practically no free or combined moisture enters the reactor. Hydrogen chloride only is then liberated during the condensation. This will not attack iron to any appreciable extent, and laboratory experience has shown that this type of reactor will give satisfactory service over a long period of years. Replacements are necessary only at the connection where the hydrogen chloride is exhausted.

The size of the horizontal reactor must be considerably out of proportion to the weight of the reacting materials. This precaution is necessary in spite of the fact that molecular proportions of the reactants are taken. During the transition from the liquid to the viscous stage, the reaction mass becomes porous, owing to the liberation of hydrogen chloride. This spongy mass tends to fill the entire vessel. This phenomenon occurs even when the weight of the charge is only one-tenth the water capacity of the reactor. When pressure develops in the vessel, some of the spongy reaction mass oozes out into the hydrogen chloride exhaust line, which is at the horizontal axis of the reactor (Fig. 2).

Effect of Agitation.—The rate of reaction is, of course, a function of the efficiency of the stirring mechanism. In fact, mixing efficiency has a vital influence on the yield and purity of the product. Insufficient or inefficient mixing may lead to uncondensed reactants or to the formation of phthalides, when phthalic anhydride is being condensed.

In the condensation of biphenyl with phthalic anhydride according to the Friedel and Crafts reaction, it was found that the yields increased with the grinding efficiency (Table VII). The experiments are divided

TABLE VII.—EFFECT OF TYPE OF AGITATION IN PREPARATION OF 4'-PHENYL-2-BENZOYLBENZOIC ACID

Phthalic anhydride, 1 mole = 148 gm.; biphenyl, 1 mole = 154 gm.; aluminum chloride sublimed (10 per cent excess), 293 gm.; yield, theory, 302 gm.

Type of agitation	Temp., °C.	Time, hr.	Yield, gm.	Yield, %	Purity, %
Experiment I					
Agitated kettle................	55 to 60	18	244	80.8	97.4
Mill with insufficient agitation[1]...	55 to 60	20	278	91.1	97.6
Mill with efficient agitation[2]......	55 to 60	18	290	96.0	97.8
Experiment II					
Agitated kettle................	60 to 65	12	208	68.9	97.5
Mill with insufficient agitation[1]...	60 to 65	12	239	79.1	97.8
Mill with efficient agitation[2]......	60 to 65	12	292	96.7	98.0

[1] Ratio weight of iron blocks in pounds to water capacity of mill, 1:3.
[2] Ratio weight of iron blocks in pounds to water capacity of mill, 1:1.

into three groups, as follows: (1) in a vertical, enamel-lined vessel fitted with an anchor-type agitator; (2) in a horizontal mill with insufficient agitation, *i.e.*, where the weight of iron blocks in pounds was one-third the water capacity of the mill; and (3) when the weight of the iron grinding blocks was equal to the water capacity of the reactor.

A reactor[1] designed according to Fig. 3, is suitable for a wide variety of Friedel and Crafts syntheses. The vulnerable inside reaction compartment is preferably made of or lined with the newer alloys which are resistant to the corrosive action of hydrochloric acid and acid chlorides. Some of the advantages of this reactor may be set forth as follows:

1. *Homogeneity.*—The reactants may be introduced in a regulated manner while the stirrer is in motion. The modified plow (*a*) insures positive agitation; (*b*) breaks the surface of the mass and thus facilitates

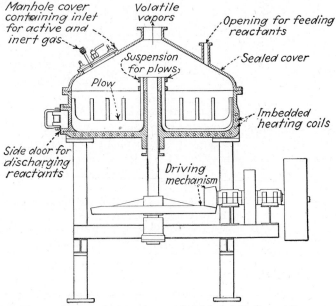

Fig. 3.—Reactor for carrying out Friedel and Crafts reactions.

the escape of the liberated hydrogen chloride; and (*c*) scrapes the walls of the vessel, thus providing satisfactory heat transfer.

2. *Removal or Retention of Hydrogen Chloride.*—By means of slightly reduced pressures, or the passage of a current of dry air over the charge, the liberated gas can be removed conveniently from the upper portion of the reactor. When alkyl or acyl halides are formed as intermediate products of reaction through the intervention of hydrogen chloride, then the gas may be retained under the desired pressure.

3. *Operating Efficiency.*—Because the reactor permits initiating and concluding a reaction at any desired temperature and with any desired ratio of active or inactive fluid components, it makes possible efficient and economical operations.

[1] Groggins, U. S. 2,008,418 (1935).

4. *Physical Properties of Reaction Mass.*—By controlling the removal of the active or inactive fluid components under reduced pressure and by the aid of jacket heating, the reaction mass can be obtained as a non-dusting granulated product or as a viscous to resinous paste. By means of the side door of the reactor which is sealed during the reaction period, the charge can be delivered to suitable containers for storage or to another vessel for subsequent treatment.

V. MECHANISM OF THE FRIEDEL AND CRAFTS REACTION

Theoretical explanations of the Friedel and Crafts reaction have kept pace with increased knowledge in the domains of physics and chemistry. What appear to be common to all of the more tenable explanations are the following points:

1. The formation of ionized solute-solvent complexes because of unsaturation or auxiliary valence in the reacting molecules. Such addition compounds are characterized by conductivity.[1]

2. Rearrangement of the unstable addition complex to one involving principal valences.[2]

3. Stabilization; the dissociation of the complex into relatively stable compounds (with splitting off of hydrogen halide). It should be noted that this procedure has been advanced by numerous students as the general mechanism for substitution in the aromatic series.

Formation of Addition Complexes.—Meerwein[1] has shown that many weak electrolytes are increased in strength by the formation of complex ions. Although simple solvation leads to ionization of molecules as a precurser of electrolytic dissociation, in complex formation there is also the formation of a chemical bond between one of the potential ions and part of its environment. This union results in the nascence of an ion of larger radius and the same charge which is consequently less firmly bound to its fellow.

In Friedel and Crafts reactions involving acyl and alkyl halides, the addition complexes which are formed may be regarded as coordination compounds containing the complex anion $(AlCl_4)^-$. Thus:

$$CH_3COCl + AlCl_3 \rightarrow (CH_3CO)^+ + (AlCl_4)^-$$

According to Fairbrother,[3] such a process constitutes effectively the conversion of a covalent carbon-chlorine bond into an ionic bond. This transition appears to occur as the first step in acylation and alkylation reactions with appropriate halides. In the complex anion $(AlCl_4)^-$ all the chlorine atoms concerned in the reaction should have an equal chance of escaping as hydrogen chloride. Fairbrother proved this experi-

[1] MEERWEIN, *Ann.*, **455**, 227 (1927).
[2] LOWRY, *Phil. Mag.*, **46**, 964 (1923).
[3] FAIRBROTHER, *J. Chem. Soc.*, **1937**, 503.

mentally by employing aluminum chloride in which part of the chlorine atoms were unstable isotopes, *i.e.*, radioactive. It was shown that an addition compound is formed in which the chlorine atoms leave the carbon atoms completely and enter the complex anion $(AlCl_4)^-$ prior to the evolution of hydrogen chloride.

Wohl and Wertyporoch,[1,2] by means of electrical conductivity measurements, have succeeded in clarifying a number of mooted questions regarding the formation of metal halide complexes. The appearance of conductivity is first to be traced to the formation of solute-solvent complexes.[3] When aluminum bromide is added to ethyl bromide, it is found that the conductivity increases from the negligible value $K < 3 \times 10^{-9}$ to 1.206×10^{-4} for a 20 per cent solution. The measurements for dilute solutions involve a time factor until equilibrium is reached. For concentrated solutions, the final conductivity per mole of $AlBr_3$ is quickly reached and is practically constant ($\mu = 0.1$, compared to $\mu = 10$ for the more soluble $(C_2H_5)_4NBr$ in ethyl bromide).

The remarkable constancy of the molar conductivity in both high and low concentration values is to be traced to the nature of the solvent ethyl bromide, which has a high dielectric constant (8.9) and dipole moment (about 2). The corresponding constants for ether are only 4.5 and 1.2, respectively. Reversion of the complex involving ethyl bromide to its original components with increasing dilution is therefore minimized. The bond between —C_2H_5 and —Br is loosened because the C_2H_5Br becomes bound in a complex cation containing aluminum.

It is known that the addition of aluminum chloride to acetyl and benzoyl chlorides results in the formation of deep-brown solutions without appreciable evolution of hydrogen chloride. The formation of such deeply colored, highly conducting addition complexes is to be traced to the presence of the $>C:O$ group. The specific conductivities of the acetyl and benzoyl chloride addition complexes in ethyl bromide are as follows:

Complexes	$K \cdot 10^7$		
	Normal conductivity	0.08 mole AlCl₃ per liter	0.2 mole AlCl₃ per liter
Benzoyl chloride..................	3.0	1,020	2,000
Acetyl chloride...................	3.2	5,500	16,170

According to WERTYPOROCH and FIRLA, *Ann.*, **500**, 287 (1933).

[1] WOHL and WERTYPOROCH, *Ber.*, **64**, 1357 (1931).

[2] WOHL and WERTYPOROCH, *Ann.*, **481**, 34 (1930).

[3] HEIN and SCHRAMM [*Z. physik. Chem.*, **151**A, 234 (1930)] made similar observations with a solution of lithiumethyl in zincethyl.

As would be expected from the evidence accumulated in the preparation of ketones according to the Friedel and Crafts reaction, acetophenone and benzophenone also form stable, highly dissociated complexes with $AlCl_3$.

The fact that stable, stoichiometric addition products of alkyl halide and aluminum halide have not yet been isolated does not preclude their existence in the course of the reaction. It should be remembered that stable, easily isolated compounds do not possess catalytic character and that the instability that makes isolation difficult constitutes the precise attributes for catalytic effectiveness of the intermediate compound.

An intermediate, particularly when it exists in equilibrium in a very limited concentration, may fully determine the course of the reaction through its decomposition, for it is the most unstable component of the equilibrium.

Maxted,[1] in discussing the specific activity of catalysts, voices the following similar opinion regarding the character of the intermediate catalytic complex: "What seems to be required is not a stable compound, but rather a body in or on which, by dissociation or otherwise, there is an active kinetic exchange of linkages between the catalyst proper and the component toward which affinity is exerted."

The following analogy may be drawn from the field of nitration. When a highly nitrated product, such as picric acid, unites with a hydrocarbon possessing special additive capacity, e.g., naphthalene, the product formed is stable. Similar forces are involved in the primary coupling of nitric acid anhydride with benzene, as is evidenced by the formation of the colored addition product. Here, however, the equilibrium is far on the side of dissociation, and the addition product, which is present only in small quantities, cannot be isolated without decomposition, the nitration process depending on its successive decomposition and reformation.

VI. TECHNICAL SYNTHESES

TREATMENT OF HYDROCARBONS

Degradation of Petroleum.—The theoretical discussion has shown that the Friedel and Crafts synthesis makes possible reactions involving fission and migration as well as those of a purely synthetical character. McAfee showed that in the treatment of petroleum hydrocarbons it was necessary to remove the more volatile degradation products as rapidly as they are formed in order to obtain the materials that are most valuable for industrial purposes. He also pointed out that it was a comparatively simple matter to control the character of the distillate by regulating

[1] MAXTED, *J. Soc. Chem. Ind.*, **50**, 149 (1931).

the temperature of the exit gases and adjusting the quantity of aluminum chloride employed. A balanced production of the various distillates may thus be made.

In the accompanying illustration[1] (Fig. 4) is shown an apparatus of a type suitable for carrying out the treatment of petroleum hydrocarbons.

In this drawing, element 1 designates a still which may be constructed of iron or steel. Within this still is mounted a stirring apparatus consisting of a shaft 2 carrying at its base a chain drag 3. Near the base of the still is an outlet 6, for withdrawing fluid oil. The manhole 7 is useful when cleaning and withdrawing coky residues. The inlet 8 may be used for supplying oil. The manhole 9 is employed for supply-

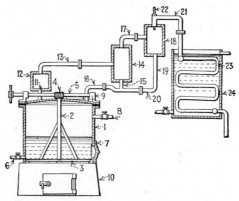

Fig. 4.—Apparatus for cracking of petroleum.

ing aluminum chloride, etc. and heat is supplied by the furnace 10. Connected with the upper part of the still is conduit 11 leading to an air-cooled condensing chamber or back trap 12 for the purpose of returning condensates of high-boiling vapors. Beyond this condensing chamber, the conduit 13 leads to another air-cooled condensing chamber 14. At its base, this chamber is provided with an outlet 15 communicating with a reflux conduit 16. Above, uncondensed vapors are led forward through 17 communicating with another air-cooled condenser 18 which has an outlet 19 leading back to the reflux device. Depression 20 in this line acts as an oil trap. The vapors are then led into and through condenser 23, which is cooled by immersion in water in tank 24.

The operation of this device is evident from the foregoing. The still 1 is charged with a suitable quantity of oil and aluminum chloride, and distillation begun. Distillation may be conducted at any rate desired, and the temperature of the boiling mass of oil and aluminum chloride will be that at which it will boil under atmospheric pressure—around 500°F. (260°C.) in the case of high-boiling petroleum oils. The temperature, as shown by the thermometer 22, should not rise above 350°F.

[1] U. S. 1,424,574 (1922).

(176°C.). When so controlled, the vapors condensing in the condenser 23 will be gasoline and kerosene, which may be afterward redistilled and separated. With a somewhat lower temperature at the point of exit of vapors from the distilling system, *e.g.*, about 300°F. (150°C.)—the distillate will all be good, clean commercial gasoline of a saturated character.

A suitable proportion of aluminum chloride for the purposes of the present process is about 2 to 5 per cent of the body of oil under treatment. With large amounts of oil under treatment in a still, about 5 per cent is a good proportion. This proportion is relative to the amount of oil temporarily in the still and not to the whole amount treated by a given amount of chloride. Considering the amount of oil treated, in obtaining complete conversion with 5 per cent in the still, 1 part of aluminum chloride will treat about 50 parts of oil before losing high activity. With a less complete conversion, it will, of course, treat much more. Much depends on the character of the particular oil treated.

By feeding a little chlorine into the still during the operation, the period of activity of the aluminum chloride is considerably prolonged. In the treatment of oil by the described process, it is found that a single charge of aluminum chloride may be used for two or three days continuously before losing its high activity.

In the practical operation of the process, as high as 85 per cent conversion of a high-boiling into a low-boiling oil may be obtained. In normal operation, about 10 per cent of the oil is converted into gas, and 5 per cent forms coke. The gas may be used in heating the still.

Because of economic considerations, the use of aluminum chloride in refinery operations is confined largely to the preparation of saturated lubricating oils.

Preparation of Alkylbenzenes.—The condensation is carried out in vertical, jacketed, agitated vessels provided with a reflux condenser. When the reaction is complete, as indicated by the reduced quantity of hydrogen chloride liberated, the charge is distilled and fractionated. In this way, the alkylbenzene is separated from the nonvolatile, oily residue, which remains behind in the reactor.

That this oily mass possessed the property of catalyzing subsequent reactions was known to many early investigators. Its industrial application is pointed out in British Patent 259,507, wherein metallic aluminum is used to maintain the quantity and activity of the oily aluminum chloride addition compound. For the ethylation of benzene, the process may be carried out as follows:

Molecular proportions of benzene and ethyl chloride are put into the reactor, using aluminum chloride as the catalyst. The catalytic mass is obtained at the end of the run and can, to a limited extent, be used for subsequent alkylations. When small quantities of metallic aluminum, *e.g.*, aluminum powder or filings, are added to the partly exhausted catalytic mass, the latter quickly regains its catalytic strength and can be used for long operating periods.

In Table VIII are given data from seven runs of a Friedel and Crafts reaction comprising the combination of benzene and ethyl chloride to form ethylbenzene. In the first, 25 gm. of aluminum chloride were used, and 76.6 gm. of oily catalytic mass obtained. In the next run, no metal chloride was added, but a small quantity of metallic aluminum was added to the oily catalytic mass obtained from the first run. In the second, 92 gm. of oily catalytic mass were obtained. At the end of the seventh run, 62.1 gm. of oily catalytic mass remained as compared with 76.6 gm. at the end of the first run. The oily catalytic mass after run 7 was practically as active as that after the first run. The importance of the method is therefore quite apparent, with respect to economy of manufacture.

TABLE VIII.—PREPARATION OF ETHYLBENZENE[1]

Run No.	Benzene, gm.	Ethyl chloride, gm.	Aluminum chloride, gm.	Aluminum metal, gm.	Oily catalytic mass produced, gm.
1	312	85	25	. . .	76.6
2	312	85	. .	1.5	92.0
3	312	85	. .	. . .	82.4
4	312	85	. .	. . .	74.1
5	312	85	. .	1.0	84.0
6	312	85	. .	. . .	79.0
7	312	85	. .	. . .	62.1

[1] Brit. 259,507 (1926).

Preparation of 3, 5-Dimethyltertiarybutylbenzene.—The following description illustrates the preparation of hydrocarbons by condensing unsaturated aliphatic with aromatic compounds. The procedure[1] involves passing isobutylene through a series of reactors, each containing aromatic hydrocarbon and aluminum chloride, thereby minimizing the loss of gas. The reaction, which may be carried out continuously, can be represented by the following equations, which relate to the condensation of *m*-xylene with isobutylene:

$$\begin{array}{l} CH_3 \\ \diagdown C:CH_2 + HCl \rightarrow \begin{array}{l}CH_3\\ \diagdown CCl\cdot CH_3 \end{array} \\ CH_3 \diagup CH_3 \diagup \end{array}$$

$$\begin{array}{l} CH_3 \\ \diagdown CCl\cdot CH_3 + C_6H_4\begin{array}{l}\diagup CH_3\\ \diagdown CH_3\end{array} \rightarrow (CH_3)_3C\cdot C_6H_3(CH_3)_2 + HCl \\ CH_3 \diagup \end{array}$$

$$\begin{array}{l} CH_3 \\ \diagdown C:CH_2 + HCl \rightarrow \begin{array}{l}CH_3\\ \diagdown CCl\cdot CH_3 \end{array} \\ CH_3 \diagup CH_3 \diagup \end{array}$$

[1] Ger. 184,230 (1906).

The reaction is started by introducing 5 kg. of *m*-xylene, 200 gm. of aluminum chloride, and 50 gm. of butyl chloride in each of a series of communicating vessels. A slow stream of isobutylene gas is led at approximately 10°C. into the first vessel. Any unabsorbed or unreacted gas travels to the following vessel. When the reaction in the first vessel is completed, it is removed and recharged and then connected as the final reactor of the series.

If the reactors are of small capacity, the contents of several vessels can be given final treatment at one time. The charge is washed with water, and the oily part separated. The latter is then fractionated for the recovery of the *tert*-butylxylene. The xylene derivative boils at 200 to 203°C., the lighter-boiling fraction being returned to the reactors for subsequent condensation.

Preparation of Tert-butylphenols. *Using (a) Butyl chloride; (b) Butyl alcohol.*—A mixture consisting of approximately equimolecular quantities of *tert*-butyl chloride and phenol, together with 1 per cent of aluminum chloride, compared with phenol employed, is reacted in a jacketed, agitated vessel. The reaction is started at about 15°C., and the temperature of the charge is gradually raised to 100°C. After completion of the reaction, the product is cooled to 90°C., and a 50 per cent solution of sodium carbonate equivalent to 4 per cent of the weight of the reactants is added to the charge under agitation.

The contents of the reactor are filtered hot, and the filtrate is distilled through a fractionating column. The distillate consists of 10.5 per cent unreacted phenol, 12 per cent 2-*tert*-butylphenol, 70.2 per cent 4-*tert*-butylphenol, and 7.1 per cent 2, 4-di-*tert*-butylphenol.

The conversion of 2-*tert*-butylphenol to the isomeric para compound may be carried out as follows: A mixture consisting of 92.5 parts (1 mole) of *tert*-butyl chloride, 94 parts (1 mole) of phenol, 150 parts (1 mole) of 2-*tert*-butylphenol, and 6 parts of aluminum chloride is stirred in a suitable reactor at 25°C. for 1 hr. The temperature is then gradually brought up to 100°C. during the next hour. The reaction mass is then neutralized by the addition of 22 parts of sodium carbonate in 10 parts of water and the charge filtered and distilled. The distillate consists of 224 parts (1.49 moles) of 4-*tert*-butylphenol, 13 parts (0.087 mole) of 2-*tert*-butylphenol, and 15 parts (0.073 mole) of 2, 4-di-*tert*-butylphenol. The 4-*tert*-butylphenol is obtained in 74.5 per cent of the theoretical yield based on the combined quantities of phenol and 2-*tert*-butylphenol used.

Because of the danger of losing some of the volatile butyl chloride (b.p., 51°C.) by entrainment with the liberated hydrogen chloride, it is desirable to have the reactor equipped with an efficient reflux condenser and to run under a slight pressure.

Instead of the butyl chloride, *tert*-butyl alcohol may be employed in the preparation of alkylphenols. Although the alkyl halides require only catalytic quantities of $AlCl_3$, the alcohols require approximately 50 molar per cent $AlCl_3$ in order to effect the conversion of the alcohol to the reactive alkyl chloride. The reactants are suspended in an inert solvent such as petroleum ether maintained at 30 to 50°C. The maintenance of a slight pressure on the reactor appears desirable.

The alkylphenols are useful antiseptics and germicides.[1] Using Staphylococcus as the testing organism, the phenol coefficients of some of these compounds are as follows:

Material	Phenol Coefficient
Phenol, U.S.P.	1.0
tert-Butylphenol	87.5
Cresol, U.S.P.	3.1
tert-Butylcresol	75.0
Xylenol	5.6
tert-Butylxylenol	150.0

Preparation of β-Phenylethyl Alcohol.

$$H_2C-CH_2 \xrightarrow{AlCl_3} ClH_2C \cdot CH_2OAlCl_2 \xrightarrow{C_6H_6} \langle\ \rangle CH_2CH_2OH$$

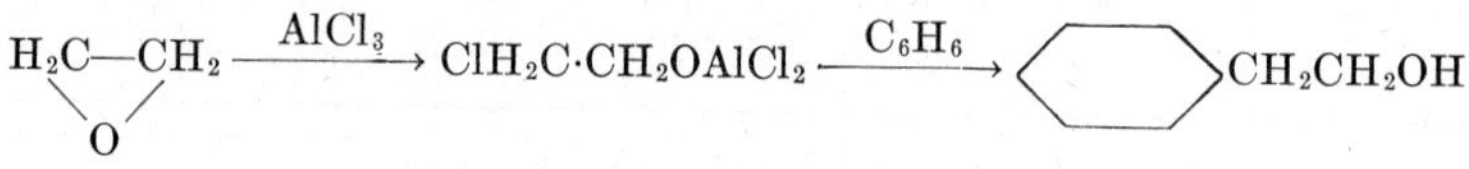

The synthesis may be carried out in a glass-lined, agitated vessel provided with a jacket for circulated brine. An apparatus similar to a "Hough" or sleeve-and-propeller nitrator is, however, preferable because success in this exothermic reaction depends largely on satisfactory temperature control. The reactor is charged with 150 parts (1 mole + 10 per cent) of pea-size aluminum chloride and 390 parts (5 moles) of benzene. Then 44 parts (1 mole) of gaseous ethylene oxide is gradually introduced in such a manner that minimal volumes of the diffused gas come into contact with a large volume of the liquid contents at a temperature of about 0°C. The introduction of air into the reactor facilitates the removal of hydrogen chloride and also serves to remove some of the heat of reaction and thus tends to inhibit the formation of chlorohydrin, β-phenylethyl chloride, and dibenzyl. The charge is stirred for about 1 hr. after the ethylene oxide has been added and is then delivered to a vessel containing about 1,000 parts of iced water.

After separation, the water layer is run off and the benzene solution of β-phenylethyl alcohol is washed with 150 parts of 2 per cent sodium carbonate. Upon ordinary distillation the excess of benzene is removed and recovered and the aromatic alcohol is then obtained by distillation *in vacuo*. The yields are approximately 75 per cent of the theoretical.

[1] Stockelbach, U. S. 2,081,284 (1937).

When used in the manufacture of perfumes, the crude β-phenylethyl alcohol must be freed from harsh-smelling impurities, and esterification of the alcohol in benzene solution has been found suitable for this purpose. The boric, phthalic, and oxalic esters are relatively nonvolatile and their distillation and subsequent hydrolysis result in a relatively pure product.[1]

ALDEHYDE SYNTHESES

The preparation of aldehydes according to the Friedel and Crafts reaction may be effected by condensing an aromatic hydrocarbon and carbon monoxide in the presence of aluminum chloride. The reaction appears to proceed through the intermediate formation of formyl chloride,

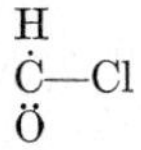

$$\begin{array}{c} H \\ \dot{C}\text{—Cl} \\ \ddot{O} \end{array}$$

a very unstable compound, which is derived from carbon monoxide and hydrogen chloride. The hydrogen chloride is usually introduced as such, although it may also be formed through an attack on the aromatic hydrocarbon by aluminum chloride.

This aldehyde synthesis may be carried out either (1) under pressure or (2) without the necessity of pressure when nitrobenzene is used as the solvent.

Preparation of Benzaldehyde.—The synthesis of benzaldehyde from benzene, in which carbon monoxide is supplied under pressure, in the presence of aluminum chloride and hydrogen chloride, may be illustrated as follows:[2]

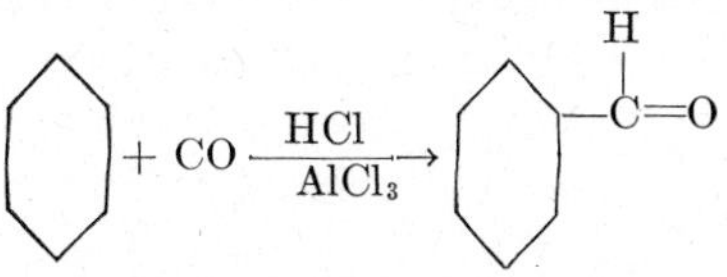

Hydrogen chloride[3] is led into an iron autoclave containing 100 liters of benzene and 45 kg. of aluminum chloride. The reaction vessel is sealed, warmed to 40 to 50°C., and for some hours, with agitation, carbon monoxide is forced in under a pressure of 90 atmos.

The reaction product is poured on ice, and the benzaldehyde and benzene removed by steam distillation. Benzaldehyde may be separated from the mixture of benzaldehyde and benzene by means of $NaHSO_3$. The crystalline addition compound of $NaHSO_3$ and benzaldehyde may

[1] Klipstein, U. S. 2,068,415 (1937).

[2] Ger. 281,212 (1914).

[3] HOLLOWAY and KRASE [*Ind. Eng. Chem.*, **25**, 497 (1933)] find that the HCl necessary for the formation of the intermediate formyl chloride may be obtained by the addition of 1.3 per cent water, compared with $AlCl_3$, to the reactants.

be removed by filtration, and benzaldehyde liberated by means of a mineral acid. A yield of 30 kg. of purified benzaldehyde, or 85 per cent based on the aluminum chloride used, may be obtained.

p-Tolualdehyde and *p*-chlorobenzaldehyde are made from toluene and chlorobenzene, respectively, in a similar manner:

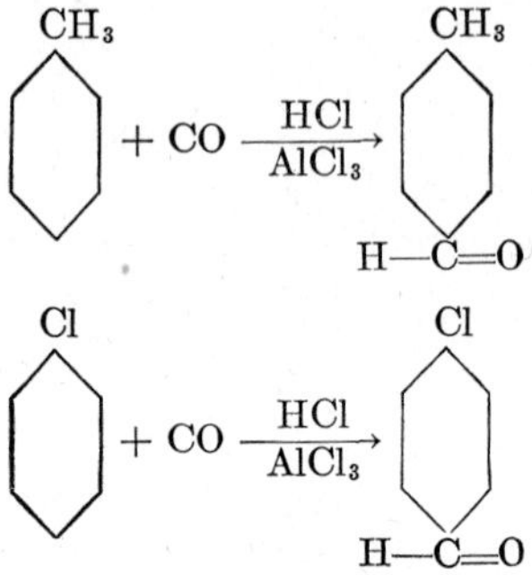

In the preparation of *p*-chlorobenzaldehyde, the chlorobenzene is first saturated with hydrogen chloride. The chlorobenzene, along with the aluminum chloride, is then agitated at a temperature of 75 to 85°C. and treated with carbon monoxide under a pressure of 70 atmos. for 10 hr.

The reaction product is treated in a manner similar to the benzaldehyde reaction product, and the isolated *p*-chlorobenzaldehyde is purified by means of vacuum distillation.

The second, or solvent, method appears as an improvement over the pressure process, in that the advantages associated with greater homogeneity of the reactants may be expected. Nitrobenzene keeps the benzene, aluminum chloride, carbon monoxide, and hydrogen chloride in contact in solution. The aluminum chloride is used in a finely divided condition to promote solubility.

The procedure is illustrated as follows:[1] 250 parts of finely divided sublimed aluminum chloride is added, with stirring, at room temperature to a mixture containing 1,000 parts of benzene and 200 parts of nitrobenzene. Solution can be seen to take place as the liquid acquires a clear reddish-yellow cast, and a slight rise in temperature occurs. A mixture of equal proportions of hydrogen chloride and carbon monoxide, previously dried by passing through a dehydrating medium such as sulfuric acid, is led into the solution, the temperature being 50 to 60°C. The gas is introduced until there no longer is a perceptible absorption, this stage being reached in about 6 to 8 hr.

The reaction mass is poured into ice water, to decompose the aluminum complex. Benzene, benzaldehyde, and nitrobenzene are then

[1] Ger. 403,489 (1924).

removed by steam distillation. After the removal of the aqueous layer, the mixture is treated with sodium bisulfite to form the crystalline sodium bisulfite-benzaldehyde compound, and the benzene and nitrobenzene may be removed and returned for use in the next charge.

The bisulfite compound is decomposed by mineral acid, giving a yield of about 90 per cent of benzaldehyde, based on the benzene converted.

CARBOXYLIC ACID SYNTHESIS

Treatment of Benzenoid Compounds with Carbon Dioxide under Pressure.

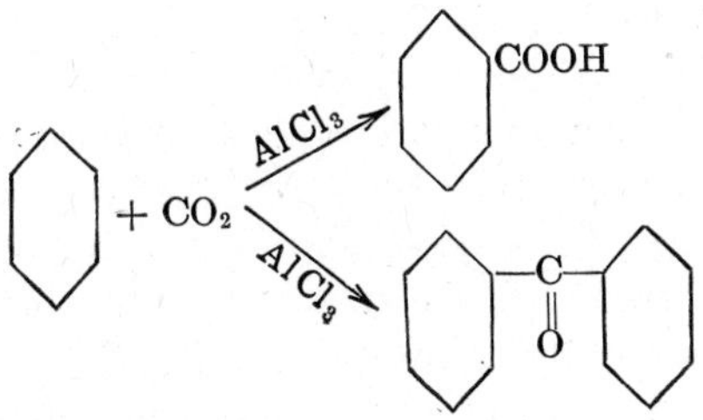

When benezenoid derivatives are treated under pressure with carbon dioxide in the presence of aluminum chloride, the principal product of reaction is a derivative of benzoic acid.

In British Patent 307,223 are shown the methods of synthesizing benzoic acid and its derivatives. Of interest in these reactions is the fact that aromatic ketones of the benzophenone series are simultaneously formed. The condensation may be carried out in the following manner:

A high-pressure autoclave, fitted with stirrers, is charged with 100 parts of benzene and 50 parts of anhydrous aluminum chloride, the air being expelled by the repeated introduction of carbon dioxide under pressure and subsequent expansion; finally, carbon dioxide is brought therein under a pressure of about 60 atmos., and the contents heated to 100°C. while stirring. After from 12 to 15 hr., the surplus carbon dioxide is discharged, the viscous reaction product is decomposed with ice, and this product, after the addition of concentrated hydrochloric acid, is extracted with benzene. After distilling off the benzene, a gray cake of crude benzoic acid remains which contains a considerable amount of benzophenone.

The initial benzene may be replaced by other aromatic hydrocarbons or their derivatives, such as chlorobenzene, toluene, xylenes, chlorotoluenes, and the like.

KETONE SYNTHESIS

Condensations with Aliphatic and Aromatic Acid Chlorides.— ω-Chloroacetophenone.

$$\text{ClCH}_2\text{COCl} + \langle\ \rangle \xrightarrow{\text{AlCl}_3} \langle\ \rangle\text{COCH}_2\text{Cl} + \text{HCl}$$

The preparation of ω-chloroacetophenone, which is described below, is similar to the procedure for making acetophenone or any of the alkyl aryl ketones. The condensation involves bringing benzene and an acyl chloride together in a suitable, agitated vessel provided with a reflux condenser.

In charging the reactor, which is an enamel-lined, jacketed vessel, 378 lb. of benzene is delivered from the feed tank (Fig. 1 page 670,) and 160 lb. of anhydrous aluminum chloride is added, the agitator being kept in motion to prevent caking. The kettle is closed, and the circulation of brine through the jacket started.

When the temperature of the material in the kettle reaches 25°C., the addition of chloroacetyl chloride is started. The rate of feed is governed by the heat-transfer capacity of the jacket in maintaining the operating temperature at 25°C. Ordinarily, about 1½ hr. is required to introduce the required 142 lb. of chloroacetyl chloride. After the reactants are added, the temperature of the charge is raised to 60°C. by replacing the brine in the jacket with steam or hot water. This temperature is maintained for 2 hr. to permit the completion of the reaction. The charge is then drowned.

The drowning tank is prepared by introducing about 550 gal. of water, which is cooled to 5°C. by the brine coil (Fig. 1). The agitator on the drowning tank is started, and the charge from the reactor is delivered at such a rate that the temperature does not exceed 15°C. The reactor is then washed out with 50 lb. of benzene, the washings also being delivered to the drowning tank underneath. The agitation in the drowning tank is continued for 30 min. to insure thorough mixing. A jet of live steam is then introduced into the mixture to bring the temperature up to 35°C., to facilitate subsequent separation. The charge is now permitted to stand until the constituents form into layers.

The separation of the upper benzene-chloroacetophenone layer from the lower water and sludge is of importance, because the presence of the metal halide during subsequent distillation operations would be deleterious. The aqueous solution of aluminum salt is run off and discarded. Any intermediate layer is withdrawn for further separation, while the benzene-chloroacetophenone layer is delivered to a blow case. Before distilling, the composite of several charges of ω chloroacetophenone is again treated with benzene, agitated, and settled in order effectively to remove any remaining contaminating aluminum compounds.

The distillation of the benzene-chloroacetophenone solution for the recovery of the ketone in a pure state may be accomplished either by vacuum distillation or by distillation with steam.

When distillation under reduced pressure is employed, the charge, consisting of approximately 70 per cent benzene and 30 per cent ketone, is first warmed to 80°C. to remove the benzene. The temperature is then raised by jacket heat to 105°C., to remove any water that may have been present. The still is now connected to the vacuum pump, so that a vacuum of 25 in. of Hg is attained. The water that was circulated through the condenser jacket is now drained, and steam is passed through it. The distillation of chloroacetophenone is indicated by the sudden rise in temperature on the still head, at which time the steam on the condenser jacket is shut off. The ketone distills over at 155 to 160°C. When the temperature drops to 125°C., the distillation is complete. A precaution should be taken finally to warm the condenser tube with steam, to insure that any crystallized ω-chloroacetophenone is removed.

When the chloroacetophenone is recovered by distillation with steam, the benzene is first removed by jacket heat and delivered to its receiver. The temperature of the still is then raised to 165°C., and live steam introduced. The still temperature is gradually raised to 190°C., and the distillation continued until the condensate shows the absence of ketone. When this method of distillation is employed, very little tarry residue is left in the still. The ratio of steam to ketone distilled is approximately 2:1 by weight.

Condensations with Aliphatic Acid Anhydrides. *General Procedure.* A solution of 1 mole of aromatic hydrocarbon or derivative in carbon disulfide or preferably in an excess of aromatic reactant is placed in a suitable vessel provided with an agitator, reflux condenser, and vent for the liberated hydrogen chloride. To this solution is added 3.3 moles of powdered aluminum chloride ($AlCl_3$), and then, with rapid stirring, 1 mole of the aliphatic acid anhydride is slowly added. After all of the acid anhydride has been introduced, the charge is heated by jacket heat until the evolution of hydrogen chloride is practically nil. The reaction mixture is then cooled to room temperature and decomposed by pouring into iced dilute mineral acid.

The ketone may be separated by permitting the aqueous suspension to separate into layers, discarding the aqueous solution of the metal halide, and working up the aromatic ketone by ordinary distillation to remove the aromatic reactant and then by distillation *in vacuo*. It is necessary thoroughly to wash the crude product prior to distillation in order to free it of aluminum compounds.

Working in accordance with the procedure outlined above, Groggins and Nagel[1] have obtained yields of 75 to 85 per cent in the preparation of a number of alkyl aryl ketones (Table II). These yields are based on both of the acyl groups in the anhydride being reactive since it was shown previously that this was possible in the presence of 3.3 moles of aluminum chloride.

Preparation of Keto Acids.—In the preparation of benzoylbenzoic and toluylbenzoic acids which are ordinarily made on a large scale, there is a distinct economic advantage in employing the mill-type reactor, which is described and discussed on page 671. It is obvious that the cost of other types of apparatus having equal productive capacity would be greater. When, however, chlorobenzene, chlorotoluenes, etc., are condensed with phthalic anhydride, a higher reaction temperature is required, and experience has further shown that an improvement in yield and purity of keto acid is obtained when 4 to 6 moles of the halogeno compounds are employed per mole of anhydride. Condensations of this character are best carried out in a vertical-type reactor.

Liquid-phase Reactions. Preparation of 4'-Chloro-2-Benzoylbenzoic Acid.—Murch[2] describes the preparation of this halogeno keto acid as follows: To a well-stirred mixture of 125 parts of phthalic anhydride and 600 parts of chlorobenzene at an initial temperature of about 30°C. is added 250 parts of anhydrous aluminum chloride at such a rate that the temperature of the mixture does not rise above 60 to 65°C. After all of the aluminum chloride has been added, the mixture is heated and maintained at a temperature of 75 to 80°C. for an hour or until the evolution of hydrogen chloride has substantially ceased.

In this condensation, Murch employs slightly over six times the quantity of chlorobenzene necessary to react with the phthalic anhydride introduced. Its recovery is effected by allowing the chlorobenzene suspension of the aluminum compound to run slowly into a solution containing 420 parts of sodium carbonate in 4,800 parts of water maintained at 90°C. Considerable heat and carbon dioxide are evolved, and large quantities of chlorobenzene distill off. The excess of chlorobenzene is removed by distillation with steam, using external heat if necessary to keep the volume of mixture approximately constant.

The charge is then filtered, and the aluminiferous residue washed free of alkali. The filtrate containing the sodium salt of the keto acid is treated at 20 to 30°C. with the necessary quantity of 66°Bé. sulfuric

[1] GROGGINS and NAGEL, *Ind. Eng. Chem.*, **26**, 1313 (1934).
[2] Murch, U. S. 1,746,737 (1930).

acid while stirring. The precipitated 4′-chloro-2-benzoylbenzoic acid is filtered off, washed, and dried.

Several modifications of this practice, particularly as they relate to the treatment of the hydrolyzed aluminum complex, have already been discussed. In U. S. patent 1,942,430 Jacobson shows that the aluminum chloride complex of the keto acid can be hydrolyzed in a limited quantity of cold acidulated water. Under such circumstances only a small portion of the keto acid remains in the supernatant aromatic reactant, most of it being precipitated out in a crystalline state. Upon filtering through a wool cloth, the keto acid is separated from the rest of the charge.

Groggins and Newton[1] obtained the results shown in Table IX in the preparation of 4′-chloro-2-benzoylbenzoic acid. In this investigation the aluminum complex was hydrolyzed with cold mineral acid, or hydrogen chloride from an ensuing run, and the excess of chlorobenzene distilled with steam. The keto acid was then filtered off from the solution of the aluminum salt in mineral acid.

TABLE IX.—EFFECT OF CHLOROBENZENE RATIO IN AGITATED VESSELS ON PREPARATION OF 4′-CHLORO-2-BENZOYLBENZOIC ACID

Semi-works Operations[1]

Expt. No.	Time of reaction, hr.	Temp. of reaction, °C.	Chloro-benzene ratio	Yield chloro-benzoylbenzoic acid		M. p., °C.	Purity by titration, %	Recovery of solvent, %
				Gm.	%			
1	5	50	6:1	509	97.7	147.0–148	98.8	99
2	4	50	3:1	506	97.1	147.0–148	99.6	95
3	5	50	3:1	510	98.0	147.0–148	99.6	95
4	6	40	2:1	508	97.5	147.0–148	99.6	90
5	5	95	6:1	456	87.5	147.0–147.8	98.0	
6[2]	5	50	3:1	334	64.1	144.4–147.2	98.7	

[1] Warm, dried air drawn over the reaction mass.
[2] Run without agitation.

Phthalic anhydride used, 2 moles = 296 gm.; aluminum chloride used, 587 gm. = 10 per cent excess. Sulfuric acid, 18 per cent H₂SO₄ was used in hydrolyzing the aluminum chloride complex of chlorobenzoylbenzoic acid. Of 2 per cent sodium hydroxide, 15 liters was used to form its sodium salt. A 10 per cent solution of sulfuric acid was used to reprecipitate the chlorobenzoylbenzoic acid. Experiment 6 shows that agitation is necessary when a low ratio of chlorobenzene is used.

Reaction between Combining Proportions of Reactants. 4′-Phenyl-2-Benzoylbenzoic Acids.—Groggins[2] has shown that it is practical to employ the mill reactor for Friedel and Crafts syntheses involving three solid reactants. When biphenyl or its halogen derivatives are condensed

[1] GROGGINS and NEWTON, *Ind. Eng. Chem.*, **21**, 376 (1929).
[2] GROGGINS, *Ind. Eng. Chem.*, **22**, 620 (1930).

with phthalic anhydride, a series of 4'-phenyl-2-benzoylbenzoic acids is obtained upon hydrolysis of the aluminum complex. When these keto acids are dehydrated, they are converted into phenylanthraquinones. The reactions of the chlorobiphenyls are shown by the following structural formulas:

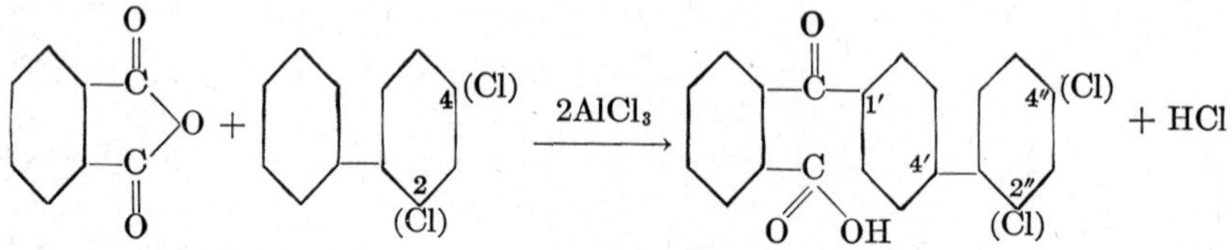

The Scholl Reaction

Scholl[1] showed that condensations in the aromatic series could be effected whereby an intramolecular union of nuclei took place with the splitting off of nuclear hydrogen. The simplest example of this reaction[2] is the transformation of α-benzoylnaphthalene into benzanthrone:

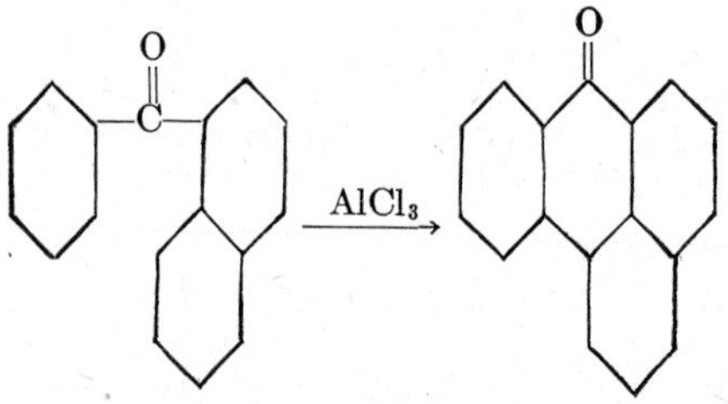

It is apparent that the synthesis comprises the preliminary formation of the benzoyl compound, by condensing benzoyl chloride and naphthalene according to the Friedel and Crafts reaction, this step being followed by a more drastic treatment with aluminum chloride to effect cyclization.

The process involves grinding 1 part of α-benzoylnaphthalene and 10 parts of aluminum chloride in a moisture-free atmosphere. The mixture is gradually warmed, and the temperature raised to 150°C. in a period of 2 hr. Cold water is added in small portions to the cooling mass. The crude product is filtered and then purified by extracting·first with dilute hydrochloric acid and then with organic solvents.

In the following synthesis of 3, 4, 8, 9-dibenzpyrene-5, 10-quinone, a combination of the Friedel and Crafts with the Scholl reactions again occurs. The first step is the condensation of benzoyl chloride with benzanthrone, to form the simple ketone. During the subsequent treatment with aluminum chloride, cyclization is effected with removal of nuclear hydrogen:

[1] Scholl, *Ann.*, **394**, 111 (1912); *Ber.*, **43**, 1737 (1910).
[2] Brit. 16,271 (1910).

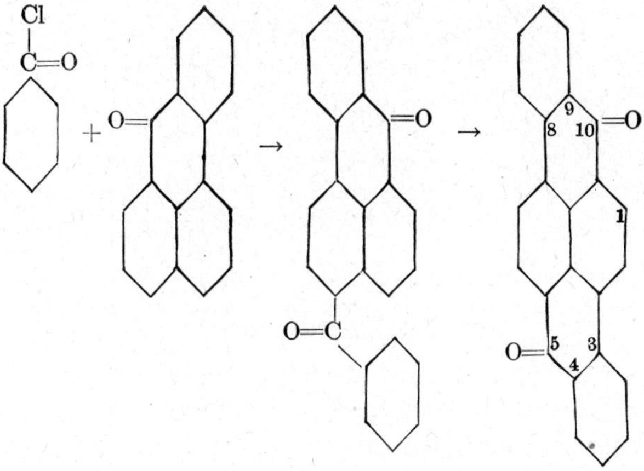

When dinaphthyl is condensed according to the Scholl reaction, perylene is formed:

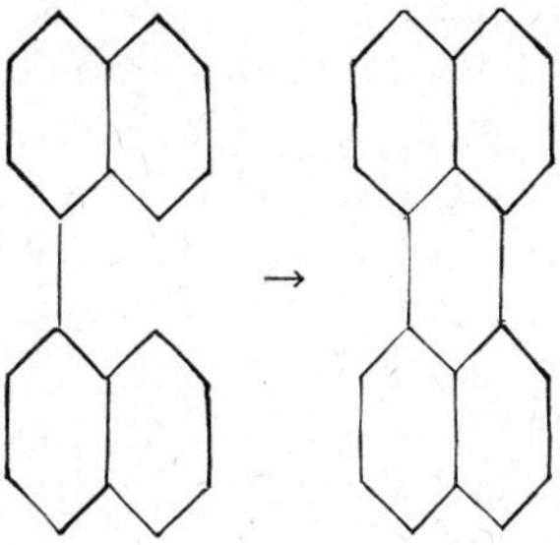

CHAPTER XIII

POLYMERIZATION

By A. J. Norton

I. INTRODUCTION[1]

Toughness, a quality which is easy to recognize but hard to define, is the necessary property of materials for a wide variety of uses. A movie film, a comb, a steering wheel must be tough; the inner layer in safety glass must be particularly so. Horn, rawhide, animal tendons are tough; so are rubber and many natural fibers. Sugar, rock salt, benzoic acid, and marble are not; they are readily pulverized. Practically all the 300,000, more or less, compounds which organic chemists have built up are crystalline; those we know as liquids crystallize at low temperatures. Crystalline substances are seldom tough. Crystals composed of identical molecules melt sharply, a familiar criterion of purity. A single crystal is usually transparent, but a mass of such crystals is not.

Acetaldehyde (C_2H_4O) (b.p., 20.2°C.) is readily converted into paraldehyde ($C_6H_{12}O_3$) (m.p., 10.5°C. and b.p., 124°C.). A pure substance, sharply characterized, is transformed into another having exactly three times the molecular weight with all the characteristics of a pure substance. This is an example of polymerization in its simplest form. Styrene ($C_6H_5 \cdot CH = CH_2$), a limpid liquid (b.p., 145°C.), passes spontaneously into a transparent tough solid. This can be shown to be a mixture, the components of which resemble each other closely and differ only in solubility and in molecular weight. No matter how far the separation of the mixture may be carried, all the fractions are still mixtures; the molecular weights of the fractions are all high, 10,000 to 100,000, compared with 104 for the original styrene. This too is polymerization but of a very different sort.

The conception of linear polymers of enormous molecular weights, containing hundreds, or even thousands of units, was brought in by Staudinger. Previously such substances were supposed to be colloidal aggregates of small molecules held together by secondary valencies or van der Waals forces.[2] Now it is believed that even a large molecule,

---

[1] The author and editor are greatly indebted to Professor E. Emmet Reid for the preparation of this introduction.

[2] Van der Waals forces are different from ordinary valence forces or those between charged particles or ions. They are the forces which exist between electrically

containing as many as 1,000 styrene units, is held together, atom to atom, by primary valencies just as is the simple styrene molecule. Strong evidence for this view is furnished by the fact that a highly polymeric substance may undergo chemical reactions without materially altering its degree of polymerization. Thus polymerized vinyl acetate may be saponified and re-esterified without being broken down.

The physical properties of a high polymer appear to be connected with the length of the chains, with the fact that they are of all possible lengths, and with their non-crystalline character. In the case of a high styrene polymer, we must imagine a chain of 2,000 carbon atoms to which are attached 1,000 phenyl groups. We may picture a number of such molecules in the liquid state as more or less coiled about each other,

FIG. 1.—Polymer chains.   FIG. 2.—Broken polymer chains.

somewhat like the strands in a plate of spaghetti. The solutions of high polymers are characterized by high viscosity; even a 2 per cent solution may be so thick that it will barely flow. When such a mass is cooled it will be extremely difficult for these long chains to orient themselves completely into crystals. They must come together in bundles but there are no joints in the bundle (see Fig. 1) where all the chains end. To pull such a bundle in two, either the molecules must break or must be pulled out as represented in Fig. 2.

The term "polymer" has been restricted to those like paraldehyde and polystyrene, which have exactly the same percentage composition as the monomers and are formed from them without the addition or subtraction of anything. Recent usage has followed Carothers in applying the term to anything in which there are recurring identical groups, particularly when the number of these is large. We speak of "high polymers" or "eupolymers" when the number of units is extremely high, *i.e.*, of the order of a thousand.

To form a linear polymer all that is needed is a recurrent reaction, one in which a reactive group remains after the reaction. An example will make this plain. In the presence of aluminum chloride an alkyl halide will react with benzene:

$$RCl + HC_6H_5 \rightarrow RC_6H_5 + HCl$$

We may use benzyl chloride with itself:

$$PhCH_2Cl + HC_6H_4CH_2Cl \rightarrow PhCH_2 \cdot C_6H_4CH_2Cl + HCl$$

neutral molecules as a result of an interaction between the electrical and magnetic fields of the molecules. It is generally assumed that the van der Waals forces account for the phenomena of change of state from gas to liquid or solid, for the phenomena of adsorption of gases on solids, and for the deviations from perfect gas laws,

The product still contains —CH_2Cl which is reactive, and the reaction may continue indefinitely. The product is:

$$C_6H_5CH_2(C_6H_4CH_2)nCl$$

In this the group —$C_6H_4CH_2$— is repeated many times. It will be observed that the end group $C_6H_5CH_2$— does not have the composition of the —$C_6H_4CH_2$— unit and there is still an active —Cl at the other end no matter how many molecules have reacted. As long as n remains small, *i.e.*, 5 to 20, the degree of polymerization can be followed by a chlorine determination. When n equals 1, the chlorine is 16.83 per cent; when n is 10, the chlorine is only 3.55 per cent. It is 0.40 per cent and 0.04 per cent when n is 100 and 1,000 respectively. Just what becomes of such end groups is a difficult question: does the amount become too small for analytical methods or is there ring formation or some other side reaction that eliminates the active end group and thus stops the reaction? It is obvious that, for a high polymer, the properties of the molecule will be determined by the repeating group.

In the example given above, the benzyl chloride is bifunctional in that the same molecule supplies both the H— and the —Cl which are to react with each other. We may obtain polymers by the reaction of two bifunctional compounds as adipic acid ($COOH(CH_2)_4COOH$) and glycol ($HOCH_2 \cdot CH_2OH$). A molecule of adipic acid may react with one of glycol. The product ($COOH(CH_2)_4COOCH_2CH_2OH$) has an acid group at one end and an alcohol group at the other. The acid end may react with a molecule of glycol and the alcoholic end with a molecule of adipic acid. The reaction product so formed has an acid group at one end and an alcoholic at the other and may react further. These reactions may continue as long as the reactants are present. The product is a polymeric ester. Glyptal, the reaction product of phthalic anhydride and glycerol, is a polymeric ester of this type. A polymer of this class is

Thickol, $\left(\begin{array}{c} \overset{S}{\overset{\|}{}}\ \overset{S}{\overset{\|}{}} \\ -CH_2-CH_2-S-S- \end{array} \right)n$, made from the bifunctional chloride $ClCH_2CH_2Cl$ and the bifunctional sodium polysulfide.

The polymerization of ethylene must go through these stages:

$$CH_2:CH_2 + CH_2:CH_2 \rightarrow CH_3 \cdot CH_2 \cdot CH:CH_2$$
$$CH_3 \cdot CH_2 \cdot CH:CH_2 + CH_2:CH_2 \rightarrow CH_3 \cdot CH_2 \cdot CH_2 \cdot CH_2 \cdot CH:CH_2$$
$$(n + 1)CH_2:CH_2 \rightarrow H(-CH_2 \cdot CH_2)_nCH:CH_2$$

This is polymerization in the narrow sense but it is to be noted that the final polymer is not simply a multiple of the ethylene but contains the end groups H— and —$CH:CH_2$. In this case analysis does not help, and in a high polymer the unsaturation would be vanishingly small. Ethylene itself is difficult to polymerize but many of its mono- and unsymmetrical di-substitution products polymerize readily to valuable plastics. Examples of these are styrene $(C_6H_5 \cdot CH:CH_2)$ vinyl chloride and acetate $(ClCH:CH_2$ and $CH_3COOCH:CH_2)$, acrylic esters $(ROCO \cdot CH:CH_2)$, and methacrylic esters $(ROCOC(CH_3):CH_2)$. The polymers may be written $H(-CHR \cdot CH_2-)_n CR:CH_2$.

A linear polymer of either of the above classes is apt to be *thermoplastic*, *i.e.*, it softens gradually over a considerable temperature range. A temperature may be found at which it is plastic enough to flow into a mold when pressure is applied as in injection molding. Or a mixture of the powdered plastic and a filling powder may be molded under pressure in a hot mold. The disadvantage of such a plastic is that the mold must be cooled somewhat before the object is ejected otherwise distortion will take place. An advantage is that all spoiled articles and scrap may be reworked.

Another type of plastic is the *thermosetting*, which means that it sets up and hardens under heat and pressure. The setting up is due to some chemical reaction which takes place in the press under the influence of the heat. The great advantage of such a resin is that the molded object can be ejected from the hot press without danger of distortion. The disadvantage is that spoiled articles and scrap can not be reworked. Bakelite, the first artificial resin to assume commercial importance, is of this type. Thermosetting is believed to be due to cross linking. A rope is flexible because its strands can slip over each other but if the strands are glued together the pliability is lost. This may be illustrated by the original and the later modified Bakelites. A para-substituted phenol reacts with formaldehyde to give a methylol derivative which may link to another and another forming a linear polymer:

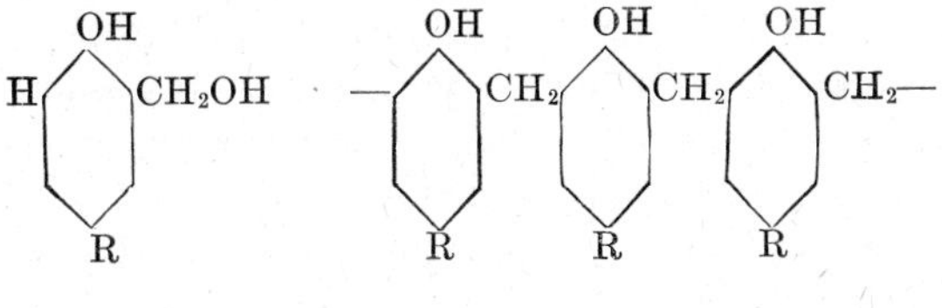

Such polymers are thermoplastic and, if the R is a large enough alkyl, are dispersible or soluble in oils. If the para position is open, as in phenol itself, other molecules of formaldehyde may tie the chains together so as to form a rigid lattice. The partially formed resin in powdered form is put into the mold with a substance, such as hexamethylene tetramine which generates formaldehyde when heated, and heat and pressure are applied. The final reaction takes place and the article is ejected from the hot mold.

II. CLASSIFICATION OF SYNTHETIC RESINS AND PLASTICS

To the consumer, the physical properties of the resins and compounds surpass in interest their constitution or derivation.　Consequently, many arbitrary classifications have arisen through industrial usage which are overlapping in character and bear no reference to the derivation of the product.　The word *resin* itself refers primarily to the physical appearance of a product rather than to its constitution.

In the generally accepted terminology, a true resin is a solid solution of many chemical compounds.　The compounds are so closely related in chemical properties that it is almost impossible to separate one from another and they are in a physical relationship so intimate that they act as one product.

The arbitrary classifications, depending on physical properties, are not exact, but they are so well embedded in the minds of the users of resins and so descriptive of the objective of resin research that they serve as one of the best means of describing synthetic resins and one of the best ways of attacking the subject.

Physical Classification

Three terms have reached a usage that makes them standard.　It is possible that new developments will lead to new classes, but all of today's products may be classified under the headings of *thermosetting* resins, *thermoplastic* resins, and *oil-soluble* or *oil-reactive* resins.

Thermosetting Resins.—By a thermosetting resin is meant a product that will not only melt and flow but which, after a short application of heat, will also set to an infusible, insoluble mass.　Thermosetting compounds are mixtures of such resins with fibrous fillers and plasticizers. Under heat and pressure, the compounds melt, flow, and take the shape of the mold and then set to a lustrous inert product, which may be taken from the hot mold without danger of warping or breaking.　To be of commercial value, the chemical and physical reactions that cause the setting of the resin must be so complete during the short interval involved that no further change takes place.　If they are not complete—and changes in physical or chemical structure should occur after taking the article from the mold—warping, checking, and cracking might result.

Thermoplastic Resins.—Thermoplastic resins are permanently fusible. They may be melted and held at elevated temperatures without changing their physical properties and, after cooling, may be remelted.　They are sometimes called *novolaks* and are used primarily in casting, *i.e.*, melting and pouring into a die and then cooling.　They may also be molded under heat and pressure, provided the mold can be cooled before the piece is removed, or by injection of the hot plastic mass into a cold mold and holding under pressure until it has cooled to a rigid mass. Many border-line resins, *i.e.*, those that will set under heat but too slowly to be of value in industrial hot molding, are included in this class as thermoplastic resins. Cellulose esters—not strictly resins but from which moldable products are made—are also included in this classification.

Oil-soluble Resins.—By an oil-soluble or oil-reactive resin is meant a product which at moderate temperatures will dissolve in, become colloidally dispersed in, or react chemically with drying oils, such as china wood oil. The resulting product will produce a homogeneous film of very different characteristics from those obtainable from either a solution of the bodied oil or the resin alone. Strictly speaking, the oil-soluble resins are a subdivision of the thermoplastic resins. But, because most thermoplastic resins are insoluble in, and incompatible with, drying oils, and because of usage in different industries, the term *oil-soluble resins* has grown to cover resins suitable for use in the paint, varnish, and lacquer industry.

Chemical Classification

To the chemist, a more exact classification is desirable. To produce a simple scheme of classification of a group of products more numerous than the organic chemicals from which they are derived is difficult. The problem is somewhat easier, however, if one bears in mind that of the many thousands of resins that are synthesized yearly, only a few ever become of commercial importance. The following classification based on the derivation of the resin may not be all-inclusive, but it does include all the resins that have reached industrial importance and those that bear the most promise for the future:

1. Products derived from phenols by condensation and polymerization with other compounds.
2. Products derived from compounds of the amino type by condensation and polymerization with formaldehyde, *e.g.*, urea-formaldehyde resins.
3. Modified resins, as:
    a. Straight esters of natural acids, ester gum (the glycerol ester of rosin) being the outstanding example.
    b. Phenolic resins that have been fluxed with natural resins or chemicals to render them dispersible in oil. The albertols are the best example.
4. Semi-polymerized esters typified by the glyptals, *i.e.*, esters of phthalic anhydride and glycerol.
5. Strictly polymerized products, the ethenoids, as represented by the vinyl, styrene, and acryloid products.
6. Cellulose plastics.

Another method of classification[1] is based on the source and properties of the reacting chemicals. Four classes are set forth:

[1] Kline, National Bureau of Standards circular, C411 (1936).

1. Synthetic resin plastics.
   a. Phenolic —aldehydic.
   b. Amino aldehydic
   c. Vinyl resins.
   d. Hydroxy dicarboxylic resins.
   e. Indene resins.
   f. Organic polysulfides.
   g. Miscellaneous.
2. Natural resin plastics.
   a. Animal resins.
   b. Vegetable resins.
   c. Mineral resins.
   d. Natural waxes.
3. Cellulose plastics.
   a. Cellulose nitrate.
   b. Cellulose acetate and other esters.
   c. Cellulose ethers.
   d. Regenerated cellulose.
4. Protein plastics.
   a. Casein.
   b. Soybean proteins.
   c. Blood albumins.

Economic Considerations.—This classification emphasizes the vast field from which products of potential value in the plastics industry may be drawn. There are several factors which seriously influence the value of the different sources.

First of these are the availability and price of the raw material, for, regardless of its properties, a resin or molding composition is of distinctly limited value if the raw material from which it is made is not available in relatively unlimited supplies at a low cost. The commercial development of many apparently valuable materials has been prevented by cost alone, for the modern successful resin and plastic must be inexpensive in order to enter fields where the consumption is large. Coal, petroleum, natural gas, cellulose, and natural proteins seem potentially good sources from which materials can be developed. The phenolic resins have always been circumscribed by the basic price of phenol and by its demand as a war material. This is particularly true now that cresols have found such a wide use in oil refining and are practically withdrawn from the resin market as their price now approaches that of pure phenol.

Second, of course, are the properties of the final product. Many synthetic products have been introduced which, in the final analysis, have no advantage over less expensive natural resins.

A clear-cut understanding of the potential outlets and their demands is as necessary to a research program in the plastics field as is a knowledge of the sources of raw materials, the chemistry of the polymerization process, and the characteristics of the final product.

III. CHEMICAL CONSTITUTION AND POLYMERIZATION

Discussion of Terms.—A large number of unsaturated, low-molecular-weight compounds have the tendency to polymerize. The transformation of such active molecules into complex derivatives of high molecular weight is generally called *polymerization*. It is to be remembered, however, that two distinct types of reactions may be distinguished *viz.*, polymerization and condensation. In a polymerization reaction, the reactants are marked by a large degree of unsaturation, and the resulting more saturated polymer is a multiple of the initial reactant. In other words the percentage composition remains unaltered. In condensation reactions, on the other hand, the final product is no longer a multiple of the monomer, and in order to obtain the formula of the final condensate it is necessary to subtract the sum of the simple compounds, *e.g.*, HCl, H_2O, NaCl, etc., which have been liberated during condensation.

Carothers[1] had indicated that the accepted polymerization of formaldehyde to polyoxymethylene may involve the formation of free radicals or condensation reactions. Thus the polymerization of pure dry formal-

$$xCH_2O \rightarrow (CH_2O)x$$

dehyde might involve the opening of the carbonyl bond [Eq. (1)] giving

$$CH_2{=}O \rightarrow -CH_2-O- \tag{1}$$

rise to free radicals whose mutual combination would result in a long chain. In the presence of water, addition according to Eqs. (2) and (3) would also lead to the formation of a large molecule.

$$CH_2{=}O + HOH \rightarrow HO-CH_2-OH \tag{2}$$
$$CH_2{=}O + HO-CH_2-OH \rightarrow HO-CH_2-O-CH_2-OH \tag{3}$$

In the presence of a strong acid, polymer formation may take place according to the intermolecular condensation [Eq. (4)].

$$HOCH_2O\,|\,H + HO\,|\,CH_2O\,|\,H + HO\,|\,CH_2OH \rightarrow HO-CH_2O-CH_2O-CH_2O- \tag{4}$$

Broadly, then, polymerization may be defined as the chemical combination of a number of similar units to form a single molecule, wherein polymerization phenomena as well as condensation reactions occur.[2] They are intermolecular combinations that are functionally capable of proceeding indefinitely, *i.e.*, leading to molecules of infinite size. Referring to the formaldehyde reactions outlined above, the functional possibilities are such that any given number of formaldehyde molecules might be combined into a single molecule. The same possibility exists with (*a*)

[1] CAROTHERS, *Trans. Faraday Soc.*, Sept. 1935.
[2] CAROTHERS, *J. Am. Chem. Soc.*, **51**, 2548 (1929).

unsaturated compounds; (*b*) cyclic compounds; and (*c*) polyfunctional compounds generally, *e.g.*, *x*—*R*—*y*, where *x* and *y* are capable of mutual reaction. The compounds formally capable of polymerization then are all *polyfunctional* compounds. Practically, the functions must be such as to permit mutual combination, and polymerization will fail only in those relatively rare cases where reaction is exclusively intramolecular. A double bond or a reactive ring will count as a double function.

Compounds Susceptible to Polymerization.—The appearance of certain unsaturated groups appears to be necessary for the occurrence of a reaction involving addition polymerization. Broadly speaking, any unsaturated grouping, as exemplified below, acts as a polymerizing

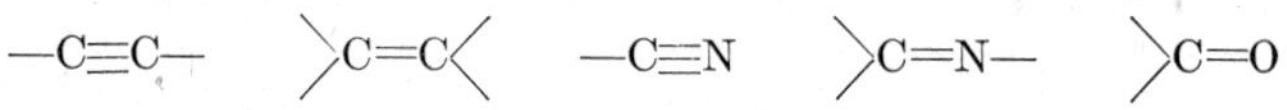

$$-C{\equiv}C- \qquad {>}C{=}C{<} \qquad -C{\equiv}N \qquad {>}C{=}N- \qquad {>}C{=}O$$

factor. The capacity for resinification is determined, however, not only by the grouping itself but also by external factors, such as heat, light, catalysts, and pressure, which are discussed later. If all the unsaturation

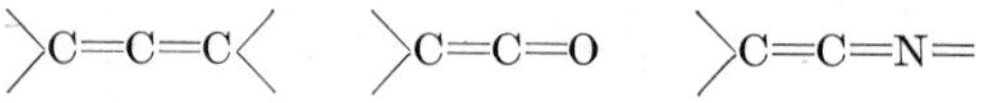

$$ {>}C{=}C{=}C{<} \qquad {>}C{=}C{=}O \qquad {>}C{=}C{=}N{=} $$

is on a single atom the tendency for polymerization is greater. Conjugation of the grouping is even more effective

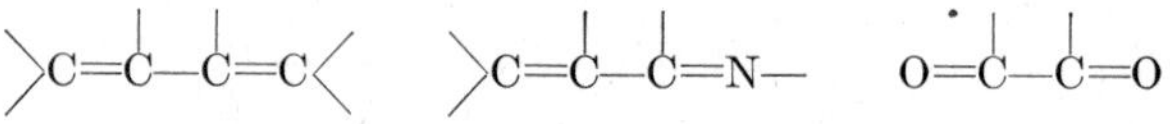

$$ {>}C{=}\overset{|}{C}{-}\overset{|}{C}{=}C{<} \qquad {>}C{=}\overset{|}{C}{-}\overset{|}{C}{=}N{-} \qquad O{=}\overset{|}{C}{-}\overset{|}{C}{=}O $$

Compounds like styrene, which contain a negative group attached to the vinyl ($CH_2{=}CH-$) radical tend to form polymers in which the degree of polymerization is very high. Other negative groups resulting in a similar behavior are:

Group	Formula	Compound
Carboxyl	$CH_2{=}CH-COOH$	Acrylic acid
Aldehyde	$CH_2{=}CH-CHO$	Acrolein
Acetyl	$CH_2{=}CH-COCH_3$	Methylene-acetone
Acetoxy	$CH_2{=}CH-OCOCH_3$	Vinyl acetate
Ethoxy	$CH_2{=}CH-OCH_2CH_3$	Vinyl ethyl ether
Chloride	$CH_2{=}CH-Cl$	Vinyl chloride

When the ethylene group is in a ring, it may still retain its ability to polymerize but giant molecules are not formed from the following:

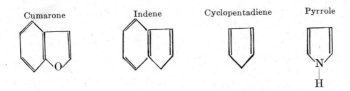

Cumarone   Indene   Cyclopentadiene   Pyrrole

The influence of the same substituents is different in the case of the C=C double bond and in that of the carbonyl (C=O) group. In the latter case, the simplest compound, formaldehyde (H₂C=O) is the least stable of all, whereas ethylene polymerizes with difficulty. In contrast with the behavior of vinyl derivatives noted in the previous paragraph, the introduction of negative components, *e.g.*, phenyl and especially chlorine, into the molecule of formaldehyde causes the tendency to polymerization to disappear; benzaldehyde and phosgene $\begin{smallmatrix} Cl \\ \\ Cl \end{smallmatrix}\!\!\!>\!\!C\!=\!O$

for instance are stable compounds. The substitution of a carbonyl or a carboxylic group makes the molecule unstable again, *e.g.*, glyoxylic acid (COOH·CHO), glyoxal (CHO·CHO), and methylglyoxal (pyruvic aldehyde) (CH₃·CO·CHO).

This difference in behavior as summarized by Staudinger[1] is shown in Table I.

TABLE I.—POLYMERIZATION TENDENCY OF ETHYLENE DERIVATIVES AND CARBONYL COMPOUNDS

C=C Compounds	Polymerizes	C=O Compounds	Polymerizes
CH₂=CH₂	With some difficulty	CH₂=O	Very easily
CH₃·CH=CH₂	With difficulty	CH₃·CH=O	Easily
(CH₃)₂·C=CH₂	Easily	(CH₃)₂C=O	Only condenses
CH₂=CH·CH=CH₂	Easily	CH₂=CH·CH=O	Very easily
C₆H₅·CH=CH₂	Very easily	C₆H₅·CH=O	Only condenses
CH₃O·CO·CH=CH₂	Very easily	CH₃O·CO·CH=O	Very easily
CH₃CO·CH=CH₂	Very easily	CH₃CO·CH=O	Easily
CH₃CO·OCH=CH₂	Easily	CH₃O·CH=O	Not
Cl₂·C=CH₂	Easily	Cl₂·C=O	Not
O=C=CH₂	Easily	O=C=O	Not

When more than one substituent is present in an ethylene derivative, it is usually found that the symmetrical compounds are more stable than the asymmetric ones. The asymmetric CH₂=CCl₂ polymerizes, for example, much more readily than the corresponding symmetrical compound ClHC=CHCl.

[1] STAUDINGER, *Trans. Faraday Soc.*, Sept. 1935.

Unsaturated compounds with conjugated double bonds are generally more reactive than those with isolated double bonds. Butadiene, for instance, polymerizes much more easily than ethylene or ethyl ethylene, and acrolein polymerizes much more readily than propionic aldehyde.

$$CH_2{=}CH{-}CH{=}CH_2 > CH_3CH_2{\cdot}CH{=}CH_2$$
$$CH_2{=}CH{-}CH{=}O \quad > CH_3CH_2CH{=}O$$

If a methyl group is introduced into a molecule with conjugated double bonds with alpha position, the polymerization tendency becomes weaker; it is raised, however, by the same substituent in the beta position. This phenomenon is further elucidated in Table II.

TABLE II.—POLYMERIZATION TENDENCY OF DIFFERENT DERIVATIVES OF ETHYLENE

Initial substance easily polymerized	Methyl group in α-position, polymerizing hardly or not at all	Methyl group in β-position, polymerizing easily
$CH_2{=}CH{-}CH{=}CH_2$ Butadiene	$CH{=}CH{-}CH{=}CH_2$ $\mid$ CH_3	$CH_2{=}C{-}CH{=}CH_2$ $\mid$ CH_3
$CH_2{=}CH{-}CH{=}O$ Acrolein	$CH{=}CH{-}CH{=}O$ $\mid$ CH_3	$CH_2{=}C{-}CH{=}O$ $\mid$ CH_3
$CH_2{=}CH{-}C{=}O$ $\mid$ OH Acrylic acid	$CH{=}CH{-}C{=}O$ $\mid \qquad \mid$ $CH_3 \qquad OH$	$CH_2{=}C{-}C{=}O$ $\mid \qquad \mid$ $CH_3 \quad OH$
$CH_2{=}CH{-}C{=}O$ $\mid$ CH_3 Methylene acetone	$CH{=}CH{-}C{=}O$ $\mid \qquad \mid$ $CH_3 \qquad CH_3$	$CH_2{=}C{-}C{=}O$ $\mid \qquad \mid$ $CH_3 \quad CH_3$

The Mechanism of Polymerization.—There is widespread agreement that the polymeric molecules are long-chain structures. The question: how do the high-polymeric products arise has been answered differently.[1] According to Staudinger,[2] the formation of high polymers must be explained by the activation of monomeric substances—by heat, light or a catalyst—and can therefore react with a second molecule. The newly formed molecule has an "active point" on each of its ends (*bifunctional*) and the polymerization process can thus proceed further, until an unknown side reaction makes the active centers disappear. The following scheme describes this process for formaldehyde,[3] isoprene, and styrene.

[1] The reader is referred to Ellis, "The Chemistry of Synthetic Resins," for a more complete survey of various theories.

[2] STAUDINGER, *Trans. Faraday Soc.*, Sept. 1935.

[3] CAROTHERS, *Trans. Faraday Soc.*, Sept. 1935.

$$CH_2{=}O \rightarrow {-}CH_2{-}O{-} \rightarrow CH_2{-}O{-}CH_2{-}O{-}CH_2{-}O{-} \cdots$$

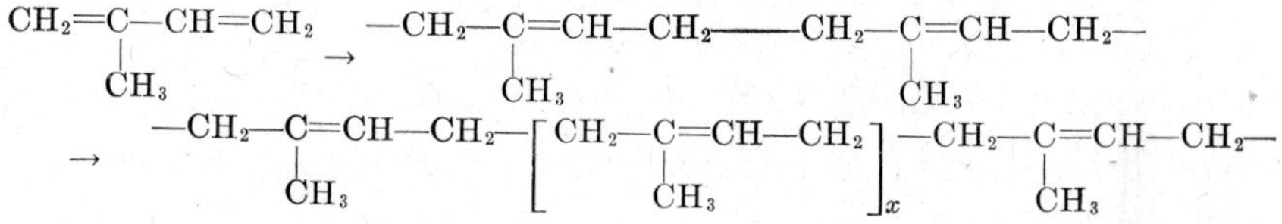

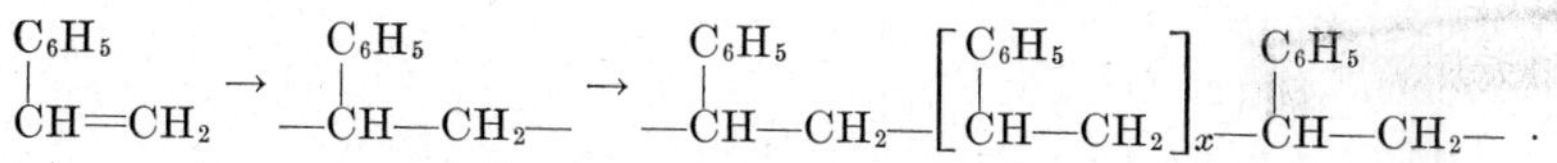

$$CH_2{=}C{-}CH{=}CH_2 \underset{\longrightarrow}{} {-}CH_2{-}C{=}CH{-}CH_2{-\!\!-\!\!-}CH_2{-}C{=}CH{-}CH_2{-}$$
$$\quad\;\; |\qquad\qquad\qquad\qquad\quad | \qquad\qquad\qquad\qquad\quad |$$
$$\quad CH_3 \qquad\qquad\qquad\qquad CH_3 \qquad\qquad\qquad\qquad CH_3$$

$$\underset{\longrightarrow}{} {-}CH_2{-}C{=}CH{-}CH_2{-}\Big[CH_2{-}C{=}CH{-}CH_2\Big]_x{-}CH_2{-}C{=}CH{-}CH_2{-}$$
$$\qquad\qquad\quad | \qquad\qquad\qquad\quad | \qquad\qquad\qquad\qquad |$$
$$\qquad\qquad CH_3 \qquad\qquad\qquad CH_3 \qquad\qquad\qquad\quad CH_3$$

$$C_6H_5 \qquad\qquad C_6H_5 \qquad\qquad C_6H_5 \quad\Big[C_6H_5\quad\Big]\quad C_6H_5$$
$$\;\; | \qquad\qquad\quad\; | \qquad\qquad\quad\; | \qquad\;\; | \qquad\qquad\quad |$$
$$CH{=}CH_2 \underset{\longrightarrow}{} {-}CH{-}CH_2{-} \underset{\longrightarrow}{} {-}CH{-}CH_2{-}\Big[CH{-}CH_2\Big]_x{-}CH{-}CH_2{-} \cdot$$

Although there are some exceptions to the quantitative aspects of this hypothesis, *e.g.*, as to isoprene where isomeric chains are formed, it nevertheless serves as a useful tool in comprehending the phenomenon of polymerization. Mark and Meyer have found by X-ray studies that there is a definite periodicity in polyoxymethylene, also in rubber, cellulose, and other products. They also consider the larger-molecular-weight compounds to be chains held together by primary valence bonds; the chains are then associated laterally by secondary valences to form micelles which act as entities.

IV. FACTORS INFLUENCING POLYMERIZATION

Temperature.—Polymerization reactions are very sensitive to heat. The generalization that low temperatures are more suitable to the formation of long-chain polymers than high temperatures has been made. Scheiber and Sändig[1] represent the effect as follows:

$$\text{Monomer} \underset{\text{Excessive temperature}}{\overset{\text{Suitable temperature}}{\longleftrightarrow}} \text{Polymer}$$

This may not always be true, as Carothers and Hill[2] have shown that some of the polyesters give no signs of being degraded by repeated exposure to high temperatures. Possibly the fact that condensation has taken place in the reaction studied by them has effected this stability. In general, however, polymerization resembles crystallization in that slow polymerization yields the largest molecules. The stability of the polymer at high temperatures may very well vary with its nature.

Polymerizations, like all chemical reactions, are accelerated by heat, and heating tends to produce short-chain polymers. An apparant exception is cyclopentadiene[3] which increases its polymer size on further heating according to the following scheme:

[1] SCHEIBER and SÄNDIG, "Artificial Resins," Sir Isaac Pitman & Sons, London (1931).

[2] CAROTHERS and HILL, *J. Am. Chem. Soc.*, **50**, 1587 (1932).

[3] HURD, "Pyrolysis of Carbon Compounds," Chemical Catalog Company, Inc., New York (1929). KISTIAKOWSKY and MEARS, *J. Am. Chem. Soc.*, **58**, 1060 (1936).

```
CH—CH              CH—CH—CH—CH              CH—CH—⎡CH—CH—⎤ CH—CH
‖   ‖    heat     ‖    ‖    ‖   ‖    heat   ‖   ‖  ⎢ ‖   ‖  ⎥  ‖   ‖
CH  CH  ────→     CH   CH—CH  CH  ────→     CH  CH ⎢ CH  CH—⎥ CH  CH
 \ /               \  /    \ /               \ /  ⎢  \ /   ⎥n  \ /
 CH₂               CH₂     CH₂               CH₂  ⎣  CH₂  ⎦   CH₂
Cyclopentadiene    Dicyclopentadiene                  Polycyclopentadiene
```

These formulas, in which n is relatively small, are supported by Staudinger and Rheiner.[1] The pentacyclopentadiene melts at 270°C. while the dicyclopentadiene (alpha form) melts at 32.5°C. A final polycyclopentadiene is obtained which is a hard white porcelainlike product decomposing above 300°C. Temperatures of the magnitude of 200°C. are used to bring about the polymerization.

On the other hand, polyoxymethylene, the polymerization product of formaldehyde, reverts to gaseous formaldehyde with the application of heat. Water, which as ice has the formula $(H_2O)_x$ where x is 3 or more, becomes the monomer in the gaseous state. Liquid water is a mixture or mutual solution of the various polymers of H_2O and even at the boiling point a considerable amount of the ice complex is present.[2]

Controlled temperature is essential in the building of all large-molecular-weight products. The effect of exothermic reactions must be carefully considered in this respect. These often occur in both polymerizations and condensations. The start of an exothermic reaction may not always be readily detected by ordinary thermometers unless excellent mixing is obtained. Local side reactions may then occur which give products that alter the desired physical properties of the final reaction product. The common expedients used to control temperature are: excellent mixing, use of moderate-sized reaction chambers, dilution by solvents, and running of the reaction at as low a temperature as possible or at some constant temperature such as the boiling point of one of the reactants.

Catalysis.—A discussion of the polymerization of cyclopentadiene under the influence of heat alone has already been given. Very different results are obtained in the presence of a strong catalyst. The end products are then rubberlike materials. Stannic chloride and antimony pentachloride both vigorously catalyze the formation of a white amorphous powder somewhat resembling rubber. The product has one double bond per C_5H_6 group and has been given the general formula

```
            CH₂            ⎡   CH₂        ⎤        CH₂
           /    \          ⎢  /    \      ⎥       /    \
··· CH—CH=CH·CH  ⎢ CH·CH=CH—CH ⎥ₙ CH·CH=CH—CH ···
```

where n is from 20 to 100.[3]

[1] STAUDINGER and RHEINER, *Helv. Chem. Acta,* **7,** 23, (1924).

[2] BARNES, "Colloidal Water and Ice," p. 103, Third Colloid Symposium Monograph, 1925.

[3] BRUSON and STAUDINGER, *Ind. Eng. Chem.,* **18,** 381 (1926).

The formation of polyoxymethylene from formaldehyde is vigorously accelerated by the presence of formic acid,[1] and many other examples can be given of reactions aided or influenced by catalysts. The usual catalysts are all the commonly used acids, salts, alkalis, and oxides. The common negative catalysts are generally phenolic, *e.g.*, quinol and resorcinol, which are used to facilitate the distillation of styrene without polymerizations, or guiacol, which inhibits the polymerization of china wood oil and is used as an anti-skinning agent in varnishes. Long side-chain phenols inhibit many polymerization reactions in petroleum distillates and are used to prevent gum formation.

For most unsaturated hydrocarbons, sulfuric or phosphoric acid is the catalyst that is commonly used. Here the reaction is probably the formation of an ester which reacts further to give the polymer with cyclic regeneration of the acid.

The selection of the proper catalyst and its form is governed by the type of products that are being reacted. Care must be taken not to inadvertently catalyze the very sensitive reactions by such things as the metal used in kettle construction or by products of the reaction itself.

Oxygen and peroxides are often used as catalysts when their effect is really one of primary oxidation, and the oxidation product is the catalyst as with formaldehyde where formic acid is a very active catalyst.

Light.—In a manner similar to the generalization that heat induces polymerization up to a certain "suitable temperature" beyond which dissociation is favored, Scheiber and Sändig[2] explain the effect of light on polymerization reactions by the equation:

$$\text{Monomer} \underset{\text{Light of short wave length}}{\overset{\text{Light of long wave length}}{\rightleftarrows}} \text{Polymer}$$

Here it is shown that, in general, the infrared favor polymerization while the shorter waves favor dissociation. Here, as with heat, the resulting effects of light on polymerizations will vary with the type of reaction involved. Where stable rearrangement products are readily obtained, it is doubtful if the generalization would hold true. In the polymerization of gaseous formaldehyde, light of 3000 Å resulted in an immediate reduction of pressure, indicating the formation of solid polyoxymethylene.

Certain types of molecules are more sensitive to activation by light than others, and the effect of light on polymerization reactions is undoubtedly of very great importance, particularly in the field of natural products. The biological activity of irradiated cholesterol indicates the type and importance of the effects that might be obtained.

[1] CARRUTHERS and NORRISH, *Trans. Faraday Soc.*, **32**, 195 (1936).

[2] SCHEIBER and SÄNDIG, "Artificial Resins," p. 71, Sir Isaac Pitman & Sons, London (1931).

Pressure.—Pressure is another important factor in effecting polymerization reactions, especially where secondary condensations or rearrangements are involved. Under reduced pressure the removal of volatile by-products often helps govern the course of a reaction. Increased pressure is often desirable where the reacting products are volatile and where high temperatures are needed. In general it might be said that increased pressure decreases the temperature at which a polymerization reaction occurs.[1]

Solubility.—Solubility effects and colloidal phenomena are part and parcel of resinification. It might be stated that the first prerequisite for true resinification is that all the constituents shall be mutually soluble at all temperatures and under all conditions. Unless this condition prevails, separation of one or another is bound to occur at some point during the use of the resin and will result in weakened structure or spotted appearance of a molded article.

Colloidal Phenomena.—Colloidal phenomena are continually met with in dealing with aggregates such as resins. Dispersion, mutual solubility of the resins in solvents are all affected by very distinctly colloidal reactions. In considering what constitutes a colloidal system, Gortner[2] calls attention to Fischer's definition stating that "colloidal systems result whenever one material is divided into a second with a degree of subdivision either coarser than molecular or where the micelles exceed 1 to 1.5 mμ in diameter."

Molecules and ions	Colloids	Matter in mass
Not visible in ultramicroscope	Visible in ultramicroscope 1.0 mμ	Visible in microscope 0.1 μ

These are arbitrary boundaries, however. It is believed that in some cases the molecules themselves in a resin reach at least colloid size, if not larger. Excellent suspensions showing some colloid characteristics can be obtained with particle sizes ranging as high as 0.002 to 0.02 mm.

The actual formation of colloidal like suspensions of resin in non-solvents is only one phase of the resin work where colloidal effects have an important bearing. Probably the actual resin itself—a solid solution of many complexes—is very much a colloid, some parts being in true, some in colloidal solution. We know that many of the oil-soluble types are resins insoluble in the natural gums in which they are dispersed

---

[1] Tamman and Pape, *Z. anorg. Chem.*, **200**, 113 (1931); Starkweather, *J. Am. Chem. Soc.*, **56**, 1870 (1934).

[2] Gortner, "Outlines of Biochemistry," p. 5, John Wiley & Sons, Inc., New York (1929).

and insoluble in the oil in which they are finally used. The apparent solubility must, therefore, be colloidal. Thermosetting varnishes are obviously semi-colloids, and even more outstanding examples of colloidal effects are obtained in some of the aggregates such as are formed from urea.

V. THERMOSETTING RESINS

Introduction.—The term *thermosetting* best describes the characteristics of the synthetic resins used in hot molding, and this term is the

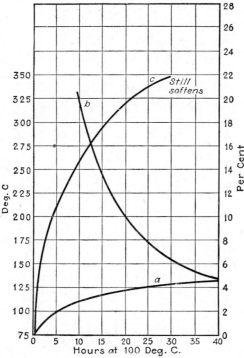

Fig. 3.—Physical properties of shellac. *a.* Loss in weight. *b.* Solubility in alcohol. *c.* Melting point.

most logical starting point of a discussion of the chemistry of these products, *as the chemical properties are only a means of accomplishing the end, the end being a product that is measured by physical rather than chemical characteristics.* Thermosetting is, in a sense, accelerated aging and is a property unique to the synthetic resins. Aside from shellac, the aging of the natural resins cannot be accelerated by the application of heat alone. Natural resins do pass, over a period of years, through the various stages represented, first, by the recent secretions; then semi-fossil and fossil types; ending with inert amber itself.[1] This transition is not only slow,

[1] FARBE and LACK, "Fossil Resins," p. 359 (1927).

however, but involves addition of oxygen, evaporation of high-boiling solvents, and many other external effects.

Shellac on the application of heat will approach a stage where it is no longer fusible but will soften only slightly with heat.   The period of time required to bring about this semi-thermoset condition is much longer than that in which a modern industrial resinoid reaches a completely set condition.   Comparative curves[1] (Figs. 3, 4) show quite distinctly

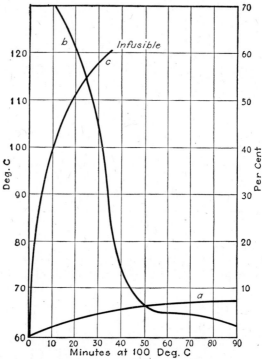

Fig. 4.—Physical properties of resinoid.   *a.* Loss in weight.   *b.* Solubility in alcohol.   *c.* Melting point.

the relative times involved.   The degree of inertness represented by high melting points and low solubilities reached in minutes by a commercial resinoid is approached only after hours by a natural resin, and the curves present graphically the requirements necessary for an industrially valuable resinoid as compared with the best of the natural products.

Rubber vulcanization is somewhat comparable to resin setting.   The times involved are again longer, and rubber never develops the hard, lustrous surface in a mold that is one of the most valuable characteristics of the thermosetting resins.   When rubber is vulcanized to a point

[1] Scheiber and Sändig, "Artificial Resins," p. 5, Unpublished communication, Laboratory of General Plastics, Inc.

as hard as a resinoid compound, it becomes very brittle. Rubber vulcanization may involve polymerization reactions similar to those of resinification. But here, as in the natural resins, heat alone is not sufficient to set the rubber. Addition of other compounds, particularly sulfur, is necessary to bring about the setting of rubber, and the physical appearance and properties are not, strictly speaking, those commonly indicated by the term *resin*. Thermoplastic rubberlike molding compounds are available but none that is thermosetting per se.

PHENOL-FORMALDEHYDE RESINS

Phenol-Formaldehyde Resins.—Of the five chemical classes of synthetic resins mentioned previously (page 697), the first two include all the thermosetting resins of commercial value today. Of these two, the first one—those products made from the reaction of phenols with formaldehyde—are by far the most important.

Probably the clearest explanation of a thermosetting reaction is the straight-line picture,[1] starting with 1 mole of phenol and an excess over 1 mole of formaldehyde at one end and ending with a finished molded article at the other.

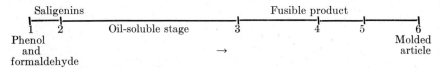

When an alkaline catalyst is present, the reaction progressing from left to right, up to point 2, is well known. The two isomeric hydroxybenzyl alcohols known as *saligenins* are the first isolable products formed.

| *p*-Hydroxybenzyl Alcohol | *o*-Hydroxybenzyl Alcohol |

These mono- and polymethylolphenols continue to condense and polymerize with each other rapidly and almost violently. They quickly pass through the water-soluble stage, through the period of oil solubility, and into three-dimensional molecular aggregates so reactive and large as to be indeterminable. After dehydration under vacuum at point 3, the resin is advanced by its own heat of reaction to a clear brittle product represented at point 4. This product is fusible (m.p. between 60 and 80°C.) and is soluble only in alcoholic solvents. Periods 1 to 4 represent 8 to 10 hr. of violent reaction both under pressure and under vacuum.

[1] DENT, Unpublished communication, Laboratory of General Plastics, Inc.

Point 4, therefore, is somewhat variable and this resin is frequently called a *resole*. The time of the incorporation of the dyes and fillers, represented by points 4 to 5 and actually taking about 5 min. in a molten state on rubber machinery, is taken advantage of to adjust the advancement accurately to the exact point required by the molder. This final period will vary from 40 sec. in some cases to 10 min. in others, and the final adjustment must be so accurate that the time required in the mold, represented by the distance from 5 to 6 is exactly right for the specific job.

In the case of an acid catalyst, point 2 on the straight line is represented by the three dihydroxydiphenylmethanes of which the first two have been isolated from resinous condensations.

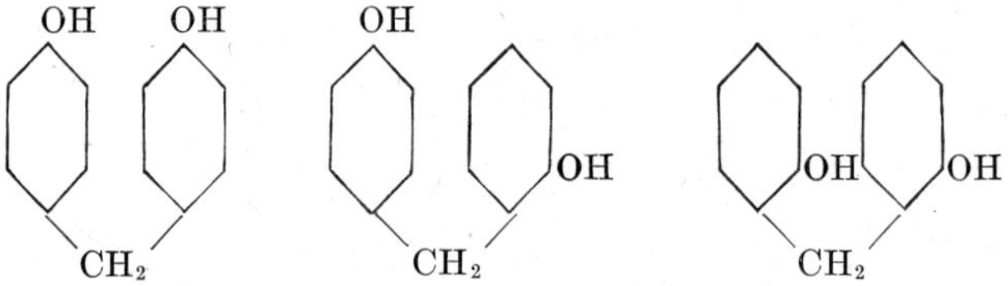

Para, Para-   Ortho, Para-   Ortho, Ortho-
Dihydroxydiphenylmethanes

At point 4, this reaction has reached an end point, and at 5 is a clear, brittle, permanently fusible product. It is soluble only in alcoholic solvents and differs little from the thermosetting resin in physical appearance. To convert it to a thermosetting resin, more formaldehyde in the form of hexamethylenetetramine is added at the time of incorporation of the fillers. In the mold, this product sets to a compound comparable to that of the alkaline reaction.

Course of Reaction.—From the preceding, it is clear that phenol-formaldehyde condensations can follow two courses leading to methylol phenols and dihydroxydiphenylmethanes, respectively. The addition of $CH_2=O$ may furthermore take place in any one of these positions in the phenol molecule, and when it is present in excess a mixture of mono- and polyalcohols is formed. In the presence of less than 1 mole of formaldehyde and in acid media, the condensation of hydroxybenzyl alcohols with phenol occurs largely in the following simplified manner:

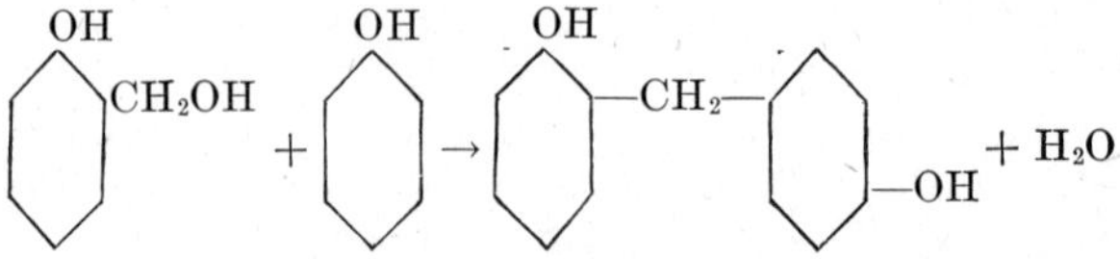

The end product above is still capable of further reaction, and larger molecules are built up by successive additions. The average molecular weight of such straight-chain addition polymers, *i.e.*, *novolaks*, is usually below 800. A typical novolak molecule would be somewhat as shown below:

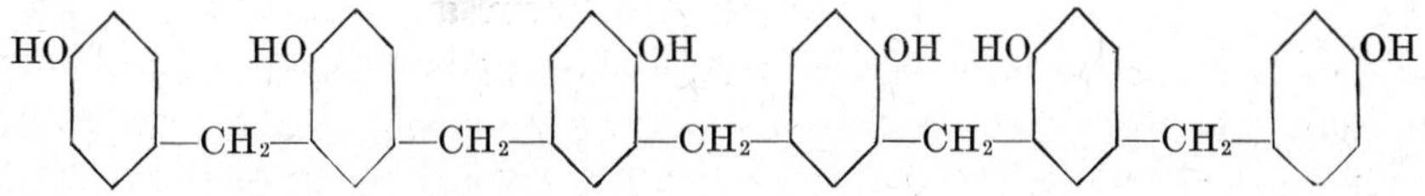

but it is clear that the three reactive positions in phenol make possible an enormous number of isomers. The final hardening of a novolak with ammonia and additional formaldehyde in the form of hexamethylene-tetramine is caused by the occurrence of cross linkages between molecules to give three-dimensional polymers, thus:

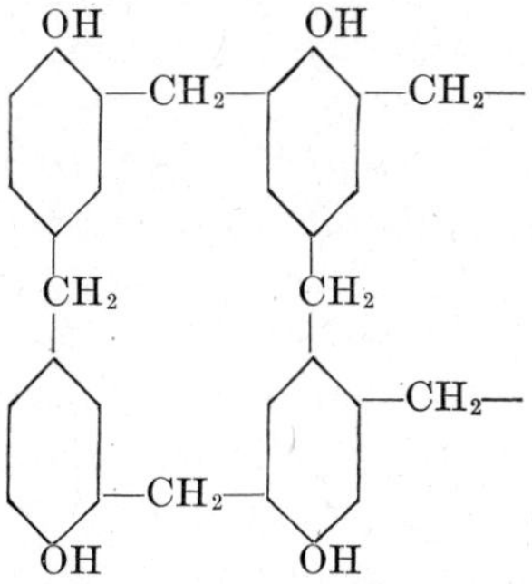

Polymers of this type, it will be recalled, are obtained directly by carrying out the reaction in alkaline media in the excess formaldehyde. The formation of polymethylolphenols is thereby facilitated, and the ease of cross linkage accentuated. Thus a typical *resole* nucleus or macro-molecule may be

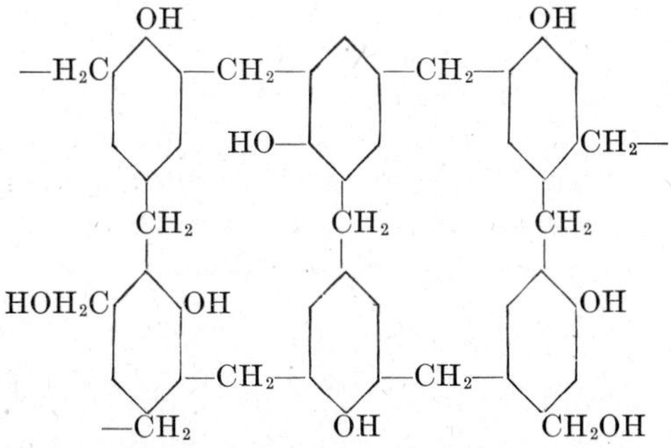

Other Phenols with Formaldehyde.—As a result of a series of studies on the reactions of various phenols and cresols with formaldehyde,[1] Megson concludes that the larger the possible number of isomers that

---

[1] MEGSON, *J. Soc. Chem. Ind.*, **52T**, 420 (1933); MORGAN and MEGSON, *ibid.*, **52T**, 418 (1933); HOLMES and MEGSON, *ibid*, **52T**, 415 (1933).

may be formed from a reacting group, the easier it is to form resins. In the formation of the permanently fusible or "novolak" resins from the acid reaction, the phenolic alcohols form and function as intermediates in the formation of the dihydroxydiarylmethanes. These in turn condense to polynuclear chain compounds. In the heat-convertible resins, the polynuclear compounds from phenol have free positions at which further condensation with formaldehyde may occur and the production of macromolecules[1] is possible.

Phenol and Other Aldehydes.—Of the thermosetting resins, those compounds resulting from the reaction of phenols and aldehydes other than formaldehyde are comparatively unimportant. It might be stated as a generalization that the larger the molecular weight of the aldehyde the slower setting and the lower the mechanical strength of the resulting resin. The stringent demands of mass production together with the lowered costs of formaldehyde have relegated acetaldehyde and furfural[2] resins to the background, *although new uses and methods of molding may minimize the importance of quick-setting properties in some fields.*

The reaction of the aldehydes of larger molecular weight with phenols is, as a rule, quite clean cut and definite. Acetaldehyde in the presence of acid will combine with phenol to give fairly good yields of p, p-dihydroxydiphenylethane.[3]

$$CH_3-CH<^{C_6H_4OH}_{C_6H_4OH}$$

Possibly this tendency to definite reactions is the reason that the resins formed from the higher aldehydes are weaker in mechanical strength and slower in their thermosetting action than the corresponding formaldehyde products.

Benzaldehyde and furfural, in particular, have been investigated very thoroughly, and more recently the availability of the higher straight-chain aldehydes has inspired numerous investigations; but all the research merely confirms the earlier conclusions that, although any aldehyde will serve as a starting point for resinification, industrial requirements can be met best with the more active formaldehyde.

AMINO-ALDEHYDIC RESINS

Aniline-Urea Condensations.—The second class of thermosetting resins—those products resulting from the condensation of *other compounds with formaldehyde*—has produced only two types of product of commercial value to date. First are the aniline resins. These are

---

[1] CHALMERS, *J. Am. Chem. Soc.*, **56**, 912 (1934).
[2] TRICKEY, MINER, and BROWNLEE, *Ind. Eng. Chem.*, **15**, 65 (1923).
[3] CLAUS and TRAINER, *Ber.*, **19**, 3004 (1886).

thermosetting but extremely slow curing. They are characterized by extreme plasticity, a brilliantly yellow basic color, and high dielectric strength. The dielectric strength is the important feature, and these resins find a limited use in products requiring special electrical properties. Second are the urea resins, characterized by their light and permanent colors, as opposed to the darker-colored resins, which are also sensitive to light.

Urea-Formaldehyde Resins.—Urea reacts with formaldehyde to give initially mono- or dimethylol urea and methylol methyleneurea.

$$
\begin{array}{ccccc}
\text{NH}_2 & & \text{NH—CH}_2\text{OH} & & \text{NH—CH}_2\text{OH} \\
| & & | & & | \\
\text{C}=\text{O} & \text{and} & \text{C}=\text{O} & \text{and} & \text{C}=\text{O} \\
| & & | & & | \\
\text{NH—CH}_2\text{OH} & & \text{NH—CH}_2\text{OH} & & \text{N}=\text{CH}_2
\end{array}
$$

On continued reaction these compounds begin to split out water and go to an infusible, relatively inert product. The reaction of the mono compound is much more rapid and difficult to control than that of the disubstituted product. In making molding compounds from these resins, the water solution of the methylol ureas is mixed with cellulose fiber and then dehydrated and heated to the point where the product will assume a rigid form under molding conditions. The chemistry here is again involved and uncertain. It is especially difficult to follow, as the end point is less stable than with the phenolic types. In fact, these products seem to be much more nearly colloidal aggregates than true resins. Addition of thiourea gives products which are more resistant to moisture and atmospheric conditions, but here the decomposition into corrosive sulfur compounds under molding conditions has been a handicap.

The colloidal nature of the reaction products of urea and formaldehyde explains the chief difficulties that are encountered in the commercial products of this type. First is the tendency to be unstable at room temperature before molding; the polymerization reaction progressing slowly even at low temperatures, whereas phenolic compounds are very stable. Second, even after taking from the mold there is a tendency to continue to react, and sometimes internal stresses and strains result which cause cracking or breaking of the finished article. The molding cycle is very critical, and too long an application of heat sets up secondary reactions which destroy the resistant resinlike characteristics of the properly cured piece. Guanidine compounds are similar to urea products but even more critical to heat. Third, the chemical and water resistance of the finished pieces is poor unless the exact conditions for proper cure are maintained.

These three handicaps have limited the use of urea products, but their excellent permanent color constitutes a definite advantage in some fields *e.g.*, lighting fixtures, where a light color is necessary.   In thin layers on a phenolic base the ureas have given excellent results.

According to Walter,[1] the methylol methylene-urea derived from dimethylol urea serves as the nucleus for straight-chain polymers:

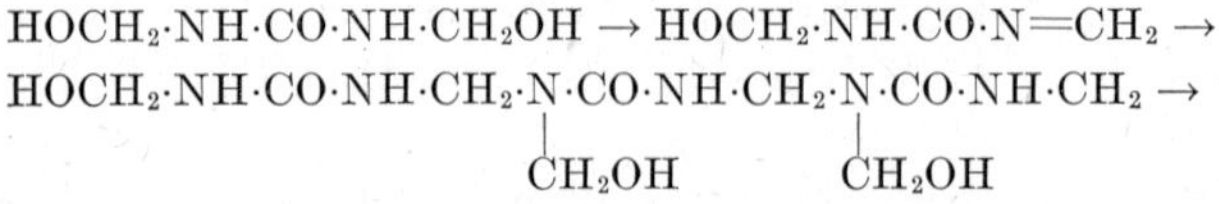

$$HOCH_2 \cdot NH \cdot CO \cdot NH \cdot CH_2OH \rightarrow HOCH_2 \cdot NH \cdot CO \cdot N{=}CH_2 \rightarrow$$

$$HOCH_2 \cdot NH \cdot CO \cdot NH \cdot CH_2 \cdot \underset{\overset{|}{CH_2OH}}{N} \cdot CO \cdot NH \cdot CH_2 \cdot \underset{\overset{|}{CH_2OH}}{N} \cdot CO \cdot NH \cdot CH_2 \rightarrow$$

which condense with the loss of water

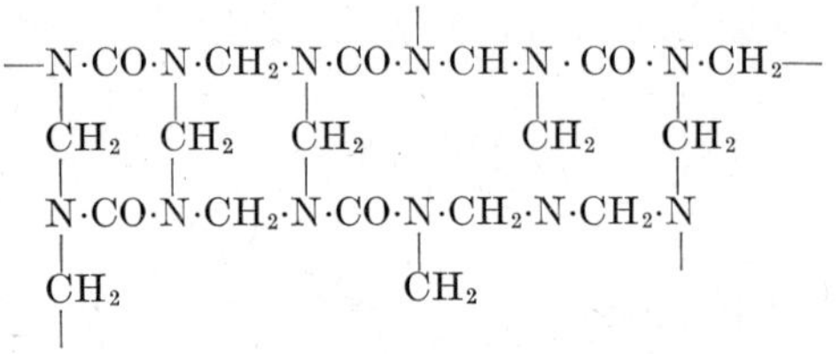

$$-N \cdot CO \cdot N \cdot CH_2 \cdot N \cdot CO \cdot \overset{|}{N} \cdot CH \cdot N \cdot CO \cdot N \cdot CH_2-$$

to form three-dimensional polymers as shown above.   The comparatively small size and relative simplicity of the urea-formaldehyde macro-molecule may account for the difficulties encountered in the technical manufacture of urea resins.   Condensations have been made in the presence of zinc chloride to give a product that sets quickly under heat and is recommended for wood bonding.   The polymerization reactions are very sensitive to changes in pH as well as temperature.

Casein-Formaldehyde Resins.—Casein and casein-formaldehyde resins have been thoroughly described by Sutermeister.[2]   These resins have reached a widespread use, here again because of the permanently light-colored products that are obtainable.   They do not set to the point of chemical inertness which characterizes other resins of this class.

Casein is a phosphoproteide having a molecular weight of 98,000 and containing about 5.5 —NH$_2$ groups in its structure.   The protein contains a large number of amino acids, among which may be mentioned

Lysine	$H_2N(CH_2)_4CH(NH_2)COOH$
Alanine	$CH_3CH(NH_2)COOH$
Valine	$(CH_3)_2CHCH(NH_2)COOH$
Leucine	$(CH_3)_2CHCH_2CH(NH_2)COOH$

As is to be expected the resins obtained by condensing casein with formaldehyde are similar to those derived from urea and formaldehyde and particularly from thiourea and formaldehyde.   The reaction of a simple amino acid with formaldehyde may be represented as follows:

$$CH_2{-}O{-} + H_2NRCOOH \rightarrow CH_2{=}NRCOOH + H_2O$$

[1] Walter, *Trans. Faraday Soc.*, **32**, 377–402 (1935).

[2] Sutermeister, "Casein and its Industrial Applications," The Chemical Catalog Company, Inc., New York (1927).

It is to be emphasized, however, that because of the variety and complexity of the amino acids that are present in the protein, the actual reactions are vastly more complicated.

Casein plastics can be made by dissolving the casein in dilute alkali and adding filler and dyestuff. The mass is stirred and then precipitated by the addition of dilute acid. The casein mixture is put into a hydraulic press, and heated with steam while under a pressure of approximately 500 lb. per square inch. It is kept under this pressure for several hours, until the desired thickness has been obtained. The molded product

TABLE III.—CONDENSATION OF SULFONAMIDES WITH FORMALDEHYDE

Amide	Composition of end product	Nature of end product	
o-Toluenesulfonamide	$R \cdot SO_2 \cdot N \underset{CH_2}{\overset{CH_2}{\diagdown}} N \cdot SO_2 R$ (I)	Resin	
	$R \cdot SO_2 \cdot N \overset{CH_2}{\diagdown} N \cdot SO_2 R$ (II) $H_2C \diagdown \underset{N}{} \diagup CH_2$ $\mid$ $R \cdot SO_2$	Fusible	Infusible
p-Toluenesulfonamide	$R \cdot SO_2 \quad R \cdot SO_2 \quad R \cdot SO_2$ (III) $HN \cdot CH_2{-}N{-}CH_2{-}N{-}CH_2OH$	*	*
m-Benzenedisulfonamide	$C_6H_4(SO_2N{=}CH_2)_2$		*
p-Sulfonamidobenzamide	$C_6H_4 \overset{SO_2N=CH_2}{\underset{CONHCH_2OH}{\diagdown}}$		**
m-Sulfonamidobenzamide	$C_6H_4 \overset{SO_2NHCH_2NHSO_2}{\underset{CONHCH_2OH \quad C_6H_4}{\diagdown}}$ $\underset{CONHCH_2OH}{\mid}$		**

** Represents extra-fast thermosetting properties.

is then removed and placed in a formaldehyde solution to effect the hardening.

Phenol is a powerful solvent for proteins such as casein, and glue, and many resins are made by condensing such a solution with formaldehyde—the addition of proteins resulting in a more flexible product.

Sulfonamide—Formaldehyde Resins.—Walter[1] has studied the tendency to form thermosetting products when the aryl sulfonamides are reacted with formaldehyde. Changing the number and nature of the substituting sulfonamide groups caused marked changes in the properties of the resulting resin. Reaction with formaldehyde proceeds in two steps: (1) the primary condensation of the amide to give —CH_2OH

[1] WALTER, Brit. 375,843 (1932); *Trans. Faraday Soc.*, 402, September, 1935.

groups; and (2) the further polymerization or condensation of these products. The second step proceeds either by intermolecular dehydration, giving unsaturated compounds capable of further polymerization, or by intramolecular dehydration and combination:

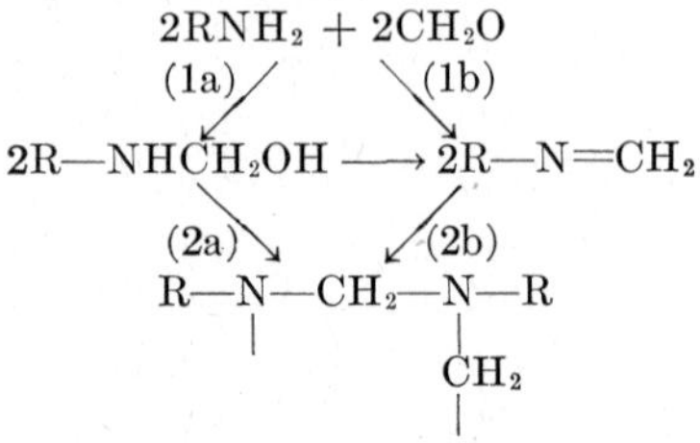

$$2RNH_2 + 2CH_2O$$

$$\overset{(1a)}{\diagup} \qquad \overset{(1b)}{\diagdown}$$

$$2R\text{—}NHCH_2OH \longrightarrow 2R\text{—}N{=}CH_2$$

$$\overset{(2a)}{\diagdown} \qquad \overset{(2b)}{\diagup}$$

$$\underset{|}{R}\text{—}N\text{—}CH_2\text{—}\underset{|}{N}\text{—}R$$

$$\underset{|}{CH_2}$$

The initial sulfonamide resins are all permanently fusible, but the substitution of a second reactive group in the ring, such as —SO_2NH_2, —$CONH_2$, or —NH_2 gives insoluble and infusible resins (Table III).

The fact that only the groups capable of cross-chain linkages and macromolecular formation give thermosetting resins substantiates the modern conception of large molecular products.

Cast Thermosetting Resins

The casting of thermosetting resins has grown to significant proportions in the past few years. The most important of the cast resins are phenol-formaldehyde derivatives essentially similar to those used as a base for molding compounds. They are not incorporated with filler, however, and the pH of the reaction mixture is kept within very narrow limits in order to get a product that is relatively light-fast and which will set uniformly and not too rapidly. Lactic acid is often used as an addition agent. Glycerine, glycols, and other high-boiling liquids, preferably those with an affinity for water, are added to the liquid condensation mass. These tend to aid in the escape of gases during the condensation and to keep the product clear by holding the last traces of water of reaction in solution. The mixtures are cast in a mold and baked at low temperatures, ranging around 65°C., for several days. The final cured piece is rich in color, it may be transparent or translucent, and it is very inert. It is then machined to final size and shape. The largest use is for jewelry and ornamental parts.

Industrially this type of resin has been mixed with fillers and cast into large forms to produce vats and containers for use in the chemical industry where resistance to non-oxidizing acids and mild alkalis is desired. The material is lighter and less brittle than stoneware.

Other resins may be cast, including some like the alkyds that are too slow setting to be useful as molding resins.

VI. THERMOPLASTIC RESINS

Chemically the number of thermoplastic resins is infinite, for included in this classification are not only those products which remelt or soften to their original consistency after cooling, but the products with semi- or slow thermosetting characteristics such as some alkyds, some furfural products, shellac, and some protein derivatives. All natural resins are thermoplastic. The chemistry of all these products is the chemistry of the thermosetting products uncomplicated by the cross linking and setting reactions. Thermoplastic resins are essentially straight-chain linkages. As before, mixtures of closely related products are necessary to avoid tendencies to crystallize; and toughness, elasticity, and other physical properties may be due either to the type of chain structure or to inclusion of extraneous groups and linkages.

Also considered in this class are derivatives of linseed and other drying oils—often semi-thermosetting in character.

In spite of the vast multitude of these products, there are very few that have reached real commercial significance due either to cost or to lack of some required property.

Oil-soluble and Oil-reactive Resins.—These products are essentially thermoplastic products and should be considered as such. Here again, the resins derived from phenols have been of the greatest commercial importance.[1]

The incorporation of resins into china-wood-oil films has such a marked effect on the durability of the films that it seems as though some definite chemical combination must have taken place. The theory involving chemical combination is also borne out by the fact that while the synthetic phenolic resins are of comparatively low melting point and are tacky feeling, the films from them after cooking with oil are comparable to or better than the films from the highest melting of the natural gums. The first type of oil-soluble resin to obtain important commercial value in the paint and varnish field, however, was one the phenolic content of which had been carried practically to the final end point.[2] This phenolic product was fluxed with ester gum in such a manner as to render it colloidally dispersed. This dispersion gave the effect of true solution in the oil, and the resulting films showed all the improved characteristics previously mentioned. The very inertness of the phenolic resin involved seems to preclude any idea of chemical reaction of this fluxed type of gum with the oil. The effects must be the result of the inert properties of the resin itself present in a colloidal dispersion that gives almost the effect of a continuous film of set-up resin.

[1] Krumbhaar, *Paint, Oil Chem. Rev.*, **98**, 22 (1936).
[2] Albert and Berend, Ger. 254,411 (1910).

Another commercial type of oil-reactive phenolic resin is that involving suspension by the use of a chemical flux such as β-naphthol.[1] This product is essentially like the fluxed ester gum resin, except that more phenolic resin can be suspended than with ester or natural gums, and a product higher in phenolic resin content can be made.

The third type of phenolic resin is the unfluxed product[2]—a compound that will dissolve by itself directly and that polymerizes to the inert stage during the cooking of the oil in the manufacture of a varnish. Here there is much more chance for chemical reaction with the oil but, as yet, there is no real evidence of such nor is there any necessity for assuming such a reaction in order to explain the properties of the resulting films.[3] However, in most cases where differences of opinion exist regarding the nature of a reaction, enough evidence to show that both effects are present is generally developed in time. Here, too, later research may show some chemical reaction with, as well as colloidal dispersions in, the oils.

To make a phenolic resin that will be soluble in oils without the use of fluxes, it is necessary to control the initial reaction very closely. The formation of compounds giving insoluble resins must be prevented and the reaction directed along lines to yield products that remain soluble in oils during the polymerization stages. For example, o-hydroxybenzyl alcohol gives resins of very different solubilities from those from the p-hydroxybenzyl alcohol. Similarly, the dihydroxydiphenylmethanes each give resins of differing properties when condensed separately. Thus, by suitably and diversely reacting the initial products of phenol-formaldehyde condensations,[4] it is possible to direct the combination into lines giving a resin truly soluble in oil.

No oil-soluble resin of commercial importance has been made from the use of the higher aldehydes. By adding phenol to amylene from oil cracking, p-amylphenol is obtained (see Chap. IX, Alkylation). This, with formaldehyde, forms a slowly heat-hardening resin which is cooked successfully with oils. It is aided in its dispersion by the presence of the uncombined phenol. Other para substituted phenols react similarly and are used extensively.

Ester Resins.—The third chemical class of resin—the straight ester type—is the most important of all classes of synthetic resins to the *paint and varnish trade*. In spite of the very conspicuous advent of phenolic resins, the fact remains that the introduction of rosin ester was really

[1] Seebach, U. S. 1,809,732 (1932).

[2] HOLMES, *J. Soc. Chem. Ind.*, 53, 757 (1934); Norton, U. S. 2,040,812 (1936).

[3] ALLEN, MEHARG and SCHMIDT, *Ind. Eng. Chem.*, **26**, 663 (1934).

[4] Dent's modifications of DeLaire's method. DEMING, "In the Realm of Carbon," John Wiley & Sons, Inc., New York (1930).

of more importance to the paint and varnish industry than any other single contribution of recent years.[1] Esterifying rosin so improved its qualities as to offer a uniform inexpensive gum of properties comparable with most natural resins. In fact, knowledge of the value of rosin esterification was necessary before the first phenolic resins of the fluxed type could be used to advantage.

Abietic anhydride is the anhydride of a monobasic acid and is present as the major constituent of ordinary gum rosin. The only other products present are small amounts of hydrocarbons and neutral bodies. It

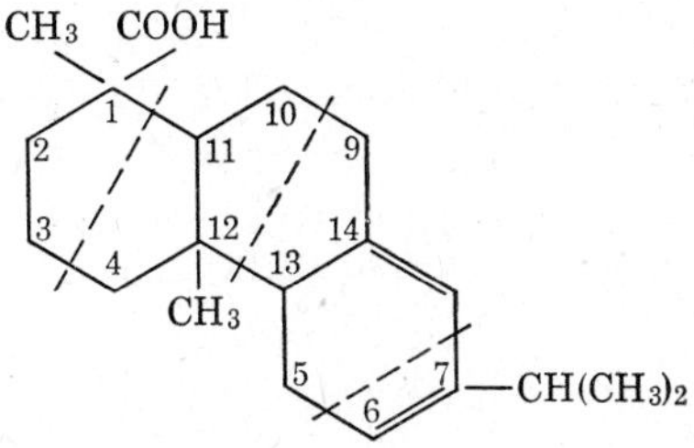

is interesting that the abietic acid molecule is resolvable into four iso-prene[2] units as indicated by the dotted lines. The isoprene groups are arranged irregularly, the chain being as follows:

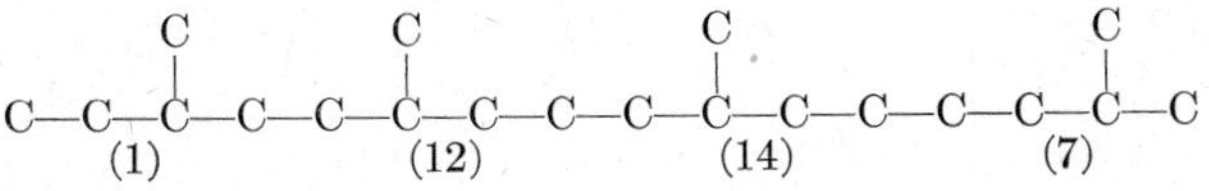

The location of the double bonds is still uncertain.

The equation involved in the esterification with glycerol is

$$3ACOOH + C_3H_5(OH)_3 \rightarrow C_3H_5(OOCA)_3 + 3H_2O$$

where A represents the abietic acid nucleus. In actual practice, the esterification is carried to a designated acid number. In the cooking of china wood oil with *ester gum*, as the rosin ester is commonly known, the acid number of the ester determines the ease of cooking. With an exactly neutral ester, it is difficult to hold the wood oil at polymerizing temperatures long enough to obtain a suitable "body" without danger of the reaction proceeding too far and the oil gelling. Rosin esters with acid numbers from 3 to 8 are commonly used. In some of the com-

---

[1] This statement refers, of course, to resins and gums and not to the introduction of new drying oils, such as tung oil.

[2] FIESER, "Chemistry of Natural Products Related to Phenanthrene," Reinhold Publishing Corporation, New York (1936).

mercial esters, portions of the abietic acid are substituted by maleic or other acids to get slightly higher melting points and lighter colors.

No polymerization reaction is present in this esterification, and the improvement in the resin results from the direct raising of the melting point and reduction of reactivity and solubility by esterification of the acid radical. There are undoubtedly other simple esters of large-molecular-weight acids and alcohols that would be of industrial importance if they were available at a low enough price to be of interest. The possibilities of either synthetic derivatives similar to rosin or of the better control of the natural process of production is indicated by the fact that rosin as well as the terpenes and rubber are all resolvable into isoprene, and therefore may all be synthesized by nature from very similar starting points.

Alkyd Resins.—It was a natural step with the advent of inexpensive phthalic anhydride to esterify this with glycerine to produce a product analogous to ester gum. It was found that mixed and simple esters could be formed and that there was a tendency to long-chain products which give light-colored products whose color is unaffected by light. Resins from phthalic anhydride and glycerine are generally termed *glyptals*. They are not only extremely important in the production of synthetic finishes of various types, but are important from a theoretical standpoint in that much of the investigation into resin structures has been made on alkyd reactions. Some of the earliest discussions of the structural formation of resins were those of Hovey, Kienle, and Hoenel.[1] They pointed out that at least one of the two ester-forming components must possess three esterifiable groups in order to reach infusibility.

The alkyd resins are polyhydric alcohol-polybasic acid ester derivatives known in commerce under many trade names. Although glycerol and phthalic anhydride are employed extensively, it is clear that a large variety of acids and alcohols are available. Obviously the properties of such resins will vary with the nature of the reactants. The simple reaction between ethylene glycol and oxalic acid may be represented thus:

$$\begin{matrix} CH_2OH \\ | \\ CH_2OH \end{matrix} + \begin{matrix} COOH \\ | \\ COOH \end{matrix} \rightarrow \begin{matrix} CH_2-O-CO \\ | \qquad\qquad | \\ CH_2-O-CO \end{matrix} + 2H_2O$$

The reaction of ethylene glycol with phthalic anhydride is more complex, and, when glycerol is used as the alcohol, the formation of the macromolecules may be represented thus:

---

[1] Hovey, Thesis from Union College, (1927); Kienle and Hovey, *J. Am. Chem. Soc.*, **51**, 509, (1929); *J. Am. Chem. Soc.*, **52**, 3636 (1930); Hoenel, *Paint, Oil Chem. Rev.*, **91**, No. 23 (1931).

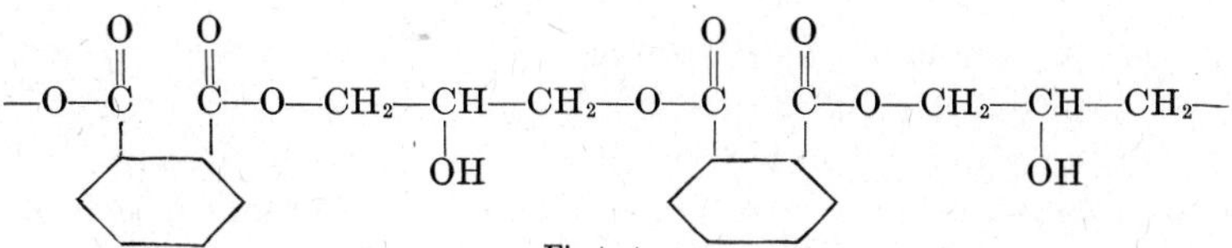

First stage

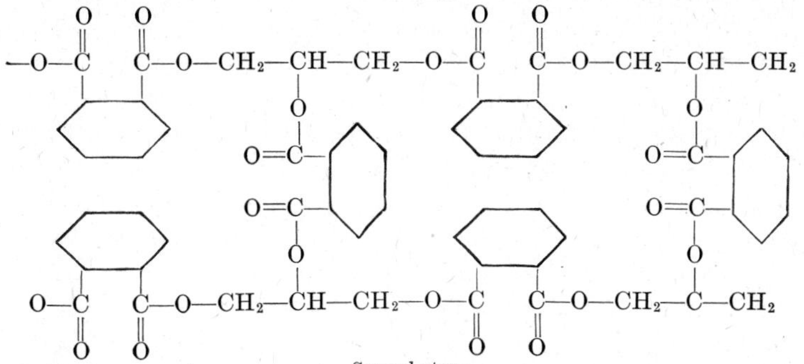

Second stage

Among the polybasic acids that have been used are:

Oxalic..................	HOOC—COOH
Succinic..............	HOOC—$(CH_2)_2$—COOH
Malic.................	HOOC—CHOH—CH_2—COOH
Maleic...............	HOOC—CH=CH—COOH (cis)
Fumaric..............	HOOC—CH=CH—COOH (trans)
Citric................	HOOC—CH_2—C(OH)(COOH)—CH_2—COOH
Adipic	HOOC—$(CH_2)_4$—COOH
Azelaic..............	HOOC—$(CH_2)_7$—COOH

Naphthalic............

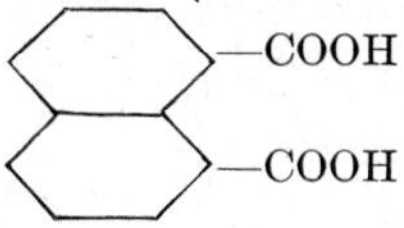

Among the polyhydric alcohols that have been used are:

Glycol.........................	HO—CH_2—CH_2—OH
Propane-1, 2—diol..............	HO—CH_2—CHOH—CH_3
Glycerol......................	HO—CH_2—CHOH—CH_2—OH
Sorbitol and Mannitol...........	HO—CH_2—$(CHOH)_4$—CH_2—OH
Pentaerythritol.................	HO·CH_2 \ / CH_2·OH

The alkyd resins can be varied indefinitely through chain linkages.[1] A large molecule with polymerizing tendencies similar to rubber can be produced. Succinic acid adds to this tendency to become resilient. The variety of possible products has also been stressed by Hovey,[2] who points out many new combinations and emphasizes the possibilities of lactone linkages with hydroxy acids. This possibility is emphasized in a study of the structure of shellac. It is believed[3] that a solid solution of chain

[1] KIENLE and SCHLESINGER, *Ind. Eng. Chem.*, **25**, 971 (1933).

[2] HOVEY, Paper at A. C. S. meeting, Chapel Hill, N. C. (1937).

[3] WEINBERGER and GARDNER, A.C.S. meeting, Rochester (1937).

intra esters of dissimilar polyhydroxy acids might account for its resinous nature.

While the glyptal resins are commonly considered and classed as gums used by the paint and varnish industry, they are more strictly a varnish or synthetic finish in themselves. China wood oil consists mainly of the glycerine ester of trielaeostearic acid and is an ester of the alkyd type. It has an unsaturated group, and oxidation complicates its polymerizing tendencies.

The alkyd resins are difficultly soluble in drying oils by themselves but go in readily in the presence of the fatty acids of linseed oil.

There are many possible "ester"-type resins, but only the inexpensive ones are of commercial importance, and even the most inert show some tendency to hydrolyze, liberating some free acid, under heat and pressure. This tendency makes them difficult to use in molding compositions.

VII. ETHENOID OR POLYMER RESINS

The fifth class chemically—those products formed by straight polymerization—has produced many interesting materials. There are three types that have become of commercial importance, the *vinyl* derivatives, the *styrene* products, and the *acryloids*.

VINYL POLYMERS

Vinylite is a polymerization product of vinyl ($CH_2\!=\!CHX$) compounds and may be considered as a synthetic shellac, having greater toughness, lighter color, and more resistant properties. The polymerization of vinyl compounds[1] is now generally considered to be a chain reaction, i.e., one which involves a chain type of transfer of the energy of activation. The reaction product also consists of a chain, here a physical chain of a great number of molecules linked together to form a polymer. The reaction may be brought about by irradiation with ultraviolet light, bombardment with alpha particles, or addition of small amounts of certain substances which are energy-rich compounds that readily break up to yield oxygen or a free radical. The oxygen possibly reacts with the vinyl compound to form a highly unstable peroxide which, in turn, reacts with another molecule. A free radical might react with a double bond, leaving a free carbon valence. A mechanism frequently offered involves the formation of an intermediate compound with the catalyst which is supposed to give a "hot" or "trigger" molecule capable of initiating polymerization, activating the reactants by a specific transfer of energy. One of the earliest, simplest, and least tenable explanations of vinyl polymer formation, the so-called stepwise mechanism, involves

---

[1] CURME and DOUGLAS, *Ind. Eng. Chem.*, **23**, 1124 (1936).

the repetition of simple addition with hydrogen migration, a process by which many known dimers are formed; a familiar example is the polymerization of unsaturated hydrocarbons in the presence of sulfuric acid. Whatever the mechanism may be, organic peroxides, metal alkyls, ozone, and many other compounds are effective catalysts for the polymerization of these vinyl compounds.

Chain reactions in general are characterized by a number of special properties; the outstanding one is the existence of an induction period and the fact that traces of impurities can have a marked inhibiting or accelerating effect, depending on whether the impurity is instrumental in breaking or initiating chains. These characteristics have all been found to be true of the polymerization of vinyl compounds and serve to establish it as a chain reaction. When such a reaction starts, its maximum velocity is not reached at once, because the number of active centers is increasing during the early part of the reaction. In the case of vinyl polymerization, this induction period ordinarily lasts for several hours. Experience has shown[1] that the induction period is at least roughly proportional to the inhibitor concentration. It decreases as the purity improves and also as the temperature rises.

Vinyl Chloride-Vinyl Acetate Copolymers.—A comparison of the various characteristics, good and bad, of the several vinyl resins shows that no single product has all the properties desired in a synthetic resin, such as adequate strength, color, stability, and water resistance, and attractive molding properties.

The simultaneous polymerization of vinyl chloride and vinyl acetate however, results in the formation of a resin which largely unites the attractive features of the two reactants.[1] These resins are not merely mechanical mixtures but a group of new chemical compounds with properties which combine the hardness, water resistance, high softening temperature, non-flammability, and chemical inertness of polyvinyl chloride, with the strength, flexibility, and, to a degree, the stability of polyvinyl acetate. A new macromolecule is formed consisting of chemically united molecules in predetermined proportions. These resins, termed *conjoint polymers*, may well be regarded as polyvinyl chloride internally plasticized with polyvinyl acetate. That is, a definite reaction, as indicated by chemical and physical tests, has taken place to produce a permanent plasticization of the vinyl chloride polymer. The extent of plasticity in the conjoint molecule can be largely controlled by varying the vinyl chloride-vinyl acetate ratio before polymerization. Such a plasticization is apparently quite different from the usual conception of this process, since a resin plasticized with high-boiling liquids, waxes, and gums is affected by evaporation or by contact with solvents.

[1] CURME and DOUGLAS, *Ind. Eng. Chem.*, **28**, 1126 (1936).

The vinyl ester resins are closely allied structurally to polystyrene, to the derivatives of polyacrylic acid, and to certain hydrocarbon polymers, all of which constitute the general class of ethenoid polymers. That is, resinification is due to self-addition of unsaturated hydrocarbon derivatives rather than to the types of condensation exemplified by the phenolic, alkyd, and urea-formaldehyde resins. The structure of the co-polymer molecule may be approximately shown by the following formula:

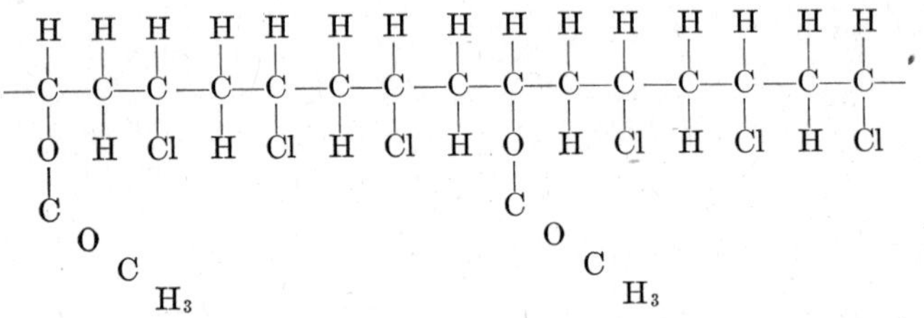

According to this conception, the resin molecule consists of a linear chain in which monomeric vinyl chloride and vinyl acetate have reacted with themselves and with each other at the double bond to form a conjoint polymer. The relative proportions of vinyl chloride and vinyl acetate in the chain depend upon the composition of the reaction mixture, and the length of the molecule is controlled by the reaction conditions at the instant of formation. Average degree of polymerization varies between approximately 200 and 250. Higher polymers are possible but unworkable by ordinary methods, because of insolubility and infusibility.

Styrene Resins[1]

When styrene ($C_6H_5CH{=}CH_2$) is heated at 200°C. for ½ hr. a solid m-styrene ($C_6H_5CH{=}CH_2)_n$ is formed. m-Styrene is quite inert and on distilling is reconverted to the monomer and dimer

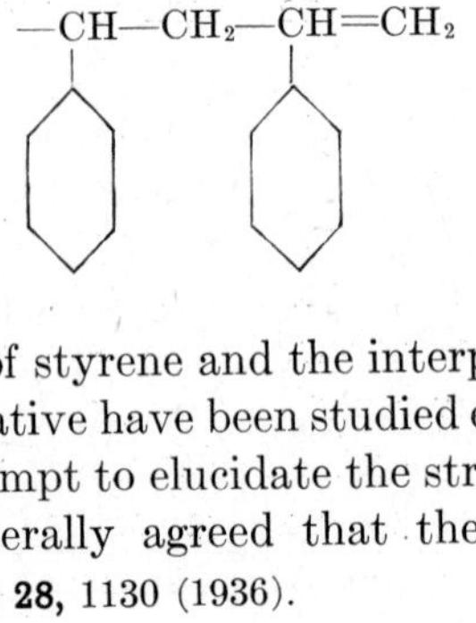

The polymerization of styrene and the interpretation of the structure of the polymerized derivative have been studied extensively by Staudinger and coworkers in an attempt to elucidate the structure of rubber. From his researches it is generally agreed that the polymerized derivative

[1] Ellis, *Ind. Eng. Chem.*, **28**, 1130 (1936).

consists of a long molecular paraffin chain to which are attached phenyl groups:

$$\cdots -CH-CH_2-CH-CH_2-CH-CH_2-CH-CH_2- \cdots$$
$$\quad\;\; | \qquad\quad | \qquad\quad | \qquad\quad |$$
$$\quad\; C_6H_5 \quad\; C_6H_5 \quad\; C_6H_5 \quad\; C_6H_5$$

The question of the end groups has not been decided; the molecule does not appear cyclic and no trivalent carbons exist. The end carbons may attach themselves to some impurities or to solvent molecules, or the compound may have one double bond at the end of the molecule, the unsaturation being wholly masked by the length of the molecule.

The long chain of polystyrene is, in effect, a single molecule and the properties of various polymeric styrenes are a function of the size. Relatively short chains dissolve readily to yield solutions of low viscosity; this low viscosity is not affected by heat. Addition of a non-solvent precipitates the polystyrene as an amorphous powder. The mean molecular weight of this type of styrene varies from 2,000 to 10,000, indicating from 50 to 100 monomeric styrene units in the molecule and is called a "hemicolloid." Where the molecule of polystyrene consists of as many as 3,000 monomeric units and where the molecular weight varies from 10,000 up into the hundred thousands, eucolloids are formed. In solution the eucolloid, in contrast to the hemicolloid, yields a solution of high viscosity which may be lowered by heat treatment. This is due to the fact that at higher temperatures the long chain is unstable and decomposes into shorter ones. On precipitation from solution, the eucolloid yields fibers. Eucolloids are formed at relatively low temperatures and by a slow polymerization. Rapid polymerization by means of catalyst or by heat results in hemicolloids.

Eucolloids are not only sensitive to heat but also appear to be decomposed by mechanical action alone. For example, when polystyrene of a molecular weight of 470,000 (or one of 163,000) is triturated in tetrahydronaphthalene, there is a progressive degradation in molecular weight until a polystyrene of mean molecular weight 103,000 is obtained.

Even the styrene polymer of high molecular weight remains soluble to some extent, in that the polymer swells in certain solvents. Staudinger and Heuer found that the polymerization of commercial styrene at 60 to 100°C. led to the formation of a polystyrene glass which was insoluble. This phenomenon of insolubility was traced to minute quantities of divinylbenzene in the commercial product. On polymerization, the substance exercised the property of bringing together the long chains of polystyrene into a three-dimensional insoluble polymer. Quantitative investigation revealed that as small an amount as 0.002 per cent divinylbenzene was sufficient to induce this effect. One per cent divinylbenzene yielded a derivative which was insoluble and swelled very little; 0.01 per cent divinylbenzene caused the resulting polymer to swell markedly.

TABLE IV.—POLYSTYRENE POLYMER HOMOLOGUES[1]

Material	Formula	Molecular weight	Nature	Solubility in ether	M.p., °C.
Dimer	$C_{16}H_{16}$	208	Fluid	Sol.	
Trimer	$C_{24}H_{24}$	312	Fluid	Sol.	
Hemicolloid SnCl₄ polymerization	$C_{240}H_{240}$	3,000	White powder	Sol.	105–110
Polymerized at 150°C. (N₂)	$C_{1840}H_{1840}$	23,000	White powder	Partly sol.	120–130
Polymerized at 100°C. (N₂)	$C_{9600}H_{9600}$	120,000	White fiber	Insol.	160–180
Polymerized at 20°C. (air)	$C_{16600}H_{16000}$	200,000	White fiber	Insol.	Undetermined
Fraction from room-temp. polymerization	$C_{48000}H_{48000}$	600,000	White fiber	Insol.	Undetermined

[1] STAUDINGER, Die hochmolekularen organischen Verbundingen.

ACRYLOIDS

A product which bids fair to exceed in importance any of the polymerized types now in general use is that made by the polymerization of derivatives of acrylic acid. The chief derivatives now in use are the methyl and the ethyl esters of methacrylic acid.

$$CH_2{=}CHCOOH \qquad CH_2{=}\underset{\underset{CH_3}{|}}{C}{-}COOH$$

Acrylic Acid   Methacrylic Acid

The first work on these products is attributed to Röhm,[1] and several papers giving general descriptions of the products and their chemistry have appeared recently.[2]

The polymerization reaction is similar to those previously described. It is autocatalytic and is accelerated by light and oxygen. The products are thermoplastic, but are clear and colorless. They can be made rubbery or brittle and are very resistant to water and petroleum solvents. They are used principally as coatings, as adhesives for glass and for sheets of curved windows, such as in airplanes.

The polymers of acrylic and methacrylic acids are not so important industrially as the alkyl esters of these acids. Methyl acrylate and methyl methacrylate are particularly important in the manufacture of organic glasses. The reactions leading to these compounds respectively are:

[1] RÖHM, *Ber.*, **34**, 573 (1901).

[2] KLEIN and PIERCE, *Ind. Eng. Chem.*, **28**, 635 (1936); E. I. DUPONT DE NEMOURS Co., *Ind. Eng. Chem.*, **28**, 1160 (1936).

TABLE V.—PROPERTIES OF METHACRYLATE ESTERS[1]

Methacrylate	Monomer B.p.		Density at 20°C.	Polymer-molded disk Softening temp., °C.	Description
	°C.	Mm.			
Methyl...............	100.3	760	0.945	125	Clear, hard, strong
Ethyl................	116.5–117	760	.....	65	Clear, tough
n-Propyl.............	141–143	765	0.921	38	Clear, tough, flexible
Isopropyl.............	125	760	0.888	95	Clear, strong
n-Butyl..............	51–52	11	0.894	33	Clear, flexible, strong
Isobutyl.............	46–47	13	0.884	70	Clear, slightly brittle
sec-Butyl...........	53–57	18	0.890	62	Clear, slightly brittle
tert-Amyl.............	67–68	20	0.887	76	Clear, brittle
Diisopropyl carbinol....	72–75	9	0.876	60	Clear, very brittle
Octyl.................	105	5	.....	Room temp.	Clear, gel
Lauryl................	142	4	.....	Room temp.	Clear, viscous liquid
Phenyl................	83–84	4	1.053	120	Clear, very brittle
o-Cresyl..............	98–103	5	1.031	106	Clear, very brittle
Cyclohexyl............	71–74	5	0.959	105	Clear, slightly brittle
p-Cyclohexyl phenyl....	M.p. 67–68	...	.....	145	Hazy, brittle, very hard
Furfuryl..............	80–82	5	1.055	78	Brown, hard, brittle
Tetrahydrofurfuryl......	81–85	4	1.039	60	Transparent, brittle
β-Chloroethyl..........	61–64	11	1.106	68	Clear, colorless, tough
β-Phenyl ethyl..........	110–117	5	1.018	40	Clear, slightly brittle
β-Methoxy ethyl........	65–67	10	0.990	30	Clear, tough
β-Ethoxy ethyl.........	91–93	35	0.996	Room temp.	Clear, rubbery
Ethylene glycol mono-..	85–86	5	1.079	70	White, slightly brittle
Ethylene glycol di-......	83	2	.....	...	Infusible, insoluble solid
α-Methyl allyl..........	56–59	15	0.921	...	Infusible, insoluble solid

[1] E. I. DUPONT DE NEMOURS & CO., *Ind. Eng. Chem.*, **28**, 1160 (1936).

$$CH_2OH \cdot CH_2Cl + NaCN \rightarrow CH_2OH \cdot CH_2CN + NaCl \qquad (1a)$$

$$CH_2OH—CH_2CN + CH_3OH + H_2SO_4 \rightarrow CH_2{=}CHCOOCH_3 + NH_4HSO_4 \quad (1b)$$

$$CH_3\overset{O}{\overset{\|}{C}}CH_3 + HCN \rightarrow CH_3\overset{OH}{\overset{|}{C}}CH_3 \qquad (2a)$$
$$\underset{CN}{}$$

$$CH_3\overset{OH}{\underset{CN}{\overset{|}{C}{|}}}CH_3 + CH_3OH + H_2SO_4 \rightarrow CH_2{=}\overset{}{\underset{CH_3}{\overset{|}{C}}}COOCH_3 \qquad (2b)$$

The polymer of methyl acrylate would have the following structure

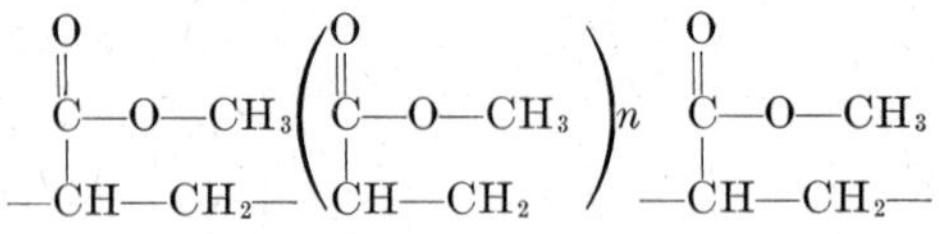

$$\underset{-\text{CH}-\text{CH}_2-}{\overset{\overset{O}{\underset{\|}{}}}{\text{C}-\text{O}-\text{CH}_3}} \left(\underset{\text{CH}-\text{CH}_2}{\overset{\overset{O}{\underset{\|}{}}}{\text{C}-\text{O}-\text{CH}_3}} \right)_n \underset{-\text{CH}-\text{CH}_2-}{\overset{\overset{O}{\underset{\|}{}}}{\text{C}-\text{O}-\text{CH}_3}}$$

The method of determining the rate and course of polymerization by the application of the Raman effect has been described by Hibben.[1] This method showed the disappearance of $=CH_2$ and $C=C$ linkages. Lower frequencies appear indicating an increased chain length. A slight decrease in the complexity of the intermediate frequency indicates an increase in the symmetry of the polymer molecules. Unlike inorganic glasses, the polymer exhibits some sharp lines and these permit an explanation of the continuing structure present throughout the solid and the mechanism by which this structure comes into existence.

Some of the properties of methacrylate esters are shown in Table V.

VIII. CELLULOSE PLASTICS

Cellulose esters and ethers form the base of the most commonly used thermoplastic compounds except shellac. Cellulose $(C_6H_{10}O_5)x$ itself is a highly polymerized product which by X-ray patterns exhibits a crystalline structure. The studies of Scherrer and of Herzog and Jancke[2] show that the crystallites are parallel to one another and parallel to the crystallographic axis of the fiber. Cellulose is now considered to be built up of anhydroglucopyranoses and the following chain structure typifies the triester, where A represents an acid radical.

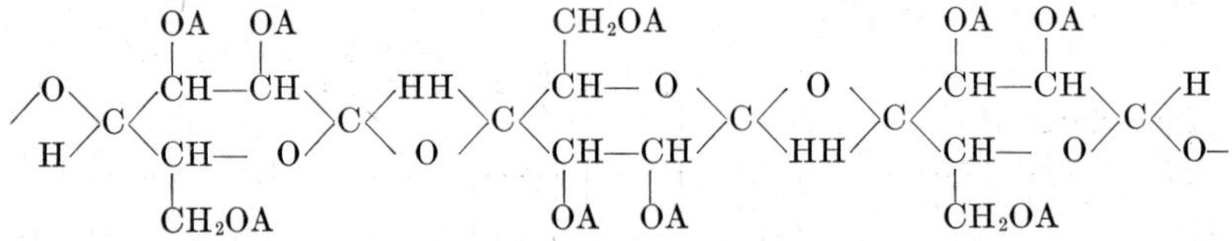

$$\underset{H}{\overset{O}{\diagdown}} C \underset{\underset{CH_2OA}{|}}{\overset{\overset{OA\ OA}{|}}{\diagup CH-CH \diagdown}} \underset{O}{\diagup} C \underset{O}{\overset{HH}{\diagdown}} C \underset{\underset{OA\ OA}{|}}{\overset{\overset{CH_2OA}{|}}{\diagup CH-O \diagdown}} C \underset{HH}{\overset{O}{\diagdown}} C \underset{\underset{CH_2OA}{|}}{\overset{\overset{OA\ OA}{|}}{\diagup CH-CH \diagdown}} C \underset{O-}{\overset{H}{\diagdown}}$$

Staudinger[3] gives the comparative data, shown in table on page 729, for cellulose, its triacetate and other high-molecular-weight polymers.

Organic esters of cellulose *e.g.*, cellulose acetate, may be polymerized by reacting them in an organic solvent solution with a suitable polymerizing agent. The solvents generally employed are acetone, methylene- and ethylene chlorides, or any other solvent which is non-reactive to the polymerizing agent. The polymerizing agents are some phos-

---

[1] HIBBEN, *J. Phys. Chem.*, **5,** 706 (1937).

[2] SCHERRER, *J. Chem. Soc.*, **1919,** 116 (2), 274; HERZOG and JANCKE, *Z. physik,* **1921,** 7, 149.

[3] STAUDINGER, "Die hochmolekularen organischen Verbundingen," p. 104.

Compound	Specific viscosity	Aver. mol. wt.	No. of atoms forming chain	Length angstrom units Å
Cellulose..............	121.4	120,000	3,800	3,900
Cellulose triacetate........	113.6	103,000	1,800	1,900
Polystyrene.............	110.0	600,000	12,000	15,000
Polyvinylacetate..........	20.0	80,000	1,800	2,200
Rubber.................	38.0	125,000	7,200	8,100

phorus-containing compounds such as $POCl_3$, P_2O_5, $C_6H_5POCl_2$, etc. Usually an organic base such as pyridine is added to the solution to remove the HCl liberated in instances where a phosphorous halogen is employed as the agent.

Polymerization of a cellulose ester modifies its properties to an extent proportional to the amount of agent combined. The change most apparent is that of the apparent viscosity of the solution. This property may be varied from a slight increase in viscosity to complete insolubility or, intermediately, to a heavy gel. Polymerization also tends to stabilize the ester and to raise its melting point. The advantages of polymerization other than that of fitting the ester to a condition requiring a higher viscosity are questionable. It is doubtful if higher strengths in the manufactured product are available through this means.

Cellulose ester molding compounds are made from the correctly polymerized ester by the incorporation of dyes and plasticizers. Their use has had a remarkable increase since the development of injection molding.

IX. METHODS OF MANUFACTURE

RESINS

The outstanding contribution of the plastic industry to industry as a whole is the development of an operating technic based on the knowledge and understanding of the value of control in manufacturing processes. The violent exothermic reactions which characterize the most important types of resins, the complexity of their chemical structure, and the close control of their physical and chemical properties make the large-scale manufacture of these products one of the most conspicuous achievements of modern industrial chemistry. The whole evolution of the ancient plastics art into the modern plastics industry has been the direct result of the ability to control these products to a degree of uniformity that permits standardization of the manufacturing processes using these new raw materials.

Phenol-Formaldehyde Resins.—These products are all the result of fairly violent exothermic reactions. When the phenols and formal-

TABLE VI.—PHYSICAL AND MECHANICAL PROPERTIES OF RESINS[1]

| | Thermoplastic Resins | | | | | Thermosetting Resins | | | |
| | | | | | | Phenolics | | | Urea formalde-hyde |
	Vinylite	Plasti-cized cellulose nitrate	Plasti-cized cellulose acetate	Poly-acrylate	Poly-styrene	Unfilled molding	Filled molding	Casting	
Sp. gr.	1.34–1.36	1.34–1.60	1.27–1.60	1.19	1.05	1.30–1.80	1.30–2.00	1.31–1.32	1.48–1.50
Refractive index	1.53	1.46–1.50	1.48–1.51	1.50	1.67	......	......	1.46	1.54
Softening temp.:									
°C	60–70	70–90	65–110	55–90	70–90				
°F	140–158	158–194	149–230	131–194	158–194				
Tensile strength, lb. per sq. in.	8,000–10,000	5,000–10,000	4,000–8,000	8,000–9,000	6,000–7,000	4,000–6,000	4,000–20,000	3,000–5,000	6,000–9,000
Impact strength, ft.-lb.:									
Izod, notched	0.30–0.60	......	......	0.26	......	0.12–0.50	0.12–3.00	9–17 (sq. in.)	1.0–2.0
Izod, unnotched	......	2.00–8.00	2.00–8.00	......	5.00	......			
Charpy	......	......	2.00–8.00	......	......	......	......	......	......
Modulus of elasticity, lb. per sq. in.	350,000–410,000	200,000–400,000	110,000–300,000	45,000	460,000	1,000,000–2,500,000	500,000–4,500,000	300,000–375,000	1,200,000–1,600,000
Modulus of rupture, lb. per sq. in.	10,000–13,000	10,000–13,000	6,000–7,000	14,000–17,000	12,000–13,000	......	6,000–20,000	7,000–12,000	10,000–14,000
Water absorption in 24 hr. at 25°C. (77°F.), %	0.05–0.15	1.50–3.00	1.40–3.00	Very slight	0	0.1–0.8	0.1–0.6	Very slight	10,000–14,000

[1] CURME and DOUGLAS, Ind. Eng. Chem., 28, 1129 (1936).

dehyde are allowed to react directly to a resin in the presence of either alkaline or acid catalyst, the violence of the reaction makes large-scale operations impractical. Ton or two-ton autoclaves are generally used; and after the reaction has progressed to the proper point, vacuum dehydration cools the mass and permits the stopping of the reaction near the point desired. At this point, the whole mass is generally cooled quickly by allowing it to run out on to the air-cooled floor where it cools, much as molasses candy does, to a brittle product, which is then pulverized. The modified DeLaire method of Dent[1] is essentially the same from a mechanical standpoint but permits much easier control, and 8 to 10 tons of the resins can be made readily in one operation.

In order to insure uniformity in the preparation of molding compound, the resins are very finely ground and air floated, after which they are blended in 40,000- to 50,000-lb. batches.

Other Resins.—Essentially the same methods are employed in all products of this type. In some cases, as the ureas, the brittle resin is not isolated, but the aqueous solution is used for incorporation with the filler. In esterifications, as that of rosin, large aluminum kettles are used. The catalyst, as metallic zinc, is introduced and the rosin heated to a comparatively high temperature, the glycerol being added gradually. All air must be excluded from this reaction to prevent discoloration. The coumarones are essentially high-temperature products, as are the vinyl derivatives. Technic is the key to resin manufacture; and large-scale production, the key to uniformity.

VARNISHES

There is considerable use for the so-called thermosetting varnishes, not only for the impregnation of paper for the molding of sheet-laminated stock but for the impregnation of insulating coils, coating of metals and paper, and for use as a cement.

These varnishes are merely solutions of the resin in alcohol, acetone, or mixed spirit solvents. They are made either by cold cutting[2] the brittle resin or by the direct cutting of the molten mass in the autoclave. The control of the viscosity is one of the most difficult features, as viscosity is a function not only of the advancement of the resin, *i.e.*, its degree of solubility, but also is affected seriously by colloidal phenomena difficult to control. Viscosity is very important, however, as it governs the penetrability of the varnish into the material with which it is being used. Various types of resin produce, of course, different types of varnish.

[1] DEMING, *loc. cit.*
[2] *I.e.*, effecting solution.

Colloidal Solutions

The availability of colloidal solutions and emulsions has opened up many new uses for thermosetting resins. These uses center primarily around cementing or gluing problems, as core binding and wood gluing.[1]

The preparation[2] of these colloids and emulsions is difficult. The primary difficulty lies, of course, in the fact that the particle size of a true colloid must be small, and yet the molecular size of some of the more advanced resins is extremely large. By the use of small amounts of protective gums, milky suspensions of a very stable character, capable of dilution with water, showing Brownian movements and, when concentrated, capable of redilution, have been made on a large scale commercially. It may be argued that these are not true colloids in spite of all the indications, because of the particle size, which runs from 0.02 to 0.002 mm. The particle-size boundaries for colloids, however, are very arbitrary and based more on actual experience than on theoretical considerations. It therefore seems correct to call these products colloids rather than stable emulsions. Emulsions have been made[3] and used as a method of incorporating resin with pulp to form a board containing resin which can later be molded. This, however, is a very different product, and emulsions of this type are not capable of transportation.

Impregnated Paper

The impregnation of paper, cloth, and similar materials with alcoholic solutions of the thermosetting resins, driving out the solvent and leaving a sheet product capable of being molded into sheets, gear blanks, or simple designs, as trays, is an old established practice. Two methods are used for the production of this product. The first is the incorporation of the resin directly into the paper as a size or filler during the beater process, before the sheet is actually formed. The second is that of starting with a good paper stock and impregnating that with resin in solution. Stock of this type is stronger mechanically than the powdered molding compound.

Molding Compound

Molding compound is, of course, the backbone of the thermosetting-resin industry. In general, its preparation is analogous to that of rubber compounds. The filler, dyes, and catalysts are mixed with the molten resin on external friction rolls (Fig. 5) or in internal mixers of the Banbury or Werner and Pfleiderer types.

[1] Dent, U. S. 1,777,998 (1928); 1,917,020 (1933).
[2] Plauson, U. S. 1,436,820 (1922); Cheetham, U. S. 1,855,384 (1932).
[3] Cheetham, U. S. 1,855,384 (1932).

In the case of molding compounds, there are five vital characteristics from the molder's angle: plasticity, cure, strength, finish, and color.

Plasticity.—Plasticity may be defined as the pressure, in pounds per square inch, required to close a press at a given temperature. Normal molding conditions are 2,500 to 3,000 lb. per square inch hydraulic pressure and a temperature of 135 to 150°C. with plenty of heat available through well-cored, well-drained, steam-heated molds. The powder is weighed out and placed in the cavity of the mold or, more commonly, briquetted in modified tableting machines into tablets containing the correct amount of material for use on a given piece. In the molding

FIG. 5.—Mixing rolls for molding compound.

(Fig. 4) of normal thermoplastic materials, plasticity is, in a sense, the viscosity of the material at a given temperature. In other words, the rate of flow increases until the material is warmed through and then becomes a constant figure. With thermosetting compounds, the rate of flow is complicated by the stiffening action due to the setting of the resins as a result of the applied heat. This curing action works diametrically opposite from plasticity as regards the rate of flow.

Cure.—The industry demands, of course, a material that flows freely in order that as many cavities as possible may be placed in a mold. At the same time, the demand is also for as quick curing a product as possible. Plasticity and cure, therefore, are so closely related that they must be considered together.

Cure may be defined as the time necessary for a compound to remain in a mold in order to complete the reaction that makes the product infusible and chemically inert. The point at which no blistering occurs when the pressure is released from the mold is generally considered to be the end point.

Normally, the plasticity and cure of a molding compound are dependent on the inherent characteristics of the resin used in the making of the compound. When phenol and formaldehyde are allowed to condense in the usual manner by the alkaline or acid method, the plasticity of molding compounds made from them increases steadily as the time required for curing decreases (Fig. 7, curve 1). In order to obtain maximum fluidity up to the time of cure (Fig. 7, curve 2), which, of

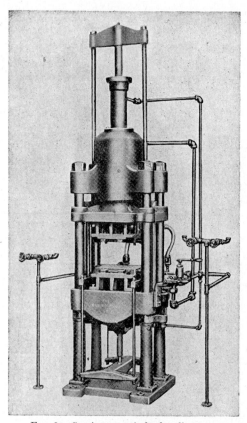

Fig. 6.—Semiautomatic hydraulic press.

course, allows the molding of the maximum number of pieces in the minimum time, it is necessary to modify the resin. This can be done in many ways. By the DeLaire method, it is possible to condense other chemicals with the first reaction products, which gives a wide variety of possibilities. In straight condensation, the control of the reaction determines the ratio of cure to plasticity. Not only the amount of formaldehyde combined, but the method of combination effects these ratios. For example, a resin made from the same amount of phenol and the same amount of combined formaldehyde may, in one case, be very soft and fast and, in another, may even reverse curve 2 and stiffen quickly and set slowly. This last condition is sometimes desirable, as in resins used for bonding the abrasive in a grinding wheel. Here the

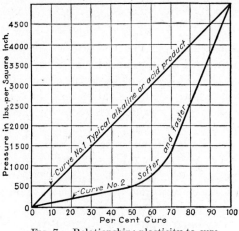

Fig. 7.—Relationship: plasticity to cure.

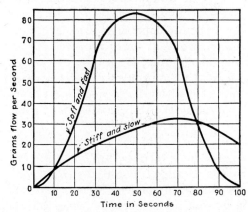

Fig. 8.—Rate of flow of molding compounds. Relationship to cure and plasticity.

resin must stiffen quickly, in order to prevent drainage flow and consequently uneven distribution of bond throughout the wheel.

Relationship of Cure and Plasticity.—Before valuable information on the chemistry of the reactions in its relation to cure and plasticity, could be compiled, it was necessary to find an accurate method of testing. Ordinary flow tests are unsatisfactory, due to the changing of the cure time during the measuring of flow. The desired curve is one showing the flow in grams per second and can be measured by plotting flow rate against time. For practical purposes, however, this is too slow, and two other methods are in vogue. One is to determine the time necessary to close a mold under constant pressure. This is interfered with by the melting rate of the compound, *i.e.*, its physical condition, and, in fast-curing materials, by the stiffening due to cure. The second and most satisfactory method has been by providing a multiple-cavity mold with constant hydraulic and constant steam pressure. The pressure per square inch is then varied by loading a different mumber of cavities to obtain the maximum area possible to close to within 0.0010 in. The cure can be obtained in the same apparatus by measuring the time the press must remain closed to prevent blistering of the piece after pressure is removed. To determine the deformation of a hot piece, it is necessary to use a suitable device in conjunction with the blister test for cure. If no gases are trapped, a piece may not blister but still not be set hard.

To measure the change of flow rate with time the rate of closing of an extrusion mold may be recorded on a revolving drum and transcribed. It is readily seen from Fig. 8, that the same quantity of a slow stiff material can be extruded as of a fast soft material, if time and rate of flow are not considered.

Plasticizer.—In molding compounds, a plasticizer refers to a product that will increase the rate of flow of a compound without affecting the rate of cure. There is no true plasticizer for a molding compound except resin itself; *i.e.*, no compound added mechanically will make a compound flow more readily at lower pressures without having a corresponding detrimental effect on the cure time. Changing the properties of the resin itself through close control is the only way of changing the plasticity of a compound without affecting its cure rate, although, over a narrow range, increasing the resin content in a compound does have this effect.

Strength.—Strength is one of the most important properties of the final molded article. Many variables are involved here:

1. The inherent strength of the resin itself. As a rule, alkaline resins are stronger than acid condensations. Formaldehyde resins are stronger than those from the higher aldehydes—probably because they approach nearer the true resin structure.

2. The type of filler used in the compound. Fibrous fillers, as wood flour, add to the mechanical strength, whereas powdered fillers, as clay, may weaken the resin.

3. The molding qualities of a compound have a pronounced effect on the strength of the final piece. Here is probably the most important factor regarding strength. An inherently strong compound that flows very readily and sets quickly in some molds may not be compressed into a piece dense enough to obtain its possible maximum strength in others. Or there may be places in the mold where gas or air is trapped, weakening

the resulting piece. In developing maximum strength, it is very essential to have a compound of the proper cure and plasticity ratio for the particular molding conditions.

Finish.—Finish, or the appearance of the molded article, is primarily a mirror reproduction of the surface of the mold. Highly polished chromium-plated molds are necessary for high gloss. Proper cure and plasticity for the molding conditions are, of course, very essential. Too soft a material gives a pebbly surface known as *dog skin,* or *orange peel,* due to the lack of pressure on the piece. The resin content of a molding compound is a determining factor in finish: the higher the resin the better the appearance of the piece. Most phenolic resins set by condensation and polymerization. Gases and water are given off and make the piece opaque and porous. It is possible however, to control the reaction so that a phenol formaldehyde resin will set by polymerization only in the final stage, and without filler can then be molded to a transparent or translucent article. The type of filler also affects the appearance of a piece. Only soft, absorbent woods, such as the best white pine, make a suitable flour, as harder particles come to the surface during molding.

Color.—Color is probably the chief handicap of the phenolic resins. They all have the weakness of darkening when exposed to ultra-violet light. This can be controlled to a certain degree and in some few cases eliminated entirely but only at the sacrifice of some other necessary qualities. Discoloration is probably due to the oxidation of the small amounts of triphenylmethane dyes, which are invariably present. These compounds are colorless when reduced, but, readily form highly colored quinone derivatives when heated or exposed to light.

Other Compounds.—Molding compounds from other products are made under very similar conditions. With thermoplastic materials, the control is uncomplicated by cure effects, and scrap can be reworked.

X. APPLICATIONS

The synthetic resins were early called the materials of infinite uses. The development of these uses progressed mostly in the molding compound field during the early stages of the industry, but new and varied uses for the resins themselves are developing rapidly.

Abrasives.—One of the first fields to adopt the resins was the grinding-wheel industry. This industry had long been searching for a strong cement which was quicker curing than the vitrified ceramic bond and more resistant to heat and alkaline solutions than shellac or rubber. Starting as a substitute for shellac wheels, synthetic resin-bonded abrasive articles have fast carved a place of their own, not only replacing shellac and clay but making possible new applications of grinding wheels through increased rate of production.

Bonded Cores.—The bonding of sand cores for foundry use is one of the most conspicuous and valuable fields recently entered by synthetic resins. The set-up resin burns out with little elimination of gas, leaving a clean sand, which runs freely out of the casting.

Resin-bonded cores are particularly valuable in aluminum work, where evolution of gas from the ordinary linseed oil bonds is apt to result

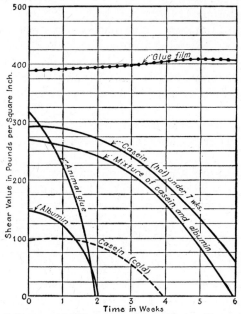

Fig. 9.—Influence of Mold and Fungi on Different Plywood Glues.[1]
Dotted line, wet glue in cold press. Full lines, wet glue in hot press. Full lines with dots, dry film glue in hot press.

in porous castings. Applied in colloidal form, it can be so much better dispersed that only one-third the amount of resin is necessary to give the same strength as with powdered resin. In brass and aluminum castings, the ordinary oil-core binder burns with such a vigorous evolution of gases that porous castings often result, while the phenolic resins, when cured, burn evenly and cleanly, with little or no sudden volatilization.

Brake Linings.—In brake linings, synthetic resins are being used in conjunction with other binding materials. The ordinary thermosetting compound sets so hard that its value as a friction material is lost. In conjunction with rubber, drying oils, and other softening agents, however, synthetic resins serve a definite purpose.

[1] R. Sorensen, Paper read at Woodworking div., A.S.M.E., Chicago, 1933.

The manufacture of a good brake lining is quite an individual task, and the type of resin that fits into consumer's process has to be designed to fit that particular process. Phenolic resins are used in brake lining, (1) to increase the water resistance; (2) to increase the oil resistance (and this is particularly important in rubber-bonded brake lining); (3) to keep the coefficient of friction more uniform during different operating conditions, particularly under heat; and, incidentally, with all these factors to increase the life of the brake lining.

Plywoods.—The most spectacular and revolutionary field for resins to be recently opened up, however, is the plywood industry.[1,2] Thermosetting resins produce a bond that is stronger than the wood, wet or dry; vermin proof; and unaffected by heat. It makes possible synthetic lumber—not a plywood or a cheap wood substitute but a new article of commerce, a homogeneously bonded, cross-grained, synthetic lumber, which is a distinct improvement mechanically over sawed lumber, less expensive when erection costs are considered, and makes possible the better utilization of our forests.[3,4]

[1] Dent, U. S. 1,917,020 (1933).

[2] Plauson, U. S. 1,436,820 (1922).

[3] SONTAG and NORTON, *Ind. Eng. Chem.*, **27**, 1114 (1935).

[4] DIKE, *Ind. Eng. Chem.*, *News Ed.*, **14**, 378 (1936).

AUTHOR INDEX[1]

A

Abernethy, C. L., 53
Aboulenc, J., 545, 546
Abramova, N. M., 571
Adams, C. C., 550
Adams, L. V., 547
Adams, R., 431, 432, 437, 438, 456, 644
Adkins, H., 392, 393, 433, 437, 438, 439,
    440, 441, 443, 444, 452, 459, 495,
    560, 570
Albert, K., 717
Alexander, L. T., 69
Alfuss, W., 570
Allen, I., 718
Allmand, A. J., 162
Almquist, J. A., 457
Aloe, M., 563
Alozerij, N. J. G., 550
Ambler, J. A., 285
Amick, M. G., 530
Ammon, R., 548
Andereau, W., 273
Andrews, C. E., 320, 343, 414
Apgar, F. A., 538
Archibald, F. M., 539
Arentz, F. B., 555
Armstrong, E. F., 434, 452
Armstrong, H. E., 239, 258
Arnold, H. R., 305, 320, 321, 343
Aronovsky, S. I., 593
Arsen'ev, D., 565
Astin, S., 371
Audibert, E., 435
Aumeras, M., 280, 554
Austerweil, G., 568
Autenreith, W., 563
Aylsworth, J. W., 629
Ayres, E., 213, 555, 565, 608, 618, 620

B

Babcock, S., 551
Bacharach, G., 18

Backer, H. J., 255
Backhaus, A. A., 550, 555, 572, 574
Bader, W., 571
Badger, W. L., 27
Bailey, G. C., 392
Bailey, K. C., 547
Bailleux, R., 551
Baker, T., 572
Bakunin, M., 563
Balandin, A. A., 598
Bancroft, W. D., 436
Bannister, W. J., 551, 555
Baranaev, M. K., 553
Barbet, P. A., 285
Barbre, C., 578
Barnes, H. T., 704
Barnet, E. de B., 639
Barrowcliff, M., 510, 517
Barsky, G., 570
Barthelmy, H., 224
Bass, S. L., 565
Bastet, M. C., 655
Bates, J. R., 603
Battegay, M., 120, 124, 126, 184
Bauer, M., 433
Bauer, W., 570
Baum, E., 569
Baumann, E., 564
Baumgarten, P., 246, 262
Bechamp, A., 68
Beckmann, E., 367
Beegle, F. M., 551
Beesley, E., 162
Béhal, A., 559, 565
Beisler, W. H., 551
Beizel, N. M., 571
Beller, H., 389
Bellucci, I., 549, 550
Bender, A., 278
Bennett, J. L., 583
Benze, B. B., 634
Berend, L., 717
Berger, G., 603

[1] The spelling of names and the style of indexing are according to the policy of *Chemical Abstracts*.

Bergius, F., 69, 70, 614
Bergmann, E., 142
Beri, M. L., 379
Berliner, J. F. T., 159
Bernthsen, A., 376
Berry, B. T., 500
Bersworth, F. C., 311
Berthelot, M. P. E., 539, 544, 549, 556
Berthold, H., 87
Bertoni, G., 558
Bezzubez, M. K., 318, 319
Bichowsky, F. R., 159
Biehringer, J., 18
Billinger, R. D., 540
Bitler, W. P., 404
Black, C. A., 398, 457
Blaikie, K. G., 570
Blair, E. W., 393, 396
Blieberger, G., 563, 564
Bliss, R. H., 621
Bloomstrand, C. W., 120
Bodenstein, M., 161, 162
Bodroux, F., 551
Böhler, O., 262
Boehringer, C. F., 517, 569
Boeseken, J., 127, 433
Bogatsky, V., 541
Bogdandy, S. von., 162
Bogojawlensky, A., 547
Boiteau, G., 561
Bolton, E. R., 550
Bone, W. A., 406
Booge, J. E., 275
Borglin, J. N., 551
Borgwardt, E., 371
Borsum, W., 18
Boswell, M. C., 173, 662
Bottoms, R. R., 313, 324, 337, 346
Boulez, V., 563
Bourion, F., 184, 220
Brand, K., 82, 83
Brandsma, W. F., 127
Branting, B. F., 435
Braun, J. v., 639
Brendel, H., 551
Brewster, R. Q., 204
Brezina, H., 547
Brezinski, L. P., 568
Bridgwater, E. R., 219
Briscoe, H. T., 547
Britton, E. C., 186, 493, 523, 605
Britton, J. W., 337, 349

Brochet, A., 90, 433, 452
Brönsted, J. N., 603
Brooks, B. T., 396, 538, 568, 621
Brown, O. W., 90, 91, 92
Brown, R. L., 435
Brownlee, H. J., 712
Bruce, J., 431
Bruck, G. van de, 565
Brunel, R. F., 541
Bruner, L., 201
Brunetti, R., 11
Bruni, G., 558
Brunjes, A. S., 553
Bruson, H. A., 704
Bryner, F., 565
Buc, H. E., 555, 556
Bucherer, H. T., 355
Buckley, J. R., 551
Bukreeva-Prozorovskaya, L. M., 571
Bull, H., 280
Burgess, H., 120
Burghardt, L. M., 556, 560
Burke, S. P., 401
Burns, R. M., 407
Burrell, G. A., 396
Burton, H., 327
Burwell, A. W., 388
Butz, R. J., 591
Byers, H. G., 69
Byrne, B. J., 435, 469

C

Cade, A. R., 488
Cadenhead, A. F. G., 383
Cain, J. C., 121
Caland, P., 267
Calcott, W. S., 219
Calkin, L. P., 402
Callis, C. C., 530
Callow, R. K., 88
Calloway, N. O., 636, 641, 653
Campbell, A. F., 285
Campbell, A. W., 313, 650
Canon, F. A., 414
Cantelo, R. C., 540
Carleton, P. W., 493
Carlson, G. H., 12, 13
Carnarius, E. H., 578
Carothers, W. H., 219, 408, 437, 456, 560, 699, 702, 703
Carpenter, C. D., 274, 276

Carpenter, G. B., 557
Carpenter, M. S., 641, 651
Carr, F. H., 510, 517
Carruthers, J. E., 705
Carswell, T. S., 550
Carter, A. S., 219
Carter, C. B., 566, 570
Carter, R. M., 564
Cauquil, G., 541
Chalkley, L. Jr., 630
Chalmers, W., 712
Chambers, L. A., 547
Chappell, J. T., 557
Charabot, E., 541
Chatterjee, N. R., 204
Chaumeton, P. C., 579
Chedin, J., 16
Cheetham, H. C., 732
Chelberg, R., 547
Chen, K. H., 551
Cheronis, N. D., 314
Child, W. C., 570
Christiansen, J. A., 162, 439
Christmann, L. J., 567
Ciocca, B., 546
Clark, K. G., 325, 358
Clark, L. H., 620
Clarke, H. T., 555, 557
Claus, A., 712
Clough, W. W., 555
Coehn, A., 162, 210
Cogan, H., 512
Cohen, E., 547
Cohen, M. J., 539
Coleman, G. H., 566, 568
Collin, G., 388
Collins, A. M., 219
Conant, J. B., 145
Conklin, E. B., 183
Connor, R., 433, 437, 438, 441, 443, 444, 452, 459
Cook, J. W., 639
Corbellini, A., 258
Corso, A. L., 540
Corson, B. B., 497
Corson, H. P., 407
Couch, H. B., 638
Courtot, C., 266, 277
Coutzen-Crowet, C., 550
Covert, L. W., 437, 438, 441, 459
Cox, E. H., 524, 525, 656
Cox, J. L., 427

Coxe, A. E., 566
Crafts, J. M., 558, 561, 634, 644
Cramer, H. I., 452, 495
Craver, A. E., 392, 412
Crowell, R. B., 550
Cryder, D. S., 435, 436, 439, 472
Curme, G. O. Jr., 342, 722, 723, 729

D

Dahlen, M. A., 337
Dains, F. B., 204
Darzens, G., 441
Datta, R. L., 204
Daudt, H. W., 530
Davidson, W. B., 117, 121
Davies, W. C., 565
Davis, A. W., 555
Davis, C. W., 77
Davis, H. S., 377, 538
Davis, T. W., 562, 568
Dawes, A. W., 83
Degering, Ed. F., 3, 14, 50, 52
Delepine, M., 177
Deming, H. G., 718, 731
Dennis, L. M., 280, 285
Dent, H. M., 709, 718, 732, 739
DeRopp, H. W., 357
Deutsch, H., 569, 639
Dick, H., 201
Dick, J., 569
Dieterle, P., 84
Dietrich, K. R., 551
Dietrich, W., 387
Dietz, W., 548
Dike, T. W., 739
Dimroth, O., 141
Dmitrov, V. V., 551
Dobrochnotow, V., 541
Dodge, B. F., 435
Dodgson, J. W., 259
Dohme, A. R. L., 524, 525
Doleman, P. H., 541
Dolgov, B. N., 571
Donleavy, J. J., 496
Dorp, G. C. A. van, 274
Dorris, T. B., 568
Dorssen, S. van, 263
Douglas, S. P., 722, 723, 729
Dow, D. B., 402
Downes, H. R., 560
Downing, F. B., 219

Downs, C. R., 238, 278, 407, 408, 412, 414

Drake, N. L., 564

Drescher, H. A. E., 351

Dressel, O., 277

Dreyfus, H., 80, 568, 571

Drumm, P. J., 128

Duckham, R., 46

DuPont, E. I., 726

Durrans, T. H., 557

Durruty, C. A., 540

Dutt, P. K., 550

Dutton, G. R., 490

Dykstra, F. J., 394

Dykstra, H. B., 565, 569

E

Ebe, S. R., 550

Edgar, G., 394, 557

Edlund, K. R., 164, 555, 568

Egloff, G., 421, 442, 497, 528

Eichenberger, E., 199

Eisleb, O., 324

Elghozy, F., 551

Elley, H. W., 378

Ellis, C., 426, 440, 441, 468, 539, 702, 724

Ellis, W. E., 557

Elvins, O. C., 435

Emley, W. E., 611

Engel, K. H.. 274

Engel, L., 142

Engelhardt, I., 570

Engelhardt, R., 539

Engs, W., 230, 538

Ephraim, F., 11, 156

Erdely, A., 435

Essex, H., 557

Euwes, P. C. J., 268

Evans, D. P., 565

Evans, T. W., 569

Ewell, R. H., 159

Eyring, H., 161, 162

F

Faber, E. M., 542

Fabisch, W., 548

Fairbrother, F., 675

Fehlandt, P. R., 560

Fenske, M. R., 419, 435, 457, 458, 459

Fenton, H. J. H., 371

Fierz-David, H. E., 49, 82, 144, 238, 268, 274, 319, 357, 381, 505

Fieser, L. F., 148, 264, 719

Firth, J. B., 371

Fischer, F., 433, 434, 435, 436, 442, 597

Fischer, O., 144

Fischer, W., 634, 648

Fischer, W. M., 551

Flett, L. H., 45

Flint, R. B., 321, 322

Florentin, D., 442

Flosdorf, E. W., 547

Fokin, S., 433

Folkers, K., 439, 452, 459

Foohey, W. L., 337

Fordyce, C. R., 563

Forjaz, A. P., 547

Forrest, H. O., 406

Forscey, L. A., 177

Fourneau, E., 503, 561

Francis, F., 17

Franke, W., 489

Friedel, C., 558, 561, 634, 644

Fries, K., 655

Fritzweiler, R., 551

Frolich, P. K., 400, 401, 402, 406, 435, 436, 439, 454, 457, 458, 459, 472, 539, 557, 568, 569

Fromm, E., 262

Fry, H. S., 591

Fryling, C. F., 401

Fuchs, O., 185, 393, 556

Fujita, Y., 546

Fulde, A., 551

Furnas, C. C., 553

G

Gabriel, C. L., 551

Gaddy, V. L., 325

Gajendragad, N. G., 557

Galloway, A. E., 435

Gardner, W. H., 721

Garner, W. E., 53, 330

Gattermann, L., 492

Gay, L., 280, 554

Gebler, I. V., 257

Gegenheimer, R. E., 594

Geiger, G. A., 182

Geoffrey, J. H., 571

George, A. B., 436

Gerard, F. W., 19, 434
Gething, H. H., 371
Ghaswalla, R. P., 598
Gibbs, H. D., 182, 285
Gibby, C. W., 559
Gibson, W., 562
Gibson, W. H., 46
Gilbe, H. F., 330
Gilchrist, P. S., 297
Gilman, H. F., 512, 641
Giordani, F., 563
Girsewald, C. von, 68, 89
Glover, T., 326
Godon, F. de, 441, 557
Goetze, K., 387
Goldschmidt, H., 143, 145
Goldstein, H., 645
Golessenko, O. M., 140
Gortner, R. A., 550, 593, 596, 706
Gottschalk, A., 548
Goudriaan, F., 80
Graebe, C., 512
Graham, J. M., 431, 441
Grant, G. H., 598
Graves, G. D., 436, 472, 473, 555, 560, 561, 568
Gray, A. E., 433
Green, A. G., 269
Green, T. G., 377
Greenewalt, C. H., 345, 571
Grether, E. F., 335, 564
Griess, J. P., 115
Grignard, V., 432, 441, 453
Grigorovich, A. N., 553
Grimm, F. V., 454, 477
Grinten, G. van der, 116
Groggins, P. H., 1, 36, 63, 99, 153, 233, 299, 306, 332, 333, 335, 336, 337, 338, 339, 634, 640, 644, 653, 658, 660, 661, 662, 663, 670, 671, 674, 688, 689
Grolea, J., 550
Gruber, F., 547
Grün, A., 377, 560
Gubelmann, I., 84, 378, 648
Guedon, A., 541
Günther, F., 487
Guthrie, F., 558
Gutorko, A. V., 600
Guyot, A., 265, 279

H

Haabestad, E. H., 565
Haag, W., 570
Haber, F., 65
Habermann, J., 547
Hachtel, F., 621
Haddan, P., 547
Haffner, A. E., 397
Hahn, D. A., 390
Haldeman, W. S., 383
Hale, W. J., 305, 383, 605
Hall, J. L., 307
Haller, A., 561
Hancock, C. W., 578
Hand, C. N., 565
Haner, C., 555
Hann, R. M., 159
Hannotte, T., 553
Hantzsch, A., 12, 15, 117, 121, 122, 124, 199
Harris, B. R., 564
Hartung, W. H., 506
Hartwell, J. L., 148
Hartwich, F., 556
Hasche, R. L., 559
Haslam, R. T., 479
Hasler, A. W., 268
Hass, H. B., 3, 4, 14, 50, 53, 165, 173, 184, 207, 210, 215
Hatch, L. F., 165, 173, 207
Hatcher, J. B., 159
Hauser, O., 557
Haworth, W. N., 538
Hazard-Flamand, M., 278
Hébert, A., 541
Heertjes, P. M., 137
Hefti, F., 565
Heim, G., 551, 553
Hein, F., 676
Heisig, G. B., 547
Held, R., 550
Helferich, O. B., 578
Heller, G., 657, 671
Hel'ms, I. E., 571
Hendricks, S. B., 325
Henke, C. O., 90, 91, 92
Henle, F., 319
Henne, A. L., 205
Hentrich, W., 118
Hermann, W. O., 569
Herold, P., 89, 305, 344

Hersh, R., 431, 441
Herstein, B., 650
Herz, W., 201
Herzberg, G., 159
Herzberg, O. W., 569
Herzfeld, K. F., 162
Herzog, R. O., 727
Hetherington, H. C., 357
Hetherington, J. A., 15, 26
Heymer, G., 162
Hibben, J. H., 727
Hibbert, E., 152
Hightower, F. W., 434
Hilcken, V., 568
Hilditch, T. P., 377, 434, 452, 465, 550
Hill, A. J., 496
Hill, J. W., 703
Hinshelwood, C. N., 598
Hinton, H. D., 490
Hirschkind, W., 567
Hodge, E. B., 3, 4, 50
Hodgson, H. H., 84, 135, 269
Hoenel, H., 720
Hofwimmer, F., 549
Hogan, J. J., 402, 454
Holdermann, K., 272
Holleman, A. F., 7, 17, 43, 46, 267
Holloway, J. H., 642, 683
Holmes, E. L., 711, 718
Holmes, R. D., 523
Holt, H. S., 551
Hoogewerff, S., 274
Hopff, H., 651
Horsley, G. F., 555
Hotson, E. E., 237
Hotz, E., 319
Houben, J., 648
Hough, A., 39, 42
Hovey, A. G., 720, 721
Howes, D. A., 377
Hsieh, T. Y., 640
Hubacher, M. H., 648
Hubbard, J. L., 549
Huber, F. C., 329
Huber, W., 238, 288
Hübner, H., 260
Hufferd, R. W., 543
Huffman, J. R., 435, 436, 445
Hultman, I. N., 555
Hund, W. J., 547
Hunt, S. B., 539
Hurd, C. D., 611, 703

Hurd, N. L., 457
Hurtley, W. R. H., 560, 570
Huston, R. C., 640

I

Iljinsky, M., 271
Ipatieff, W., 487, 497, 498, 499, 527, 528, 568
Ipatiev, V., 432, 433, 441
Irvine, J. C., 538
Irschick, A., 143
Isajev, V., 568
Isenhour, L. L., 611
Isham, R. M., 568
Izmailskii, V. A., 564

J

Jacobson, B. H., 671
Jaeger, A. O., 547, 557
James, J. H., 404
Jancke, W., 727
Jansson, J. I., 564
Jatkar, S. K. K., 557
Jayne, D. W., 567
Jenkins, R. L., 225
Johner, H., 116
Johnson, T. B., 496
Johnston, A. C., 550, 566
Jones, W. J., 565
Jordan, H., 124
Joubert, J. M., 377
Judefind, W. L., 565
Jung, G., 162

K

Kailan, A., 543
Kaiser, H. F. G., 547, 550
Kaisha, S. K., 564
Kametaka, T., 431
Kane, H. L., 546
Kane, T., 640
Kao, C. H., 551
Karlsson, S., 602
Karvé, D. D., 559
Kassel, L. S., 162
Kaufmann, W. E., 437
Kauter, C. T., 322
Keener, J. L., Jr., 335
Keim, R., 205
Kekulé, F. A., 125

Kendall, J., 274, 275, 276
Kenner, J., 326, 327
Keunecke, E., 387
Keyes, D. B., 533
Khaikin, I. S., 494
Kharasch, M. S., 175, 532
Khotinskii, E. S., 551
Kienle, R. H., 720, 721
Kiewiet, T. E., 78
Kiliani, H., 367
Kimball, J. W., 542
King, C. G., 564
King, H. H., 307
Kirby, J. E., 219
Kireev, V. A., 553
Kistiakowsky, G. B., 703
Klatte, F., 569
Klein, L., 726
Kline, G. M., 697
Kling, A., 442
Klinov, I. Ya., 553
Klipstein, K. H., 651, 683
Klotz, A., 557
Knapp, F., 126
Knecht, E., 152
Knilling, W. von, 550
Knoblauch, O., 540
Knoevenagel, E., 563
Knox, W. J., Jr., 557
Knuth, C. A., 465, 466
Kobelev, V. A., 332, 347
Kokatnur, V. R., 595
Kolb, A. L., 137
Kolhatkar, G. B., 560, 598
Komarewsky, V. I., 499
Koppe, P., 89
Koppengerg, H., 421
Kornfeld, G., 162
Korolev, A. I., 547
Kotake, M., 546
Kothe, R., 277
Koton, M. M., 571
Kozminskaya, T. K., 598
Kranzlein, G., 637, 650
Krase, H. J., 325, 358
Krase, N. W., 642, 683
Krauch, C., 388
Kraus, C. A., 530
Krebser, A., 250, 254, 271
Krehma, I. J., 560, 571
Kremann, R., 560, 564
Kremp, F., 571

Krüger, D., 579
Krumbhaar, W., 717
Kuh, E., 538
Kurbatow, A., 258

L

Lacourt, A., 491
Ladenburg, A., 137
Ladewig, H., 547
Lang, W., 382
Lang, W. R., 550
Langmeier, A., 566
Laptev, N. G., 494
Lapworth, A., 602
Larson, A. T., 642
Laska, A. L., 565
Lauer, K., 9, 250, 252, 256, 266, 270, 271, 272, 293, 295, 315
Lawrie, J. W., 513
Lawson, W. E., 566
Lazier, W. A., 435, 439, 475, 571
Lebo, R. B., 539
Lecart, M., 553
Ledbury, W., 393, 396
Lefort, T. E., 403
Leighton, W. B., 553
Lel'chuk, S. L., 571
Lenher, S., 403
Leroux, H., 432
Lesser, R., 647
Leuck, G. J., 550
Levenstein, I., 237, 243
Lewis, H. F., 512
Lewis, W. K., 27, 401, 435, 436, 472
Lichtenthaeler, F. E., 546
Lifschits, J., 122, 124
Lillienfeld, L., 538
Lind, S. C., 162
Lipp, A., 560
Livingston, J. W., 41, 493
Lloyd, S. J., 590, 597
Locquin, R., 551
Loehr, O., 570
Lommel, W., 539
Longinov, V., 551
Longinov, V. V., 553
Loon, C. van, 561
Lowry, T. M., 675
Lowy, A., 640
Lubman, N., 541
Lubs, H. A., 152

Lush, E. J., 433, 454, 468, 550
Luther, M., 387, 389, 550
Luther, R., 208
Lux, H., 177
Lyford, C. A., 112
Lyons, E., 565
Lyons, R. E., 73, 75, 76

Mc

McAdams, W. H., 27
McBee, E. T., 165, 173, 207, 210, 215
McCabe, W. L., 27
McCleary, R. F., 3, 14, 50, 52
McCormack, H., 32
McCorkle, M., 641
McKee, R. H., 20, 594
McKenzie, A., 541
McKinney, P. V., 542, 561
McLaughlin, R. R., 173, 662
McMaster, L., 329, 335
MacMullin, R. B., 594
MacQueen, D. E., 493

M

Mackert, A., 547
Mackey, J. F., 550
Madinaveitia, A., 560
Magill, P. L., 562
Magoun, G. L., 565
Mahr, J., 83
Maier, W., 116, 126
Mailhe, A., 320, 432, 433, 438, 441, 443, 502, 512, 545, 557
Malkina-Okum, R., 540, 547
Malm, C. J., 563
Mann, M. D., Jr., 491, 556
Manzetti, R., 550
Mardles, E., 407
Marek, L. F., 362, 390
Marekwald, W., 541
Marker, R., 532
Markovich, M. V., 538
Markownikoff, W., 14, 552, 615
Marks, E. C. R., 555
Marshall, A. L., 162, 165
Marshall, J. R., 431
Marshall, W., 558
Martin, F., 185
Martin, J., 320, 343, 344, 560, 571
Martin, L. F., 172, 493

Martinsen, H., 248
Marvel, C. S., 433, 489
Marx, C., 55
Mason, J., 185
Masson, I., 15, 26
Mathes, W., 310
Matheson, H. W., 569, 570
Matievic, A., 541
Matsumoto, G., 551
Maxted, E. B., 406, 410, 412, 452, 467, 677
May, P., 506
Mears, W. H., 703
Meer, W. ter, 80, 90
Meerwein, H., 675
Megson, N. J. L., 711
Meharg, V. E., 392, 393, 718
Meisenheimer, J., 541
Meldrum, A. N., 263
Menalda, F. A., 564
Menke, J. B., 18
Menschutkin, N., 541, 562
Merk, B., 367
Merley, S. R., 539
Merriman, R. W., 556
Merz, A., 143
Meyer, K. H., 143, 144
Meyer, V., 543
Meyer, W. A., 433, 437
Michael, A., 12, 13, 541
Michael, W., 570
Michels, M., 126
Middleton, E. B., 568
Midgley, T., Jr., 205
Milas, N. A., 376
Miller, E., 524, 525
Miller, G. E., 662
Miller, P., 560
Miller, S. P., 114
Milligan, C. H., 465, 466, 557
Mills, G. D., 556
Mills, L. E., 310, 329
Miner, C. S., 712
Mion, P., 280, 554
Mixter, W. G., 325
Modersohn, A., 82
Mohr, G., 262
Molinari, E., 44, 47
Mom, C. P., 433
Monnet, P., 382, 570
Moore, C. G., 243
Moore, G. V., 566

Moore, H. K., 465
Moore, T. S., 68
Moravec, R. Z., 538
Morgan, G. T., 120, 124, 326, 711
Morrell, J. C., 442
Morris, J. C., 161
Morrison, G. O., 569
Moses, C. G., 565
Mounier, D., 122
Mühlbock, O., 548
Müller, F. H. S., 260
Müller, H., 162
Mugdan, M., 569
Mullin, C. E., 579
Mund, W., 551, 553
Murat, M., 441
Murch, W. M., 688

N

Nafash, M. S., 177, 178, 312
Nagel, R. H., 644, 658, 660, 663, 688
Nakaya, U., 551
Narbut, J., 547
Nash, A. W., 377, 435
Natelson, S., 490
Nazarova, Z. N., 640
Nedden, W. ter, 433
Nelson, C. C., 24, 38
Nernst, W., 162
Nesvizhskii, M. P., 598
Neuberg, C., 548
Neumann, P., 564
Newitt, D. M., 397, 398, 400, 406, 435, 469
Newman, A. C. C., 371
Newton, H. P., 153, 335, 338, 660, 662, 670, 689
Nicholl, L., 565
Nicodemus, O., 321
Nicolai, F., 565
Nicoll, F., 121
Nicoll, W. D., 582
Niederl, J. B., 490, 496
Niemann, G., 570
Nieuwland, J. A., 219, 490, 546, 562, 568
Noller, C. R., 490, 644, 663
Norman, G. M., 551, 561
Norris, J. F., 377, 638
Norrish, R. G. W., 705
Norton, A. J., 692, 718, 739

Noyes, W. A., 543
Nussbaum, R. Jr., 457

O

Oda, R., 560
Oddo, B., 128
Oechslin, K. J., 541
Oliver, S. C. J., 603
Ollano, Z., 11
Orton, K. J. P., 546, 547
Ostwald, W., 545
Otto, R., 255
Oxley, H. F., 571

P

Paal, C., 432
Pabst, J. A., 19
Paden, J. H., 143
Pallemaerts, F. A. F., 424
Palmer, G. D., 590
Palomaa, M. H., 564
Panickar, K. G. R., 204
Panoff, C., 541
Pape, A., 706
Pardee, A. M., 559
Parkin, M., 326
Parks, C., 437
Parks, G. S., 436, 445
Parmelee, A. E., 530
Partridge, E. P., 385
Patterson, J. A., 3, 14, 53
Pauling, H., 60
Payman, J. B., 562
Péan de Saint-Gilles, L., 539, 544, 549, 556
Pease, R. N., 161, 163, 211
Peer, A. A., 402, 454
Perkin, W., 68
Perkins, G. A., 561, 641
Perman, E. P., 306
Perry, L. R., 457
Peterkin, A. G., Jr., 281
Peterson, W. D., 145
Petrenko-Kritschenko, P., 541
Pfannf, M., 558
Pfeiffer, P., 570
Phelps, I. K., 546, 549
Phillips, M., 595
Pichler, H., 397, 403
Pictet, A., 10, 17

Pierce, J. S., 437, 726
Pigulerskii, V. V., 538
Pinck, L. A., 20, 21
Pines, H., 497, 498
Pinnow, J., 559
Piotrowski, W. J. de, 405
Pistor, K., 561
Plant, J. H. G., 571, 621
Plauson, H., 569, 732, 739
Polak, J. J., 267
Polányi, M., 162
Pope, J. C., 394
Poznanski, S., 540, 551, 557
Prager, W. L., 541, 543
Prahl, W., 310
Pratt, L. S., 542
Prillwitz, H. H. C., 565
Prins, H. J., 65
Pugh, J. W., 401
Pukirev, A. G., 553
Punnett, E. B., 392
Pupko, S. L., 551
Purdie, T., 558

Q

Qua, M. C., 644, 657
Quiggle, D., 435, 457, 458, 459
Quilico, A., 263
Quimby, O. T., 164
Qureshi, M., 606

R

Rabald, E., 569
Rahlfs, O., 634
Raineau, A., 435
Randall, M., 434
Raschig, F., 382, 627, 631
Rather, J. B., 565
Razorenov, B. A., 564
Reder, R., 397, 403
Redmond, A., 230
Reed, C. F., 196
Regnault, V., 266
Reicher, L. T., 541
Reid, E. E., 329, 432, 500, 533, 542, 557, 558, 559, 562, 565, 652, 692
Reilly, J., 128
Reimer, M., 560
Reverdin, F., 10
Rheiner, A., 704

Rhodes, F. H., 24, 38
Rice, F. O., 602
Richardson, A. S., 21, 465, 466
Richter, G. A., 465
Riddell, W. A., 663
Riedel, J. D., 490
Riegler, R., 413
Riley, H. L., 371
Rinkenbach, W. H., 53
Rist, C. E., 325
Roberts, K. C., 552
Rodebush, W. H., 560, 566
Rodionov, V., 517
Röhm, O., 726
Röse, B., 559
Rogers, D. G., 88, 595
Roka, K., 556
Rona, P., 548
Rosanoff, M. A., 543
Rosenmund, K. W., 655
Rosenstein, L., 547, 567
Rossini, F. D., 159
Rost, T., 569
Rozhdestvenskii, M. S., 533
Rubidge, C. R., 644, 657
Ruder, C., 568
Ruff, O., 116, 205
Ruggli, P., 126
Russell, R. P., 479

S

Sabatier, P., 320, 432, 433, 434, 436, 438, 441, 443, 502, 512, 557
Sabetay, S., 561, 564
Sachs, J. H., 542
Sändig, K., 703, 705, 708
Salmi, E. J., 564
Salo, T., 564
Salzberg, P. L., 321, 322
Sandor, S., 142
Saunders, K. H., 119, 354
Schaarschmidt, A., 19, 20
Schaffer, J. M., 524, 526
Scheiber, J., 703, 705, 708
Schenk, O., 439
Scherrer, P., 727
Schilt, W., 565
Schlattmann, O., 421
Schlenker, E., 645
Schlesinger, N., 540, 547, 721
Schlösser, H., 143

Schmidt, A., 551
Schmidt, J., 116, 120, 126
Schmidt, J. H., 718
Schmidt, L., 568
Schmidt, O., 90, 570
Schmidt, R. E., 271
Schmidt, W., 321, 400, 541
Schneider, F., 492
Schneider, H. G., 568
Schnitzspahn, K., 116
Schnurr, W., 655
Schönberg, C., 565
Scholl, R., 646, 656, 690
Schotten, C., 564
Schotz, S. P., 533
Schoutissen, H. A. J., 123, 127, 129, 134, 142
Schrader, H., 442, 599
Schramm, H., 676
Schrauth, W., 439
Schülke, K., 671
Schümann, M., 127
Schumann, T. E. W., 401
Schuyler, W. H., 557
Schwab, L. C., 543
Schwabe, E., 551
Schweitzer, H., 148, 319
Schwenk, E., 256, 371
Schwing, P. F. H., 564
Schwyzer, J., 494, 495, 503, 510, 517, 518, 521
Seebach, F., 718
Seixas Palma, J. de, 262
Sekera, V. C., 489
Semproni, A., 546
Senderens, J. B., 90, 434, 436, 438, 441, 491, 545, 546
Senseman, C. E., 273
Seyewetz, A., 122
Shaffer, S., 512
Shah, M. S., 263
Shaw, T. P. G., 569
Sherman, A., 159, 161, 163, 164, 165
Shreve, R. N., 289, 485, 494, 495, 626
Shuikin, N. I., 598
Shukoff, A. A., 539
Sidgwick, N. V., 88, 123, 621
Simon, L. J., 539
Simpson, W. A., 233
Skirrow, F. W., 569
Skita, A., 432, 433, 437, 438
Sklyarenko, S. I., 553

Skrabal, A., 541
Slotta, K. H., 489
Small, L. F., 517, 519
Smeykal, K., 305, 320, 321, 344
Smith, A., 65
Smith, A. E., 546, 547
Smith, D. F., 435
Smith, F. B., 207
Smith, H. G., 562
Smith, L. I., 143
Smith, L. T., 73, 75, 76
Smith, R. A., 496
Smolenski, E., 320
Snow, C. C., 128
Söhne, A. E., 517
Sontag, L., 739
Sorensen, R., 738
Southwick, C A., Jr., 435
Sowa, F. J., 490, 562, 568
Spellmeyer, E. F., 547
Spiegel, L., 570
Spring, O., 539
Sprung, M. M., 330
Starkweather, H. W., 706
Staudinger, H., 645, 701, 702, 704, 728
Steffins, J. A., 551
Stehlby, E. T., 550
Steimmig, G., 560, 570
Stein, V., 116
Steiner, A., 329, 335
Stephan, A., 568
Stephen, H., 78
Stewart, F. B., 542, 561
Stewart, T. D., 164
Stickdorn, K., 439
Stieglitz, J., 594
Stimmel, B. F., 564
Stirton, A. J., 299, 306, 332, 333, 335, 336, 337, 338, 339, 644, 658, 662
Stockelbach, F. E. E., 682
Störmer, R., 547
Stoesser, W. C., 207
Stolle, R., 646
Stone, H. G., 671
Storch, E. A., 490, 496
Strahler, F., 621
Strain, D. E., 569
Strange, E. H., 546, 568
Strecker, A., 123
Stritar, M. J., 201
Strong, H. W., 435, 469
Strosacher, C. J., 180

Sudborough, J. J., 559
Suida, H., 568
Sumiya, K., 571
Sun, C. E., 163
Sutermeister, E., 714
Sutherland, R. O., 164
Suzuki, T., 127, 129
Suzuki, Y., 564
Svetlov, I., 551
Swallen, L. C., 305, 320, 343, 344
Swarts, F., 205
Sweeney, W. J., 479, 481
Swern, D., 640, 661
Swietoslawski, W., 540, 551, 557
Symmes, E. M., 551
Szego, P., 406
Szydlowsky, H., 570

T

Täufel, K., 600
Tahir, N. A., 606
Tajima, Y., 571
Tamayo, M., 561
Tammann, G., 706
Tassilly, E., 127
Tauch, E., 401, 402
Tauch, E. J., 454
Taveau, R. de M., 538
Taylor, G. B., 21
Taylor, H. A., 562
Taylor, H. S., 603
Taylor, P. S., 435
Taylor, T. W. J., 177
Theimer, E. T., 651
Thielepape, E., 551
Thoenges, E. E., 587
Thomae, G., 563
Thomas, V., 661
Thompson, J. G., 358
Thompson, T. J., 550
Thomsen, J., 539
Tidwell, H. C., 557
Tietze, E., 118
Tilley, F. W., 524, 526
Tischenko, V., 570
Tobler, R., 319, 357
Tochtemann, H., 143
Tolman, R. C., 330
Tomlins, H. P., 124
Traill, D., 515
Trainer, E., 712

Trent, W. R., 453
Trickey, J. P., 712
Trieschmann, W., 512
Tropsch, H., 433, 434, 481
Truffi, F., 558
Trusler, R. B., 562
Twitchell, E., 546, 550, 610
Tyrer, D., 279
Tsukervanik, I. P., 640

U

Ueno, S., 127, 129
Ulffers, F., 568
Ulich, H., 634
Ullmann, F., 304, 511, 512, 648
Ulrich, H., 560, 570
Unger, W., 162
Urech, F., 539

V

Vail, W. E., 571
Vakil, K. H., 269
Valik, I., 651
Valik, L., 651
Van Arsdel, W. B., 465
Vanderbilt, B. M., 4, 50
Van Schaack, R. H., Jr., 550
Van't Hoff, J. H., 539
Van Vleck, J. H., 161
Varma, P. S., 19, 204
Varvoglis, G. A., 546
Vassallo, E., 546
Vaughen, J. V., 435
Vavon, G., 437, 438, 541
Verley, A., 487
Vesterdal, H. G., 389
Ville, L., 177
Voorhees, V., 432, 438
Voorhies, A., Jr., 479, 481
Vorbrodt, J., 201
Vorontzov, I. I., 84
Vorozhtzov, N. N. Jr., 332, 347, 348, 600

W

Wacker, A., 551, 560
Wade, J., 552, 566
Wagner, E. C., 496
Wagner, G., 377
Wagner, P., 556

Wahl, A., 551
Waldo, J. H., 532
Waldschmidt-Leitz, E., 596
Walker, J., 135
Walker, T. K., 142
Walker, W. H., 27
Walle, H. van de, 548
Walter, G., 714, 715
Walton, R. P., 613
Walz, G. F., 163, 211
Ware, G. C., 307
Warren, T. E., 401
Waser, E., 432
Wassermann, P., 261
Wassiljewa, A., 210
Waterman, H. I., 137
Waters, W. A., 559
Watson, E. R., 507
Webb, H. W., 55
Weber, F., 548
Weber, P., 165, 173, 210, 215
Wecker, E., 550
Weddige, A., 559
Weibezahn, W., 569
Weide, O. B. van der, 433
Weil, H., 261
Weinberger, H., 721
Weiss, J. M., 407
Wenner, P., 512
Werner, E. A., 325
Werner, K., 548
Wertyporoch, E., 339, 676
Weyler, J. L., 550
Wheeler, T. S., 560
Whitacre, F. M., 547
White, A. H., 434
Whitney, W. R., 69
Wickert, J. N., 322, 323, 551
Wieland, H., 13, 114
Wiesler, K., 385
Wietzel, R., 551, 556, 571
Wiezevich, P. J., 400, 568, 652
Wijs, J. J. A., 603
Wilcox, M., 541
Wilhelm, R. H., 20

Willard, M. L., 127
Williams, I., 219
Williams, W. H., 305, 337, 345, 493
Williamson, B. F., 551
Willstätter, R., 431
Wilson, T. A., 306, 308
Wilson, W. S., 539
Winkler, J., 405
Witt, O. N., 238, 492
Wittka, F., 377
Wizinger, R. K., 145
Wohl, A., 68, 339, 412, 676
Wolff, A., 124
Wolgast, K., 541
Woodhouse, J. C., 571
Woodruff, J. C., 571
Woodward, H. E., 115
Woodward, J. D., 493
Worden, E. C., 579
Wuyts, H., 491, 551
Wynne, E. W., 239

Y

Yamada, J., 551
Yamada, S., 571
Yamamoto, E., 121, 128
Yanuisheva, Z. S., 571
Yarsley, V. E., 579
Yeaw, J., 426
Yost, D. M., 159
Young, C. O., 393
Young, P. L., 539, 568
Youtz, M. A., 193, 227

Z

Zaganiaris, J. N., 546
Zakharov, A. I., 279
Zanden, J. M., van der, 255
Zeisberg, F. C., 55, 60, 571
Zeltner, J., 564
Zerner, E., 387
Zimmerli, A., 494, 550
Zwecker, O., 543

SUBJECT INDEX[1]

A

Abietic acid, 719
Abrasives, utilization of resins, 737
Absorption systems, HCl recovery, 231
  NH₃ recovery, 359
Absorption tower, 59
Acetaldehyde, ammonolysis of, 302
  oxidation of, 376, 383
  polymerization of, 692, 712
  preparation of, 393, 401, 403
  reduction of, 436, 437
  sulfonation of, 247
Acetamide, 63
Acetanilide, nitration of, 10, 17, **44**
  preparation of, 63
Acetic acid, chlorination of, 180, **215**
  in esterification, 534, 540, 552
  iodination of, 156, 157
  in nitration, 1, 9, 10, 12
  preparation of, 383, 385, 401
  reduction of, 439
  sulfonation of, 258
Acetic anhydride, acetylating agent, 562, 563
  in nitration, 1, 10, 12, 18
  in sulfonation, 274
Acetoacetic esters, hydrogenolysis of, 444
Acetone, iodination of, 203
  reduction of, 438, 441, 452
Acetophenetidine, 488, 491, **509**
Acetophenone, in Friedel and Crafts reaction, 653
  preparation of, 644, 658
  reduction of, 438, 441
Acetylation, 124
  of cellulose, 563, 579
Acetyl chloride, acetylating agent, 9, 564
  preparation of, 181, 652
p-Acetyl-o-cresol, 656
p-Acetyl diphenyl ether, 656
Acetylene, chlorination of, 193, 207, 208
  esterification of, 536, 568
  hydrolysis of, 596
Acetyl fluoride, fluorinating agent, 159
Acetyl nitrate, nitrating agent, 1, 10, 15–17
Acid anhydrides, in esterification, 534, 562, 566
  in Friedel and Crafts reaction, 635, 687
Acid chlorides, in esterification, 534, 563
  in Friedel and Crafts reaction, 635, 686
  preparation of, 194, 197, 643, 652
Acidolysis, 534, 561
Acids, in diazotization, 128
  hydrogenation of, 436, **473**
  in hydrolysis, 593, 603

Acids, in oxidation, 366, 376
  unsaturated, reduction of, 433
Acid sulfates, sulfonating agents, 235, 257
Acriflavine, 488, 489, 495
Acrolein, ammonolysis of, 302
  in polymerization, 700, 702
Acrylic acid, 700
  in polymerization, 700, 726
Acryloids, 726
Actinic rays, in chlorination, 154, 171
Activation energies, of halogens, 160, 161
Acylation, 8
Addition complexes, in Friedel and Crafts reaction, 675
  in sulfonation, 274
Addition reactions, in bromination, 156, 201
  in chlorination, 154, 175, 193
  in halogenation, 153, 189
  in iodination, 203
Agitation, in ammonolysis, 328
  in Friedel and Crafts reaction, 673
  in nitration, 28
  in reduction, 73, 74, 94
  in sulfonation, 265, 274
Air, oxidizing agent, 382
Alcohols, alkylating agents, 487
  ammonolysis of, 299, 301, 320, 343
  esterification of, 191, 533, 570
  in Friedel and Crafts reaction, 635
  oxidation of, 362
  preparation of, 394–403, 438, 469, 473, 620, 623, 624
Alcoholysis, 534, 558, 560
Aldehydes, ammonolysis of, 299, 302, 321, 322
  esterification of, 570
  oxidation of, 362
  reduction of, 436
  in resin preparation, 692, 712
  synthesis of, 362, 637, 642, **683**
Aliphatic alkylamines, 492
Aliphatic compounds, nitric acid esters of, 6
  oxidation of, 390, 394, 400
  treated with chlorosulfonic acid, 258
  treated with oleum, 236, 247
  treated with sulfites, 260
  treated with sulfuric acid, 236
Aliphatic ethers, 491
Alizarin, 374, 380
Alkalene oxides, ammonolysis of, 303
  in Friedel and Crafts reaction, 635
Alkali fusions, in hydrolysis, 594
  in oxidation, 374
Alkaline hypochlorites, in oxidation, 376

[1] The spelling of names and style of indexing are according to the policy of *Chemical Abstracts*. Principal references are in **bold faced** type.

Alkaline oxidation, 366, 376
Alkaline reduction with hydrogen, 64, 65, 89
Alkali nitrates, nitrating agents, 1, 16
Alkali salts, in sulfonation, 270, 273
Alkali sulfides, in reduction, 67, 111
Alkaloidal amines, 494
Alkaloids, 492
Alkanolamines, 303, 322
Alkyd resins, 720
Alkyl, bound to carbon, 485, 495, **524**
   bound to metal, 485, 500, 530
   bound to oxygen, 485, 491, **509**
   bound to pentavalent nitrogen, 485, 495, **524**
   bound to trivalent nitrogen, 485, 492, **521**
Alkylating agents, 487
   physical condition, 503
Alkylation, 485
   effect of, 506
   equipment, 503
   factors, 500
   by Friedel and Crafts reaction, 496, 637, 638
   products, 486
   ratio of reactants, 502
   technical, 509
   types, 485, **490**
Alkylation products, recovery of, 503
Alkylbenzenes, preparation of, 497, 498, 679
Alkylchlorides, alkylating agents, 488
   hydrolysis of, 598
   preparation of, 191
Alkyl halides, alkylating agents, 488
   in esterification, 534, 565
   in Friedel and Crafts reaction, 637, 639
   preparation of, 189, 191, 651
Alkylphenols, 637, 640
Alkyl quaternary ammonium compounds, 489
Alkyl sulfates, alkylating agents, 488
Aluminum, in ammonolysis, 316
   in chlorination, 183
Aluminum chloride, in chlorination, 196
   disruptive influence, 654
   in Friedel and Crafts reaction, 634, 635, 657, 663
   in nitration, 20
   in reduction, 69
Amides, esterification of, 534, 562
   hydrolysis of, 64
Amination, by ammonolysis, **299**
   by reduction, **63**
   survey of reactions, 309
Amines, from alcohols, 299, 301, 320, 343
   aliphatic, 311–313, 320–324, 343–346
   nitration of, 8, 10
   preparation of, 63, **96**
   primary, 63, 119, 650
   secondary, 63, 637, 646, 650
   tertiary, 63, 637
Amino acids, preparation of, 313
Amino-aldehyde resins, 712
1-Aminoanthraquinone, diazotization of, 228
2-Aminoanthraquinone, 63
   chlorination of, 188
   oxidation of, 374
   preparation of, 300, 301, 315, **349, 356**

Aminoazobenzene, 118
Aminoazotoluene, diazotization of, **138**
1-Aminobenzene-4-sulfonic acid, 238
2-Aminobenzoic acid, 125
4-Aminobenzoic acid, iodination of, 157
2-Amino-1-bromo-3-chloroanthraquinone, 188
3-Aminocarbazole, 116
Aminocarboxylic acids, diazotization of, 125, 135
2-Amino-3-chloroanthraquinone, 188
2-Amino-7-chloroanthraquinone, 84
Amino compounds, coupling of, 151
   manufacture of, 342
   oxidation of, 364
2-Amino-4, 6-dinitrophenol, 115
Amino-G-acid, 246
1-Aminonaphthalene, 114
2-Aminonaphthalene-3-carboxylic acid, 319
1-Aminonaphthalene-2, 4-disulfonic acid, 261
1-Aminonaphthalene-4-sulfonic acid, 244, 261
1-Aminonaphthalene-3, 6, 8-trisulfonic acid, 248
1-Amino-5-naphthol, 318
1-Amino-8-naphthol-3, 6-disulfonic acid, 124
1-Amino-2-naphthol-4-sulfonic acid, diazotization
   of, 116, 120, 126, 136
   preparation of, 260, **290**
2-Amino-5-naphthol-7-sulfonic acid, 124
Aminonaphthols, diazotization of, 125, 136
1-Amino-5-nitroanthraquinone, 87
2-Amino-4-nitrophenol, 84
m-Aminophenol, 126
o-Aminophenol, 88
p-Aminophenol, alkylation of, 494
   preparation of, 85
   sulfonation of, 262
Aminophenols, diazotization of, 125, 136
p-Aminophenyl-diisopropylamine, 116
Amino-R-acid, 246
Aminosulfonic acids, diazotization of, 135
   sulfonating agents, 235, 263
Ammonia, 63
   alcoholic, in ammonolysis, 326
   aqueous, partial pressure of, 308
      pH of, 305, 306
      physical properties of, 306
      reaction of, 303
      vapor pressure of, 306, 328
   concentration in ammonolysis, 330, 331, 333, 348
   recovery from ammonolysis, 359
Ammonium nitrate, in ammonolysis, 350
Ammonium sulfite, in ammonolysis, 317
Ammonolysis, 299
   continuous, 355
   equipment, 340
   factors, 327
   liquid phase, 300, 329, 357
   mechanism, 339
   metal catalysts, 334
   oxidants in, 315, 338
   replacement of halogen, 300, 329, 334
   replacement of hydroxyl, 299, 301
   replacement of labile nitro groups, 299, 303, 325
   replacement of sulfonic acid radical, 299, 301
   technical, 342

Ammonolysis, vapor phase, 300
Amyl acetates, 558, 576
Amyl alcohols, 213, 558, 618
Amyl chlorides, alkylation, 526
  hydrolysis of, 618
  preparation of, 213
t-Amylphenol, 526
Anilides, nitration of, 9
Aniline, 63
  alkylation of, 496
  diazotization of, 122, **132**
  distillation of, 98, 99, 100
  nitration of, 9, 18, 19
  oxidation of, 376, 379
  in polymerization, 712
  preparation of, 74, 79, 90, **96,** 300, 309, 316,
    346
  sulfonation of, **287**
Aniline Black, 376
Aniline hydrochloride, chlorination of, 155
  diazotization of, 123
  in reductions, 69
Aniline nitrate, 17
Aniline-m-sulfonic acid, 151
Aniline-Urea condensations, 712
p-Anisidine. 10
Anisole, 491, 492
  preparation of, 511
Anthracene Yellow C, 363
Anthranilic acid, diazotization of, 125, 136
  preparation of, 366
Anthraquinone, halogenation of, 188
  hydrogenation of, 432
  nitration of, 8
  preparation of, 652
  sulfonation of, 248, 249, 252, 269, **292–294**
1, 5-Anthraquinonedisulfonic acid, 254, 271, 294
1, 8-Anthraquinonedisulfonic acid, 254, 271
2,6-Anthraquinonedisulfonic acid, 228, 250,
    253, 269
2,7-Anthraquinonedisulfonic acid, 228, 250,
    253, 269
α, α-Anthraquinonedisulfonic acids, 255
β, β-Anthraquinonedisulfonic acids, 253
1-Anthraquinonesulfonic acid, 192, 271
  preparation of, 252, 254, 255, 272, **294**
2-Anthraquinonesulfonic acid, 294
  ammonolysis of, 301, 315, **350**
  oxidation of, 374, 380
  preparation of, 228, 250, **292**
  sulfonation of, 271
Anthraquinonesulfonic acids, ammonolysis of,
    314
  fusion of, 374, 380
Antimony pentachloride, in chlorination, 172,
    196, 207
  in fluorination, 158, 229
Antimony trichloride, in chlorination, 155, 172,
    207
Antimony trifluoride, in fluorination, 205, 229
Antipyrine, 489, 492
Apparatus, catalytic oxidation, **413–418**
  chlorination, 208, 211, 214, 216, 217, 222, 224,
    225, 227, 230

Apparatus, continuous ammonolysis, 355
  sulfonation, 281
Aralkyl halides, alkylating agents, 489
  in Friedel and Crafts reaction, 639
Aromatic alcohols, reduction of, 432
Aromatic alkylamines, 492, 493
Aromatic chlorides, preparation of, 182
Aromatic compounds, chlorination of, 182, 195
  nitration of, 7, 12
  sulfonation of, 237, 248, 261
Aromatic hydrocarbons, hydrogenation of, 430,
    431
  oxidation of, 405
Aromatic ketones, reduction of, 432
Aromatic nitro compounds, 7, 12
Arsenic acid, oxidizing agent, 374
Arylalkanols, 637, 651
Aryloxamic acid chlorides, 646
Arylsulfonic alkyl esters, 489
Auramine, 494
Autoclaves, for continuous operation, 355
  corrosion of, 336
  direct fired, 340
Auxiliary high-pressure equipment, 341
Azeotropic agents, 551
Azobenzene, 66, 79, 81, 364, 376
Azo Blue, 508
Azo dyes, 118, 140
Azoxybenzene, 66, 79

B

Bakelite, 695
Barbet and Ambler-Gibbs process, 286
Barbital, 495
Batch esterifications, 573, 578
Batch sulfonations, 277
Beckmann mixture, 367
Benzal chloride, preparation of, 182, 184
Benzaldehyde, fluorination of, 159
  in Friedel and Crafts reaction, 653
  polymerization of, 701, 712
  preparation of, 382, 409, **683**
  reduction of, 437, 441
Benzamide, 63
Benzanthrone, 374, 656, 690
Benzene, alkylation of, 497, 498, 527
  chlorination of, 183, 184, 185, 186, 190, **220**
  hydrogenation of, 430, 431
  iodination of, 204
  nitration of, 13, 20–22, **33, 38**
  oxidation of, 406, **407**
  sulfonation of, 237, **284**
Benzene-2-diazonium carboxylate, 136
Benzenediazonium chloride, 117, 120, 133, 198,
    206
Benzenediazonium hydroxide, 121
Benzenediazonium-4-sulfonate, 123
1, 3-Benzenedisulfonic acid, 116, 237, 267, **286**
Benzenesulfamic acid, 262
Benzenesulfonic acid, hydrolysis of, 593, **628**
  preparation of, 237, **284**
Benzil, 373
Benzoazurine, 508

Benzoic acid, preparation of, 382, 406, 409, 685
  reduction of, 433
Benzoin, 373
Benzophenone, preparation of, 643, 644, 658, 666, 685
  reduction of, 438, 441
o-Benzoquinone, 371
Benzotrichloride, 182, 184
2-Benzoylbenzoic acid, 647, 665
Benzoyl chloride, in acylation, 9, 564
p-Benzoyl-o-cresol, 656
p-Benzoyl diphenyl ether, 656
1-Benzoylnaphthalene, 656, 690
Benzoyl nitrate, nitrating agent, 1, 15, 16, 17
Benzoyl peroxide, 202, 371
Benzyl acetate, 534
Benzyl alcohol, 540
  reduction of, 441
Benzyl benzoate, 534
Benzyl cellulose, 489, 517
Benzyl chloride, alkylating agent, 489
  in esterification, 534, 565
  in Friedel and Crafts reaction, 693
  in polymerization, 693, 694
  preparation of, 184
  sulfonation of, 262
Benzylethylaniline, 489, 493
Bergius process, 594, 606
Binaries, in esterification, 552, 553, 554
Biphenyl, chlorination of, 186, 187, **225**
Biphenyl-2, 2'-dicarboxylic acid, 371
Bismarck Brown, 137
Bisulfites, sulfonating agents, 260
Bonded cores, utilization of resins, 738
Boric acid, sulfonation catalyst, 270, 274
Bornyl chloride, 378
Borofluoric acid, 206
Boron trifluoride, 158, 205
Brake linings, utilization of resins, 738
Bromination, 155, 200
Bromine, brominating agent, 156, 201
  catalyst in chlorination, 154, 175, 176, 207
  catalyst in fluorination, 205
  oxidizing agent, 376
Bromine chloride, 177, 178
1-Bromoanthraquinone, 228
4'-Bromo-2-benzoylbenzoic acid, 662
4-Bromochlorobenzene, 300, 310
Brönner acid, 246
Bucherer process, 246, 317
Butadiene, 702
n-Butane, nitration of, 52
  oxidation of, 396
Butene-1, 498
Butyl acetate, 576, **578**
n-Butyl alcohol, esterification of, 540
  preparation of, 401
t-Butyl alcohol, 640
Butylamine, 302, 322
Butyl chloride, 650, 661, 681
  hydrolysis of, 616
i-Butyl chloride, hydrolysis of, 615
t-Butyl phenols, 640, 681

t-Butylxylene, 639
Butyric acid, production of, 5

C

C-acid, 124
Caffeine, 488, 489, 492
Camphor, preparation of, **378**
Caproic acid, 526
Caprokol, 524
Carbitol, 490, 512
Carbohydrates, hydrolysis of, 597, 611
Carbon, chlorination catalyst, 209
Carbon dioxide, ammonolysis of, 299, 303, 324, **357**
  in Friedel and Crafts reaction, 637, 642, 648, **685**
Carbon disulfide, xanthate preparation, 567
Carbon linkages, destruction, 363
Carbon monoxide, esterification of, 536, 571
  in Friedel and Crafts reaction, 652, **683**
  hydrogenation of, 434, 435, **469**
Carbon tetrachloride, fluorination of, 229
  preparation of, 207
Carbonyl linkages, hydrogenation of, 419, 432
Carboxylic acid derivatives, 637, 642
Carboxylic acids, in Friedel and Crafts reaction, 660, 657
  preparation of, 642, **685**
Carboxyl, reduction of, 419
Carbyl sulfate, 254, **284**
Carius process, 372
Caro's acid, 376
Carvacrol, 641
Casein, polymerization of, 714
Casein formaldehyde resins, 714
Castor oil, 234
Cast thermosetting resins, 716
Catalysts, alkylation, 497, 500
  ammonolysis, 317
  chlorination, 154, 172, **206**
  esterification, 544, 545
  hydrogenation, 430, 431, 432, 433, 435, 437, 438, 439, 441, **455**
  hydrolysis, 606
  iodination, 157
  oxidation, 376, 387, 412
  polymerization, 704
  reduction, 74, 77, 88
  sulfonation, 252, 265, 270, 294
Cellosolve, 490, 513
Cellulose, acetylation of, 579
  alkylation of, 516
  hydrolysis of, 597
  nitration of, 7, 20, 537, 587
  xanthation of, 582
Cellulose acetate, 580, 728
Cellulose dekanitrate, 6
Cellulose esters, 537, 727
Cellulose nitrate, 587
Cellulose plastics, 698, 727
Cellulose xanthate, 582
Chalcone, 653
Charcoal, in chlorination, 209

Chicago acid, 148
Chlorates, oxidizing agents, 369
Chloric acid, 369
Chlorinating agents, 154, 165
Chlorination, 154, 165
  with catalysts, 154, 155
  factors, 168, 169, 183, 186
  liquid phase, 154, 168, 182
  mechanism, 159–165
  in nucleus, 183, 200
  photocatalytic, 200
  rules, 165
  in side chain, 182, 200
  vapor phase, 154, 168, 184, 185, 186, 190
Chlorination catalysts, 154, 172, **206**
Chlorine, chlorinating agent, 154, 165, 172, 182, 185
  oxidizing agent, 378
N-Chloroacetanilide, 650
Chloroacetic acid, ammonolysis of, 301, 314, 331
  chlorination of, 180, **216**
  preparation of, 180, 181, **215**
Chloroacetic anhydride, 181
ω-Chloroacetophenone, 208, 217, 662, **670, 686**
Chloroacetyl chloride, 182, 194, **216,** 686
Chloroalkanes, 166
o-Chloroaniline, 649
4-Chloroaniline, 310, 649
1-Chloroanthraquinone, 192
2-Chloroanthraquinone, ammonolysis of, 300, 327, 338, **349**
4-Chlorobenzaldehyde, 684
Chlorobenzene, ammonolysis of, 300, 309, **346**
  hydrolysis of, 593, 599, **629, 630**
  nitration of, 7, 20, **40–44**
  preparation of, 183, 185, 198, 207, **220**
3-Chlorobenzoic acid, sulfonation of, 255
4-Chlorobenzoic acid, 366
4′-Chloro-2-benzoylbenzoic acid, 261, 663, 688, 689
2-Chlorobiphenyl, 187, **225**
4-Chlorobiphenyl, 187, **225,** 331
2-Chloro-1, 3-butadiene, preparation of, 219
2-Chloro-3, 4-dinitrotoluene, 326
2-Chloro-5, 6-dinitrotoluene, 326
Chloroform, 195, 196, 551
3-Chloro-4-hydroxybiphenyl, 194
4-Chloro-(N-Methyl)-aniline, 300, 310
1-Chloronaphthalene, 186, 334
4-Chloro-2-nitroaniline, 221
2-Chloro-7-nitroanthraquinone, 84
2-Chloronitrobenzene, **41**
4-Chloronitrobenzene, alkylation of, 492, 510
  ammonolysis of, 300, 332, **351, 354**
  hydrolysis of, 599, 605, 606
  preparation of, **41**
  solidifying points of, 43
6-Chloro-2-nitrotoluene, 186
6-Chloro-3-nitro-o-toluidine, 303
Chloropentanes, hydrolysis of, 618
  preparation of, 166, 167, **213**
4-Chloro-o-phthalic acid, 187
Chloroprene, preparation of, 219
Chloropropanes, 166, 173

α-Chloropropionic acid, 181
β-Chloropropionic acid, 181, 644
Chlorosulfonic acid, 235, 258, 290
4-Chlorotoluene, 366
2, 6-Chlorotoluidine, 186
  sulfonation of, 268
4-Chloroxenene, ammonolysis of, 331
Chromic acid, oxidizing agent, 367
Chrysophenine G, 486, 490
Cinnamic acid, oxidation of, 377
  reduction of, 433
Cleve's acids, 241
Coal, hydrogenation of, 421, 440, **476, 483,** 484
Coconut oil, 439
Codeine, 489, 491, 492, **517,** 518
Colloidal phenomena, polymerization, 706
Colloidal solutions, 732
Color, molding compound, 737
Combustion, heat of, 54, 55, 56
Concentration factor, in alkylation, 500
  in ammonolysis, 330
  of catalyst in reduction, 74
  in coupling, 145
  in diazotization, 127
  in hydrolysis, 606
  in nitration, 12
  of nitric acid, 60, 61
  of spent sulfuric acid, 297
  of sulfides in reduction, 86
  in sulfonation, 251, 253, 255, 265
Continuous aminations, 355
Continuous chlorinations, 224
Continuous esterifications, 574, 575
Continuous hydrogenations, 469
Continuous nitrations, 31
Continuous sulfonations, 280, 285
Copper, in ammonolysis, 335
  in chlorination, 173
  in diazonium group replacement, 119, 199
  in oxidation, 390
  as reducing agent, 65, 90
Copper salts, in ammonolysis, 335
  oxidizing agents, 373
Copper sulfate, in diazotization, 136
Corrosion, in alkylation, 503
  in ammonolysis, 336
Cost factors, in aniline production, 98, 106
  in hydrogen production, 427
  in nitrobenzene production, 37
  in p-phenylene diamine production, 111
Coupling, 115, 140
  concentration, 145
  factors, 145
  H-ion concentration, 146
  mechanism of reaction, 144
  solvent, 147
  technical, 148
  temperature, 145
  time, 147
Coupling component, structure of, 143
m-Cresol, reduction of, 442
o-Cresol, hydrogenolysis of, 442, 443
  nitration of, 20
Cresol mixture, hydrogenation of, 442, 443

m-Cresotic acid, 643
Crocein acid, 244
Crocein Orange, 120
Crystallization, heat of, 54, 55, 56
Crystal Violet, 494, 508
Cumarone, 701
Cupric chloride, in chlorination, 172, 190, 219
Cupric nitrate, in nitration, 18
Cupric sulfate, oxidizing agent, 381
Cuprous chloride, chlorinating agent, 172, 191
Cure, molding compound, 733, 735
Cyanuric chloride, 643
Cyaphenine, 637, 643
Cycle acid, in nitration, 24
Cyclohexanone, 302, 322, 421, 545
Cyclohexylamine, 302, 322
Cyclopentadiene, 701, 703, 704
Cymene, hydrogenation of, 430, 431

D

Deacon process, 173, 190
Degradation, by Friedel and Crafts reaction, 677
  of petroleum, 677
Dehydration, 109, 637, 652
Dehydrogenation, 362, 363
Denitration, of spent acid, 57
Denitration tower, 57
Dennis process, 280
2, 2'-(Diacetyl chloride)-biphenyl, 645
Diacetyl-*o*-nitric acid, 15, 18
1, 4-Diaminoanthraquinone, 319
1, 5-Diaminoanthraquinone, 228
1, 8-Diaminoanthraquinone, 228
2, 3-Diaminoanthraquinone, 300
Diamino compounds, diazotization of, 137
1, 3-Diaminopropanol, 301, 303
Dianisidine, 116, 491, 509
  tetrazotization of, 137
Diazoamino compounds, 118
Diazo compounds, analysis of, 140
  in fluorinations, 206
  preparation of, 123
  production of azo dyes, 118, 140
  reactions, 115
  structure, 142
  uses of, 115, 118, 140
Diazo hydroxide, 117
Diazonium carboxylates, 125
Diazonium chlorides, 116
Diazonium compounds, decomposition, 122, 206
Diazonium formula, 116, 120
Diazonium group replacement, 119, 198
Diazonium hydroxide, 117
Diazonium iodides, 122
Diazonium salts, coupling activity, 115, 140
  properties of, 116, **119**
  reactions of, 119
Diazonium sulfates, 116
Diazonium sulfonates, 116
  properties of, 123
  reactions, 123
Diazo oxide, 125
Diazo reaction, in fluorination, 206

Diazo reaction, in halogenation, 198, 228
  in iodination, 204
Diazotates, 117
Diazotization, 115
  equipment, 130
  factors, 126
  technical, 131
1, 5-Dibenzoylnaphthalene, 646
3, 4, 8, 9-Dibenzpyrene-5,10-quinone, 690
2, 3-Dichloroanthraquinone, 300
2, 6-Dichlorobenzaldehyde, 200
1, 2-Dichlorobenzene, 220
1, 4-Dichlorobenzene, hydrolysis of, 599
  preparation of, 220
  sulfonation of, 255
4, 4'-Dichlorobenzophenone, 660
Dichlorodifluoromethane, 205, 229
Dichloroethylene, 178, 193
s-Dichloroethylether, 301, 312
3, 4-Dichloro-1-fluorobenzene, 158
Dichloromethane, 196
1, 2-Dichloro-4-nitrobenzene, 221
1, 4-Dichloro-2-nitrobenzene, 221
Dichloropropanes, 174
1, 3-Dichloropropanol-2, 301
2, 6-Dichlorotoluene, 186, 200
Dichromates, as oxidizing agents, 367
Dicyclopentadiene, 704
Diethanolamine, 303
Diethylamine, 492
Diethyl disulfide, 364
Diethylene glycol ethyl ether, 512
Diethylenetriamine, 301
Diethyl ketone, reduction of, 438
Diethyl sulfate, alkylating agent, 488
o-Dihydroxybenzene, 371
1, 2-Dihydroxy-4, 6-dinitrobenzene, 115
Dihydroxydiphenylmethane, 710, 712
1, 6-Dihydroxypyrene, 645
Dihydroxystearic acid, 363
Dihydroxystearylsulfuric acid, 295
3, 4-Dimethoxyacetophenone, 2
4, 4'-Dimethoxynaphthil, 645
Dimethylamine, preparation of, 345, 521
4-Dimethylaminobenzoic acid, 643, 649
Dimethylaniline, 63, 518
  oxidation of, 381
  preparation of, 487, 493, 496, 522
1, 6-Dimethylnaphthalene, 647
Dimethyl sulfate, alkylating agent, 488, 492, 493, 494, 511
3, 5-Dimethyltertiarybutylbenzene, 680
Dinaphthyl, 691
1, 5-Dinitroanthraquinone, 87
1, 3-Dinitrobenzene, preparation of, **38**
  reduction of, 83, 86, **111**
  solubility in sulfuric acid, 25
4, 6-Dinitrobenzene-2, 1-diazooxide, 125
5, 6-Dinitro-*o*-chlorotoluene, 303, 326
4, 4'-Dinitrodiphenylamine, reduction of, **78**
2, 4-Dinitrophenol, 84
Dinitrophthalic acid, 372
2, 3-Dinitrotoluene, 326
4, 5-Dinitroveratrole, 2

Dinitroxylene, 372
Diphenic acid, 371
Diphenylamine, 63
Diphenyl ether, 656
Diphenylmethane, hydrogenation of, 430
  oxidation of, 366
Diphenylurea, 649
Discontinuous sulfonation, 279
3, 5-Disulfophthalic anhydride, 256, 272
Distillation, with azeotropic agents, 551, 573
D. V. S. or dehydrating value of sulfuric acid,
  22, 23, 42
Dypnone, 653

E

Economic considerations of polymerization, 698
Economic survey, manufacture of aniline, 105
Electrochemical methods, in chlorination, 155
Energy factors, in ammonolysis, 330
  in hydrogenation, 446, 447
Enzymes, in esterification, 547
  in hydrolysis, 595
Epichlorohydrin, 303
Equilibrium, in alcoholysis, 558–560
  in ammonolysis, 337
  in esterification, 540, 548, 558
  in hydrolysis, 604
Equipment, alkylation, 503
  ammonolysis, 340
  diazotization, 130
  esterification, 560, 572
  Friedel and Crafts reaction, 670–674
  halogenation, 211
  hydrogenation, 461
  hydrolysis, 607
  nitration, 26, 584
  oxidation, 383, 413–418
  reduction, 92
  sulfonation, 281
Ester gum, 551, 719
Esterification, 533
  catalytic, 544, 557
  completing, 548
  equilibrium, 540, 548, 558
  equipment, 560, 572
  with inorganic acids, 537
  mass action law, 540, 543, 548
  with organic acids, 539
  rates and limits, 540, 542
  reactions, 533
  speeding up, 544
  technical, 578
  vapor phase, 556
Ester resins, 718
Esters, boiling points of, 554
  esterification of, 558
  hydrogenation of, 436, 473
  hydrolysis of, 597, 602
  preparation of, 573
  reduction of, 433
Ethane, nitration of, 4
  oxidation of, 396, 399
Ethanedisulfonic acid, 247

Ethanesulfonic acid, 364
Ethanol, alkylating agent, 487, 513
  esterification of, 534, 540, 558
  oxidation of, 362, 364, 385, 393
  preparation of, 401
  sulfonation of, 284
1-Ethanol-2-sulfonic acid, 254
Ethers, hydrolysis of, 598
Ethionic acid, 254, **284**
4-Ethoxy-4'-hydroxyazobenzene, 510
Ethyl acetate, 534, 551, 552, 558, **573**
Ethylamine, 346
4-Ethylaminobenzoic acid, 643
Ethylbenzene, hydrogenation of, 430, 431
  oxidation of, 406, 409
  preparation of, 638, **679,** 680
Ethyl benzoate, 433, 534, 558
Ethyl borate, 551
Ethyl bromide, 488
Ethyl cellulose, 515
Ethyl chloride, alkylating agent, 488, **530,** 679
Ethylene, chlorination of, 175, 176, 193, **227**
  esterification of, 535, 568
  hydration of, 237, 596
  oxidation of, 403
  sulfonation of, 284
Ethylene chlorohydrin, preparation of, 193, **227**
Ethylene derivatives, polymerization of, 701, 702
Ethylenediamine, 301, 311
  preparation of, 342
Ethylene dibromide, 158, 176, 203, 312
Ethylene dichloride, ammonolysis of, 301, 311,
  342
  preparation of, 175, 178, 207
Ethylene glycol, 536, 720
  preparation of, 624
Ethylene glycol ethyl ether, 490, **513,** 515
Ethylene oxide, 303, 570
  alkylation of, 514
  esterification of, 536
  preparation of, 403
Ethylenic linkages, hydrogenation of, 419, 429,
  431
  oxidation of, 377
Ethyl ether, reduction of, 441
Ethylidene glycol, 536, 568
Ethyl iodide, 203, 488
Ethyl mercaptan, 364
Ethyl nitrate, 534
Ethyl nitrite, 3, 4, 551, 558
  hydrolysis of, 601
Ethyl sulfate, 489, 534, 538
  preparation of, 237
Ethylsulfuric acid, 237, 538
Explosive limits of gases, 426

F

F-Acid, 245
Factors, alkylation, 500
  ammonolysis, 327
  chlorination, 168, 169, 183, 186
  coupling, 145
  diazotization, 126

Factors, Friedel and Crafts reaction, 657
  hydrogenation, 444
  nitration, 24 /
  polymerization, 703
  reduction, 72
  sulfonation, 251, 253, 255, **265**
Fat hardening, 464
Fatty acids, 465
  preparation of, 386, 608, 609
  sulfonation of, 295
Fehling's solution, 373
Ferric chloride, in ammonolysis, 316
  in chlorination, 154, 155, 172, 185, 190, 191, 196, 206
  in Friedel and Crafts reaction, 661
  oxidizing agent, 372
  in reduction, 75, 76
Ferric nitrate, nitrating agent, 18
Ferric salts, oxidizing agents, 372
Ferrous chloride, reducing agent, 71
Ferrous sulfate, in ammonolysis, 319, 357
  in reduction, 67, 77, 86
Finish, molding compound, 737
Fischer-Tropsch process, 421, 434
Fluorinating agents, 158
Fluorination, 157, 204
Fluorine. in fluorination, 157, 205
  properties, 157
Fluorobenzene, 206
Formaldehyde, in polymerization, 705, 709, 711, 712, 713, 714, 715
  preparation of, 390, 395, 401, 403
Formamide. 63
Formation, heat of, in nitration, 54, 55, 56
Formic acid, 9, 401
Formyl chloride, 652
IV-acid, 241
Freeboard, in ammonolysis, 333
Freund's acid, 241
Friedel and Crafts reaction, 634
  chemical engineering problems, 668
  classification of syntheses, 637
  effect of agitation, 673
  effect of solvents, 657
  equipment, 669–674
  factors, 656
  function of AlCl$_3$, 635
  liquid phase, 669, 688
  mechanism, 659, **675**
  technical preparations, **677**
  types, 635
Fries migration, 637, 655
Fumaric acid, 376
  sulfonation of, 255
Fuming sulfuric acid, 375
Furans, alkylation of, 637, 641
Furfural, oxidation of, 376
  polymerization of, 712
  reduction of, 437

G

G-acid, 245. 246, 264, 291
Gamma acid, 246

Gas oil, hydrogenation of, 482
Gattermann reaction, 155, 199
Gay, Aumeras, and Mion process, 280
Glucamine, 302, 321
Glucose, ammonolysis of, 302
Glycerol, 597, 608
  esterification of, 537
  nitration of, 6, 7, 583
  oxidation of, 371
  polymerization of, 721
Glycerol dichlorohydrin, 312
Glyceryl trinitrate, 6, 7
  preparation of, 537, 583
Glyceryl tristearate, 597, 609
Glycine, 301, 313
Glycol acetate, 570
Glycol dinitrate, 537
Glycols, 363, 377, 721
  esterification of, 537, 570
Glyoxal, 248, 701
Glyptal resins, 410, 567, 694
Gold, reduction with, 90
Guaiacol, 491
  alkylation, 509
Guanidine derivatives, **713**
Guyot process, 279

H

H-acid, 124, 140, 241
Halogenations, 153
  equipment, 211
  of olefins, 175, 178, 189
  progressive, 199
  survey of, 165
  technical, 213
  theoretical basis of, 159
Halogeno compounds, preparation of, 637, 651
Halogens, ammonolysis of, 299, 300, 309, 329
  heat of reaction, 164
  reactions with halogen hydrides, 163
  reactions with hydrocarbons, 162
  reactions with hydrogen, 160, 161
Hart condenser, 58
Heat, of combustion, 54, 55, 56
  of crystallization, 54, 55, 56
  of formation, in nitration, 54, **55**, 56
  of nitration, 32, 54, 55, 56
  of reaction, in halogenation, 163, 164
    in hydrogenation, 478
    in reduction, 76
Heat transfer, in sulfonation, 281
Heat transfers, in vapor phase oxidation, 414
Heptaldehyde, reduction of, 437
Heptanes, oxidation of, 400
Heterocyclic amines, 492, 495
Hexanes, oxidation of, 400
Hexylresorcinol, 495
  preparation of, 524
Hough nitrator, 30
Hydration, 596
Hydrazoanisole, 112

Hydrazobenzene, 67, 79, **81**
Hydriodic acid, 157, 203
Hydrobromic acid, in bromonitation, 156, 201
Hydrocarbon derivatives, 653
Hydrocarbons, halogenation of, 162, 212
  hydrogenolysis of, 443
  hydrolysis of, 596
  oxidation of, 362, 386, 394–403
  source of hydrogen, 424
  synthesis of, 635, 637, 638
Hydrochloric acid, as chlorinating agent, 154, 188, 191
  in esterification, 544
  recovery, 231
Hydrogen, consumption, 423
  cost of, 427
  production of, 422
  properties of, 426
  ratios in hydrogenation, 453
  reducing agent, 65, 67, 88, 89
  solubility of, 454
Hydrogenated oils, 465
Hydrogenated quinoline bases, in reduction, 67, 87
Hydrogenation, 419
  of carbonyl, 419, 432
  of carboxyl, 419
  equipment, 461
  of ethylenic linkages, 419, 429, 431
  exothermic, 454, 478
  mechanism, 445–450
  physical factors, 444
  technical, 419, 464
  types, 419, 429
Hydrogenation catalysts, 430–433, 435, 437–439, 441, **455**
Hydrogen chloride, in chlorination, 181, 189, 190, 191, 212
  removal in Friedel and Crafts reaction, 657, 663, 664, 674
Hydrogen fluoride, in fluorination, 158
Hydrogen ions, in hydrolysis, 603
Hydrogenolysis, 419, 437, 440, 441
Hydrogen peroxide, 370, 376
Hydrolysis, 590
  acid, 591, 593, 603
  alkali, 591, 594
  catalysts, 606
  enzymatic, 591, 595
  equipment, 607
  mechanism, 602
  susceptible materials, **596**
  technical, 608
  temperature, 604
  types, 591
  vapor phase, 591, 607, 630
  water, 591, 592
Hydrolyzing agents, 591
Hydroquinone, oxidation of, 362
  preparation of, 380
Hydroxyanthraquinones, ammonolysis of, 319
Hydroxybenzyl alcohols, 709
Hydroxy biphenyl, chlorination of, 194
Hydroxy compounds, ammonolysis of, 319

Hydroxy compounds, coupling of, 148
1-Hydroxynaphthalene-4-carboxylic acid, 644
2-Hydroxynaphthalene-3-carboxylic acid (*see* 3-Hydroxy-2-naphthoic acid)
2-Hydroxy-3-naphthoic acid (*see* 3-Hydroxy-2-naphthoic acid)
3-Hydroxy-2-naphthoic acid, 116
  ammonolysis of, 319, **357**
Hypochlorites, in chlorination, 193
Hypochlorous acid, chlorinating agent, 193
  oxidizing agent, 368, 376
Hyposulfites, 210
  sulfonating agents, 262

I

Impregnated paper, 732
Indanthrene Blue RS, 374
Indanthrene Dark Blue BO, 374
Indene, 701
Indigo, reduction of, 88
  synthesis of, 389
Indophenol, 368
Indoxyl, 389
Iodination, 156, 202
Iodine, in chlorination, 171, 180, 183, 185, 207
  in iodination, 156, 203
Iodine monochloride, in iodination, 157
Iodobenzene, 204
2-Iodobenzoic acid, oxidation of, 367
Iodoform, 203
2-Iodosobenzoic acid, preparation of, 367
Iron, in acid reduction, 68, 72
  in alkali reduction, 67, 79, **81**
  halogen carrier, 182, 183
  reducing agent, 65, 67
Iron oxides, in oxidation catalysis, 392
  as reducing agents, 90
Iron salts, in chlorination, 207
Isatins, 646
Isoborneol, 378
Isobornyl acetate, 378
Isobutyl alcohol, esterification of, 542
Isobutylamine, 302
Isobutylene, 230, 422, 680
  oxidation of, 377
Isobutylene glycol, 377
Isoeugenol, oxidation of, 377
Isopropyl alcohol, 538, 641
  preparation of, 538, 621, 622
Isothermals of NH_3 and H_2O, 306, 328

J

J-acid, 124
Jacket reduction, 93, 94, **101**
Jacketed vessels, in ammonolysis, 340, 351
James process, 404

K

Kerosene, oxidation of, 404
Ketene, esterification with, 535, 567
Ketimides, 637, 648

Keto acids, 637, 647, 688
Ketones, ammonolysis of, 302
    reduction of, 438
    synthesis of, 637, 644, 686
Kiliani mixture, 367
Koch acid, 241, 248
Krafft process, 372

L

Lactic acid, chlorination of, 181
Laurent's acid, 241
Lead, chlorination catalyst, 154
Lead peroxide, oxidizing agent, 369, 381
Lead tetraethyl, 500, **530**
Leuco bases, oxidation of, 381
Light, in diazotization, 130
    in polymerization, 705
Limits of esterification, 540, 542
Liquid phase, alkylation, 501
    amination, 329, 357
    chlorination, 154, 168, 183
    Friedel and Crafts reaction, 669, 688
    hydrogenation, 453
    nitration, 3
    oxidation, 365, **376**, 382, 413
    reduction, 89, 431–433, 437–439, 441

M

Magenta, 508
Malachite Green, 494
    preparation of, 381
Maleic acid, 255, 366, 405, 407, 543
Malic acid, 408
Manganese acetate, in oxidation, 383
Manganese dioxide, in chlorinations, 190
    oxidizing agent, 370, 376, 382
Mass action law, in esterification, 540, 543
Mechanism, of ammonolysis, 339
    of coupling, 144
    of Friedel and Crafts reaction, 675
        addition complexes, 675
    of hydrogenation, 444–450
    of hydrolysis, 602
    of nitration, 12
    of polymerization, 699, 702
    of reduction, 68, 69
Mercaptans, esterification, 542
Mercury, catalyst in oxidation, 375
    catalyst in sulfonation, 252, 270, **294**
Merthiolate, 500, **531**
Mesidine, 496
Mesitylene, 143, 430
Metal catalysts, in ammonolysis, 334, 357
Metal nitrates, in nitration, 1, 18
Metal nitrites, in nitration, 3
Metal salts, in esterification, 565
Metal sulfides, in reduction, 67, 83
Metanilic acid, 139, 151
Methacrylates, 726, 727, 728
Methacrylic acid, 726
Methallyl chloride, preparation of, 230
Methane, chlorination of, 171, 173, 189, 195, 196
    oxidation of, 395, 396, 398

Methanol, alkylating agent, 487, 496
    ammonolysis of, 302, **343**
    esterification of, 540, 558
    oxidation of, 390
    preparation of, 401, 420, 435, 469
Methoxybiphenyl, 194
Methyl acetate, hydrolysis of, 545
4-Methylacetophenone, 661
Methylamine, 302, **343**, 344, 346, 492
Methylaniline, 63
2-Methylanthraquinone, 363
Methylation, 518
Methylbenzenesulfonate, alkylating agent, 489
Methyl chloride, alkylating agent, 511
    preparation of, 172, 189, 196
Methylene acetone, in polymerization, 702
Methylene Blue, 368, 494
Methylene chloride, 172, 191, 196
Methyl formate, 210
Methyl iodide, 203, 492
Methyl nitrate, 4
2-Methylquinoline, reducing agent, 67, 87
Methyl p-toluenesulfonate, 489, 495
Methyl Violet, 381, 494, 508
Metol, 494
Michler's ketone, 486, 649
Mixed acids, composition of, 15, 16, **21**, 38, 537
    for nitration, 1, 6, 10, 12, 15, **21**
    system, 39
Molding compound, 732
Molybdenum oxide, 409, 412
Monosulfonation, 252, 292, 294
Morpholine, 301, 312, 490, 518
Motor fuel, synthetic gasoline, 527

N

Naphthalene, chlorination of, 186
    hydrogenation of, 421
    nitration of, 8, 19, **49**
    oxidation of, 363, 366, 405, 407, 410
    sulfonation of, 238, 266, **288, 289**
Naphthalene-1-diazonium-4-sulfonate, 135
Naphthalene-1, 2-diazooxide-4-sodium sulfonate, 136
1, 5-Naphthalenedicarbonyl chloride, 646
1, 5-Naphthalenedisulfonic acid, 258, 264, 268
1,6-Naphthalenedisulfonic acid, 239, 264, 268, 269
1-Naphthalenesulfonic acid, 239
    hydrolysis of, 593, 601
2-Naphthalenesulfonic acid, 239, 241, 243, 264, 284
    hydrolysis of, 290, 601
    preparation of, **288, 289**
    sodium salt of, 290
Naphthalenesulfonic acids, 238, 240
Naphthionic acid, 244
    diazotization of, 135
1-Naphthol, in Friedel and Crafts reaction, 644
    sulfonation of, 272
2-Naphthol, ammonolysis of, 302, 317, 318, **355**
    preparation of, 601, 625
    sulfonation of, 244, 256, 269, **290, 291**

2-Naphthol-1, 6-disulfonic acid, 274
2-Naphthol-3, 6-disulfonic acid, 245, 264, 291
2-Naphthol-6, 8-disulfonic acid, 245, 264, 291
1-Naphthol-2-sulfonic acid, 272
1-Naphthol-7-sulfonic acid, 318
2-Naphthol-1-sulfonic acid, 245, 246, 256, 274, **290**
2-Naphthol-6-sulfonic acid, 120, 245, **291**
2-Naphthol-7-sulfonic acid, 245, 274, 277
2-Naphthol-8-sulfonic acid, 274
2-Naphtholsulfonic acids, 244
α-Naphthoquinone, 405
α-Naphthoylbenzoic acid, 667
1-Naphthylamine, 114, 139, 151
    sulfonation of, 244, 263
2-Naphthylamine, preparation of, 302, 317, **355**
    sulfonation of, 256, 269
2-Naphthylamine-4, 8-disulfonic acid, 124
1-Naphthylamine-2-sulfonic acid, 244, 263
1-Naphthylamine-7-sulfonic acid, 318
2-Naphthylamine-1-sulfonic acid, 135, 256
2-Naphthylamine-5-sulfonic acid, 242
1-Naphthylaminesulfonic acids, 241, 243
2-Naphthylaminesulfonic acids, 241, 242
β-Naphthyl methyl ether, 488, 491
Natural resin plastics, 698
Neutral oxidation, 366, 376
Nickel, in hydrogenation, 434, 440, 441, 466
    reduction with, 65, **90**
Nitrating agents, 1
    examination, 14, **15**
Nitrating apparatus, 26
Nitration, **1**
    continuous, 31
    factors, 24
    heat of, 32, 54, 55, 56
    liquid phase, 3
    mechanism of, 12
    solubility, 26
    technical, 33
    temperature, 8, **24,** 34, 52
    vapor phase, 2, 3, 4, 50
Nitrators, 26, 584
Nitric acid, concentration of, 60, 61
    consumption of, 26
    dual capacity of, 11
    esters, 6, 12
    fuming, 10
    in iodination, 157
    in nitration, 1, 3, 4, 9, 10, **11,** 13, 14
    oxidizing agent, 3, 372, 378
    spent acid, 22, 55, 57, 59
Nitric acid anhydride, in nitration, 15
Nitriles, esterification of, 536, 569
    formation, 119
    reduction of, 64
o-Nitroacetanilide, 10, 17, 18
p-Nitroacetanilide, preparation of, 10, **44**
    reduction of, 69
Nitroamines, diazotization of, 133
3-Nitro-4-aminotoluene, 116
m-Nitroaniline, diazotization of, 121
    preparation of, 45
p-Nitroaniline, diazotization of, 85, 121, **133**

p-Nitroaniline, operating budget, 354
    preparation of, 300, 332, **351, 354**
    reduction of, 107
3-Nitro-p-anisidine, 10
o-Nitroanisole, 487, 491, 509
    reduction of, 112
2-Nitroanthraquinone-7-sulfonic acid, 192
Nitrazo compounds, reduction of, 85
m-Nitrobenzaldehyde, reduction of, 86
Nitrobenzene, nitration of, 38
    operating losses, 35
    oxidizing agent, 372, 378
    preparation of, 22, **33**
    reduction of, 64, 66, 72, 73, 74, 76, 81, 90, 91 **96**
    solubility losses, 36
    sulfonation of, 273
p-Nitrobenzenediazonium chloride, 117, 133, 143
Nitro-tert-butyl glycerol, 6
Nitro compounds, 1
    aromatic, **7**
    in Friedel and Crafts reaction, 637, 649
    reduction of, 64, **83**
    survey of, 2
    thermal data of, 53
3-Nitro-o-cresol, 20
5-Nitro-o-cresol, 20
Nitroethane, 3, 4
Nitrogen compounds, hydrolysis, 600
Nitrogen dioxide, in nitration, 4
Nitrogen peroxide, in nitration, 2, 15
Nitrogen tetroxide, in nitration, 1, 13, 15, **19,** 20
Nitrogen trioxides, in nitration, 13
Nitroglycerin, 583
Nitro groups, in ammonolysis, 299, 303, 325, 329
    orientation of, **7**
α-Nitronaphthalene, preparation of, **49**
    reduction of, 114
5-Nitro-1-naphthylamine, preparation of, 84
Nitroparaffins, 2, 4, **5, 50**
    raw material cost, 52
p-Nitrophenetole, 487, **510**
o-Nitrophenol, 366
    alkylation of, 488
    preparation of, 48
    reduction of, 88
p-Nitrophenol, preparation of, 48, 599
p-Nitrophenolate, 10, 11
p-Nitrophenyl-o-nitro-p-toluenesulfonate, 11
Nitrosoamines, 117
Nitrosobenzene, 66
1-Nitroso-2-naphthol, 260, 291
Nitrosophenols, reduction of, 69
Nitro substituents, effect in ammonolysis, 329
Nitrosulfonic acid, in nitration, 1, 18, 19
Nitrosulfuric acid, 13, 15, 16
Nitrosylsulfuric acid, 25, 57
    in nitration, 18, 20
m-Nitrotoluene, preparation of, 45
o-Nitrotoluene, chlorination of, 186
    preparation of, 45
p-Nitrotoluene, preparation of, 45
o-Nitrotoluene-p-sulfonate, 11
2-Nitro-p-toluidine, 10
3-Nitro-o-toluidine, 326

3-Nitro-p-toluidine, 10
Nitrous acid, in diazotization, 115, 119, 123–126
3-Nitro-o-4-xylidine, 327
4-Nitro-o-3-xylidine, 327

O

m-Octadecyl alcohol, ammonolysis of, 302
Oil-soluble resins, 696, 697, **717**
Olefins, alkylation of, 489
    alkylation with, 497
    chlorination of, 175
    in Friedel and Crafts reaction, 635
    halogenation of, 178, 189
    hydrogenation of, 429
    hydrolysis of, 620, 621, 624
    oxidation of, 363, 377, 403
    nitration of, 13
Oleic acid, esterification of, 550
    hydrogenation of, 475, 476
    oxidation of, 363, 377
    reduction of, 433, 439
Olein, hydrogenation of, 464
Oleum, in nitration, 1
    oxidizing agent, 375
    sulfonating agent, 234, 246, 278
Olive oil, 234
Operating data, nitration of benzene, 36
    preparation of p-nitroaniline, 354
Organic halides, hydrolysis of, 598
Organic nitrates, in nitration, 1, 17
Orientation, of nitro groups, 7
    in nuclear chlorination, 183, 200
    in sulfonation, 270
Oxalic acid, 9
Oxalyl chloride, 645, 652
Oxidants, in ammonolysis, 315, 338, 350
Oxidation, 362
    catalysts, 376, 412
    equipment, 413–418
    liquid phase, 365, 376, 382, 413
    types, 362
    vapor phase, 365, 390, 405, 407, 410, 414
Oxidizing agents, 365
Oxygen, in chlorination, 173, 189
    oxidizing agent, 362, 382
Ozone, oxidizing agent, 375

P

Paraffins, chlorination of, 165, 167, 195
    nitration of, 2, 4, 14, **50**
    oxidation of, 387, 394
Paraldehyde, 692
Pentamethylbenzene, 372
Pentane, chlorination of, 166, 167, 213
n-Pentane, oxidation of, 396
Perchloric acid, in esterification, 546
Peri-acid, 241
Permanganates, oxidizing agents, 365
Peroxides, in bromination, 202
    oxidizing agents, 369
Petrohol, 538, 621
Petroleum, cracking of, 678

Petroleum, degradation of, 677
    hydrogenation of, 421, 440, 476, **479**
    oxidation of, 403
pH, of aqueous ammonia solutions, 305
    in ammonolysis, 336
    in coupling, 146
    of reductions, 82
Phenacetin, 509
Phenanthraquinone, 371
p-Phenetidine, 510
Phenetole, 489, 491
Phenol, alkylation of, 487, 490, **511, 526,** 681
    ammonolysis of, 299, 301, 316
    hydrogenation of, 432
    hydrogenolysis of, 441–443
    iodination of, 204
    manufacture of, 407, **627,** 631, 632
    nitration of, 2, 8, 18, 19, 20, **48**
    polymerization of, 709, 712, **729**
Phenoldisulfonic acid, 2
Phenol ethers, 492
Phenol-formaldehyde resins, 709, **729**
Phenolphthalein, 410, 648
2-Phenylanthraquinone, 653
4'-Phenyl-2-benzoylbenzoic acid, cyclization of, 653
    preparation, 673, 689
m-Phenylenediamine, diazotization of, 137
p-Phenylenediamine, distillation of, 110
    plant, 107
    preparation of, 107
β-Phenylethyl alcohol, 682
Phenylglyceric acid, 377
Phenylglycine, 389
Phenylhydroxylamine, 66
Phenyl isocyanate, 535
Phenyl-p-toluenesulfonate, 10
Phenyltrimethylammonium chloride, 489, **518**
Phosgene, chlorinating agent, 155, 194
    in esterification, 563
    in Friedel and Crafts reaction, 637, 643
Phosphorus, in chlorination, 180
    in iodination, 157
Phosphorus oxychloride, chlorinating agent, 197
Phosphorus pentachloride, chlorinating agent, 180, 181, 197
Phosphorus pentoxide, in nitration, 1
Phosphorus trichloride, in chlorination, 154, 155, 197
Phosphorus trifluoride, in fluorination, 159
Phosphorus triiodide, in iodination, 203
Photocatalysis, in chlorination, 209
Photochlorinator, 211
o-Phthalic acid, chlorination of, 187
    preparation of, 366
Phthalic anhydride, in esterification, 566
    in Friedel and Crafts reaction, 647, 657, 660
    polymerization of, 720
    preparation of, 363, 407, 409, 410
    sulfonation of, 272
Phthalonic acid, 366
Picramic acid, diazotization of, 125
Picric acid, 2, 18

Plant assembly, in ammonolysis, 352
Plasticity of molding compound, 733, 735
Plasticizers, 736
Plastics, classification of, 696
    chemical, 697
    physical, 696
Plywoods, utilization of resins, 739
Polyhydric alcohols, nitration of, 32
    polymerization of, 720, 721
Polymerization, 692
    catalysts, 704
    compounds susceptible to, 700
    discussion of terms, 699
    economic considerations of, 698
    factors, 703
    mechanism of, 699, 702
Polymer resins, 711, **722**
Polymers, 693
Polyoxymethylene, 704, 705
Polystyrene, 725
    polymers, 725, 726
Potassium chlorate, oxidizing agent, 369, 380
Potassium dichromate, oxidizing agent, 379
Potassium ferricyanide, oxidizing agent, 375
Potassium fluoride, in fluorination, 158
Potassium nitrate, nitrating agent, 6
Potassium permanganate, oxidizing agent, 363,
    376, 377
Pressure, in alkylation, 501
    in hydrogenation, 430, 431, 435, **451,** 462, 480
    partial, of NH₃, 308
    in polymerization, 706
    in vapor phase oxidation, 397, 398
Products derived by alkylation, 503
Propane, chlorination of, 171, 173, 174
    oxidation of, 396, 398
Propionic acid, 5, 258
n-Propylamine, preparation of, 302, 322
i-Propylbenzene, 527
Propylene, alkylating agent, 527
    hydrolysis of, 622
    oxidation of, 403
Propylene oxide, ammonolysis of, 323
Protein plastics, 698
N-Pyridiniumsulfonic acid, sulfonating agent,
    235, 262
Pyrolysis, 403
Pyrrole, 701

Q

Quick-vinegar process, 385, 552
Quinizarin, ammonolysis of, 319
Quinone, preparation of, 362, 376, 379, 407
    reduction of, 380, 438

R

R-acid, 245, 246, 264, 291
Rapid Fast Red GL, 116
Raschig process, 631, 632
Rates, of chlorination, 168, 171
    of esterification, 540, 542
Reaction, catalytic reduction, 74

Reaction, of diazo compounds, 115, 123
    heat of, in reductions, 76
    of polymerization, 710
Recovery, of catalyst in reduction, **77**
    of hydrochloric acid, 231
    of NH₃ in ammonolysis, 359
    of spent acid from nitration, 55
Reducers, 93, 94, 95
Reduction, agitation in, 73, 74, 94
    amination by, 63
    catalysts, 65, 74, 77, 88
    chemical factors, 72
    equipment, 92
    liquid phase, 89
    mechanism of, 68, 69
    methods, 67
    technical, 96
    temperature, 75
    types, 419
    vapor phase, 67, 90, 91
Replacement reaction, in ammonolysis, 300, 329,
    334
    in bromination, 156
    in chlorination, 153, 154, 191
    in iodination, 203
Resinoid, 708
Resins, applications, 737
    manufacture, 729
    oil-soluble, 696, 697
    properties, 707, 708, **729**
    thermoplastic, 695, 696, **717**
    thermosetting, 695, 696, **707**
    utilization of, 731, 732
Resorcinol, 115, 526
Rezyl resins, 410
Rosaniline, 508
Rosin esters, 719, 720

S

Saccharification, of wood, 613
Saccharin, preparation of, 259
S-acid, 241
Safranine, 368
Salicyl chloride, 194
Salicylic acid, 194, 643
Sandmeyer reaction, in chlorination, 155, 186,
    198, 199, 200, **228**
Schäffer acid, 244, 245, 246, 291
Schäffer salt, 120
Scholler-Tornesch process, 613
Scholl reaction, 637, 656, **690**
Schotten-Baumann method, 564
Selenium dioxide, oxidizing agent, 371
Shellac, 707
Silica gel, in nitration, 20
Silver, in ammonolysis, 234
    in oxidation, 371
    in reduction, 90
Silver fluoride, in fluorination, 158
Silver oxides, oxidizing agents, 371
Sludge analysis, 72
Soap, preparation of, 608
Sodium acetate, in esterification, 534, 565

Sodium bisulfate, in reduction, 69
Sodium bisulite, in ammonolysis, 318
  in sulfonation, 257, 290
Sodium chlorate, oxidizing agent, 369, 376
Sodium chloride, in reduction, 76
Sodium dichromate, oxidizing agent, 364, 379
Sodium ethylate, 518
Sodium fluoride, in fluorination, 158
Sodium hydrosulfite, in ammonolysis, 319
  reducing agent, 67, 87
  sulfonating agent, 262
Sodium hypochlorite, in chlorination, 154
  oxidizing agent, 368
Sodium naphthalene-1, 2-diazooxide-4-sulfonate, 136
Sodium peroxide, oxidizing agent, 371
Sodium phenolate, 10
Sodium salicylate, chlorination of, 194
Sodium stearate, 609
Sodium sulfate, in sulfonation, 273
Solubility, aniline in water, 100
  of hydrogen, 454
Solvent, in alkylation, 501
  in ammonolysis, 327
  in bromination, 200
  in chlorination, 155, 186
  in coupling, 147
  in diazotization, 127
  in Friedel and Crafts reaction, 657, **666,** 689
  in nitration, 26
  in polymerization, 706
Spent acid, denitration, 57, 59
  from nitrations, composition of, 22
  recovery, 55
  from sulfonations, concentration of, 297
Stannous chloride, chlorinating agent, 78, 191
  in reduction, 78
Starch, hydrolysis of, 611
Steam, in distillation of aniline, 99
Stearic acid, 464, 597
  esterification of, 549
  reduction of, 439
Stilbene, 363
Strength, molding compound, 736
Structure, of the coupling component, 143
  of diazo compounds, 142
Styrene, 692, 700, 725
Styrene resins, 724
Substitution reactions, in bromination, 156
  in chlorination, 154, 171, 189, 194
  in halogenations, 153
  in iodination, 204
Succinic acid, 376
Sulfamic acid derivatives, 259, 261
p-Sulfanilic acid, 123, 124
  preparation of, 238, **287**
  sulfonating agent, 263
Sulfides, in reduction, 85
Sulfites, 235
  sulfonating agents, 260
Sulfoacetic acid, 258
4-Sulfoanthranilic acid, 118
3-Sulfobenzene-azo-1-naphthalene-4-d i a z o n i u m
    chloride, 139

m-Sulfobenzoic acid, 260
Sulfomaleic acid, 255
Sulfonamide-formaldehyde resins, 715
Sulfonating agents, 234, 246, 258
Sulfonation, 233
  catalytic, 252, 265, 294
  continuous, 280, 285
  discontinuous, 277, 279
  equipment, 281
  factors, 251, 253, 255, **265**
  of fatty acids, 295
  formation of addition compounds, 274
  technical methods, 277
  technical preparations, 283
Sulfonation catalysts, 252, 265, 294
Sulfonator, 282
Sulfonic acids, ammonolysis of, 299, 301 314,
  hydrolysis of, 269, 601
  preparation of, 283
  separation of, 263
  uses of, 234
Sulfonyl chlorides, 265, 564
3-Sulfophthalic anhydride, 272
4-Sulfophthalic anhydride, 256, 272
Sulfopropionic acid, 258
Sulfur, in chlorination, 185, 208
Sulfur chloride, in chlorination, 208
Sulfur compounds, oxidation of, 364
Sulfur dioxide, 234
  reducing agent, 67
  sulfonating agent, 235, 259
Sulfuric acid, in chlorination, 184
  in esterification, 544
  heat capacity of, 24
  in nitration, 1, 16, 19
  oxidizing agent, 375
  properties, 235
  in saccharification, 613
  sulfonating agent, 234, 236
Sulfur trioxide, 234
  sulfonating agent, 234, 254
Sulfuryl chloride, chlorinating agent, 155, 195
Synthetic resin plastics, 696, 697
Synthin, 434

T

Tar, hydrogenation of, 421, 440, **476, 481**
Technical, alkylations, 509
  ammonolyses, 342
  couplings, 148
  diazotizations, 131
  esterifications, 578
  Friedel and Crafts reactions, 677
  halogenations, 213
  hydrogenations, 419, 464
  manufacture of resins, 730
  nitrations, 33
  operations involving hydrolysis, 608
  reductions, 96
  sulfonations, 277, 283
Temperature as a factor, in alkylations, 500
  in ammonolysis, 330
  in chlorination, 168, 169, 183, 186

Temperature as a factor, in coupling, 145
  in diazotization, 127, 128
  in Friedel and Crafts reaction, 657, **665**
  in hydrogenation, 450, 480
  in hydrolysis, 604
  in nitration, 8, **24**, 34, 52
  in oxidation, 365, 391, 392, 396
  in polymerization, 703
  in reduction, 75
  in sulfonation, 251, 253, 255, 265, **267**
Ternaries, use in esterification, 552, 553, 554
Tetraalkylammonium fluorides, 159
Tetrachloroethane, 207
Tetralin, 421
Tetramethylbenzoic acid, 372
Tetramethyldiaminotriphenylmethane, 381
Theobromine, 492
Thermal data, in nitrations, 53
Thermoplastic resins, 695, 696, **717**
Thermosetting resins, 695, 696, **707**
Thioisatins, 646
Thiokol, 694
Thionyl chloride, in chlorination, 194
Thymol, 495, 540, 641
Time as a factor, in coupling, 147
  in diazotization, 130
  in hydrogenation, 453
  in sulfonation, 251, 253, 255, 265, 270
Tin, in reduction, 65, 67, 77, 90
Tobias acid, 135, 246
Tolidine, 148
p-Tolualdehyde, 684
Toluene, chlorination of, 182, 184
  hydrogenation of, 430, 431
  nitration of, 20, **45–47**
  oxidation of, 363, 382, 406, 409, 410
  sulfonation of, 267
2, 5-Toluenedisulfonic acid, 265
Toluene-ω-sulfonic acid, 233
  preparation of, 262
m-Toluenesulfonic acid, 260, 267
p-Toluenesulfonic acid, 267, 489, 492, 546
o-Toluenesulfonyl chloride, 258
p-Toluenesulfonyl chloride, 9, 10
o-Toluic acid, oxidation of, 366
m-Toluidine, 122, 238
o-Toluidine, 122, 238
p-Toluidine, 122, 238
  nitration of, 10
o-Tolyl acetate, 655
2-Tolylazo-3-tolyl-4-diazonium chloride, 138
o-Tolyl benzoate, 656
Trialkyl phosphates, 564
Triaryl phosphates, 564
1, 2, 3-Trichloroisobutane, 617
ω-Trichloromethyl-p-tolyl ketone, 648
Triethanolamine, 303
Triisobutylborate, 639
Triisopropylbenzene, 527
2, 4, 6-Trinitrobenzenediazonium sulfonate, 143
Triphenylfluoromethane, 159
Triphenylmethane, oxidation of, 366
  preparation of, 638

Tubular pressure systems, in ammonolysis, 341
Twitchell process, 610
Tyrer process, 279

U

Urea, polymerization of, 712, 713
  preparation of, 303, 324, 326, **357**, 637, 648
Urea-formaldehyde resins, 713

V

Vacuum, use in sulfonation, 278
Vanadium, in sulfonation, 270, 273
Vanadium pentoxide, oxidation catalyst, 376,
    392, 408, 409, 411, 412
  sulfonation catalyst, 273
Vanillin, 377, 491, 492
  preparation of, 520
Vapor phase, alkylation, 501
  ammonolysis, 299, 312
  chlorination, 154, 168, 184, 185, 186, 190
  esterification, 556
  hydrolysis, 623, 624, 630
  nitration, 2, 20, 50
  oxidation, 365, 390, 405, 407, 410, 411, 414
  reduction, 67, 90, 91, 431–433, 437–439, 441, 454
Vapor pressure, comparative, of NH₃ and H₂O,
    306, 328
Varnishes, 731
Vinyl acetate, 536, 700
Vinylacetylene, 219
Vinyl bromide, 202
Vinyl chloride, 178, 179, 700
Vinyl chloride—vinyl acetate, copolymers, **723**
Vinyl esters, 568, 724
Vinyl polymers, 722
Vinyl resins, 722

W

Water, hydrolyzing agent, 591, 592
  source for hydrogen, 423, 424
Williamson synthesis, 491
Wood, saccharification of, 613

X

Xanthates, 567
Xanthation of cellulose, 582
Xenylamine, 331, 333, 650
Xylene, hydrogenation of, 430, 431
m-Xylene, 639, 680
o-Xylene, oxidation of, 372, 409
s-Xylenol, 301, 317
s-Xylidene, 301, 317
m-Xylidine, 256

Z

Zinc, as reducing agent, 65, 67, 79, 82, 112
Zinc chloride, in chlorination, 217
  in hydrolysis, 546
Zinc-chloride ammonia, 199